ENCYCLOPEDIA OF PHYSICS

EDITED BY

S. FLÜGGE

VOLUME XI/1

ACOUSTICS I

WITH 183 FIGURES

SPRINGER-VERLAG
BERLIN · GÖTTINGEN · HEIDELBERG
1961

HANDBUCH DER PHYSIK

HERAUSGEGEBEN VON

S. FLÜGGE

BAND XI/1

AKUSTIK I

MIT 183 FIGUREN

SPRINGER-VERLAG
BERLIN · GÖTTINGEN · HEIDELBERG
1961

Druck der Universitätsdruckerei H. Stürtz AG., Würzburg.

Inhaltsverzeichnis.

Linear Acoustic Theory.

By

PHILIP M. MORSE and K. UNO INGARD.

With 2 Figures.

A. Basic concepts and formulas.

Acoustical motion is, almost by definition, a perturbation. The slow compressions and expansions of materials, discussed in thermodynamics, are not thought of as acoustical phenomena, nor is the steady flow of air usually called sound. It is only when the compression is irregular enough so that over-all thermodynamic equilibrium may not be maintained, or when the steady flow is deflected by some obstacles so that wave motion is produced, that we consider part of the motion to be acoustical. In other words, we think of sound as a by-product, wanted or unwanted, of slower, more regular mechanical processes. And, whether the generating process be the motion of a violin bow or the rush of gas from a turbo-jet, the part of the motion we call sound usually carries but a minute fraction of the energy present in the primary process, which is not considered to be acoustical.

This definition of acoustical motion as being the small, irregular part of some larger, more regular motion of matter, gives rise to basic difficulties when we try to develop a consistent mathematical representation of its behavior. When the irregularities are large enough, for example, there is no clear-cut way of separating the "acoustical" part from the "non-acoustical" part of the motion. For example, in the midst of turbulence, the pressure at a given point varies with time as the flow vortices move past; should this variation be called a sound wave or should it be classed as the necessary concomitant of turbulent flow? Of course this vorticity produces pressure waves which extend beyond the region of turbulence, travelling in the otherwise still fluid with the speed of sound. Here we have no trouble in deciding that this part of the motion is acoustic. For the far field the distinction between acoustic and non-acoustic motion is fairly clear; for the near field the distinction often must be arbitrary.

So any definition of the nature of sound gives rise to taxonomic difficulties. If sound is any fluid motion involving time variation of pressure, then the theory of turbulence is a branch of acoustical theory. On the other hand, if sound is that fluid disturbance which travels with the speed of sound, then not only is turbulent motion not acoustic motion but also shock waves and other, non-linear or near-field effects are not included. In fact only in the cases where the non-steady motions are first-order perturbations of some larger, steady-state motion can one hope to make a self-consistent definition which separates acoustic from non-acoustic motion and, even here, there are ambiguities in the case of some types of near field, as will be indicated later in this article.

Thus it is not surprising that the earliest work in—and even now the majority of—acoustic theory has to do with situations where the acoustical part of the motion is small enough so that linear approximations can be used. These situations, and the linear equations which represent them, are the subject of this article. Strictly speaking, the equations to be discussed here are valid only when the acoustical component of the motion is "sufficiently" small; but it is only in this limit that we can unequivocably separate the total motion into its acoustical and its non-acoustical parts. As we have said, even here there are cases where the line of division is not completely clear, particularly when we try to represent the motion by partial differential equations and related boundary conditions; only when the representation is in terms of integral equations is the separation fairly straight-forward, even in the small-amplitude limit.

Still another limitation of the validity of acoustical theory is imposed by the atomicity of matter. The thermal motions of individual molecules, for instance, are not representable (usually) by the equations of sound; these equations are meant to represent the average behavior of large assemblies of molecules. Thus in this article, for instance, when we speak of an element of volume we implicitly assume that its dimensions, while being smaller than any wavelength of acoustical motion present, are large compared to inter-molecular spacings. Thus also, when we discuss the production of sound by the motion of boundaries, we take for granted that the boundary velocity is not greater than the mean thermal velocity of the fluid molecules.

In the present article we shall first develop the linear equations of acoustics, both their differential and integral counterparts, and discuss the various forms which are appropriate for different circumstances as well as the various basic techniques of their solution. We also discuss the effect, on these equations, of regular changes (in both time and space) of pressure, density, temperature and flow. The remainder of the article will deal with examples of the solution of these equations for situations of interest at the present time. No attempt will be made for complete coverage; the available space would preclude any such exhaustiveness, even if the authors had desired it.

I. The differential equations of linear acoustics.

1. Basic equations of motion [*1*], [*13*], [*16*], [*29*], [*60*], [*70*], [*73*]. Considering the fluid as a continuous medium, two points of view can be adopted in describing its motion. In the first, the Lagrangian description, the history of each individual fluid element, or "particle", is recorded in terms of its position as a function of time. Each particle is identified by means of a parameter, which usually is chosen to be the position vector $\boldsymbol{r}_0$ of the element at $t=0$. Thus the Lagrangian description of fluid motion is expressed by the set of functions $\boldsymbol{r}=\boldsymbol{r}(\boldsymbol{r}_0, t)$.

In the second, or Eulerian, description, on the other hand, the fluid motion is described in terms of a velocity field $\boldsymbol{V}(\boldsymbol{r}, t)$ in which $\boldsymbol{r}$ and t are now independent variables. The variation of $\boldsymbol{V}$ (or of any other fluid property, in this description) with time thus refers to a fixed point in space rather than to a specific fluid element, as in the Lagrangian description. If a field quantity is denoted by Ψ_L in the Lagrangian and by Ψ_E in the Eulerian description, the relation between the time derivatives in the two descriptions is

$$\frac{d\Psi_L}{dt} = \frac{\partial \Psi_E}{\partial t} + (\boldsymbol{V}\cdot\nabla)\,\Psi_E. \tag{1.1}$$

We note that in the case of linear acoustics for a homogeneous medium at rest we need not be concerned about the difference between $(d\Psi_L/dt)$ and $(\partial\Psi_E/\partial t)$, since the term $(\boldsymbol{V}\cdot\nabla)\,\Psi_E$ is then of second order. However in a moving or inhomogeneous medium the distinction must be maintained even in the linear approximation.

We shall ordinarily use the Eulerian description and if we ever need the Lagrangian time derivative we shall express it as $(d\Psi/dt) = (\partial\Psi/\partial t) + (\boldsymbol{V}\cdot\nabla)\Psi$ (without the subscripts). In this article the fluid motion is expressed in terms of the three velocity components V_i of the velocity vector $\boldsymbol{V}$. In addition, of course, the state of the fluid is described in terms of two independent thermodynamic variables such as pressure and temperature or density and entropy (we assume that thermodynamic equilibrium is maintained within each volume element). Thus in all we have five field variables; the three velocity components and the two independent thermodynamic variables. In order to determine these as functions of $\boldsymbol{r}$ and t we need five equations. These turn out to be the conservation laws; conservation of mass (one equation), conservation of momentum (three equations) and conservation of energy (one equation).

The *mass flow* in the fluid can be expressed by the vector components

$$\varrho V_i$$

and the *total momentum flux* by the tensor

$$t_{ij} = P_{ij} + \varrho V_i V_j,$$

in which the first term is the contribution from the thermal motion and the second terms the contribution from the gross motion of the fluid. The term P_{ij} is, of course, the *fluid stress tensor*

$$P_{ij} = (P - \varepsilon\nabla\cdot\boldsymbol{V})\,\delta_{ij} - 2\eta\,U_{ij} = P\,\delta_{ij} - D_{ij},$$

P is the total pressure in the fluid, D_{ij} is the viscous stress tensor, ε and η are two coefficients of viscosity, and

$$U_{ij} = \frac{1}{2}\left(\frac{\partial V_i}{\partial x_j} + \frac{\partial V_j}{\partial x_i}\right)$$

is the shear-strain tensor. In this notation the bulk viscosity would be $3\varepsilon + 2\eta$, and if this were zero (as STOKES assumed for an ideal gas) then η would equal $-3\varepsilon/2$. However acoustical measurement shows that bulk viscosity is not usually zero (in some cases it may be considerably larger than η) so we will assume that ε and η are independent parameters of the fluid.

In addition, we define the *energy density* of the fluid as

$$h = \tfrac{1}{2}\varrho V^2 + \varrho E,$$

the sum of its kinetic energy and the internal energy (E is the internal energy per unit mass) and the *energy flow vector*

$$I_i = h V_i + \sum_j P_{ij} V_j - K\frac{\partial T}{\partial x_i}$$

in which $-K(\partial T/\partial x_i)$ is the *heat flow vector*. The term $\sum_j P_{ij} V_j$ contains the work done by the pressure as well as the dissipation caused by the viscous stresses.

The basic equations of motion for the fluid, representing the conservation of mass, momentum and energy (exactly) can thus be written in the forms

$$\frac{\partial \varrho}{\partial t} + \sum_i \frac{\partial (\varrho V_i)}{\partial x_i} = Q(\boldsymbol{r}, t), \tag{1.2}$$

$$\frac{\partial (\varrho V_i)}{\partial t} + \sum_j \frac{\partial t_{ij}}{\partial x_j} = F_i(\boldsymbol{r}, t), \tag{1.3}$$

$$\frac{\partial h}{\partial t} + \sum_i \frac{\partial I_i}{\partial x_i} = H(\boldsymbol{r}, t) \tag{1.4}$$

in which Q, F_i and H are *source terms* representing the time rate of introduction of mass, momentum and heat energy into the fluid, per unit volume. The energy equation can be rewritten in a somewhat different form;

$$\varrho \frac{dE}{dt} \equiv \varrho \left(\frac{\partial E}{\partial t} + \boldsymbol{V} \cdot \nabla E \right) = K \nabla^2 T + D - P \nabla \cdot \boldsymbol{V} + H \tag{1.5}$$

which represents the fact that a given element of fluid has its internal energy changed either by heat flow, or by viscous dissipation

$$D = \sum_{ij} D_{ij} U_{ij} = \varepsilon \sum_j U_{jj}^2 + 2\eta \sum_{ij} U_{ij}^2,$$

or by direct change of volume, or else by direct injection of heat from outside the system.

This last form of the energy equation can, of course, be obtained directly from the first law of thermodynamics $(dE/dt) = T(dS/dt) + (P/\varrho^2)(d\varrho/dt)$ if, for the rate of entropy production per unit mass, we introduce

$$T \frac{dS}{dt} = \frac{K}{\varrho} \nabla^2 T + \frac{D}{\varrho} + \frac{H}{\varrho} \tag{1.6}$$

and for the density change $d\varrho/dt$ we use $(\partial \varrho/\partial t) + \boldsymbol{V} \cdot \nabla \varrho = -\varrho \nabla \cdot \boldsymbol{V}$.

If we wish to change from one pair of thermodynamic variables to another we usually make use of the *equation of state* of the gas. For a perfect gas this is, of course,

$$P = R \varrho T \quad \text{[see also Eq. (3.1)]}. \tag{1.7}$$

2. The wave equation. Returning to Eqs. (1.2) to (1.4), by elimination of $\partial^2(\varrho V_i)/\partial x_i \, \partial t$ from the first two, we obtain

$$\frac{\partial^2 \varrho}{\partial t^2} - c_0^2 \nabla^2 \varrho = \frac{\partial Q}{\partial t} - \sum_i \frac{\partial F_i}{\partial x_i} + \nabla^2 (P - c_0^2 \varrho) + \sum_{ij} \left[\frac{\partial^2 D_{ij}}{\partial x_i \, d x_j} + \frac{\partial^2 (\varrho V_i V_j)}{\partial x_i \, \partial x_j} \right]. \tag{2.1}$$

We have here subtracted the term $c_0^2 \nabla^2 \varrho$ from both sides of the equation, where c_0 is the space average of the velocity of sound (c_0 can depend on t). The right-hand terms will vanish for a homogeneous, loss-less, source-free medium at rest; the result is the familiar wave equation

$$\nabla^2 \varrho - \frac{1}{c_0^2} \frac{\partial^2 \varrho}{\partial t^2} = 0$$

for the density. Under all other circumstances the right-hand side of Eq. (2.1) will not vanish, but will represent some sort of sound "source", either produced by external forces or injections of fluid or by inhomogeneities, motions or losses in the fluid itself (this will become more apparent when we separate the equation into its successive approximations, in the next section).

The first term, representing the injection of fluid, gives rise to a monopole wave, as will be seen in Sect. 14. For air-flow sirens and pulsed-jet engines, for example, it represents the major source term. The second term, corresponding to body forces on the fluid, gives rise to dipole waves, as will be indicated in Sect. 14. Even when this term is independent of time it may have an effect on sound transmission, as we shall see later, in the case of the force of gravity, for example.

The third term on the right of Eq. (2.1) represents several effects. From Eq. (3.1) we will see that a variation of pressure is produced both by a density and an entropy variation. When the fluid changes are isentropic the term corresponds to the scattering or refraction of sound by variations in temperature or composition of the medium. It may also correspond to a source of sound, in the case of a fluctuating temperature in a turbulent medium. We shall return to this term in a later sub-section. If the motion is not isentropic, the term $\nabla^2(P - c_0^2\varrho)$ also contains contributions from entropy fluctuations in the medium. These effects will include losses produced by heat conduction and also the generation of sound by heat sources.

The fourth term, the double divergence of D_{ij}, represents the effects of viscous losses and/or the generation of sound by oscillating viscous stresses in a moving medium. If the coefficients of viscosity should vary from point to point, one would also have an effect of scattering from such inhomogeneities, but these are usually quite negligible. Finally the fifth term, the double divergence of the term $\varrho V_i V_j$ represents the scattering or the generation of sound caused by the motion of the medium [*30*], [*31*], [*52*]. If the two previous terms are thought of as stresses produced by thermal motion, this last term can be considered as representing the "Reynolds stress" of the gross motion; it is the major source of sound in turbulent flow. As will be indicated later, this term produces quadrupole radiation.

3. The linear approximation. After having summarised the possible effects in fluid motion we shall now consider the problem of linearisation of Eqs. (1.2) to (1.4) and the interpretation of the resulting acoustic equations. Eqs. (1.2) to (1.4) are non-linear in the variables ϱ and V_i. Not only are there terms where the product ϱV_i occurs explicitly, but also terms such as h and I_i implicitly depend on ϱ and V in a non-linear way. Furthermore, the momentum flux t_{ij} is not usually linearly related to the other field variables. In the first place the gross motion of the fluid (if there is such motion) contributes a stress $\varrho V_i V_j$ and in the second place there is a non-linear relationship between the pressure P and the other thermodynamic variables. For example, in an isentropic motion we have $(P/P_0) = (\varrho/\varrho_0)^\gamma$ and, for a non-isentropic motion we have

$$\frac{P}{P_0} = \left(\frac{\varrho}{\varrho_0}\right)^\gamma e^{(S-S_0)/C_v}. \tag{3.1}$$

Expanding this last equation, we can obtain

$$\left.\begin{aligned} P - P_0 &= \frac{\partial P_0}{\partial \varrho_0}(\varrho-\varrho_0) + \frac{\partial P_0}{\partial S_0}(S-S_0) + \\ &\quad + \frac{1}{2}\left[\frac{\partial^2 P}{\partial \varrho_0^2}(\varrho-\varrho_0)^2 + \frac{\partial^2 P}{\partial S_0^2}(S-S_0)^2\right] + \cdots \\ &= c^2(\varrho-\varrho_0) + \frac{P_0}{C_v}(S-S_0) + \frac{1}{2}(\gamma-1)\,c^2(\varrho-\varrho_0)^2 + \\ &\quad + \frac{P_0}{2C_v^2}(S-S_0)^2 + \cdots \end{aligned}\right\} \tag{3.2}$$

where the C's are specific heats, $\gamma = (C_p/C_v)$ and $c^2 = (\gamma P_0/\varrho_0)$. Thus only when the deviation of P from the equilibrium value P_0 is small enough is the linear relation

$$P \approx P_0 + c^2(\varrho - \varrho_0) + \frac{P_0}{C_v}(S - S_0) \tag{3.3}$$

a good approximation.

As was noted in the introduction, in acoustics we are usually concerned with the effects of some small, time-dependent deviations from the "equilibrium state" of the system. When the equilibrium state is homogeneous and static, the perturbation can easily be separated off and the resulting first-order equations are relatively simple. But when the "equilibrium state" involves inhomogeneities or steady flows the separation is less straight-forward. Even here, however, if the inhomogeneities are confined to a finite region of space, the equilibrium state outside this region being homogeneous and static, then the separating out of the acoustic motions in the outer region is not difficult. This will be discussed again in the Division on integral equations (Sects. 12 to 17).

In any case, we assume that the medium in the equilibrium state is described by the field quantities $\boldsymbol{V}_0 = \boldsymbol{v}$, P_0, ϱ_0, T_0 and S_0, for example, and define the *acoustic* velocity, pressure, density, temperature and entropy as the differences between the actual values and the equilibrium values

$$\left.\begin{array}{c} \boldsymbol{u} = \boldsymbol{V} - \boldsymbol{V}_0 = \boldsymbol{V} - \boldsymbol{v}; \quad p = P - P_0; \quad \delta = \varrho - \varrho_0, \\ \theta = T - T_0; \quad \sigma = S - S_0. \end{array}\right\} \tag{3.4}$$

If $\boldsymbol{u}$, p etc., are small enough we can obtain reasonably accurate equations, involving these acoustic variables to the first order, in terms of the equilibrium values (not necessarily to the first order). If we have already solved for the equilibrium state, the equilibrium values $\boldsymbol{V}_0 = \boldsymbol{v}$, P_0, etc., may be regarded as known parameters, p, $\boldsymbol{u}$, etc., being the unknowns. Thus the first order relationship between the acoustic pressure, density and entropy arising from Eq. (3.2) is

$$p \approx c^2\delta + \frac{P_0}{C_v}\sigma. \tag{3.5}$$

Our procedure will thus be to replace the quantities ϱ, $\boldsymbol{V}$, T etc., in Eqs. (1.2) to (1.5) by $(\varrho_0 + \delta)$, $(\boldsymbol{v} + \boldsymbol{u})$, $(T_0 + \theta)$, etc., and to keep only terms in first order of the acoustic quantities δ, $\boldsymbol{u}$, θ, etc. The terms containing only ϱ_0, $\boldsymbol{v}$, T_0, etc. (which we will call the *inhomogeneous terms*) need not be considered when we are computing the *propagation* of sound. On the other hand, in the study of the *generation* of sound these inhomogeneous terms are often the source terms.

In general the linear approximation thus obtained will be valid if the mean acoustic velocity amplitude $|\boldsymbol{u}|$ is small compared to the wave velocity c. There are exceptions however. In the problem of the diffraction of sound by a semi-infinite screen, for example, the acoustic velocity becomes very large in the regions close to the edge of the screen. In such regions non-linear effects are to be expected.

The linearised forms for the equations of conservation of mass, momentum and energy, and the equation of state (perfect gas), for a moving, inhomogeneous medium, are

$$\frac{\partial \delta}{\partial t} + \delta \sum_i \frac{\partial v_i}{\partial x_i} + \varrho_0 \sum_i \frac{\partial u_i}{\partial x_i} + \sum_i u_i \frac{\partial \varrho_0}{\partial x_i} \approx Q \quad (\boldsymbol{v} = \boldsymbol{V}_0), \tag{3.6}$$

$$\frac{\partial}{\partial t} (\varrho_0 u_i + \delta v_i) + \sum_j \frac{\partial}{\partial x_j} [\varrho_0 (u_i v_j + u_j v_i) + \delta v_i v_j + p_{ij}] \approx F_i, \tag{3.7}$$

$$\varrho_0 T_0 \left(\frac{\partial \sigma}{\partial t} + u \cdot \nabla S_0 \right) + \frac{p}{\mathsf{R}} \frac{d S_0}{dt} \approx K \nabla^2 \theta + 4\eta \sum_{ij} u_{ij} v_{ij} + H, \tag{3.8}$$

$$p \approx \mathsf{R} \varrho_0 \theta + \mathsf{R} T_0 \delta = c^2 \delta + \frac{P_0}{C_v} \sigma \tag{3.9}$$

where

$$\frac{d}{dt} = \frac{\partial}{\partial t} + (\boldsymbol{V} \cdot \nabla);$$

$$u_{ij} = \frac{1}{2} \left(\frac{\partial u_i}{\partial x_j} + \frac{\partial u_j}{\partial x_i} \right)$$

and

$$p_{ij} = p\, \delta_{ij} - d_{ij},$$
$$d_{ij} = \varepsilon \operatorname{div} (\boldsymbol{u})\, \delta_{ij} + 2\eta\, u_{ij}$$

are acoustic counterparts of the quantities defined earlier. The source terms Q, $\boldsymbol{F}$ and H are the "non-equilibrium" parts of the fluid injection, body force and heat injection; the equilibrium part of Q, for example, having been cancleed against $(\partial \varrho_0/\partial t) + \operatorname{div} (\varrho_0 \boldsymbol{v})$ from the left-hand side of (1.2).

These results are so general as to be impractical to use without further specialisation. For example, one has to assume that $\operatorname{div} \boldsymbol{v} = 0$ (usually a quite allowable assumption) before one can obtain the linear form of the general wave equation,

$$\left(\frac{\partial}{\partial t} + \boldsymbol{v} \cdot \nabla \right)^2 \delta - \nabla^2 p \approx \frac{\partial Q}{\partial t} - \nabla \cdot \boldsymbol{F} + \nabla \cdot \mathfrak{D} \cdot \nabla \tag{3.10}$$

where the last term is the double divergence of the tensor $\mathfrak{D}$, which has elements d_{ij}. In order to obtain a wave equation in terms of acoustic pressure p alone, we must determine δ and d_{ij} in terms of p. To do this in the most general case is not a particularly rewarding exercise; it is much more useful to do it for a number of specific situations which are of practical interest. This will be done in the next sections.

But, before we go to special cases, it is necessary to say a few words about the meaning of such quadratic quantities as acoustic intensity, acoustic energy density and the like. For example the energy flow vector

$$\boldsymbol{I} = (\tfrac{1}{2} \varrho V^2 + \varrho E)\, \boldsymbol{V} + \mathfrak{P} \cdot \boldsymbol{V} - K \operatorname{grad} T \tag{3.11}$$

where $\mathfrak{P}$ is the fluid stress tensor, with elements P_{ij}. The natural definition of the acoustic energy flow would be

$$\boldsymbol{i} = (\boldsymbol{I})_{\text{with sound}} - (\boldsymbol{I})_{\text{without sound}} = \boldsymbol{I} - \boldsymbol{I}_0 \tag{3.12}$$

with corresponding expressions for the acoustic energy density, $w = W - W_0$, and mass flow vector, $(\varrho \boldsymbol{V})_{\text{with sound}} - (\varrho_0 \boldsymbol{V}_0)$. Similarly with the momentum flow tensor, from which the acoustic radiation pressure tensor is obtained,

$$m_{ij} = (P_{ij} + \varrho V_i V_j)_{\text{with sound}} - (P_{ij} + \varrho V_i V_j)_{\text{without sound}}. \tag{3.13}$$

These quantities clearly will contain second order terms in the acoustic variables, therefore their rigorous calculation would require acoustic equations which are correct to the second order. As with Eq. (3.10), it is not very useful to perform this calculation in the most general case; results will be obtained later for special cases of interest. It is sufficient to point out here that the acoustic energy flow, etc., correct to second order, can indeed be expressed in terms of products of the first order acoustic variables.

In the general acoustic equations (3.6) to (3.9) we have included the source terms Q, $\boldsymbol{F}$ and H, corresponding to the rate of transfer of mass, momentum and heat energy from external sources. The sound field produced by these sources can be expressed in terms of volume integrals (see subsection 13) over these source functions. As mentioned above, we have not included terms, such as $\varrho V_i V_j$ or $\nabla^2 P_0$, which do not include the acoustic variables. The justification for this omission is that these terms balance each other locally in the equations of motion, for example fluctuations in velocities are balanced by local pressure fluctuations, and the like. These fluctuations produce sound (i.e. acoustic radiation), but in the region where the fluctuations occur (the near field) the acoustic radiation is small compared to the fluctuations themselves. However, the acoustic radiation produced by the fluctuations extends *outside* the region of fluctuation, into regions where the fluid is otherwise homogeneous and at rest (the far field) and here it can more easily be computed (and, experimentally, more easily measured).

Thus, in the study of the generation of sound by fluctuations in the fluid itself, it is essential to retain in the source terms the terms which do not contain the acoustic variables themselves. Within the region of fluctuation, the differentiation between sound and "equilibrium motion" is quite artificial (the local fluid motion could be regarded as part of the acoustic near field) and in many cases it will be more straightforward to use the original equations (1.2) to (1.5) and (2.1) in their integral form (see Sect. 13), where the net effect of the sources will appear as an integral over the region of fluctuation.

4. Acoustic equations for a fluid at rest. In this section and the next we will discuss the special forms taken on by Eqs. (3.6) to (3.13) when the equilibrium state of the fluid involves only a few of the various possible effects discussed above. At first we will assume that, in the equilibrium state, the fluid is at rest and that the acoustic changes in density are isentropic ($\sigma = 0$). In this case the relation between the acoustic pressure p and the acoustic density δ is simply

$$p = c^2 \delta; \qquad c^2 = \frac{\gamma P}{\varrho} \tag{4.1}$$

from Eq. (3.3). [From here on we will omit the subscript 0 from the symbols for equilibrium values, in situations like that of Eq. (4.1), where the difference between P and P_0 or ϱ and ϱ_0 would make only a second-order difference in the equations. We also will use the symbol $=$ instead of $\approx$; from now on we are committed to the linear equations.] The wave equation (3.10) then reduces to the familiar

$$\nabla^2 p - \frac{1}{c^2} \frac{\partial^2 p}{\partial t^2} = 0. \tag{4.2}$$

Once the pressure has been computed, the other acoustic variables follow from the equations of the previous subsection;

$$\left.\begin{aligned}
&\text{Velocity,} & \boldsymbol{u} &= -\frac{1}{\varrho}\int \operatorname{grad} p\, dt \\
& & &= \frac{1}{i k \varrho c} \operatorname{grad} p \quad (p = p_0\, e^{-i\omega t},\ \omega = k c), \\
&\text{Displacement,} & \boldsymbol{d} &= \int \boldsymbol{u}\, dt = -\frac{1}{k^2 \varrho c^2} \operatorname{grad} p \quad (p = p_0\, e^{-i\omega t},\ \omega = k c), \\
&\text{Temperature,} & \theta &= (\gamma - 1)\frac{T}{\varrho c^2}\, p \quad \left(\gamma = \frac{C_p}{C_v}\right), \\
&\text{Density} & \delta &= \frac{p}{c^2}.
\end{aligned}\right\} \tag{4.3}$$

All these variables satisfy a homogeneous wave equation such as Eq. (4.2). For a plane sound wave, which has the general form $p = f(ct - \boldsymbol{n}\cdot\boldsymbol{r})$ (where $\boldsymbol{n}$ is a unit vector normal to the wave front), the acoustic velocity is

$$\boldsymbol{u} = \frac{\boldsymbol{n}}{\varrho c} f(ct - \boldsymbol{n}\cdot\boldsymbol{r}). \tag{4.4}$$

The quantity ϱc is called the characteristic acoustic impedance of the medium. Since $\operatorname{div} \boldsymbol{d}$ is the relative volume change of the medium, we can use Eq. (4.1) to obtain another relation between $\boldsymbol{d}$ and p;

$$p = -\varrho c^2 \operatorname{div} \boldsymbol{d} \tag{4.5}$$

which states that the isentropic compressibility of the fluid is equal to $(1/\varrho c^2)$.

The sound energy flow vector (the *sound intensity*) is

$$\boldsymbol{i} = p\,\boldsymbol{u} = \varrho c\, u^2\, \boldsymbol{n} = \frac{p^2}{\varrho c}\, \boldsymbol{n}. \tag{4.6}$$

It is tempting to consider this equation as self-evident, but it should be remembered that $\boldsymbol{i}$ is a second-order quantity which must be evaluated from Eq. (3.12). In the special case of a homogeneous medium at rest the other second-order terms cancel out and Eq. (4.6) is indeed correct to second order [*35*], [*65*]. In a moving medium, the result is not so simple [*61*].

The situation is also not so straightforward in regard to the mass flow vector. One might assume that it equals $\delta\boldsymbol{u}$, but this would result in a non-zero, time-average, mass flow for a plane wave, an erroneous result. In this case the additional second-order terms in the basic equations do contribute, making the mass flow vector zero in the second-order approximation.

On the other hand the magnitude of the acoustic momentum flux is correctly given by the expression ϱu^2 to the second order. The rate of momentum transfer is, of course, equal to the *radiation pressure* on a perfect absorber [*3*].

Generally we are interested in the time average of these quantities. For single-frequency waves (time factor $e^{-i\omega t}$) these are

$$\boldsymbol{i} = \tfrac{1}{2}\operatorname{Re}(p\,\boldsymbol{u}^*) \tag{4.7}$$

where the asterisk denotes the complex conjugate. For a plane wave [see Eq. (4.4)]

$$\boldsymbol{i} = \frac{1}{2}\varrho c\,|u|^2 \boldsymbol{n} = \frac{\boldsymbol{n}}{2\varrho c}|p|^2. \tag{4.8}$$

The acoustic energy density is

$$w = \frac{1}{2}\varrho\,|u|^2 + \frac{1}{2\varrho c^2}|p|^2 \tag{4.9}$$

where the first term is the kinetic energy density and the second term the potential energy density. In a plane wave these are equal. We note that the magnitude of the acoustic radiation pressure is thus equal to the acoustic energy density.

The simple wave equation (4.2) is modified when there are body forces or inhomogeneities present, even though there is no motion of the fluid in the equilibrium state, as two examples will suffice to show. For example, the force of gravity has a direct effect on the wave motion, in addition to the indirect effect produced by the change in density with height. In this case the body force $\boldsymbol{F}$ is equal to $\varrho \boldsymbol{g}$, where $\boldsymbol{g}$ is the acceleration of gravity and thus the term div $\boldsymbol{F}$ in Eq. (3.10) becomes $\boldsymbol{g} \cdot \nabla \varrho + \varrho \nabla \cdot \boldsymbol{g}$, where the magnitude of the second term is to that of the first as the wavelength is to the radius of the earth, so the second term can usually be neglected. Therefore the wave equation, in the presence of the force of gravity is

$$\frac{\partial^2 p}{\partial t^2} = c^2 \nabla^2 p + \boldsymbol{g} \cdot \nabla p. \tag{4.10}$$

The added term has the effect of making the medium anisotropic. For a simple harmonic, plane wave exp $(i k \boldsymbol{n} \cdot \boldsymbol{r} - i \omega t)$ if $\boldsymbol{n}$ is perpendicular to $\boldsymbol{g}$ then $k = (\omega/c)$, but if $\boldsymbol{n}$ is parallel to $\boldsymbol{g}$ the propagation constant k is

$$k_g = i \frac{g}{2c^2} + \frac{\omega}{c} \sqrt{1 - \frac{g^2}{4c^2 \omega^2}}\,. \tag{4.11}$$

We note that a wave propagating downward (in the direction of $\boldsymbol{g}$) is attenuated at a rate $e^{-\alpha z}$, where $\alpha = (g/2c^2)$, independent of the frequency, and its phase velocity is $c/\sqrt{1 - (g^2/4c^2\omega^2)}$. If the frequency of the wave is less than $(g/4\pi c)$ there will be no wave motion downward.

A similar anisotropy occurs when the anisotropy is not produced by a body force but is caused by an inhomogeneity in one of the characteristics of the medium. In a solid or liquid medium the elasticity or the density may vary from point to point (as is caused by a salinity gradient in sea-water, for instance). If the medium is a gas the inhomogeneity must manifest itself by changes in temperature and/or entropy density. For a source-free medium at rest, Eq. (3.10) shows that $(\partial^2 \delta/\partial t^2) = \nabla^2 p$, but this equation reduces to the usual wave equation (4.2) only when the equilibrium entropy density is uniform and the acoustical motions are isentropic. If the equilibrium entropy density S_0 is *not* uniform the wave equation is modified, even though the acoustic motion is still isentropic.

If the acoustic disturbance is isentropic then $(dS/dt) = (\partial S/\partial t) + \boldsymbol{u} \cdot \nabla S = 0$, and if the equilibrium entropy density S_0 is a function of position but not of time, then

$$\frac{\partial \sigma}{\partial t} + \boldsymbol{u} \cdot \nabla S_0 = 0. \tag{4.12}$$

Referring to Eqs. (3.5) and (4.3), we obtain

$$\frac{\partial \delta}{\partial t} = \frac{1}{c^2} \frac{\partial p}{\partial t} - \frac{\varrho}{C_p} \frac{\partial \sigma}{\partial t} = \frac{1}{c^2} \frac{\partial p}{\partial t} + \frac{\varrho}{C_p} \boldsymbol{u} \cdot \nabla S_0,$$

and thus

$$\frac{\partial^2 \delta}{\partial t^2} = \frac{1}{c^2} \frac{\partial^2 p}{\partial t^2} - \frac{1}{C_p} \nabla p \cdot \nabla S_0$$

which, when inserted into Eq. (3.10) for a source-free medium at rest finally produces the equation

$$\frac{1}{c^2} \frac{\partial^2 p}{\partial t^2} = \nabla^2 p + \frac{1}{C_p} \nabla p \cdot \nabla S_0 \tag{4.13}$$

which has the same form as Eq. (4.10) representing the effect of gravity. Thus an entropy gradient in the equilibrium state will produce anisotropy in sound propagation. As with the solutions for Eq. (4.10), sound will be attenuated in the direction of entropy increase, will be amplified in the direction of decreasing S_0. However a much larger effect arises from the fact that a change in entropy will produce a change in c from point to point, so that the coefficient of $(\partial^2 p/\partial t^2)$ in Eq. (4.13) will depend on position.

5. The effects of motion and of transport phenomena. The effects of fluid motion can be demonstrated by discussing the behavior of a non-viscous, source-free, isentropic fluid moving with uniform velocity v in the x direction, with respect to the coordinates x, y, z. In this case the wave equation (3.10) reduces to

$$\frac{\partial^2 p}{\partial t^2} + 2v\frac{\partial^2 p}{\partial x\,\partial t} + v^2\frac{\partial^2 p}{\partial x^2} - c^2\nabla^2 p = 0. \tag{5.1}$$

The relation between the various acoustic variables may be obtained from Eqs. (3.6) to (3.9),

$$\left.\begin{aligned} \left(\frac{\partial}{\partial t} + v\frac{\partial}{\partial x}\right)\delta = -\varrho\,\mathrm{div}\,\boldsymbol{u}; \quad \varrho\left(\frac{\partial}{\partial t} + v\frac{\partial}{\partial x}\right)\theta = (\gamma - 1)\,T, \\ \varrho\left(\frac{\partial}{\partial t} + v\frac{\partial}{\partial x}\right)\boldsymbol{u} = -\,\mathrm{grad}\,p. \end{aligned}\right\} \tag{5.2}$$

It is clear that in a coordinate system moving with the medium, $x' = x - vt$, $y' = y$, $z' = z$, Eq. (5.1) reduces to the simple wave equation (4.2). However in many problems we have to do with boundaries which are at rest in the x-coordinates, so it is convenient to use Eq. (5.1). This can be simplified somewhat by changing the scale in the x direction,

$$x_1 = \frac{x}{\sqrt{1-M^2}}; \quad M = \frac{v}{c}; \quad y_1 = y; \quad z_1 = z$$

in terms of which Eq. (5.1) becomes

$$\frac{\partial^2 p}{\partial t^2} - \frac{2Mc}{\sqrt{1-M^2}}\,\frac{\partial^2 p}{\partial t\,\partial x_1} - c^2\nabla_1^2 p = 0. \tag{5.3}$$

An alternative coordinate system, useful in studying the radiation from stationary source in a moving medium, is one moving with the medium, but contracted in the direction of motion,

$$x_2 = \frac{x'}{\sqrt{1-M^2}} = \frac{x - vt}{\sqrt{1-M^2}} = x_1 - \frac{vt}{\sqrt{1-M^2}}; \quad y_2 = y; \quad z_2 = z$$

which results in the wave equation

$$\frac{1}{1-M^2}\,\frac{\partial^2 p}{\partial x_2^2} + \frac{\partial^2 p}{\partial y_2^2} + \frac{\partial^2 p}{\partial z_2^2} + \frac{1}{c^2}\,\frac{\partial^2 p}{\partial t^2} = 0. \tag{5.4}$$

To study the effects of transport phenomena, such as viscosity and heat conduction [22], we consider a homogeneous, source-free medium at rest. The linearised Eqs. (3.6) to (3.9) then become

$$\left.\begin{aligned} \frac{\partial\delta}{\partial t} + \varrho\,\mathrm{div}\,\boldsymbol{u} = 0; \quad \varrho\left(\frac{\partial u_i}{\partial t}\right) + \sum_j\left(\frac{\partial p_{ij}}{\partial x_j}\right) = 0, \\ \varrho\,C_v\left(\frac{\partial\theta}{\partial t}\right) = K\nabla^2\theta - P\,\mathrm{div}\,\boldsymbol{u}; \quad p = RT\,\delta + R\varrho\,\theta \end{aligned}\right\} \tag{5.5}$$

where, as before, $p_{ij} = (p - \varepsilon \operatorname{div} \boldsymbol{u})\, \delta_{ij} - \eta [(\partial u_i/\partial x_j) + (\partial u_j/\partial x_i)]$. The presence of viscosity introduces vorticity into the fluid motion, in which case it is convenient to express the acoustic velocity as the sum of an irrotational part $\boldsymbol{u}_g$ ($\operatorname{curl} \boldsymbol{u}_g = 0$) and a rotational part $\boldsymbol{u}_v$ ($\operatorname{div} \boldsymbol{u}_v = 0$). The equation for $\boldsymbol{u}_v$ comes from the second of Eqs. (5.5),

$$\varrho \frac{\partial \boldsymbol{u}_v}{\partial t} = \eta \nabla^2 \boldsymbol{u}_v = -\eta \operatorname{curl} (\operatorname{curl} \boldsymbol{u}_v) \tag{5.6}$$

which corresponds to the diffusion of vorticity, caused by viscosity, into the sound field.

The irrotational part of $\boldsymbol{u}$ can most easily be obtained from the gradient of θ. By eliminating $\operatorname{div} \boldsymbol{u}$ between the second and third of Eqs. (5.5), we can obtain a differential equation for θ. In the case of harmonic time dependence, where the time factors are $e^{-i\omega t}$ and $(\omega/c) = k$, this equation simplifies to the fourth-order form

$$(\nabla^2 + k_p^2)(\nabla^2 + k_h^2)\, \theta = 0 \tag{5.7}$$

where

$$\left.\begin{aligned}
k_p^2 &= -\frac{B}{2D}(1 - A); \qquad k_h^2 = -\frac{B}{2D}(1 + A),\\
A^2 &= 1 + \frac{4\omega^2 D}{B^2}; \qquad B = c^2 \left[1 - \frac{2}{3} i k^2 (l_v^2 + \gamma l_h^2)\right],\\
D &= i \frac{l_h^2 c^2}{2} \left[1 - \frac{2}{3} i \gamma (k l_v)^2\right],\\
l_v^2 &= \frac{2\eta}{\omega \varrho}; \qquad l_h^2 = \frac{2K}{\varrho \omega C_p}.
\end{aligned}\right\} \tag{5.8}$$

As will be shown in Sect. 11, the lengths l_v and l_h are the viscous and thermal boundary layer thicknesses. For air at normal pressure and temperature l_v and l_h are both approximately 0.007 cm at 1000 cps, quite small compared to most wavelengths. In this case, when $k l_v$ and $k l_h$ are small, the two propagation constants are approximately

$$\left.\begin{aligned}
k_p &\approx k \left\{1 + i \left[\frac{1}{3}(k l_v)^2 + \frac{1}{4}(\gamma - 1)(k l_h)^2\right]\right\};\\
k_h &\approx \frac{1 + i}{l_h}.
\end{aligned}\right\} \tag{5.9}$$

The solution of Eq. (5.7) is $\theta = \theta_p + \theta_h$, where the two components are solutions of the separated equations $(\nabla^2 + k_p^2)\, \theta_p = 0$ and $(\nabla^2 + k_h^2)\, \theta_h = 0$, respectively. The exact forms and magnitudes of the two components will be determined by the boundary conditions, as will be shown in the next Division (Sect. 11). Propagation constant k_p corresponds to the usual wave motion, with a small attenuation caused by both viscosity and heat conduction. Constant k_h corresponds to thermal boundary waves near a conducting surface; these waves are negligible more than a distance l_h away from the surface.

The corresponding acoustic velocity and pressure can be obtained once θ_p and θ_h have been found. For example the velocity is

$$\boldsymbol{u} = \boldsymbol{u}_v + \frac{i\omega}{T k_p^2}\left[1 - \frac{1}{2}\gamma (k_p l_h)^2\right] \operatorname{grad} \theta_p + \frac{i\omega}{T k_h^2}\left[1 - \frac{1}{2}\gamma (k_s l_h)^2\right] \operatorname{grad} \theta_h. \tag{5.10}$$

The first and last terms are important only near boundary surfaces, the first forming the viscous boundary layer and the third the thermal boundary layer. The second term represents the main contribution to the acoustic field away from these boundary layers.

6. Internal energy losses. For some purposes it may be sufficient to compute the energy lost per unit volume of the fluid, as a quadratic function of the acoustic variables, rather than to work out the solution of Eqs. (5.6) and (5.7). In this Division we consider the losses in the main body of the medium; in the next Division (Sect. 11) we treat losses near a boundary surface. We also confine our discussion to the effects of viscosity and heat conduction on a homogeneous fluid at rest.

The average rate of energy loss per unit volume of the fluid can be calculated from the time average of the "loss function"

$$L = -\sum_{ij} P_{ij}\, U_{ij},$$

where, from Sect. 1, P_{ij} are elements of the stress tensor and U_{ij} elements of the strain tensor. Separating

$$P_{ij} = (P_0 + p)\,\delta_{ij} - D_{ij}$$

into its pressure and viscous components, we have

$$L = -(P_0 + p)\,\nabla\cdot\boldsymbol{u} + \sum_{ij} D_{ij}\, U_{ij}. \tag{6.1}$$

If we consider harmonic time dependence (time factor $e^{-i\omega t}$) only and disregard second-order terms, the time average of $P_0 \nabla\cdot\boldsymbol{u}$ is zero. Since also $\nabla\cdot\boldsymbol{u} = -(1/\varrho)\,(\partial\delta/\partial t)$, we can write the average acoustic energy loss per unit volume per second as

$$\overline{L} = \left[\frac{p}{\varrho}\,\frac{\partial\delta}{\partial t}\right]_{\rm av} + \left[\sum_{ij} D_{ij}\, U_{ij}\right]_{\rm av}. \tag{6.2}$$

The first term represents the average work done on the medium by the acoustic pressure, which results in an increase of the internal energy of the medium and a "leakage" of energy due to heat conduction. The heat leakage produces a phase difference between the pressure p and the density δ so that the time average of $p\,(\partial\delta/\partial t)$ differs from zero.

When the time factor is $e^{-i\omega t}$ the first term in (6.2) can be expressed as $\frac{1}{2}\,\mathrm{Re}\,[-i\omega p^*\,\delta/\varrho]$ where p^* is the complex conjugate of p. Introducing the compressibility $\varkappa = (\delta/\varrho p)$ of the fluid, we obtain

$$\overline{L} = \tfrac{1}{2}\,\mathrm{Re}\,(-i\,\omega\,\varkappa\,|p|^2) + \overline{D};\quad \overline{D} = \left[\sum_{ij} D_{ij}\, U_{ij}\right]_{\rm av}. \tag{6.3}$$

The viscous dissipation function $\overline{D}$ can be calculated directly from the acoustic velocity field, and needs no further discussion here. The evaluation of the compressibility $\varkappa$, however, requires further discussion.

From the linearised equations (3.5) to (3.9) we have (when v is zero and S_0 is constant)

$$\left.\begin{aligned} &\varrho\, T\,\frac{\partial\sigma}{\partial t} = K\,\nabla^2\theta \approx \frac{K}{\varrho\, C_p}\,\nabla^2 p \approx -k^2\,\frac{K p}{\varrho\, C_p};\\ &p = c^2\,\delta + \frac{P}{C_v}\,\sigma;\quad k = \frac{\omega}{c}\end{aligned}\right\} \tag{6.4}$$

where we have used $\theta = (p/\varrho\, C_p) + (T\sigma/C_p)$ and have discarded the term containing $K\sigma$ as being of order K^2. By eliminating σ in these two equations we obtain a first-order expression for the compressibility

$$\varkappa = \frac{1}{\varrho\, c^2}\left[1 + i\,\frac{\gamma-1}{2\gamma}\,(k\, l_h)^2\right] \tag{6.5}$$

where

$$c^2 = \frac{\gamma P}{\varrho}; \quad l_h^2 = \frac{2K}{\varrho\omega C_v}.$$

Therefore, according to Eq. (6.3), the average rate of energy loss per unit volume in a sound field can be expressed as

$$\left.\begin{aligned} \bar{I} &= \frac{\gamma-1}{2\gamma}\,\omega\,(k\,l_h)^2\,\frac{|p|^2}{2\varrho c^2} + \bar{D} \\ &= (\gamma-1)\,\frac{K\omega^2}{\varrho C_p c^3}\,\frac{|p|^2}{2\varrho c} + \bar{D}. \end{aligned}\right\} \tag{6.6}$$

In obtaining this expression we have neglected terms higher than first order in the conduction and viscosity coefficients; it will thus be consistent to use in Eq. (6.6) the pressure and velocity obtained from a "loss-free" solution.

As an example of the use of Eq. (6.6) we compute the attenuation of a plane wave. The viscous dissipation function in this case becomes

$$\bar{D} = \frac{4\eta}{3}\left[\left(\frac{\partial u}{\partial x}\right)^2\right]_{\text{av}} = \left(\frac{4\eta}{3}\right) k^2 (u^2)_{\text{av}} = \frac{4\eta\omega^2}{3\varrho c^3}\,\frac{\varrho c}{2}\,|u|^2 \tag{6.7}$$

where we have assumed that $\varepsilon = -(2\eta/3)$ [see discussion preceding Eq. (1.2)]. Since the intensity in a plane wave is

$$\frac{|p|^2}{2\varrho c} = \frac{\varrho c\,|u|^2}{2} = I,$$

we can consider Eq. (6.6) to give the attenuation of intensity,

$$\frac{dI}{dx} = -I\left[\frac{4\eta}{3} + (\gamma-1)\,\frac{K}{\varrho C_p}\right]\frac{\omega^2}{c^3} \tag{6.8}$$

which results in an *energy attenuation* factor $e^{-\alpha x}$ with an attenuation constant

$$\alpha_t = \left[\frac{4\eta}{3} + (\gamma-1)\,\frac{K}{\varrho C_p}\right]\frac{\omega^2}{c^3} \tag{6.9}$$

as could have been obtained from Eq. (5.9). The corresponding pressure attenuation constant is $\alpha/2$. It should be noted that the method of this section is applicable to non-plane waves; similar extension of Sect. 5 is much more difficult.

In addition to the thermal relaxation caused by heat conduction, as discussed above, in polyatomic gases and in most liquids there are additional relaxation effects resulting from energy transfer from translational to rotational and vibrational degrees of freedom of the molecules [*23*], [*24*], [*36*]. These effects produce an additional imaginary term in the expression for the compressibility and a corresponding increase in loss. In the case of a plane wave this attenuation, per wavelength $\lambda = 2\pi c/\omega$ can be written in the form

$$\lambda\,\alpha_r = \frac{2\alpha_{\max}\,(f/f_r)}{1+(f/f_r)^2} \qquad (\omega = 2\pi f) \tag{6.10}$$

where f is the sound frequency and f_r the relaxation frequency. The maximum attenuation $\alpha_{\max}$ (occurring when $f = f_r$) and also f_r itself, vary widely from one gas to another, and depend markedly on the temperature and the impurities in the gas. In air the attenuation α_r produced by this latter effect is much larger than that produced by viscosity and heat conduction, α_t, in most circumstances. The total attenuation constant α is, of course, the sum of α_r and α_t.

II. Boundary conditions.

7. Reaction of the surface to sound [*40*], [*43*]. We now must discuss the behavior of sound in the neighborhood of a boundary surface, and see whether we can express this behavior in terms of boundary conditions on the acoustic field. It will turn out that in many cases the sorts of boundary conditions familiar in the classical theory of boundary-value-problems, such as that the ratio of value to normal gradient of pressure is specified at every point on the boundary, is at least approximately valid.

At first sight it may seem surprising that the ratio of pressure to its normal gradient, which to first order [see Eq. (4.3)] equals the ratio of pressure to normal velocity at the surface, could be specified, even approximately, at each point of the surface, independently of the configuration of the incident wave. Of course if the wall is perfectly rigid, so that the value of the ratio is infinite everywhere, the assumption that this ratio is independent of the nature of the incident wave is not so surprising. But many actual boundary surfaces are not very rigid, and in many problems in theoretical acoustics the effect of the yielding of the boundary to the sound pressure is the essential part of the problem. When the boundary does yield, for the "classical" boundary conditions to be valid would imply that the ratio of incident pressure to normal displacement of the boundary would be a characteristic of each point of the surface by itself, independent of what happens at any other point on the surface. To see what this implies, regarding the acoustic nature of the boundary surface, and when it is likely to be valid, let us discuss the simple case of the incidence of a plane wave of sound on a plane boundary surface.

Suppose the boundary is the y-z plane, with the boundary material occupying the region of positive x and the fluid carrying the incident sound wave occupying the region of negative x, to the left of the boundary plane. Suppose also that the incident wave has frequency $\omega/2\pi$ and that its direction of propagation is at the angle of incidence ϕ to the x axis, the direction normal to the boundary. The incident wave, therefore, has a pressure and fluid-velocity distribution, within the fluid, given by [see Eqs. (4.4)]

$$\left.\begin{aligned} p &= p_i \exp\left(i k x \cos\phi + i k y \sin\phi - i \omega t\right), \\ \boldsymbol{u} &= \frac{p}{\varrho c}\left(\boldsymbol{a}_x \cos\phi + \boldsymbol{a}_y \sin\phi\right), \qquad k = \frac{\omega}{c} = \frac{2\pi}{\lambda}, \end{aligned}\right\} \tag{7.1}$$

where ϱ is the fluid density, c is the velocity of sound waves and λ the wave length of the wave in the fluid in the region $x < 0$.

At $x = 0$ the wave is modified because the boundary surface does not move in response to the pressure in the same way that the free fluid does. In general the presence of the acoustic pressure p produces motion of the surface, but the degree of motion depends on the nature of the boundary material and its structure. If the fluid viscosity is small we can safely assume that the tangential component of fluid velocity close to the surface need not be equal to the tangential velocity of the boundary itself; thus a discontinuity in tangential velocity is allowed at the boundary. But there must be continuity in normal velocity through the boundary surface, and there must also be continuity in pressure across the surface [*10*], [*78*].

If the surface is porous, so that the fluid can penetrate into the surface material, then there can be an average fluid velocity into the surface without motion of the boundary material itself. If the pores do not interconnect then it would be true that the mean normal velocity of penetration of the fluid into the pores would bear a simple ratio to the pressure at the surface, independent of the pressure and velocity of the wave at other points on the surface. In this case we could expect the ratio between pressure and normal velocity at the surface to be a point property of the surface, perhaps dependent on the frequency of the incident wave but independent of its configuration.

8. Acoustic impedance. The ratio between pressure and velocity normal to a boundary surface is called the *normal acoustic impedance* z_n of the surface. When it is a point property of the surface, independent of the configuration of the incident wave (and we have indicated that this is the case in practice for many porous surfaces) then the "classical" type of boundary condition is applicable. For with a wave of frequency $\omega/2\pi$ the normal fluid velocity just outside the surface is equal to $(1/i\omega\varrho)$ times the normal gradient of the pressure there. Thus the ratio of pressure to its normal gradient at a point of the surface would equal the value of the normal impedance of the surface at the point, divided by $ik\varrho c$, where $k=\omega/c=2\pi/\lambda$ and where ϱc is the characteristic impedance of the fluid medium [see Eq. (4.4)];

$$\frac{p}{\partial p/\partial n} = \frac{z_n}{ik\varrho c} = \frac{\zeta}{ik} = \frac{1}{ik}(\chi - i\xi) \tag{8.1}$$

where ζ is the dimensionless *specific impedance* of the surface and χ and ξ are its resistive and reactive components[1]. If z_n is a point property of the surface then "classical" boundary conditions can be used for single-frequency incident waves.

For example, for the conditions of Eq. (7.1), the ratio between the reflected amplitude p_r and the incident amplitude p_i in the total wave in the region $x<0$

$$p = (p_i e^{ikx\cos\phi} + p_r e^{-ikx\cos\phi})\, e^{iky\sin\phi - i\omega t} \tag{8.2}$$

is easily shown from Eq. (8.1) to be

$$R = \frac{p_i}{p_r} = \frac{-1+\zeta\cos\phi}{1+\zeta\cos\phi} = -\frac{(1-\chi\cos\phi)+i\xi\cos\phi}{(1+\chi\cos\phi)-i\xi\cos\phi} \tag{8.3}$$

and the ratio of reflected to incident intensity is

$$|R|^2 = 1-\alpha = \frac{(1-\chi\cos\phi)^2+\xi^2\cos^2\phi}{(1+\chi\cos\phi)^2+\xi^2\cos^2\phi} \tag{8.4}$$

where α is called the *absorption coefficient* of the surface. If χ and ξ are point properties of the surface, independent of the configuration of the incident wave (independent, in this case, of the angle of incidence ϕ) then the problem is solved. The fraction α of energy absorbed by the surface can be computed from Eq. (8.4) as a function of the incident angle ϕ, considering χ and ξ to be independent of ϕ. For example, if the specific resistance χ is larger than unity the absorption coefficient has a maximum for an angle of incidence $\phi = \operatorname{arc}\cos(1/\chi)$, dropping to zero at grazing incidence, $\phi=90°$.

But if $z_n=\varrho c\zeta$ is not a point function of position on the boundary surface then the problem is not really solved, for the value of z_n will depend on the configuration of the motion of the boundary surface itself, and to obtain the appropriate values of χ and ξ to use in Eq. (8.4) we will have to investigate the behavior of the sound wave inside the boundary material, an investigation we do not need to undertake when z_n is a point function of position and the "classical" boundary conditions of Eq. (8.1) can be used.

[1] It should be pointed out that the time factor used in this article is $\exp(-i\omega t)$, so that the reactance of a mass is $-i\omega m$. Using the negative sign in the definition of ξ thus makes it correspond to the usual definitions; thus $\xi=+\omega m$ is a mass reactance.

9. Exceptions to the classical boundary conditions. To appreciate the nature of the difficulties which then arise let us continue to discuss the simple example of Eq. (7.1), that of a plane wave incident on a plane boundary, for the case where we do have to consider the wave motion inside the boundary. To keep the example simple, we suppose the material forming the boundary to fill the region $x > 0$ uniformly. We will also suppose that the material is "homogeneous" to the extent that we can talk about a mean displacement and velocity of the material (see discussion in Sect. 4). The wave properties of the material may not be isotropic, however; we shall assume that the wave velocity in the x direction is c_n and that in a direction parallel to the boundary plane is c_t, where both these quantities may be complex and also frequency dependent. In other words, pressure waves are possible in the material, the wave equation and the relation between pressure and material velocity,

$$\left.\begin{aligned} & c_n^2 \frac{\partial^2 p}{\partial x^2} + c_t^2 \left(\frac{\partial^2 p}{\partial y^2} + \frac{\partial^2 p}{\partial z^2}\right) + \omega^2 p = 0, \\ & u_x = \frac{1}{i\omega \varrho_n} \frac{\partial p}{\partial x}, \quad u_y = \frac{1}{i\omega \varrho_t} \frac{\partial p}{\partial y}, \quad u_z = \frac{1}{i\omega \varrho_t} \frac{\partial p}{\partial z} \end{aligned}\right\} \tag{9.1}$$

serving to define the quantities c_n, c_t, ϱ_n and ϱ_t.

If the pressure inside the boundary ($x > 0$) is to satisfy this wave equation and also to fit the wave form of Eq. (8.2) at $x = 0$, then the pressure and velocity waves inside the material must be

$$\left.\begin{aligned} & p = p_t \exp\left[i k_n x \sqrt{1 - \left(\frac{c_t}{c}\right)^2 \sin^2\phi} + i k y \sin\phi - i\omega t\right], \\ & \boldsymbol{u} = \frac{p}{\varrho_n c_n} \boldsymbol{a}_x \sqrt{1 - \left(\frac{c_t}{c}\right)^2 \sin^2\phi} + \frac{p}{\varrho_t c_t} \boldsymbol{a}_y \frac{c_t}{c} \sin\phi \end{aligned}\right\} \tag{9.2}$$

where $k_n = \omega/c_n$, $k = \omega/c$ and c is the sound velocity in the fluid outside the boundary ($x < 0$). Equating p and u_x at $x = 0$ with those from Eq. (8.2), we find for the ratio of reflected to incident pressures, outside the boundary surface,

$$R = \frac{p_r}{p_i} = \frac{-\sqrt{1 - (c_t/c)^2 \sin^2\phi} + (\varrho_n c_n/\varrho c) \cos\phi}{\sqrt{1 - (c_t/c)^2 \sin^2\phi} + (\varrho_n c_n/\varrho c) \cos\phi}. \tag{9.3}$$

The absorption coefficient α is $1 - |R|^2$, as before.

Comparison with Eq. (8.3) shows that the specific surface impedance in this instance is

$$\zeta(\phi) = \frac{\varrho_n c_n}{\varrho c} \left[1 - \left(\frac{c_t}{c}\right)^2 \sin^2\phi\right]^{-\frac{1}{2}} \tag{9.4}$$

which is *not* independent of ϕ unless c_t, the transverse velocity in the boundary material, is negligibly small compared to c, the wave velocity in the fluid outside the boundary. Unless c_t is small compared to c the impedance of the surface is not a point property of the surface, independent of the configuration of the incident wave (in the example, independent of ϕ), and to find its value for any specific configuration of incident wave we must work out the corresponding wave configuration *inside* the boundary material.

From the point of view of the theoretical acoustician, therefore, there are two general types of boundary-value problems which are encountered. The first type is where the boundary material is such that its normal acoustic impendance is a point property of the surface, independent of the configuration of the incident wave. For this type the ratio of pressure to normal gradient of pressure at each point of the boundary is uniquely specified for each frequency, and the well-known methods of the classical theory of boundary-value problems can be employed. The second type is where it is not possible to consider the surface impedance to be independent of the configuration of the incident wave. In these types of problems it is not possible to substitute a surface impedance for an analysis of the wave inside the boundary; here the internal wave must be studied in detail and its reaction to the incident external wave must be calculated for each configuration of incident wave. These types of problems are usually much more difficult of solution than are the first type.

The survey of the theory of linear acoustics which follows Chapter A will therefore be divided into two chapters. The first, Chapter B, will be devoted to problems of the first type, where it is assumed that surface velocities or surface impedances can be specified for each point of the boundary surfaces involved, and where it is necessary only to compute the wave motion in the fluid medium "outside" these boundaries. The second, Chapter C, will deal with problems of the second type, where the interaction between the waves on both sides of the boundary surface must be worked out in detail for each problem. Here some of the newer techniques of boundary-value theory, such as the variational principles for continuous eigenvalues, and the Wiener-Hopf method, demonstrate their power and their utility.

10. Effects of relative motion of fluid and boundary. The tangential motion of the medium past the boundary produces special effects which should be discussed. If the boundary is a perfectly rigid plane and the medium flows past it tangentially then, except for the effects of viscous drag (touched on in the next section and discussed again in Chapter B), no effect of the relative motion will be apparent and Eqs. (8.2) to (8.4) (for $\zeta\to\infty$ since the boundary is rigid) will hold in the coordinates which are at rest with respect to the medium. But if the boundary is not rigid ($|\beta|=|1/\zeta|>0$) its surface will not be perfectly plane in the presence of an incident sound wave, and relative motion of the fluid medium past this non-plane surface will produce acoustic effects. To analyze this in a simple manner it is best to deal, not with the normal velocity of the surface, but with its normal displacement [*19*], [*28*], [*61*].

As before, the boundary, when no sound waves are present, is the plane $x=0$. The fluid medium is in the region $x<0$ and, in this case, is moving with constant velocity V in the y direction. The boundary is specified acoustically by its admittance, $1/z=\beta/\varrho c=(\varkappa-i\sigma)/\varrho c$. We wish again to determine the reflection of a plane sound wave from the boundary, as a function of its angle of incidence ϕ, as in Sect. 8, except that now the medium has tangential velocity V. To begin with we shall assume that the incidence-reflection plane is the x-y plane, parallel to the mass flow of the medium. The coordinates are taken to be at rest with respect to the boundary, not the medium, and the angle of incidence ϕ is with respect to the boundary at rest.

The wave equation (5.1) for a sound wave in a uniformly moving fluid now reduces to

$$\frac{1}{c^2}\left(\frac{\partial}{\partial t}+V\frac{\partial}{\partial y}\right)^2 p=\nabla^2 p. \tag{10.1}$$

For an incident wave of the form $p_i\exp(ik_x x+ik_y y-i\omega t)$, with the ratio $(k_y/k_x)=\tan\phi$, we obtain from (10.1),

$$k_x=\frac{k\cos\phi}{M\sin\phi+1};\qquad k_y=\frac{k\sin\phi}{M\sin\phi+1};\qquad k=\frac{\omega}{c};\qquad M=\frac{V}{c}. \tag{10.2}$$

The acoustic pressure at the boundary produces a displacement of the boundary d_x which, according to the discussion of Sect. 8, is related to the pressure by the equation

$$\frac{\partial d_x}{\partial t} = \frac{\beta}{\varrho c} p \tag{10.3}$$

where β is the specific admittance of the surface, assumed at present to be a point function of the surface.

When the boundary is thus displaced we can no longer consider the fluid flow to be exclusively in the y direction; it will follow the boundary and thus have a velocity in the x direction. This component is of first order in the acoustic variables and thus must be included in the matching of boundary conditions. From Eqs. (3.10) and (4.3) we obtain the relation between acoustic pressure and acoustic displacement for this case,

$$\varrho\left(\frac{\partial}{\partial t} + V\frac{\partial}{\partial y}\right)^2 d_x = -\frac{\partial p}{\partial x} \quad \text{at } x = 0. \tag{10.4}$$

As in Eq. (8.2), we take for the total wave

$$p = p_i(\mathrm{e}^{ik_x x} + R\,\mathrm{e}^{-ik_x x})\,\mathrm{e}^{ik_y y - i\omega t}$$

and, by using Eqs. (10.2) to (10.4) we obtain for the reflection coefficient R the modified formula

$$R = \frac{\zeta(M\sin\phi + 1)\cos\phi - 1}{\zeta(M\sin\phi + 1)\cos\phi + 1} = \frac{(M\sin\phi + 1)\cos\phi - \beta}{(M\sin\phi + 1)\cos\phi + \beta} \tag{10.5}$$

which is to be compared to Eq. (8.2). The effect of the fluid motion is to add a factor $(M\sin\phi + 1)$, which can either be thought of as modifying the impedance ζ or else as modifying the angle factor $\cos\phi$. The corresponding absorption coefficient is

$$\alpha = \frac{4\varkappa(M\sin\phi + 1)\cos\phi}{[(M\sin\phi + 1)\cos\phi + \varkappa]^2 + \sigma^2}; \quad \beta = \varkappa - i\sigma. \tag{10.6}$$

If the incidence-reflection plane is at an angle θ to the fluid flow $\boldsymbol{V}$, then M is replaced by $M\cos\theta$ in these formulas.

It is not difficult to compute R and α when β is not a point function of the boundary. As shown in Eq. (9.4) the results for an incident plane wave simply are that β (or ζ) may now be considered to be functions of ϕ, the angle of incidence. For example, suppose the material on both sides of the boundary $x=0$ is the same, only the fluid in $x > 0$ is at rest and that in $x < 0$ is moving with velocity V in the y direction. The angle of incidence of the wave in the moving fluid (with respect to fixed axes) is again ϕ. The angle of refraction, giving the direction of propagation of the wave in the quiescent fluid in $x > 0$, ϕ_r, must satisfy the boundary condition $k_y = k\sin\phi_r$, so that

$$\sin\phi_r = \frac{\sin\phi}{M\sin\phi + 1}. \tag{10.7}$$

The equivalent admittance is then $(u_x/p) = (1/\varrho c)\cos\phi_r$ and the corresponding reflection coefficient R, and T the transmission coefficient, the ratio of transmitted to incident amplitudes,

$$R = \frac{\sin 2\phi - \sin 2\phi_r}{\sin 2\phi + \sin 2\phi_r}; \quad T = \frac{2\sin 2\phi_r}{\sin 2\phi + \sin 2\phi_r}. \tag{10.8}$$

The formula for T can be used to estimate the transmission of high frequency sound away from a jet, for example.

11. Viscous and conduction losses near a boundary [*10*], [*25*]. Near heat-conducting boundary surfaces the viscous and heat-conduction losses are considerably larger than in regions away from a boundary. In the free field the quantity $\nabla^2\theta$ is of the order θ/λ^2, whereas close to a good heat conductor $\nabla^2\theta$ is more nearly equal to θ/l_h^2, where l_h is the small quantity defined in Eq. (5.8).

In the present analysis we assume the tangential acoustic velocity u_t to be zero at the boundary (we assume that the medium in equilibrium is at rest and homogeneous). Furthermore we shall consider the thermal conductivity and heat capacity of the surface material to be so much larger than those of the medium that we can take the temperature at the boundary to be constant, i.e., that the acoustic temperature there is zero.

This analysis is based on the fact that the tangential velocity and the acoustic temperature decrease rapidly to zero at the boundary inside a boundary layer having thickness small compared to the usual wavelength. In this layer the viscous shear forces produce losses and, in addition, the compressibility of the medium is complex as it varies from the almost adiabatic value outside the layer to the isothermal value at the surface. The problem thus reduces to the determination of the velocity distribution and the complex compressibility in the boundary layer. The losses can then be obtained by using Eq. (6.2).

We start by considering the boundary to be the y, z plane, as before (the medium in the region of positive x) and the acoustic velocity to be in the x, y plane (plane of incidence the x, y plane). The tangential component of the velocity, u_y, is zero at $x=0$ and increases rapidly with x, within the boundary layer, to a value u_t roughly equal to the velocity the medium would have next to the surface of it had no viscosity. In calculating the velocity distribution within the layer we neglect $(\partial^2 u_y/\partial y^2)$ in comparison with $(\partial^2 u_y/\partial y^2)$ in the second of Eqs. (5.5), which then becomes

$$\varrho\frac{\partial u_y}{\partial t}+\frac{\partial p}{\partial y}-\eta\frac{\partial^2 u_y}{\partial x^2}=0. \tag{11.1}$$

For wavelengths large compared to the layer thickness p will not vary much across the layer, so that $(\partial p/\partial y)$ should equal $-\varrho(\partial u_t/\partial t)$ [from Eq. (4.3)] where u_t is the tangential velocity just outside the layer. Thus

$$\varrho\frac{\partial(u_y-u_t)}{\partial t}\approx\eta\frac{\partial^2 u_y}{\partial x^2}. \tag{11.2}$$

If we assume that the time factor is $e^{-i\omega t}$ then the solution which is zero at $x=0$ and is u_t at "infinity" is

$$u_y=|u_t|\left[1-e^{-(1-i)x/l_v}\right]e^{-i\omega t};\qquad l_v^2=\frac{2\eta}{\varrho\omega} \tag{11.3}$$

where l_v is the thickness of the acoustic viscous boundary layer; the tangential velocity u_y rapidly approaches u_t beyond this layer. As mentioned above, u_t is the tangential velocity at $x=0$ in the solution obtained when viscosity is neglected.

The rate of viscous dissipation per unit area of the boundary can now be calculated as $\int\bar{D}\,dx$, where $\bar{D}$ is the viscous dissipation function of Eq. (6.3). The major term in D is $\eta(\partial u_y/\partial x)^2$, and from (11.3) we obtain

$$\left.\begin{aligned}(\text{Viscous loss per unit area})&=\int_0^\infty\bar{D}\,dx\\&=\frac{1}{2}\eta\frac{|u_t|^2}{l_v}=\frac{1}{2}R_v|u_t|^2,\\R_v=\frac{\eta}{l_v}&=\sqrt{\frac{\eta\omega\varrho}{2}}=\frac{1}{2}(k l_v)\,\varrho c.\end{aligned}\right\} \tag{11.4}$$

R_v may be considered as a viscous surface resistance, although we shall see in Sect. 18 that R_v does not behave like an additional acoustic resistance of the boundary surface. For air at 15° C we find that $R_v \approx (0.83 \times 10^{-3}) \sqrt{f}$.

The effect of heat conduction on the temperature distribution can be computed in a similar manner. If we neglect $(\partial^2\theta/\partial y^2)$ in comparison to $(\partial^2\theta/\partial x^2)$, the third of Eqs. (5.5) can be written as

$$\varrho C_v \frac{\partial \theta}{\partial t} \approx K \frac{\partial^2 \theta}{\partial x^2} - P \operatorname{div} u.$$

In the region where $(\partial^2\theta/\partial x^2)$ is small we have

$$\varrho C_v \frac{\partial \theta}{\partial t} = P \frac{\partial \delta}{\partial t},$$

which is the same as

$$\theta = \frac{P}{C_v \varrho} \delta = (\gamma - 1)\, T \frac{\delta}{\varrho},$$

the usual isentropic relationship between temperature and density in a sound wave. This temperature variation will exist outside the boundary layer. If we neglect the variation of density within the layer (any variation of δ with x will be proportional to K, so the term proportional to $\partial^2\delta/\partial x^2$ will be proportional to K^2, which can be neglected) we can obtain a simplified equation

$$\frac{\partial \theta'}{\partial t} \approx \frac{K}{\varrho C_v} \frac{\partial^2 \theta'}{\partial x^2} \tag{11.5}$$

where $\theta' = \theta - (P/\varrho C_v)\,\delta$. For a time factor $e^{-i\omega t}$ this has a solution

$$\left.\begin{aligned} \theta &= \frac{P|\delta|}{\varrho C_v}\left[1 - e^{-(1-i)x/l_h}\right] e^{-i\omega t}, \\ l_h^2 &= \frac{2K}{\omega \varrho C_v} \end{aligned}\right\} \tag{11.6}$$

where l_h is the thickness of the acoustic thermal boundary layer.

From the last two of Eqs. (5.5) and from (6.4) we now can obtain the compressibility $\varkappa = (\delta/\varrho p)$ in the boundary layer,

$$\varkappa = \frac{1}{\gamma P}\left[1 + (\gamma - 1)\, e^{-(1-i)\,x/l_h}\right]. \tag{11.7}$$

As x increases, the compressibility goes from the isothermal value $(1/P)$ to the adiabatic value $(1/\gamma P)$.

The loss per unit area caused by heat conduction is then [see Eq. (6.3)]

$$\left.\begin{aligned} &(\text{conduction loss per unit area}) \\ &\quad \approx \frac{1}{2} \operatorname{Re} \int_0^\infty (-i\omega\varkappa)\, |p|^2\, dx = \frac{1}{2} (\gamma - 1)\, \frac{k l_h}{2\varrho c} |p|^2 \end{aligned}\right\} \tag{11.8}$$

in which we have again neglected the variation of p with x within the layer. The total rate of acoustic loss in both layers is

$$\left.\begin{aligned} \overline{L} &= \tfrac{1}{2} R_v |u_t|^2 + \tfrac{1}{2} R_h |p|^2, \\ R_v &= \sqrt{\frac{\eta\omega\varrho}{2}} \approx (0.83 \times 10^{-3}) \sqrt{f} \text{ cgs units for air at } 15^\circ\text{C}, \\ R_h &= \frac{\gamma - 1}{\varrho c^2} \frac{K\omega}{2\varrho C_v} \approx (0.25 \times 10^{-6}) \sqrt{f} \text{ for air at 1 atm, } 15^\circ\text{C}. \end{aligned}\right\} \tag{11.9}$$

These results, of course, are also applicable to any curved boundary, as long as the radius of curvature is large compared to the boundary layer thicknesses.

As an example, we shall compute the attenuation caused by these effects for a sound wave propagating along the inside of a circular tube with diameter much larger than the layer thicknesses, again taking the time factor to be $e^{-i\omega t}$. The total power transmitted along the tube is $IA = (A/2)\, p u = \frac{1}{2} A \varrho c |u|^2 = \frac{1}{2} A |p|^2/\varrho c$, where $A = \pi r^2$ is the area of the tube. The loss per unit length is

$$-\pi r^2 \frac{dI}{dx} = 2\pi r I \left[\tfrac{1}{2} k l_v + \tfrac{1}{2} (\gamma - 1) k l_h\right]$$

which results in $I = I_0\, e^{-\alpha x}$, where the energy attenuation constant is

$$\alpha = \frac{1}{r} \left[k l_v + (\gamma - 1) k l_h\right] \tag{11.10}$$

in agreement with the classical result, obtained by KIRCHHOFF by the direct integration of Eqs. (5.5).

III. The integral equations of linear acoustics.

12. GREEN's functions. The differential equations derived in Division I are basic to linear acoustics, and are often solved directly. In some problems, however, it is convenient to convert them to integral equations; in this form approximate calculations can often be more easily carried out and variational procedures can be set up more directly than with the differential form. The basis of the integral equation formulation is the GREEN's function [*44*], [*72*], which is the solution of an inhomogeneous equation, with the inhomogeneity a unit one confined to a single point. For linear acoustics the GREEN's function is the wave produced at x, y, z (vector $\boldsymbol{r}$) by a unit, point source at the point x_0, y_0, z_0 (vector $\boldsymbol{r}_0$).

Two GREEN's functions are of particular utility; one is for simple-harmonic waves, the other for waves with more general time dependence. The first is used when the sources and fields have a single frequency, or else when the total field has been analyzed into its frequency components and we are studying one of these components. Here all aspects of the wave have a common time factor $e^{-i\omega t}$ and the space part of the pressure or density wave [see Eqs. (2.1) and (3.10)] satisfies the Helmholtz equation, in the variables x, y, z (vector $\boldsymbol{r}$)

$$\nabla^2 \Psi + k^2 \Psi = q(\boldsymbol{r}); \quad k = \frac{\omega}{c}, \tag{12.1}$$

where Ψ may be the density ϱ, in which case q represents $-(1/c_0^2)$ times the quantities on the right-hand side of Eq. (2.1), with the time factor $e^{-i\omega t}$ divided out, or else, if we are using the linear approximations of Eq. (4.3), Ψ may be the acoustic pressure p, in which case q may be some of the terms on the right-hand side of Eq. (3.10). Some of these quantities are truly inhomogeneous terms, being completely specified functions of the coordinates represented by vector $\boldsymbol{r}$; other terms are linear in the unknown Ψ or its derivatives and still other terms are quadratic in Ψ and its derivatives (the quadratic terms are neglected in our present discussion). From Ψ, of course, we can obtain the other properties of the wave, its fluid velocity, temperature, etc., by means of the relations given in Eq. (4.3).

The GREEN's function for the single-frequency case is

$$G(\boldsymbol{r}|\boldsymbol{r}_0) = g(\boldsymbol{r}|\boldsymbol{r}_0) + \Phi(\boldsymbol{r}|\boldsymbol{r}_0); \quad g = -\frac{e^{ikR}}{4\pi R}, \tag{12.2}$$

where $\boldsymbol{R}=\boldsymbol{r}-\boldsymbol{r}_0$ is the vector distance between source point $\boldsymbol{r}_0$ and observation point $\boldsymbol{r}$ and R is its magnitude. Function g is the GREEN's function for a region with all boundaries at infinity (the infinite domain) and Φ is a solution of the homogeneous equation $(\nabla^2+k^2)\,\Phi=0$ such that G satisfies boundary conditions, on other possible boundaries, in both $\boldsymbol{r}$ and $\boldsymbol{r}_0$ coordinates, which may be chosen to simplify the solution. Function g, and therefore function G, satisfies the equation

$$(\nabla^2+k^2)\,G(\boldsymbol{r}\,|\,\boldsymbol{r}_0)=\delta(\boldsymbol{r}-\boldsymbol{r}_0) \tag{12.3}$$

where the Laplace operator ∇^2 is in the $\boldsymbol{r}$ coordinates and where δ is the three-dimensional Dirac delta function.

The GREEN's function g for the infinite domain may be expanded in spherical coordinates about the common origin of $\boldsymbol{r}$ and $\boldsymbol{r}_0$, in terms of the spherical harmonics

$$Y_{lm}(\vartheta,\varphi)=\mathrm{e}^{im\varphi}\,\mathscr{P}_{lm}(\vartheta)$$

and the spherical Bessel functions

$$j_l(x)=\sqrt{\frac{\pi}{2x}}\,J_{l+\frac{1}{2}}(x) \quad \text{and} \quad h_l(x)=\sqrt{\frac{\pi}{2x}}\,H^{(1)}_{l+\frac{1}{2}}(x),$$

$$g(\boldsymbol{r}\,|\,\boldsymbol{r}_0)=-\frac{\mathrm{e}^{ikR}}{4\pi R}=-ik\sum_{lm}\bar{Y}_{lm}(\vartheta_0,\varphi_0)\,Y_{lm}(\vartheta,\varphi)\,j_l(kr_0)\,h_l(kr) \tag{12.4}$$

for $r>r_0$. G can also be expanded as a series of eigenfunctions inside a finite region. Let $\Psi_n(\boldsymbol{r})$ be a normalized solution of $(\nabla^2+\lambda_n^2)\,\Psi_n=0$ which satisfies the boundary conditions desired for G. Then,

$$G(\boldsymbol{r}\,|\,\boldsymbol{r}_0)=\sum_n \Psi_n(\boldsymbol{r}_0)\,\Psi_n(\boldsymbol{r})/(k^2-\lambda_n^2)\,. \tag{12.5}$$

Both (12.4) and (12.5) illustrate the *reciprocity condition* for single-frequency GREEN's functions, that $G(\boldsymbol{r}_0\,|\,\boldsymbol{r})=G(\boldsymbol{r}\,|\,\boldsymbol{r}_0)$; the field at the observation point $\boldsymbol{r}$ from a unit source at $\boldsymbol{r}_0$ is equal to the field measured at $\boldsymbol{r}_0$ from a source at $\boldsymbol{r}$.

The GREEN's function for more general time dependence is used to solve the more general wave equation

$$\nabla^2\Psi-\frac{1}{c^2}\,\frac{\partial^2\Psi}{\partial t^2}=q(\boldsymbol{r},t) \tag{12.6}$$

where again q is proportional to the right-hand side of Eq. (2.1), expressed in terms of the various inhomogeneous quantities and of Ψ and its derivatives, with second-order terms omitted. The GREEN's function for this equation, for the infinite domain, is

$$g(\boldsymbol{r},t\,|\,\boldsymbol{r}_0,t_0)=-\frac{\delta\left(\frac{R}{c}-t+t_0\right)}{4\pi R}\,. \tag{12.7}$$

It is a solution of the equation

$$\nabla^2 g-\frac{1}{c^2}\,\frac{\partial^2 g}{\partial t^2}=\delta(R)\,\delta(t-t_0)\,. \tag{12.8}$$

In this case the reciprocity condition is

$$G(\boldsymbol{r},t\,|\,\boldsymbol{r}_0,t_0)=G(\boldsymbol{r}_0,-t_0\,|\,\boldsymbol{r},-t)\,.$$

13. The basic integral equation. We suppose that the region H, in which we wish to compute the sound wave, is completely surrounded by a boundary surface B, some part of which may be at infinity. The solution of Eq. (12.1) in this enclosed region turns out [2], [44] to be a sum of a volume integral over H and a surface integral over B,

$$\left.\begin{aligned}&\iiint\limits_{\text{over } H} G(\boldsymbol{r}\,|\,\boldsymbol{r}_0)\, q(\boldsymbol{r}_0)\, d v_0 + \iint\limits_{\text{over } B} \left[\Psi(\boldsymbol{r}_0^B)\frac{\partial}{\partial n_0} G(\boldsymbol{r}\,|\,\boldsymbol{r}_0^B) - G(\boldsymbol{r}\,|\,\boldsymbol{r}_0^B)\frac{\partial}{\partial n_0}\Psi(\boldsymbol{r}_0^B)\right] d s_0\\ &\qquad = \begin{cases}\Psi(\boldsymbol{r}) & \text{if } \boldsymbol{r} \text{ is in } H \text{ or on } B\\ 0 & \text{if } \boldsymbol{r} \text{ is outside } H \text{ and } B.\end{cases}\end{aligned}\right\}\tag{13.1}$$

Both integrals are in terms of the $\boldsymbol{r}_0$ coordinates, so the resulting quantity is a function of the $\boldsymbol{r}$ coordinates. The symbol $(\partial/\partial n_0)$ is the gradient, in the $\boldsymbol{r}_0$ coordinates, normal to the surface B at the point $\boldsymbol{r}_0^B$ on the surface, in the direction *away* from the region H.

As mentioned earlier, the linearized function q has inhomogeneous terms (completely specified functions of $\boldsymbol{r}_0$) and homogeneous terms (specified functions of $\boldsymbol{r}_0$ times Ψ or its derivatives). Consequently the volume integral has inhomogeneous terms, which can be integrated directly and which represent *sources* of sound, and also has homogeneous terms, which have the unknown Ψ inside the integral. The boundary conditions for Ψ on the boundary surface B may be inhomogeneous (Ψ or its normal gradient specified on B) or homogeneous (Ψ or its normal gradient or a linear combination of the two equal to zero on B). Consequently the surface integral of (13.1) has inhomogeneous terms, for those portions of the boundary where the boundary conditions are inhomogeneous, and homogeneous terms, involving the unknown Ψ or its normal gradient. The inhomogeneous volume and surface integrals are thus known functions of $\boldsymbol{r}$; they represent sources of sound. The homogeneous integrals, when they are present, make Eq. (13.1) a true integral equation for the function Ψ.

It often is possible to simplify the surface integrals by a proper choice of boundary conditions for G. If, for example, the normal gradient of Ψ is specified at every point on B, then we can choose G so that its normal gradient on B is zero (for both the $\boldsymbol{r}$ and $\boldsymbol{r}_0$ coordinates) and (13.1) becomes

$$\Psi(\boldsymbol{r}) = \iiint G(\boldsymbol{r}\,|\,\boldsymbol{r}_0)\, q(\boldsymbol{r}_0)\, d v_0 - \iint G(\boldsymbol{r}\,|\,\boldsymbol{r}_0^B)\frac{\partial}{\partial n_0}\Psi(\boldsymbol{r}_0^B)\, d s_0 \tag{13.2}$$

in H and on B. The surface integral then has no homogeneous part.

Similarly if the boundary has a normal acoustic impedance $\varrho c \zeta$ which is a point function of $\boldsymbol{r}_B$, the position on B, independent of the configuration of the wave in H, then we may choose the boundary conditions for G so that the ratio between its value to its normal gradient at the point $\boldsymbol{r}_0^B$ is $\alpha(\boldsymbol{r}_0^B)/i k$ and, in H and on B

$$\left.\begin{aligned}\Psi(\boldsymbol{r}) &= \iiint G(\boldsymbol{r}\,|\,\boldsymbol{r}_0)\, q(\boldsymbol{r}_0)\, d v_0 + {}\\ &\qquad + \frac{1}{i k}\iint \left[\alpha(\boldsymbol{r}_0^B) - \zeta(\boldsymbol{r}_0^B)\right]\frac{\partial}{\partial n_0} G(\boldsymbol{r}\,|\,\boldsymbol{r}_0^B)\frac{\partial}{\partial n_0}\Psi(\boldsymbol{r}_0^B)\, d s_0\\ &= \iiint G(\boldsymbol{r}\,|\,\boldsymbol{r}_0)\, q(\boldsymbol{r}_0)\, d v_0 + \frac{1}{i k}\iint\left[\frac{1}{\zeta(\boldsymbol{r}_0^B)} - \frac{1}{\alpha(\boldsymbol{r}_0^B)}\right] G(\boldsymbol{r}\,|\,\boldsymbol{r}_0^B)\,\Psi(\boldsymbol{r}_0^B)\, d s_0\end{aligned}\right\}\tag{13.3}$$

the surface integral being a homogeneous one in either Ψ or its normal gradient. If we can make α equal to the actual impedance ζ over any part of the surface, the surface integral over this part will be zero. If we can make α equal to the average value of ζ over some part of B, then the remaining integrand is small and can be treated as a correction term.

If, however, the acoustic impedance of some part A of the boundary is not a point function of position on B then, as shown in the previous discussion of boundary conditions, we must analyze the wave in the boundary material "outside" that part of B. In other words we must solve the acoustic equations in another region H', which directly adjoins H along the surface A; H being on one side of A and H' being on the other.

In these cases we can set up two integral equations, one for region H and the other for H', which coincide over parts of their boundary surfaces and which can thus be combined to obtain a solution in both H and H'. For example, suppose that Ψ is the pressure and that the boundaries of both H and H' are rigid ($\partial\Psi/\partial n=0$) everywhere except along the common boundary A. We then use GREEN's functions G and G' for the two regions H and H', which have zero normal gradient along the whole of their respective boundaries B and B' (including A). The equation for the pressure Ψ in H is then (13.2), where the surface integral is just over the common surface A, since $\partial\Psi/\partial n$ is zero everywhere else on B. There is a similar equation for the pressure Ψ in H', with the surface integral again confined to the common boundary A. If now both pressure and normal velocity $(1/ik\varrho c)(\partial\Psi/\partial n)$ are continuous across the boundary, we can equate Ψ on A with Ψ' on A and $(1/ik\varrho c)(\partial\Psi/\partial n)$ on A with $-(1/ik\varrho' c')(\partial\Psi'/\partial n')$ on A (the minus sign because the normal gradient away from H is opposite in direction from the normal gradient away from H') and obtain finally an integral equation for $u_n(\boldsymbol{r}^A)=(1/ik\varrho c)(\partial/\partial n)\,\Psi(\boldsymbol{r}^A)$, the normal velocity of the surface A, which is common to both regions,

$$\left.\begin{aligned} ik\iiint\limits_{\text{over } A} [\varrho c\, G(\boldsymbol{r}^A|\boldsymbol{r}_0^A) + \varrho' c' G'(\boldsymbol{r}^A|\boldsymbol{r}_0^A)]\, u_n(\boldsymbol{r}_0^A)\, dA_0 \\ = \left\{\iiint\limits_{\text{over } H} G(\boldsymbol{r}^A|\boldsymbol{r}_0)\, q(\boldsymbol{r}_0)\, dv_0 - \iiint\limits_{\text{over } H'} G'(\boldsymbol{r}^A|\boldsymbol{r}_0')\, q'(\boldsymbol{r}_0')\, dv_0'\right\} \end{aligned}\right\} \tag{13.4}$$

where $\boldsymbol{r}^A$ is some specified point on A, the surface integral is over A in the common coordinate $\boldsymbol{r}_0=\boldsymbol{r}_0'=\boldsymbol{r}_0^A$, one volume integral is over H in the coordinate $\boldsymbol{r}_0$ and the other is over H' in $\boldsymbol{r}_0'$.

If the source functions q and q' are completely specified (all inhomogeneous) then the volume integrals are specified functions of $\boldsymbol{r}^A$ and Eq. (13.4) is a Fredholm integral equation [*45*] of the first kind in the unknown function $u_n(\boldsymbol{r}^A)$, with a symmetric kernel given by the expression in the square brackets, and the known function of $\boldsymbol{r}^A$ being the expression in braces. This equation may sometimes be solved exactly, it can usually be solved by successive approximations and it often may be solved by variational methods. Once the exact or approximate solution for u_n is obtained, the pressure Ψ in H, which we had originally set out to find, is obtained by use of Eq. (13.2) again;

$$\iiint\limits_{\text{over } H} G(\boldsymbol{r}|\boldsymbol{r}_0)\, q(\boldsymbol{r}_0)\, dv_0 - ik\varrho c \iint\limits_{\text{over } A} G(\boldsymbol{r}|\boldsymbol{r}_0^A)\, u_n(\boldsymbol{r}_0^A)\, dA_0 = \Psi(\boldsymbol{r}) \text{ in } H. \tag{13.5}$$

This sort of technique will be utilized extensively in the third part of this article, where we discuss problems which cannot be solved by "classical" boundary-value theory.

When the wave motion is not periodic and we do not choose to separate the motion into its harmonic components, but wish to solve Eq. (12.6) directly, we use the GREEN's function of Eq. (12.7) for the infinite domain and modify it appropriately, by means of some "image function" $\Phi(\boldsymbol{r}, t|\boldsymbol{r}_0, t_0)$ to fit boundary conditions on nearby boundaries (if any). The basic integral equation, corresponding to (13.1), involves integration over time as well as space. We consider the motion as having started at $t=0$ and continuing to the present $t=t$. The integration over t_0 thus goes from 0 to t^+, which is just enough larger than t so that we do not stop the integration in the middle of a Dirac delta function. The generalized boundary surface thus includes the surface $t=0$. The integral equation is

$$\left.\begin{aligned}\Psi(\boldsymbol{r},t) &= \int_0^{t^+} dt_0 \iiint G(\boldsymbol{r},t|\boldsymbol{r}_0,t_0)\,q(\boldsymbol{r}_0,t_0)\,dv_0 + \\ &+ \int_0^{t^+} dt_0 \iint \left[\Psi(\boldsymbol{r}_0^B)\frac{\partial}{\partial n_0}G(\boldsymbol{r},t|\boldsymbol{r}_0^B,t_0) - G\frac{\partial}{\partial n_0}\Psi\right] ds_0 + \\ &+ \frac{1}{c^2}\iiint\left[\left(\frac{\partial G}{\partial t_0}\right)_0 \Psi_0(\boldsymbol{r}_0) - G_0\left(\frac{\partial \Psi}{\partial t_0}\right)_0\right] dv_0\end{aligned}\right\} \tag{13.6}$$

where the subscripts 0 in the last integral indicate that these quantities are to be taken for $t_0=0$ (initial conditions). From this, by integrating over t_0, we can obtain the familiar retarded potential solution of KIRCHHOFF.

Very much the same discussion can be given, for the possible forms this equation can take on, as has been given for the case of the Helmholtz equation solution, Eq. (13.1). The resulting integrals are enough more difficult than those of Eq. (13.1) that it is often better to separate the motion into harmonic components by a Laplace transform and then to use Eq. (13.1) for the harmonic components.

14. The source terms. The inhomogeneous terms in Eqs. (13.1) and (13.6), both in the volume and surface integrals, represent the introduction of forces, or additional fluid, from outside the system and thus correspond to the generation of sound. For example, the first term in Eq. (2.1), $(\partial Q/\partial t)$, represents the rate of mass flow of fluid into the region surrounding the point $\boldsymbol{r}$. If the component of this term having the frequency $(\omega/2\pi)$ differs from zero only near the origin of coordinates then the volume integral of Eq. (13.1) will have a term equal to the integral of $G(\boldsymbol{r}|\boldsymbol{r}_0)$ times the component of $(-1/c_0^2)\,(\partial Q/\partial t)$ over the small volume in question (assuming that Ψ is the density ϱ; if Ψ were pressure, all terms would be multiplied by c_0^2).

To be specific, let us take Ψ to be the pressure p and let $-(\partial Q/\partial t)=i\omega Q_0\,\mathrm{e}^{-i\omega}$ differ from zero only in the region inside a sphere of radius a around the origin. If we wish to compute the radiated wave at distances r large compared to a, in the infinite domain, then we can use an approximate form for g,

$$g(\boldsymbol{r}|\boldsymbol{r}_0) = -\frac{\mathrm{e}^{ikR}}{4\pi R} \approx -\frac{\mathrm{e}^{ikr}}{4\pi r}\,\mathrm{e}^{-ik\boldsymbol{a}_r\cdot\boldsymbol{r}_0} \qquad (r\gg a) \tag{14.1}$$

where the vector $\boldsymbol{r}$, specifying the observation point, is expressed in terms of the spherical coordinates r, ϑ, φ and where $\boldsymbol{a}_r$ is the unit vector in the r direction ($\boldsymbol{a}_r\cdot\boldsymbol{r}_0 = z_0\cos\vartheta + x_0\sin\vartheta\cos\varphi + y_0\sin\vartheta\sin\varphi$). If, in addition, a is small compared to the wavelength $\lambda=2\pi c/\omega$ of the radiated wave the second exponential can be expanded and

$$g(\boldsymbol{r}|\boldsymbol{r}_0) \approx -\frac{\mathrm{e}^{ikr}}{4\pi r}\left[1 - ik(\boldsymbol{a}_r\cdot\boldsymbol{r}_0) - \tfrac{1}{2}k^2\,\boldsymbol{a}_r\cdot(\boldsymbol{r}_0\boldsymbol{r}_0)\cdot\boldsymbol{a}_r + \cdots\right] \tag{14.2}$$

where the dyadic $(\boldsymbol{r}_0\boldsymbol{r}_0)$ has tensor components x_0x_0, x_0y_0, etc.

Consequently the sound wave produced by the periodic rate of introduction of fluid of mass Q_0 into a region inside the sphere $r=a$ has the asymptotic form

$$\left.\begin{aligned} p(\boldsymbol{r}) &= i\omega \iiint g(\boldsymbol{r}|\boldsymbol{r}_0)\, Q_0(\boldsymbol{r}_0)\, dv_0 \\ &\approx -\frac{i\omega}{4\pi}\frac{e^{ikr}}{r}\left[\iiint Q_0\, dv_0 - ik\,\boldsymbol{a}_r\cdot\iiint \boldsymbol{r}_0\, Q_0\, dv_0 - \cdots\right] \quad (r \gg a). \end{aligned}\right\} \tag{14.3}$$

If $ka<1$ the successive terms in the brackets are successively smaller and the series converges rapidly. The first term thus usually predominates at low frequencies; it is independent of the direction of $\boldsymbol{r}$, the vector between the source and the observation point, and is called *monopole* radiation. The integral of Q_0 over the source region ($r_0<a$) is called the *strength* of the monopole source.

The second term inside the brackets does depend on the direction of $\boldsymbol{r}$ through the factor $\cos\theta$, where θ is the angle between $\boldsymbol{r}$ and the direction of the integral of $\boldsymbol{r}_0 Q_0$ over the source region. This vector integral is called the *dipole* moment of the source; if Q_0 is symmetrically placed about the origin it is zero. The higher terms in expansion (14.3) produce terms with still more complicated dependence on direction, but as long as $ka<1$ these terms are usually smaller than the monopole and dipole terms, for this part of q. When $ka>1$ it is necessary to use the exact expansion of g given in Eq. (12.4); the angular dependence of the radiated wave being thus given as a series of spherical harmonics of ϑ and φ. The coefficients of these spherical harmonics are integrals of Q_0, times $Y^*_{lm}(\vartheta_0, \varphi_0)\, j_l(kr_0)$, over the source region, which are the extensions of the integrals of Eq. (14.3) for $ka>1$.

The second inhomogeneous term in Eq. (2.1), which corresponds to a term $\operatorname{div}\boldsymbol{F}$ in q, represents a possible oscillating body force, such as would be produced by an oscillating electromagnetic field in a conducting fluid. Here we can simplify the result by using integration by parts,

$$\iiint g(\boldsymbol{r}|\boldsymbol{r}_0)\operatorname{div}_0\boldsymbol{F}\, dv_0 = -\iiint \boldsymbol{F}(\boldsymbol{r}_0)\cdot\operatorname{grad}_0 g\, dv_0 + \iint g F_n\, ds_0$$

where the surface integral vanishes if we assume that $\boldsymbol{F}$ differs from zero only inside the sphere $r=a$. For $ka<1$, as before, we use the expansion of Eq. (14.2). Taking the gradient in the r_0 coordinates, we have, for the equation corresponding to (14.3) for radiation caused by body forces,

$$p(\boldsymbol{r}) \approx +\frac{e^{ikr}}{4\pi r}\left[ik\,\boldsymbol{a}_r\cdot\iiint \boldsymbol{F}_0\, dv_0 + k^2\boldsymbol{a}_r\cdot\iiint(\boldsymbol{r}_0\boldsymbol{F}_0)\, dv_0\cdot\boldsymbol{a}_r - \cdots\right] \tag{14.4}$$

where

$$\boldsymbol{F} = \boldsymbol{F}_0(\boldsymbol{r})\, e^{-i\omega t}.$$

We thus see that, since the effect of a body-force enters the source expression q as a divergence, there can be no monopole radiation produced by body forces (in the long-wavelength limit, that is; there may be some spherically symmetric radiation produced when $ka>1$). The volume integral of $\boldsymbol{F}_0$ is the dipole moment of the body-force and the volume integral of the dyadic $(\boldsymbol{r}_0\boldsymbol{F}_0)$ can be called its *quadrupole* moment. As long as $ka<1$ the quadrupole radiation is usually small compared to the dipole term.

The inhomogeneous part of the fourth term on the right-hand side of (2.1) contributes a term $\varrho\nabla\cdot(\boldsymbol{V}\boldsymbol{V})\cdot\nabla$ to the inhomogeneous part of q for the pressure wave, where $(\boldsymbol{V}\boldsymbol{V})$ is the dyadic with tensor components equal to products of the components of the flow velocity $\boldsymbol{V}$, and where the expression with two gradient operators is a short-hand way of writing the double divergence of $(\boldsymbol{V}\boldsymbol{V})$. If $\boldsymbol{V}$ corresponds to turbulent flow, there may be a component of $(\boldsymbol{V}\boldsymbol{V})$ which has the frequency $\omega/2\pi$, in which case the contribution to q will be the amplitude $(\boldsymbol{V}\boldsymbol{V})_0$ of this frequency component. Again assuming that this term also vanishes outside $r=a$, we can integrate twice by parts and obtain, for the turbulence-produced radiation

$$p(\boldsymbol{r}) \approx \frac{\varrho e^{ikr}}{8\pi r}\left[k^2 \boldsymbol{a}_r \cdot \iiint (\boldsymbol{V}\boldsymbol{V})_0 \, dv_0 \cdot \boldsymbol{a}_r + \cdots\right] \tag{14.5}$$

under the same conditions as hold for Eqs. (14.3) and (14.4). The first two terms in the brackets of expansion (14.2) have vanished because of the double differentiation, thus showing that sound generated by turbulence cannot have monopole or dipole characteristics; its major contribution (at long wavelengths) must be quadrupole-type radiation.

If some part of the boundary surface is closer than infinity and if some part of this is moved to and fro at frequency $\omega/2\pi$, then the corresponding part of the surface integral of (13.1) is inhomogeneous and represents the wave generated by the vibrating surface. The portion of the boundary B which is generating sound (call it B_r) may be simply connected to the rest of the boundary, as for the case of a loudspeaker set in a room wall, for example. Or it may be a part of the surface of an object placed in H, as for a separate loudspeaker, not simply connected with the rest of B. In either case, it is usually easiest to adjust the GREEN'S function $G(\boldsymbol{r}|\boldsymbol{r}_0)$ so that the boundary condition on B_r is that the normal gradient of G is zero there. Then the contribution to the generated pressure wave caused by boundary vibration is

$$p(\boldsymbol{r}) = i k \varrho c \iint\limits_{\text{over } B_r} G(\boldsymbol{r}|\boldsymbol{r}_0^B)\, \boldsymbol{v}_0(\boldsymbol{r}_0^B)\, ds_0 \tag{14.6}$$

where v_0 is the normal velocity amplitude at frequency $\omega/2\pi$.

There are cases, of course, when it is not convenient to analyze the motion of the source into its simple harmonic components and then to use formulas (14.3) to (14.6) to calculate the radiated wave. In such cases we can use the formulation (13.6) for the time dependent wave, using Eq. (12.7) for the GREEN'S function for the infinite domain. If $t=0$ is so long ago that the initial conditions no longer matter then the source terms in q will produce a wave in the infinite domain

$$\int\limits_0^{t+} dt_0 \iiint q(\boldsymbol{r}_0, t_0)\, \delta\!\left(\frac{R}{c} - t - t_0\right) \frac{dv_0}{4\pi R} = \iiint q\left(\boldsymbol{r}_0, t - \frac{R}{c}\right) \frac{dv_0}{4\pi R}. \tag{14.7}$$

This is the well-known retarded potential solution of the wave equation. It can also be used when the boundaries are closer than infinity, by suitably modifying G to fit appropriate boundary conditions and by adding the surface integrals of Eq. (13.6). These integrals are usually more difficult to carry out than are the ones for the single-frequency case. Also, since the time-dependent GREEN'S function cannot be expanded in a manner similar to Eq. (14.2), non-periodic radiation cannot be separated into monopole, dipole, etc., terms.

15. The scattering of sound. We have just shown that the inhomogeneous parts of the volume and surface integrals of Eqs. (13.1) and (13.6) represent the production of sound waves in the medium. These terms are completely specified by describing the forces or fluid flows which generate the sound; once they are specified the volume and surface integrals can be computed directly. There are also homogeneous parts of q and homogeneous parts of the surface integral, where the integrand is proportional to the unknown Ψ or its derivatives, such as the cross terms $u_i V_j$ in the fourth term of (2.1) and the deviations of the diagonal term $P - \varrho c_0^2$, in the third term, from its zero average value. These terms produce, not radiation, but a distortion of the wave motion which, if the primary wave is a travelling wave, is called scattering.

As mentioned, the terms in q responsible for scattering have the form $\varkappa(\boldsymbol{r})\Psi$ or else $\boldsymbol{K}(\boldsymbol{r}) \cdot \operatorname{grad}\Psi$ or $\nabla \cdot (\boldsymbol{V} \operatorname{grad}\Psi) \cdot \nabla$. We shall discuss the effects of the first type of term; the effects of the other types can be found by analogous methods. Term $\varkappa(\boldsymbol{r})\Psi$ corresponds to a local change in index of refraction of the medium. Since c_0 was adjusted so that the third term on the right in (2.1) is zero on the average, $\varkappa$ will usually differ from zero in isolated regions, where the acoustic properties of the fluid differ from the average. These regions, and similar regions where the other homogeneous terms in q happen to differ from zero, will be called *bulk scatterers*. These regions refract the sound.

Scattering is also caused by the presence of one or more "foreign bodies" in the fluid, which reflect or absorb the incident wave. Here it is the boundary surface which is fragmented, so to speak; the surface B which "encloses" the region H consists of the large surface actually enclosing it, plus the separate surfaces of the foreign bodies, separating the fluid from the other material which constitutes the bodies. From the point of view of the fluid, these surfaces also "enclose" it, and the surface integrals of Eqs. (13.1) and (13.6) must also include integrals over these surfaces. These foreign bodies can be called *surface scatterers*.

To show how such calculations go, let us suppose a plane wave $e^{ikz-i\omega t}$ is sent in from infinity, to be scattered from a finite number of bulk and surface scatterers. The outer surface is then the sphere at infinity and the appropriate GREEN'S function is the g of Eq. (12.2). Then Eq. (13.1) involves a set of volume integrals of $g\varkappa\Psi$ over those regions where $\varkappa$ differs from zero, plus surface integrals over surface scatterers, plus a surface integral over the sphere at infinity. The sound wave in the fluid can then be thought of as composed of an *incident wave* Ψ_i, which would be the complete solution if there were no scatterers, plus the volume and surface integrals which represent the various scattered waves.

The surface integral over the sphere at infinity simply produces the incident wave, so Eq. (13.1) can be written

$$\left.\begin{aligned} \Psi(\boldsymbol{r}) = \Psi_i(\boldsymbol{r}) + \sum_i \underset{\text{over } i}{\iiint} g(\boldsymbol{r}|\boldsymbol{r}_0)\,\varkappa(\boldsymbol{r}_0)\,\Psi(\boldsymbol{r}_0)\,dv_0 + \\ + \sum_j \underset{\text{over } j}{\iint} \left[\Psi(\boldsymbol{r}_0^B)\frac{\partial g}{\partial n_0} - g(\boldsymbol{r}|\boldsymbol{r}_0^B)\frac{\partial \Psi}{\partial n_0}\right] ds_0. \end{aligned}\right\} \tag{15.1}$$

This is a Fredholm integral equation [45] of the second kind for the unknown wave function Ψ, where Ψ_i, $\varkappa$ and g are specified. The individual volume and surface integrals are over the individual scatterers i and j and the effects are added. Let us first consider the effect of each separately, taking the volume integral first.

16. Bulk scattering. Suppose, at first, that $\varkappa$ differs from zero only inside a sphere of radius a around the origin. Then, if $2\pi a$ is small compared to $\lambda = 2\pi/k$ and if $\varkappa$ is small compared to k^2, we might expect that the incident wave will not be distorted much by the presence of the scatterer and that a good first approximation for Ψ will be obtained by setting Ψ in the integral equal to Ψ_i,

$$\Psi(\boldsymbol{r}) \approx \Psi_i(\boldsymbol{r}) + \iiint g(\boldsymbol{r}|\boldsymbol{r}_0)\,\varkappa(\boldsymbol{r}_0)\,\Psi_i(\boldsymbol{r}_0)\,dv_0. \tag{16.1}$$

This approximate solution is called the *first Born approximation*.

Suppose our incident wave is the plane wave e^{ikz}. If the observation point $\boldsymbol{r}$ is some distance from the scatterer ($r \gg a$) we can, as before, set $g \approx -(e^{ikr}/4\pi r) \times e^{-ik\boldsymbol{a}_r \cdot \boldsymbol{r}_0}$, where $\boldsymbol{a}_r$ is the unit vector in the $\boldsymbol{r}$ direction. The first Born approximation then is

$$\left.\begin{aligned} \Psi(\boldsymbol{r}) &\approx e^{ikz} - \frac{e^{ikr}}{r} f(\vartheta, \varphi), \\ f(\vartheta, \varphi) &= \frac{1}{4\pi} \iiint e^{i\boldsymbol{\mu}\cdot\boldsymbol{r}_0} \varkappa(\boldsymbol{r}_0)\, dv_0 \\ &\approx \frac{1}{4\pi}\left[\iiint \varkappa(\boldsymbol{r}_0)\, dv_0 + i\boldsymbol{\mu}\cdot\iiint \boldsymbol{r}_0 \varkappa(\boldsymbol{r}_0)\, dv_0 - \cdots\right] \quad (\mu a < 1) \end{aligned}\right\} \tag{16.2}$$

where

$$\boldsymbol{\mu} = k(\boldsymbol{a}_z - \boldsymbol{a}_r) = \mu(\boldsymbol{a}_z \sin\tfrac{1}{2}\vartheta - \boldsymbol{a}_x \cos\tfrac{1}{2}\vartheta\cos\varphi - \boldsymbol{a}_y \cos\tfrac{1}{2}\vartheta \sin\varphi)$$

and the magnitude

$$\mu = 2k\sin\tfrac{1}{2}\vartheta.$$

If it were particles instead of waves which were being scattered, vector $\boldsymbol{\mu}$ would be proportional to the momentum imparted to the scatterer by the scattered particle; hence $\boldsymbol{\mu}$ is often called the *recoil vector*.

The plane wave is thus modified by the presence of a scattered wave radiating out from the scatterer, having an amplitude proportional to $f(\vartheta, \varphi)$. Function f, the scattered amplitude, is a function of the spherical angles ϑ and φ defining the direction of $\boldsymbol{r}$, the vector to the point of observation from the scatterer. We see that for very long wavelengths f is practically independent of ϑ and φ; waves scattered from bulk scatterers are spherically symmetric in the long-wavelength limit. As the wavelength is decreased the first dependence on ϑ and φ is through the induced dipole moment $\int \boldsymbol{r}_0 \varkappa\, dv_0$. We note that the dipole component along the recoil vector $\boldsymbol{\mu}$ enters, not that along z.

This scattered wave derives its energy from the incident wave. Detailed study of the interference effects between incident and scattered waves shows that the energy transmitted in the incident wave along the positive z axis (beyond the scatterer) is reduced by just the amount of energy which is absorbed or radiated away in the scattered wave. In fact we can compute the amount of energy lost to the incident wave by calculating the scattered power. The intensity of the scattered wave is proportional to $|f(\vartheta, \varphi)|^2/r^2$ and the ratio of the total power scattered, at all angles, to the incident intensity is

$$\sigma = \int_0^{2\pi} d\varphi \int_0^{\pi} |f(\vartheta, \varphi)|^2 \sin\vartheta\, d\vartheta. \tag{16.3}$$

Since f has the dimension of length, σ has the dimension of area, and is called the *scattering cross section* of the scatterer. It is the area a totally absorbing surface would have to show to the incident beam to absorb from it a power equal to that scattered.

On the other hand, if $a\mu$ is not less than 1, or if $\varkappa$ is not small compared to k^2, then we cannot assume that Ψ, inside the scattering region $r < a$, is approximately equal to Ψ_i, and the Born approximation is not good enough. We could try a successive approximation scheme, solving Eq. (16.1) for $r < a$ and putting this solution, instead of Ψ_i, into the volume integral, and so on. Usually, however, the difficulties of carrying out the successive integrations make this procedure impractical. A more promising approach is to use a variational procedure [*46*], [*48*].

To illustrate the technique, we start with the exact integral equation (16.1), for the scattering of a plane wave $\Psi_i = e^{i\boldsymbol{k}_i\cdot\boldsymbol{r}}$ from a single region enclosed by the sphere $r=a$. Vector $\boldsymbol{k}_i$ has magnitude $k=\omega/c$ and direction that of the incident wave,

$$\left.\begin{aligned}\Psi(\boldsymbol{r}) &= e^{i\boldsymbol{k}_i\cdot\boldsymbol{r}} + \iiint g(\boldsymbol{r}|\boldsymbol{r}_0)\,\varkappa(\boldsymbol{r}_0)\,\Psi(\boldsymbol{r}_0)\,dv_0 \\ &\to e^{i\boldsymbol{k}_i\cdot\boldsymbol{r}} - \frac{e^{ikr}}{r} f(\boldsymbol{k}_i|\boldsymbol{k}_s) \qquad (r\gg a) \\ \text{where}\qquad f(\boldsymbol{k}_i|\boldsymbol{k}_s) &= \frac{1}{4\pi}\iiint e^{-i\boldsymbol{k}_s\cdot\boldsymbol{r}_0}\varkappa(\boldsymbol{r}_0)\,\Psi(\boldsymbol{r}_0)\,dv_0\end{aligned}\right\} \tag{16.4}$$

where vector $\boldsymbol{k}_s$ has magnitude k but is directed along $\boldsymbol{r}$, in the direction in which the scattered wave is being measured. Since we are not assuming that $\Psi\approx e^{i\boldsymbol{k}_i\cdot\boldsymbol{r}_0}$ in the integral, we cannot compute the angle-distribution function f directly, but we can devise a variational expression for it.

We multiply and divide the first term in (16.4) by f, obtaining

$$\Psi(\boldsymbol{r}) = \frac{e^{i\boldsymbol{k}_i\cdot\boldsymbol{r}}}{4\pi f}\iiint e^{-i\boldsymbol{k}_s\cdot\boldsymbol{r}_0}\varkappa(\boldsymbol{r}_0)\,\Psi(\boldsymbol{r}_0)\,dv_0 + \iiint g(\boldsymbol{r}|\boldsymbol{r}_0)\,\varkappa(\boldsymbol{r}_0)\,\Psi(\boldsymbol{r}_0)\,dv_0. \tag{16.5}$$

Now we multiply this equation by $\varkappa(\boldsymbol{r})\,\widetilde{\Psi}(\boldsymbol{r})$ (where $\widetilde{\Psi}$ will be defined shortly) and integrate over the region $r<a$,

$$\left.\begin{aligned}\iiint \widetilde{\Psi}(\boldsymbol{r})\,\varkappa(\boldsymbol{r})\,\Psi(\boldsymbol{r})\,dv &= \frac{1}{4\pi f}\iiint e^{i\boldsymbol{k}_i\cdot\boldsymbol{r}}\varkappa(\boldsymbol{r})\,\widetilde{\Psi}(\boldsymbol{r})\,dv \iiint e^{-i\boldsymbol{k}_s\cdot\boldsymbol{r}_0}\times \\ &\times\varkappa(\boldsymbol{r}_0)\,\Psi(\boldsymbol{r}_0)\,dv_0 + \iiint \varkappa(\boldsymbol{r})\,\widetilde{\Psi}(\boldsymbol{r})\,dv\iiint g(\boldsymbol{r}|\boldsymbol{r}_0)\,\varkappa(\boldsymbol{r}_0)\,\Psi(\boldsymbol{r}_0)\,dv_0.\end{aligned}\right\} \tag{16.6}$$

We now note that if we perform a variation of shape of the unknown function $\widetilde{\Psi}$ in this equation, assuming that f is unchanged, to first order, by varying $\widetilde{\Psi}$, then setting the coefficient of $\delta\widetilde{\Psi}$ equal to zero produces Eq. (16.5). To see what sort of function Ψ is we vary Ψ in (16.6) and set the coefficient of $\delta\Psi$ zero, assuming again that f is also unchanged to first order by varying Ψ. We then obtain an equation for the *adjoint function* $\widetilde{\Psi}$

$$\widetilde{\Psi}(\boldsymbol{r}_0) = \frac{e^{-i\boldsymbol{k}_s\cdot\boldsymbol{r}_0}}{4\pi f}\iiint e^{i\boldsymbol{k}_i\cdot\boldsymbol{r}}\varkappa(\boldsymbol{r})\,\widetilde{\Psi}(\boldsymbol{r})\,dv + \iiint g(\boldsymbol{r}|\boldsymbol{r}_0)\,\varkappa(\boldsymbol{r})\,\widetilde{\Psi}(\boldsymbol{r})\,dv \tag{16.7}$$

which is the equation for the scattering of an incident plane wave $e^{-i\boldsymbol{k}_s\cdot\boldsymbol{r}_0}$, coming in from the observation point and being scattered in the negative z direction [i.e., back to the source of the incident wave of Eq. (16.5)]. In other words the adjoint function $\widetilde{\Psi}$ is the wave solution for the reciprocal situation, when source and observation point are interchanged.

But we have obtained these results from (16.6) only when we assumed that the first order variation of f, caused by simultaneous variation of Ψ and $\widetilde{\Psi}$, is zero. Solving for f, we have

$$[f(\boldsymbol{k}_i|\boldsymbol{k}_s)] = \left[\frac{\iiint e^{i\boldsymbol{k}_i\cdot\boldsymbol{r}}\varkappa\widetilde{\Psi}\,dv\iiint e^{-i\boldsymbol{k}_s\cdot\boldsymbol{r}_0}\varkappa\widetilde{\Psi}\,dv_0}{\iiint\widetilde{\Psi}\varkappa\,\Psi\,dv - \iiint\widetilde{\Psi}\varkappa\,dv\iiint g(\boldsymbol{r}|\boldsymbol{r}_0)\,\varkappa\,\Psi\,dv_0}\right]. \tag{16.8}$$

The brackets around these expressions indicate that if Ψ and $\widetilde{\Psi}$ are varied to obtain a stationary value (i.e., a maximum, minimum or saddle point) for the quantity on the right, its stationary value is equal to $f(\boldsymbol{k}_i|\boldsymbol{k}_s)$. Because all integrals are over the interior of the sphere $r<a$ we need only vary the shape of Ψ and $\widetilde{\Psi}$ inside this sphere. The shape of Ψ outside $r=a$ can then be found by inserting the optimal shape of Ψ (for $r<a$) into the volume integral of Eq. (16.4).

If Ψ and $\widetilde{\Psi}$ are adjusted to obtain an exactly stationary value of f, they will be exact solutions of Eqs. (16.5) and (16.7). But even if the exact solution is too difficult to find, one can choose reasonable forms for Ψ and $\widetilde{\Psi}$, equipped with parameters which can be varied; the values of the parameters which make stationary the expression in brackets in (16.8) are the values which result in the best value of f and the best form for Ψ which is possible within the limitations of the chosen expression. Even setting $\Psi = e^{i k_i \cdot r}$ and $\widetilde{\Psi} = e^{-i k_s \cdot r}$ results in a better value for f than does the first Born approximation, because of the presence of the sextuple integral in the denominator of (16.8). These integrals, of course, are not easy to compute, but they are usually less difficult than is a solution of (16.4) by iteration. We shall discuss variational principles in more detail later.

17. Surface scatterers. We next should examine the effects of the "foreign bodies", which give rise to the surface integrals of Eq. (15.1). In these cases we will find that the Born approximation is not good enough, even in the long-wavelength limit. To demonstrate this in as simple a matter as possible, let us suppose a plane wave $e^{ikz - i\omega t}$ is incident on a spherical object of radius a, centered at the origin. If this were a bulk scatterer, with the region inside $r = a$ having only a slightly different index of refraction than that of the medium, we have shown that in the long-wavelength limit ($k a \ll 1$) the scattered radiation is monopole; the dipole strength of the scattered wave is $k a$ times smaller than the monopole strength. We will now show that if the material inside the sphere $r = a$ is perfectly rigid then, in the long-wavelength limit, the dipole and monopole scattered radiation will have the same order of magnitude.

To show this we shall have to assume a distribution of pressure Ψ and normal velocity (proportional to $\partial\Psi/\partial r$) at the sphere $r = a$, next adjust these distributions so they satisfy Eq. (15.1) to the first order in $k a$, and then finally compute the scattered wave resulting from this self-consistent solution. In other words we will first solve, to the first order in $k a$, the Fredholm equation of the second kind which results when, in the special form of (15.1),

$$\Psi(\boldsymbol{r}) = e^{ikr\cos\vartheta} + \iint \left[\Psi(\boldsymbol{r}_0^B)\,\frac{\partial g}{\partial n_0} - g(\boldsymbol{r}|\boldsymbol{r}_0^B)\,\frac{\partial \Psi}{\partial n_0}\right] d s_0 \qquad (17.1)$$

appropriate for a surface scatterer, vector $\boldsymbol{r}$ is placed on the surface of the sphere $r = a$. When the surface values of Ψ and $\partial\Psi/\partial n$ are determined we can then use the asymptotic form for the GREEN's function,

$$g \to -\frac{e^{ikr}}{4\pi r}\, e^{-ikr_0\cos\theta}$$

(where θ is the angle between $\boldsymbol{r}$ and $\boldsymbol{r}_0$) to determine the form of the scattered wave

$$\left.\begin{aligned} \Psi_s(\boldsymbol{r}) &\to \frac{e^{ikr}}{r}\, f(\vartheta) \qquad (r \gg a)\,, \\ f(\vartheta) &= +\left(\frac{a^2}{4\pi}\right)\iint \left[\Psi(a)\,\frac{\partial}{\partial a}\, e^{-ika\cos\theta} - e^{-ika\cos\theta}\,\frac{\partial}{\partial a}\,\Psi(a)\right] d\Omega_0 \end{aligned}\right\} \qquad (17.2)$$

where $d\Omega_0$ is the element of solid angle $\sin\vartheta_0\, d\vartheta_0\, d\varphi_0$ for integration over the surface of the sphere $r_0 = a$.

Suppose the surface values of Ψ and its normal gradient at $r = a$ are (we omit the time factor $e^{-i\omega t}$)

$$\left.\begin{aligned} \Psi(\boldsymbol{a}) &= \Psi_0 + i k a \gamma \cos\vartheta + \cdots \\ \left(\frac{\partial\Psi}{\partial r}\right)_{r=a} &= -\left(\frac{\partial\Psi}{\partial n}\right)_B = -\frac{\alpha}{a} + i k \eta \cos\vartheta + \cdots \end{aligned}\right\} \qquad (17.3)$$

to the first order in the small quantity ka where γ, α and η are constants to be determined. If the surface has a normal acoustic impedance there would be a constant ratio between Ψ_0 and α and between γ and η, but we shall ignore this for the moment. The other quantities which enter the surface integral are the GREEN's function and its normal gradient at $r_0 = a$, for which we use the expansion of Eq. (12.4),

$$\left.\begin{aligned} g(\mathbf{r}|\mathbf{r}_0^B) &= -\frac{ik}{4\pi}\left[j_0(ka)\,h_0(kr) + 3\cos\theta\, j_1(ka)\,h_1(kr) + \cdots\right] \\ &\approx -\frac{1}{4\pi r}\left[\left(1-\tfrac{1}{6}k^2a^2\right) + \frac{a}{r}\cos\theta + \cdots\right] \qquad (r\to a \ll 1/k) \\ &\approx \frac{e^{ikr}}{4\pi r}\left[\left(1-\tfrac{1}{6}k^2a^2\right) - ika\cos\theta + \cdots\right] \qquad (r\to\infty), \\ \frac{\partial g}{\partial n_0} &= -\frac{\partial g}{\partial a} \approx \frac{1}{4\pi r}\left[-\tfrac{1}{3}k^2 a + \frac{1}{r}\cos\theta + \cdots\right] \qquad (r\to a\ll 1/k) \\ &\approx \frac{e^{ikr}}{4\pi r}\left[-\tfrac{1}{3}k^2 a - ik\cos\theta + \cdots\right] \qquad (r\to\infty) \end{aligned}\right\} \tag{17.4}$$

where

$$\cos\theta = \cos\vartheta\cos\vartheta_0 + \sin\vartheta\sin\vartheta_0\cos(\varphi-\varphi_0).$$

Inserting these expressions into Eq. (17.2), integrating over $d\Omega_0$, and setting $r = a$, we find the following relationships between Ψ_0, α, η and γ must hold if the integral equation is to satisfy (17.1) to the first order in ka,

$$\left.\begin{aligned} \Psi_{r=a} &= \Psi_0 + ika\gamma\cos\vartheta \\ &\approx e^{ika\cos\vartheta} + \frac{1}{4\pi}\iint\left[(\Psi_0 + ika\gamma\cos\vartheta_0)\cos\theta + \right. \\ &\qquad \left. + (1+\cos\theta)(\alpha - ika\eta\cos\vartheta_0)\right] d\Omega_0 \\ &\approx 1 + ika\cos\vartheta + \tfrac{1}{3}ika\gamma\cos\vartheta + \alpha - \tfrac{1}{3}ika\eta\cos\vartheta, \\ a\left(\frac{\partial\Psi}{\partial r}\right)_{r=a} &= -\alpha + ika\eta\cos\vartheta \\ &\approx ika\cos\vartheta + \frac{1}{4\pi}\iint\left[(\Psi_0 + ika\gamma\cos\vartheta_0)(-2\cos\theta) - \right. \\ &\qquad \left. - (1+2\cos\theta)(\alpha - ika\eta\cos\vartheta_0)\right] d\Omega_0 \\ &\approx ika\cos\vartheta - \tfrac{2}{3}ika\gamma\cos\vartheta - \alpha + \tfrac{2}{3}ika\eta\cos\vartheta, \end{aligned}\right\} \tag{17.5}$$

or

$$\Psi_0 \approx 1 + \alpha; \qquad \gamma \approx 1 + \tfrac{1}{2}(1-\eta)$$

for Eq. (17.1) to be satisfied to the first order. The scattered wave, to the second order in ka, is then $\Psi_S \to (e^{ikr}/r)\, f(\vartheta)$, where

$$\left.\begin{aligned} f(\vartheta) &\approx \frac{a}{4\pi}\iint\left[(\Psi_0 + ika\gamma\cos\vartheta_0)\left(-\tfrac{1}{3}k^2a^2 - ika\cos\theta\right) + \right. \\ &\qquad \left. + (\alpha - ika\eta\cos\vartheta_0)(1 - ika\cos\theta)\right] d\Omega_0 \\ &= a\left[\alpha - \tfrac{1}{3}k^2a^2 + \tfrac{1}{2}k^2a^2(1-\eta)\cos\vartheta\right]. \end{aligned}\right\} \tag{17.6}$$

Several comments should be made about this result. In the first place we note that, even when the scattering sphere is rigid and held fixed in space (so that $\alpha = \eta = 0$) the distribution of pressure $\Psi_{r=a}$ at the surface is not that of the incident wave $e^{ika\cos\vartheta}$ at the surface (for γ is not 1 when $\eta = 0$, but is $\frac{3}{2}$). Thus the Born approximation, which consists of setting $\Psi = \Psi_i$ inside the integral, is not good here, even in the first approximation. When $\alpha = \eta = 0$ the correct form for the scattered amplitude is $f(\vartheta) \approx \frac{1}{2}k^2a^3(\cos\vartheta - \frac{2}{3})$, which scatters more in the backward direction ($\vartheta > \frac{1}{2}\pi$) than in the forward direction ($\vartheta < \frac{1}{2}\pi$), but which has some scattered wave directly forward ($\vartheta = 0$). The Born approximation would have $f(\vartheta) \approx \frac{1}{3} k^2 a^3 (\cos\vartheta - 1)$, which goes to zero in the forward direction. True, the difference is in the second order in ka, but (when $\alpha = \eta = 0$) this is the order of magnitude of the whole scattered wave, so the error is not negligible. A small, rigid sphere does not scatter much sound, and to compute the right form for the small amount scattered, we must use a better approximation than the Born approximation provides.

The second comment is that the scattered radiation from a small, rigid sphere ($\alpha = \eta = 0$) is not just monopole or just dipole radiation, it is a combination of both, to the same order in ka, the dipole strength being $\frac{3}{2}$ the monopole strength. This is because the sphere material has a different compressibility than the medium and also the region as a whole is held fixed. If the material of the sphere had a compression modulus $\varrho_m c_m^2$ (compared to ϱc^2 for the medium outside) then the surface of the sphere would yield to the average pressure and the quantity α in (17.6) would be $\frac{1}{3} k^2 a^2 (\varrho c^2/\varrho_m c_m^2)$, not zero. Likewise if the material had density ϱ_m, not infinite, its center would not be fixed at the origin, but would move somewhat with the medium, and the quantity η would be $3\varrho/(\varrho + 2\varrho_m)$, not zero. In this case the scattered amplitude, to the second order in ka, would be

$$f(\vartheta) \approx -\frac{1}{3} k^2 a^3 \left[\frac{\varrho_m c_m^2 - \varrho c^2}{\varrho_m c_m^2} - \frac{3\varrho_m - 3\varrho}{2\varrho_m + \varrho} \cos\vartheta\right]. \tag{17.7}$$

We note that if the sphere has the same density as that of the fluid medium there is no dipole scattering; the sphere moves to and fro as though it were the fluid. Alternately, if the sphere has the same compressibility as the fluid medium, there is no monopole scattering; the sphere compresses as though it were the fluid. As long as $\varrho_m > \varrho$ and $\varrho_m c_m^2 > \varrho c^2$, more sound is scattered backward than forward.

The formula (17.7) holds, for small values of ka, even for cases where the density and compressibility of the material are smaller than that of the fluid medium (as, for instance, for air bubbles in water). In such cases it is occasionally necessary to include the fact that energy is lost in compressing and expanding the bubble; energy from the incident wave is absorbed by the bubble as well as dispersed by scattering.

When the radius of the sphere is large compared to the wavelength, the second-order result of (17.7) is no longer valid; an exact solution is needed [*42*], or a variational calculation similar to that of Eq. (16.8). This will be touched on again in the next chapter.

B. The behavior of simple acoustic systems.

Having derived the basic equations of linear acoustics and indicated their range of validity, the remainder of this article will be devoted to examples of the solution of those equations, for a variety of conditions of interest. The present Chapter B will be devoted to the analysis of sound waves in a single region, not coupled to any other region. In view of the discussion preceding Eq. (8.1), this is equivalent to assuming that the normal acoustic impedance of the boundary surrounding the region is a point function of position on the boundary, independent of the configuration of the enclosed wave, at every point on the boundary. In the final Chapter C we will discuss more complicated cases, where the waves in two regions are coupled across a common boundary, as was exemplified in Eq. (13.4).

The single region we are to discuss in the present chapter is presumed filled with a fluid of density ϱ and sound velocity c. The acoustic impedance of the boundary surface at the point $\boldsymbol{r}^B$ is $\varrho c\,\zeta(\boldsymbol{r}^B) = \varrho c/\beta(\boldsymbol{r}^B)$, where ζ, called the *specific acoustic impedance* (or sometimes just *impedance*) and β, called the *specific acoustic admittance*, are point functions of $\boldsymbol{r}^B$ and of the frequency $(\omega/2\pi)$ of the wave.

I. Reflection from a plane boundary.

18. Uniform impedance. We have already discussed the case of a single-frequency plane wave striking a plane boundary at an angle of incidence ϕ, when the surface has uniform admittance β. The incident-plus-reflected wave is [*10*], [*42*], [*43*].

$$\left.\begin{aligned} p(\boldsymbol{r}) &= p_i\left[e^{i\boldsymbol{k}_i\cdot\boldsymbol{r}} + R(\phi)\, e^{i\boldsymbol{k}_r\cdot\boldsymbol{r}}\right] e^{-i\omega t},\\ R(\phi) &= \frac{\zeta\cos\phi - 1}{\zeta\cos\phi + 1} = \frac{\cos\phi - \beta}{\cos\phi + \beta} \qquad (0 \leqq \phi < \tfrac{1}{2}\pi) \end{aligned}\right\} \tag{18.1}$$

where $\boldsymbol{k}_i$ is the wave vector of the incident wave, at an angle ϕ to the normal $\boldsymbol{a}_z$ to the surface, $\boldsymbol{k}_r$ is the reflected wave vector, also at angle ϕ to the normal and $\boldsymbol{k}_i$, $\boldsymbol{a}_z$ and $\boldsymbol{k}_r$ are in the x, z plane. The pressure and the fluid velocity at the surface $z=0$ are then

$$\left.\begin{aligned} p(\boldsymbol{r}^B) &= p_i\left(\frac{2\cos\phi}{\cos\phi+\beta}\right) e^{ikx\sin\phi - i\omega t};\\ u_x(\boldsymbol{r}^B) &= \left(\frac{\sin\phi}{\varrho c}\right) p(\boldsymbol{r}^B); \quad u_z(\boldsymbol{r}^B) = \left(\frac{-\beta}{\varrho c}\right) p(\boldsymbol{r}^B). \end{aligned}\right\} \tag{18.2}$$

We should note that Eq. (18.1) is not valid for ϕ identically $\frac{1}{2}\pi$, unless β is identically zero. At grazing incidence the reflected wave is exactly equal and opposite in sign to the incident wave, so the two cancel. The difficulty is [*68*] that a truly plane wave cannot travel tangential to an infinite plane surface which yields, however slightly, to the acoustic pressure. For a truly plane wave tangential to the surface would have acoustic velocities exactly parallel to the surface, and if the surface yields to the pressure there would have to be a component of velocity normal to the surface. We will come back to this apparent paradox later in this chapter, when we discuss transmission through ducts (Sect. 23).

The specific acoustic admittance $\beta = \varkappa - i\sigma$ of the surface usually has a magnitude smaller than 1; by the time it has become as large or larger than 1, β is usually no longer a point function of position. Quantity $\varkappa$ is the specific acoustic conductance of the surface and σ is its susceptance. The fraction of the incident energy which is absorbed by the surface is

$$\alpha(\phi) = 1 - |R(\phi)|^2 = \frac{4\varkappa\cos\phi}{|\cos\phi+\beta|^2}. \tag{18.3}$$

While we are at it we can utilize the results of Eq. (11.8) to compute the energy the energy lost because of viscosity and thermal conduction near the surface. The power lost per unit area is

$$\frac{1}{4}\varrho c k l_v |u_x|^2 + \frac{1}{4}(\gamma-1)\frac{k l_h}{\varrho c}|p|^2 = \frac{k|p_i|^2}{2\varrho c}\left[l_v\frac{2\cos^2\phi\sin^2\phi}{|\cos\phi+\beta|^2} + (\gamma-1)\, l_h\frac{2\cos^2\phi}{|\cos\phi+\beta|^2}\right]$$

where l_v and l_h are the boundary layer thicknesses for viscous and thermal loss, respectively. Since the incident intensity is $|p_i|^2/2\varrho c$ and since a unit area of incident wave irradiates an area $(1/\cos\phi)$ of surface, the fraction of the incident energy which is lost by viscosity and heat conduction is

$$\alpha_{vh} = \frac{2k\cos\phi}{|\cos\phi+\beta|^2}\,[l_v\sin^2\phi + (\gamma-1)\,l_h]. \tag{18.4}$$

The thermal loss has the same dependence on the angle of incidence as does the loss in the wall itself [according to Eq. (18.3)]; in fact we can consider the heat conduction loss as equivalent to an additional surface conductance $\varkappa_h = \frac{1}{2}(\gamma-1)\,k l_h$. This is not possible for the viscous losses, because of the additional factor $\sin^2\phi$. For air, the energy lost to the surface itself is usually much larger than the energy lost to viscosity and conductivity, unless the boundary surface is exceptionally rigid and non-porous. Consequently, we can often neglect these latter effects in comparison with the effects of surface absorption.

If, instead of a single-frequency wave, the incident wave is the simple pulse $\delta[t-(\boldsymbol{a}_i\cdot\boldsymbol{r}/c)]$, which is the inverse Laplace transform of $\exp(i\boldsymbol{k}_i\cdot\boldsymbol{r})$ $(\boldsymbol{k}_i = k\boldsymbol{a}_i$, $k=\omega/c=is/c)$, the reflected wave is the inverse Laplace transform of the reflected wave of (18.1), where ω in $\boldsymbol{k}_r=\boldsymbol{a}_r(\omega/c)$ and in β is replaced by is. For example if $\zeta=\chi+(i\,\Upsilon/\omega)$ (the surface having friction and stiffness) the reflected wave is

$$\frac{\chi\cos\phi-1}{\chi\cos\phi+1}\,\delta\left(t-\frac{\boldsymbol{a}_r\cdot\boldsymbol{r}}{c}\right)+\frac{2\Upsilon\cos\phi}{(\chi\cos\phi+1)^2}\,u\left(t-\frac{\boldsymbol{a}_r\cdot\boldsymbol{r}}{c}\right)\exp\left[\frac{-\Upsilon\cos\phi}{1+\chi\cos\phi}\left(t-\frac{\boldsymbol{a}_r\cdot\boldsymbol{r}}{c}\right)\right]$$

where u is the unit step function. The reflected wave is thus an initial pulse of amplitude $(\chi\cos\phi-1)/(\chi\cos\phi+1)$, involving the resistance term χ, plus an exponentially decaying "wake", which continues after the pulse has passed.

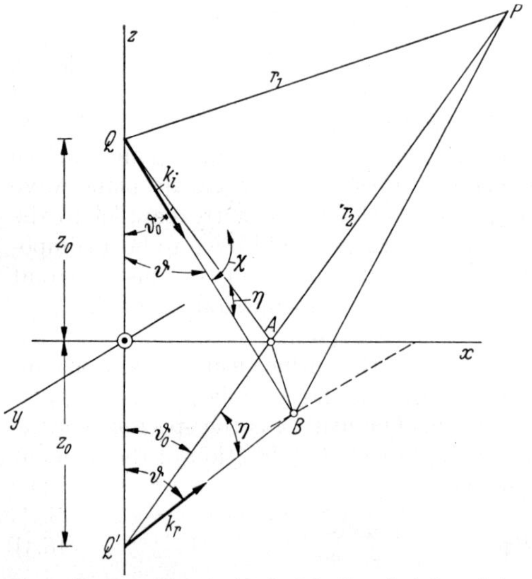

Fig. 1. Vectors and angles involved in the calculation of the reflection of a spherical wave from an absorbing surface.

19. The GREEN's function. We can also use Eq. (18.1) to obtain the GREEN's function [*18*], [*62*], [*67*], [*74*] for a semi-infinite region bounded by an infinite plane boundary, which has a specific acoustic admittance $\beta=(1/\zeta)$. For we can express a single-frequency monopole wave [*43*] by a superposition of plane waves in different directions,

$$\frac{e^{ikr}}{r}=\frac{ik}{2\pi}\iint\limits_C e^{i\boldsymbol{k}\cdot\boldsymbol{r}}\,d\Omega \tag{19.1}$$

where vector $\boldsymbol{k}$ has magnitude $k=\omega/c$ and direction given by the spherical angles ϑ, φ, where $d\Omega$ is the element of solid angle $d\varphi\sin\vartheta\,d\vartheta$ and where the range of integration implied by C is from 0 to 2π for φ but from 0 to $\frac{1}{2}\pi-i\infty$ (or from 0 to $-\frac{1}{2}\pi+i\infty$) for ϑ ($\cos\vartheta$ goes from 1 to $i\infty$). The polar axis for φ, ϑ can be in any direction with respect to vector $\boldsymbol{r}$.

When the source of the spherical wave is the point Q, at the point $(0, 0, z_0)$ above the boundary which is the x, y plane, as shown in Fig. 1, we can choose the angles η, χ to be the spherical angles for the integration in (19.1). The wave reaching the point of measurement P from Q is of course the direct wave e^{ikr_1}/r_1 (where $\boldsymbol{r}_1$ is the vector from Q to P) plus the wave reflected from the plane boundary $z=0$. For each plane wave in the integral of (19.1) for the incident wave, there is a reflected plane wave with amplitude given by (18.1). For example, for that part of the incident integrand having the incident wave with wave vector $\boldsymbol{k}_i$ at the angles η, χ to line QA ($\boldsymbol{k}_i$ points along QB) there is a reflected plane wave $R(\vartheta)\exp(i\boldsymbol{k}_r\cdot\boldsymbol{r}_2)$ where $\boldsymbol{r}_2$ is the vector from image point Q' to P and $\boldsymbol{k}_r$ points along line $Q'B$. For this component plane wave the reflection coefficient is $R(\vartheta)=(\cos\vartheta-\beta)/(\cos\vartheta+\beta)$ where β is the surface admittance and $\cos\vartheta=\cos\vartheta_0\cos\eta+\sin\vartheta_0\sin\eta\cos\chi$. Consequently the reflected part of the GREEN's function can be expressed as the integral

$$\left.\begin{aligned}\frac{ik}{2\pi}\iint\limits_C e^{i\boldsymbol{k}_r\cdot\boldsymbol{r}_2}R(\vartheta)\,d\Omega &= \frac{k\,e^{ikr_2}}{2\pi}\int\limits_0^{2\pi}d\chi\int\limits_0^{\infty}e^{-kr_2t}R(\vartheta)\,dt\\ &=\frac{e^{ikr_2}}{r_2}\int\limits_0^{\infty}e^{-kr_2t}\,d(kr_2t)\left[\frac{1}{2\pi}\int\limits_0^{2\pi}\frac{\cos\vartheta-\beta}{\cos\vartheta+\beta}\,d\chi\right]\end{aligned}\right\}\tag{19.2}$$

where

$$\cos\eta = 1+it$$

and thus

$$\cos\vartheta=(1+it)\cos\vartheta_0+\sin\vartheta_0\cos\chi\sqrt{t^2-2it}.$$

The integral over χ can be carried out in closed form, resulting in

$$1-\frac{2\beta}{\sqrt{(1+\beta\cos\vartheta_0+it)^2-(1-\beta^2)\sin^2\vartheta_0}}.$$

The integral over t cannot be carried out in closed form, but the first term in the asymptotic expansion for kr_2 large is $1-2\beta\{[1-F(\xi)]/(\cos\vartheta_0+\beta)\}$, where

$$\left.\begin{aligned}&[1-F(\xi)]\approx\sqrt{\pi\xi}\,e^{\xi}\,\mathrm{Erfc}(\sqrt{\xi});\qquad \xi=-ikr_2\frac{(\cos\vartheta_0+\beta)^2}{2(1+\beta\cos\vartheta_0)}\\ &\mathrm{Erfc}(y)=\frac{2}{\sqrt{\pi}}\int\limits_y^{\infty}e^{-u^2}\,du.\end{aligned}\right\}\tag{19.3}$$

Consequently the GREEN's function for the sound pressure at point P caused by the constant-frequency unit sound source at Q, in the presence of a plane boundary of admittance β a distance z_0 from Q is

$$g(\boldsymbol{r}_0|\boldsymbol{r})=-\frac{e^{ikr_1}}{4\pi r_1}-\{R(\vartheta_0)+[1-R(\vartheta_0)]\,F(\xi)\}\frac{e^{ikr_2}}{4\pi r_2}\tag{19.4}$$

where $\boldsymbol{r}_0$ points to the source point Q, $\boldsymbol{r}$ to the observation point P, $\boldsymbol{r}_1$ the vector from Q to P, $\boldsymbol{r}_2$ is the vector from image point Q' to P, making an angle ϑ_0 with the normal to the surface (thus a ray path from Q, via specular reflection, to P would have an angle of incidence ϑ_0) and $R(\vartheta_0)$ is the reflection coefficient for this angle. Expansion of the error function shows that as long as $\xi>10$,

$$F(\xi)=1-2\sqrt{\xi}\,e^{\xi}\int\limits_{\sqrt{\xi}}^{\infty}e^{-u^2}du\approx\frac{1}{\xi}=\frac{2i(1+\beta\cos\vartheta_0)}{kr_2(\cos\vartheta_0+\beta)^2}.\tag{19.5}$$

Thus when kr_2 is very large (point P a large number of wavelengths away from the image point Q') $F(\xi)$ is negligibly small for all values of the angle ϑ_0 unless β is very small, in which case the asymptotic formula (19.5) for F is not valid when $\vartheta_0\to\frac{1}{2}\pi$. But when $\beta=0$ we know that the factor in braces in (19.4) is exactly 1, corresponding to $1-R=0$, no matter what value F has.

Therefore, for kr_2 large enough, the quantity in braces in Eq. (19.4) reduces to $R(\vartheta_0)$, the reflection coefficient appropriate for the ray path from Q to P via specular reflection from the surface, and the complete GREEN'S function has the asymptotic form

$$g(\boldsymbol{r}_0|\boldsymbol{r}) \approx -\frac{e^{ik|\boldsymbol{r}-\boldsymbol{r}_0|}}{4\pi|\boldsymbol{r}-\boldsymbol{r}_0|} - \left(\frac{\cos\vartheta_0-\beta}{\cos\vartheta_0+\beta}\right)\frac{e^{ik|\boldsymbol{r}-\boldsymbol{r}_0'|}}{4\pi|\boldsymbol{r}-\boldsymbol{r}_0'|} \tag{19.6}$$

where the source is at $\boldsymbol{r}_0$, the image at $\boldsymbol{r}_0'$ and the observation point is at $\boldsymbol{r}$, and ϑ_0 is the angle between the vector $\boldsymbol{r}_0-\boldsymbol{r}_0'$ and vector $\boldsymbol{r}-\boldsymbol{r}_0'$. When P is close to Q' the more accurate formula (19.4) must be used. When P and Q are both on the boundary ($\vartheta_0\to\frac{1}{2}\pi$) Eq. (19.6) goes to zero; Eq. (19.4) shows that the actual pressure at the boundary diminishes as $(1/r^2)$.

20. Radiation from a circular piston in a plane. If the portion of the boundary surface (x, y plane) within a circle of radius a, centered at the origin, is moved with velocity $v_0\,e^{-i\omega t}$ normal to the surface, the rest of the boundary being at rest, we can use the general equation (13.1) to compute the generated sound wave [42], [55], [75] using the GREEN'S function we have just devised. We assume that the surface has an admittance β, including the circular area which is forced to move. What we mean by the phrase "the rest of the surface being at rest" is that, if the instantaneous acoustic pressure at a given point on the rest of the surface is $p_0\,e^{-i\omega t}$, then the instantaneous normal velocity of the surface is $-(\beta p_0/\varrho c)\,e^{-i\omega t}$ at that point. The phrase "is moved with velocity $v_0\,e^{-i\omega t}$" can have several meanings; we will choose it to mean that the normal velocity of the fluid near the surface, plus $(\beta/\varrho c)$ times the pressure there, is $v_0\,e^{-i\omega t}$. This is the same as saying that the pressure at the surface is equal to $(\varrho c/\beta)$ times the difference between $v_0\,e^{-i\omega t}$ and the actual fluid velocity there, normal to the surface.

To use Eq. (13.1) to find the radiated sound we must use the GREEN'S function of Eq. (19.4) or (19.6). If we are satisfied to obtain the asymptotic form for large distances from the generating disk, we use Eq. (19.6). To use it in Eq. (13.1), we need its value and the value of its normal gradient when $z_0=0$,

$$\left.\begin{aligned} g(\boldsymbol{r}_0^B|\boldsymbol{r}) &\approx \left(\frac{-2\cos\vartheta}{\cos\vartheta+\beta}\right)\frac{1}{4\pi r}\exp[ik(r-r_0\sin\vartheta\cos\Psi)] \quad (r\gg r_0,\ kr\gg 1)\,,\\ \frac{\partial}{\partial z_0}g(\boldsymbol{r}_0^B|\boldsymbol{r}) &\approx \left(\frac{2ik\beta\cos\vartheta}{\cos\vartheta+\beta}\right)\frac{1}{4\pi r}\exp[ik(r-r_0\sin\vartheta\cos\Psi)] \quad \left(\frac{\partial}{\partial n_0}=-\frac{\partial}{\partial z_0}\right)\end{aligned}\right\} \tag{20.1}$$

where r, ϑ, φ are the coordinates of the observation point P, r_0, φ_0 the coordinates of the source point Q_0 (which is on the x, y plane) and where $\psi=\varphi-\varphi_0$.

Inserting these into Eq. (13.1) we find for the pressure at P, $p(\boldsymbol{r})=(e^{ikr}/r)\,f(\vartheta)$, where

$$f(\vartheta) \approx \frac{-1}{4\pi}\iint\left(\frac{2\cos\vartheta}{\cos\vartheta+\beta}\right)[ik\beta p(\boldsymbol{r}_0^B)+ik\varrho c u(\boldsymbol{r}_0^B)]\,e^{-ikr_0\sin\vartheta\cos\psi}\,ds_0 \tag{20.2}$$

and where we have used the relation $(\partial p/\partial z)=ik\varrho c u_z$. As we have already explained, for $r_0>a$, where the surface is "at rest", $u_z=-(\beta p/\varrho c)$ so the quantity in brackets is zero; for $r_0<a$ the quantity in brackets is $ik\varrho c v_0$. Therefore the asymptotic form for the angle distribution factor f is

$$\left.\begin{aligned} f(\vartheta) &\approx -\frac{ik\varrho c v_0\cos\vartheta}{2\pi(\cos\vartheta+\beta)}\int_0^{2\pi}d\psi\int_0^a e^{-ikr_0\sin\vartheta\cos\psi}\,r_0\,dr_0\\ &= -\frac{1}{2}ik\varrho c v_0 a^2\left[\frac{2\cos\vartheta\,J_1(ka\sin\vartheta)}{(\cos\vartheta+\beta)\,ka\sin\vartheta}\right]\end{aligned}\right\} \tag{20.3}$$

and the intensity at P is $(|f|^2/2\varrho c r^2)$.

When the surface, except for the vibrating disk, is perfectly rigid ($\beta=0$), the angular distribution of intensity has the well-known Fraunhofer diffraction factor

$$[2J_1(k a \sin\vartheta)/k a \sin\vartheta]^2 .$$

If β is not zero, however, the angular distribution of intensity is modified by the additional factor

$$[\cos^2\vartheta/|\cos\vartheta+\beta|^2] ,$$

which is a little less than unity at $\vartheta=0$ and which goes to zero at $\vartheta=\frac{1}{2}\pi$, for radiation tangential to the surface. The fact that the surface yields somewhat to the pressure means that somewhat less sound is radiated straight out from the disk and very little sound survives at large distances tangential to the surface.

Useful as it is in computing the far field, the GREEN's function formulation of Eqs. (20.1) is not satisfactory for calculations of the near field, such as the determination of the acoustic reaction on the driving piston. The form which is advantageous here is one expressed in terms of the cylindrical coordinates z, r, φ. The GREEN's function for free space in these coordinates is

$$-\frac{e^{ikR}}{4\pi R} = \frac{-1}{4\pi}\sum_{m=0}^{\infty} \varepsilon_m \cos m(\varphi-\varphi_0) \int_{\infty}^{0} e^{i\mu|z-z_0|} J_m(u r) J_m(u r_0) \frac{u\,du}{\mu} \tag{20.4}$$

where

$$\varepsilon_0 = 1, \qquad \varepsilon_n = 2\,(n>0),$$

and where

$$\mu = \sqrt{k^2-u^2}.$$

If we orient the coordinate system so that the boundary is at $z=0$, then it is not difficult to modify this expansion to obtain the GREEN's function appropriate for the half-space $z \geqq 0$, when the surface $z=0$ has specific acoustic admittance β;

$$\left.\begin{aligned} G(\boldsymbol{r}|\boldsymbol{r}_0) &= \frac{-1}{4\pi}\sum_{m=0}^{\infty} \varepsilon_m \cos m(\varphi-\varphi_0) \times \\ &\times \int_0^{\infty} \left[e^{i\mu|z-z_0|} + \left(\frac{\mu-k\beta}{\mu+k\beta}\right) e^{i\mu(z+z_0)}\right] J_m(u r) J_m(u r_0) \frac{u\,du}{\mu} \end{aligned}\right\} \tag{20.5}$$

which can be used instead of the asymptotic expression of Eq. (20.2) when we wish to calculate the near field. It should be noted that the integration over u is taken so that $\mu=\sqrt{k^2-u^2}$ is positive real when $u<k$, is positive imaginary when $u>k$.

If the piston of Eq. (20.3) is the disk $z=0$, $r<a$, then the total reaction force on it is

$$\left.\begin{aligned} F &= \int_0^{2\pi} d\varphi \int_0^a p(0,r,\varphi)\, r\, dr \\ &= 2\pi k \varrho c v_0 \int_0^a r\,dr \int_0^a r_0\,dr_0 \int_0^{\infty} J_0(u r) J_0(u r_0) \frac{u\,du}{\mu+k\beta} \\ &= 2\pi k \varrho c v_0 \int_0^{\infty} \frac{[J_1(u a)]^2}{\sqrt{k^2-u^2}+k\beta} \frac{du}{u}. \end{aligned}\right\} \tag{20.6}$$

When $\beta = 0$ the impedance $Z = F/v_0$ becomes

$$Z = \pi a^2 \varrho c \left[2ka \int_0^{ka} \frac{[J_1(w)]^2 dw}{w\sqrt{k^2a^2 - w^2}} - 2ika \int_{ka}^{\infty} \frac{[J_1(w)]^2 dw}{w\sqrt{w^2 - k^2a^2}} \right]. \tag{20.7}$$

The first term in the brackets is $1 - (1/ka)\, J_1(2ka)$ and the second term is (i/ka) times the Struve function of $2ka$ of order 1. When $\beta \neq 0$ the integral of Eq. (20.6) must be computed numerically.

21. Scattering from an inhomogeneity in surface impedance. If an area of the surface around the origin has specific acoustic admittance β which differs from the value β_0 which the x, y plane has everywhere else, then a plane wave incident at angle ϕ will produce a wave scattered by the inhomogeneity [*5*], [*9*], [*21*], [*44*], in addition to the reflected wave given in Eq. (18.1). The basic integral equation (13.1) can be modified, by methods by now familiar, to correspond to this case. We suppose the incident wave vector $\boldsymbol{k}_i$ is in the x, z plane at angle ϕ to the z axis and that the measurement point $P(r, \vartheta, \varphi)$ is a great distance from the origin. The area A, around the origin, has admittance β, whereas the rest of the x, y plane has admittance β_0.

Using the asymptotic forms of Eq. (20.1), the pressure at P is

$$\left.\begin{aligned} p(\boldsymbol{r}) \approx p_i\, e^{ik(-z\cos\phi + x\sin\phi)} + p_i \left(\frac{\cos\phi - \beta}{\cos\phi + \beta}\right) e^{ik(z\cos\phi + x\sin\phi)} - \\ - \frac{e^{ikr}}{4\pi r}\left(\frac{2ik\cos\vartheta}{\cos\vartheta + \beta}\right) \iint_A (\beta - \beta_0)\, p(x_0, y_0)\, e^{-ik(x_0\sin\vartheta\cos\varphi + y_0\sin\vartheta\sin\varphi)}\, dx_0\, dy_0 . \end{aligned}\right\} \tag{21.1}$$

The first term is the incident wave, the second the reflected wave and the third term is the wave scattered by the inhomogeneity in surface admittance.

If the difference $(\beta - \beta_0)$ is not large we can consider the factor p in the integral to be approximately equal to the plane-plus-reflected pressure at the surface (Born approximation), so that the scattered wave p_s, for large r, is $p_i(e^{ikr}/r) \times$ $\times f(\boldsymbol{k}_i, \boldsymbol{k}_s)$, with

$$\left.\begin{aligned} f(\boldsymbol{k}_i, \boldsymbol{k}_s) &\approx \frac{-ik\cos\phi\cos\vartheta}{\pi(\cos\phi + \beta)(\cos\vartheta + \beta)} \iint_A b(x_0, y_0)\, e^{i\boldsymbol{\mu}\cdot\boldsymbol{r}_0}\, dx_0\, dy_0 \\ &\to \frac{-ik\cos\phi\cos\vartheta}{\pi(\cos\phi + \beta)(\cos\vartheta + \beta)} \iint_A b(x_0, y_0)\, dx_0\, dy_0 \quad (A \ll \lambda^2) \end{aligned}\right\} \tag{21.2}$$

where the limiting second form is valid when the dimensions of area A are small compared to the wavelength $(2\pi/k)$. Quantity b is the difference in admittance $(\beta - \beta_0)$ for area A and vector $\boldsymbol{\mu}$ is the projection of vector $\boldsymbol{k}_r - \boldsymbol{k}_s$ on the x, y plane;

$$\boldsymbol{\mu} = \boldsymbol{a}_z \times [(\boldsymbol{k}_r - \boldsymbol{k}_s) \times \boldsymbol{a}_z],$$

$$\boldsymbol{\mu}\cdot\boldsymbol{r}_0 = k\, x_0 (\sin\phi - \sin\vartheta\cos\varphi) - k\, y_0 \sin\vartheta\sin\varphi .$$

When the dimensions of A are small compared to a wavelength the inhomogeneity acts like a point source of strength proportional to the integrated difference b of admittance.

When the area A, over which b differs from zero, is large compared to a wavelength, we must use the first expression of (21.2). In the opposite limit, when $\beta(x, y)$ varies with x and y over the whole x, y plane, we choose β_0 to be the average value of β, so that the integral of b over the plane is zero. Then the area A in the first line of (21.2) is the area irradiated by the incident plane wave.

To measure the scattered sound we must usually screen the observation point P from the incident and reflected waves. This can be done by limiting the extent of the wave front of the incident wave by some collimating device, so that, near the x, y plane, the incident wave fronts have non-zero amplitude only within a specified area of dimensions large compared to the wavelength but small compared to r and to the dimensions of the wall. Within this area the incident wave is effectively a plane wave, though at the edges diffraction effects occur.

Now suppose this collimated plane wave is incident, at an angle ϕ on an area A of the x, y plane around the origin and suppose the point $P(r, \vartheta, \varphi)$ is out of the incident and reflected beams and is far enough away so that the solid angle $(A\cos\vartheta/r^2)$, subtended by A at P, is small. Then the scattered waves will arrive at P all with approximately the same directionality, and the scattered intensity at P will be $|p(r)|^2/2\varrho c$. To compute this power we use the first line of (21.2), the integration being over the irradiated area A. We note that the integral is proportional to the two-dimensional Fourier transform of b,

$$B(\boldsymbol{\mu}) = \frac{1}{2\pi}\iint\limits_A b(x_0, y_0)\, e^{i\mu_x x_0 + i\mu_y y_0}\, dx_0\, dy_0 .$$

The pressure at P is

$$p_s(r) = -\frac{2ik\,p_i\cos\vartheta\cos\phi}{(\cos\vartheta+\beta)(\cos\phi+\beta)}\, B(\boldsymbol{\mu})\,\frac{e^{ikr}}{r} \tag{21.3}$$

and the ratio between the scattered intensity at P to the incident intensity $|p_i|^2/2\varrho c$ is

$$\sigma(\boldsymbol{k}_i, \boldsymbol{k}_s) = \frac{4k^2\cos^2\phi\cos^2\vartheta}{|\cos\phi+\beta|^2\,|\cos\vartheta+\beta|^2}\iiiint\limits_{\text{over } A} b(x_0, y_0)\, b^*(x_1, y_1)\times$$
$$\times\exp\left[i\mu_x(x_0-x_1) + i\mu_y(y_0-y_1)\right] dx_0\, dx_1\, dy_0\, dy_1$$

where

$$\mu_x = k\sin\phi - k\sin\vartheta\cos\varphi \quad\text{and}\quad \mu_y = -k\sin\vartheta\sin\varphi .$$

The variables of integration in this can be changed to x_1, y_1 and $X = x_0 - x_1$, $Y = y_0 - y_1$. The integral over x_1, y_1 is proportional to the *auto-correlation function* of the inhomogeneities b of the surface admittance,

$$S(X, Y) = \frac{1}{A}\iint\limits_A b^*(x_1, y_1)\, b(x_1 + X, y_1 + Y)\, dx_1\, dy_1 . \tag{21.4}$$

Thus the quadruple integral is proportional to the Fourier transform of this auto-correlation function,

$$s(\boldsymbol{\mu}) = \frac{1}{2\pi}\iint\limits_A S(X, Y)\, e^{i\mu_x X + i\mu_y Y}\, dX\, dY . \tag{21.5}$$

In fact the intensity ratio at P is just

$$\sigma(\boldsymbol{k}_i, \boldsymbol{k}_s) = \left(\frac{A\cos\vartheta}{r^2}\right)\left[\frac{8\pi k^2\cos\vartheta\cos^2\phi}{|\cos\vartheta+\beta|^2\,|\cos\phi+\beta|^2}\, s(\boldsymbol{\mu})\right] \tag{21.6}$$

where the components of the vector $\boldsymbol{\mu}$ have been given above.

If the irregularities in surface admittance are randomly placed, the correlation function S will drop off exponentially with $(X^2 + Y^2)$ and $s(\boldsymbol{\mu})$ will be largest for $\boldsymbol{\mu} = 0$ (scattering in the same direction as the reflected beam) dropping off in intensity away from this direction uniformly as μ increases, the "half-width" of the scattered beam being inversely proportional to the "grain-size" of the variations in b. If b has a periodic structure, S will be periodic with the same period, s will also be periodic, with inverse periods, and the scattered wave will have beams of extra intensity at the appropriate Bragg reflection angles (see Sect. 37). Thus an exploration of the distribution of scattered intensity can give us data regarding the statistics of the fluctuations in admittance of the surface.

If, instead of confining the incident-plus-reflected wave, we collimate the solid angle from which the scattered wave comes to P, we can still use formula (21.6). Since $(A \cos\vartheta/r^2)$ is the solid angle subtended at P by A, the intensity at P in a small solid angle $d\Omega$ at the angles ϑ, φ is the quantity in brackets in (21.6), multiplied by $d\Omega$.

A second way of measuring the scattered wave is by pulsing the incident wave. For example, the collimated incident beam (of frequency $\omega/2\pi$) could be turned on at time $t=0$ and turned off at time $t=T$, where T is long compared to a period $(2\pi/\omega)$ but short compared to the time required for the sound to go from the surface to P. This arrangement enables us to measure the intensity scattered back to the original source, for example, where $\boldsymbol{k}_s = -\boldsymbol{k}_i$ ($\vartheta = -\phi$ and $\mu = 2k \sin\frac{1}{2}\phi$). Appropriate modifications of (21.6) can be used to compute the scattering for this and other configurations.

Solutions (21.2) to (21.6) are approximate solutions, valid as long as the difference $(\beta - \beta_0)$ is small. Exact solutions can be obtained for the scattering of sound from a patch of wall surface which differs in admittance from the rest of the boundary plane, when the patch is of simple shape, such as a strip or disk. An exact solution can also be obtained when the admittance varies sinusoidally over the boundary surface. In the great majority of cases of practical interest, however, the approximate solutions discussed above will adequately predict the general behavior of the sound field, and can be used for patches of any shape.

22. Scattering from a rough surface [*58*], [*76*]. An "element of roughness" on a surface may be thought of as a "foreign body" (in the sense of Sect. 15) half-imbedded in the surface, which is otherwise smooth in the immediate neighborhood. It is equivalent, for surface effects, to the surface scatterer of Sect. 15; each roughness element of a rough surface contributes a scattered wave to the incident-plus-reflected wave which would be the complete solution if the surface were not rough. In the region above the surface $(z>0)$ the sound field is nearly the same as it would be if the smooth surface between the roughness elements were removed and there were two waves, $p_i e^{i\boldsymbol{k}_i\cdot\boldsymbol{r}}$ and $R(\phi)\, p_i e^{i\boldsymbol{k}_r\cdot\boldsymbol{r}}$, incident on a distribution of surface scatterers on the plane $z=0$. The two fields would be identical if the admittance of the inter-element surface were 0 or ∞ and if the surface scatterers in the second case were all symmetric with respect to the plane $z=0$. But since the roughness elements of a rough surface usually display variability in size and shape, we will have to express our final results in terms of average shapes and equivalent scattering powers anyway, so that the approximate equivalence of the two problems will suffice.

Usually, also, the dimensions of the roughness elements are small compared to a wavelength. In this case Eq. (17.7) gives the angular distribution of the wave scattered from each incident wave by each scatterer. For our purposes here it suffices that the wave scattered in the direction $\boldsymbol{k}_s$ from the wave with wave vector $\boldsymbol{k}_i$, by the n-th scatterer has the form

$$g(\boldsymbol{r}_n|\boldsymbol{r})\,[k^2 \Gamma_n - (\boldsymbol{k}_i\cdot\boldsymbol{k}_s)\,\Delta_n] \tag{22.1}$$

where g is the GREEN's function for the source at the n-th scatterer (on the x, y plane) and the observation point at $\boldsymbol{r}$ (r, ϑ, φ). Quantity Γ_n can be called the monopole scattering strength of the n-th roughness element and Δ_n its dipole scattering strength. Both Γ_n and Δ_n have the dimensions of a volume. If the n-th element is completely incompressible, Γ_n would equal twice the volume of the roughness element which protrudes above the x, y plane; if the element is compressible Γ_n will be less than this and may be complex. If the element is completely immobile, quantity Δ_n would equal three times the protruding volume of the element; if it does move under the influence of the sound wave, Δ_n will be smaller than this and may be complex, if friction accompanies the motion. The GREEN's function g is affected by the presence of the admittance surface and should thus be

$$\frac{\cos\vartheta}{\cos\vartheta+\beta} \; \frac{-\mathrm{e}^{ik|\boldsymbol{r}-\boldsymbol{r}_n|}}{4\pi|\boldsymbol{r}-\boldsymbol{r}_n|}$$

instead of the function $(-\mathrm{e}^{ikr}/4\pi r)$ used in Eq. (17.2) for a free scatterer at the origin.

Combining the scattering from both incident and reflected waves of Eq. (18.1), the wave at (r, ϑ, φ) scattered by the roughness element at (r_n, φ_n), from an incident-plus reflected wave, with angle of incidence ϕ, is

$$g(\boldsymbol{r}_n|\boldsymbol{r})\,[p(\boldsymbol{r}_n)\,k^2\,\Gamma_n - k^2(\sin\phi\sin\vartheta\cos\varphi - \beta\cos\vartheta)\,p(\boldsymbol{r}_n)\,\Delta_n]$$

where $p(\boldsymbol{r}_n)$ is the total pressure wave at $\boldsymbol{r}_n$; to the first approximation it is the pressure

$$\frac{2\cos\phi}{\cos\phi+\beta}\,\mathrm{e}^{ikx_n\sin\phi}$$

of the incident-plus-reflected wave. The first term in the brackets is the monopole scattering. The second term can be written as

$$-k\varrho c\,\boldsymbol{u}(\boldsymbol{r}_n)\cdot\boldsymbol{k}_s\,\Delta_n = i\,\boldsymbol{k}_s\cdot\mathrm{grad}_0\,[p(\boldsymbol{r}_n)]\,\Delta_n,$$

where $\boldsymbol{u}$ is the acoustic velocity of the plane-plus-scattered wave, with x component $(\sin\phi/\varrho c)\,p(\boldsymbol{r}_n)$ and z component $-(\beta/\varrho c)\,p(\boldsymbol{r}_n)$. Note that the whole velocity, not just the normal velocity, enters here; if β were zero this velocity would be parallel to the x, y plane.

If the roughness of the surface is "fine-grained", i.e. if the roughness elements are considerably smaller than a wavelength and if they are distributed more or less evenly over the $x\,y$, plane so that the mean distance between them is less than a wavelength, then we can put our results into forms similar to those of the previous section. We suppose the sums of the Γ's and Δ's for all scatterers in an area $dx_0\,dy_0$ small compared to the wavelength are

$$\sum_n \Gamma_n = \Gamma(\boldsymbol{r})\,dx_0\,dy_0; \qquad \sum_n \Delta_n = \Delta(\boldsymbol{r}_0)\,dx_0\,dy_0 \tag{22.2}$$

where the "mean roughness factors" $\Gamma(\boldsymbol{r}_0)$ and $\Delta(\boldsymbol{r}_0)$ (which have the dimensions of length) are more or less smoothly varying functions of x_0 and y_0. Then the total wave at (r, ϑ, φ) scattered from an area A of the rough surface surrounding the origin, can be written as $p_i(\mathrm{e}^{ikr}/r)\,f(\boldsymbol{k}_i, \boldsymbol{k}_s)$ when r is much larger than the dimensions of A and where

$$\left.\begin{aligned} f(\boldsymbol{k}_i,\boldsymbol{k}_s) \approx {} & \frac{-k^2\cos\phi\cos\vartheta}{2\pi(\cos\phi+\beta)(\cos\vartheta+\beta)}\times \\ & \times\iint_A [\Gamma(\boldsymbol{r}_0) - \Delta(\boldsymbol{r}_0)(\sin\phi\sin\vartheta\cos\varphi-\beta\cos\vartheta)]\,\mathrm{e}^{i\boldsymbol{\mu}\cdot\boldsymbol{r}_0}dx_0\,dy_0. \end{aligned}\right\} \tag{22.3}$$

As with Eq. (21.2)

$$\mu = \boldsymbol{a}_x (\sin\phi - \sin\vartheta\cos\varphi) - \boldsymbol{a}_y \sin\vartheta\sin\varphi .$$

This result is to be compared with Eq. (21.2) for the scattering from irregularities in surface impedance. The monopole scattering term, in Γ, cannot be distinguished from the effect of an irregularity in impedance [term b in (21.2)], but the dipole part of the roughness scattering, dependent on Δ, has a different dependence on the angles of incidence and of scattering. In addition to the usual factor

$$\frac{\cos\phi\cos\vartheta}{(\cos\phi+\beta)(\cos\vartheta+\beta)}$$

there is a factor proportional to $(\boldsymbol{u}_s \cdot \boldsymbol{k}_s)$ where $\boldsymbol{u}_s$ is the velocity of the air at the surface.

From here on the calculation of the scattering of sound from an area of "fine-grained roughness" can be carried out analogously to that for admittance variations discussed in the previous section. The scattered amplitudes can be expressed in terms of the Fourier transforms of the mean roughness factors and the scattered intensity can be expressed in terms of their auto- and cross-correlation functions.

If the roughness elements are larger and are separated by distances not small compared to a wavelength, then the scattering from each element must be considered separately and the first approximation formulas, used above, may not be adequate. When the surface is "everywhere rough" and cannot be separated into elements separated by a smooth surface (as, for instance, the surface of the ocean) other methods of computation must be used [*34*], [*46*] though the results often can be expressed in terms of equivalent values of Γ and Δ.

II. Transmission through ducts.

23. Uniform ducts. The analysis of the transmission of sound along the interior of cylindrical enclosures is of interest, in part because there is occasional industrial need for tubes which allow air, but not sound, to flow freely through them, in part because many acoustical measurement procedures involve ducts, within which sound pressure is measured.

We will first discuss the propagation of sound along the interior of a uniform duct of infinite length [*10*], [*41*], [*42*], having its axis parallel to the z axis. The cross section of the duct is bounded by some closed boundary curve, of total parameter l, parallel to the x, y plane. At the boundary surface we assume (for this chapter, at any rate) that the ratio of acoustic pressure to normal velocity at the surface is a point function of position on the surface. If this surface impedance is a function of the transverse position on the boundary, but not of z, then a single-frequency wave inside the duct, propagated to the right, will have the form

$$p = \sum_m A_m \Phi_m(x, y) \exp(i k_m z - i k c t); \qquad \omega = k c \tag{23.1}$$

where Φ_m is one of the eigenfunction solutions of the equation

$$\left(\frac{\partial^2}{\partial x^2} + \frac{\partial^2}{\partial y^2}\right)\Phi_m + \mu_m^2 \Phi_m = 0; \qquad k_m^2 = k^2 - \mu_m^2 \tag{23.2}$$

which satisfies the boundary condition

$$\frac{\Phi_m}{\partial \Phi_m/\partial n} = \frac{\zeta(s)}{i k}$$

at the point on the perimeter of the cross section which is designated by the parameter s [the perimeter is defined by the parametric equations $x = X(s)$, $y = Y(s)$, where $(dX/ds)^2 + (dY/ds)^2 = 1$ to simplify scale factors] $\partial/\partial n$ is the normal component of the gradient, pointing away from the inside of the duct.

If $\zeta(s)$, the specific impedance of the surface, is everywhere zero, or infinity or everywhere pure imaginary (reactive), then all the eigenvalues μ_m^2 will be real and all (or all but one) will be positive. They thus can be placed in order along the real axis, with μ_0^2 farthest to the left, μ_1^2 next, and so on. Eq. (23.1) indicates that the wave consists of a set of partial waves, each travelling with different phase velocity, the m-th wave being characterized in transverse distribution by the transverse eigenfunction $\Phi_m(x, y)$. The propagation constant for the m-th partial wave is k_m, which is real for all μ_m's smaller than $k = (\omega/c)$ and which is pure imaginary for all μ_m's larger than k (as long as ζ has no real component). Thus the partial waves for all m's larger than some value m_0 have no true wave motion but die out exponentially; those for $m \leqq m_0$ are propagated with phase velocity $(ck/k_m) = ck/\sqrt{k^2 - \mu_m^2}$, larger than c, the sound velocity in free space. The higher the frequency the higher is m_0, i.e., the more partial waves are propagated. Alternatively, for the m-th partial wave there is a cut-off frequency $(\omega_m/2\pi) = (\mu_m c/2\pi)$, above which the wave is propagated, below which it dies out exponentially.

When the duct wall impedance is not purely reactive, but has a resistive component, then all the eigenvalues μ_m^2 will have imaginary components, in which case all the propagation constants k_m will be complex, not just those for $m > m_0$, and thus all the partial waves are attenuated. There is still a difference between the behavior of the lower modes and the higher ones, however, for the real part of μ_m^2 is usually considerably smaller than its imaginary part. Consequently those waves for which the real part of μ_m^2 is smaller than k^2 ($m \leqq m_0$, by definition) have propagation constants with imaginary parts much smaller than their real parts, and thus behave as true waves, somewhat attenuated. On the other hand, those waves for which the real part of μ_m^2 is larger than k^2 ($m > m_0$) have propagation constants which are almost purely imaginary; though there is some propagation, these waves rapidly damp out.

Power flows along the duct and, in most cases, it also is lost into the duct walls. The time average flow along the duct, across the section at z, is

$$\frac{1}{2\varrho c} \sum_{m,n} \left[A_m A_n^* \iint \Phi_m \Phi_n^* \, dx\, dy\right] \mathrm{Re}\, \frac{k_m}{k} \exp\left[\frac{-z}{k} \mathrm{Im}\,(k_m + k_n)\right] \tag{23.3}$$

which is non-increasing as $z \to \infty$ since the imaginary part of μ_m^2 is always non-positive. Two major comments should be made about this expression. First, the cross terms in the double summation do not vanish, since Φ_m is not orthogonal to Φ_n^*, but to Φ_n;

$$\iint \Phi_m \Phi_n \, dx\, dy = \Lambda_n \delta_{mn}. \tag{23.4}$$

The function Φ_m^* (the asterisk denotes the complex conjugate) is an eigenfunction for complex conjugate boundary conditions (i.e., for frequency $-\omega/2\pi$). Second, though the sum in Eq. (23.3) is over all values of m and n, it is effectively over m equal to or less than m_0, because the real part of (k_m/k) is negligibly small for $m > m_0$, as we have stated above and will illustrate later.

The GREEN's function for a unit point source, of frequency $\omega/2\pi$, at point (x_0, y_0, z_0) inside the duct is

$$G_k(\boldsymbol{r}|\boldsymbol{r}_0) = \sum_{m=0}^{m_0} \frac{\Phi_m(x_0, y_0)\,\Phi_m(x, y)}{2ik_m\Lambda_m} \exp(i\,k_m|z-z_0|) - \sum_{m>m_0} \frac{\Phi_m(x_0, y_0)\,\Phi_m(x, y)}{2K_m\Lambda_m} \exp(-K_m|z-z_0|) \qquad (23.5)$$

where

$$k_m = \sqrt{k^2-\mu_m^2} \quad \text{and} \quad K_m = \sqrt{\mu_m^2-k^2}\,.$$

The partial waves for $m>m_0$ are concentrated close to the source point; the lower modes, for $m\leqq m_0$, carry most of the wave energy away from the source.

If the duct is driven from one end, the surface $z=0$ having a z component of velocity $v_k(x, y)\,e^{-i\omega t}$ and the end at $z\to\infty$ being open, then the magnitudes A_m of Eq. (23.1) are adjusted so that $(\partial p/\partial z)_{z=0} = ik\varrho c v_k(x, y)$ and the wave has the form

$$p = \sum_{m=0}^{m_0} \left[\frac{k\varrho c}{\Lambda_m k_m} \iint v_k\,\Phi_m\,dx\,dy\right] \Phi_m(x, y)\,e^{ik_m z - i\omega t} - \sum_{m>m_0} \left[\frac{ik\varrho c}{\Lambda_m K_m} \iint v_k\,\Phi_m\,dx\,dy\right] \Phi_m(x, y)\,e^{-K_m z - i\omega t}. \qquad (23.6)$$

If the surface impedance of the sides of the duct has no real part then all the partial waves for $m\leqq m_0$ are propagated clear to $z\to\infty$, but all the modes for $m>m_0$ are rapidly attenuated and are not present as $z\to\infty$.

If the surface at $z=0$ is driven by a pulse

$$v_{z=0} = v_\delta(x, y)\,\delta(t) = \text{Laplace transform of } v_\delta(x, y)$$

then the Laplace transform of the generated wave is

$$\sum_m \frac{s\varrho c}{\sqrt{s^2+\omega_m^2}} \left[\frac{1}{\Lambda_m} \iint v_\delta\,\Phi_m\,dx\,dy\right] \Phi_m(x, y) \exp\left(-\frac{z}{c}\sqrt{s^2+\omega_m^2}\right) \quad (\omega_m = c\,\mu_m) \qquad (23.7)$$

and the wave itself, the transform with respect to $s=-i\omega$, is

$$\varrho c \frac{d}{dt} \sum_m \left[\frac{1}{\Lambda_m} \iint v_\delta\,\Phi_m\,dx\,dy\right] \Phi_m(x, y)\, u\left(t-\frac{z}{c}\right) J_0\left(\omega_m \sqrt{t^2-\left(\frac{z}{c}\right)^2}\right) \qquad (23.8)$$

where $u(x)=0$ $(x<0)$, $=1$ $(x>0)$ and $(d/dx)\,u(x)=\delta(x)$, and where we have assumed that the ω_m's are independent of ω. Thus the wave generated by the impulsive motion of the "piston" at $z=0$ is, first a pulse $p c v_\delta(x, y)\,\delta\left(t-\frac{z}{c}\right)$ equal to ϱc times the velocity pulse of the piston, travelling with velocity c along the duct with no change in form as it travels, followed by a "wake"

$$p_\delta(t, r) = \varrho c \sum_m \left[\frac{1}{\Lambda_m} \iint v_\delta\,\Phi_m\,dx\,dy\right] \frac{\omega_m t\,\Phi_m(x, y)}{\sqrt{t^2-(z/c)^2}}\, J_1\left(\omega_m \sqrt{t^2-\left(\frac{z}{c}\right)^2}\right) \quad \left(t>\frac{z}{c}\right)$$

which does change with t and z.

Strictly speaking, of course, a pulse of any magnitude constitutes a shock wave, which is not a linear phenomenon. However we can construct a continuous motion of the piston out of a sequence of pulses,

$$v_0(t; x, y) = \int v_\delta(t_0; x, y)\,\delta(t-t_0)\,dt_0$$

and obtain the resulting continuous generated wave by a corresponding integration

$$p(t, \mathbf{r}) = \int p_\delta(t - t_0, \mathbf{r})\, dt_0 \tag{23.9}$$

and, if v_0 is small enough, the radiated wave $p(t, \mathbf{r})$ will be satisfactorily represented by our linear formulae. A more serious limitation is imposed by our assumption that ω_m is independent of ω, which is equivalent to assuming that the impedance of the duct wall is independent of frequency. This is correct if the walls are perfectly rigid, and Eq. (23.8) is approximately valid if the impedance is large compared to ϱc, but it is not correct otherwise. When ω_m depends on ω $(=is)$ in a non-trivial manner, we must take this into account when taking the Laplace transform of (23.7). A good approximation is to use for ω_m in (23.8) the value which $\omega_m(\omega)$ would have if for ω we use the real part of ω_m, an implicit equation which can be solved by successive iteration.

The foregoing has been worked out for the case of the medium in the duct at rest with respect to the duct walls, in the equilibrium state. For completeness we should see what effect a steady flow of velocity V, in the direction of propagation of the wave, will have on the wave (if V is positive the wave motion is with the flow, if V is negative it is against the flow). Referring to Eq. (10.1) we see that Eq. (23.1) is unchanged in form, but the equation relating k_m to $k=\omega/c$ and the eigenvalue μ_m is not $k_m^2 = k^2 - \mu_m^2$ but

$$k_m = \left[\sqrt{k^2 - \mu_m^2(1 - M^2)} + kM\right]/(1 - M^2); \quad M = \frac{V}{c}. \tag{23.10}$$

Correspondingly the eigenfunction solutions Φ_m of Eq. (23.2) do not satisfy the boundary condition $ik\Phi_m = \zeta(\partial\Phi_m/\partial n)$ on the boundary, but instead satisfy the condition

$$i\left[k(1 - M^2) + 2M\sqrt{k^2 - \mu_m^2(1 - M^2)}\right]\Phi_m = (1 - M^2)\,\zeta\,\frac{\partial\Phi_m}{\partial n}. \tag{23.11}$$

This boundary condition is an implicit one, having the ratio between value and normal gradient of Φ dependent on the eigenvalue μ_m^2; it must thus be solved by successive approximations. We note that if $\zeta = \infty$ the eigenvalues μ_m^2 are independent of M and thus of V and therefore the eigenfunctions are also independent; relative motion of the medium has no effect when the duct walls are perfectly rigid.

We have neglected the effects of viscosity and of thermal conduction in this subsection. This is justified if the duct walls are soft ($|\zeta| < 10$) because the energy absorption by the soft walls is usually much larger than that lost by these other effects (unless ζ is purely reactive). In the case of a duct with highly rigid walls, however, it is sometimes necessary to compute these small losses. Eq. (11.9) provides a means of approximate computation. By using Eq. (23.1), neglecting viscosity and heat conduction, we compute values of p and u_t at the duct surface. The integral of $\frac{1}{2}R_v|u_t|^2 + \frac{1}{2}R_h|p|^2$ around the perimeter of the duct will give the power lost, as was shown in Eq. (11.10) for the circular duct, lowest mode.

24. Transmission in narrow, non-uniform ducts. Before we consider the more general problems, where more than one partial wave is involved, let us deal with the simpler case, where the wavelength $\lambda = 2\pi c/\omega$ of the sound transmitted is considerably larger than the perimeter of the duct. In this case only the lowest mode $(m=0)$ is transmitted and the analysis simplifies enough so that we can deal with non-uniform ducts nearly as easily as with uniform ones [*42*], [*44*], [*70*]. Since Φ_0 is practically independent of x and y for such narrow ducts, we can consider the motion to be preponderantly in the z direction, and discuss the total flow of fluid, Su, along the duct, where $S(z)$ is the area of cross section of the duct at a distance z from the origin (for this sub-section only, S is allowed to be a function of z).

Corresponding to Eq. (3.7) for momentum, we have

$$-S\frac{\partial p}{\partial z}\,dz = \varrho S\frac{\partial u}{\partial t}\,dz \tag{24.1}$$

where the left-hand side is the net force (p is thus an average pressure across the section) on all the fluid within the duct between z and $z+dz$. The left-hand side is the change in momentum of this fluid in the z direction (u is thus also an average velocity over the section at z).

The combination of Eqs. (3.6) and (4.1) relates the mass flow into a region with the change in pressure in the region. Increase in pressure compresses the fluid and thus makes room for more fluid in the slice of thickness dz; the term representing this is $(S\,dz/\varrho c^2)(\partial p/\partial t)$. But pressure also produces a motion of the duct walls, which increases laterally the volume of the slice. If the integral of the duct wall admittance around the perimeter is $(l\beta/\varrho c)$, where $l(z)$ is the duct perimeter and $\beta(z)$ is the average admittance of the duct walls at z, then the term representing the wall motion is $(l\beta/\varrho c)\,p$ and the second equation is

$$-\frac{\partial S u}{\partial z} = \frac{S}{\varrho c^2}\frac{\partial p}{\partial t} + \frac{l\beta}{\varrho c}\,p. \tag{24.2}$$

If the time factor is $e^{-i\omega t}$ the two equations combine to produce a wave equation for p and a relation between volume flow Su and p;

$$\left.\begin{aligned} &\frac{1}{S}\frac{\partial}{\partial z}\left(S\frac{\partial p}{\partial z}\right) + \left[k^2 + ik\frac{l\beta}{S}\right]p = 0,\\ &Su = \frac{S}{ik\varrho c}\frac{\partial p}{\partial z};\quad \omega = kc \end{aligned}\right\} \tag{24.3}$$

or, if one prefers a self-adjoint equation to deal with,

$$\frac{\partial^2 f}{\partial z^2} + \left[k^2 + ik\left(\frac{l}{S}\right)\beta + \frac{1}{4}\left(\frac{S'}{S}\right)^2 - \frac{1}{2}\left(\frac{S''}{S}\right)\right]f = 0 \tag{24.4}$$

where $f = p\sqrt{S}$ and the prime on S indicates differentiation with respect to z.

Solutions of this equation may be obtained in terms of simple functions when the quantity in brackets in Eq. (24.4) is independent of z and also in the case when it has the form $[K^2 - (q/z)^2]$. In the first case, both β and S (and of course l) must change exponentially with z:

Exponential Horn: $S = S_0\,e^{2z/h}$; $l = l_0\,e^{z/h}$; $\beta = \beta_0\,e^{z/h}$.

$$p = (p_0\,e^{-z/h})\,e^{\pm ik_e z - i\omega t};\qquad k_e^2 = k^2 - \left(\frac{1}{h}\right)^2 + ik\frac{l_0\beta_0}{S_0}. \tag{24.5}$$

There is wave propagation for frequencies above about $(c/2\pi h)$, when the real part of k_e^2 begins to be positive [but still below the frequencies where the higher partial waves begin to propagate, of course; otherwise Eqs. (24.3) and (24.4) do not hold].

In the second case S must be proportional to a power of z:

Hyper-conical Horn: $S = S_0(z/h)^{2\alpha}$; $l/l_0 = \beta/\beta_0 = (z/h)^{\alpha}$.

$$p = p_0 H_{\alpha-\frac{1}{2}}(k_r z)\,e^{-i\omega t};\qquad k_r^2 = k^2 + ik\frac{l_0\beta_0}{S_0} \tag{24.6}$$

where $H_n(x)$ is a Hankel function of either the first or second kind, of argument x and order n. The parabolic horn corresponds to $\alpha = \frac{1}{2}$, the true conical horn to $\alpha = 1$. The dependence of β on z can also be as $\beta_0 (z/h)^{-\alpha}$, in which case $k_r = k$ and the order of the Hankel function is

$$\sqrt{(\alpha - \tfrac{1}{2})^2 - i k h \frac{\beta_0 l_0 h_0}{S_0}}\,.$$

It can also be independent of z, in which case the solution is a confluent hypergeometric function instead of a Bessel function.

When S, l and β have other dependence on z, Eq. (24.4) must usually be solved numerically. However when S, l and β vary periodically with z (which is the case with many acoustic filters) other methods of computation may be used [7], [20].

Suppose, for example, that the cross section S, the perimeter l and the mean specific admittance β all have the same period (one or two of these could be independent of z, of course) the period z_0 being small compared to the wavelength $\lambda = 1/2\pi k$. We can then extend Eqs. (24.2) and (24.3) to cover the whole volume between z and $z + z_0$, dealing with the average behavior of a full period of the duct. We imagine the duct to be broken up into a sequence of units of length z_0, the first stretching from $z = 0$ to $z = z_0$, the second from $z = z_0$ to $z = 2z_0$, and so on. We measure pressure and flow only at the beginning and end of each unit, $S_0 p_n$ and $S_0 u_n$ being respectively the net force and volume flow across the section at $z = n z_0$, S_0 being the cross sectional area of the beginning and end of each unit.

Our two equations then become one relating the net force on the medium in one unit to the acceleration of the whole fluid therein, another relating the net influx of fluid into the unit to the change of pressure therein. To set up such equations for a full periodic unit of the duct (even though the unit is small compared to λ) requires a certain amount of averaging. For example if S is a periodic function of z, then some parts of the fluid will move faster than others and, when net force is applied to a unit, some parts will be accelerated more than others. The analogue to Eq. (24.1) should state that the net force on one unit, $S_0(p_n - p_{n+1})$, equals the total change in z component of momentum of the fluid in the unit. If S varies with z, then this momentum will not be $\varrho S_0 z_0$ times the mean velocity $\frac{1}{2}(u_n + u_{n+1})$, but can be written $V_e \varrho$ times mean velocity, where V_e is the effective volume for acceleration. It can be shown that V_e can be obtained by integrating the total kinetic energy of the fluid in a unit and dividing this by $(\varrho/2)$ times the square of the mean velocity. Thus one of the two equations becomes

$$S_0(p_n - p_{n+1}) = \frac{1}{2}\varrho V_e \frac{d}{dt}(u_n + u_{n+1}) = -\frac{1}{2} i k d \varrho c S_0 (u_n + u_{n+1}) \qquad (24.7)$$

where d is defined as the ratio of V_e to S_0; it only equals z_0 if $S(z) = S_0$ everywhere. In the second form for the right-hand side we have, of course, assumed that the time factor is $e^{-i\omega t}$.

The analogue to Eq. (24.2) relates the net flow into a unit to the change in pressure brought about by compression of the fluid in the unit and that caused by the yielding of the duct walls,

$$\left.\begin{aligned} S_0(u_n - u_{n+1}) &= \frac{V_0}{2\varrho c^2}\frac{\partial}{\partial t}(p_n + p_{n+1}) + \frac{S_0 B}{2\varrho c}(p_n + p_{n+1}) \\ &= \frac{\gamma^2}{2 i \varrho c k d}(p_n + p_{n+1}); \\ \gamma^2 = k^2 d^2 \frac{V_0}{V_e} &+ i k d B = i(\Gamma - i\Sigma) k d \end{aligned}\right\} \qquad (24.8)$$

where V_0 is the equilibrium volume enclosed by each periodic unit of the duct and B is the integral of the specific admittance β over the surface of a duct unit, divided by S_0 (thus B is dimensionless and usually smaller than unity). Constant γ^2 is the analogue of the quantity in brackets in Eq. (24.3). The complex quantity $\Gamma - i\Sigma$ is the effective specific admittance of each duct unit, including both the stiffness susceptance $-ikd(V_0/V_e)$ of the medium itself and the admittance B of the duct walls.

We can manipulate these two equations to obtain equations relating p_{n+1} and u_{n+1} to p_n and u_n,

$$\left.\begin{aligned} p_{n+1} &= \frac{4-\gamma^2}{4+\gamma^2}\, p_n + \frac{4 i \varrho c k d}{4+\gamma^2}\, u_n ; \\ u_{n+1} &= \frac{-4\gamma^2}{i \varrho c k d (4+\gamma^2)}\, p_n + \frac{4-\gamma^2}{4+\gamma^2}\, u_n . \end{aligned}\right\} \tag{24.9}$$

To have a solution corresponding to a "travelling wave" we must have both pressure and velocity at the end of each periodic unit equal to the same constant, e^{ih}, times their counterparts at the beginning of the same unit. Thus we set $p_{n+1} = e^{ih} p_n$ and $u_{n+1} = e^{ih} u_n$ into Eqs. (24.9); for self-consistency of the resulting homogeneous equations for p_n and u_n, we must have the determinant of their coefficients,

$$\left(e^{ih} - \frac{4-\gamma^2}{4+\gamma^2}\right)^2 + \frac{16\gamma^2}{(4+\gamma^2)^2} \quad \text{be zero.}$$

One root of this equations is

$$e^{ih} = \frac{2+i\gamma}{2-i\gamma}, \quad \text{another is } \frac{2-i\gamma}{2+i\gamma} = e^{-ih}, \tag{24.10}$$

the second root representing a travelling wave to the left.

We can compute the propagation parameter h from the equation

$$\cos h = \frac{4-\gamma^2}{4+\gamma^2} = \frac{4 - \Sigma k d - i \Gamma k d}{4 + \Sigma k d + i \Gamma k d} . \tag{24.11}$$

We note that when there is no energy loss at the duct walls ($\Gamma = 0$) the propagation parameter h can be real (corresponding to a wave travelling without attenuation to the right) *if* the real fraction $(4-\gamma^2)/(4+\gamma^2)$ is not greater than unity. But if Σ, the mean susceptance of the duct unit, is negative (an inertial susceptance) then the fraction is larger than unity and h has to be pure imaginary, a situation analogous to the rapid attenuation of the upper partial waves in a uniform duct, above their cut-off frequencies. In the periodic duct, however, the range of frequency over which this can be so may be adjusted, by proper design of the duct units, to cover any desired frequency band (low enough so that $\lambda \gg z_0$). Thus the periodic structure can be made into a high-pass, a band-pass or a low-pass acoustic filter. The analogy with electric filter networks is complete.

When a travelling wave is set up in the duct, the relations between p and u at the beginning of the n-th unit are

$$p_n = p_0 \left[\frac{2+i\gamma}{2-i\gamma}\right]^n ; \quad u_{\imath} = u_0 \left[\frac{2+i\gamma}{2-i\gamma}\right]^n ; \quad u_n = \frac{\Sigma + i\Gamma}{\varrho c}\, p_n . \tag{24.12}$$

The ratio $(u_n/p_n) = (\Sigma + i\Gamma)/\varrho c$ is called the *characteristic admittance* of the periodic duct. The power transmitted into the n-th unit is

$$\frac{1}{2} S_0 \operatorname{Re}(p_n u_n) = \frac{1}{2\varrho c} S_0 \Sigma |p_n|^2 = \frac{1}{2\varrho c} \Sigma S_0 |p_0|^2 \exp(-n \operatorname{Im} h) \tag{24.13}$$

where the imaginary part of h can be obtained from Eq. (24.11).

25. Rectangular ducts. To deal with more complicated problems of sound transmission along ducts we must become more specific in our treatment of the transverse eigenfunctions for the higher partial waves; the simplest way to do this is to consider a specific duct shape. We choose the rectangular shape, of width a in the x direction and height b in the y direction; it is a relatively simple case to work out [*42*], [*44*], [*68*] and it is a shape often encountered in practice.

For comparison, and for use later, we first write down the solution when all four duct walls are perfectly rigid. Referring to Eqs. (23.1) and (23.5) we have

$$\left.\begin{aligned} \Phi_{mn}(x,y) &= \cos\frac{\pi m x}{a}\cos\frac{\pi n y}{b}; \\ \Lambda_{mn} &= \frac{ab}{\varepsilon_m\varepsilon_n}; \quad \mu_{mn}^2 = \left(\frac{\pi m}{a}\right)^2 + \left(\frac{\pi n}{b}\right)^2 \end{aligned}\right\} \tag{25.1}$$

where $\varepsilon_m = 1$ $(m=0)$, $=2$ $(m>0)$. In this case it is more convenient to characterize the eigenfunctions by two integers, rather than a single integer, even though this does not order the eigenvalues in order of increasing magnitude (as was done before). If μ_{mn}^2 is smaller than k^2 the (m, n)-th partial wave propagates without attenuation; if μ_{mn}^2 is larger than k^2, the corresponding $k_{mn} = \sqrt{k^2 - \mu_{mn}^2}$ is positive imaginary and the mode does not propagate.

For the rigid duct, where no energy is lost by duct wall motion, the viscous and heat conduction losses in the medium near the walls become the only cause of attenuation. If we confine our attention to regions of the duct more than a few wavelengths from the source, so that the partial waves for which $k_{mn}^2 < 0$ have disappeared, the sums over m and n need only be over the waves which are propagated. The unperturbed wave is

$$p = \sum_{m,n} A_{m,n}\cos\frac{\pi m x}{a}\cos\frac{\pi n y}{b}\exp(i k_{mn} z - i\omega t)$$

where the sum is over the values of m and n for which k_{mn} is real. The energy loss from viscosity and heat conduction, per unit length of duct (assuming that the duct walls are good heat conductors) can be computed by using Eqs. (11.9),

$$\left.\begin{aligned} -\frac{dI}{dz} = \frac{1}{4\varrho c}\sum_{m=0}^{M}\varepsilon_m k a \Biggl\{\left[(\gamma-1)\,l_h + \left(\frac{\pi m}{ka}\right)^2 l_v\right]\left|\sum_{p=0}^{P} A_{m,p}\right|^2 + \\ + l_v\left|\sum_{p=0}^{P}\frac{k_{mp}A_{m,p}}{k}\right|^2\Biggr\} + \\ + \frac{1}{4\varrho c}\sum_{n=0}^{N}\varepsilon_n k b\left\{\left[(\gamma-1)\,l_h + \left(\frac{\pi n}{kb}\right)^2 l_v\right]\left|\sum_{q=0}^{Q}A_{q,n}\right|^2 + l_v\left|\sum_{q=0}^{Q}\frac{k_{qn}A_{q,n}}{k}\right|^2\right\} \end{aligned}\right\} \tag{25.2}$$

where M is the largest integer less than π/ka and P the largest integer less than $\sqrt{(kb/\pi)^2 - (mb/a)^2}$, N and Q being similar limits with a and b, m and n interchanged. We see that the cross terms, coupling m, n with m', n', enter this expression; we cannot discuss the loss of energy and attenuation of each mode separately, viscosity and thermal conduction couple them together.

Turning now to ducts with non-rigid walls, suppose the specific admittance of the duct wall at $x=0$ is β_1, that of the wall at $x=0$ is β_2, for wall $y=0$ is β_3 and for wall $y=b$ is β_4 (all independent of z and of y or x respectively, but functions of ω). In this case the eigenfunction is

$$\left.\begin{aligned} \Phi_{mn} &= \mathrm{Cos}\left[M_m(k)\frac{\pi i x}{a} - \mathrm{ArTan}\frac{\beta_1 k a}{\pi M_m}\right]\mathrm{Cos}\left[N_n(k)\frac{\pi i y}{b} - \mathrm{ArTan}\frac{\beta_3 k b}{\pi N_n}\right], \\ \mu_{mn}^2 &= \left(\frac{\pi M_m}{a}\right)^2 + \left(\frac{\pi N_n}{b}\right)^2 \end{aligned}\right\} \tag{25.3}$$

where, to satisfy the boundary conditions

$$\left(\frac{\partial \Phi}{\partial x}\right)_{x=a} = i k \beta_2 \Phi_{x=a}, \qquad \text{etc.},$$

we must have M_m and N_n the m-th and n-th roots, respectively of the following equations;

$$\left.\begin{aligned} \pi i M_m(k) &= \operatorname{ArTan}\frac{k a \beta_1}{\pi M_m} + \operatorname{ArTan}\frac{k a \beta_2}{\pi M_m}; \\ \pi i N_n(k) &= \operatorname{ArTan}\frac{k b \beta_3}{\pi N_n} + \operatorname{ArTan}\frac{k b \beta_4}{\pi N_n}. \end{aligned}\right\} \tag{25.4}$$

When all the β's are small the following series expansions,

$$\left.\begin{aligned} M_0 &= \frac{1}{\pi}\sqrt{-i k a(\beta_1+\beta_2)}\left[1+\frac{i k a}{6}\frac{\beta_1^3+\beta_2^3}{(\beta_1+\beta_2)^2}+\cdots\right] \quad \left(\beta_1, \beta_2 \ll \frac{\pi}{k a}\right); \\ M_m &= m - \frac{i k a}{\pi^2 m}(\beta_1+\beta_2) + \frac{k^2 a^2}{\pi^4 m^3}(\beta_1+\beta_2)^2 + \cdots \quad \left(\beta_1, \beta_2 \ll \frac{m\pi}{k a}\right), \end{aligned}\right\} \tag{25.5}$$

and similar ones for N_n (with n, b and β_3, β_4 instead of m, a and β_1, β_2) are rapidly convergent. If the β's are too large for the series to converge well, the values of M and N can be read from charts or tables [*41*], [*42*].

The propagation constant for the (m, n)-th partial wave, k_{mn}, is given by the usual equation

$$\left.\begin{aligned} k_{mn} &= \sqrt{k^2 - \left(\frac{\pi M_m}{a}\right)^2 - \left(\frac{\pi N_n}{b}\right)^2} \\ &\approx k_{mn}^0 + \frac{k}{k_{mn}^0}\left[\frac{\varepsilon_m}{2a}(\sigma_1+\sigma_2+i\varkappa_1+i\varkappa_2) + \frac{\varepsilon_n}{2b}(\sigma_3+\sigma_4+i\varkappa_3+i\varkappa_4)\right]; \\ (k_{mn}^0)^2 &= k^2 - \left(\frac{\pi m}{a}\right)^2 - \left(\frac{\pi n}{b}\right)^2, \qquad \beta = \varkappa - i\sigma, \end{aligned}\right\} \tag{25.6}$$

the second line being a first-order approximation for small admittances. The imaginary part of k_{mn}, of course, measures the degree of attenuation of the wave. We note that, in this first approximation, the lowest partial wave is less affected by the wall admittance than are the higher modes, both because of the factor $\frac{1}{2}$ (coming from the factors ε_m and ε_n) but also, as m and n increase, k_{mn} diminishes until it finally becomes imaginary. The lowest mode goes as directly along the duct as it can, avoiding the walls, so to speak; the higher modes involve reflection from one wall to another and thus are affected more by the wall admittance [see also the discussion following Eq. (26.9)]. This statement is in general true even when the β's are large, though there are a few exceptions for particular magnitudes and phases of β, for which one mode may be more strongly absorbed for a range of frequencies than are the modes immediately above or below.

To treat the non-uniform duct more adequately than was done in the previous subsection will usually require the techniques of joining solutions across an interface [see discussion of Eq. (13.4)] which we are postponing until Chapt. C. A special case which can be discussed here, however, is the one where the cross section is uniform but the wall admittance is a function of z. Two examples will be worked out: one where the duct walls are rigid except for one "soft region"; the other where half of one duct wall is soft, the rest of the duct being rigid. In both cases we consider the duct to be rectangular, with sides a and b, as before.

We take the duct walls $x=a$, $y=0$ and $y=b$ as rigid and assume the wall $x=0$ has specific admittance β in either the region $-l/2<z<+l/2$ or else the region $0<z$, being rigid elsewhere. In this duct an incident wave, coming from

$-\infty$, would be affected by the "soft spot"; some of the wave would be reflected back to $-\infty$ and the rest would be transmitted on to $+\infty$ or else would be absorbed by the soft spot. The integral equation provides the best means of attack on such problems.

The appropriate GREEN's function is that of Eq. (23.5), with the eigenfunctions of Eq. (25.1). Since the incident wave is independent of y (so we assume) and the irregularity in wall admittance is also independent of y, therefore the solution $p(x, z)$ is independent of y and we need only consider the $n=0$ terms in the sum for G. The part of G of interest is thus

$$\left.\begin{aligned} g(0, z_0|x, z) &= \int_0^b G_k(\mathbf{r}_0^B|\mathbf{r})\, d y_0 \\ &= \frac{e^{ik|z-z_0|}}{2ika} + \sum_{m=1}^{M} \frac{\cos(\pi m x/a)}{i k_m a} e^{ik_m|z-z_0|} - \\ &\qquad - \sum_{m>M} \frac{\cos(\pi m x/a)}{K_m a} e^{-K_m|z-z_0|} \end{aligned}\right\} \tag{25.7}$$

where

$$k_m^2 = k^2 - \left(\frac{\pi m}{a}\right)^2 = -K_m^2$$

and M is the largest integer less than ak/π. Thus the first sum represents those partial waves which are propagated and the second sum those waves with cut-off frequencies above $kc/2\pi$, which are only large near $z=z_0$.

Inserting this into Eq. (13.1), we see that the surface integrals over the duct walls all vanish except for the soft spot, where $\partial p/\partial n_0 = ik\beta p$. The integral over the duct opening at $z\to+\infty$ vanishes if we assume that p is there a sum of transmitted waves, with factors $e^{ik_m z}$ (for $m>0$ the integral over x vanishes, for $m=0$ the two parts of the surface integral cancel each other). At $z\to-\infty$ the pressure wave should be an incident wave $p_i e^{ikz}$ plus a set of reflected waves, with factors $e^{-ik_m z}$, which integrates to zero except for the incident wave. Consequently the integral equation for the first example, the finite soft spot, is

$$\left.\begin{aligned} p(x, z) &\approx p_i e^{ikz} - ik\beta \int_{-\frac{1}{2}l}^{\frac{1}{2}l} p(0, z_0)\, g(0, z_0|x, z)\, dz_0 \\ &\xrightarrow[z\to-\infty]{} p_i e^{ikz} - \frac{1}{a}\sqrt{\frac{\pi}{2}} \sum_{m=0}^{M} \frac{\varepsilon_m k}{k_m} B(k_m) \cos\frac{\pi m x}{a} e^{-ik_m z} \\ &\xrightarrow[z\to\infty]{} \left[p_i - \frac{\sqrt{\pi}}{a} B(-k)\right] e^{ikz} - \frac{\sqrt{2\pi}}{a} \sum_{m=1}^{M} \frac{k}{k_m} B(-k_m) \cos\frac{\pi m x}{a} e^{ik_m z} \end{aligned}\right\} \tag{25.8}$$

where

$$B(h) = \frac{1}{\sqrt{2\pi}} \int_{-\frac{1}{2}l}^{\frac{1}{2}l} \beta p(0, z_0)\, e^{ihz_0}\, dz_0,$$

is the Fourier transform of the function $\beta(z)\, p(0, z)$, considering $\beta(z)$ to be a discontinuous function, equalling β for $-\frac{1}{2}l<z<\frac{1}{2}l$ and being zero elsewhere.

The first term in the asymptotic expansion for $z\to-\infty$ is the incident wave, the sum is the set of reflected waves, the principal reflected wave being the one for $m=0$. The first term in the limiting expression for $z\to+\infty$ is the principal transmitted wave. We note that the amplitudes of all the reflected and transmitted waves can be expressed in terms of the Fourier transforms of the function $\beta(z)\, p(0, z)$.

The Born approximation [see Eq. (16.1)] for the solution of Eq. (25.6) is obtained by setting $p(0, z)$ equal to the incident wave $p_i\, e^{ikz}$;

$$\left.\begin{aligned} p(x,z) &= p_i\, e^{ikz} - ik\beta p_i \int_{-\frac{1}{2}l}^{\frac{1}{2}l} e^{ikz_0}\, g(0, z_0|x, z)\, dz_0 \qquad (\beta k l \ll 1)\\ &\xrightarrow[z\to-\infty]{} p_i\, e^{ikz} - \beta p_i \sum_{m=0}^{M} \frac{\varepsilon_m k \sin[\frac{1}{2}(k+k_m)\,l]}{k_m (k+k_m)\, a} \cos\left(\frac{\pi m x}{a}\right)\cdot e^{ik_m x}\\ &\xrightarrow[z\to+\infty]{} p_i \left(1 - \frac{\beta}{2a}\right) e^{ikz} - \beta p_i \sum_{m=1}^{M} \frac{2k \sin[\frac{1}{2}(k-k_m)\,l]}{k_m (k-k_m)\, a} \cos\left(\frac{\pi m x}{a}\right)\cdot e^{ik_m z}. \end{aligned}\right\} \tag{25.9}$$

The fraction of the incident power, $(ab/2\varrho c)\,|p_i|^2$, which is reflected is, to this approximation

$$\sum_{m=0}^{M} \varepsilon_m |\beta|^2 \left(\frac{k}{k_m}\right) \left\{\frac{\sin[\frac{1}{2}(k+k_m)\,l]}{(k+k_m)\,a}\right\}^2 = P_r.$$

This quantity is second order in $|\beta|$, but since the formula for the reflected waves has no zero order term the formula for P_r should be good to second order. In the case of the transmitted waves, the expression for the principal transmitted wave is a combination of zero and first order terms, so its square would not be good to second order. To find the fraction of incident power transmitted in the principal wave we first compute the power transmitted by the higher modes,

$$\sum_{m=0}^{M} 2|\beta|^2 \left(\frac{k}{k_m}\right) \left\{\frac{\sin[\frac{1}{2}(k-k_m)\,l]}{(k-k_m)\,a}\right\}^2 = P_{ht},$$

which also is good to second order. The fraction of power transmitted in the principal mode is therefore (to the second order) 1 minus P_r minus P_{ht} minus the fraction $(l/a)\,\mathrm{Re}(\beta)$ of incident power which is absorbed by the soft spot. According to Eq. (25.9) the fraction of power transmitted in the principal mode is $|1-(\beta l/2a)|^2$, which corresponds to the foregoing only to the first order in $|\beta|$; as noted above this term is not good to second order. However, by using the terms already computed, we see that the total fraction of power transmitted is $1-(l/a)\,\mathrm{Re}(\beta) - P_r$, correct to second order in $|\beta|$.

A better expression for p and the reflected and transmitted power can be obtained by using a variational procedure. We vary the related shapes of $p(0, z)$ and $\tilde{p}(0, z)$ (which is the counterpart of p with the incident wave coming in from $+\infty$) in the region $-\frac{1}{2}l < z < +\frac{1}{2}l$ until the first order variation of the quantity

$$\frac{\int \tilde{p}\, e^{ikz}\, dz \int p\, e^{-ikz_0}\, dz_0}{\int \tilde{p}\, p\, dz + \beta \int \tilde{p}\, dz \int g(0, z_0|0, z)\, p\, dz} \tag{25.10}$$

is zero. Since the integrals are between $-\frac{1}{2}l$ and $+\frac{1}{2}l$ the shape of $p(0, z)$ within this range only is being varied. The stationary value of this quantity is proportional to the transform $B(-k)$ of Eq. (25.8) and the shape of p which results in the stationary value is the optimal shape, which can then be used in Eq. (25.8) to compute the reflected and transmitted waves.

The second example to be considered here is for the case where the soft part of the duct wall $x=0$ extends from $z=0$ clear to $z\to+\infty$. We can then modify our procedure to simplify the integral equation and, in the special case of $k<\pi/a$ $(M=0)$, can even obtain an exact solution. As was pointed out in Sect. 12, we can add to the Green's function any solution of $(\nabla^2+k^2)\,\Psi=0$ satisfying the same boundary conditions as G and still be able to use the result in Eq. (13.1).

We therefore choose the function

$$\left.\begin{aligned}\gamma(0, z_0|0, z) &= \frac{1}{2ika}\left(e^{ik|z-z_0|} - e^{ik(z-z_0)}\right) + \\ &+ \sum_{m=1}^{M} \frac{\cos(\pi m x/a)}{i k_m a} e^{ik_m|z-z_0|} - \sum_{m>M} \frac{\cos(\pi m x/a)}{K_m a} e^{-K_m|z-z_0|}\end{aligned}\right\} \quad (25.11)$$

which has no principal wave for $z > z_0$. This together with the fact that $p \to 0$ as $z \to \infty$, as long as β has any real part, results in the integral expression for p,

$$p(x, z) = -ik\beta \int_0^\infty p(0, z_0)\, \gamma(0, z_0|x, z)\, dz_0 \quad (25.12)$$

which becomes a homogeneous integral equation for the pressure along the soft wall when we set $x = 0$.

This homogeneous integral equation can be solved, more easily than the inhomogeneous equation (25.8), for it is amenable to solution by taking Fourier transforms and then using the Wiener-Hopf factorization procedure. The functions

$$P_+(h) = \frac{1}{\sqrt{2\pi}} \int_0^\infty p(0, z)\, e^{ihz}\, dz; \qquad P_-(h) = \frac{1}{\sqrt{2\pi}} \int_{-\infty}^{0} p(0, z)\, e^{ihz}\, dz \quad (25.13)$$

are the Fourier transforms of the pressure along the soft part of the wall $x = 0$ and that along the hard part of the wall, respectively. The integral for P_+ converges for $\mathrm{Im}(h)$ greater than some negative quantity $-q$ (since p attenuates as $z \to \infty$) whereas the integral for P_- converges for $\mathrm{Im}(h) < 0$, so that both integrals converge in the band $0 > \mathrm{Im}(h) > -q$. Function $\gamma(0, z_0|0, z)$ is a function of $(z - z_0)$ and its transform with respect to $(z - z_0)$ is

$$\frac{1}{\sqrt{2\pi}} \int_{-\infty}^{\infty} \gamma(z - z_0)\, e^{ih(z-z_0)}\, d(z - z_0) = \frac{1}{\sqrt{k^2 - h^2}} \cot\left(a\sqrt{k^2 - h^2}\right) \quad (25.14)$$

which converges in the band $0 > \mathrm{Im}(h) > -\sqrt{(\pi/a)^2 - k^2}$ (if $k < \pi/a$, that is, if $M = 0$).

The Fourier transform of the integral equation arising from (25.12) by setting $x = 0$ is then

$$P_+(h) + P_-(h) = -ik\beta\, P_+(h) \frac{\cot(a\sqrt{k^2 - h^2})}{\sqrt{k^2 - h^2}},$$

or

$$P_+(h) = \frac{-\sqrt{k^2 - h^2}\,\sin(a\sqrt{k^2 - h^2})\, P_-(h)}{ik\beta\cos(a\sqrt{k^2 - h^2}) + \sqrt{k^2 - h^2}\,\sin(a\sqrt{k^2 - h^2})}. \quad (25.15)$$

By factoring the quantity multiplying P_- into a factor which has no zeros or poles in the region $\mathrm{Im}(h) > -\sqrt{(\pi/a)^2 - k^2}$ (call it Y_+) divided by a factor Y_- which has no zeroes or poles in the region $\mathrm{Im}(h) < 0$, we obtain an equation $(P_+/Y_+) = (P_-/Y_-)$ which has no poles or zeroes in overlapping half planes and thus, by analytic continuation, both sides must equal a constant C. The poles of the quantity multiplying P_- in (25.15) are at the values of $M = (a/\pi)\sqrt{k^2 - h^2}$ for which

$$(\pi M) \cdot \tan(\pi M) = -ika\beta. \quad (25.16)$$

The m-th root of this equation, M_m, is the root of Eq. (25.4) for the case where $\beta_2 = \beta_3 = \beta_4 = 0$. This is not surprising, for in the present problem the duct for $z>0$ has just such a distribution of admittances and we might expect that the eigenvalues for a doubly infinite soft wall (uniform from $-\infty$ to $+\infty$) would also enter the solution for a semi-infinite soft wall.

The factored solution for the Fourier transform P_+ turns out to be (see [*48*] for details)

$$P_+(h) = \frac{C}{h+k_0} \frac{\prod_{n=1}^{\infty} \left[\sqrt{1-(ka/\pi n)^2} - i(ha/\pi n)\right] e^{iha/\pi n}}{\prod_{m=1}^{\infty} \left[\sqrt{1-(ka/\pi M_m)^2} - i(ha/\pi M_m)\right] e^{iha/\pi M_m}} \tag{25.17}$$

where $-ik_0 = \sqrt{(\pi M_0/a)^2 - k^2}$. This can, if we so desire, be re-transformed to give $p(0, z)$ for $z>0$ and, from this by using Eq. (25.12), the pressure anywhere in the duct may be computed. But if we wish only to compute the amplitude of the wave reflected back to $-\infty$ (only the principal wave when $k<\pi/a$) we need not transform the solution. For the asymptotic form for Eq. (25.12), for the limit $z\to-\infty$ (when $k<\pi/a$) is

$$\left.\begin{aligned} p(x,z) &\to \sqrt{\tfrac{1}{2}\pi}\,\frac{\beta}{a}\left[P_+(-k)\,e^{ikz} - P_-(k)\,e^{-ikz}\right] = p_i e^{ikz} + R\,p_i e^{-ikz};\\ R &= -\frac{P_+(k)}{P_-(-k)} = \frac{\sqrt{1-(\pi M_0/ka)^2}-1}{\sqrt{1-(\pi M_0/ka)^2}+1} \prod_{m=1}^{\infty} \frac{\sqrt{1-(ka/\pi M_m)^2} + i(ka/\pi M_m)}{\sqrt{1-(ka/\pi m)^2}+i(ka/\pi m)}. \end{aligned}\right\} \tag{25.18}$$

This is an exact solution for the reflection coefficient. The Born approximation for this case would result in the first factor only, without the infinite product. The infinite product corresponds to the fact that the higher modes do contribute to the shape of the wave near $z=0$, even though (in the present case where $k<\pi/a$) all of them attenuate to zero as $|z|\to\infty$.

When $k>\pi/a$, so that one or more of the higher modes can carry reflected energy, a factorization of Eq. (25.15) is not possible, so an exact solution cannot be obtained. In this case we must be satisfied with the Born approximation or with a variational technique derived from Eq. (25.12).

26. Resonance and reverberation in enclosures. The study of acoustic waves inside finite enclosures encompasses much of the theory of architectural acoustics [*10*], [*42*], [*43*], which is beyond the scope of this article. Consequently we will append the few remarks to be made on this subject to the end of the section on ducts. After all, most enclosures encountered in practice can be considered to be ducts of finite length, closed at both ends.

The solutions of the three-dimensional Helmholtz equation,

$$(\nabla^2 + \mu^2)\,\Phi = 0,$$

inside a finite surface B, on which the boundary condition

$$\frac{\partial \Phi}{\partial n} = i k \beta(\mathbf{r}^B)\,\Phi$$

holds, constitute a triply infinite set of eigenfunctions $\Phi_m(\mathbf{r}, k)$, where m represents a trio of integers, corresponding to the eigenvalue $\mu_m^2(k)$. Since $k\beta$ is a function of the driving frequency $\omega/2\pi = kc/2\pi$, the Φ's and the μ's are functions of k. These functions, for any specified value of k, are mutually orthogonal; their normalization constant is $\Lambda_m(k)$. If the real part of β is zero everywhere on B the eigenvalues μ_m^2 are all real and the eigenfunctions Φ_m can be all made real everywhere inside and on B. If, however, the real part of β is not zero everywhere on B, the Φ's and μ's are complex, corresponding to energy absorption by the boundary. When the real part of β is everywhere positive, it turns out that the imaginary part of μ_m^2 is negative for all m.

The GREEN's function for a unit, point source of frequency $kc/2\pi$, inside B, can be expanded in terms of these eigenfunctions [see Eq. (12.5)]

$$G(k\,|\,\boldsymbol{r}\,|\,\boldsymbol{r}_0) = \sum_m \frac{\Phi_m(\boldsymbol{r}_0, k)\,\Phi_m(\boldsymbol{r}, k)}{\Lambda_m(k)\,[k^2 - \mu_m^2(k)]}\,. \tag{26.1}$$

If the acoustic system is driven by a source which can be expressed as an inhomogeneous term $q_k(r)\,\mathrm{e}^{-ikct}$ in the Helmholtz equation, which differs from zero only in a small region R_q inside B then, by Eq. (13.1), the solution for forced acoustic motion in the enclosure is

$$p_k(r, t)\,\mathrm{e}^{-ikct} = \sum_m \left[\iiint\limits_{R_q} \Phi_m(r_0)\,q_k(r_0)\,dv_0\right] \frac{\Phi_m(r, k)}{(k^2 - \mu_m^2)\,\Lambda_m}\,\mathrm{e}^{-ikct}. \tag{26.2}$$

If the μ's are all real (if no energy is absorbed at the boundary) then as the driving frequency $kc/2\pi$ approaches the m-th resonance frequency $\mu_m c/2\pi$ of the enclosure, the wave amplitude approaches infinity. If energy is absorbed each μ will have an imaginary part, in which case the amplitude of p_k will be large but not infinite at resonance. Because of the three-fold nature of m, the number of resonance frequencies between k and $k+dk$ increases proportionally to $k^2\,dk$ as k increases, so that at high enough driving frequencies the resonance peaks overlap and the response $p_k(r, t)$ is practically a uniform function of k.

At lower frequencies, however, the resonance peaks do not overlap, and the response is a very irregular function of k, the m-th term in the sum predominating (usually) as k approaches μ_m. For these frequencies a measurement of the width of the m-th resonance peak will provide a measure of the real and imaginary part of μ_m^2. The ratio between the m-th resonance frequency and the half-width of its resonance peak (the half-width is twice the difference between the resonance frequency and the frequency at which the response $|p|^2$ is one half that at resonance) is called the Q of the system at the m-th resonance. We see that $Q_m = \mathrm{Re}(\mu_m^2)/\mathrm{Im}(\mu_m^2)$ and, since the resonance frequency itself is $(c/2\pi)\sqrt{\mathrm{Re}(\mu_m^2)}$, a measurement of Q and the resonance frequency determines the value of the complex quantity μ_m^2.

The Fourier transform can be used to obtain the wave motion produced by a point source of "strength" $q(t)$ at $\boldsymbol{r}_0$. The acoustic pressure at $\boldsymbol{r}$ caused by this source is $p(t)$, a solution of the equation

$$\left(\nabla^2 - \frac{1}{c^2}\frac{\partial^2}{\partial t^2}\right) p(t\,|\,\boldsymbol{r}\,|\,\boldsymbol{r}_0) = q(t)\,\delta(\boldsymbol{r} - \boldsymbol{r}_0)\,. \tag{26.3}$$

The Fourier transform of this

$$P(\boldsymbol{k}\,|\,\boldsymbol{r}\,|\,\boldsymbol{r}_0) = \frac{1}{\sqrt{2\pi}} \int\limits_{-\infty}^{\infty} p(t\,|\,\boldsymbol{r}\,|\,\boldsymbol{r}_0)\,\mathrm{e}^{ikct}\,d(ct)$$

is a solution of the inhomogeneous Helmholtz equation

$$(\nabla^2 + k^2)\,P(\boldsymbol{k}\,|\,\boldsymbol{r}\,|\,\boldsymbol{r}_0) = Q(k)\,\delta(\boldsymbol{r} - \boldsymbol{r}_0)$$

which is simply $Q(k)$ times the GREEN's function of Eq. (26.1). Function $Q(k)$ is the Fourier transform of $q(t)$. Taking the inverse transform, we have

$$p(t\,|\,\boldsymbol{r}\,|\,\boldsymbol{r}_0) = \frac{1}{\sqrt{2\pi}} \int\limits_{-\infty}^{\infty} \mathrm{e}^{-ikct}\,Q(k)\,G(k\,|\,\boldsymbol{r}\,|\,\boldsymbol{r}_0)\,dk\,. \tag{26.4}$$

A few examples will illustrate the difficulties encountered and the results obtained. In the first example, $q(t)$ is the Dirac delta function $\delta(t-t_0)$, having transform $(c/\sqrt{2\pi})\,e^{ikct_0}$, the resulting wave from the explosive pulse starting from $\boldsymbol{r}_0$ at t_0 is

$$g(t,\boldsymbol{r}|t_0,\boldsymbol{r}_0)=\frac{c}{2\pi}\int\limits_{-\infty}^{\infty} e^{-ikc(t-t_0)}\sum_m \frac{\Phi_m(\boldsymbol{r}_0,k)\,\Phi_m(\boldsymbol{r},k)\,dk}{\Lambda_m(k)\,[k-\mu_m(k)]\,[k+\mu_m(k)]}\,.$$

Each integral in the sum is evaluated by computing residues at the poles, the two roots of the equation $k^2-\mu_m^2(k)=0$.

An important property of the eigenvalues $\mu_m^2(k)$ are that they change to their complex conjugate when k changes sign, $\mu_m(-k)=\mu_m^*(k)$; similarly with the eigenfunctions $\Phi_m(\boldsymbol{r},k)$. Consequently if we can compute the root of the implicit equation $k-\mu_m(k)=0$ (which we will write as $k_m-i\varkappa_m$) then the root of the equation $k+\mu_m(k)=0$ can be written as $-k_m-i\varkappa_m$. And if the eigenfunction $\Phi_m(\boldsymbol{r},k)$ which results when k is set equal to $k_m-i\varkappa_m$ is called $\Psi_m(\boldsymbol{r})$ then the corresponding function for $k=-k_m-i\varkappa_m$ is the complex conjugate $\Psi_m^*(\boldsymbol{r})$. Therefore the residues only are included within the contour when $t<t_0$ and the pulse GREEN'S function is

$$g(t_0,\boldsymbol{r}_0|t,\boldsymbol{r})=\begin{cases}0 & (t<t_0),\\ c\sum\limits_m e^{-c\varkappa_m(t-t_0)}\,\mathrm{Im}\left[\dfrac{\Psi_m(\boldsymbol{r}_0)\,\Psi_m(\boldsymbol{r})}{k_m N_m}\,e^{-ick_m(t-t_0)}\right] & (t>t_0)\end{cases} \tag{26.5}$$

where N_m is the normalizing constant $\iiint[\Psi_m(\boldsymbol{r})]^2\,dv$.

Several points should be noted about this solution. In the first place each standing wave (each trio of numbers corresponding to m) has its own frequency of oscillation $(ck_m/2\pi)$ and its own rate of decay $c\varkappa_m$, where k_m and $\varkappa_m$ are the real and imaginary parts of one of the solutions of the implicit equation $k=\mu_m(k)$. In the second place the functions $\Psi_m(\boldsymbol{r})$ which represent the shape of the m-th standing wave, are *not* members of a family of mutually orthogonal eigenfunctions They are not mutually orthogonal, for each Ψ_m satisfies a boundary condition, $(\partial\Psi_m/\partial n)=i(k_m-i\varkappa_m)\,\beta\,\Psi_m$, corresponding to its own frequency and decay rate, which is not usually the same as for any other Ψ. When the system is driven by a source of single frequency $(ck/2\pi)$ the forced-motion waves $\Phi_m(\boldsymbol{r},k)$ *are* mutually orthogonal, but the partial waves for free vibration of the system, Ψ_m, are not.

A second example is one where $q(t)$ is zero until $t=0$ and is $q_0(\boldsymbol{r}_0)\,e^{-i\omega t}$ thereafter. In this case $Q(k)=iq_0/[k-(\omega/c)]$ and the resulting pressure wave is zero for $t<0$ and is, for $t>0$,

$$\left.\begin{aligned}&q_0(\boldsymbol{r}_0)\,G\left(\frac{\omega}{c}\,|\boldsymbol{r}_0|\boldsymbol{r}\right)e^{-i\omega t}+\sum_m\frac{q_0(\boldsymbol{r}_0)\,\Psi_m(\boldsymbol{r}_0)\,\Psi_m(\boldsymbol{r})}{2N_m k_m[k_m-i\varkappa_m-(\omega/c)]}\,e^{-c(ik_m+\varkappa_m)t}+\\&\qquad+\sum_m\frac{q_0(\boldsymbol{r}_0)\,\Psi_m(\boldsymbol{r}_0)\,\Psi_m(\boldsymbol{r})}{2N_m k_m[k_m+i\varkappa_m+(\omega/c)]}\,e^{c(ik_m-\varkappa_m)t}\,.\end{aligned}\right\} \tag{26.6}$$

The first term is the steady-state motion; the second and third together make up the transient.

To find the solution for the case when the source for Eq. (26.6) is on from $t\to-\infty$ and is turned *off* at $t=0$, we subtract expression (26.6) from the steady state solution $q_0G\,e^{-i\omega t}$. The solution is thus the first term of (26.6) for $t<0$, and minus the second and third terms for $t>0$. These second and third terms thus represent the reverberation in the enclosure after the source has been shut off. If the source is extended in space, these solutions can be integrated, over r_0, over the region for which q_0 differs from zero.

For rectangular enclosures of sides a, b and d, with admittance β_{x1} over the wall $x=0$, β_{x2} over the wall $x=0$, and so on, the forced-motion eigenfunctions and eigenvalues are related to those of Eq. (25.3);

$$\left.\begin{aligned}
\Phi_m(\mathbf{r}, k) &= \phi_l(x, a, k)\, \phi_m(y, b, k)\, \phi_n(z, d, k);\\
\phi_m(y, b, k) &= \operatorname{Cos}\left[M_m^y(k)\frac{\pi i y}{b} - \operatorname{Ar\,Tan}\frac{\beta_{y1} k b}{\pi M_m^y}\right], \qquad \text{etc.}\\
\mu_m^2(k) &= \left[\frac{\pi M_l^x(k)}{a}\right]^2 + \left[\frac{\pi M_m^y(k)}{b}\right]^2 + \left[\frac{\pi M_n^z(k)}{d}\right]^2\\
&\approx \left(\frac{\pi l}{a}\right)^2 + \left(\frac{\pi m}{b}\right)^2 + \left(\frac{\pi n}{d}\right)^2 - i k\left[\frac{\varepsilon_l}{a}(\beta_{x1}+\beta_{x2}) + \right.\\
&\quad \left. + \frac{\varepsilon_m}{b}(\beta_{y1}+\beta_{y2}) + \frac{\varepsilon_n}{d}(\beta_{z1}+\beta_{z2})\right] + \cdots
\end{aligned}\right\} \tag{26.7}$$

where the last expression is appropriate for small values of the β's.

Solving for the two roots of the equation $k^2-\mu_m^2=0$ gives us, to the first order in the admittances β,

$$\left.\begin{aligned}
k &= \pm k_{lmn} - i\varkappa_{lmn}; \qquad k_{lmn}^2 \approx \left(\frac{\pi l}{a}\right)^2 + \left(\frac{\pi m}{b}\right)^2 + \left(\frac{\pi n}{d}\right)^2;\\
\varkappa_{lmn} &\approx \frac{\varepsilon_l}{2a}(\varkappa_{x1}+\varkappa_{x2}) + \frac{\varepsilon_m}{2b}(\varkappa_{y1}+\varkappa_{y2}) + \frac{\varepsilon_n}{2d}(\varkappa_{z1}+\varkappa_{z2})
\end{aligned}\right\} \tag{26.8}$$

where $\varkappa_{x1}$ is the real part of β_{x1}, etc., and the corresponding expressions for the partial waves for the free vibration are

$$\left.\begin{aligned}
\Psi_m &= \psi_l(x, a)\, \psi_m(y, b)\, \psi_n(z, d); \qquad N_m = \Lambda_l^x \Lambda_m^y \Lambda_n^z;\\
\psi_0(x, a) &\approx \operatorname{Cos}\left[\frac{x}{a}\sqrt{i k a(\beta_{x1}+\beta_{x2})} - \sqrt{\frac{i k a \beta_{x1}}{(\beta_{x1}+\beta_{x2})}}\right];\\
\psi_l(x, a) &\approx \operatorname{Cos}\left[\left(\frac{\pi i l x}{a}\right) + \left(\frac{k x}{\pi l}\right)(\beta_{x1}+\beta_{x2}) - \beta_{x1}\left(\frac{k a}{\pi l}\right)\right] \quad (l>0);\\
\Lambda_0^x &\approx a\left[1 - \left(\frac{i k a}{3}\right)\frac{\beta_{x1}^3+\beta_{x2}^3}{(\beta_{x1}+\beta_{x2})^2}\right];\\
\Lambda_l^x &\approx \frac{1}{2} a\left[1 + \frac{i k a}{l^2}(\beta_{x1}+\beta_{x2})\right] \quad (l>0); \quad \text{etc.}
\end{aligned}\right\} \tag{26.9}$$

We see that, to this approximation, the partial waves divide into eight classes in regard to their decay rates $\varkappa$, since the difference between these rates depends only on the three factors ε. The lowest mode, for $l=m=n=0$, has the slowest decay rate ($\varepsilon_0=1$) (this mode is the one where the walls move more than the air in the room; it has zero frequency for rigid walls); next, those waves for which $l=m=0$ and $n>0$ suffer twice the absorption from the "z-walls" (those perpendicular to the z axis) because $\varepsilon_n=2$ for $n>0$. These waves reflect back and forth between the z-walls, moving parallel to the x- and the y-walls. Two other classes are those moving parallel to the x- and the y-walls ($l=n=0$, $m>0$) and those parallel to the y- and the z-walls. Three classes with somewhat greater decay rates are those moving parallel to only one pair of walls and, finally, those partial waves which reflect from all walls all have the largest decay rate (l, m, $n>0$).

At the beginning of Sect. 18 we pointed out that it is impossible for a wave to travel completely parallel to a "soft" wall. The present discussion is an example of this fact. When $\beta_{x1}=\beta_{x2}=0$ then all the waves for which $l=0$ move exactly parallel to the x walls, but as soon as these β's differ from zero there is some component of motion in the x direction for these waves, and thus some absorption by the x walls. The interesting point is that, to the first approximation, the waves adjust their "lack of parallelism" so that they are absorbed half as rapidly by the x walls as are the waves for $l>0$, which did not "try to be parallel" [see also the discussion following Eq. (25.6)].

When the wall admittance is not constant over a whole wall the integral equation is a more convenient way of computing steady-state and transient behavior. For example, for the rectangular rooms discussed above, we use the GREEN's function for rigid walls. The series of (26.1) holds, with

$$\left.\begin{aligned} \Phi_{lmn}(\boldsymbol{r}) &= \cos\frac{\pi l x}{a}\cos\frac{\pi m y}{b}\cos\frac{\pi n z}{d}; \\ \mu^2_{lmn} &= \left(\frac{\pi l}{a}\right)^2+\left(\frac{\pi m}{b}\right)^2+\left(\frac{\pi n}{d}\right)^2; \\ \Lambda_{lmn} &= \frac{abd}{\varepsilon_l\varepsilon_m\varepsilon_n}, \end{aligned}\right\} \tag{26.10}$$

all of these being independent of k. If now the area B_s of the boundary is the source of sound, moving with normal velocity $v_0(t)\,e^{-ikct}$, and the specific admittance of the rest of the wall surface is $\beta(\boldsymbol{r}^B)$, then the pressure amplitude at point $\boldsymbol{r}$ inside B is

$$p(k,\boldsymbol{r}) = i k\varrho c v_0(k)\iint_{B_s} G(k|\boldsymbol{r}|\boldsymbol{r}_0^B)\,ds_0 - ik\iint_B \beta(\boldsymbol{r}_0^B)\,p(k,\boldsymbol{r}_0^B)\,G(k|\boldsymbol{r}|\boldsymbol{r}_0^B)\,ds_0 \tag{26.11}$$

which is an inhomogeneous integral equation for p.

The pressure may be expanded in a series of the eigenfunctions Φ, and we can define the following coefficients

$$p=\sum_m p_m\Phi_m;\quad A_m=\frac{1}{\Lambda_m}\iint_{B_s}\Phi_m\,ds;\quad B_{mn}=\frac{1}{2\Lambda_m}\iint_B\beta\,\Phi_m\Phi_n\,ds \tag{26.12}$$

for use in computing the expansion (we have returned to the simpler practice of letting m stand for the trio l, m, n and n stand for l', m', n'). Coefficient A_m measures the coupling between the source and the m-th mode; coefficient B_{mn} measures the coupling between the m-th and the n-th waves and the wall impedance. We can then convert the integral equation (26.11) into a set of simultaneous algebraic equations for the coefficients p_n,

$$(k^2-\mu_m^2)\,p_m + 2ik\sum_n B_{mn}p_n = ik\varrho c v_0(k)\,A_m.$$

The wall admittance couples the various modes, the elements of the coupling matrix B_{mn} being the measure of this coupling.

Solution of this set of equations by successive approximations is not difficult if the elements of the coupling matrix are small (to be specific, if $B_{mn}\ll k$). In this case

$$p_m\approx\frac{ik\varrho c v_0(k)}{(k^2-\mu_m^2)+2ikB_{mm}}\left[A_m - ik\sum_{n\neq m}\frac{B_{mn}A_n}{(k^2-\mu_n^2)+2ikB_{nn}}\right]. \tag{26.13}$$

We note that even to this degree of approximation there are resonance peaks of finite height, exhibiting a Q equal to $\mu_m/\mathrm{Re}(B_{mm})$ the real part of the diagonal terms of the coupling matrix being measures of the rate of decay of the mode.

Finally we can apply the Fourier transform to this, to obtain an approximate expression for the acoustic response to an impulsive motion of the source part of the wall. If $v_0(t) = \delta(t)$ then $v_0(k) = (c/\sqrt{2\pi})$ and the acoustic response is a sum involving the inverse transforms of (26.13),

$$p_\delta(t, \boldsymbol{r}) \approx \begin{cases} 0 \quad (t < 0); \\ \varrho c^2 \sum_m \mathrm{Re}\left[\frac{\mu_m - i B_{mm}}{\mu_m} A_m \mathrm{e}^{-c(i\mu_m + B_{mm})t} \Phi_m(\boldsymbol{r})\right] + \\ \quad + \varrho c^2 \sum_m \mathrm{Im}\left\{\sum_{n \neq m} \frac{B_{mn} A_n \Phi_m(\boldsymbol{r})}{(\mu_m - i B_{mm})^2 - (\mu_n - i B_{nn})^2} \times \right. \\ \quad \left. \times \left[\frac{(\mu_m - i B_{mm})^2}{\mu_m} \mathrm{e}^{-c(i\mu_m + B_{mm})t} - \frac{(\mu_n - i B_{nn})^2}{\mu_n} \mathrm{e}^{-c(i\mu_n + B_{nn})t}\right]\right\} \\ \qquad\qquad (t > 0). \end{cases} \tag{26.14}$$

The first, single sum represents the waves directly excited by the impulsive motion of the source area B_s. The second, double sum represents the additional waves which are created, after the impulse, by the interaction between the directly excited waves and the wall. For example, the source area may be so located that $A_M = 0$ for a given M; the M-th wave cannot be directly excited by the source. Nevertheless this wave *will* appear in the second term unless $B_{Mn} A_n$ is zero for *all* $n \neq M$. If any wave is coupled to the M-th one via the wall then, if this is coupled to the source ($A_n \neq 0$), the M-th wave will eventually appear. Corresponding to this, we see that, for small values of t, the first term rises linearly with t, but the second term increases quadratically with t.

The elements of the coupling matrix B_{mn} are functions of k, because β usually is a function of k. In Eq. (26.13) they are functions of k but in Eq. (26.14) the k in B_{mn} must be replaced by μ_m, to the degree of approximation used here.

Other examples of calculations of transient and steady-state motion could be worked out, but most of the techniques of computation have by now been exemplified, so we will turn to another subject.

III. Radiation and scattering.

27. Radiation from spheres. In Sect. 20 we have discussed the near and the far field from a vibrating disk set in a plane, the prototype of surface radiators which are set in the main boundary surface. There also are sound radiators placed away from the main boundary; some of the general properties of the far field from such generators was discussed in Sect. 14. However, we should treat at least one case in enough detail to be able to compute the near field and thus to find the reactive force, on the vibrating surface, of the acoustic field caused by its motion. Only a few geometrical shapes allow an exact calculation of such a field; we will discuss the radiation from a spherical source, as a representative example [*42*], [*47*], [*64*], [*75*].

Suppose the sphere is of radius a, that its surface has acoustic admittance $(\beta/\varrho c)$ and that an area A of its surface is vibrating with radial velocity $v_0 \mathrm{e}^{-i\omega t}$. If the sphere is in free space the radiation from its surface can be expressed in terms of spherical harmonics $Y_{mn}(\vartheta, \varphi)$ (normalized to unity) and spherical Hankel functions $h_n(kr)$,

$$p = \sum_{mn} Q_{mn} Y_{mn}(\vartheta, \varphi) h_n(kr) \mathrm{e}^{-i\omega t} \quad (\omega = kc), \quad (r \geq a) \tag{27.1}$$

where r, ϑ, φ are spherical coordinates centered on the sphere, with polar axis appropriately oriented. The properties of the spherical Bessel functions of use in this and succeeding sections are:

$$\left.\begin{aligned} & h_n(z) = \sqrt{\frac{\pi}{2z}}\, H^{(1)}_{n+\frac{1}{2}}(z)\,; \qquad \mathrm{Re}[h_n(z)] = j_n(z)\,,\\ & h_n(z) \to \begin{cases} -i\,\dfrac{(2n)!}{2^n\, n!\, z^{n+1}} & (z\to 0)\,,\\ \dfrac{1}{i^{n+1} z}\, e^{iz} & (z\to\infty)\,, \end{cases}\\ & j_n(z)\, h_n'(z) - j_n'(z)\, h_n(z) = \frac{i}{z^2} \end{aligned}\right\} \tag{27.2}$$

where the prime denotes differentiation with respect to the argument z. Tables of the spherical Bessel functions $j_n(z)$, and of the magnitudes and phase angles of the complex functions h_n and h_n' are available.

The radial component of the acoustic velocity is

$$u_r = \frac{1}{i\varrho c} \sum_{mn} Q_{mn}\, Y_{mn}(\vartheta,\varphi)\, h_n'(kr)\, e^{-i\omega t}. \tag{27.3}$$

If the boundary condition at the surface of the sphere is that $[u_r + (\beta/\varrho c)\, p]_{r=a}$ is equal to $v_0\, e^{-i\omega t}$ over area A and is zero elsewhere, then the values of the coefficients Q_{mn} must be

$$Q_{mn} = \frac{i\varrho c\, v_0 A_{mn}}{h_n'(ka) + i\beta h_n(ka)}\,; \qquad A_{mn} = \iint\limits_{\text{over } A} Y^*_{mn}(\vartheta,\varphi)\, d\varphi \sin\vartheta\, d\vartheta \tag{27.4}$$

if β is constant over the surface of the sphere. Limiting values of these coefficients are

$$Q_{mn} \to \left\{\begin{aligned} & \frac{\varrho c\, 2^n n!\, (ka)^{n+2} A_{mn}}{(2n)!\, [(n+1) - i\beta ka]}\, v_0 && (ka \ll 1)\,;\\ & \frac{i^{n+1}\varrho c k a}{1+\beta}\, A_{mn} v_0\, e^{-ika} \quad (n < ka)\,; \quad \to 0 \quad (n > ka) && (ka \gg 1)\,. \end{aligned}\right\} \tag{27.5}$$

The quantity A_{00} is the fraction of surface area of the sphere which is moving with radial velocity $v_0\, e^{-i\omega t}$. The far-field pressure and time-average intensity is then

$$\left.\begin{aligned} & p \xrightarrow[r\to\infty]{} \frac{e^{ik(r-ct)}}{kr} \sum_{mn} i^{-n-1} Q_{mn}\, Y_{mn}(\vartheta,\varphi)\,;\\ & I \xrightarrow[r\to\infty]{} \frac{1}{2\varrho c k^2 r^2} \Big|\sum_{mn} i^{-n} Q_{mn}\, Y_{mn}(\vartheta,\varphi)\Big|^2. \end{aligned}\right\} \tag{27.6}$$

To find the total reaction force back on the moving part of the sphere's surface, we integrate the surface pressure over the area A. The ratio of this to the surface velocity,

$$\left.\begin{aligned} Z_r &= 4\pi a^2 \sum_{mn} \frac{i\varrho c\, |A_{mn}|^2\, h_n(ka)}{h_n'(ka) + i\beta h_n(ka)}\\ &\to \begin{cases} 4\pi a^2 \varrho c k a \sum\limits_{mn} |A_{mn}|^2\, [i(n+1) + (n+1+\beta)\, ka]^{-1} & (ka \ll 1)\,;\\ 4\pi a^2 \varrho c A_{00} (1+\beta)^{-1} & (ka \gg 1) \end{cases} \end{aligned}\right\} \tag{27.7}$$

is the radiation impedance load on the moving part of the surface.

At low frequencies each partial wave (each m, n) couples separately to the medium, the impedance for the (m, n)-th wave being approximately that of three shunt elements, a "radiation resistance"

$$(4\pi a^2 |A_{mn}|^2)\, \frac{\varrho c}{(n+1)}\,,$$

a "radiation mass reactance"

$$-(4\pi a^2 |A_{mn}|^2 \frac{i\varrho c k a}{(n+1)}$$

and the impedance

$$(4\pi a^2 |A_{mn}|^2) \frac{\varrho c}{\beta}$$

from the sphere's surface, all in parallel. At high frequencies the partial waves "work together", each element of the moving area coupling directly to the medium, so that the total impedance is the area of the moving part, $(4\pi a^2 A_{00})$, times an impedance per unit area, which is equivalent to a radiation resistance ϱc shunted by the surface impedance $(\varrho c/\beta)$ of the moving surface itself.

To see what effect the presence of a boundary surface has on the radiation from the sphere, and on the radiation reaction on the sphere, we bring up a plane boundary of surface admittance β_0, perpendicular to the polar axis of the sphere, to a distance h from the center of the sphere. Every partial wave $Y_{mn} h_n$ of Eq. (27.1) now is accompanied by a wave reflected from this surface. The methods of Sect. 19 can be used to compute the form of this reflected wave. It can most compactly be expressed in terms of the distance and angle of the observation point from the image point, a distance h below the plane. The position of the observation point is (r, ϑ, φ) with respect to the center of the radiating sphere; it is $(r_r, \vartheta_r, \varphi)$ with respect to the image sphere. The lines r, r_r and $2h$ (the line between centers) form a triangle, angle $(r, 2h)$ being ϑ and angle $(r_r, 2h)$ being ϑ_r. As long as $2kh$ is larger than unity a good approximation to the reflected wave, which accompanies $Y_{mn} h_n$, is $[(\cos\vartheta_r - \beta_0)/(\cos\vartheta_r + \beta_0)]\, Y_{mn}(\vartheta_r, \varphi)\, h_n(k r_r)$, analogous to Eq. (19.6).

The reflected wave, is, of course, reflected again from the radiating sphere, and so on, ad infinitum. But if $2kh$ is large the effects of re-reflection are negligible and we can then approximately represent the far field at (r, ϑ, φ) above the plane, by the direct and reflected waves,

$$\left.\begin{aligned} p \approx \sum_{mn} \frac{i\varrho c v_0 A_{mn}}{h'(ka) + i\beta h_n(ka)} \times \\ \times \left[Y_{mn}(\vartheta, \varphi)\, h_n(kr) + \frac{\cos\vartheta_r - \beta_0}{\cos\vartheta_r + \beta_0}\, Y_{mn}(\vartheta_r, \varphi)\, h_n(k r_r) \right] e^{-i\omega t} \end{aligned}\right\} \tag{27.8}$$

for $kr \gg 1$, $h > a$. This expression exhibits interference effects, as the primary and reflected waves cancel or reinforce each other.

It is not satisfactory to use both sets of coordinates when computing the near field at the surface of the radiating sphere. We must expand each reflected wave in a series of waves referred to the origin of the coordinates (r, ϑ, φ). If a is small enough, compared to h, then $\cos\vartheta_r \approx 1$ on the surface of the sphere, so that factor $(\cos\vartheta_r - \beta_0)/(\cos\vartheta_r + \beta_0)$ is approximately $(1-\beta_0)/(1+\beta_0)$ there. It also can be shown that

$$Y_{mn}(\vartheta_r, \varphi)\, h_n(k r_r) = \sum_l i^{n+l}\, Y_{ml}(\vartheta, \varphi)\, j(kr) \sum_\nu i^\nu L_\nu^m(n|l)\, h_\nu(2kh) \tag{27.9}$$

where $L_\nu^m(n|l)$ is the Gaunt factor defined by the equation

$$4\pi Y^*_{mn}(\vartheta, \varphi)\, Y_{ml}(\vartheta, \varphi) = \sum_\nu L_\nu^m(n|l)\, P_\nu(\cos\vartheta)$$

P_ν being the un-normalized Legendre function, which goes to unity as $\vartheta \to 0$. Integer ν in the sum takes on the values $|n-l|, |n-l|+2, \ldots, n+l-2, n+l$.

We can thus express the pressure at the point (a, ϑ, φ) on the surface of the radiating sphere by the multiple series

$$\left.\begin{aligned} p_{r=a} \approx i\varrho c v_0 \sum_{mn} \Big\{ \frac{A_{mn} h_n(ka)}{h_n'(ka) + i\beta h_n(ka)} + \frac{1-\beta_0}{1+\beta_0} \times \\ \times \sum_l i^{l+n} \frac{A_{ml} j_n(ka)}{h_l'(ka) + i\beta h_l(ka)} \sum_\nu i^\nu L_\nu^m(l|n)\, h_\nu(2kh) \Big\} Y_{mn}(\vartheta, \varphi)\, e^{-i\omega t}. \end{aligned}\right\} \quad (27.10)$$

The second term in the braces is, of course, the effect of the presence of the surface. The factors $h_\nu(2kh)$ provide the interference effects, h being the distance of the sphere center from the surface. In the limit of wavelength large compared to the sphere radius ($ka \ll 1$) but not large compared to h, the radiation impedance on the moving part of the sphere, becomes, to the first order in the small quantity ka,

$$\left.\begin{aligned} Z_r \approx 4\pi a^2 A_{00} \times \\ \times \Big\{ \sum_{mn} \frac{\varrho c(|A_{mn}|^2/A_{00})}{\beta + (n+1) + i[(n+1)/(ka)]} + \frac{1-\beta_0}{1+\beta_0} \frac{ka}{2kh} \frac{\varrho c A_{00}}{\beta + 1 + (i/ka)} e^{ik(2h-a)} \Big\} \end{aligned}\right\} \quad (27.11)$$

where $4\pi a^2 A_{00}$ is the area of the moving part of the sphere. The first term in the braces is the limiting form, for waves long compared to a, for the radiation impedance when the surface is not present. The second term is the effect of the surface, to first order in ka. We see that only the monopole radiation from the sphere ($m = n = 0$) has any first-order effect as far as the reflected wave is concerned; this effect is modified by the admittance β_0 of the surface. This second term also contains the interference factor $e^{ik(2h-a)}$ which changes phase depending on the relative distance between sphere and plane. At higher frequencies the higher multipoles begin to produce their interference effects until, for $ka \approx 1$, the full series of Eq. (27.10) must be used.

Similar computations can be carried out for other bodies, of shape differing from spherical, if the wave equation can be separated in the coordinate system appropriate to the body shape. In practice this means that oblate and prolate spheroids are the only other shapes for which calculations can be made. Approximate solutions, of course, may be obtained for other shapes.

28. Scattering from spheres. We have discussed sound scattering briefly and approximately in Sect. 17; we should now indicate how one goes about obtaining an exact solution [*42*], [*47*] for the scattering of an incident wave p_i by a sphere of radius a and specific admittance β. We start again from the integral equation

$$p(\mathbf{r}) = p_i(\mathbf{r}) + \iint \left[g(\mathbf{r}|\mathbf{r}_0^B) \left(\frac{\partial p}{\partial r_0}\right) - p(\mathbf{r}_0^B) \left(\frac{\partial g}{\partial r_0}\right) \right] ds_0 \quad (28.1)$$

as in (17.1), where $(\partial/\partial r_0) = -(\partial/\partial n_0)$, where p_i is the incident wave and the integration is over the surface of the sphere. Utilizing Eq. (12.4) for the expansion of g in spherical coordinates we obtain

$$\left.\begin{aligned} p(r, \vartheta, \varphi) &= p_i(r, \vartheta, \varphi) + p_s(r, \vartheta, \varphi), \\ p_s(r, \vartheta, \varphi) &= i k^2 a^2 \sum_{mn} Y_{mn}(\vartheta, \varphi)\, h_n(kr) \times \\ &\times \int_0^{2\pi} d\varphi_0 \int_0^{\pi} [j_n'(ka) + i\beta j_n(ka)]\, p(a, \vartheta_0, \varphi_0)\, Y_{mn}^*(\vartheta_0, \varphi_0) \sin\vartheta_0\, d\vartheta_0 \end{aligned}\right\} \quad (28.2)$$

where the Y_{mn} are normalized spherical harmonics, as before. Function p_s is the scattered wave.

Setting $r=a$ and utilizing the expression for the Wronskian, $j_n h_n' - j_n' h_n = (i/k^2 a^2)$ in Eq. (27.2), we obtain an integral equation for the pressure distribution $p(a, \vartheta, \varphi)$ on the surface of the sphere

$$\left.\begin{aligned} p_i(a,\vartheta,\varphi) &= \int_0^{2\pi} d\vartheta_0 \int_0^{\pi} G_k(\vartheta,\varphi\,|\,\vartheta_0,\varphi_0)\, p(a,\vartheta_0,\varphi_0)\sin\vartheta_0\, d\vartheta_0, \\ G(\vartheta,\varphi\,|\,\vartheta_0,\varphi_0) &= -i k^2 a^2 \sum_{mn} Y_{mn}(\vartheta,\varphi)\, j_n(ka)\,[h_n'(ka) + i\beta\, h_n(ka)]\, Y_{mn}^*(\vartheta_0,\varphi_0) \end{aligned}\right\} \qquad (28.3)$$

which is a Fredholm equation of the first kind, with a G which is symmetric if β is independent of ϑ or φ, the incident wave p_i being the known function and p being the unknown. If β is independant of ϑ and φ an exact solution may be obtained by expanding both p_i and p in spherical harmonics. Since the incident wave would be regular at $r=0$ if the sphere were not present, it must be expandable in the spherical Bessel functions

$$p_i(r,\vartheta,\varphi) = \sum_{ml} A_{ml}\, Y_{lm}(\vartheta,\varphi)\, j_l(kr)$$

and consequently

$$p(a,\vartheta,\varphi) = \frac{i}{k^2 a^2} \sum_{mn} \frac{A_{mn} Y_{mn}(\vartheta,\varphi)}{h_n'(ka) + i\beta\, h_n(ka)}\,. \qquad (28.4)$$

From this, of cource, we can compute the net force on the sphere,

$$\boldsymbol{F} = \frac{-\sqrt{\frac{2\pi}{3}}\,\frac{1}{k^2}}{h_1'(ka) + i\beta\, h_1(ka)}\,[i\,\boldsymbol{a}_x(A_{11} + A_{-11}) + \boldsymbol{a}_y(A_{11} - A_{-11}) + i\sqrt{2}\,\boldsymbol{a}_z A_{01}]\,. \qquad (28.5)$$

By setting the expression for $p(a,\vartheta,\varphi)$ into Eq. (28.2) we can obtain the series for the total field p and also the asymptotic form of the scattered wave, in terms of the coefficients R_n,

$$\left.\begin{aligned} p(r,\vartheta,\varphi) &= \sum_{mn} A_{mn} Y_{mn}(\vartheta,\varphi)\,[j_n(kr) - \tfrac{1}{2}(1-R_n)\, h_n(kr)] \\ &\xrightarrow[r\to\infty]{} \frac{1}{2kr}\sum_{mn} A_{mn} Y_{mn}(\vartheta,\varphi)\,[i^{n+1} e^{-ikr} + i^{-n-1} R_n\, e^{ikr}]; \\ p_s(r,\vartheta,\varphi) &\longrightarrow \frac{e^{ikr}}{r} f(\vartheta,\varphi); \quad f = \frac{i}{2k}\sum_{mn} i^{-n} A_{mn} Y_{mn}(\vartheta,\varphi)\,(1-R_n); \\ R_n &= -\frac{[h_n'(ka)]^* + i\beta\,[h_n(ka)]^*}{h_n'(ka) + i\beta\, h_n(ka)}; \quad 1 - R_n = 2\,\frac{j_n'(ka) + i\beta\, j_n(ka)}{h_n'(ka) + i\beta\, h_n(ka)}\,. \end{aligned}\right\} \qquad (28.6)$$

The second line, which expresses the whole wave in terms of an incoming and an outgoing wave, indicates that R_n is analogous to a reflection coefficient. If β is purely imaginary then the magnitude of R_n is unity, no energy is absorbed by the sphere and the waves are simply changed in phase on reflection, If β has a real part then the magnitude of R_n is less than unity and energy is absorbed by the sphere. The function f gives the distribution-in-angle of the scattered wave. The quantities $(1-R_n)$ have appreciable size for $n<ka$, rapidly approach zero for $n>ka$, so the series for f converges absolutely.

When the incident wave is a plane wave

$$p_i(r,\vartheta,\varphi) = p_0\, e^{ikr\cos\vartheta} = \sum_n \sqrt{4\pi(2n+1)}\, i^n\, Y_{0n}(\vartheta,\varphi)\, j_n(kr)\, p_0\,. \qquad (28.7)$$

The quantities F of Eq. (28.5) and f of (28.6) become

$$\left.\begin{aligned} \boldsymbol{F} &= \frac{2\pi a^2 p_0 e^{-ika}\boldsymbol{a}_z}{(1/ka)+(1+\frac{1}{2}\beta)-ika(1+\beta)}, \\ f(\vartheta) &= \frac{i}{k}\sum_n \sqrt{\pi(2n+1)}\, Y_{0n}(\vartheta,\varphi)\,(1-R_n) \\ &\to a\left[ika\beta - \tfrac{1}{3}k^2a^2(1+\beta)+\tfrac{1}{2}k^2a^2\cos\vartheta\right] \qquad (ka\to 0). \end{aligned}\right\} \tag{28.8}$$

The last expression should be compared with Eq. (17.6). Note that β corresponds to neither α nor η, but the two expressions are equal when $\alpha=\beta=\eta=0$.

The integral of the scattered intensity over the sphere at infinity is the power scattered and the integral of the total energy flow into the sphere $r=a$ is the power absorbed by the sphere. The ratios of these powers to the incident intensity $(1/2\varrho c)|p_0|^2$ are called the scattering cross section Q_s and the absorbing cross section Q_a;

$$\left.\begin{aligned} Q_s &= \frac{\pi a^2}{k^2a^2}\sum_n (2n+1)\,|1-R_n|^2 \to \\ &\to \begin{cases} 4\pi a^4k^2\left[|\beta|^2-\frac{2}{3}ka\sigma+k^2a^2(\frac{7}{36}+\frac{2}{3}\varkappa+|\beta|^2)\right] & (ka\to 0), \\ 2\pi a^2(1+|\beta|^2)/[(1+\varkappa)^2+\sigma^2] & (ka\to\infty); \end{cases} \\ Q_a &= \frac{\pi a^2}{k^2a^2}\sum_n (2n+1)\,(1-|R_n|^2) \to \\ &\to \begin{cases} 4\pi a^4k^2\varkappa\left[1+2ka\sigma+k^2a^2(2-2\varkappa-\varkappa^2\varepsilon 3\sigma^2)\right] & (ka\to 0), \\ 4\pi a^2\varkappa/[(1+\varkappa)^2+\sigma^2] & (ka\to\infty) \end{cases} \end{aligned}\right\} \tag{28.9}$$

where $\beta=\varkappa-i\sigma$, as defined earlier. These cross sections measure the equivalent areas of the incident beam which are scattered and absorbed, respectively, by the sphere. Both absorption and scattering are small when ka is small; both approach asymptotic values as $ka\to\infty$.

If the admittance of the spherical surface is a function of position on the sphere, $\beta(\vartheta,\varphi)$, then an exact solution of Eq. (28.3) is not possible, though an approximation series can be used if the variation of β with ϑ and φ is not large. We define the matrix B as follows:

$$B_{nm}^{jl} = \int_0^{2\pi} d\varphi \int_0^{\pi} \beta(\vartheta,\varphi)\, Y_{jl}(\vartheta,\varphi)\, Y_{mn}^*(\vartheta,\varphi)\sin\vartheta\, d\vartheta. \tag{28.10}$$

Then, to the first order in the non-diagonal terms of B,

$$\left.\begin{aligned} p(a,\vartheta,\varphi) &\to \frac{i}{k^2a^2}\sum_{mn}\frac{Y_{mn}(\vartheta,\varphi)}{h_n'(ka)+iB_{mn}^{mn}h_n(ka)} \times \\ &\times\left\{A_{mn} - i h_n(ka)\sum_{j,l\neq m,n}\frac{B_{mn}^{jl}A_{jl}}{h_l'(ka)+iB_{jl}^{jl}h_l(ka)}\right\} \end{aligned}\right\} \tag{28.11}$$

where the last sum is over all pairs of values of j and l except for the pair m, n.

The scattered wave cannot be simply expressed in terms of reflection coefficients R for each partial wave, because of the coupling of these waves by the irregularities of the surface admittance. The far field takes on the form

$$\left.\begin{aligned} p_s &\to \frac{i e^{ikr}}{kr}\sum_{mn}\frac{i^{-n}Y_{mn}(\vartheta,\varphi)}{h_n'(ka)+iB_{mn}^{mn}h_n(ka)} \times \\ &\times\left\{A_{mn}[j_n'(ka)+iB_{mn}^{mn}j_n(ka)] - \frac{1}{k^2a^2}\sum_{j,l\neq m,n}\frac{B_{mn}^{jl}A_j}{h_l'(ka)+iB_{jl}^{jl}h_l(ka)}\right\} \end{aligned}\right\} \tag{28.12}$$

from which the scattering and absorption cross sections can be computed. If β is so large that these approximate series do not converge rapidly, we have to solve Eq. (28.3) by other means, perhaps by variational techniques.

Finally we might compute the effect, on the sound field radiated by a piston of radius b in a plane of admittance β_0, produced by the insertion of a sphere of radius a and admittance β, with its center on the axis of the piston, a distance h from the center of the piston. Referring to Eq. (20.5), the pressure wave radiated from the piston, in cylindrical coordinates z, R, φ (origin at center of piston, piston axis the z axis) when no sphere is present, is

$$p_i(z, R, \varphi) = k \varrho c b v_0 \int_0^\infty e^{iz\sqrt{z^2-u^2}} J_0(uR) \frac{J_1(ub)\, du}{\sqrt{k^2-u^2}+k\beta_0}. \tag{28.13}$$

This can be considered to be the incident wave on the sphere, but we cannot use Eqs. (28.4) to (28.6) unless we can express the wave in spherical coordinates (r, ϑ, φ) about the sphere's center. Such an expansion is

$$\left.\begin{aligned}(p_i(z, R, \varphi) &= k \varrho c b v_0 \sum_n (2n+1)\, i^n P_n(\cos\vartheta)\, j_n(kr) \times \\ &\times \left\{ \int_0^{\frac{1}{2}\pi} e^{ikh\cos\alpha} P_n(\cos\alpha)\, J_1(kb\sin\alpha) \frac{\cos\alpha\, d\alpha}{\cos\alpha+\beta_0} + \right. \\ &\left. + \int_0^\infty e^{-khw} P_n(iw)\, J_1\!\left(kb\sqrt{w^2+1}\right) \frac{w\, dw}{(\beta_0+iw)\sqrt{w^2+1}} \right\}\end{aligned}\right\} \tag{28.14}$$

where $P_n(\cos\vartheta)$ is the un-normalized Legendre function $\sqrt{4\pi/(2n+1)}\, Y_{0n}(\vartheta, \varphi)$. The quantity in braces can be evaluated, at least approximately, in most cases. We thus can find the coefficients A_{mn} of Eq. (28.4) and then compute the wave scattered by the sphere. This, according to Eq. (28.2), is expressed in terms of partial waves $Y_{mn} h_n$, which now should be expressed in terms of cylindrical coordinates (because of the symmetry of location of the sphere, we need only consider the terms for $m=0$), if we wish to find the effect of the scattered wave on the piston.

But the inverse expansion is

$$P_n(\cos\vartheta)\, h_n(kr) = i^n \int_0^\infty e^{i(h-z)\sqrt{k^2-u^2}} J_0(Rw)\, P_n\!\left(\frac{\sqrt{k^2-w^2}}{k}\right) \frac{w\, dw}{k\sqrt{k^2-w^2}} \tag{28.15}$$

for $z<h$. To this must be added the wave

$$i^n \int_0^\infty e^{i(h+z)\sqrt{k^2-w^2}} J_0(Rw)\, P_n\!\left(\frac{\sqrt{k^2-w^2}}{k}\right) \frac{\sqrt{k^2-w^2}-k\beta_0}{\sqrt{k^2-w^2}+k\beta_0}\, \frac{w\, dw}{k\sqrt{k^2-w^2}}$$

which represents its reflection from the surface at $z=0$. Thus each term $Y_{0n} h_n$ in the expansion of the wave scattered by the sphere can be replaced by

$$2i^n \int_0^\infty e^{ih\sqrt{k^2-w^2}} J_0(Rw)\, Y_{0n} \frac{w\, dw}{\sqrt{k^2-w^2}+k\beta_0} \tag{28.16}$$

to obtain the pressure on the surface $z=0$, where the Y_{0n} in the integrand is $\sqrt{4\pi(2n+1)}\, P_n(\sqrt{k^2-w^2}/k)$.

If kh is large and if h is large compared to a, we need not go on to calculate the effect of the scattering of this wave from the sphere again. We will only give the final results when $\beta_0=0$ and when ka is small enough so that only the monopole term is important in the scattered wave. The coefficient A_{00} is

$$A_{00} = -\varrho c v_0 \sqrt{4\pi}\,(e^{ik\sqrt{h^2+b^2}} - e^{ikh}) \approx -i\varrho c v_0 \sqrt{\pi}\,\frac{k b^2}{h}\,e^{ikh}$$

and the reaction force back on the piston because of the presence of the sphere is, for ka small,

$$F_s \approx \pi \frac{k^2 a^2 b^4}{h^2}\,\varrho c v_0 [\beta + ika(\tfrac{1}{3}+\beta)]\,e^{2ikh} \tag{28.17}$$

which exhibits the interference factor e^{2ikh}. The quantity F_s, divided by v_0, should be added to the radiation impedance of Eq. (20.7); it expresses, approximately, the additional load on the piston because of the presence of the sphere.

29. Scattering from disks [*64*]. Another problem of practical interest is that of the scattering of sound from a circular disk of radius a. For convenience we place it in the x, y plane, with center at the origin and we call the side facing the positive z axis face 1, the other face 2. The problem can be solved exactly in terms of oblate spheroidal functions [*4*], by methods completely similar to those used for spherical functions in the previous section. We shall, instead, use the problem to demonstrate the use of the variational techniques mentioned earlier, in part because the problem turns out to be particularly amenable to such techniques and in part because prolate spheroidal wave functions are quite complicated functions. We start with the integral equation (13.1) for an incident wave p_i, of frequency $(\omega/2\pi)$,

$$p(\boldsymbol{r}) = p_i(\boldsymbol{r}) + \iint \left(p\,\frac{\partial g}{\partial n_0} - g\,\frac{\partial p}{\partial n_0}\right) d s_0 \tag{29.1}$$

which involves integration over both sides of the disk. Over face 1, $(\partial/\partial n_0) = -(\partial/\partial z_0)$; over face 2 $(\partial/\partial n_0) = (\partial/\partial z_0)$. Therefore the first term in the integral is $-(p_1 - p_2)(\partial g/\partial z_0)$, where p_1 is the pressure at a given value of r_0, ϕ_0 on face 1 and p_2 the pressure on face 2 for the same r_0, ϕ_0. As before the GREEN's function is

$$g = -\frac{e^{ik|\boldsymbol{r}-\boldsymbol{r}_0|}}{4\pi|\boldsymbol{r}-\boldsymbol{r}_0|}.$$

The form taken by the second term in the integral depends on the acoustic nature of the disk surface. We will consider two cases.

Case I will be that of porous disk (such as one made of cloth) through which the air can be made to move by applying a pressure differential between the two faces. Since we assume the disk has no thickness, the flow into one face must equal that out the other face, so the normal gradient of p on one surface must equal minus the normal gradient of p at the corresponding point on the other face. In this case the second term in the integral of Eq. (29.1) will cancel out, leaving

$$\left.\begin{aligned} p(\boldsymbol{r}) &= p_i(\boldsymbol{r}) - \int_0^{2\pi} d\phi_0 \int_0^a \frac{\partial g}{\partial z_0}(p_1 - p_2)\, r_0\, d r_0 \qquad \text{(porous disk)} \\ &\to p_i(\boldsymbol{r}) - \frac{e^{ikr}}{r} f_d \quad (r\to\infty), \\ f_d &= -\frac{ik}{4\pi}\cos\theta_s \int_0^{2\pi} d\phi_0 \int_a^a (p_1 - p_2)\, e^{-i\boldsymbol{k}_s\cdot\boldsymbol{r}_0}\, r_0\, d r_0, \end{aligned}\right\} \tag{29.2}$$

where the vector $\boldsymbol{k}_s$ in the asymptotic form has magnitude k and is pointed in the direction of the observation point, at an angle θ_s to the z axis. The function f_d

is the angular distribution factor for the scattered wave, as with Eqs. (16.2) and (28.6). It can be computed as soon as we have computed the distribution of the pressure difference (p_1-p_2) over the disk.

Case II will be that of a disk with faces which have surface admittance $(\beta/\varrho c)$ but which are impervious to flow from one side to the other (this is the other limiting case; most actual disks are intermediate between the two). We call this disk an impedance disk. For it the normal velocity at one face is not related to that of the other; in fact the normal velocity into face 1 is equal to $(\beta/\varrho c)\, p_1$, that into face 2 is $(\beta/\varrho c)\, p_2$, and the two may simultaneously point into the disk [this could not happen if the disk were truly of infinitesimal thickness, but it can be thick enough to exhibit compression and still be of negligible thickness in regard to the integral of Eq. (29.1)]. For such a disk the second term in the integral will be $-ik\beta(p_1+p_2)$ and

$$\left.\begin{aligned} p(\boldsymbol{r}) &= p_i(\boldsymbol{r}) - \iint\left[\frac{\partial g}{\partial z_0}(p_1-p_2) + ik\beta\, g\,(p_1+p_2)\right] ds_0 \quad \text{(impedance disk)}\\ &\to p_i(\boldsymbol{r}) - \frac{e^{ikr}}{r}(f_d+f_s) \qquad (r\to\infty);\\ f_s &= \frac{ik\beta}{4\pi}\int_0^{2\pi} d\phi_0 \int_0^{\pi} (p_1+p_2)\, e^{-i\boldsymbol{k}_s\cdot\boldsymbol{r}_0}\, r_0\, dr_0 . \end{aligned}\right\} \tag{29.3}$$

For f_d see Eq. (29.2). In this case we must compute both the difference and the sum of p_1 and p_2, in order to calculate the scattering.

In both cases, therefore, we must compute the near field in order to calculate the scattering. It will not suffice to use the Born approximation (putting p_i in for p in the integral) for then p_1-p_2 would be zero and we would obtain no scattering from the porous disk (and none from the impedance disk either if β were zero). To compute the near field we must use the form of the GREEN's function given in Eq. (20.4). We first place $z_0=0$, after which we must distinguish between the case $z>0$, which is used when we make the p on the left side of the equation into p_1, and the case $z<0$, which is used if $p(\boldsymbol{r})$ is to become p_2. Thus the first line of Eq. (29.2) and that of Eq. (29.3) involve an integral which becomes

$$\frac{1}{4\pi}\int_0^{2\pi} d\phi_0 \int_0^{\pi} r_0\, dr_0 \sum_m \varepsilon_m \cos m(\phi-\phi_0) \int_0^{\infty} (p_1-p_2)\, e^{iz\sqrt{k^2-u^2}} J_m(u r_0)\, J_m(u r)\, u\, du \qquad (\text{for } z>0),$$

$$-\frac{1}{4\pi}\int_0^{2\pi} d\phi_0 \int_0^{\pi} r_0\, dr_0 \sum_m \varepsilon_m \cos m(\phi-\phi_0) \int_0^{\infty} (p_1-p_2)\, e^{-iz\sqrt{k^2-u^2}} J_m(u r_0)\, J_m(u r)\, u\, du \qquad (\text{for } z<0).$$

When we set $z\to 0$ and keep r between 0 and a, because of the properties of the Bessel transform,

$$f(r) = \int_0^{\infty} J_m(u r)\, u\, du \int_0^{\infty} f(r_0)\, J_m(u r_0)\, r_0\, dr_0 \tag{29.4}$$

and of the properties of Fourier series, the first integral above becomes simply $\frac{1}{2}(p_1-p_2)$ which, when taken over to the left-hand side of the equation, combines with the p_1 there to give $\frac{1}{2}(p_1+p_2)$ in the range $0\leqq r<a$. The second integral $(z<0)$ becomes $-\frac{1}{2}(p_1-p_2)$ in the range $0\leqq r<a$, which combines with the p_2 on the left-hand side to become $\frac{1}{2}(p_1+p_2)$ again. Thus Eqs. (29.2) and (29.3)

become

$$\left.\begin{aligned}&\tfrac{1}{2}(p_1+p_2)=p_i \quad \text{(porous disk)}\\ &\tfrac{1}{2}(p_1+p_2)=p_i+\frac{k\beta}{2\pi}\int_0^{2\pi}d\phi_0\int_0^a r_0\,dr_0\sum_m \varepsilon_m\cos m(\phi-\phi_0)\times\\ &\qquad\times\int_0^\infty \tfrac{1}{2}(p_1+p_2)\,J_m(u\,r)\,J_m(u\,r_0)\frac{u\,du}{\sqrt{k^2-u^2}} \quad \text{(impedance disk)}\end{aligned}\right\}\tag{29.5}$$

where (p_1+p_2) on the left-hand side is a function of r,ϕ, in the integral is a function of r_0,ϕ_0.

This solves only half of the problem, for we need to compute p_1-p_2 also. To obtain this we differentiate both sides of the equations with respect to z. For the porous disk we now use the fact that the flow through the disk, $(1/ik\varrho c)\times(\partial p/\partial z)$, is equal to the pressure difference (p_2-p_1) times the flow admittance $(\beta/\varrho c)$, so that $(\partial p/\partial z)_{z=0}=-(ik\beta)(p_1-p_2)$. The real part of β is the specific conductance for flow through the disk pores; the imaginary part is related to the mass and, perhaps, the stiffness of the disk for motion in the z direction.

For the impedance disk we use the facts that $(\partial p_1/\partial z)=-(ik\beta)p_1$ and $(\partial p_2/\partial z)=ik\beta p_2$. The results, after using the Bessel transform again, are (for $0\leqq r<a$)

$$\left.\begin{aligned}(2\beta)\,\tfrac{1}{2}(p_1-p_2)&=-\frac{1}{ik}\frac{\partial p_i}{\partial z}-\frac{1}{2\pi k}\int_0^{2\pi}d\phi_0\int_0^a r_0\,dr_0\sum_m\varepsilon_m\cos m(\phi-\phi_0)\times\\ &\qquad\times\int_0^\infty\tfrac{1}{2}(p_1-p_2)\,J_m(u\,r)\,J_m(u\,r_0)\sqrt{k^2-u^2}\,u\,du\end{aligned}\right\}\tag{29.6}$$

for the porous disk. The equation for the impedance disk only differs from this by having β instead of 2β on the left-hand side. In one case, of course, the β is a flow admittance, in the other it is a surface admittance.

It might appear that these integral equations can be solved exactly by the use of Bessel transforms. This is not so because the equations are only valid in the range $0\leqq r<a$, whereas the Bessel transform should range over $0\leqq r<\infty$. The complication is similar to that encountered in Eq. (25.12) where z goes from $-\infty$ to $+\infty$ whereas z_0 goes from 0 to $+\infty$, and the Wiener-Hopf method had to be used on the Fourier transform. Unfortunately there is no analogue to the Wiener-Hopf method for Bessel transforms, so we must be satisfied with approximate results (or else turn to the oblate spheroidal wave functions).

One possibility, which is not too bad for long wavelengths, is to use the steady-state flow solutions in the integrals of Eq. (29.6). In this case the velocity potential Ψ is computed for steady flow; the velocity is then grad Ψ and, to the first approximation in ka, the pressure is $ik\varrho c\Psi$. Here we do use oblate spheroidal coordinates, the steady-state velocity potential coming out in Legendre functions of these coordinates. Assuming that the incident wave near the disk is $p_0+k\varrho c v_0[z\cos\theta_i+x\sin\theta_i]$ these solutions are

$$\left.\begin{aligned}&\tfrac{1}{2}(p_1+p_2)\approx p_0+\varrho c v_0\sin\theta_i\,k\,r\cos\phi;\\ &\tfrac{1}{2}(p_1-p_2)\approx\frac{2}{\pi}\varrho c v_0\cos\theta_i\frac{k\sqrt{a^2-r^2}}{1-(8/3\pi)\,ik\,a\beta}\quad\text{(porous disk)}\end{aligned}\right\}\tag{29.7a}$$

and

$$\tfrac{1}{2}(p_1+p_2)\approx p_0+\varrho c v_0\sin\theta_i\frac{kr\cos\phi}{1-(3\pi/32)\,ik\,a\,\beta}\quad\text{(impedance disk)}\tag{29.7b}$$

with the equation for $\frac{1}{2}(p_1 - p_2)$ for the impedance disk the same as that for the porous disk, except that the $(8/3\pi)$ in the denominator is changed to $(4/3\pi)$.

These expressions may be reasonably good approximations, at long wavelengths, to the near field, but steady-state flow theory provides no means for computing the scattered radiation, which does not enter in steady-state flow. However, we might expect that insertion of these near-field approximations into the integrals for f_d and f_s given in Eqs. (29.2) and (29.3) might result in a satisfactory approximation for the angular distribution of the scattered wave. When this is done, after evaluating the integrals, using the following relationships,

$$\left.\begin{aligned} &\int_0^{2\pi} \cos(m\phi)\, e^{iz\cos(\varphi-\varphi_0)}\, d\phi = 2\pi\, i^m J_m(z)\cos(m\phi_0), \\ &\int_0^1 J_m(k a x \sin\theta)\,(1-x^2)^n\, x^{m+1}\, dx = \frac{(ka\sin\theta)^m}{2(n+1)(n+2)\ldots(n+m)}\,\Upsilon_{m+n-1}(\theta) \end{aligned}\right\} \quad (29.8)$$

where

$$\Upsilon_n(\theta) = \frac{2^n\,\Gamma(n+1)}{(ka\sin\theta)^n}\, J_n(ka\sin\theta) \to 1 - \frac{k^2a^2\sin^2\theta}{2(n+1)} \qquad (ka\sin\theta\to 0),$$

we find that the first approximation is

$$\left.\begin{aligned} f_d &\approx \left(\frac{k^2a^2}{\pi}\right)\cos\theta_i\cos\theta_s\,\Upsilon_{\frac{3}{2}}(\theta_s) \quad \text{(porous disk)}; \\ f_s + f_d &\approx \frac{1}{2}\, i k a^2 \beta\, \Upsilon_1(\theta_s) + \frac{1}{\pi} k^2 a^3 \cos\theta_i \cos\theta_s\, \Upsilon_{\frac{3}{2}}(0) - \\ &\quad - \frac{1}{4}\, i k^3 a^4 \sin\theta_i \sin\theta_s\, \Upsilon_2(\theta) \quad \text{(impedance disk)}. \end{aligned}\right\} \quad (29.9)$$

This is certainly better than the Born approximation, for it differs from zero. Comparison with Eq. (28.8) (last line) for the scattering from a sphere, shows that the first term differs only by a factor $\frac{1}{2}\Upsilon_1(\theta_s)\to\frac{1}{2}$; since this term arises from the contraction of the surface under pressure, and since the surface area of a disk of radius a is half that of a sphere of radius a, the factor $\frac{1}{2}$ is not surprising. The higher-order terms do not correspond to those for the sphere, but we should not expect the angular distribution of a wave scattered by a disk to be the same as that for a sphere. A more serious deficiency, however, is the lack of symmetry between the angles of incidence, θ_i, $\phi_i = 0$ and the angles of scattering, θ_s, ϕ_s; Eqs. (29.9) do not obey the principle of reciprocity. These equations can only be valid as long as ka is small enough so that the quantities Υ are equal to unity.

One way to obtain a better result is to use a variational procedure. By methods analogous to those which obtained Eq. (16.8) we can show that, as the shape of φ on the disk surface is varied, the particular shape for which the first-order variation of the quantity

$$\left(\frac{ik\beta}{2\pi}\right)\left[\frac{\iint \tilde{\varphi}(\boldsymbol{r})\, e^{i\boldsymbol{k}_i\cdot\boldsymbol{r}}\, ds \iint \varphi\, e^{-i\boldsymbol{k}_s\cdot\boldsymbol{r}}\, ds}{\iint \tilde{\varphi}(\boldsymbol{r})\,\varphi(\boldsymbol{r})\, ds - \beta \iint \tilde{\varphi}(\boldsymbol{r})\, ds \iint G_s(\boldsymbol{r}|\boldsymbol{r}_0)\,\varphi(\boldsymbol{r}_0)\, ds_0}\right] = [f_s] \qquad (29.10)$$

is zero is the correct shape of $\frac{1}{2}(p_1 + p_2)$ and the corresponding stationary value is the correct value of f_s. We have here taken the incident wave to be a plane wave with angles of incidence θ_i, $\phi_i = 0$, corresponding to $\varrho c v_0$ of Eq. (29.7) equalling $i p_0$.

Even if we do not choose the correct form for φ, if it differs from the correct shape of $\frac{1}{2}(p_1 + p_2)$ by first order terms, the above expression will differ from the correct f_s by second-order terms. Only the shape of φ matters, not its magnitude;

the expression is insensitive to changes of magnitude of φ. The function $\tilde{\varphi}$ is the adjoint trial function, corresponding to a wave incident in the direction $-\boldsymbol{k}_s$, scattered in direction $-\boldsymbol{k}_i$ (the reciprocity relation). The GREEN'S function in the denominator comes from Eq. (29.5),

$$G_s(\boldsymbol{r}|\boldsymbol{r}_0) = \frac{k}{2\pi}\sum_m \varepsilon_m \cos m(\phi-\phi_0)\int_0^\infty J_m(u\,r)\,J_m(u\,r_0)\,\frac{u\,du}{\sqrt{k^2-u^2}}. \tag{29.11}$$

The variational procedure has one other advantage, it avoids the necessity of first computing the field and then the scattering; the angle-distribution factors f are obtained directly. We assume a form for φ, with parameters, vary the parameters until $[f_s]$ is stationary and take this as the best value of f_s. If we wish further details of the field, near or far, we insert the best form for φ into the expression

$$\tfrac{1}{2}(p_1+p_2) = \varphi(\boldsymbol{r})\iint\tilde{\varphi}\,e^{i\boldsymbol{k}_i\cdot\boldsymbol{r}}\,ds\Big/\left(\iint\tilde{\varphi}\,\varphi\,ds - \beta\iint\tilde{\varphi}\,ds\iint G_s\,\varphi\,ds_0\right)$$

and use it for $\frac{1}{2}(p_1+p_2)$ in the first line of Eq. (29.3) (together with p_1-p_2, to be obtained shortly) to compute a better approximation for p.

For example, Eqs. (29.7) suggest that we try, as forms for insertion into (29.10),

$$\varphi = 1+\gamma\sin\theta_i\,k\,r\cos\phi;\qquad \tilde{\varphi} = 1-\gamma\sin\theta_s\,k\,r\cos(\phi-\phi_s) \tag{29.12}$$

where γ is the variational parameter. Note the reciprocity relationship between φ and $\tilde{\varphi}$. The various terms in (29.10) become

$$\left.\begin{aligned}
\iint\varphi\,e^{-i\boldsymbol{k}_s\cdot\boldsymbol{r}}\,ds &= \pi a^2\left[\Upsilon_1(\theta_s) - \tfrac{1}{2}i\gamma k^2a^2\sin\theta_i\sin\theta_s\cos\phi_s\,\Upsilon_2(\theta_s)\right],\\
\iint\tilde{\varphi}\,e^{i\boldsymbol{k}_i\cdot\boldsymbol{r}}\,ds &= \pi a^2\left[\Upsilon_1(\theta_i) - \tfrac{1}{2}i\gamma k^2a^2\sin\theta_i\sin\theta_s\cos\phi_s\,\Upsilon_2(\theta_i)\right],\\
\iint\tilde{\varphi}\,\varphi\,ds &= \pi a^2\left[1-\tfrac{1}{5}k^2a^2\gamma^2\sin\theta_i\sin\theta_s\cos\phi_s\right],\\
\iint\tilde{\varphi}\,ds\iint G_s\,\varphi\,ds_0 &= 2\pi a^2\int_0^\infty[J_1(k\,a\,w)]^2\frac{dw}{w\sqrt{1-w^2}} - \\
&\quad -\pi a^2\gamma^2k^2a^2\sin\theta_i\sin\theta_s\cos\phi_s\int_0^\infty[J_2(k\,a\,w)]^2\frac{dw}{w\sqrt{1-w^2}}.
\end{aligned}\right\} \tag{29.13}$$

The first integral in the last expression can be evaluated in terms of the Bessel function J_1 and the Struve function H_1. The second integral cannot, but since it is of higher order in ka, we can perhaps be satisfied with an approximate value. The result is

$$\begin{aligned}
\iint\tilde{\varphi}\,ds\iint G_s\,\varphi\,ds_0 \approx \pi a^2\Big\{&1-\frac{1}{ka}J_1(2ka) - \frac{i}{ka}H_1(2ka) + \\
&+\tfrac{1}{2}i\,k^2a^2\gamma^2\sin\theta_i\sin\theta_s\cos\phi_s\left[1-k^2a^2(1-i)\right]\Big\}.
\end{aligned}$$

Inserting all these into Eq. (29.10), differentiating with respect to γ, setting the result equal to zero and solving, we finally obtain for the optimal value

$$\left.\begin{aligned}
f_s &\approx \frac{1}{2}i\,k\,a^2\beta\,\Upsilon_1(\theta_i)\,\Upsilon_1(\theta_s)\,\frac{1}{Q} + \\
&\quad+\frac{1}{2}i\,k^3a^4\beta\sin\theta_i\sin\theta_s\cos\phi_s\,\Upsilon_2(\theta_i)\,\Upsilon_2(\theta_s)\,\frac{1}{R} + \\
&\quad+\frac{1}{8}i\,k^3a^4\beta\sin\theta_i\sin\theta_s\cos\phi_s\,\frac{[\Upsilon_1(\theta_i)\,\Upsilon_2(\theta_s)+\Upsilon_2(\theta_i)\,\Upsilon_1(\theta_s)]^2}{\Upsilon_1(\theta_i)\,\Upsilon_1(\theta_s)\,R},\\
Q &= 1-\beta\left[1-\frac{1}{ka}J_1(2ka) - \frac{i}{ka}H_1(2ka)\right],\\
R &\approx 1+2i\beta-\tfrac{1}{2}k^2a^2(1+i)\,\beta.
\end{aligned}\right\} \tag{29.14}$$

This *is* symmetrical with respect to incident and scattering angles and thus satisfies the reciprocity condition. It corresponds to Eq. (29.9) to the first order in $k\,a$ (for the symmetric part) and, presumably, is accurate to at least the second order. It is thus a more satisfactory result than (29.9). A still more accurate result, of course, could be obtained by using a more complicated trial function, with more parameters to vary.

The variational expression for the pressure difference,

$$[f_d] = \frac{i\,k}{2\pi}\left[\frac{\cos\theta_i\cos\theta_s\iint\tilde{\varphi}(\boldsymbol{r})\,e^{i\boldsymbol{k}_i\cdot\boldsymbol{r}}\,ds\iint\varphi(\boldsymbol{r})\,e^{-i\boldsymbol{k}_s\cdot\boldsymbol{r}}\,ds}{\beta\iint\tilde{\varphi}(\boldsymbol{r})\,\varphi(\boldsymbol{r})\,ds+\iint\tilde{\varphi}(\boldsymbol{r})\,ds\iint G_d(\boldsymbol{r}\,|\,\boldsymbol{r}_0)\,\varphi(\boldsymbol{r}_0)\,ds_0}\right] \tag{29.15}$$

for the impedance disk, where

$$G_d = \frac{1}{2\pi k}\sum_m \varepsilon_m\cos m\,(\phi-\phi_0)\int_0^\infty J_m(u\,r)\,J_m(u\,r_0)\sqrt{k^2-u^2}\,u\,du \tag{29.16}$$

is similar to (29.10). For the porous disk, the factor β in the denominator is replaced by 2β. The suggested form in Eq. (29.7) has only one term, so that a linear variational parameter is not easily devised. However inserting the single terms

$$\varphi = \cos\theta_i\sqrt{1-\left(\frac{r}{a}\right)^2}\,;\qquad \tilde{\varphi} = -\cos\theta_s\sqrt{1-\left(\frac{r}{a}\right)^2}$$

should result in an expression for f_d which is correct to at least second order in $k a$ [and will turn out to be as accurate as (29.14)]. The various integrals are

$$\left.\begin{aligned}
&\iint\varphi\,e^{-i\boldsymbol{k}_s\cdot\boldsymbol{r}}\,ds = \pi\,a^2\cos\theta_i\,\Upsilon_{\frac{3}{2}}(\theta_s)\,;\qquad \iint\tilde{\varphi}\,e^{i\boldsymbol{k}_i\cdot\boldsymbol{r}}\,ds = -\pi\,a^2\cos\theta_s\,\Upsilon_{\frac{3}{2}}(\theta_i)\,,\\
&\qquad\qquad\iint\tilde{\varphi}\,\varphi\,ds = -\tfrac{2}{3}\,\pi\,a^2\cos\theta_i\cos\theta_s\,,\\
&\iint\tilde{\varphi}\,ds\iint G_d\,\varphi\,ds_0 = -\pi^2\frac{a}{k}\cos\theta_i\cos\theta_s\int_0^\infty\left[J_{\frac{3}{2}}(k\,a\,w)\right]^2\frac{\sqrt{1-w^2}}{w^2}\,dw\\
&\qquad\qquad\approx -\tfrac{1}{3}\,i\,\pi^2\frac{a}{k}\cos\theta_i\cos\theta_s\left[1-\frac{2}{9\pi}\,k^2\,a^2\,(1+i)\right]
\end{aligned}\right\} \tag{29.17}$$

and the result for the pressure-difference part of the angle-distribution factor is

$$f_d \approx \frac{3}{2\pi}\,k^2\,a^3\,\frac{\cos\theta_i\cos\theta_s\,\Upsilon_{\frac{3}{2}}(\theta_i)\,\Upsilon_{\frac{3}{2}}(\theta_s)}{1-2i\beta k a-\dfrac{2}{9\pi}\,k^2 a^2(1+i)}\quad\text{(impedance disk)}. \tag{29.18}$$

The total scattering factor for the impedance disk is then the sum of (29.14) and (29.18). The scattering factor for the porous disk is just the f_d of (29.18), but with the term $2i\beta k a$ in the denominator changed to $4i\beta k a$. These formulas should be compared with the less accurate formulas of Eq. (29.9) and also with the scattering factor for the sphere, given in Eq. (28.8). We note that the disk scatters most when it is perpendicular to the direction of the incident wave ($\theta_i=0$) and that the porous disk does not scatter at all when it is parallel to the incident direction ($\theta_i=\frac{1}{2}\pi$). We also note that the scattering from a disk of intermediate type would have the β of (29.14) differ from the β of (29.18).

30. Scattering in enclosures. The previous section dealt with the effect on a wave in free space of the presence of a sphere or a disk. It is sometimes of interest to compute the effect of such an object on the standing waves in an enclosure, in particular its effect on the resonance frequencies and rates of decay of the standing waves [*48*]. We will thus be able to complete the discussion begun in Sect. 26. Here again variational procedures will turn out to be useful.

Suppose we have obtained the exact solution for an enclosure R_0, with specified boundary conditions on the boundary B_0 for a driving frequency $(kc/2\pi)$ [as was done in Eqs. (26.7) for a rectangular enclosure]. The eigenfunctions for the forced motion waves are $\Phi_m(\boldsymbol{r})$, corresponding to the eigenvalues $\mu_m = \pm k_m(k) - i\varkappa_m(k)$, where $(k_m/2\pi)$ is the resonance frequency and $\varkappa_m$ is the damping factor for the m-th standing wave. If now we wish to compute the resonance frequencies and damping factors for an enclosure which differs from this only in having a small "foreign body" present in the enclosure, excluding the medium from the volume R_s, which has specific acoustic admittance β_s on its surface B_s, we can start with the homogeneous integral equation for standing waves,

$$p(\boldsymbol{r}) = \iint\limits_{B_0} \left[p(\boldsymbol{r}_0)\frac{\partial G}{\partial n_0} - G(\boldsymbol{r}|\boldsymbol{r}_0)\frac{\partial p}{\partial n_0}\right] ds_0 + \iint\limits_{B_s}\left[p\frac{\partial G}{\partial n_0} - G\frac{\partial p}{\partial n_0}\right] ds_0. \quad (30.1)$$

We use the GREEN'S function expansion (12.5) or (26.1) in eigenfunctions appropriate to the enclosure without the body present,

$$G(\boldsymbol{r}|\boldsymbol{r}_0) = \sum_n \frac{\Phi_n(\boldsymbol{r})\,\Phi_n(\boldsymbol{r}_0)}{\Lambda_n[k^2 - (k_n - i\varkappa_n)^2]} \quad (30.2)$$

where we include the normalization constant Λ_n since the Φ's are not necessarily normalized. With this GREEN'S function the integral over the enclosure walls B^0 is identically zero except when $k = k_m - i\varkappa_m$, in which case the integral is the free wave $\Psi_m(\boldsymbol{r})$ [see Eq. (26.9)]. When the body is present the correct value of k will be near, but not exactly equal to $k_m - i\varkappa_m$, in which case the second integral of Eq. (30.1) will be present but not the first. Now multiply through by $\Phi_m(\boldsymbol{r})$ and integrate over R_0. Because of the orthogonality of the Φ's we obtain, after multiplying by $k^2 - (k_m - i\varkappa_m)^2$,

$$[k^2 - (k_m - i\varkappa_m)^2] \iiint\limits_{R_0} p\,\Phi_m\,dv = \iint\limits_{B_s}\left[p(\boldsymbol{r}_0)\frac{\partial \Phi_m}{\partial n_0} - \Phi_m(\boldsymbol{r}_0)\frac{\partial p}{\partial n_0}\right] ds_0.$$

If the object is small enough, p will not differ much from Ψ_m over most of region R_0 (see subsection 26 for the relationship between the Φ_s and the Ψ's) and the volume integral will closely approximate to Λ_m. We thus obtain an equation for the perturbed eigenvalue

$$k \approx k_m - i\varkappa_m + \frac{1}{2\Lambda_m(k_m - i\varkappa_m)}\iint\limits_{B_s}\left[p\frac{\partial \Psi_m}{\partial n_0} - \Psi_m\frac{\partial p}{\partial n_0}\right] ds_0. \quad (30.3)$$

If this correction term is small compared to k_m itself (if the perturbing body is small) then $k^2 - (k_m - i\varkappa_m)^2$ will be small and, in series (30.2), the predominating term will be the one containing Ψ_m. Thus by far the largest term on the right in Eq. (30.1) will be Ψ_m times a surface integral. Since (30.1) is homogeneous, we can change the scale of p by this factor and thus obtain an integral equation for the perturbed eigenfunction which is near to Ψ_m,

$$p(\boldsymbol{r}) = \Psi_m(\boldsymbol{r}) + \iint\limits_{B_s}\left[p(\boldsymbol{r}_0^B)\frac{\partial G_m}{\partial n_0} - G_m(\boldsymbol{r}|\boldsymbol{r}_0)\frac{\partial p}{\partial n_0}\right] ds_0 \quad (30.4)$$

where G_m is the GREEN'S function of (30.2) with the term in Φ_m removed. However as long as the body is not close to surface B_0 this modified GREEN'S function is not very different from the free-space GREEN'S function g at the surface of the body (i.e., when $\boldsymbol{r}$ is on B_s as well as $\boldsymbol{r}_0$). Therefore the integral equation for $p(\boldsymbol{r})$ on the surface of the perturbing body, in the presence of the m-th standing wave, is, to a close approximation,

$$p(\boldsymbol{r}^B) = \Psi_m(\boldsymbol{r}^B) + \iint\limits_{B_s} \left[p(\boldsymbol{r}_0^B) \frac{\partial g}{\partial n_0} - g(\boldsymbol{r}^B | \boldsymbol{r}_0^B) \frac{\partial p}{\partial n_0} \right] d s_0 \tag{30.5}$$

which is the same as Eq. (29.1) for the pressure on the surface of a scattering object when the incident wave is the eigenfunction Ψ_m. Thus we solve the scattering problem to determine $p(\boldsymbol{r}^B)$ and its normal gradient on the surface of the scatterer and then we set the result into Eq. (30.3) to determine the perturbed eigenvalues.

If the perturbing body is a sphere we can use the results of Eq. (28.4) to carry out the calculations. We place the new origin of coordinates at the center of the sphere and orient the axes for convenience, not necessarily parallel to the enclosure walls. Near the object the unperturbed standing wave can be expressed by its Taylor series

$$\left.\begin{aligned} \Psi_m(\boldsymbol{r}) &= \Psi_m(\boldsymbol{r}_c) + \varrho c v_m \boldsymbol{k}_i \cdot \boldsymbol{r} + \cdots \\ &= \Psi_m(\boldsymbol{r}_c) + \varrho c v_m k (z \cos\theta_i + x \sin\theta_i \cos\phi_i + y \sin\theta_i \sin\phi_i) \cdots \end{aligned}\right\} \tag{30.6}$$

where $\boldsymbol{r}_c$ is the vector from the origin (the "old origin") for the functions Ψ_m to the center of the sphere, where $\boldsymbol{r}$ is the radius vector from the center of the sphere (the new origin) and where vector $\varrho c v_m \boldsymbol{k}_i$ is the gradient of Ψ_m at this new origin. The expansion coefficients A_{mn} of $p_i = \Psi_m$ to use in Eq. (28.4) are thus

$$A_{00} = \sqrt{4\pi}\, \Psi_m(r_c); \quad A_{01} = \sqrt{12\pi}\, \varrho c v_m \cos\theta_i; \quad A_{11} = \sqrt{6\pi}\, \varrho c v_m \sin\theta_i e^{-i\phi_i} = A_{-11}.$$

Consequently the perturbed eigenvalue for the m-th standing wave, when distorted by the presence of a sphere of radius a with center at $\boldsymbol{r}_c$, is

$$k \approx k_m - i\varkappa_m - \frac{2\pi i \beta a^2 \Psi_m^2(r)}{(1 - i k_m \alpha \beta) \Lambda_m} - \frac{\pi k_m a^3 \varrho^2 c^2 v_0^2}{\Lambda_m} \frac{1 + i k_m a \beta}{1 - \frac{1}{2} i k_m a \beta} \tag{30.7}$$

which is valid for small values of $ka\beta$. In the correction terms we have neglected $i\varkappa_m$ in comparison to k_m (though $k_m - i\varkappa_m$ can be used instead of k_m if necessary).

The first correction term is the effect of the yielding of the spherical surface; it is proportional to β and may be said to be the effect of the change of potential energy in the standing wave. The real part of β modifies the damping factor $\varkappa$; the imaginary part of β changes the frequency $k_m/2\pi$. The second term would not vanish if β were zero; it is caused by the fact that the presence of the sphere distorts the flow and changes the kinetic energy of the standing wave. The dependence of the term on β is a higher-order effect.

If the perturbing body is a porous disk, with center at r_c and with axis along the z axis then the surface integrand of Eq. (30.3) becomes $-\frac{1}{2}(p_1 - p_2)(\partial\Psi_m/\partial z)\, ds$ and Eq. (30.5) becomes

$$(2\beta)\frac{1}{2}(p_1 - p_2) + \frac{1}{ik}\frac{\partial \Psi_m}{\partial z} + \iint G_d(\boldsymbol{r}^B | \boldsymbol{r}_0^B)\frac{1}{2}(p_1 - p_2)\, d s_0 = 0$$

where G_d is given in Eq. (29.16). The corresponding variational expression is

$$[A(k)] = \left[\frac{-(1/ik)\{\iint (\partial\Psi_m/\partial z)\, \varphi\, ds\}^2}{2\beta \iint \varphi^2\, ds + \iint \varphi\, ds\, G_d(\boldsymbol{r}|\boldsymbol{r}_0)\, \varphi\, d s_0} \right] \quad \text{(porous disk)} \tag{30.8}$$

where we have not used the adjoint function, because reciprocity does not enter here. The stationary value of A, divided by $\Lambda_m(k_m - i\varkappa_m)$, is the correction to the eigenvalue, as required by Eq. (30.3). Thus

$$k \approx k_m - i\varkappa_m - \frac{a^2}{3\Lambda_m}\left\{\frac{\varrho^2 c^2 v_m^2\, a k_m \cos^2\theta_i}{1-(3/4\pi)\, i a k \beta - (2/9\pi)\, a^2 k_m^2 (1+i)}\right\} \tag{30.9}$$

where we have used $\sqrt{1-(r/a)^2}$ as a trial function and carried out the integrations as in Eq. (29.17). Angle θ_i is the angle between the disk axis and the direction of unperturbed flow at $\boldsymbol{r}_c$. Evidently the effect of the porous disk on the eigenvalue is greatest when the disk is in a nodal plane of pressure, where the fluid velocity is greatest. It is zero if the disk is at a pressure loop, where the velocity is zero; it is also zero if the plane of the disk is parallel to the unperturbed velocity.

If the disk has acoustic surface admittance β and no flow through it (impedance disk) then the surface integral of Eq. (30.3) has the form

$$\iint (p_1 - p_2)\frac{\partial \Psi_m}{\partial z}\, ds - i k \beta \iint (p_1 + p_2)\, \Psi_m\, ds \tag{30.10}$$

and Eq. (30.5) divides into the two equations of (29.5) and (29.6). The variational expression for the first of these is the same as (30.8), with the factor 2β in the denominator changed to β. The variational expression for the second part is

$$[B(k)] = \left[\frac{ik\beta\left(\iint \Psi_m \varphi\, ds\right)^2}{\iint \varphi^2\, ds - \beta \iint \varphi\, ds\, G_s(\boldsymbol{r}|\boldsymbol{r}_0)\, \varphi\, ds_0}\right] \quad \text{(impedance disk)}. \tag{30.11}$$

Using the trial function $\varphi = 1 + \gamma k r \cos\phi$ and making the derivative of B with respect to γ zero, we obtain, finally, the eigenvalue for the m-th standing wave perturbed by an impedance disk,

$$\left.\begin{aligned} k &\approx k_m - i\varkappa_m - \frac{A(k_m - i\varkappa_m) + B(k_m - i\varkappa_m)}{(k_m - i\varkappa_m)\Lambda_m} \\ &\approx k_m - i\varkappa_m - \frac{i\pi a^2 \beta}{\Lambda_m}\left\{\frac{\Psi_m^2(r_c)}{1-(8i/3\pi)\beta k_m a} + \frac{\varrho^2 c^2 v_m^2 k_m^2 a^2 \sin^2\theta_i}{4(1-\frac{1}{2}i\beta)}\right\} - \\ &\quad - \frac{a^2}{3\Lambda_m}\left\{\frac{\varrho^2 c^2 v_m^2 k_m a \cos^2\theta_i}{1-(3i/8\pi)\beta k_m a - (2/9\pi)\, a^2 k_m^2 (1+i)}\right\}. \end{aligned}\right\} \tag{30.12}$$

The first correction term depends on the over-all pressure effect, being directly proportional to β; this term is maximum when the disk is at a pressure loop and is independent of the orientation of the loop (to this approximation). The second and third terms depend on the pressure gradient; they are maximum at a pressure node and depend on the orientation of the disk. This result should be compared with Eq. (30.7) for a sphere as perturbing body. The first correction terms differ by approximately a factor 2, which is the ratio between the surface areas; the other two terms differ entirely because the disk has orientation, which the sphere does not possess.

IV. Propagation in moving and inhomogeneous media.

31. Relative motion of source and medium. When a sound source moves relative to the surrounding fluid the flow around the source (as around any other body) is generally quite complex and often is unstable. Under such conditions the analysis of the radiation from the source becomes quite involved [*1*], [*54*], [*77*]. To bring out the salient features we shall limit ourselves to simple situations, in which the flow distortion around the source can be neglected. We start by investigating the acoustic field from a small pulsating sphere, small enough so we can describe it mathematically as a delta function

$$Q(\boldsymbol{r}, t) = F(t)\,\delta(\boldsymbol{r} - \boldsymbol{r}_s). \tag{31.1}$$

The location of the source, as well as the wave motion it produces, will be given in terms of a coordinate system at rest with respect to the fluid. Although we later will specialize to the case of uniform motion, it is of interest to carry through the formal analysis for an arbitrary motion of the source, given by the position vector $\boldsymbol{r}_s(t)$. According to Eq. (3.10) the source term in the equation is $(\partial Q/\partial t)$, so the wave equation is

$$\frac{1}{c^2}\frac{\partial^2 p}{\partial t^2} - \nabla^2 p = \frac{\partial Q}{\partial t}$$

and the formal solution of the equation is [see Eq. (13.6)]

$$p(\boldsymbol{r}, t) = \frac{1}{4\pi}\frac{\partial}{\partial t}\iiint Q\left(\boldsymbol{r}_0, t - \frac{R}{c}\right)\frac{dv_0}{R} \tag{31.2}$$

where $\boldsymbol{R} = \boldsymbol{r} - \boldsymbol{r}_s$ is the distance between the source and the observation point at time t.

In this case we have

$$Q\left(\boldsymbol{r}_0, t - \frac{R}{c}\right) = [F(t)]\,\delta(X)\,\delta(Y)\,\delta(Z),$$

where

$$X = x_0 - [x_s(t)], \quad Y = y_0 - [y_s(t)], \quad Z = z_0 - [z_s(t)].$$

The quantities inside the brackets should be evaluated at the retarded times $t - (R/c)$, where R is still to be determined. The solution (31.2) can then be expressed as

$$p(\boldsymbol{r}, t) = \frac{1}{4\pi}\frac{\partial}{\partial t}\left\{\frac{[F(t)]}{RI}\right\}_{X=Y=Z=0} \tag{31.3}$$

where I, the Jacobian determinant, can be expressed in terms of the retarded velocity $[\boldsymbol{V}] = [d\boldsymbol{r}_s/dt]$ of the source,

$$I = 1 - \{[\boldsymbol{V}]\cdot\boldsymbol{n}/c\} \tag{31.4}$$

where $\boldsymbol{n}$ is the unit vector $\boldsymbol{R}/R$. It remains to determine the retarded value of R corresponding to $X = Y = Z = 0$ from the equation

$$R^2 = \left\{x - x_s\left(t - \frac{R}{c}\right)\right\}^2 + \left\{y - y_s\left(t - \frac{R}{c}\right)\right\}^2 + \left\{z - z_s\left(t - \frac{R}{c}\right)\right\}^2. \tag{31.5}$$

To find R explicitly from this equation, we need to specify the motion of the source. We shall now consider the special case when the source moves along the x axis with a constant velocity V, so that $x_s = Vt$, $y_s = z_s = 0$. Eq. (31.5) then reduces to $R^2 = (x - Vt + MR)^2 + y^2 + z^2$, with the solution

$$R = \frac{M}{1-M^2}(x - Vt) \pm \sqrt{\left(\frac{x - Vt}{1-M^2}\right)^2 + \frac{y^2+z^2}{1-M^2}}, \quad M = \frac{V}{c}. \tag{31.6}$$

When the source speed is sub-sonic ($M < 1$), only the plus sign in this expression results in a positive value of R. In other words only one source point will contribute to the field at the observation point $\boldsymbol{r}$ at a given time. However when the speed of the source is super-sonic ($M > 1$) both signs in (31.6) result in positive values of R when $x < x_s$ and $(M^2 - 1)(y^2 + z^2) \leqq (x - Vt)^2$, i.e., for points inside a cone with vertex at the source and with half angle ϕ defined by $\sin\phi = (1/M)$. Outside this so-called Mach cone there are no real values of R and thus there is no sound.

In the sub-sonic case it is convenient to introduce the quantities

$$x_1 = \frac{x - Vt}{\sqrt{1-M^2}}\,; \qquad R_1 = \sqrt{x_1^2 + y^2 + z^2}$$

in terms of which the expression for R has the simpler form

$$R = \frac{M x_1 + R_1}{\sqrt{1-M^2}}\,.$$

Inserting this into Eq. (31.3) we obtain $(RI)_{X=Y=Z=0} = \sqrt{1-M^2}\,R_1$, and

$$p = \frac{1}{4\pi}\,\frac{\partial}{\partial t}\left\{\frac{F(t-R/c)}{\sqrt{1-M^2}\,R_1}\right\}$$

or

$$p = \frac{1}{4\pi}\left\{(1-M^2)^{-\frac{3}{2}}\left(\frac{F'}{R_1}\right)\left(1 + M\,\frac{x_1}{R_1}\right) + \frac{V}{1-M^2}\,\frac{x_1}{R_1^3}\,F\right\} \tag{31.7}$$

where the prime indicates the derivative with respect to its argument $(t - R/c)$.

The second term in this expression for p contributes to the near field, and can be neglected when R_1 is sufficiently large. The first term can be divided into two parts (by separating the 1 from the $M x_1/R_1$); the first term corresponds to a monopole term and the second to a dipole term, the exact division being conditioned by our choice of coordinates, x_1, y, z.

When the relative speed of source and medium is supersonic, it is convenient to use the variables

$$x_2 = \frac{x - Vt}{\sqrt{1-M^2}}\,; \qquad R_2 = \sqrt{x^2 - y^2 - z^2}\,.$$

As indicated earlier, there are two possible values of R when the observation point is inside the Mach cone,

$$R_+ = \frac{M x_2 + R_2}{\sqrt{M^2-1}}\,; \qquad R_- = \frac{M x_2 - R_2}{\sqrt{M^2-1}} \tag{31.8}$$

which, when inserted in (31.3) give us

$$\left.\begin{aligned} p = &-\frac{1}{4\pi}(M^2-1)^{-\frac{3}{2}}\,\frac{1}{R_2}\left\{\left(1 - \frac{M x_2}{R_2}\right)F'\left(t - \frac{R_+}{c}\right) + \right.\\ &\left.+\left(1 + \frac{M x_2}{R_2}\right)F'\left(t - \frac{R_-}{c}\right)\right\} + \frac{1}{4\pi}\,\frac{V x_2}{R_2^3}\left\{F\left(t - \frac{R_+}{c}\right) + F\left(t - \frac{R_-}{c}\right)\right\}.\end{aligned}\right\} \tag{31.9}$$

As before, the second term can be neglected when R_2 is large.

We note that, when there is relative motion of source and medium, the surfaces of constant phase do not coincide with the surfaces of constant pressure amplitude. In the subsonic case, for example, the surfaces of constant phase are given by $R = (M x_1 + R_1)/\sqrt{1-M^2} = \text{const}$, whereas the surfaces of constant pressure amplitude are determined by $(M x_1 + R_1)/R_1^2 = \text{const}$.

If we are to use these solutions as GREEN'S functions it would be desirable to express them in terms of coordinates at rest with respect to the source. Let these coordinates by ξ, η and ζ, parallel respectively to x, y and z (the motion of the fluid is along the ξ axis, in the negative direction).

The free-field GREEN's function for a constant frequency source in a moving medium is thus (for the sub-sonic case)

$$\left.\begin{aligned} g(\boldsymbol{r}|\boldsymbol{r}_0) &= \frac{-1}{1-M^2}\,\frac{e^{ikR}}{4\pi R_1}\left(\frac{R}{R_1}+iM\frac{x_1}{R_1}\,\frac{1}{kR_1}\right); \\ k &= \frac{\omega}{c}; \qquad x_1=\chi-\chi_0; \qquad \chi=\frac{\xi}{\sqrt{1-M^2}}; \\ R_1^2 &= (\chi-\chi_0)^2+(\eta-\eta_0)^2+(\zeta-\zeta_0)^2; \\ R &= \frac{M x_1+R_1}{\sqrt{1-M^2}}. \end{aligned}\right\} \tag{31.10}$$

As an example we compute the radiation from a rectangular piston set in an otherwise rigid plane, coincident with the ξ,η plane, with the fluid moving past in the negative ξ direction with speed V. The piston, which has dimensions $2a$ and $2b$, has velocity $U e^{-i\omega t}$ in the ζ direction, and therefore displacement $(iU/\omega)\,e^{-i\omega t}$. The acoustic field is therefore obtained by integrating $2i\omega\varrho g$ times the fluid velocity in the ζ direction, over the region $-a<\xi_0<+a$, $-b<\eta_0<+b$. Because of the fluid motion, its normal velocity is not just the piston velocity, $U\,e^{-i\omega t}$, over the area of the piston; there are also the discontinuous jumps of velocity, $(iUV/\omega)\,[\delta(\xi-a)-\delta(\xi+a)]\,e^{-i\omega t}$, from $\eta=-b$ to $\eta=+b$, arising when the fluid flows over the edge of the piston, as it moves up and down. Since we have assumed that the flow is in the ξ direction, these jumps are only at the $\xi=\pm a$ edges, not at the others.

The integration over the first term in g, adequate for the far field, is then

$$\left.\begin{aligned} p &\to -\frac{2i\varrho c U k a b}{\pi(1-M^2)^2}\,\frac{e^{ikR}}{r_1}\,\frac{R}{r_1}\,\frac{\sin X}{X}\,\frac{\sin Y}{Y}\left(1+M\frac{\chi}{r_1}\right) \qquad (kR\gg 1); \\ r_1^2 &= \chi^2+\eta^2+\zeta^2; \qquad\qquad R=\frac{r_1+M\chi}{\sqrt{1-M^2}}; \\ X &= ka\left(M+\frac{\chi}{r_1}\right)\Big/(1-M^2); \qquad Y=kb\,\eta/r_1\sqrt{1-M^2}. \end{aligned}\right\} \tag{31.11}$$

It is interesting to note that, although the GREEN's function of Eq. (31.10) diverges as $M\to 1$, the field from an extended source, as given in Eq. (31.11), does not. To find the field from the piston when the flow is super-sonic, we must use Eq. (31.9) to obtain the g for the super-sonic case. The resulting radiation is, of course, confined to the Mach cone on the downstream side of the piston.

32. Inhomogeneous media, the geometric approximation [*1*], [*17*], [*27*], [*57*], [*69*]. In many problems of sound propagation, in the atmosphere as well as in the sea, it is necessary to take into account the fact that the medium is neither quiescent nor homogeneous. The motion of the medium makes it acoustically anisotropic and the inhomogeneities cause scattering and refraction. All of these effects, of course, are contained in the basic equations (1.2) to (1.4) and have been mentioned in the first Chapter. In this Chapter we expect to indicate how these effects can be computed.

As indicated in Sect. 3, the appropriate wave equation for regions where the speed of sound c and the steady-state fluid velocity $\boldsymbol{v}$ vary, but where the fractional changes of these quantities in a distance of a wavelength are small, is

$$\frac{1}{c^2}\left(\frac{\partial}{\partial t}+\boldsymbol{v}\cdot\nabla\right)^2 p=\nabla^2 p. \tag{32.1}$$

Two general techniques of approximate solution of this equation are useful. The first, appropriate when the inhomogeneities in c and $\boldsymbol{v}$ are random and "fine-grained" (i.e. when λ times the Laplacian of either c or $\boldsymbol{v}$ is the same order of magnitude as its gradient) is the Born approximation, first discussed in Sect. 16. The second, to be discussed in this section, is appropriate when c and $\boldsymbol{v}$ vary slowly and "smoothly" (i.e., when λ times the Laplacian of c and $\boldsymbol{v}$ are negligible compared to their gradients). In this case we use what is known in quantum mechanics as the WKB approximation.

When the variations of c and $\boldsymbol{v}$ are "smooth" we can keep a clear separation between the phase of a sound wave and its amplitude. We write

$$\left.\begin{aligned} p(\boldsymbol{r},t) &= A(\boldsymbol{r})\,e^{ik_0\Phi - i\omega t} = A_0\,e^{i\Psi(\boldsymbol{r}) - i\omega t}, \\ \Psi(\boldsymbol{r}) &= k_0\,\Phi - i\ln\frac{A}{A_0} \end{aligned}\right\} \tag{32.2}$$

where Φ, the so-called *eikonal function*, defines the surfaces of equal phase and $A(\boldsymbol{r})$ is the amplitude function. The quantity A_0 is the constant reference amplitude and $k_0 = (\omega/c_0)$ corresponds to the constant reference value c_0 of sound velocity. We thus see that phase and amplitude can be written as real and imaginary parts of a complex phase function $\Psi(\boldsymbol{r})$.

Since this representation of p in terms of its phase and amplitude is most useful when the wavelength $(2\pi/k_0)$ is small compared to the distances over which v and c change appreciably, when we substitute (32.2) into (32.1), we at the same time neglect all but the highest powers of k_0 in the resulting equation. Separating real and imaginary parts, we finally obtain a pair of approximate equations which will serve to determine Φ and A,

$$|\operatorname{grad}\Phi|^2 \approx \left(\frac{c_0}{c}\right)^2 (1 - \boldsymbol{M}_0 \cdot \operatorname{grad}\Phi)^2, \tag{32.3}$$

$$2(\operatorname{grad}\Phi + |\operatorname{grad}\Phi|\,\boldsymbol{M}) \cdot \operatorname{grad}(\ln A) \approx -\nabla^2\Phi \tag{32.4}$$

where $\boldsymbol{M}_0 = \boldsymbol{v}/c_0$ and $\boldsymbol{M} = \boldsymbol{v}/c$ may be called Mach vectors. Eq. (32.3), the so-called eikonal equation, can be written in the form

$$|\operatorname{grad}\Phi| = \frac{c_0}{c + v_s} \tag{32.5}$$

where $v_s = \boldsymbol{v} \cdot \hat{\mathbf{s}}$ is the component of $\boldsymbol{v}$ in the direction of the unit vector

$$\hat{\mathbf{s}} = \frac{\operatorname{grad}\Phi}{|\operatorname{grad}\Phi|} \tag{32.6}$$

normal to the phase surface $\Phi = \text{const.}$

In a fluid at rest the magnitude of the gradient of the eikonal is the index of refraction (c_0/c), which is the same in all directions. In a moving fluid, however, the index of refraction $c_0/(c + \boldsymbol{v} \cdot \hat{\mathbf{s}})$ depends on the direction of propagation of the wave. If we denote the distance along the normal $\mathbf{s}$ to the phase surface by s, the velocity of propagation of the phase surfaces along s is

$$\frac{\omega}{k_0\,(\partial\Phi/\partial s)} = \frac{c_0}{\partial\Phi/\partial s} = c + \boldsymbol{v} \cdot \hat{\mathbf{s}}. \tag{32.7}$$

The Eq. (32.4) for the amplitude function, can be written

$$(c\,\hat{\mathbf{s}} + \boldsymbol{v}) \cdot \operatorname{grad}(\ln A) = |c\,\hat{\mathbf{s}} + \boldsymbol{v}|\,\frac{\partial}{\partial q}(\ln A) = -\frac{c\,\nabla^2\Phi}{2|\nabla\Phi|}$$

in which q is the distance in the direction of $c\hat{\boldsymbol{s}}+\boldsymbol{v}$ or $\hat{\boldsymbol{s}}+\boldsymbol{M}$. Note that this is not the same as the direction of the wave normal $\hat{\boldsymbol{s}}$, unless $\boldsymbol{v}=0$. We can formally express Φ and A in terms of line integrals. For example, by integrating (32.5) along s, we have

$$\Phi=\int\frac{c_0\,ds}{c+\boldsymbol{v}\cdot\hat{\boldsymbol{s}}}+\text{const}. \tag{32.8}$$

Similarly, integrating Eq. (32.7) along q, we have

$$\ln\left(\frac{A}{A_0}\right)^2=-\int\frac{c}{c_0}\,\frac{1+\boldsymbol{M}\cdot\hat{\boldsymbol{s}}}{|\hat{\boldsymbol{s}}+\boldsymbol{M}|}\,\nabla^2\Phi\,dq. \tag{32.9}$$

These equations provide the formal solution for the propagation of short wavelength sound in an inhomogeneous fluid. Numerical or graphical procedures can readily be developed for the detailed solution of specific problems; closed-form, analytic solutions are not often found. We will confine our further remarks here to a discussion of the general effects of temperature and flow-velocity gradients on the ray paths.

As noted above, the direction of the amplitude gradient (and also the direction of the "ray" of sound) is given by the unit vector in the direction of q,

$$\hat{\boldsymbol{q}}=\frac{\hat{\boldsymbol{s}}+\boldsymbol{M}}{|\hat{\boldsymbol{s}}+\boldsymbol{M}|}=\frac{c\hat{\boldsymbol{s}}+\boldsymbol{v}}{|c\hat{\boldsymbol{s}}+\boldsymbol{v}|} \tag{32.10}$$

where $\hat{\boldsymbol{s}}$ is the unit vector normal to the phase surface, as defined in Eq. (32.6), and $\boldsymbol{M}$ is the Mach vector. The curvature of a ray is obtained from $(1/R)=|d\hat{\boldsymbol{q}}/ds|$ where R is the radius of curvature. Let us determine the curvature of the rays in the special case when the flow is parallel to the x, y plane and the gradients of the temperature and flow velocity are in the z direction, a situation approximating the conditions in the atmosphere and in the sea.

If we confine ourselves to rays which are parallel or almost parallel to the x axis, we have

$$\frac{1}{R}\approx\frac{1}{|\hat{\boldsymbol{s}}+\boldsymbol{M}|}\left|\frac{d\hat{\boldsymbol{s}}}{ds}\right|\approx\frac{1}{|\hat{\boldsymbol{s}}+\boldsymbol{M}|}\,\frac{\partial}{\partial z}\left(\frac{\partial\Phi/\partial x}{|\nabla\Phi|}\right). \tag{32.11}$$

For sufficiently small Mach numbers, we can set $|1/\nabla\Phi|\approx(c+v_x)/c_0$, and Eq. (32.11) reduces to

$$\frac{1}{R}\approx\frac{1}{c_0}\,\frac{\partial c}{\partial z}+\frac{1}{c_0}\,\frac{\partial v_x}{\partial z}=\frac{1}{c_0}\left(\frac{dc}{dz}+\frac{dv}{dz}\cos\gamma\right) \tag{32.12}$$

where v_x is the component of flow velocity in the x direction and γ is the angle between $\boldsymbol{v}$ and the x axis. Under these conditions the curvature contributions from flow and temperature gradients are additive.

The rays are bent upward when the effective gradient $(dc/dz)+(dv/dz)\cos\gamma$ is negative. The effect of the temperature gradient is the same in all directions of propagation, but the effect of the wind gradient varies as $\cos\gamma$. If the ray is perpendicular to the flow velocity the bending effect of the wind gradient vanishes (to the degree of approximation used here). Consequently the bending effects of wind and temperature will cooperate or oppose each other, depending on the direction of propagation. The effects will cancel each other when

$$\frac{dc}{dz}=-\frac{dv}{dz}\cos\gamma_c. \tag{32.13}$$

As a result of this refractive curvature, it is possible that so-called "zones of silence" or "shadow zones" will form. The most common of these is the one formed because of the obstruction produced by a boundary such as the ground or sea surface, as illustrated in Fig. 2. This figure corresponds to sound propagation in the atmosphere; we see that a shadow zone will be formed when the rays are bent upward. The limiting ray, denoted by L in the figure, is horizontal at the point where it touches the ground. In the case of a negative temperature gradient and a positive wind gradient such that $(dv/dz) < (-dc/dz)$ it follows that the shadow zone is limited to the region outside the down-wind sector defined by $\gamma < \gamma_c$, as given in (32.13).

When the atmosphere is stratified in the z direction, it can be shown that the trace velocity in the x direction is constant,

$$\frac{c + v\cos\gamma\cos\theta}{\cos\theta} = \frac{c}{\cos\theta} + v\cos\gamma = \text{const} = A \tag{32.14}$$

where θ is the elevation angle of the trajectory. For the limiting ray which defines the shadow zone, $\theta = 0$ when $z = 0$, so that the constant A is $c(0) = v\cos\gamma$. The horizontal distance along this ray from the source is x and the equation for trajectory can be written as $(dx/dz) = \cos\theta$. Using (32.14) to determine $\cos\theta$, if the source is a height h above the x, y plane, the horizontal distance between the source and a point on the shadow boundary a height z above the x, y plane is

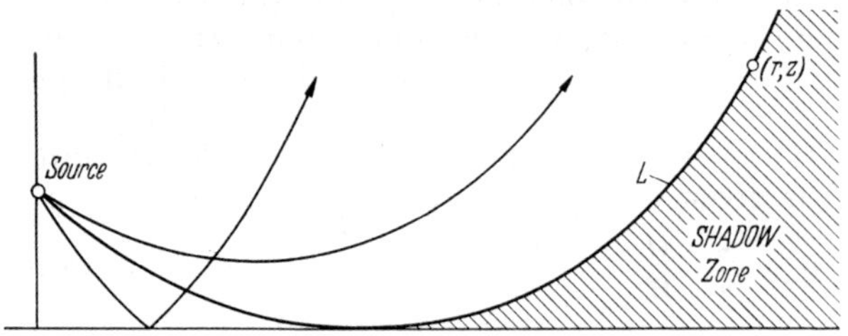

Fig. 2. Sound rays generated by a point source above a reflecting plane, in an inhomogeneous medium.

$$X = \int_0^h f(z)\,dz + \int_0^z f(z)\,dz, \qquad f(z) = \frac{c(z)}{\sqrt{(A - c\cos\gamma)^2 - c^2(z)}}. \tag{32.15}$$

The time of travel along the trajectory to the point on the shadow limit a distance z above the x, y plane is

$$t_0 = \int_0^h g(z)\,dz + \int_0^z g(z)\,dz, \qquad g(z) = \frac{(A - v\cos\gamma)^2}{cA\sqrt{(A - v\cos\gamma)^2 - c^2}}. \tag{32.16}$$

For the special case (which will be discussed again in the next section) where $v = 0$ but there is a temperature or salinity gradient such that the sound speed has the following dependence on z,

$$c(z) = \frac{c_0}{\sqrt{1 + \alpha z}} \tag{32.17}$$

the distance horizontally from the source (at height h) to the point on the shadow zone at height z is

$$X = 2\left(\sqrt{\frac{z}{\alpha}} + \sqrt{\frac{h}{\alpha}}\right) \tag{32.18}$$

and the time of travel to this point is

$$t_0 = \frac{1}{c_0}\left[2\left(\sqrt{\frac{z}{\alpha}} + \sqrt{\frac{h}{\alpha}}\right) + \frac{2}{3}\left(z^{\frac{3}{2}} + h^{\frac{3}{2}}\right)\right]. \tag{32.19}$$

These results will be referred to later.

33. Penetration into the shadow zone. Geometrical acoustics is adequate for the calculation of the acoustic field in the "illuminated" regions, when the inhomogeneities of the medium vary slowly in comparison to the wavelength. It clearly fails in the shadow zones, such as the one pictured in Fig. 2. To compute the field in these zones one must use wave acoustics [*6*], [*56*], [*57*]. The particular type of temperature- and wind-created shadow shown in Fig. 2 is of considerable interest in connection with sound propagation in the atmosphere and in the sea; we shall select this case for study here.

For simplicity we assume the fluid quiescent and consider the effect only of a vertical temperature (or salinity) gradient in the region $z > 0$, where the plane boundary at $z=0$ is specified acoustically by the impedance Z. The sound source will be a point monopole located at $x=y=0$, $z=h$, having frequency $(\omega/2\pi)$. The temperature, and therefore the speed of sound, is diminishing monotonically with z, slowly enough so that the fractional change $\Delta c/c$ in the distance of a wavelength is much less than unity. Under such conditions we can neglect the term $(\nabla p \cdot \nabla S_0)/c_p$ in the linear wave equation (4.13), so that the inhomogeneity is accounted for solely by the variation of c with z.

The wave equation is then

$$\left[\frac{1}{c(z)}\right]^2 \frac{\partial^2 p}{\partial t^2} - \nabla^2 p = \frac{\partial Q}{\partial t} \tag{33.1}$$

where Q is the source strength per unit volume. If the source is at the point $r=0$, $z=h$ in cylindrical coordinates and has unit strength and frequency $(\omega/2\pi)$ then the equation for p is

$$\nabla^2 p + \left[\frac{\omega}{c(z)}\right]^2 p = i\omega\,\delta(\boldsymbol{r} - \boldsymbol{a}_z h)\,\mathrm{e}^{-i\omega t} \tag{33.2}$$

and p will be $i\omega$ times the GREEN's function $G(\boldsymbol{r}|\boldsymbol{a}_z h)$.

The use of the Hankel transform is a fairly obvious procedure. We set

$$p = \int_0^\infty J_0(kr)\,F(k,z)\,k\,dk; \qquad F = \int_0^\infty J_0(kr)\,p\,r\,dr. \tag{33.3}$$

The equation for F is then

$$\left(\frac{d^2 F}{\partial z^2}\right) + \left\{\left[\frac{\omega}{c(z)}\right]^2 - k^2\right\} F = i\omega\,\delta(z-h) \tag{33.4}$$

which is to be solved subject to the boundary conditions that $-i\omega\varrho F = ZF'$ at $z=0$ (where Z is the surface impedance and where the prime indicates differentiation with respect to z), and that F is an outgoing wave at $z\to\infty$. To do this, we first solve the homogeneous equation, $y'' + [(\omega/c)^2 - k^2]\,y = 0$ for the two solutions, $U(z,k)$ which has up-going waves at $z\to\infty$, and $D(z,k)$ which has down-going waves at $z\to\infty$. The Wronskian of these two solutions, $W = DU' - UD'$, is independent of z.

The solution of Eq. (33.4) which satisfies these boundary conditions is

$$F(k,z) = \left\{\begin{array}{ll} \dfrac{U(z,k)}{W}\left[D(h,k) - \dfrac{D(0,k)+\gamma D'(0,k)}{U(0,k)+\gamma U'(0,k)}\,U(h,k)\right] & (0<z<h), \\[2ex] \dfrac{U(h,k)}{W}\left[D(z,k) - \dfrac{D(0,k)+\gamma D'(0,k)}{U(0,k)+\gamma U'(0,k)}\,U(z,k)\right] & (0<h<z) \end{array}\right\} \tag{33.5}$$

where $\gamma = (Z/i\omega\varrho)$ has the dimensions of length. For out-going waves at $z\to\infty$ the contour of integration is above the real axis of k for $k<0$, below the real axis for $k>0$. Because of the symmetry of the integrand of Eq. (33.3) we can extend the integral from $-\infty$ to $+\infty$ for k, and then evaluate the residues at the poles of the integrand. We separate J_0 into its outgoing and incoming waves,

$J_0(kr) = \frac{1}{2}[H_0^{(1)}(kr) + H_0^{(2)}(kr)]$ and complete the contour around the upper half k-plane for the $H_0^{(1)}$ term, about the lower half k-plane for $H_0^{(2)}$. Since the poles of the integrand are the zeros of the denominator of the second term in F, and since these zeros are in the first quadrant of the k-plane, only the outgoing $H_0^{(1)}$ terms survive, as was required.

For simplicity we shall consider the case of a rigid boundary plane, so that $\gamma = \infty$. In this case the integral becomes

$$p = -\pi\omega \sum_n k_n \frac{H_0^{(1)}(k_n r)\, U(h, k_n)\, U(z, k_n)}{U(0, k_n)\, K(k_n)} \tag{33.6}$$

where

$$K(k_n) = \left[\frac{\partial^2 U(z,k)}{\partial z\, \partial k}\right]_{z=0,\, k=k_n}$$

where the summation is over all the roots k_n of the equation $U'(0,k) = 0$ and where $W(k_n) = -D'(0, k_n)\, U(0, k_n)$. This is the formal solution for the radiation from a point source at $z = h$, $r = 0$, above a rigid, plane boundary at $z = 0$. This series is divergent close to the source but, as we shall see, it can be used as an asymptotic series to compute the field strength in the shadow zone.

Let us now return to the example of Eq. (32.17), of a medium at rest but having a sound speed $c(z) = c_0/\sqrt{1+\alpha z}$ which is maximum at $z = 0$ and diminishes as z increases, thus producing the conditions for a shadow zone. The equation for F then becomes

$$\left(\frac{d^2F}{dz^2}\right) + [k_0^2(1 + \alpha z) - k^2]\, F = 0 \tag{33.7}$$

where $k_0 = (\omega/c_0)$. The two solutions turn out to be

$$U = u^{\frac{1}{2}} H_{\frac{1}{3}}^{(1)}(\tfrac{2}{3} u^{\frac{3}{2}}); \qquad D = u^{\frac{1}{2}} H_{\frac{1}{3}}^{(2)}(\tfrac{2}{3} u^{\frac{3}{2}}) \tag{33.8}$$

where

$$u(k, z) = \frac{[k_0^2(1 + \alpha z) - k^2]}{(\alpha k_0^2)^{\frac{2}{3}}}$$

and the Wronskian is

$$W = \left(\frac{6}{i\pi}\right)(\alpha k_0^2)^{\frac{1}{3}}.$$

The roots k_n of Eq. (33.6) are obtained from the equation

$$H_{-\frac{2}{3}}^{(1)}[\tfrac{2}{3} u^{\frac{3}{2}}(k, 0)] = 0;$$

they are

$$\tfrac{2}{3} u^{\frac{3}{2}}(k, 0) = A_n\, e^{-i\pi},$$

where

$$A_1 = 0.685, \quad A_2 = 3.903, \ldots, A_n \approx (n - \tfrac{3}{4})\,\pi \quad (n \text{ large}). \tag{33.9}$$

This leads to the following equation for k_n^2,

$$k_n^2 = k_0^2 - (\tfrac{3}{2} A_n \alpha k_0^2)^{\frac{2}{3}}\, e^{-2\pi i/3}$$

and, since we have assumed that (α/k_0) is small, it leads to the following approximate equation for k_n,

$$k_n \approx k_0(1 - \delta_n); \qquad \delta_n = \frac{1}{2}\left(\frac{\frac{3}{2} A_n \alpha}{k_0}\right)^{\frac{2}{3}} e^{-2\pi i/3} \tag{33.10}$$

which lie in the first quadrant, as indicated earlier.

For large values of $k_0 r$ and k_0/α we can use the asymptotic expressions for H and U in Eq. (33.6)

$$\left.\begin{aligned} H_0(kr) &\approx \left(\frac{2}{\pi k r}\right)^{\frac{1}{2}} e^{i(kr-\frac{1}{4}\pi)},\\ U(z,k) &\approx \left(\frac{3}{\pi}\right)^{\frac{1}{2}} u^{-\frac{1}{4}} e^{i(\frac{2}{3}u^{\frac{3}{2}}-\frac{5}{12}\pi)},\\ \tfrac{2}{3}u^{\frac{3}{2}} &\approx \tfrac{2}{3}k_0\alpha^{\frac{1}{2}}z^{\frac{3}{2}}\left[1+3\left(\frac{\delta_n}{\alpha z}\right)\right]\end{aligned}\right\} \tag{33.11}$$

when $k_0 r$, $k_0 z$ and $(\alpha z/\delta_n)$ are large compared to unity. The series of Eq. (33.6) is then a series of exponentials, the n-th term having the exponential argument

$$\left.\begin{aligned} i\left\{(k_0-\delta_n)\,r+\tfrac{2}{3}\alpha^{\frac{1}{2}}k_0(z^{\frac{3}{2}}+h^{\frac{3}{2}})+2k_0\delta_n\left(\sqrt{\frac{z}{\alpha}}+\sqrt{\frac{h}{\alpha}}\right)\right\}\\ =i\left\{k_0[r-(r-r_0)\,\delta_n]+\tfrac{2}{3}\alpha^{\frac{1}{2}}(z^{\frac{3}{2}}+h^{\frac{3}{2}})\right\}\end{aligned}\right\} \tag{33.12}$$

where

$$r_0=2\left(\sqrt{\frac{z}{\alpha}}+\sqrt{\frac{h}{\alpha}}\right).$$

Since $-\delta_n$ is complex, with a positive imaginary part, this result shows that beyond the horizontal distance $r=r_0$ from the source (at height z, for a source at height h), all the asymptotic terms in (33.6) begin to diminish exponentially For $r<r_0$ the series is not convergent; for $r>r_0$ it is rapidly convergent. Reference to Eq. (32.18) shows that this limit of convergence is just the boundary of the shadow zone. In fact, using Eq. (32.19), we can write the asymptotic form of (33.6) as

$$p\approx\sum_n C_n\left(\frac{1}{\sqrt{r}}\right)\exp\left\{i\,\omega\left[\frac{1-\delta_n}{c_0}(r-r_0)-(t-t_0)\right]\right\} \tag{33.13}$$

with

$$\delta_n\approx\frac{1}{2}\left(\frac{\frac{3}{2}A_n\alpha}{k_0}\right)^{\frac{2}{3}}e^{-2\pi i/3}$$

where, according to the earlier discussion, t_0 is the travel time from the source to the shadow boundary at (z, r_0).

At a sufficient distance inside the shadow zone the field can be represented by the first term in the series alone;

$$p\approx\frac{C_1}{\sqrt{r}}\exp\left\{i\omega\left[\frac{r-r_0}{c_0}(1-0.255\,\alpha^{\frac{2}{3}}k_0^{-\frac{2}{3}})-(t-t_0)\right]-0.441\,\alpha^{\frac{2}{3}}k_0^{\frac{1}{3}}(r-r_0)\right\}. \tag{33.14}$$

Thus, in the shadow region, the sound pressure field decays exponentially with the horizontal distance from the shadow boundary. The decay constant is proportional to the two-thirds power of the characteristic velocity gradient α and to the one-third power of the frequency.

Returning to Eq. (33.13) we see that the time of travel of the n-th mode from the source to the point of observation (r, z) in the shadow zone is $t_0+[(r-r_0)/c_0](1-\mathrm{Re}\,\delta_n)$. If one were to interprete this time in terms of a ray picture the result shows that the sound entering the shadow zone travels (1) along the downward leg of the limiting ray, (2) penetrates the shadow a distance $(r-r_0)$ along the ground (where c is maximum) and (3) travels along a path parallel to the shadow boundary from the ground up to the point (r, z). Paths (1) and (3) together make up time t_0 and path (2) corresponds to time $(r-r_0)/c_0$ $(\delta_n\ll 1)$. This path, being the shortest path from source to (r, z) in regard to time of travel, satisfies FERMAT's principle.

34. Small-scale inhomogeneities, geometric approximation [8], [27], [39], [71]. In the discussion of the previous section it was assumed tacitly that the variations of the index of refraction were not only "smooth" (small in a distance of a wavelength) but also correlated in space and time over a large region. Under such conditions the waves scattered from the various points of the medium are coherent and the effect of the inhomogeneity is best described as a refraction of the sound wave.

In a turbulent fluid the medium is broken up into a large number of smooth regions, inside which the changes of index are correlated but where the correlation from region to region is very small. The waves scattered from separate regions will thus be uncorrelated and their superposition results in an irregular wave field. In addition to this random spatial field, the motion and interaction of the turbulence causes a random variation in time of the field at a fixed point.

Under such circumstances the description of the field cannot be as detailed as it could for the cases previously discussed; it cannot be given in terms of a known function of space and time. Even the specification of the index of refraction n has to be limited to certain statistical properties of n. The most commonly used property is the two-point correlation function

$$K(r', t' | r'', t'') = \langle n(r', t')\, n(r'', t'')\rangle \tag{34.1}$$

where $\langle\ldots\rangle$ signifies the time average. In the case of homogeneous and isotropic turbulence this correlation function depends only on the separations $\xi = r' - r''$ and $\tau = t' - t''$. Under such conditions the correlation function often can be approximated by

$$K(\xi, \tau) \approx n_0^2 \exp\left[-\left(\frac{\xi}{L}\right)^2 - \left(\frac{\tau}{T}\right)^2\right] \tag{34.2}$$

where L is a measure of the size of an individual inhomogeneity and T the mean life-time of the inhomogeneity at some point in space.

Since the properties of the medium cannot be specified with any better accuracy than this, it is clear that we cannot expect to calculate the exact behavior of the sound wave, as in the previous sections, but must limit our demands to the determination of certain statistical properties of the field, which can be obtained from the correlation function. We can distinguish between several different effects of weak random inhomogeneities, such as phase and amplitude fluctuations, energy scattering and corresponding attenuation of the propagated wave, and the frequency broadening of a single-frequency sound wave. The relative importance of these effects depends on the geometry of the field and, of course, on the nature of the particular application which is under study. For example, in the case of propagation of a plane or spherical wave in a large, inhomogeneous region, the attenuation produced is often insignificant, the phase and amplitude fluctuations are instead of major interest. On the other hand, when the sound field consists of a sharply collimated beam, the scatter attenuation is of considerable interest.

First let us use the geometrical approximation to study the behavior of an initially plane wave which inters a large, randomly inhomogeneous region. This approximation will neglect the diffraction effects; they will be studied in the next section. Let the region $x > 0$ be inhomogeneous, with an index of refraction $n = |\text{grad}\, \Phi| = 1 + \mu$ [see Eq. (32.3)] which deviates only slightly from unity, so that $n^2 \approx 1 + 2\mu$. The region $x < 0$ is homogeneous, with index of refraction unity. A plane wave, travelling in the positive x direction enters the inhomogeneous region at $x = 0$; we wish to determine the correlation between the phases and amplitudes at two different points in the inhomogeneous region; in particular, we wish to compute the r.m.s. value of the phase and amplitude fluctuations as functions of the depth of penetration of the wave.

We start with the geometrical approximation discussed in Sect. 32 and express the phase and amplitude of the wave as

$$k_0\,\Phi = k_0(\Phi_0 + \varphi); \qquad A = A_0 + a \tag{34.3}$$

where $\Phi_0 = x$ and $A_0 = \text{const}$ are the unperturbed values and φ and a the perturbations produced by the inhomogeneity. Considering only a first-order perturbation, keeping only the terms in φ and a, we have $|\operatorname{grad}\Phi|^2 \approx 1 + 2(\partial\varphi/\partial x)$ and Eq. (32.8) reduces to

$$\varphi(x, t) \approx \int_0^x \mu(x, t)\, dx. \tag{34.4}$$

Thus the average value of φ is zero. The r.m.s. value of the phase fluctuation at the point x is then

$$\langle\varphi^2\rangle = \left\langle\left(\int_0^x \mu\, dx\right)^2\right\rangle = \int_0^x\int_0^x \langle\mu_1\mu_2\rangle\, dx_1\, dx_2 = \int_0^x\int_0^x K\, dx_1\, dx_2. \tag{34.5}$$

If we assume that the correlation function $K = \langle\mu_1\mu_2\rangle$ depends on the difference $\xi = |x_1 - x_2|$ only, we can replace the double integral by the single integral

$$\langle\varphi^2\rangle = 2\int_0^x (x - \xi)\, K(\xi)\, d\xi. \tag{34.6}$$

Using the expression (34.2) for K and considering $x \gg a$, we find

$$\langle(k_0\,\varphi)^2\rangle \approx \sqrt{\pi}\,(k_0 L)\,(k_0\,x)\,\langle\mu^2\rangle. \tag{34.7}$$

In other words the r.m.s. value of the phase fluctuation increases with the square root of x, the distance traversed in the inhomogeneous region.

In complete analogy we obtain from Eq. (32.9) the mean variance of the amplitude

$$\left\langle\left(\ln\frac{A}{A_0}\right)^2\right\rangle \approx \left\langle\frac{a^2}{A_0^2}\right\rangle = \frac{1}{4}\int_0^x\int_0^x \langle\nabla^2\varphi_1\nabla^2\varphi_2\rangle\, dx_1\, dx_2.$$

Without going into detailed calculations, we see that $\nabla^2\varphi_1 \sim (\partial\mu/\partial x_1)$ and that, with $x_1 > x_2$

$$\left\langle\left(\frac{\partial\mu}{\partial x_1}\right)\left(\frac{\partial\mu}{\partial x_2}\right)\right\rangle \sim \frac{\partial^2\left(e^{-(x_1-x_2)^2/L^2}\right)}{\partial(x_1 - x_2)^2} \sim \frac{(x_1 - x_2)^2}{L^4}.$$

Therefore

$$\int_0^x dx_1 \int_0^{x_1} \langle\ldots\rangle\, dx_2 \sim \left(\frac{x^3}{L^3}\right)$$

and with a similar expression for $\int_0^x dx_1 \int_{x_1}^x \langle\ldots\rangle\, dx_2$, we find

$$\left\langle\left(\frac{a}{A_0}\right)^2\right\rangle \sim \left(\frac{x}{L}\right)^3 \langle\mu^2\rangle. \tag{34.8}$$

In other words, according to the geometric approximation, the r.m.s. value of the amplitude fluctuation of the wave increases as the three-halves power of x, independent of the wavelength.

In the foregoing analysis the effects of lateral scattering or diffraction are clearly not accounted for. However, an approximate evaluation of these effects can be obtained, by a method which might be called the method of lateral diffusion [53]; a method of use in other propagation problems. The general equation $\nabla^2 p = k_0^2(1+\mu)^2 p$, when expressed in terms of the complex phase function Ψ, becomes

$$(\operatorname{grad}\Psi)^2 - i\,\nabla^2\Psi = k_0^2(1+\mu)^2$$

and the corresponding first-order equation for the perturbation $\psi = \Psi - \Psi_0$ is

$$2k_0\left(\frac{\partial\psi}{\partial x}\right) - i\,\nabla^2\psi = 2\mu\,k_0^2,$$

since

$$\nabla\psi\cdot\nabla\Psi_0 = k_0\left(\frac{\partial\psi}{\partial x}\right).$$

If we neglect $(\partial^2\psi/\partial x^2)$ in comparison to $k_0\,(\partial\psi/\partial x)$, which is possible when the fractional change of $(\partial\psi/\partial x)$ in a wave-length is small, we obtain the equation

$$2k_0\frac{\partial\psi}{\partial x} - i\left(\frac{\partial^2\psi}{\partial y^2} + \frac{\partial^2\psi}{\partial z^2}\right) = 2\mu\,k_0^2 \tag{34.9}$$

which has the solution

$$\psi = -\frac{i k_0^2}{2\pi}\int_0^x\iint_{-\infty}^{+\infty}\exp\left[\frac{i\varrho^2 k_0}{2(x-\xi)}\right]\mu(\xi,\eta,\zeta)\,\frac{d\xi\,d\eta\,d\zeta}{(x-\xi)} \tag{34.10}$$

where

$$\varrho^2 = (y-\eta)^2 + (z-\zeta)^2.$$

The real and imaginary parts of ψ are the perturbations of the phase and the amplitude, respectively,

$$(k_0\,\varphi) \approx k_0\int_0^x\iint_{-\infty}^{\infty} S(x-\xi,\varrho)\,\mu(\xi,\eta,\zeta)\,d\xi\,d\eta\,d\zeta, \tag{34.11}$$

$$\left(\frac{a}{A_0}\right) \approx k_0\int_0^x\iint_{-\infty}^{\infty} C(x-\xi,\varrho)\,\mu(\xi,\eta,\zeta)\,d\xi\,d\eta\,d\zeta \tag{34.12}$$

where

$$\begin{matrix}S\\C\end{matrix}(x-\xi,\varrho) = \frac{k_0}{2\pi(x-\xi)}\begin{matrix}\sin\\\cos\end{matrix}\left(\frac{k_0\varrho^2}{x-\xi}\right). \tag{34.13}$$

Let us now determine the r.m.s. values of φ and a at a location $(x, 0, 0)$, by forming the variances $\langle\varphi^2\rangle$ and $\langle a^2\rangle$. For $\langle\varphi^2\rangle$ we get

$$\langle k_0^2\varphi^2\rangle \approx k_0^2\iint d\xi_1\,d\xi_2\iiiint S(x-\xi_1,\varrho_1)\,S(x-\xi_2,\varrho_2)\,K\,d\eta_1\,d\eta_2\,d\zeta_1\,d\zeta_2$$

where, as before, $K = \langle\mu_1\,\mu_2\rangle$. We evaluate this integral as follows. Change the variables to $\eta_- = \eta_1 - \eta_2$, $\eta_+ = \frac{1}{2}(\eta_1+\eta_2)$, etc., and replace the product of sines by a sum. We can then integrate over the variables η_+ and ζ_+ and, after some algebra, find

$$\left.\begin{aligned}
&\langle k_0^2\varphi^2\rangle \approx \tfrac{1}{2}(I_1+I_2);\\
&I_1 = k_0^2\iint_{-\infty}^{+\infty} d\eta_-\,d\zeta_-\iint_x^0 S(\xi_1-\xi_2,\varrho)\,d\xi_1\,d\xi_2;\\
&I_2 = k_0^2\iint_{-\infty}^{\infty} d\eta_-\,d\zeta_-\iint_0^x S(2x-\xi_1-\xi_2,\varrho)\,d\xi_1\,d\xi_2.
\end{aligned}\right\} \tag{34.14}$$

Then, using Eq. (34.2) we finally obtain the following expression for the variance of the phase [8]

$$\langle k_0^2 \varphi^2 \rangle \approx (2\pi)^2 \sqrt{\pi} \left(\frac{xL}{2}\right) \left(1 + \frac{1}{D} \arc\tan D\right) \langle \mu^2 \rangle \tag{34.15}$$

where we have assumed that $x \gg L$ and that $k_0 L \gg 1$ and where $D = (4/k_0 L)(x/L)$. In the same way we can show that the variance of the amplitude at $(x, 0, 0)$ is

$$\left\langle \left(\frac{a}{A_0}\right)^2 \right\rangle \approx \tfrac{1}{2}(I_1 - I_2)$$

where I_1 and I_2 are given in (34.14). In the high-frequency limit $D \to 0$ and the expression for the phase variance reduces to the value given by Eq. (34.7), obtained from geometrical acoustics (as, of course, it should). The amplitude variance, in the short-wave limit, becomes

$$\left\langle \left(\frac{a}{A_0}\right)^2 \right\rangle \to \tfrac{8}{3} \sqrt{\pi} \left(\frac{x}{L}\right)^3 \langle \mu^2 \rangle \tag{34.16}$$

which provides the missing factor, which was not worked out in Eq. (34.8).

However, the lateral diffusion analysis was not presented just to check the values obtained by the purely geometrical analysis, but to extend these results. It is clear that the lateral scattering is insignificant as long as D in Eq. (34.15) is small, i.e., when $(x/L) \ll (k_0 L/4)$; in this case the wave has not penetrated deep enough for the lateral scattering to have an appreciable effect on the fluctuations in phase and amplitude. In these regions, we have seen that the r.m.s. value of the fluctuation in wave amplitude is independent of frequency and proportional to the three-halves power of the distance of penetration. As the wave penetrates more deeply, however, the amplitude fluctuation becomes frequency dependent and, at very deep penetration, when $D \gg 1$, the amplitude variance becomes

$$\left\langle \left(\frac{a}{A_0}\right)^2 \right\rangle \approx \tfrac{1}{2} \sqrt{\pi}\, (k_0 L)\, (k_0 x) \langle \mu^2 \rangle, \tag{34.17}$$

a result which could not be obtained from the purely geometric analysis. In this region the r.m.s. amplitude fluctuations are proportional to the frequency and to the one-half power of x. Thus, as x is increased from zero, the r.m.s. amplitude fluctuation changes from the $\frac{3}{2}$ power dependence on depth of penetration x to a $\frac{1}{2}$ power law, at a distance approximately given by

$$x_c \approx \frac{4L\lambda}{\sqrt{2\pi}} \approx \sqrt{L\lambda}. \tag{34.18}$$

The r.m.s. value of the phase fluctuations, on the other hand, does not change significantly as x increases; for very large x it has the same value as given in (34.17) for a, which is larger than that given for the shallower penetration by the factor $\sqrt{2}$.

In the analysis we have considered only the variances at a given point. It is clear that the results can be extended to include the correlations between amplitudes and phases at two different points. We need only replace ζ by $\zeta + z_b$ in the formulae for I_1 and I_2 of Eqs. (34.14).

35. The Born approximation [30], [46], [51]. In the foregoing section the effect of random inhomogeneities was investigated for sound waves with a wavelength λ considerably smaller than the scale L of the inhomogeneities. In the geometric limit we found that the effect on the amplitude and phase was influenced only by the properties of the medium along the path of the ray leading to the point of observation, implying that the scattering produced by the inhomogeneities is entirely in the forward direction. By including some of the diffraction-producing terms, this approximation could be improved to account for lateral scattering, and we found that the geometrical analysis is clearly invalid for depths of penetration greater than a critical distance of the order of $\sqrt{L\lambda}$. However this improved analysis still assumes that $(\lambda/L) \gg 1$; to obtain results which are less restricted in regard to frequency we must use wave acoustics.

As an illustration of the wave techniques we shall discuss the scattering of a plane wave penetrating a region of isotropic turbulence. The basis of the analysis is the Born approximation, first discussed in Sect. 16, a valid approximation if the inhomogeneities are "weak". Furthermore we shall neglect multiple scattering, which neglect is allowable if the inhomogeneous region is sufficiently small. An adequate treatment of multiple scattering would lead us too deeply into the intricacies of radiative diffusion (see [*49*]) to be appropriate for this article.

Suppose the turbulent region occupies a volume V which is considerably larger than the characteristic scale L of the inhomogeneities. A plane sound wave $p = p_0 \, e^{i\boldsymbol{k}_0 \cdot \boldsymbol{r} - i\omega t}$ is scattered by this turbulent region; we wish to determine the angular dependence of the scattered intensity and the total power scattered. Furthermore it is of interest to determine the frequency spectrum of the scattered sound, as influenced by the random Doppler shifts produced by the turbulence.

Basically, the scattering is produced as a result of the influence of the acoustical particle velocity upon the local pressure fluctuations in the turbulent region. These pressure fluctuations are of the form ϱv^2 and when the acoustic fluid velocity u is superimposed, there will result a linear pressure component of the form $2\varrho u v$, producing the scattered field. As indicated by the general wave equation (2.1), the source term for this coupling is actually $(\partial^2 t_{ij}/\partial x_i \partial x_j)$ where

$$t_{ij} = \varrho (u_i v_j + v_i u_j) . \tag{35.1}$$

The turbulent motion will also produce local fluctuations in the speed of sound because of temperature fluctuations. But these thermal effects turn out to be small compared to those produced by t_{ij}, so they will be neglected here.

We denote the point of integration in the source region by the vector $\boldsymbol{r}_0$, as before, and the observation point (outside the source region) by $\boldsymbol{r}$. Then, for the far field, where $|\boldsymbol{r}_0| \ll |\boldsymbol{r}$, we can replace

$$\left[\frac{\partial^2 t_{ij}}{\partial x_{0i} \partial x_{0j}}\right] \text{ by } \frac{x_i x_j}{c^2 r^2} \frac{\partial^2 [t_{ij}]}{\partial t^2} .$$

where the quantities in brackets are retarded values. Then the expression for the scattered field becomes

$$p_s(\boldsymbol{r}, t) \approx \frac{\varrho}{4\pi c^2} \sum_{i,j} \frac{x_i x_j}{r^3} \frac{\partial}{\partial t^2} \iiint t_{ij} \left(r_0, \, t - \frac{|\boldsymbol{r} - \boldsymbol{r}_0|}{c}\right) d v_0 . \tag{35.2}$$

If the incident wave is a plane wave in the x direction, then

$$u_i = U_0 \, \delta_{i1} \, e^{i(\boldsymbol{k}_0 \cdot \boldsymbol{r} - \omega t)} \tag{35.3}$$

where the propagation vector $\boldsymbol{k}_0$ has magnitude (ω/c) and is directed along x. If we assume that the characteristic frequencies of fluctuation in the turbulent flow are all considerably smaller than ω, we can set $(\partial^2/\partial t^2) = -\omega^2$ in (35.2) and thus obtain

$$p_s(\boldsymbol{r}, t) \approx -\frac{\varrho U_0 \omega^2}{2\pi c^2} \sum_i \frac{x_i x_1}{r^3} \iiint v_i \, e^{i(\boldsymbol{k}_0 \cdot \boldsymbol{r}_0 - \omega t)} \, d v_0 . \tag{35.4}$$

It should be noted that the scattered pressure in the i-th direction depends on the turbulent velocity component in this direction.

The corresponding pressure auto-correlation function for the scattered wave,

$$\Psi(\tau) = \tfrac{1}{2}\,\mathrm{Re}\langle p_s(\boldsymbol{r}, t)\, p_s(\boldsymbol{r}, t-\tau)\rangle\,,$$

then becomes

$$\Psi(\tau) \approx \varrho^2 U_0^2 \left(\frac{k_0^2}{2\pi}\right)^2 \sum_{ij} \frac{x_1^2 x_i x_j}{2r^6}\, \mathrm{Re}\left\{\iint K_{ij}\, e^{i(\boldsymbol{k}_0-\boldsymbol{k}_1)\cdot(\boldsymbol{r}_0-\boldsymbol{r}_1) - i\omega\tau}\, d v_0\, d v_1\right\} \tag{35.5}$$

where

$$K_{ij} = \langle v_i(\boldsymbol{r}_0, t)\, v_j(\boldsymbol{r}_1, t_1)\rangle\,,$$

$$t_1 = t_0 - \tau - \frac{1}{c}\left\{|\boldsymbol{r}-\boldsymbol{r}_0| - |\boldsymbol{r}-\boldsymbol{r}_1|\right\} \approx t_0 - \tau - \left(\frac{\boldsymbol{R}\cdot\boldsymbol{r}}{c r}\right)$$

and

$$\boldsymbol{R} = \boldsymbol{r}_0 - \boldsymbol{r}_1\,.$$

The symbols $\langle\ldots\rangle$ stand for the time average, as before; $\boldsymbol{k}_0$ and $\boldsymbol{k}_1$ are the propagation vectors in the incident and scattered directions respectively. The recoil vector $\boldsymbol{\mu} = \boldsymbol{k}_0 - \boldsymbol{k}_1$ [see Eq. (16.2)] has magnitude $2k_0 \sin(\theta/2)$, where θ is the scattering angle between vector $\boldsymbol{r}$, to the observation point, and the x axis, the direction of incidence.

The total scattered intensity is proportional to $\Psi(0)$. On account of the turbulent motion there will be Doppler shifts, so that the scattered sound is not strictly single-frequency but has a small band width, proportional to the characteristic Mach number of the turbulent motion. This spectrum of the scattered sound can be obtained from the Fourier transform of the correlation function [*14*].

For homogeneous and isotropic turbulence the correlation function K will be a function of $\boldsymbol{R} = \boldsymbol{r}_0 - \boldsymbol{r}_1$ and of $t_1 - t_0$ only. It will go rapidly to zero when $|\boldsymbol{R}|$ is larger than the characteristic eddy size L and when $|t_1 - t_0|$ is larger than the "relaxation time" T of an eddy. Since only values of R less than L will be of importance in (35.5), the term $(\boldsymbol{R}\cdot\boldsymbol{r})/c r$ will be smaller than L/c, i.e., less than the time of travel of sound across an eddy. Since we have already assumed that T is much larger than this travel time, we may neglect $(\boldsymbol{R}\cdot\boldsymbol{r})/c r$ in (35.5); the result for the scattered intensity is then

$$\left.\begin{aligned} I_s &= \frac{1}{\varrho c}\langle p^2\rangle = \frac{1}{\varrho c}\Psi(0) \\ &\approx \varrho c\, U_0^2\left(\frac{k_0^2}{2\pi c}\right)^2 V \sum_{ij}\frac{x_1^2 x_i x_j}{r^6}\,\mathrm{Re}\left\{\iiint K_{ij}(R)\, e^{i(\boldsymbol{k}_0-\boldsymbol{k}_1)\cdot\boldsymbol{R}}\, d v_R\right\} \end{aligned}\right\} \tag{35.6}$$

where V is the volume occupied by the turbulent region.

Consequently, if we introduce the Fourier transform of the velocity correlation function

$$\Phi_{ij}(\boldsymbol{K}) = \frac{1}{(2\pi)^3}\iiint K_{ij}(R)\, e^{i\boldsymbol{K}.\boldsymbol{R}}\, d v_R \tag{35.7}$$

the scattered intensity per unit volume of turbulence can be expressed as

$$\frac{I_s}{V} \approx I_0 \frac{2\pi}{c^2} k_0^4 \sum_{ij} \frac{x_1^2 x_i x_j}{r^6}\, \Phi_{ij}(\boldsymbol{k}_0 - \boldsymbol{k}_1) \tag{35.8}$$

where $I_0 = (\varrho c\, U_0^2/2)$ is the incident intensity. As mentioned earlier, the scattered intensity depends only on the turbulent velocity components in the direction of the observer.

In the theory of turbulence it is shown that the spectrum function $\Phi_{ij}(\boldsymbol{K})$ can be expressed in terms of the kinetic energy spectrum $E(K)$ of turbulence as follows:

$$\Phi_{ij}(\boldsymbol{K}) = \frac{E(K)}{4\pi K^2}\left[\delta_{ij} - \frac{K_i K_j}{K^2}\right] \tag{35.9}$$

for isotropic turbulence. Inserting this into Eq. (35.8) we find

$$\frac{I_s}{V} \approx I_0 \frac{k_0^2}{8c^2 r^2} \cos^2\theta \cot^2(\tfrac{1}{2}\theta)\, E(2k_0 \sin\tfrac{1}{2}\theta)\,. \tag{35.10}$$

The function $E(K)$ represents the analysis of the turbulent kinetic energy into wave number bands. It has its maximum value for K about equal to $(2\pi/L)$, where L is the turbulent cell dimension, dropping in value for K larger or smaller than this. By definition the integral

$$\int_0^\infty E(K)\, dK = \tfrac{1}{2}\langle v^2\rangle \tag{35.11}$$

is the mean kinetic energy per unit mass of the fluid

Because of the $\cot^2(\frac{1}{2}\theta)$ term in (35.10) most of the scattered intensity is in the forward direction; because of the peak in the function E an appreciable amount of scattering occurs at an angle such that $u = 2k_0 \sin(\frac{1}{2}\theta)$ is about equal to $(2\pi/L)$. The total power scattered, per unit volume of turbulent fluid per unit incident intensity, is

$$Q = \frac{\pi k_0^2}{c^2}\int_0^{2k_0} E(u)\left[1 - \frac{1}{2}\left(\frac{u}{k_0}\right)^2\right]^2\left[1 - \frac{1}{4}\left(\frac{u}{k_0}\right)^2\right]\frac{du}{u}\,. \tag{35.12}$$

If the incident wave has sufficiently high frequency, so that $k_0 \gg 2\pi/L$, this becomes approximately

$$Q \approx \frac{\pi k_0^2}{c^2}\int_0^\infty E(u)\,\frac{du}{u} \approx \frac{\pi L k_0^2}{c^2}\langle v^2\rangle. \tag{35.13}$$

In other words the scattering cross section per unit volume of turbulent fluid for high-frequency sound is proportional to the square of the frequency and to the variance of the turbulent velocity. The attenuation of the incident beam is therefore $I = I_0\, e^{-\alpha x}$, where the attenuation constant α is, approximately

$$\alpha \approx \frac{2}{\pi} k^2 L \langle M^2\rangle \tag{35.14}$$

where

$$\langle M^2\rangle = \frac{1}{c^2}\langle v^2\rangle$$

is the Mach number variance.

In the high-frequency limit, as we have seen, almost all the scattering is in the forward direction. The energy, therefore, is not removed from the initial direction of propagation (except by multiple scattering), but is converted from coherent to incoherent wave motion, which modifies the primary wave by producing fluctuations in its amplitude. The variance of the amplitude fluctuations will increase with distance x of penetration and, from (35.14) will be proportional to $kx \cdot kL\langle M^2\rangle$, which is to be compared with Eq. (34.17), obtained from geometrical analysis.

A calculation of the actual attenuation of the wave would lead us too deeply into solutions of the integral equations of radiative diffusion. A rough estimate can be obtained, however, by noting that the intensity scattered in the backward direction corresponds to values of u in the integrand of (35.12) between $\sqrt{2}k_0$ and $2k_0$; only eddies with size of the order of a wavelength contribute to the back scattering. In the so-called inertial sub-range of isotropic turbulence we have $E(K)\sim K^{-\frac{5}{3}}$. Thus, from Eq. (35.13), the total amount of back scattering, and therefore the attenuation constant, must be proportional to $k_0^{\frac{1}{3}}$. This dependence has been observed in experimental studies of scatter attenuation in the atmosphere.

36. Sound generation by turbulent flow. Sound can be said to be produced by local pressure fluctuations in the medium. In a fluid at rest these fluctuations are usually produced by action of the boundaries, less often by heat sources. However when the fluid is in motion, local pressure fluctuations can be generated in the main body of the fluid, without boundary motion [*31*], [*37*], [*50*], [*59*]. For example the fluid pressure at a stagnation point at a fixed boundary will fluctuate and produce sound when the flow speed varies with time. Similarly, in a turbulent fluid the collisions of the eddies in the flow produce pressure fluctuations in the main body of the fluid, away from boundaries. These local pressure fluctuations can be regarded as an acoustic near field, analogous to the field near an oscillating source boundary, in terms of which the acoustic far field can be expressed.

The pressure fluctuations in a moving, incompressible fluid are related to the fluid flow velocity components v_i by the equation

$$\nabla^2 P_0 = -\sum_{ij} \frac{\partial^2 \varrho\, v_i v_j}{\partial x_i\, \partial x_j} \tag{36.1}$$

Consequently if we neglect the additional increments contributed by the acoustic velocities, the source term $\sum_{ij} (\partial^2 \varrho v_i v_j/\partial x_i \partial x_j)$ in the general wave equation (2.1) can be approximated by the term $\nabla^2 P_0$. The acoustic radiation field from the fluctuating pressure region, in the absence of boundaries, is then

$$p(\boldsymbol{r}, t) = -\frac{1}{4\pi} \iiint \frac{[\nabla_0^2 P_0]}{|\boldsymbol{r}-\boldsymbol{r}_0|}\, d v_0 \tag{36.2}$$

where the quantity in brackets is evaluated at time $t_r = t - |\boldsymbol{r}-\boldsymbol{r}_0|/c$, as before. The point of observation is at $\boldsymbol{r}$ and the source point is at $\boldsymbol{r}_0$, with the corresponding volume element $d v_0$. Outside the finite source region the fluid is assumed to be at rest and in this outer region the only fluctuating pressures are those produced by the pressure fluctuations in the source region. Neglecting terms involving the factor $(1/r)$, we can replace $[\nabla_0^2 P_0]$ by

$$\nabla^2 P_0(r_0, t_r) \approx -\frac{1}{c^2} \frac{\partial^2 P_0(r_0, t_r)}{\partial t^2}.$$

In the far field, Eq. (36.2) then becomes

$$p(\boldsymbol{r}, t) \approx \frac{1}{4\pi r c^2} \frac{\partial^2}{\partial t^2} \left\{ \iiint P_0(\boldsymbol{r}_0, t)\, d v_0 \right\}. \tag{36.3}$$

If P_0 were regular and could be written down as a regular function of r and t the discussion could stop here; examples of solution have been discussed in earlier sections. But the pressure is here a stochastic function, which cannot be expressed in terms of simple functions. As we have indicated in the last two sub-sections, we can most easily express its statistical properties in terms of its auto-correlation function. In this case the function of interest is the time correlation function

$$\Psi(\tau) = \langle p(\boldsymbol{r}, t)\, p(\boldsymbol{r}, t-\tau)\rangle \tag{36.4}$$

where, as before, the symbols $\langle\ldots\rangle$ indicate the time average. The acoustic intensity at a given point is then $\Psi(0)/\varrho c$ and the total acoustic power flowing across a surface is the surface integral of this. The intensity spectrum, $E(\omega)$, is related to the Fourier transform of Ψ,

$$E(\omega) = \frac{1}{2\pi\varrho c}\int_{-\infty}^{\infty}\Psi(\tau)\, e^{i\omega\tau}\, d\tau; \qquad I = \frac{\Psi(0)}{\varrho c} = \int_{-\infty}^{\infty} E(\omega)\, d\omega. \tag{36.5}$$

It follows from Eq. (36.3) that this auto-correlation function is related to the space-time correlation of the local pressure fluctuations in the source region by the equation

$$\Psi(\tau) = \left(\frac{1}{4\pi r c^2}\right)^2 \iint K(\boldsymbol{r}_0, t_{r0}; \boldsymbol{r}_1, t_{r1})\, dv_0\, dv_1 \tag{36.6}$$

where the space-time correlation function is

$$K(\boldsymbol{r}_0, t_{r0}; \boldsymbol{r}_1, t_{r1}) = \left\langle\left[\frac{\partial^2 P_0(\boldsymbol{r}_0, t_{r0})}{\partial t^2}\right]\left[\frac{\partial^2 P_0(\boldsymbol{r}_1, t_{r1})}{\partial t^2}\right]\right\rangle$$

and

$$t_{r0} = t - \frac{|\boldsymbol{r}-\boldsymbol{r}_0|}{c}; \qquad t_{r1} = t - \tau - \frac{|\boldsymbol{r}-\boldsymbol{r}_1|}{c}.$$

A calculation of the function $\Psi(\tau)$ and the related acoustic power and its spectrum requires knowledge of the correlation function K. However, even if we do not know in detail the dependence of K on $|\boldsymbol{r}_0-\boldsymbol{r}_1|$ and on τ, dimensional considerations enable us to determine the dependence of the radiated acoustic power on the fluid velocities in the source region. The fluctuating portion of the fluid pressure is proportional to the square of the velocity fluctuations. If L is the characteristic eddy size in the source region and U the characteristic oscillating flow velocity, then the characteristic time of oscillation of the fluid is L/U. Thus each application of the operator $(\partial/\partial t)$ would bring in a factor proportional to (U/L) and, as indicated earlier, since P_0 must be proportional to ϱU^2, K must equal a dimensionless constant times $(\varrho^2 U^8/L^4)$ and the total acoustic power radiated must be

$$\left.\begin{aligned} W &\approx \frac{4\pi r^2}{\varrho c}\Psi(0) = \frac{L^2\varrho^2 U^8}{4\pi\varrho c^5}\iint\left(\frac{K}{\varrho^2 U^8 L^2}\right)_{\tau=0} dv_0\, dv_1 \\ &\approx (\text{const})\, M^5\,\frac{\varrho U^3 L^2}{2}, \quad \text{where} \quad M = \frac{U}{c} \end{aligned}\right\} \tag{36.7}$$

in which the integral is a dimensionless constant which depends on the geometry and the time dependence of the flow in the source region. We thus find that the acoustic power output is proportional to the eighth power of the characteristic flow velocity in the source region [*31*]. If we divide by ϱL^3 we obtain the mean acoustic power generated per unit mass of fluid in the source region,

$$w = \frac{W}{\varrho L^3} \approx (\text{const})\,\frac{M^5 U^3}{2L}. \tag{36.8}$$

In the case of a statistically stationary oscillation of the fluid some constant power is applied from outside the system, which power is dissipated by viscosity and other loss mechanisms and by acoustic radiation. The power first goes into the kinetic energy of eddies of the order of size L of the driving mechanism. If the power transfer per unit mass of the fluid is denoted by ε the velocity fluctuation in these large eddies is expected to be of the order of $U \approx (\varepsilon L)^{\frac{1}{3}}$. Consequently the acoustic power radiated from unit mass of fluid in the source region is

$$w \approx (\text{const})\, M^5\, \varepsilon \tag{36.9}$$

which shows that the efficiency of conversion of fluid flow energy into sound via turbulent fluctuations is proportional to the fifth power of the r.m.s. Mach number fluctuation. In the particular case of homogeneous, isotropic turbulence, the dimensionless constant in Eqs. (36.8) and (36.9) turns out [59] to be approximately equal to 38, i.e.,

$$w \approx 38\,\frac{M^5\,U^3}{L} \approx 38\,M^5\,\varepsilon\,. \tag{36.10}$$

Returning now to Eq. (36.6) we note that if the fluctuations in flow are statistically stationary the time dependence of the correlation function K involves only the time difference

$$t_{r\,0} - t_{r\,1} = \tau - \left[\frac{|\boldsymbol{r}-\boldsymbol{r}_0|}{c} - \frac{|\boldsymbol{r}-\boldsymbol{r}_1|}{c}\right] \approx \tau - \frac{\boldsymbol{R}\cdot\boldsymbol{r}}{r\,c} \tag{36.11}$$

with $\boldsymbol{R} = \boldsymbol{r}_0 - \boldsymbol{r}_1$ [see Eq. (35.5)]. The variables of integration in (36.6) can be changed to $\boldsymbol{R} = \boldsymbol{r}_0 - \boldsymbol{r}_1$ and $\boldsymbol{X} = \boldsymbol{r}_0 + \boldsymbol{r}_1$, so that K can be written as $K(\boldsymbol{R}, \tau - \tau_0, \boldsymbol{X})$, where $\tau_0 = (\boldsymbol{R}\cdot\boldsymbol{r}/r\,c)$, and

$$\Psi(\tau) = \left(\frac{1}{4\pi r c^2}\right)^2 \iiint d v_X \iiint K(\boldsymbol{R}, \tau - \tau_0, \boldsymbol{X})\, d v_R\,. \tag{36.12}$$

The corresponding intensity spectrum is therefore

$$E(\omega) = \frac{1}{16\pi^2 r^2 \varrho c^5} \iiint d v_X \iiint \phi(\boldsymbol{R}, \omega, \tau_0, \boldsymbol{X})\, d v_R \tag{36.13}$$

where

$$\phi(\boldsymbol{R}, \omega, \tau_0, \boldsymbol{X}) = \frac{1}{2\pi} \int_{-\infty}^{\infty} K(\boldsymbol{R}, \tau - \tau_0, \boldsymbol{X})\, e^{i\omega\tau}\, d\tau$$

is the Fourier transform of the correlation function K for the pressure fluctuations in the source region. Eqs. (36.12) and (36.13) are the formal solution to the problem of the radiation of sound from a turbulent region. The solution is expressed with reference to a coordinate system following the mean motion of the fluid, so that the fluctuating velocities used in the equations represent the total velocities in the chosen reference system.

In homogeneous turbulence K is independent of $\boldsymbol{X} = \boldsymbol{r}_0 + \boldsymbol{r}_1$, and is substantially different from zero only when $R = |\boldsymbol{r}_0 - \boldsymbol{r}_1|$ is of the order of L or smaller. Therefore if the linear size of the source region is considerably larger than L, we need not be concerned with boundary effects in the integration in the equations for E and ϕ. The acoustic intensity spectrum radiated per unit volume of source region is then

$$e(\omega) = \frac{1}{32\pi^3 r^2 \varrho c^5} \iiint d v_R \int_{-\infty}^{\infty} K(\boldsymbol{R}, \tau - \tau_0)\, e^{i\omega\tau}\, d\tau\,. \tag{36.14}$$

Reference to Eq. (36.11) indicates that τ_0 corresponds to the time of travel of sound from one end of an eddy to the other, in the integral of (36.12). The characteristic time of oscillation of an eddy is of the order of $(L/U) = (L/c\,M) \approx$

(τ_0/M). Thus as long as the Mach number of the fluctuations in velocity is considerably smaller than unity the period of oscillation of the eddy will be much larger than τ_0, so there will be no significant change in the eddy during a time τ_0. Under such circumstances it is justified to neglect τ_0 in the argument of K, and we shall do so in our subsequent analysis.

The detailed form of the function K and of it Fourier transform generally have to be determined experimentally. But if we limit ourselves to the so-called inertial subrange of isotropic turbulence, we can deduce some properties of K directly from dimensional considerations. In this subrange the statistical properties are supposed independent of viscosity and of the geometry of the driving mechanism, and dependent only on the driving power ε supplied per unit mass of fluid. The size of the eddies in this inertial or similarity range are smaller than the size L of the largest eddies but are larger than the "micro-scale" eddies, which are influenced more by viscosity than by inertial effects. The size of the micro-eddies is of the order of $l \approx (\nu^3/\varepsilon)^{\frac{1}{4}}$, where ν is the kinematic viscosity. The velocity of the largest eddies is $U \approx (\varepsilon L)^{\frac{1}{3}}$ and the Reynolds number of the turbulence, $\Re = (UL/\nu)$ can be expressed in terms of the large and small scales as

$$\Re^{\frac{3}{4}} = \frac{L}{l}. \tag{36.15}$$

Thus, in the inertial range the magnitude of R will lie in the range $l < R \ll L$. Dimensional considerations indicate that the correlation function K is of the form $K \sim \varrho^2 (\varepsilon R)^{\frac{8}{3}} \Phi$, where Φ is a dimensionless function of τ, R and ε. The characteristic time of oscillation of an eddy of size R is of the order $R^{\frac{2}{3}} \varepsilon^{-\frac{1}{3}}$ and the dimensionless argument of Φ is then $(\tau/R^{\frac{2}{3}} \varepsilon^{-\frac{1}{3}})$. If we limit ourselves to eddies in the inertial range we can use

$$K_i \sim \varrho^2 (\varepsilon R)^{\frac{8}{3}} \Phi\left(\frac{\tau}{R^{\frac{2}{3}} \varepsilon^{-\frac{1}{3}}}\right) \tag{36.16}$$

in (36.14) to obtain the acoustic power spectrum $4\pi r^2 e(\omega)$ of the sound radiated from the inertial sub-range;

$$4\pi r^2 e(\omega) = \frac{4\pi}{8\pi^2 \varrho c^5} \int_l^{L_i} R^2 \, dR \int_{-\infty}^{\infty} K_i(R, \tau) \, e^{i\omega\tau} \, d\tau \tag{36.17}$$

in which L_i is the largest eddy size in the inertial range.

The lower limit in this integral goes to zero as the Reynolds number $\Re$ goes to infinity. With this choice of lower limit and using the dimensionless variables $x = (\tau/R^{\frac{2}{3}} \varepsilon^{-\frac{1}{3}})$ and $y = \omega R^{\frac{2}{3}} \varepsilon^{-\frac{1}{3}}$ in (36.17), we obtain [37]

$$4\pi r^2 e(\omega) = \frac{4}{3} \pi \varrho c^2 M^{\frac{21}{2}} \left(\frac{c}{\omega L}\right)^{\frac{7}{2}} \int_0^{y_m} y^{\frac{5}{2}} \, dy \int_{-\infty}^{\infty} e^{iyx} \Phi(x) \, dx \tag{36.18}$$

where $y_m = (\omega L_i/cM)$. To obtain the acoustic contribution from the rest of the eddies, for $L_i < R < L$, we must add to this integral a portion in which K does not have the similarity form, but depends on the geometry of the driving mechanism. However, as one increases the frequency the upper limit of the integral over y goes to infinity and the additional contribution from these larger eddies becomes negligible (assuming proper convergence of K as $\omega \to \infty$). Therefore in the frequency range $\omega \gg (cM/L)$ the acoustic spectrum should be "universal", in the sense that it does not depend on the geometry of the driving mechanism.

The acoustic power spectrum in this range is

$$4\pi r^2 e(\omega) \approx (\text{const})\, \varrho\, c^2 M^{\frac{21}{2}} \left(\frac{c}{\omega L}\right)^{\frac{7}{2}} \quad \left(\omega \gg \frac{c M}{L}\right) \tag{36.19}$$

the constant involving the value of the double integral, with the integral over y extended to ∞.

As we saw earlier, the total acoustic power generated by the turbulent region is proportional to M^8 [see Eq. (36.8)]. The high-frequency portion of the power increases with $M^{\frac{21}{2}}$ and decreases with frequency as $1/\omega^{\frac{7}{2}}$.

37. Sound generation by a turbulent jet. In the previous section the turbulent region was considered to be at rest on the average. Under such conditions the radiation will be spherically symmetric, with total output proportional to the eighth power of the velocity fluctuations. In many situations of practical interest, however, the turbulent air is in rapid motion with respect to the observer. The effect of this relative motion is to give directionality to the radiated sound [*32*], more energy being radiated downstream than upstream.

A detailed theoretical analysis of the noise spectrum from moving turbulence, as in a jet, by an application of Eqs. (36.12) to (36.14) is difficult, not only because of the inhomogeneity and non-isotropy of the turbulence but particularly on account of the gradients of the mean velocity of the stream [*37*]. These gradients amplify the pressure fluctuations transverse to the mean flow and also refract the sound coming from the center of the jet. The GREEN's function for a moving source in a fluid at rest certainly cannot be used to compute the radiation field; it must be modified to account for the refraction. Although we can write down an appropriate formal solution, we shall not pursue this analysis further, but will turn to a comparison of some of the known characteristics of jet noise with the results we have already obtained.

First we note that measured values of the total acoustic power radiated from jets are consistent with the eighth power dependence on flow velocity indicated by Eq. (36.8). In fact the experimental results [*15*], [*50*] for circular jets are that

$$w \approx C\, M_0^5\, \frac{A\, \varrho\, v^3}{2} = C\, A\, \frac{\varrho\, c^3}{2}\, M_0^8 \tag{37.1}$$

where A is the jet area, $M_0 = v_0/c$, v_0 is the mean exit velocity and c is the speed of sound in the region outside the jet. The dimensionless constant C has been found to be of the order of 10^{-4}. In this equation $(A\, \varrho\, v^3/2)$ represents the total mechanical power of the jet and $C M_0^5 \approx 10^{-4} M_0^5$ represents the "acoustic efficiency".

It is interesting to compare this result with the theory of the previous section, given in Eq. (36.10). There we saw that the efficiency of conversion of the driving power of the turbulence into sound is about $38 M^5 = 38\,(v/c)^5$ where v is the r.m.s. value of the fluctuations in velocity. Experiments with jets have shown that the fluctuating velocity component is about one tenth of the mean flow velocity. The experimentally determined efficiency of a circular jet is thus roughly $10^{-4} M_0^5 \approx 10 M^5$, which is the same order of magnitude as that predicted by Eq. (36.10).

The spectra of circular jets have been found experimentally to be expressible in the general form

$$E(\omega) = E_0\, F(\gamma)\,; \quad \gamma = \frac{\omega}{\omega_0} \tag{37.2}$$

where E_0 is the maximum value of the spectrum and $(\omega_0/2\pi)$ the frequency at which this maximum occurs. This peak frequency has been found to be related to the flow velocity v_0 and diameter d of the jet as follows,

$$\omega_0 \approx 2\pi \frac{0.15\, v_0}{d}. \tag{37.3}$$

From Eq. (37.1) we then obtain

$$E(\omega) \approx A \frac{C \varrho c^3}{2N} M^8 \left[\frac{2\pi F(\gamma)}{\omega_0}\right] \tag{37.4}$$

where

$$N = \int_0^\infty F(\gamma)\, d\gamma.$$

Measured acoustic spectra of subsonic jets can be approximated by the empirical formula

$$F(\gamma) \approx \frac{\gamma^2}{(\frac{5}{9} + \frac{4}{9}\gamma^{1.5})^3}. \tag{37.5}$$

Thus at the high frequency end of the spectrum the energy is proportional to $M_0^{9.5}$ and at the low frequency end it is proportional to M_0^5, whereas the total radiated power is proportional to M_0^8.

When a turbulent fluid is in contact with a boundary surface it will produce pressure fluctuations on the boundary and the boundary in turn will react on the fluid; the result being a dipole source distribution over the surface [*12*], [*26*]. From Eq. (14.4) the radiation from an elementary local force is

$$-\frac{1}{4\pi r}[\operatorname{div} \boldsymbol{f}(\boldsymbol{r}, t)] \approx \frac{1}{4\pi c r} \boldsymbol{a}_r \cdot \left[\frac{\partial}{\partial t} \boldsymbol{f}(\boldsymbol{r}, t)\right] \quad (r \to \infty)$$

where the quantities in brackets are retarded. When there is a pressure distribution P_s on some boundary S, the reaction force produced by the surface element $d\boldsymbol{S}$ (direction normal to surface) is

$$p(r, t) \approx \frac{1}{4\pi r c} \boldsymbol{a}_r \cdot \left[\frac{\partial}{\partial t} \iint P_s(\boldsymbol{r}_s, t_r)\, d\boldsymbol{S}\right] \tag{37.6}$$

where $t_r = t - (|\boldsymbol{r} - \boldsymbol{r}_s|/c)$. The acoustic intensity at the observation point is thus

$$I(r) \approx \frac{1}{16\pi^2 \varrho c^3 r^2} \boldsymbol{a}_r \cdot [\iint K_s(\boldsymbol{r}_1, t_1; \boldsymbol{r}_2, t_2)\, d\boldsymbol{S}_1\, d\boldsymbol{S}_2] \cdot \boldsymbol{a}_r \tag{37.7}$$

where the quantity in brackets is a dyadic and where the correlation function

$$K_s(\boldsymbol{r}_1, t_1; \boldsymbol{r}_2, t_2) = \left\langle \frac{\partial}{\partial t} P_s(\boldsymbol{r}_1, t_1) \frac{\partial}{\partial t} P_s(\boldsymbol{r}_2, t_2)\right\rangle;$$

$$t_1 = t - \frac{|\boldsymbol{r} - \boldsymbol{r}_1|}{c}; \quad t_2 = t - \frac{|\boldsymbol{r} - \boldsymbol{r}_2|}{c}.$$

From dimensional considerations, similar to those made earlier in this subsection, we can rewrite this in the form

$$I(r) \approx \frac{\varrho c^3 L^2 M^6}{16\pi^2 r^2} \boldsymbol{a}_r \cdot \left[\iint \frac{K_s}{\varrho^2 U^6 L^2}\, d\boldsymbol{S}_1\, d\boldsymbol{S}_2\right] \cdot \boldsymbol{a}_r \tag{37.8}$$

in which U is a characteristic velocity fluctuation and L a characteristic size of the turbulent eddies; and the integral is dimensionless. The chief interest in this result is that the dependence of the output goes with the sixth power of the velocity fluctuations M, in contrast to the sound generated in the body of the fluid, which goes with the eighth power of M, as indicated by Eq. (36.8). Thus for smaller values of U the surfaces in contact with turbulence produce the majority of the noise; for larger values of U the noise from the body of the fluid predominates.

When an object, whether a microphone or an airplane, moves with respect to the surrounding fluid, the fluctuating pressures produced on the object can arise either because it is moving through air already turbulent or because the motion itself causes the turbulence. This last becomes important when the Reynolds number of the flow is sufficiently large. In either case the resulting fluctuating force will produce a sound field of the sort represented by Eq. (37.8); a surface dipole field with an acoustic power output proportional to the sixth power of the Mach number of the fluctuations. Examples of such radiation are the Aeolian tone from a cylinder in a stream and the low-frequency radiation from the oscillatory drag and lift forces on an airplane.

C. Coupled acoustic systems.

In the previous chapter we have worked out some of the implications of the assumption that the boundary surface has an acoustic impedance, a point function of the position on the surface, independent of the configuration (but not of the frequency) of the incident wave. The advantages of such a formulation are clear; the acoustic medium and its yielding boundary surface form a single acoustic system, the surface responding only passively to the waves. Calculations based on this assumption will correspond closely to reality in most cases where the boundary surface does not respond strongly, where the magnitude of the specific surface admittance $|\beta|$ is everywhere considerably less than unity. But when the boundary surfaces, or part of them, respond strongly to the incident wave the assumption that the boundary is a passive adjunct of the wave in the medium is no longer valid. We must take into account that such boundary surfaces are acoustic systems in their own right, which are coupled to the wave in the medium.

This chapter will consider a few such coupled systems and will discuss how their behavior can be calculated. The calculations are usually more difficult than the single-system ones exhibited in Chap. B. Only a few special cases have been worked out; new techniques may have to be developed before many others can be solved.

I. Coupling incident wave with boundary.

38. Transmission through membranes and plates. The simplest example of the coupling of waves in the medium with waves in the boundary surface occurs when the boundary is an infinite, plane membrane or plate. If the surface material is thin enough and is under tension T it will act more or less like a membrane with mass δ per unit area. Transverse waves can propagate in this membrane with velocity $c_m = \sqrt{T/\delta}$, in the absence of the medium. With the medium present, the coupled system can be set into motion by projecting a sound wave against the membrane [*10*], [*28*], [*66*], or by applying an oscillating force directly to the membrane.

We first consider the former situation. We suppose that the membrane is in the x, z plane, that a fluid of density ϱ_+ and sound velocity c_+ occupies the region of positive y and that one of density ϱ_- and sound velocity c_- is in the region of negative y. A plane wave of frequency $(\omega/2\pi)$ comes toward the membrane from $y \to +\infty$, with direction of propagation in the x, y plane, making an angle of incidence ϕ_i with the y axis. The pressure wave in the upper region is then

$$p_+ = p_0\, e^{i k_+ x \sin\phi_i - i\omega t}\left(e^{-i k_+ y\cos\phi_i} + R\, e^{i k_+ y \cos\phi_i}\right) \tag{38.1}$$

where $k_+ = (\omega/c_+)$ and the reflection coefficient is to be computed. Some of this wave will be transmitted through the membrane and will continue on to $y \to -\infty$. The wave in the lower region is thus

$$p_- = p_0\, S\, e^{i k_+ x\sin\phi_i - i k_- y\cos\phi_t - i\omega t} \tag{38.2}$$

where $k_- = (\omega/c_-)$ and where $(1/c_+)\sin\phi_i = (1/c_-)\sin\phi_t$, ϕ_t being the angle the transmitted wave makes with the y axis.

The membrane displacement η in the y direction, away from its plane of equilibrium, will have a similar dependence on x and t. The equation of motion for η is

$$-\delta\frac{\partial^2\eta}{\partial t^2} + \delta c_m^2\left[\frac{\partial^2\eta}{\partial x^2} + \frac{\partial^2\eta}{\partial z^2}\right] = (p_+ - p_-)_{y=0} \tag{38.3}$$

where, in the present case, the p's and η are independent of z. Setting

$$\eta = A\, e^{i k_+ x\sin\phi_i - i\omega t} \tag{38.4}$$

we obtain one equation relating R, S and A,

$$A(\omega^2 - c_m^2 k_+^2 \sin^2\phi_i) = p_0(1 + R - S).$$

Other equations come from the fact that the y component of the acoustic velocity in both media, at $y=0$, must equal $(\partial\eta/\partial t) = -i\omega\eta$,

$$-i\omega\eta = u_y = \frac{1}{i\omega\varrho_+}\frac{\partial p_+}{\partial y} = \frac{1}{i\omega\varrho_-}\frac{\partial p_-}{\partial y} \quad \text{at} \quad y = 0,$$

or

$$-i\omega A = p_0\frac{\cos\phi_i}{\varrho_+ c_+}(-1 + R) = -p_0\frac{\cos\phi_t}{\varrho_- c_-}S.$$

To simplify writing the solution we define three "impedance factors"

$$\left.\begin{aligned} Z_+ &= \frac{\varrho_+ c_+}{\cos\phi_i}; \quad Z_- = \frac{\varrho_- c_-}{\cos\phi_t},\\ \cos\phi_t &= \sqrt{1 - \left(\frac{c_-}{c_+}\right)^2 \sin^2\phi_i},\\ Z_m &= i\omega\left(\frac{T}{c_+}\right)^2 \sin^2\phi_i - i\omega\delta = i\omega\delta\left[\left(\frac{c_m}{c_+}\right)^2\sin^2\phi_i - 1\right].\end{aligned}\right\} \tag{38.5}$$

Z_+ is always real; Z_- is real for normal incidence ($\phi_i = 0$) and is real for all angles of incidence if $c_- < c_+$, but will be imaginary (total reflection) for large enough values of ϕ_i if $c_- > c_+$. The membrane impedance factor Z_m is reactive; its first term represents the inter-relation between the stiffness of the medium and that of the membrane tension; the second term is the mass reactance of the membrane. Impedance Z_m is zero if the velocity $(c_+/\sin\phi_i)$ of the incident wave fronts along the x axis is equal to the velocity c_m of waves in the unperturbed membrane (which we might call *travelling resonance*). This can only occur when $c_m > c_+$ and even then only at a particular angle of incidence but, when it does occur, the membrane is transparent to the wave.

In terms of these impedance factors, A, the amplitude of the membrane waves, and R and S, the reflection and transmission coefficients, are

$$A = \frac{(2p_0/i\omega)}{Z_+ + Z_- + Z_m}; \quad S = \frac{2Z_-}{Z_+ + Z_- + Z_m}; \quad R = \frac{-Z_+ + Z_- + Z_m}{Z_+ + Z_- + Z_m}. \tag{38.6}$$

The power incident on a unit area of membrane is $(|p_0|^2/2\varrho_+ c_+)\cos\phi_i$; the power reflected and transmitted by this area are the fractions I_r and I_t of this, where

$$I_r = \frac{(Z_+ - Z_-)^2 + |Z_m|^2}{(Z_+ + Z_-)^2 + |Z_m|^2}; \quad I_t = \frac{4 Z_+ Z_-}{(Z_+ + Z_-)^2 + |Z_m|^2} = 1 - I_r \tag{38.7}$$

if Z_- is real (i.e., if total reflection is not occurring). If Z_- is imaginary then $I_r = 1$ and no power is transmitted into the second medium. Ordinarily Z_m is much larger then Z_+ or Z_-, so most of the energy is reflected, except when $\sin\phi_i = (c_+/c_m)$ (travelling resonance) and the wave motion is as though no membrane separated the two media.

If the medium below the panel, in which the transmitted wave travels, is moving with uniform velocity V in the x direction, the equations of Sect. 10 show that these results are changed only in the expressions for Z_- and for the angle of the transmitted wave ϕ_t,

$$\sin\phi_t = \frac{c_- \sin\phi_i}{c_+ + V\sin\phi_i}; \quad Z_- = \frac{\varrho_- c_-}{\cos\phi_t}\,\frac{c_+ + V\sin\phi_i}{c_+} = \frac{\varrho_- c_-}{\cos\phi_i}\,\frac{c_-}{c_- - V\sin\phi_t}. \tag{38.8}$$

We used the flexible membrane, with its simple properties, to work out the coupling equations. In practice the boundary panel is more likely to resemble a stiff plate, with internal stiffness providing the restoring force, rather than tension. The equation of motion for transverse displacement η away from the x, z plane of equilibrium of a thin plate of mass δ per unit area and of thickness h is

$$\delta\left[\frac{\partial^2\eta}{\partial t^2} + \frac{E h^3}{12\delta(1-\sigma^2)}\left(\frac{\partial^2}{\partial x^2} + \frac{\partial^2}{\partial z^2}\right)^2 \eta\right] = (p_2 - p_1) \tag{38.9}$$

where E is the modulus of elasticity of the panel material and σ is its Poisson ratio. The velocity of transverse waves in this panel, in the absence of the media, is proportional to the square root of the frequency. It thus is convenient to express the stiffness constant of the panel in terms of the frequency $(\nu_+/2\pi)$ at which the panel wave velocity equals the velocity c_+ of waves in the upper medium,

$$\nu_+^2 = \frac{12\delta(1-\sigma^2)\,c_+^4}{E h^3} \tag{38.10}$$

The velocity of transverse waves in the uncoupled panel is then $c_+\sqrt{\omega/\nu_+} = c_p$.

The derivation given earlier for the reflection and transmission of a plane wave from a membrane can now be repeated for the stiff plate, with Eqs. (38.1) to (38.8) unchanged except that, in Eqs. (38.5) and (38.7) the panel impedance factor is changed from Z_m to

$$Z_p = \frac{i\omega^3}{\nu_+^2}\,\delta\sin^4\phi_i - i\omega\delta = i\omega\delta\left[\left(\frac{c_p}{c_+}\right)^4 \sin^4\phi_i - 1\right] \tag{38.11}$$

For frequencies smaller than $(\nu_+/2\pi)$, and for normal incidence at all frequencies, the mass reactance term $-i\omega\delta$ in this impedance predominates. But for higher frequencies the plate impedance depends strongly on ϕ_i and is zero when $\sin\phi_i = \pm\sqrt{\nu_+/\omega}$ (travelling resonance).

39. Scattering from a flexible sphere. For a different example, let us consider the scattering of sound from a spherical membrane [*47*], [*63*], such as a balloon (or a bubble in water) which is kept under tension by a slight excess pressure p_T in the fluid inside the sphere. The relation between this pressure, the tension T in the membrane and the radius a of the sphere is $p_T = (2T/a)$. If the membrane has thickness h and modulus of elasticity E, the excess pressure p_T also has increased the radius of the sphere by an amount $\Delta_T = (a^2 p_T/4hE)$. Thus at equilibrium the membrane surface is a sphere of radius a, with uniform excess pressure p_T inside, to keep the membrane under tension T.

When a sound wave strikes this membrane, the pressure differential Δp at various points on the sphere will differ from the equilibrium difference p_T; this excess differential will produce radial motion of that part of the membrane. If the radial displacement of the point on the membrane defined by the spherical angles ϑ, φ is $\eta(\vartheta, \varphi)$ then the dependence of η on the pressure differential Δp will depend not only on the frequency $(\omega/2\pi)$ but also on the over-all dependence of Δp on ϑ and φ. If, for example, both pressure differential and membrane displacement are expanded in spherical harmonics,

$$\Delta p - p_T = \sum_{m,n} F_{mn}(t)\, Y_{mn}(\vartheta, \varphi); \qquad \eta = \sum_{m,n} \Delta_{mn}\, Y_{mn}(\vartheta\, \varphi), \tag{39.1}$$

then the equations of motion for Δ_{mn} are

$$\left.\begin{aligned} &\delta \frac{\partial^2 \Delta_{00}}{\partial t^2} + \frac{4hE}{a^2} \Delta_{00} = F_{00}(t), \\ &\delta \frac{\partial^2 \Delta_{mn}}{\partial t^2} + (n-1)(n+2) \frac{T}{a^2} \Delta_{mn} = F_{mn}(t) \quad (n>0) \end{aligned}\right\} \tag{39.2}$$

where the positive direction for $\Delta p - p_T$ and for η is away from the origin and where δ is the mass of the membrane per unit area.

The symmetrical mode of vibration $(m=n=0)$ requires an actual stretching of the membrane, so the modulus of elasticity E enters into the stiffness term. The modes for $n=1$ involve displacement of the sphere as a whole, so only the mass reactance enters. The restoring force for the higher modes involve changes of curvature of the spherical surface but no stretching of the membrane as a whole (at least to the first order in the small quantity η/a); consequently the tension T enters into the stiffness reactance, not E.

Now suppose a plane wave of frequency $(\omega/2\pi)$ and wave length $(2\pi c/\omega) = (2\pi/k)$, propagated parallel to the polar axis of the angles ϑ, φ is incident on this sphere. The pressure of this incident wave can be expanded in terms of Legendre functions of ϑ and spherical Bessel functions of r [see Eq. (28.7)],

$$p_i = p_0\, e^{ikr\cos\vartheta - i\omega t} = p_0 \sum_{n=0}^{\infty} (2n+1)\, i^n P_n(\cos\vartheta)\, j_n(kr)\, e^{-i\omega t}. \tag{39.3}$$

The scattered wave p_s must be entirely outgoing and thus must involve the spherical Hankel functions, whereas the waves inside the sphere must stay finite at $r=0$ and thus must involve the Bessel functions;

$$\left.\begin{aligned} p_s &= \sum_{n=0}^{\infty} (2n+1)\, i^n A_n P_n(\cos\vartheta)\, h_n(kr)\, e^{-i\omega t}, \\ p_- &= p_T + \sum_{n=0}^{\infty} (2n+1)\, B_n P_n(\cos\vartheta)\, j_n(kr)\, e^{-i\omega t} \end{aligned}\right\} \tag{39.4}$$

where we have assumed that the fluid inside the sphere is the same as that outside and that p_T is small enough so that the sound velocity inside is the same as that outside.

The pressure differential expansion coefficients of Eq. (39.1) are therefore

$$F_n = (2n+1)\, i^n [B_n j_n(ka) - p_0 j_n(ka) - A_n h_n(ka)]\, e^{-i\omega t},$$

where we have omitted the subscript m on F because all the waves are symmetrical about the polar axis and only the $m=0$ terms enter. The values of B_n, A_n and Δ_n (membrane displacement) are then determined by three equations. The first of these is the equation of motion (39.2); the other two are that the radial velocity of the membrane must equal that of the fluid just inside and just outside the membrane,

$$\varrho c \omega \Delta_n = B_n j_n'(ka) = j_n'(ka) + A_n h_n'(ka) \tag{39.5}$$

where, as in Sect. 28, the primes indicate differentiation with respect to the argument ka.

The solution of these three equations is expressible, as with the plane panel, in terms of impedances; in this case a set for each spherical harmonic,

$$\left.\begin{aligned} Z_{rn} &= \frac{\varrho c}{k^2 a^2 j_n'(ka)\, h_n'(ka)} \to \begin{cases} \dfrac{3 i \varrho c}{ka} & (n=0,\ ka \ll 1), \\[2mm] \dfrac{i \varrho c k a (2n+1)}{n(n+1)} & (n>0,\ ka \ll n+1), \end{cases} \\ &\to \frac{i^n \varrho c\, e^{-ika}}{\cos(ka - \frac{1}{2}\pi n)} \qquad (ka - n \gg 1), \\ Z_{s0} &= -i\omega\delta + i\frac{4hE}{a^2\omega}, \\ Z_{sn} &= -i\omega\delta + i(n-1)(n+2)\frac{T}{\omega a^2} \qquad (n>0). \end{aligned}\right\} \tag{39.6}$$

The wave impedance coefficient $Z_{rn}(n>0)$ is a mass reactance at low frequencies $(ka \ll n)$, approaches zero as $n\to\infty$; the membrane impedance coefficient Z_{sn} is that of a mass δ per unit area plus a stiffness $(n-1)(n+2)(T/a^2)$ (for $n>0$), it goes to zero at a frequency such that these two reactances just cancel each other. As the frequency is increased (as ka becomes larger than some specified integer n) the n-th wave impedance factor shows the effects of standing wave resonance within the sphere, when $j_n'(ka)$ becomes zero and Z_{rn} goes to infinity.

The three sets of coefficients turn out to be

$$\left.\begin{aligned} A_n &= -\frac{j_n'(ka)}{h_n'(ka)}\, \frac{Z_{sn}\, p_0}{Z_{sn}+Z_{rn}}; \qquad B_n = \frac{Z_{rn}\, p_0}{Z_{sn}+Z_{rn}}, \\ \Delta_n &= \frac{j_n'(ka)}{\varrho c \omega}\, \frac{Z_{rn}\, p_0}{Z_{sn}+Z_{rn}} = \frac{j_n'(ka)}{\varrho c \omega} B_n. \end{aligned}\right\} \tag{39.7}$$

Consequently the asymptotic form of the scattered wave turns out to be

$$p_s = p_0 \frac{e^{ikr - i\omega t}}{r} f(\vartheta); \quad f(\vartheta) = \frac{i}{k}\sum_{n=0}^{\infty}(2n+1)\, P_n(\cos\vartheta)\, \frac{j_n'(ka)}{h_n'(ka)}\, \frac{Z_{sn}}{Z_{sn}+Z_{rn}} \tag{39.8}$$

where $f(\vartheta)$ is the angle-distribution factor defined in subsection 28. Finally, the scattering cross section, the total power scattered per unit incident intensity, is

$$Q_s = \frac{2\pi}{k^2}\sum_{n=0}^{\infty}(2n+1)\left|\frac{j_n'(ka)}{h_n'(ka)}\right|^2 \left|\frac{Z_{sn}}{Z_{sn}+Z_{rn}}\right|^2. \tag{39.9}$$

At certain frequencies the coefficients of the n-th Legendre function in the scattered wave become zero, as though the sphere had become transparent to the n-th partial wave. This happens at the n-th membrane resonance frequency, when Z_{sn} becomes zero (it cannot happen for the $n=1$ wave, but it can for all others) and also at the various standing wave resonance frequencies, when $j_n'(ka)$

goes to zero. At no frequency does the denominator become zero, though it might become quite small if $|Z_{rn}|$ should happen to become nearly equal to $|Z_{sn}|$, if in addition Z_{rn} happens then to be purely imaginary. In this unlikely case the one partial scattered wave would predominate.

40. Transmission through a periodically supported membrane. Suppose an infinite membrane, of density δ per unit area and under tension T per unit length, is stretched across a set of identical supporting bars, all parallel to the z axis in the x, z plane, spaced a distance l apart. We will assume that these supports are not perfectly rigid, but move in the y direction in response to the transverse forces arising when the membrane is set into motion. They do not respond directly to the acoustic pressure of a sound wave incident on the membrane but they respond indirectly, because the membrane is moved, which thus brings forces to bear on the supports. When the membrane is in motion there will be discontinuity of the x derivative of the transverse displacement η of the membrane at each support; the ratio between T times this slope discontinuity and the transverse velocity of the support is assumed to be a constant (for a given frequency), the transverse impedance Z_s of the support per unit length.

The calculation of the coupled motion of such a periodic structure and the medium with which it is in contact requires the development of a set of periodic GREEN'S functions, set up so that the basic integral equation will involve integration over only one period of the structure (from $x=0$ to $x=l$, say) rather than over the whole extent of the membrane. If the incident wave has frequency $(\omega/2\pi)$ and angle of incidence ϕ_0 (and direction of incidence in the x, y plane) then the motion of the membrane between the support at $x=nl$ and the next one, at $x=(n+1)\,l$, will differ from the motion of the strip between $x=0$ and $x=l$ only by the phase factor $e^{inkl\sin\phi_0}$, where $k=(\omega/c)$, c being the sound velocity in the medium (assumed constant). The two-dimensional GREEN'S function for the membrane must therefore be the product of the phase factor $e^{ikx\sin\phi_0}$ times a function which is periodic in x with period l.

This GREEN'S function $g_p(x|x_1)$ (we leave out the dependence on z because we have, for simplicity, assumed that the incident wave function is independent of z; the case where the functions depend on z can also be solved, but it adds no new principles, only burdensome detail) must thus have the following properties, over the range $0\leqq x\leqq l$;

$$\left.\begin{aligned} g(l|x_1) &= e^{ikl\sin\varphi_0}\, g(0|x_1), \\ T\left(\frac{\partial^2 g}{\partial x^2}\right)+\delta\omega^2 g &= -\,\delta(x-x_1) \quad (T=\delta c_p^2), \\ T\left(\frac{\partial^2 g}{\partial x^2}\right)+\delta\omega^2 g &= -\,i\omega Z_s\, g\,\delta(x) \end{aligned}\right\} \tag{40.1}$$

where c_p is the velocity of transverse waves in the membrane. The first of these equations introduces the phase factor $e^{iknl\sin\phi_0}$ in the periodicity; the function in the n-th strip then being $e^{iknl\sin\phi_0}$ times that in the first strip. The second equation gives the relation between the shape of the membrane and the unit line force at $x=x_1$, which is characteristic of GREEN'S functions. By integrating this over the range $x_1-\Delta<x<x_1+\Delta$ (Δ small) we can rewrite it as

$$T\left(\frac{\partial g}{\partial x}\right)_{x_1+\Delta}-T\left(\frac{\partial g}{\partial x}\right)_{x_1-\Delta}=-1$$

plus the requirement that g satisfy the homogeneous equation $(\partial^2 g/\partial x^2)+(\omega/c_p)^2 g=0$ when $x\neq x_1$. The third equation expresses the relationship between the shape of the membrane and the motion of the support at $x=0$, Z_s being the impedance of the support per unit length. It can be rewritten as

$$T\left(\frac{\partial g}{\partial x}\right)_\Delta - T\,e^{-ikl\sin\phi_0}\left(\frac{\partial g}{\partial x}\right)_{l-\Delta} = -\,i\omega\,\delta c_p z_s g(0|x_1)$$

where we have used the first of Eqs. (40.1) to avoid computing $(\partial g/\partial x)$ at $x=-\Delta$, outside the range $0\leqq x\leqq l$. The support impedance is $\delta c_p z_s$ per unit length, z_s being a dimensionless quantity, usually considerably larger than unity.

The solution of this set of equations can be expressed either as a Fourier series (which emphasizes its periodicity) or as a sequence of closed functions in successive periods (which is easier to manipulate). For example, in the range $0\leqq x\leqq l$,

$$g(x|x_1) = \begin{cases} a\,\{2i\sin k_p(x+l-x_1) - 2i\,e^{-ikl\sin\phi_0}\sin k_p(x-x_1) + \\ \qquad + z_s[\cos k_p(x+x_1-l) - \cos k_p(x-x_1+l)]\} \\ \qquad\qquad (0\leqq x\leqq x_1\leqq l); \\ a\,\{2i\,e^{ikl\sin\phi_0}\sin k_p(x-x_1) - 2i\sin k_p(x-x_1-l) + \\ \qquad + z_s[\cos k_p(x+x_1-l) - \cos k_p(x-x_1-l)]\} \\ \qquad\qquad (0\leqq x_1\leqq x\leqq l). \end{cases} \tag{40.2}$$

In the other ranges of values for x and x_1 we use the relations

$$g(x+ml|x_1) = e^{ikml\sin\phi_0}\,g(x|x_1)$$

and

$$g(x|x_1+nl) = e^{-iknl\sin\phi_0}\,g(x|x_1).$$

The amplitude is

$$a = \frac{(i/4\,\delta c_p\,\omega)}{\cos(kl\sin\phi_0) - \cos(k_p l) + \frac{1}{2} i z_s \sin(k_p l)}$$

and $k_p=(\omega/c_p)$, $k=(\omega/c)$ are the propagation constants in the membrane and in the medium, respectively.

The series form for g is

$$\left.\begin{aligned} g(x|x_1) &= \frac{1}{\delta c_p^2 l}\sum_{m=0}^{\infty}\frac{e^{ik_m(x-x_1)}}{(k_m^2-k_p^2)} - \\ &\quad - \frac{(k_p z_s/\delta c^2 l^2)\,[\cos(k_0 l) - \cos(k_p l)]}{\cos(k_0 l) - \cos(k_p l) + i z_s\sin(k_p l)}\sum_{m,n=-\infty}^{\infty}\frac{e^{ik_m x - ik_n x_1}}{(k_m^2-k_p^2)(k_n^2-k_p^2)} \end{aligned}\right\} \tag{40.3}$$

where $k_m = k\sin\phi_0 + (2\pi m/l)$. This form shows, more clearly than Eq. (40.2), the reciprocity relationship between x and x_1, and the periodicity in x and x_1.

We will assume that the medium on both sides of the membrane is the same, with density ϱ and wave velocity c. The net upward force per unit area on the membrane is $(p_- - p_+)$, where p_- is the pressure on the under side of the membrane and p_+ that on the upper side. This pressure difference has the time factor $e^{-i\omega t}$ and if its value at $x+nl$ differs by the factor $e^{iknl\sin\phi_0}$ from its value at x, then the displacement η of the membrane is given by the integral

$$\eta = \int_0^l (p_- - p_+)\,g(x|x_1)\,dx_1. \tag{40.4}$$

This expression has in it all the interaction between the membrane, the upper and lower media and the periodically placed supports; the GREEN's function g embodies the effect of the support impedance z_s. Because of the periodicity of g, we need only integrate over one period, from $x=0$ to $x=l$.

Next we must work out the interaction between the wave in the medium and the wave in the membrane. The GREEN's functions $G(x, y|x_0, y_0)$ for the regions $y>0$ and $y<0$ must satisfy the requirements

$$\left.\begin{aligned} &G(x+nl, y|x_0, y_0) = e^{iknl\sin\phi_0} G(x, y|x_0, y_0), \\ &(\nabla^2+k^2) G = \delta(x-x_0)\,\delta(y-y_0), \\ &\left[\frac{\partial}{\partial y} G(x, y|x_0, y_0)\right]_{y=0} = 0 \end{aligned}\right\} \tag{40.5}$$

where we have left out the z coordinate since it does not enter into this problem. The solution for the region $y \geqq 0$ is

$$G_+(x, y|x_0, y_0) = \sum_{m=-\infty}^{\infty} \frac{e^{ik_m(x-x_0)}}{ilw_m} \left\{\begin{matrix} \cos(w_m y_0)\, e^{iw_m y} & (0 \leqq y_0 \leqq y) \\ \cos(w_m y)\, e^{iw_m y_0} & (0 \leqq y \leqq y_0), \end{matrix}\right\} \tag{40.6}$$

where $k_m = k\sin\phi_0 + (2\pi m/l)$ as was given before, and $w_m^2 = k^2 - k_m^2$, the quantity w_m being positive real when $|k_m| < k$ and being positive imaginary when $|k_m| > k$. The function G_-, for the region $y \leqq 0$, has the signs of y and y_0 changed.

The integral equation for the wave in the region $y \geqq 0$ then [see Eq. (13.1)] involves an integral over the "cell" with sides $x_0=0$, $y_0=0$, $x_0=l$, $y_0=\infty$. The surface integral over this cell boundary at $y=\infty$ results in the incident-plus-reflected wave $2p_0 e^{ik_0x}\cos w_0 y = p_0 e^{ik_0x}(e^{-iw_0y}+e^{+iw_0y})$, which would be the complete solution if the membrane were rigid. (We remember that $k_0 = k\sin\phi_0$ and $w_0 = k\cos\phi_0$.) The integral along the cell boundary $x_0=0$, from $y_0=0$ to $y_0=\infty$ just cancels the integral over the boundary at $x_0=l$ (going from $x_0=0$ to $x_0=l$ brings a factor e^{ik_0l} for p, a factor e^{-ik_0l} for G; the product pG is periodic in x_0 with period l; the normal gradients are in opposite directions so the two integrals cancel). Consequently

$$\left.\begin{aligned} p(x, y) &= p_i + \int_0^l G_+(x, y|x_0, 0)\left(\frac{\partial p}{\partial y_0}\right)_{y_0=0} dx_0 \qquad (y \geqq 0) \\ &= p_i + \varrho\omega^2 \int_0^l G_+(x, y|x_0, 0)\,\eta(x_0)\,dx_0 \\ &= p_i - \varrho\omega^2 \int_0^l G_+(x, y|x_0, 0)\,dx_0 \int_0^l (p_+ - p_-)\, g(x_0|x_1)\,dx_1 \end{aligned}\right\} \tag{40.7}$$

where $p_i = 2p_0 e^{ik_0x}\cos w_0 y$, and where we have used the fact that the normal velocity $(1/i\omega\varrho)(\partial p/\partial y)$ at $y=0$ must equal the velocity $-i\omega\eta$ of the membrane, in addition to Eq. (40.4).

The wave in the region $y \leqq 0$ is

$$p(x, y) = \varrho\omega^2 \int_0^l G_-(x, y|x_0, 0)\,dx_0 \int_0^l (p_+ - p_-)\, g(x_0|x_1)\,dx_1. \tag{40.8}$$

Setting $y=0$ in these and subtracting, we find an integral equation for the pressure difference $\Psi(y) = p_+ - p_-$,

$$\left.\begin{aligned} \Psi(x) &= 2p_0 e^{ik_0x} - 2\varrho\omega^2 \int_0^l G(x, 0|x_0, 0)\,dx_0 \int_0^l \Psi(x_1)\, g(x_0|x_1)\,dx_1 \\ &= 2p_0 e^{ik_0x} + \frac{2i\varrho k_p^2}{\delta l} \sum_{m=-\infty}^{\infty} \frac{e^{ik_mx}}{w_m(k_m^2-k_p^2)} \int_0^l \Psi(x_1)\,dx_1 \times \\ &\quad \times \left\{ e^{-ik_mx_1} - \frac{(z_s k_p/l)(\cos k_0 l - \cos k_p l)}{\cos k_0 l - \cos k_p l + iz_s \sin k_p l} \sum_{n=-\infty}^{\infty} \frac{e^{-ik_nx_1}}{k_n^2 - k_p^2} \right\} \end{aligned}\right\} \tag{40.9}$$

where we have carried out the integration over x_0 and thus have obtained a Fredholm equation of the second kind for Ψ. The kernel of this equation is symmetric for interchange of x and x_1.

If we assume that Ψ can be represented by a Fourier series, the integral equation can be changed to a set of algebraic equations,

$$\left.\begin{aligned} &\Psi(x) = \sum_n A_n\, e^{i k_n x}; \qquad k_n = k \sin\phi_0 + \left(\frac{2\pi n}{l}\right); \qquad w_n^2 = k^2 - k_p^2, \\ &A_0 = 2p_0 + \frac{2 i \varrho k_p^2/\delta w_0}{(k_0^2 - k_p^2)} \left\{A_0 - k_p^2 C \sum_{n=-\infty}^{\infty} \frac{A_n}{k_n^2 - k_p^2}\right\}, \\ &A_m = \frac{2 i \varrho k_p^2/\delta w_m}{(k_m^2 - k_p^2)} \left\{A_m - k_p^2 C \sum_{n=-\infty}^{\infty} \frac{A_n}{k_n^2 - k_p^2}\right\} \qquad (m \neq 0) \end{aligned}\right\} \tag{40.10}$$

where

$$C = \frac{(z_s/k_p l)(\cos k_0 l - \cos k_p l)}{\cos k_0 l - \cos k_p l + i z_s \sin k_p l}$$

is the factor representing the coupling of the membrane to the supports. It is zero when $z_s = 0$ (support resonance) or when $k_p = (\omega/c_p)$ is equal to $k_0 = (\omega/c)\sin\phi_0$ (membrane travelling resonance, see discussion after Eq. (38.7)].

To express the solution of these equations in understandable form we need to define a number of angles of reflection and transmission and a number of impedances. Since the periodic membrane-support system is a kind of diffraction grating, we expect that the reflected and transmitted waves will be a diffraction pattern. The primary reflected or transmitted beam comes off at the angle of incidence ϕ_0 but, in addition (unless the frequency is too low to allow it) there are other beams, at angles ϕ_m, such that $\sin\phi_m = \sin\phi_0 + (2\pi m/k l)$, where m is any integer, positive or negative, such that $|\sin\phi_m| < 1$. Our summation in Eq. (40.10) is over all values of m. All the waves exist near the surface, of course, but for those values of m such that $|\sin\phi_m| > 1$, the y-propagation factor $w_m = k\cos\phi_m$ is imaginary and the wave attenuates as $|y|$ is increased. We define the angles ϕ_m for all values of m

$$\sin\phi_m = \sin\phi_0 + \left(\frac{2\pi m}{k l}\right); \qquad \cos^2\phi_m = 1 - \sin^2\phi_m \tag{40.11}$$

and take the cosine to be positive real or positive imaginary, depending on whether $|\sin\phi_m|$ is smaller or larger than unity.

In addition we must define a number of impedance factors, which can be used to simplify the writing of the formulas for the diffracted amplitudes. There is, of course, the radiation impedance Z_{rm} of the medium for radiation at the angle ϕ_m [see Eq. (38.5)]. There is also the impedance of the membrane Z_{bm} (without the supports)

$$\left.\begin{aligned} &Z_{rm} = \left(\frac{\varrho c}{\cos\phi_m}\right); \qquad Z_{bm} = X + Y_m; \\ &X = -i\omega\delta; \qquad Y_m = i\omega\left(\frac{T}{c^2}\right)\sin^2\phi_m \end{aligned}\right\} \tag{40.12}$$

where X and Y_m are imaginary for all values of m, but Z_{rm} is real for those values of m for which $|\sin\phi_m| < 1$, corresponding to actual, not virtual, diffraction.

The exact solutions of Eqs. (40.10) are then

$$\left.\begin{aligned} &A_0 = \frac{2 Z_{b0} p_0}{Z_{b0} + 2 Z_{r0}} - B_0; \qquad A_m = -B_m \qquad (m \neq 0), \\ &B_m = \frac{4 Z_{r0} X C p_0}{(Z_{b0} + 2 Z_{r0})(Z_{bm} + 2 Z_{rm})} \left[1 + \sum_{m=-\infty}^{\infty} \frac{2 Z_{rm} X C}{Z_{bm}(Z_{bm} + 2 Z_{rm})}\right]^{-1}. \end{aligned}\right\} \tag{40.13}$$

The reflected and transmitted beams can be expressed in terms of these coefficients From Eqs. (40.7) and (40.8) we see that, far from the membrane

$$\left.\begin{aligned} p_r &\to \frac{Z_{b0}}{Z_{b0}+2Z_{r0}}\, e^{ik(x\sin\phi_0+y\cos\phi_0)} - \sum_m B_m\, e^{ik(x\sin\phi_m+y\cos\phi_m)} \quad (y\to\infty),\\ p_t &\to \frac{2Z_{r0}}{Z_{b0}+2Z_{r0}}\, e^{ik(x\sin\phi_0-y\cos\phi_0)} + \sum_m B_m\, e^{ik(x\sin\phi_m-y\cos\phi_m)} \quad (y\to-\infty)\end{aligned}\right\} \qquad (40.14)$$

where the summation is over all the values of m for which $\sin\phi_m = \sin\phi_0 + (2\pi m/kl)$ is not greater in magnitude than unity. When the support impedances z_s are zero, C is zero and therefore the coefficients B_m are all zero; there is then only one reflected and one transmitted wave and the formulas reduce to those of Eq. (38.6) for the simple membrane (for $Z_+ = Z_- = Z_{r0}$, $Z_m = Z_{b0}$). The diffracted beams, for $m \neq 0$, all have amplitudes proportional to z_s, the support impedance factor, through the factor C.

This factor C goes to zero when there is support resonance ($z_s = 0$) or when there is membrane resonance, $\cos(kl\sin\phi_0) = \cos k_p l$, which includes the "travelling resonance" $k\sin\phi_0 = k_p$ as well as higher resonances. In any of these cases the diffracted beams vanish, though the simple reflected beam does not, except for the travelling resonance case, $(c_p/c)\sin\phi_0 = 1$, when Z_{b0} also is zero. If z_s is large compared to unity, the factor C becomes large when $\sin(k_p l) = 0$, corresponding to resonance of the strips of membrane between supports. In these cases the diffracted beams have their largest amplitude.

II. Forced motion of coupled boundary.

41. Uniform membrane, line force. Instead of being set into motion by an incident wave, the membrane of Sect. 38 may be driven by an oscillating force applied directly to its surface. We will first compute the motion produced on the membrane, and the coupled motion of the media, when the force is a sinusoidal one, extending over the whole membrane. Then, by use of the Fourier transform, we can obtain the response when the force is concentrated at a point or along a line.

The membrane, as before, is in the x, z plane, has a mass δ per unit area and is under tension $T(=\delta c_m^2$, where c_m is the velocity of free, uncoupled, transverse waves on the membrane). If a transverse force $F(x_0)\, e^{-i\omega t}$ per unit length is applied along the line $x = x_0$ then the displacement of the membrane, in the absence of any coupled medium, is

$$\eta = \frac{iF(x_0)}{2Tk_u}\, e^{ik_u|x-x_0|-i\omega t} \qquad \left(k_u = \frac{\omega}{c_m}\right) \qquad (41.1)$$

and the driving impedance, the ratio of the driving force $F(x_0)$ to the membrane velocity $-i\omega\eta$ at $x - x_0$, is $(2T/c_m) = 2\delta c_m$.

To find the corresponding quantities when a medium is coupled to the membrane will take us more time. To avoid excess symbols we will assume that the medium in the region $y > 0$ has large enough density so it affects the motion of the membrane whereas the reaction of the medium in the region $y < 0$ is negligible (water on one side, air on the other, for example). First we assume that the driving force per unit area at point x, z on the membrane is $F(k)\, e^{ikx-i\omega t}$, where the values of k and of ω are arbitrary. The displacement of the membrane and the pressure in the medium above the membrane then must have the values

$$\eta = A\, e^{ikx-i\omega t}; \qquad p = p_0 \exp\left[ikx + iy\sqrt{\left(\frac{\omega}{c}\right)^2 - k^2} - i\omega t\right] \qquad (41.2)$$

which are related to each other and to the driving force by the equations

$$\frac{\partial p}{\partial y} = i\omega\varrho \frac{\partial \eta}{\partial t} = \omega^2 \varrho \eta,$$

$$F(k)\, e^{ikx - i\omega t} = p + \delta \frac{\partial^2 \eta}{\partial t^2} - T \frac{\partial^2 \eta}{\partial x^2},$$

so that

$$\left.\begin{aligned} \eta &= \frac{[F(k)/T]\, e^{ikx-i\omega t}}{k^2 - \left(\frac{\omega}{c_m}\right)^2 \left[1 + \frac{(\varrho/\delta)}{\sqrt{k^2-(\omega/c)^2}}\right]}, \\ p &= \frac{[\omega^2 \varrho F(k)/T] \exp\left[ikx - y\sqrt{k^2-(\omega/c)^2} - i\omega t\right]}{[k^2-(\omega/c_m)^2]\sqrt{k^2-(\omega/c)^2} - (\omega/c_m)^2(\varrho/\delta)} \end{aligned}\right\} \qquad (41.3)$$

where, if $k^2 < (\omega/c^2)$ the square root becomes *negative* imaginary.

For any given value of ω there are four values of k for which the denominators become zero, for which there can be motion without applied force; in other words free wave motion is possible for these values of k. If the wave velocity of the uncoupled membrane, c_m, is less then the wave velocity c of the medium, then these four roots for k are all real, corresponding to unattenuated wave motion. They can be written as $\pm k_m$ and $\pm k_r$, where, if $(\varrho\lambda/2\pi)$ is considerably smaller than δ, approximate formulas are

$$\left.\begin{aligned} k_m &\approx \frac{\omega}{c_m} + \frac{(\varrho/2\delta)}{\sqrt{1-(c_m/c)^2}} \qquad (c_m < c); \\ k_s &\approx \frac{\omega}{c} + \frac{(\varrho^2 c/2\delta^2\omega)}{[1-(c_m/c)^2]^2} \qquad (\varrho c \ll \omega\delta). \end{aligned}\right\} \qquad (41.4)$$

The first type of wave, with propagation constant $\pm k_m$, has a velocity slightly smaller than c_m, the wave velocity for the uncoupled membrane. For these waves, the majority of the energy is carried by the membrane; the wave in the fluid dies out rapidly with y since $\sqrt{k_m^2-(\omega/c)^2}$ is fairly large. These waves can be called "membrane waves"; their velocity is approximately $\sqrt{T/[\delta+(\varrho\lambda_m/2\pi)]}$, as though the mass of a layer of the medium a thickness $(1/2\pi)$ times the membrane wavelength were simply added to the mass of the membrane.

The second type of wave, with wave number $\pm k_r$ might be called the fluid wave, for it travels with a velocity slightly smaller than c. In this case most of the energy is carried in the fluid, though (as long as $c_m < c$) this energy moves parallel to the membrane and does not go to $y = \infty$; the attenuation factor $\sqrt{k_r^2-(\omega/c)^2}$ is not large, so the amount of medium in motion is large, though finite. As long as $c_m < c$, however, all these waves are surface waves, no energy is propagated to $y = \infty$.

If $c_m > c$, on the other hand, two of the four roots become complex,

$$\left.\begin{aligned} k_m &\approx \frac{\omega}{c_m} - \frac{i(\varrho/2\delta)}{\sqrt{(c_m/c)^2-1}} \qquad (c_m > c), \\ k_r &\approx \frac{\omega}{c} + \frac{(\varrho^2 c/2\delta^2\omega)}{[(c_m/c)^2-1]^2} \qquad (\varrho c \ll \omega\delta) \end{aligned}\right\} \qquad (41.5)$$

corresponding to the fact that k_m is now smaller than (ω/c) and consequently the waves in the medium can propagate to $y = \infty$; thus energy is lost by radiation and the wave along the membrane must attenuate, i.e., k_m is complex. The other pair of roots are still real; these waves are still surface waves, though the energy is still carried to a considerably extent in the fluid.

In the special case when $c_m = c$, the approximate formulas for the four roots are $\pm k_m$ and $\pm k_r$ again, with

$$k_m \approx \frac{\omega}{c} - \frac{1}{2} e^{i\pi/3} \left(\frac{\omega \varrho^2}{c\delta^2}\right)^{\frac{1}{3}}; \qquad k_r \approx \frac{\omega}{c} + \left(\frac{\omega \varrho^2}{c\delta^2}\right)^{\frac{1}{3}} \tag{41.6}$$

again the set k_m corresponds to attenuated wave motion, the set k_r to unattenuated surface waves.

However, we started out to compute the forced motion of the membrane. This has been done, of course, for the sinusoidal force of Eq. (41.3), for any values of k and ω. If k is greater than (ω/c), radiation to $y=\infty$ is impossible and the ratio between force and membrane velocity is imaginary; no energy is lost to the membrane. If k is smaller than (ω/c), however, the denominators of Eqs. (41.3) are complex and some energy radiates away from the membrane.

To determine the response of the membrane-medium system to a concentrated line force, we use Fourier transforms, integrating over k. For example, the Fourier transform of a line force $F(x_0)\,\delta(x-x_0)\,e^{-i\omega t}$ is $F(k) = (1/\sqrt{2\pi})\, e^{-ikx_0 - i\omega t}$ and the responses to such a force are the corresponding Fourier transforms

$$\left.\begin{aligned} \eta(x,t) &= \frac{F(x_0)}{2\pi T} \int_{-\infty}^{\infty} \frac{e^{ik(x-x_0)-i\omega t}\, dk}{k^2 - \left(\frac{\omega}{c_m}\right)^2 \left[1 + \frac{(\varrho/\delta)}{\sqrt{k^2-(\omega/c)^2}}\right]}; \\ p(x,y,t) &= -\frac{\omega^2 \varrho F(x_0)}{2\pi T} \int_{-\infty}^{\infty} \frac{e^{ik(x-x_0)-y\sqrt{k^2-(\omega/c)^2}-i\omega t}\, dk}{[k^2-(\omega/c_m)^2]\sqrt{k^2-(\omega/c)^2} - (\omega^2\varrho/\delta c_m^2)} \end{aligned}\right\} \tag{41.7}$$

where the contour of integration goes above the real axis from $-\infty$ to 0 and below the real axis from 0 to $+\infty$ for k. The poles of the integrands are at $k = \pm k_m$ and the branch points are at $\pm k_r$, the roots discussed earlier. The branch cuts can run from k_r to $i\infty$ and from $-k_r$ to $-i\infty$. When $x > x_0$ the contour can be deformed into one around the pole at k_m plus a loop from $i\infty$ to the left of the cut, around k_r in a counter-clockwise direction and then back to $i\infty$. When $x < x_0$ the pole at $-k_m$ is involved and the loop goes from $-i\infty$ around $-k_r$.

A closed expression, in terms of known functions, is not possible; nevertheless good approximations can be obtained for various situations of interest. The contribution from the pole is straightforward; it is

$$\frac{iF(x_0)}{2Tk_m} e^{ik_m|x-x_0|-i\omega t} \quad \text{for } \eta$$

and

$$-\frac{i\omega^2\varrho F(x_0)}{2Tk_m\sqrt{k_m^2-(\omega/c)^2}} e^{ik_m|x-x_0|-y\sqrt{k_m^2-(\omega/c)^2}-i\omega t} \quad \text{for } p.$$

The first of these should be compared with Eq. (41.1). Evidently this part of the wave represents the membrane wave, only slightly modified by the presence of the fluid. When $c_m < c$, k_m is real and no energy leaves the membrane. The wave spreads outward from x_0 to $x = \pm\infty$ with a speed slightly less than c_m, as though the membrane were loaded with an additional mass of a layer of fluid $(\lambda_m/2\pi)$ thick. If $c_m > c$, however, the membrane as a whole radiates, so k_m is complex and the membrane wave attenuates as its spreads out from $x = x_0$.

This part cannot be all of the wave, however. It is possible to have a discontinuous slope in the membrane at $x = x_0$, but it is not possible to have a discontinuous gradient in the fluid pressure, as is implied by the factor $e^{i k_m |x - x_0|}$. The integral around the branch cut repairs this; it corresponds to the radiation from the discontinuity in slope at $x = x_0$ and represents the only radiation away from the membrane when $c_m < c$.

To show this more clearly we will obtain an asymptotic form for the pressure in the medium. For the integral around the branch point, the only range of k for which the integrand is large is near the branch point. Even near here, the quantity (ϱ/δ) is usually small compared to $\sqrt{k^2 - (\omega/c)^2}$, so the denominator of the integrand for this integral is approximately equal to $[k_r^2 - (\omega/c_m)^2] \sqrt{k^2 - k_r^2}$. Using the integral representation of the Hankel function,

$$H_0^{(1)}\left(\frac{\omega R}{c}\right) = \frac{1}{\pi} \int_{-\infty}^{\infty} \exp\left[i k (x - x_0) + i y \sqrt{\left(\frac{\omega}{c}\right)^2 - k^2}\right] \frac{d k}{\sqrt{(\omega/c)^2 - k^2}} \tag{41.8}$$

where $R^2 = (x - x_0)^2 + y^2$, we see that the integral for the pressure wave, including contributions from the pole and also from the branch point, is thus approximately

$$\left.\begin{aligned} p \approx & - \frac{i \omega^2 F(x_0)}{2 T k_m \sqrt{k_m^2 - (\omega/c)^2}} \exp\left[i k_m |x - x_0| - y \sqrt{k_m^2 - \left(\frac{\omega}{c}\right)^2} - i \omega t\right] - \\ & - \frac{\omega^2 \varrho F(x_0)}{2 T [k_r^2 - (\omega/c_m)^2]} H_0^{(1)}(k_r R)\, e^{-i \omega t} \end{aligned}\right\} \tag{41.9}$$

as long as $|x - x_0|$ is large.

The second term is the asymptotic form, arising from the integral around the branch cut, for the cylindrical out-going wave produced by the discontinuity in slope of the membrane at $x = x_0$, the line of application of the force. When (ω/c) is smaller than $k_m \approx (\omega/c_m)$ this is the only radiation to $y = \infty$ from the membrane, since then the first term represents a surface wave, carrying energy to $|x| = \infty$ but confined, in the y direction, to the fluid within a distance $1/\sqrt{k_m^2 - (\omega/c)^2}$ of the membrane. When c_m is smaller than c there is no way true waves in the medium can be coupled to the membrane motion *except* at the line of discontinuity of slope at $x = x_0$, which produces a cylindrical wave which does carry away some energy. If the membrane were finite in extent, there would also be radiation from the membrane edges.

On the other hand, if the acoustical velocity c is smaller than the wave velocity c_m in the membrane, then outgoing waves can arise from every part of the membrane, the exponential in the first term becomes $\exp[i k_m |x - x_0| + i y \sqrt{(\omega/c)^2 - k_m^2} - i \omega t]$ and all parts of the membrane lose energy, not just the discontinuity at $x = x_0$. In this case the root k_m is complex [Eq. (41.5)] indicating that the first term is largest near $x = x_0$ and attenuates away from this line of application of the force.

The admittance imposed on the driving force, $Y(\omega) = -i \omega \eta(x_0)/F(x_0)$, can be obtained from the integral for η of (41.7). Setting $k_0 = (\omega/c)$, $k_u = (\omega/c_m)$, $\beta = (k_0/k_u) = (c_m/c)$, we have

$$Y(\omega) = \frac{1}{2\pi T} \int_{-\infty}^{\infty} \frac{d k \sqrt{k^2 - k_0^2}}{(k^2 - k_u^2)\sqrt{k^2 - k_0^2} - (\varrho/\delta)\, k_u^2} = \frac{\omega}{2 T k_m} + \frac{(\varrho/\delta k_0)}{\pi \delta c} J(\omega) \tag{41.10}$$

where k_m is the propagation constant for the loaded membrane, as given in Eqs. (41.4) to (41.6). The function $J(\omega)$ arises from the contour around the branch cut;

$$\left.\begin{aligned} J &= i\int_{-i}^{\infty} \frac{du\sqrt{1+u^2}}{(1+\beta^2 u^2)^2(1+u^2)+(\varrho/\delta k_0)^2} \\ &\xrightarrow[k_0<k_u]{} \int_0^{\frac{1}{2}\pi} \frac{\sin^2 w\, d\, w}{(1-\beta^2\cos^2 w)^2 \sin^2 w + (\varrho/\delta k_0)^2} - i\int_{-\infty}^{\infty} \frac{dt}{(1+\beta^2 \operatorname{Sin}^2 t)^2} \\ &\approx \frac{\pi}{2}\left[1 - \frac{\varrho}{\delta k_0} + \cdots\right] + \frac{i/2}{1-\beta^2}\left[1 + \frac{2-\beta^2}{\sqrt{1-\beta^2}} \ln\left(\frac{1-\frac{1}{2}\beta^2 - \sqrt{1-\beta^2}}{1-\frac{1}{2}\beta^2+\sqrt{1-\beta^2}}\right)\right] \end{aligned}\right\} \quad (41.11)$$

the last, approximate form, valid when $\beta = c_m/c$ is less than unity.

The first term in Y, $(\omega/2Tk_m)$, is the membrane load; it differs from the admittance of the unloaded membrane, as obtained from Eq. (41.1), only by the ratio (k_u/k_m). When $c_m < c$, k_m is real and this first term is real, corresponding to the fact that the membrane surface waves carry the energy to ∞, as with a loss-less transmission line. When $c_m > c$, however, k_m is complex, corresponding to the fact that the membrane is now a "leaky transmission line", with a complex input admittance.

The second term in Y is the result of the cylindrical wave generated in the medium by the discontinuity in slope of the membrane at the region of application of the force. Part of this term is real, corresponding to energy radiation; part is imaginary, the stiffness reaction of the near field of the cylindrical wave. This second term is small when the membrane mass δ is considerably larger than the fluid mass load (ϱ/k_0). If the medium is air and the membrane is metal or plastic, it may often be neglected, compared to the first term.

When $\beta > 1$ $(c_m > c)$ the evaluation of J is somewhat more complicated. Numerical evaluation is always possible, however.

Thus the effect, on the motion of the membrane, caused by the coupling of the medium is two-fold: a load on each element of area of the membrane and also an extra load near where the force is applied. When $c \gg c_m$ the area load is mass-like; the membrane acts as though its mass were not δ but were $\delta + (\varrho/k_m)$, an added mass of a thickness $(1/k_m) = (\lambda_m/2\pi)$ of the medium ($2/k_m$ if the medium is also in region $y<0$). When $c \ll c_m$ the area load is resistive, the impedance per unit area is not $-i\omega\delta$ but $-i\omega\delta + \varrho c$, because every part of the membrane radiates. In addition, if the force is applied along a line, there is an added radiation load (in both cases) as though a strip of width $(\sqrt{8}/k_m)$ were radiating directly into the medium. This strip load, arising from the cylindrical wave, is in parallel with the membrane area load, so that the input admittances add.

42. Uniform plate, point force. The same sort of analysis can be applied to a uniform thin plate of mass δ per unit area, thickness h, elastic modulus E and Poisson ratio σ [see Eq. (38.9)] in the x, z plane, coupled to a fluid of density ϱ and wave velocity c in the upper region $y > 0$. If the plate is subjected to a force $F(k)\, e^{ikx - i\omega t}$ per unit area then the equations, analogous to (41.3), for the transverse displacement of the plate and for the pressure wave in the fluid are

$$\left.\begin{aligned} \eta &= \frac{[12(1-\sigma^2)\,F(k)/E h^3]}{k^4 - k_u^4\left[1 + \dfrac{(\varrho/\delta)}{\sqrt{k^2-k_0^2}}\right]} \exp(i k x - i\omega t), \\ p &= \frac{12[(1-\sigma^2)\,\omega^2 \varrho F(k)/E h^3]}{(k^4-k_u^4)\sqrt{k^2-k_0^2} - k_u^4(\varrho/\delta)} \exp\left[i k x - y\sqrt{k^2-k_0^2} - i\omega t\right] \end{aligned}\right\} \quad (42.1)$$

where $k_0 = (\omega/c)$, $k_u = \sqrt{\nu\omega}/c$ and where $\nu^2 = [12\delta(1-\sigma^2)\,c^4/E h^3]$ is the value of ω for which the velocity of transverse waves in the plate is equal to the wave velocity in the fluid.

Here there are six roots to the denominator; one pair, $k = \pm k_p$, is nearly equal to the propagation constant k_u of the unloaded plate, another pair, $k = \pm k_q$, is near $i k_u$ and the third pair, $k = \pm k_r$ is near $k_0 = \omega/c$. If the velocity of waves in the uncoupled plate, $(c\sqrt{\omega/\nu})$, is smaller than c, the wave velocity in the medium, then two pairs of these roots are real;

$$k_p \approx \left(\frac{\sqrt{\omega\nu}}{c}\right) + \frac{(\varrho/4\delta)}{\sqrt{1-(\omega/\nu)}} \approx -i k_q; \qquad k_r \approx \left(\frac{\omega}{c}\right) + \frac{(\varrho^2 c/2\delta^2\omega)}{[1-(\omega/\nu)^2]^2}. \tag{42.2}$$

The waves travelling with propagation constant k_p are the "plate waves", with energy mainly carried by the plate itself, but accompanied by a surface wave of thickness $(\lambda_p/2\pi)$ in the fluid. The waves with wave number k_r are the fluid waves; if $\omega < \nu$ these waves also are surface waves.

If now we wish to compute the plate displacement and the resulting pressure wave when a point force $F_0\,\delta(x-x_0)\,\delta(z-z_0)\,\mathrm{e}^{-i\omega t}$ drives the plate, we must use the two-dimensional Fourier integral,

$$\left.\begin{aligned}
\eta &= \frac{3(1-\sigma^2)\,F_0\,\mathrm{e}^{-i\omega t}}{\pi^2 E h^3}\int_{-\infty}^{\infty}\int_{-\infty}^{\infty}\frac{\mathrm{e}^{i k_x(x-x_0)+i k_z(z-z_0)}\,d k_x\,d k_z}{(k_x^2+k_z^2)^2 - k_u^4\left[1+\dfrac{(\varrho/\delta)}{\sqrt{k_x^2+k_z^2-k_0^2}}\right]}\\
&= \frac{6(1-\sigma^2)\,F_0}{\pi E h^3}\int_0^{\infty}\frac{J_0(kR)\,\mathrm{e}^{-i\omega t}\,k\,dk}{k^4 - k_u^4\left[1+\dfrac{(\varrho/\delta)}{\sqrt{k^2-k_0^2}}\right]}; \quad R^2 = (x-x_0)^2+(z-z_0)^2,\\
p &= \frac{6(1-\sigma^2)\,\omega^2\varrho F_0}{\pi E h^3}\int_0^{\infty}\frac{J_0(kR)\,\mathrm{e}^{-y\sqrt{k^2-k_0^2}-i\omega t}}{(k^4-k_u^4)\sqrt{k^2-k_0^2}-k_u^4(\varrho/\delta)}\,k\,dk; \quad k_u^2 = \frac{\omega\nu}{c^2}; \quad k_0 = \frac{\omega}{c}
\end{aligned}\right\} \tag{42.3}$$

which can be treated in a fashion analogous to those of (41.7).

As with the membrane, asymptotic expressions can be obtained. The results for the pressure wave, for $k_0 R \gg 1$, are

$$\left.\begin{aligned}
p \approx \frac{-\varrho F_0}{2\pi\delta}\,\frac{\mathrm{e}^{i k_r|\boldsymbol{r}-\boldsymbol{r}_0|-i\omega t}}{[1-(k_r/k_u)^4]\,|\boldsymbol{r}-\boldsymbol{r}_0|} &- \frac{i k_p^2 F_0\,\mathrm{e}^{-y\sqrt{k_p^2-k_0^2}-i\omega t}}{8\delta\sqrt{k_p^2-k_0^2}}\,H_0^{(1)}(k_p R) +\\
&+ \frac{k_p^2 F_0\,\mathrm{e}^{i y\sqrt{k_p^2+k_0^2}-i\omega t}}{8\delta\sqrt{k_p^2+k_0^2}}\,H_0^{(1)}(i k_p R).
\end{aligned}\right\} \tag{42.4}$$

When $\omega < \nu$ (i.e., when the plate as a whole cannot radiate) only the first term represents radiation to $y = \infty$; it is a hemispherical wave radiated by the discontinuity in third derivative caused by the point force at x_0, z_0. The second term is a circular wave staying near the plate as it goes out in the x, z plane; the third term is concerned with the discontinuity at x_0, z_0, it dies out rapidly as R increases.

When $\omega > \nu$ and the plate as a whole can couple to the waves in the fluid, then k_p is complex and $k_0^2 > Re\,k_p^2$, so that the second term represents radiation to $y = \infty$, as well as the first term; the plate as a whole radiates, as well as the point of application of the force. In this treatment we have neglected longitudinal wave motion in the plate. It only occasionally gives rise to external effects.

We thus can conclude this section with some general statements regarding the effect of a coupled medium on the behavior of a plate or membrane. If the velocity c of sound in the medium is larger than that of transverse waves in the plate or membrane then the effect of the medium on most of the plate area is, approximately, to increase the effective mass per unit area from δ to $\delta+(\varrho\lambda_p/2\pi)$, where λ_p is the wavelength in the plate. If $c<c_p$ then the additional load is not mass-like but resistive, the impedance per unit area changing from $-i\omega\delta$ to $-i\omega\delta+\varrho c$ or, alternatively, the effective mass is $\delta+i(\varrho\lambda/2\pi)$ instead of δ, where λ is now the wavelength in the medium. In addition, for all values of c and c_p, if the driving force is applied along a line, a cylindrical wave is radiated into the medium, as though a strip $(\sqrt{8}/k_p)$ wide were radiating; if the driving force is applied to a point, a sphercial wave is radiated as though a circular area of diameter $(\sqrt{8}/k_p)$ were radiating, the amplitude of vibration of strip or disk being that of the plate at the point of application of the force.

When $c>c_p$ this cylindrical or spherical wave is the only part of the wave which carries energy to $y=\infty$. When $c<c_p$ every part of the plate or membrane can radiate.

43. Forced motion of periodically supported membrane. As a last example of forced motion we return to the membrane of mass δ and tension T, supported by parallel struts at $x=ml$ (m an integer, positive or negative) each having a transverse impedance Z_s per unit length. As with the uniform membrane, we first apply forces to all supports, phased with propagation constant k,

$$F(x)=F(k)\,\mathrm{e}^{-i\omega t}\sum_m \mathrm{e}^{ikx}\,\delta(x-m\,l) \tag{43.1}$$

and then integrate over k to obtain the forced motion for a force concentrated just along the line $x=0$. For the phased force of Eq. (43.1), concentrated on every strut, the membrane will have a displacement $\eta(x)$ which has discontinuities in slope at $x=ml$ and which is phased so that $\eta(x+nl)=\mathrm{e}^{inkl}\,\eta(x)$. The propagation constant k_m for the membrane is that for a membrane in contact with the medium in the region $y>0$ and thus will differ from $k_1=(\omega/c_m)=\omega\sqrt{\delta/T}$. The effect of the medium should be obtained by using a phased-periodic GREEN'S function like that of (40.6), which should be adjusted so as to give a self-consistent value of k_m, a rather tedious procedure (as will be demonstrated in Sect. 47). However we can use the results of Sect. 41 to obtain an approximate expression for k_m. We can say the load of the medium is approximately that which results in the propagation constant k_m of Eqs. (41.4), (41.5) and (41.6).

For example, when $c_m<c\,(k_1>k_0=\omega/c)$ we can say that the propagation constant k_m for the membrane is approximately $k_1+(\varrho/2\delta\sqrt{1-\beta^2})$, where $\beta=(k_0/k_1)=(c_m/c)$. To this approximation the shape of the membrane is

$$\eta(k,x)\approx\left\{\begin{array}{ll}A\,[\sin k_m(x+l)-\mathrm{e}^{-ikl}\sin k_m x]\,\mathrm{e}^{-i\omega t} & (-l<x<0),\\ A\,[\mathrm{e}^{ikl}\sin k_m x+\sin k_m(l-x)]\,\mathrm{e}^{-i\omega t} & (0<x<l),\\ A\,[\mathrm{e}^{2ikl}\sin k_m(x-l)+\mathrm{e}^{ik}\sin k_m(2l-x)]\,\mathrm{e}^{-i\omega t} & (l<x<2l)\end{array}\right\} \tag{43.2}$$

and so on. The ratio between $F(k)$ of Eq. (43.1) and the amplitude A is obtained by working out the impedance at each point of application of the force. This force must not only drive the membrane, it must move the strut and must also generate the cylindrical wave produced at the line of application of the force, which is responsible for the admittance $(\varrho/2\pi\delta^2k_0c)\,J$ of Eq. (41.10). The membrane admittance, however, is not the quantity $(\omega/2Tk_m)$ of Eq. (41.10), for the shape of the membrane is not $A\,e^{ik_m x - i\omega t}$, as it was in Sect. 41, but is that given in Eq. (43.2). In this case the force required to produce the motion of the support plus the discontinuity in slope of the membrane is

$$T\left(\frac{\partial\eta}{\partial x}\right)_{x=-\Delta} - T\left(\frac{\partial\eta}{\partial x}\right)_{x=+\Delta} - i\,\omega\,\eta\,Z_s \qquad (\Delta\to 0)$$
$$= 2A\,T\,k_m(\cos k_m l - \cos k\,l) - i\,\omega\,A\sin k_m l.$$

Consequently the total admittance $-i\omega\eta/F(k)$ is

$$\left.\begin{aligned} Y(k) \approx {} & \frac{i\sin k_m l}{2\delta c_m(\cos k\,l - \cos k_m l + \tfrac{1}{2} i z_s \sin k_m l)} + \\ & + \frac{\varrho}{\delta k_0}\,\frac{J}{\pi\delta c}\left[\frac{\cos k\,l - \cos k_m l}{\cos k\,l - \cos k_m l + \tfrac{1}{2} i z_s \sin k_m l}\right]^2 \end{aligned}\right\} \qquad (43.3)$$

where $z_z = (Z_s/\delta c_m)$, as in Eqs. (40.3) and (40.9), is the specific support impedance. We have here assumed that $\varrho J \ll \delta k_0$.

When the second term, representing the admittance of the cylindrical wave radiating from the discontinuity in slope of the membrane, is small enough to be neglected, the value of A, to be inserted in Eq. (43.2), is

$$A \approx \frac{-F(k)}{2\delta c_m \omega(\cos k\,l - \cos k_m l + \tfrac{1}{2} i z_s \sin k_m l)} \qquad (43.4)$$

where the effect of the coupled medium enters only in the difference between k_m and $k_1 = (\omega/c_m)$. This approximation is valid only when the density of the medium is considerably smaller than the membrane density.

We now can ask again whether free waves can travel along the periodic structure, whether there exists a value or values of k for which the denominator of (43.4) is zero, so that A can be non-zero when F is zero. If z_s is pure imaginary (i.e., if the support impedance is purely reactive) and if $\frac{1}{2} z_s \sin k_m l$ is small enough, then this can occur for real values of kl, and non-attenuated waves can travel along the structure. If z_s is imaginary but not small (a more likely circumstance) then a root for kl, which occurs when

$$\cos k\,l = \cos k_m l - \tfrac{1}{2} i\,z_s \sin k_m l \qquad (43.5)$$

corresponds to a complex value of k, and the wave attenuates. The general form of the root, for complex z_s, is $k_n = (\alpha + i\beta + n\pi)/l$, where n is any integer. As long as $c_m < c$ the wave motion is a surface wave, except for the cylindrical waves generated at each membrane discontinuity. Note the similarity with Eq. (24.11).

If the system is driven by a single line force $F_0\,e^{-i\omega t}$ applied along the line $x = 0$, the membrane shape will be

$$\eta \approx \frac{-F_0}{4\pi\delta c_m\omega}\oint \frac{e^{ikl}\sin k_m x + \sin k_m(l-x)}{\cos kl - \cos k_m l + \tfrac{1}{2} z_s \sin k_m l}\,dk \qquad (0 < x < l) \qquad (43.6)$$

where the integral is a contour around the pole at $kl = \alpha + i\beta$. Thus the resulting shape will be a function of the form given in Eq. (43.2), with phase factor $kl = \alpha + i\beta$ and amplitude

$$A = \frac{F_0}{2\delta\omega c_m}\left[(\cos k_m l - \tfrac{1}{2} i\,z_s \sin k_m l)^2 - 1\right]^{-\frac{1}{2}} \qquad (43.7)$$

for $x > 0$ and another set, with $kl = -\alpha + i\beta$ and the same value of A, for $x < 0$. Thus the driven motion of the periodically supported membrane combines the behavior of the unsupported membrane of Sect. 41 with the filter-like behavior of the periodic duct discussed in Sect. 24. If $c_m < c$ most of the energy stays near the membrane, but, if z_s is large, waves are rapidly attenuated except for driving frequencies for which $|\cos k_m l - (i/2)\, z_s \sin k_m l|$ is less than unity. When $c_m > 0$, the membrane as a whole can radiate and the wave is attenuated for all driving frequencies.

III. Coupled motion in ducts.

44. Constriction in a circular duct. As an example of the computation of coupled motion in ducts, we will consider the case of a rigid, cylindrical duct of radius a, of infinite length, partially obstructed by a rigid plate with a concentric hole of radius b in it [*41*], [*72*], [*75*]. In terms of the cylindrical coordinates z, r, ϕ the obstruction is in the $z=0$ plane, with the area from $r=0$ to $r=b$ open and the annulus from $r=b$ to $r=a$ (the radius of the duct) being rigid and impervious to motion of the fluid. Suppose a plane wave of frequency $(\omega/2\pi)$ is sent along the duct in the positive z direction from $z=-\infty$. It will be affected by the obstruction, part of the wave will be reflected by the flange and part will traverse the hole to be transmitted on to $z=+\infty$. To compute the distortion of the field near the obstruction and the intensity of the reflected and transmitted waves, we proceed to match the field across the opening in the obstruction, as was discussed in connection with Eq. (13.4).

We choose a GREEN's function G_+ for the region $z \geqq 0$ to have zero normal gradient at $z=0$ and $r=a$ and to be an outgoing wave at $z \to \infty$. Since the whole problem is symmetric about the cylindrical axis, we need not consider dependence on ϕ. The appropriate GREEN's function is

$$\left.\begin{aligned} G_+(r, z | r_0, z_0) &= \frac{1}{i\pi a^2} \sum_{n=0}^{\infty} \frac{J_0(x_n r_0/a)\, J_0(x_n r/a)}{k_n J_0^2(x_n)} \times \\ &\quad \times \begin{cases} \cos(k_n z_0)\, e^{i k_n z} & (0 \leqq z_0 \leqq z), \\ \cos(k_n z)\, e^{i k_n z_0} & (0 \leqq z \leqq z_0), \end{cases} \\ k_n^2 = k^2 - \left(\frac{x_n}{a}\right)^2; &\quad k = \frac{\omega}{c}; \quad J_0'(x_n) = 0. \end{aligned}\right\} \tag{44.1}$$

The GREEN's function G_-, for the region $z \leqq 0$ is obtained by reversing the signs of z and z_0 in G_+. Once the normal gradient of the pressure, $(\partial p/\partial z)_0 = i k \varrho c u_z^0(r_0)$, in the opening $z=0$, $0 \leqq r \leqq b$, is known, these GREEN's functions enable us to compute the pressure anywhere in the duct.

The constant x_n is the n-th root of the equation $[\partial J_0(x)/\partial x] = 0$ or of $J_1(x) = 0$; the first few values are $x_0 = 0$, $x_1 = 3.8317$, $x_2 = 7.0156$, $x_3 = 10.1735, \ldots$, and the asymptotic values are $x_n \to \pi n + \frac{1}{4}\pi$. The functions $J_0(x_n r/a)$ are mutually orthogonal eigenfunctions; their normalization constant is $\frac{1}{2} a^2 J_0^2(x_n)$. The pressure wave is then

$$p(r, z) = \begin{cases} 2\pi i k \varrho c \int_0^b G_+(r, z | r_0, z_0)\, u(r_0)\, r_0\, d r_0 & (z \geqq 0) \\ 2A \cos(kz) - 2\pi i k \varrho c \int_0^b G_-(r, z | r_0, z_0)\, u_z^0(r_0)\, r_0\, d r_0 & (z \leqq 0), \end{cases} \tag{44.2}$$

where, in the region $z \leqq 0$, we have included the incident wave $A\, e^{ikz}$ (we omit the factor $e^{-i\omega t}$) plus the wave $A\, e^{-ikz}$ which would be reflected if there were no hole in the barrier at $z=0$.

To simplify the discussion we assume that ka is smaller than x_1, so that only the plane-wave mode $(n=0)$ is propagated along the duct; all higher modes attenuate. In this case the wave which reaches $z \to \infty$ will be just the lowest mode and, from the form of G_+ we see that

$$p \to \frac{\tau A}{\pi a^2} e^{ikz} \qquad (z \to \infty) \qquad (k a < x_1) \tag{44.3}$$

where

$$\tau = \frac{2\pi \varrho c}{A} \int_0^b u_z^0(r_0)\, r_0\, d r_0$$

is the ratio of the amplitude of total flow through the hole to the acoustic velocity amplitude $(A/\varrho c)$ of the incident wave (so that τ has the dimensions of an area). The ratio of the square of the pressure amplitude at $z \to \infty$ to the square of A the incident pressure amplitude, $T = |\tau/\pi a^2|^2$, is the *transmission factor* for the opening, the ratio of transmitted to incident power. The *reflection factor* R is, of course, $1 - T$. We thus see that, if we know the value of the acoustic velocity $u_z^0(r)$ at each point in the hole, we can compute the reflection and transmission without needing to know any other details of the near field. We thus look for an integral equation for u_z^0.

Such an integral equation is easily obtained by requiring that the pressure in the opening, $z=0$, $0 \leqq r \leqq b$, computed using G_+, is the same as that computed using G_-; from Eq. (44.2) we have

$$A = 2\pi i k \varrho c \int_0^b G(r, 0 | r_0, 0)\, u_z^0(r_0)\, r_0\, d r_0 \qquad (0 \leqq r \leqq b) \tag{44.4}$$

where we have removed the subscripts from G because $G_+(r, 0|r_0, 0) = G_-(r, 0|r_0, 0)$. We could, of course, obtain the solution by expanding u_z^0 in a series of the eigenfunctions $J_0(x_n r/b)$, appropriate for the hole, and compute the series coefficients. But these new eigenfunctions are not orthogonal to the set $J_0(x_n r/a)$, used for G, so that the equation for each expansion coefficient includes all the others, and there is no simple way to find the eigenvalues of the resulting infinite matrix.

A method of successive approximations, which is usually satisfactory, is by use of a variational formula for τ, followed by successive use of the integral equation, if necessary. It can be shown that when the shape of the trial function $\varphi(r)$ in

$$\left.\begin{aligned} [\tau] &= \frac{1}{ik}\left[\frac{(\int \varphi r\, dr)^2}{\int \varphi r\, dr \int G(r|r_0)\, \varphi r_0\, d r_0}\right] = \pi a^2 \left[\frac{U^2}{U^2 - i k a W}\right]; \\ U &= \int_0^b \varphi(r)\, r\, dr; \quad W = \sum_{n=1}^{\infty} \frac{[\int \varphi(r)\, J_0(x_n r/a)\, r\, dr]^2}{J_0^2(x_n) \sqrt{x_n^2 - k^2 a^2}} \end{aligned}\right\} \tag{44.5}$$

is varied to give a stationary value for the quantity in brackets, this stationary value will be the correct value of τ and the shape of φ which yields this stationary value is related to the solution of Eq. (44.4) by the formula

$$u_z^0(r) = \frac{A a^2 U \varphi(r)}{2\varrho c (U^2 - i k a W)} \qquad (0 \leqq r < b). \tag{44.6}$$

This expression for u_z^0 can then be inserted back in (44.2) to obtain $p(r, z)$, if the near field is required; the far field is given immediately by the value of τ. Incidentally, we have used the fact that k is assumed to be smaller than (x_1/a), to change $\sqrt{k^2 a^2 - x_n^2}$ into $i\sqrt{x_n^2 - k^2 a^2}$ for $n > 0$ in these expressions.

If $b \ll a$ the velocity distribution for steady flow through the hole would be $u_z^0 \to B/\sqrt{1-(r/b)^2}$, whereas as b approaches a $u_z^0 \to C$. Consequently an appropriate form to use for a trial function is

$$\varphi(r) = \gamma + \left[\frac{1}{\sqrt{1-(r/b)^2}}\right] \tag{44.7}$$

where γ is a variational parameter. Using the integral relations

$$\int_0^b \frac{J_0(x_n r/a)}{\sqrt{1-(r/b)^2}}\, r\,dr = \left(\frac{a\,b}{x_n}\right)\sin\left(\frac{x_n b}{a}\right) \xrightarrow[n=0]{} b^2,$$

$$\int_0^b J_0\left(\frac{x_n r}{a}\right) r\,dr = \left(\frac{a\,b}{x_n}\right) J_1\left(\frac{x_n b}{a}\right) \xrightarrow[n=0]{} \tfrac{1}{2}\, b^2$$

we find that the optimal values of γ, of the transmission factor τ and the velocity u_z^0 can all be expressed in terms of the convergent series

$$\left.\begin{aligned}
S_0 &= \sum_{n=1}^{\infty} \frac{\sin^2(x_n b/a)}{J_0^2(x_n)(x_n b/a)^2\sqrt{x_n^2-k^2a^2}} \to \begin{cases} 0.785\left(\frac{a}{b}-1\right)+0.197\,k^2a^2 & (b \gg a),\\ 0.0873+0.0035\,k^2a^2 & (b\to a),\end{cases}\\
S_1 &= \sum_{n=1}^{\infty} \frac{2\sin(x_n b/a)\,J_1(x_n b/a)}{J_0^2(x_n)(x_n b/a)^2\sqrt{x_n^2-k^2a^2}} \to \begin{cases} 0.785\left(\frac{a}{b}-1\right)+0.197\,k^2a^2 & (b\ll a),\\ -[0.480+0.0087\,k^2a^2]\,\varepsilon & (b\to a),\end{cases}\\
S_2 &= \sum_{n=1}^{\infty} \frac{4\,J_1^2(x_n b/a)}{J_0^2(x_n)(x_n b/a)^2\sqrt{x_n^2-k^2a^2}} \to \begin{cases} 0.907\,\frac{a}{b}-0.785+0.197\,k^2a^2 & (b\ll a),\\ [-0.859-2.546\ln\varepsilon+0.090\,k^2a^2]\,\varepsilon^2 & (b\to a)\end{cases}
\end{aligned}\right\} \tag{44.8}$$

where the expressions at the right are limiting values when ka is small; quantity ε equals $(a-b)/a$. All three sums diverge as $b\to 0$. Sum S_0 is positive in the range $0 \leqq b \leqq a$ and approaches a small, positive value as $b\to a$. Sum S_1 oscillates in the range $0<b<a$ and approaches zero from a negative value as $b\to a$. Sum S_2 is positive in the range $0<b<a$; it approaches zero proportional to $\varepsilon^2\ln\varepsilon$ as $b\to a$.

Using these definitions, the optimal values of γ, τ, u_z^0 and the transmission constant T are then

$$\left.\begin{aligned}
\gamma &= -2\,\frac{S_0-S_1}{S_1-S_2}; \quad \left(\frac{\pi a^2}{\tau}\right) = 1 + i\,k\,a\,\frac{S_1^2+S_0S_2}{S_0-2S_1+S_2},\\
u_z^0 &\approx \frac{A\,a^2}{\varrho c b^2}\,\frac{(S_0-S_1)-\frac{1}{2}F(S_1-S_2)}{S_0-2S_1+S_2+i\,k\,a(S_1^2-S_0S_2)} \to\\
&\to \begin{cases} \dfrac{(A\,a^2/2\varrho c b^2)\,F}{1-0.785\,i\,(k\,a^2/b)} & (b\ll a),\\[2mm] \dfrac{A\,a^2}{\varrho c b^2}\,[1+5.50\,\varepsilon+2.75\,\varepsilon F] & (b\to a),\end{cases}\\
T &\approx \frac{(S_0-2S_1+S_2)^2}{(S_0-2S_1+S_2)^2+k^2a^2(S_1^2-S_0S_2)^2} \to\\
&\to \begin{cases} 1/[1+0.616\,(k^2a^4/b^2)] & (b\ll a),\\ 1-12.25\,k^2a^2\varepsilon^4\,(1+0.729\ln\varepsilon)^2 & (b\to a)\end{cases}
\end{aligned}\right\} \tag{44.9}$$

where $F = 1/\sqrt{1-(r/b)^2}$ and, as before, $\varepsilon = (a-b)/a$. The limiting-value expressions are for $ka < 1$. We see that when the hole expands and the flange disappears ($b \to a$) the distortion of the wave field at $z = 0$ disappears and the whole wave continues on to $z \to \infty$ ($T \to 1$). On the other hand when the hole shrinks in size the velocity there is distributed proportional to the function $F = 1/\sqrt{1-(r/b)^2}$, concentrating near the sharp edge of the flange; the fraction T of power transmitted goes to zero quadratically with b, though the amount which does get through is inversely proportional to the square of the frequency ($T \propto b^2/k^2 a^4$); long waves can more easily leak through small holes.

Many other joining problems in ducts can be computed by similar methods. The reflection from and transmission past a change in duct cross-section are cases which have been worked out. Calculation of the transmission of sound past a change in direction of the duct axis is also possible [*47*]; the results need not be detailed here. The radiation of sound from the open end of a cylindrical duct can be solved exactly by the Wiener-Hopf method [*46*], [*47*], illustrated in Sect. 25. Limitations of space forbid further elaboration here. Instead, we go on to other types of duct problems.

45. Transmission in duct with flexible walls [*11*], [*33*]. We pointed out in Chap. B that if the walls of a duct yield to the pressure of the wave inside, the wave velocity inside the duct will be different from the value c for free space. In Sect. 23 we considered the case where the yielding was proportional to the pressure at a given point and where there was no coupling to any medium outside the duct; here we take up the case where the duct walls couple with the medium outside, which is assumed to have the same ϱ and c as the medium within the duct. We attack the problem in two steps. In this section we investigate the reaction of the medium outside the duct on the duct walls and thus on the wave motion inside, using a simple form of duct for the analysis. In the next subsection we consider in more detail the coupling of a less simple form of duct with the medium inside, using the previous analysis to provide the reaction of the external medium. In each case we assume that the transverse dimensions of the duct are small compared to the wavelength.

In this first step we consider a cylindrical duct of radius a, where $a \ll (c/\omega)$. The wave inside the duct will have a velocity somewhat different from c, but the difference will not be large for the "plane-wave" mode if the duct walls are stiff. We can thus assume that the dependence of the pressure inside and outside the duct, and the radial displacement of the duct wall, all depend on t and on z, the distance along the duct axis, through the common factor $\exp\left(iz\sqrt{k^2-(\alpha/a)^2} - i\omega t\right)$, where $k = (\omega/c)$ and where the value of the constant α is to be determined by equating motions and pressures at the duct walls.

Inside the duct the lowest mode is the pressure wave

$$p_1 = p_0\, J_0\left(\frac{\alpha r}{a}\right) \exp\left(i z \sqrt{k^2 - \left(\frac{\alpha}{a}\right)^2} - i\omega t\right). \tag{45.1}$$

Outside the duct the wave is

$$p_2 = A H_0^{(1)}\left(\frac{\alpha r}{a}\right) \exp\left(i z \sqrt{k^2 - \left(\frac{\alpha}{a}\right)^2} - i\omega t\right), \tag{45.2}$$

where $H_0^{(1)}(x)$ is the Hankel function for outgoing waves (if α is real power flows away from the duct; if α is imaginary the wave clings to the duct and power is not lost to $r \to \infty$). The radius of the duct will change in response to the difference in pressure $(p_1 - p_2)_a$ so that the radius is $a + \eta$, where η is a function of z and of t. The reaction force of the duct walls to this pressure difference will be proportional to the change in curvature of the walls; if the wavelength is long compared to a this reaction, for a cylindrical duct, is a point reaction, practically independent of λ. Thus, if the duct wall has a mass δ per unit area and a natural frequency for radial oscillation, in the absence of the medium, of $(\omega_0/2\pi)$, the relation between the radial extension η and the pressure difference $(p_1 - p_2)_a$ is approximately

$$\left.\begin{aligned} &(p_1 - p_2)_a = \delta\eta(\omega_0^2 - \omega^2); \quad \eta = D\exp\left(iz\sqrt{k^2 - \left(\frac{\alpha}{a}\right)^2} - i\omega t\right) \\ \text{or}\quad & \\ &p_0 J_0(\alpha) - A H_0^{(1)}(\alpha) = \delta D(\omega_0^2 - \omega^2) \end{aligned}\right\} \tag{45.3}$$

where the term $+\delta\eta\,\omega_0^2$ is the stiffness reaction and $-\delta\eta\,\omega^2$ the mass reaction of the duct wall.

In addition the radial velocity $-i\omega\eta$ of the wall must equal the radial velocities $(1/ik\varrho c)\,(\partial p_1/\partial r)_a$ and $(1/ik\varrho c)\,(\partial p_2/\partial r)_a$,

$$-i\omega D = -\frac{\alpha p_0}{i\varrho c k a} J_1(\alpha) = -\frac{\alpha A}{i\varrho c k a} H_1^{(1)}(\alpha). \tag{45.4}$$

Combining these equations, and using the expression for the Wronskian

$$J_1(\alpha)\,H_0^{(1)}(\alpha) - J_0(\alpha)\,H_1^{(1)}(\alpha) = \frac{2i}{\pi\alpha}$$

we obtain the equation for α,

$$\pi\alpha^2 J_1(\alpha)\,H_1^{(1)}(\alpha) = \frac{2i\varrho a\omega^2}{\delta(\omega_0^2 - \omega^2)}. \tag{45.5}$$

This equation has several roots; the root for the fundamental mode is the smallest one. If ϱa is small compared to δ and/or if ω^2 is small compared to ω_0^2 then α is small and, for the lowest mode, we can use the first terms in the series expansions for J_1 and H_1. The equation for α then becomes

$$\alpha^2 \approx -\frac{2\varrho a\omega^2}{\delta(\omega_0^2 - \omega^2)}. \tag{45.6}$$

Thus, if $\omega_0 > \omega$ (if the walls have stiffness reaction), the constant α is imaginary. In this case the phase velocity $\omega/\sqrt{k^2 - (\alpha/a)^2}$ inside the duct is smaller than c and the waves outside the duct do not radiate to $r \to \infty$ but cling to the tube. On the other hand if ω is larger than ω_0 [but if $\varrho a \ll \delta$, so that (45.6) still holds] then α is real, the phase velocity is greater than c and a small amount of energy radiates to $r \to \infty$ [this would imply that α should be complex, which is correct if we solve the exact Eq. (45.5), but the imaginary part is small if $\varrho a \ll \delta$].

In this simple example we have really just considered the coupling of the wave inside the duct with the wave outside. For a duct of radius small compared to the wavelength we can consider the wall reaction to be a point reaction and need not bring in the effects of wave motion in the duct wall itself. In this the cylindrical tube differs from the flat side of a rectangular duct, where it would be a poor approximation to consider the wall reaction to be point impedance. What we have done, however, is to work out the reaction of the medium outside the tube, and this part of the analysis can be used in other, more complicated calculations. What is needed is the fact that, when the mean radius of the duct is small compared to the wavelength then, no matter what the cross-sectional shape of the duct, the acoustic pressure p_2 of the external wave is approximately constant over the perimeter of the duct and is related to the amplitude q of the total radial flow of fluid outward (for the cylinder, $q=2\pi a v_r$) by the relation

$$p_2 \approx \frac{q}{2\pi i \alpha \varrho c k a} \frac{H_0^{(1)}(\alpha)}{H_1^{(1)}(\alpha)} \to \frac{i\omega\varrho q}{2\pi} \ln(\alpha) \quad (k a \to 0) \tag{45.7}$$

where a is the mean radius of cross section of the duct and α is the quantity we have computed for the case of the tube and will compute again for a rectangular duct. As long as ka is small the reaction pressure of the external wave is uniform over the outside of the duct and its magnitude depends only on the mean outward velocity of the surface of the duct.

46. Coupling of rectangular duct with transmitted wave. To see, in more detail, how one can calculate the coupling of duct walls with the internal-external acoustic waves, we consider next a rectangular duct of transverse (x and y) dimensions a and b, with three walls rigid but with the fourth side (the one in the x, z plane, of width a) a membrane of mass δ per unit area and under tension T. The boundary conditions on the internal pressure wave p_1 are thus that $(\partial p/\partial x)=0$ at $x=0$ and $x=a$ $(\partial p/\partial y)=0$ at $y=b$ and $(\partial p/\partial y)=\varrho\omega^2\eta$ at $y=0$, where η is the displacement (in the positive y direction) of the membrane which constitutes the side $y=0$. The equation of motion of the membrane is

$$\delta c_p^2 \nabla^2 \eta + \delta\omega^2 \eta = (p_1 - p_2)_{y=0}; \qquad c_p^2 = \frac{T}{\delta} \tag{46.1}$$

where p_1 is the pressure on the internal (upper) face and p_2 that on the external (lower) face of the membrane. The boundary conditions on the membrane are that $\eta=0$ at $x=0$ and $x=a$.

As in the previous sub-section, we assume that p_1, p_2 and η vary with z and t according to the factor $\exp\left(iz\sqrt{k^2-(\alpha/a)^2}-i\omega t\right)$ where the parameter α is to be determined. In this case the net outward flow from the outside of the duct is $q=i\omega\int\eta\,dx$ and, according to Eq. (45.7), if a and b are smaller than (c/ω), the external pressure p_2 is nearly independent of x,

$$p_2 \approx -\frac{\omega^2\varrho}{2\pi} \ln(\alpha) \int_0^a \eta\, dx. \tag{46.2}$$

Having decided on the z and t dependence we need only match forces and velocities across the membrane in the transverse direction, from $x=0$ to $x=a$. The one-dimensional GREEN'S function for the membrane, with z propagation constant $\sqrt{k^2-(\alpha/a)^2}$, as specified, for a unit upward point force at $x=x_1$ is

$$g(x|x_1) = \frac{a}{\delta c_p^2 \beta \sin\beta} \begin{cases} \sin\frac{\beta x}{a} \sin\frac{\beta}{a}(a-x_1) & (0 \leqq x \leqq x_1 \leqq a), \\ \sin\frac{\beta}{a}(a-x) \sin\frac{\beta x_1}{a} & (0 \leqq x_1 \leqq x \leqq a) \end{cases} \tag{46.3}$$

where

$$\beta^2 = (k_p a)^2 - (k a)^2 + \alpha^2, \qquad k_p = \frac{\omega}{c_p}, \qquad k = \frac{\omega}{c}.$$

Therefore, if the pressures are known, the membrane displacement dependence on x would be

$$\eta(x) = \int_0^a (p_2 - p_1)\, g(x|x_1)\, dx_1 \tag{46.4}$$

where $(p_1 - p_2)$ is the pressure differential at point x on the membrane (the common z dependence is the exponential, as given above).

However the internal pressure is not known, it is determined by η. The GREEN's function for the x, y dependence of p_1, assuming the exponential z and t dependence, is

$$\left.\begin{aligned} G(x, y|x_0, y_0) &= \sum_{m=0}^{\infty} \frac{\varepsilon_m\, a \cos\frac{\pi m y}{b} \cos\frac{\pi m y_0}{b}}{b\, \alpha_m \sin(\alpha_m)} \times \\ &\times \begin{cases} \cos\frac{\alpha_m x}{a} \cos\frac{\alpha_m}{a}(a - x_0) & (0 \leqq x \leqq x_0 \leqq a), \\ \cos\frac{\alpha_m}{a}(a - x) \cos\frac{\alpha_m x_0}{a} & (0 \leqq x_0 \leqq x \leqq a) \end{cases} \end{aligned}\right\} \tag{46.5}$$

where $\varepsilon_m = 1\ (m=0) = 2\ (m>0)$, $\alpha_m^2 = \alpha^2 - (\pi m a/b)^2$ and, since we are assuming that $\alpha < ka < 1$, the higher α's are all imaginary, $\alpha_m \approx i(\pi m a/b)$ $(m>0)$. In terms of this GREEN's function the internal pressure is

$$p_1(x, y) = \varrho\, \omega^2 \int_0^a G(x, y|x_0, 0)\, \eta(x_0)\, dx_0 \tag{46.6}$$

where η is the membrane displacement at the point $(x_0, 0, z)$ and where the z dependence of both p_1 and η is $\exp\left(i z \sqrt{k^2 - (\alpha/a)^2}\right)$ as noted earlier.

We can now combine Eqs. (46.4) and (46.6) in two ways; one results in an integral equation for η, the other in an integral equation for the internal pressure at the membrane surface. We choose the latter because we expect the pressure amplitude across the membrane, for the principle wave, to be nearly independent of x, which makes it easier to solve for. The result of substituting (46.4) in (46.6) is

$$\left.\begin{aligned} p_1(x, 0) &= -\varrho\, \omega^2 \int_0^a G(x, 0)|x_0, 0)\, dx_0 \int_0^a g(x_0|x_1)\,(p_1 - p_2)\, dx_1 \\ &= \frac{-\varrho\, k_p^2 a^2}{\beta \sin\beta} \int_0^a \Gamma(x|x_1)\,(p_1 - p_2)\, dx_1; \\ \Gamma(x|x_1) &= \sum_{m=0}^{\infty} \frac{\varepsilon_m\, a\, \beta}{b\, \alpha_m (\beta^2 - \alpha_m^2) \sin\alpha_m} \Big[\cos\frac{\alpha}{a}(a - x) \sin\frac{\beta}{a}(a - x_1) + \\ &\quad + \cos\frac{\alpha_m x}{a} \sin\frac{\beta x_1}{a} - F_m(x|x_1)\Big]; \\ F_m(x|x_1) &= \begin{cases} \sin\beta \cos\frac{\alpha_m}{a}(a - x) \cos\frac{\alpha_m x_1}{a} + \\ \qquad + \frac{\alpha_m}{\beta} \sin(\alpha_m) \sin\frac{\beta}{a}(a - x) \sin\frac{\beta x_1}{a} & (x_1 < x), \\ \sin\beta \cos\frac{\alpha_m x}{a} \cos\frac{\alpha_m}{a}(a - x_1) + \\ \qquad + \frac{\alpha_m}{\beta} \sin(\alpha_m) \sin\frac{\beta x}{a} \sin\frac{a}{p}(a - x_1) & (x < x_1) \end{cases} \end{aligned}\right\} \tag{46.7}$$

which satisfies the p boundary conditions (zero slope) for x and the η conditions (zero value at $x = 0, a$) for x_1.

If we neglect p_2, Eq. (46.7) is a homogeneous Fredholm equation for p_1. The solution is $p_1=0$ except for a discrete set of values of α. We wish to find the smallest allowed value of α, and to obtain the corresponding solution for p and then for η. Examination of function Γ shows that the magnitude of the principle term $(m=0)$ varies sharply with $\alpha(=\alpha_0)$ when α is small; small shifts of value of α produce large shifts in the size of the integral of Γ. Consequently, adjusting α so that an equality of average value on both sides of the equation will produce a good approximation to the correct value of α.

To demonstrate these statements, let us carry out the equivalent of a Born approximation on Eq. (46.7) and assume, for the first approximation, that $(p_1-p_2)=P$, a constant, inside the integral, and see whether the result of the integration is nearly independent of x. The result of the integration is a second approximation for p_1,

$$\left.\begin{aligned} p_1(x,0) \approx \frac{-\varrho k_p^2 a^4 P}{b\,\delta\,\beta^2\alpha^2}\Big\{\frac{1}{\beta}\tan\Big(\frac{1}{2}\beta\Big)\Big[\cos\frac{\alpha}{a}(a-x)+\cos\frac{\alpha x}{a}\Big]-1-\\ -\frac{\alpha^2}{\beta^2}\,\frac{\sin(\beta x/a)+\sin(\beta/a)(a-x)}{\sin\beta}-2\alpha^2\sum_{m=1}^{\infty}\Big(\frac{b}{\pi m a}\Big)^2 f_m(x)\Big\}\end{aligned}\right\} \tag{46.8}$$

where

$$\left.\begin{aligned} f_m=\Big\{\frac{\beta\,\alpha_m}{\beta^2-\alpha_m^2}\tan\Big(\frac{1}{2}\beta\Big)\frac{\cos(\alpha_m x/a)+\cos(\alpha_m/a)(a-x)}{\sin\alpha_m}-1-\\ -\frac{\alpha_m^2}{\beta^2-\alpha_m^2}\,\frac{\sin(\beta x/a)+\sin(\beta/a)(a-x)}{\sin\beta}\Big\},\\ \alpha_m=i\sqrt{\Big(\frac{\pi m a}{b}\Big)^2-\alpha^2};\qquad \beta=\sqrt{(k_p^2-k^2)\,a^2-\alpha^2};\\ \beta^2-\alpha_m^2=\Big(\frac{\pi m a}{b}\Big)^2+(k_p^2-k^2)\,a^2.\end{aligned}\right\} \tag{46.9}$$

The functions f_m involve ratios of hyperbolic cosines to hyperbolic sines and other terms, all of the order of magnitude of unity. Therefore when α is small this second approximation to p_1 is the sum of a quantity which is nearly independent of x [the first line of (46.8)] plus small correction terms; it is a quantity nearly independent of x with magnitude inversely proportional to α^2. To determine α to the first approximation we can simply equate the average value of p_1 (call it P_1) by integrating both sides of (46.8) over x from 0 to a,

$$P_1=\frac{1}{a}\int_0^a p_1(x,0)\,dx=-\frac{\varrho k_p^2 a^4 P}{b\beta^2}\Big[\frac{2}{\beta}\tan\Big(\frac{1}{2}\beta\Big)-1\Big]\sum_{m=0}^{\infty}\frac{\varepsilon_m}{\alpha_m^2} \tag{46.10}$$

where $\alpha_0=\alpha$.

To determine α we now must compute the average value of p_2 over the outer surface of the membrane. Using Eq. (46.4) and inserting $(P_1-P_2)=P$ as before, we obtain

$$\left.\begin{aligned} \eta(x)\approx\frac{-P a^2}{\delta c_p^2\beta^2}\Big[\frac{\sin(\beta x/a)+\sin(\beta/a)(a-x)}{\sin\beta}-1\Big];\\ q=i\omega\int_0^a\eta\,dx\approx-\frac{i\omega P a^3}{c_p^2\beta^2}\Big[\frac{2}{\beta}\tan\Big(\frac{1}{2}\beta\Big)-1\Big];\\ P_2\approx\frac{\varrho k_p^2 a^3 P}{2\pi\delta\beta^2}\ln\alpha\Big[\frac{2}{\beta}\tan\Big(\frac{1}{2}\beta\Big)-1\Big].\end{aligned}\right\} \tag{46.11}$$

The expression for η satifies the boundary conditions and is a first approximation for its shape. Now we can insert $P_1 = P + P_2$ into the left-hand side of Eq. (46.10) and finally arrive at a second approximation equation for α,

$$\alpha^2 \approx -\left\{\frac{(\delta b \beta^2/\varrho k_p^2 a^4)}{(2/\beta)\tan(\beta/2) - 1} - \left(\frac{b^2}{3a^2}\right) + \left(\frac{b}{2\pi a}\right) + \ln\alpha\right\}^{-1} \tag{46.12}$$

where, in the logarithm and in the expression for β, we can use the value of α obtained by neglecting the second and third terms in the braces, since these terms are small as long as $\varrho a \ll \delta$. We have also used the relationship

$$\sum_{m=0}^{\infty} \frac{\varepsilon_m}{\alpha_m^2} \approx \frac{1}{\alpha^2} - \sum_{m=1}^{\infty} \frac{2b^2}{\pi^2 m^2 a^2} = \frac{1}{\alpha^2} - \frac{1}{3}\left(\frac{b}{a}\right)^2.$$

As with Eq. (45.6) the appropriate value of α is imaginary, unless the membrane is so "flabby" that we are above its natural frequency [i.e., unless $(2/\beta)\tan(\beta/2) - 1$ is negative]. Thus the wave motion outside the duct is a surface wave which stays within a distance $(a/|\alpha|)$ of the duct as it travels along. Since we have assumed that ka (and, presumably $k_p a$) is small compared to 1 and since for air, $\varrho a \ll \delta$ (this would not necessarily be true for water) we see that the first term in the braces is usually very large and, consequently $|\alpha|$ is usually small. Often the second and third terms in the braces (which arise from the distortion of the "plane wave" near the membrane and from the reaction of the external wave) can be neglected and the simpler formula

$$\left.\begin{aligned} \alpha^2 &\approx \frac{-\varrho a^2}{\delta b[1-(c_p/c)^2]}\left[\frac{2}{\beta}\tan\left(\frac{1}{2}\beta\right) - 1\right] \to \frac{-\varrho\omega^2 a^4}{3\delta b c_p^2} \qquad (\omega \to 0), \\ \beta &\approx \left(\frac{\omega a}{c_p}\right)\sqrt{1 - \left(\frac{c_p}{c}\right)^2} \end{aligned}\right\} \tag{46.13}$$

is sufficient.

Thus for very low frequencies α is imaginary and proportional to ω; the pressure inside the duct is uniform, the transverse shape of the membrane is parabolic and the external wave is a surface wave. If $c_p < c$ parameter β is real and, as ω is increased further, $|\alpha|$ increases faster than the first power of ω, until, when $\beta \approx \pi$, Eq. (46.13) is no longer valid; there is transverse resonance of the membrane. If the membrane is very stiff and/or very light, so that $c_p > c$, β is imaginary and there is no resonance, α rising from zero to some small, imaginary, limiting value as ω is increased from 0 to ∞.

If a more accurate expression for η than (46.11) is needed we can insert Eq. (46.8) into (46.4). A still better approximation for p_1 can be obtained by inserting (46.8) into (46.7). Alternatively p_1 and α can be computed more accurately by using a variational expression derived from Eq. (46.7). For example, if p_2 can be neglected, a variational expression for $\alpha \sin \alpha$ would involve the quantity

$$\frac{\int \chi \varphi \, dx}{\int \chi \, dx \int \Gamma(x|x_1) \varphi \, dx_1}$$

where φ is the trial function satisfying the boundary conditions for p_1 and χ the trial function satisfying the boundary conditions for η. This suggests we would have done better to have used the weighting factor $\sin(\pi x/a)$, instead of 1, when we integrated Eq. (46.8) to obtain (46.10). However the resulting formula for α does not differ appreciably from (46.12) until the magnitude of α becomes as large as 1, and the formula is more complicated.

47. Coupling with a periodically supported duct wall. Many other illustrations of the use of the GREEN'S function for the computation of the coupling between waves in the medium and wave s in the boundary surface could be given, but nearly all the basic techniques have by now been discussed. One last example will be given, that of a system similar to the one just analysed, except that the flexible membrane at $y=0$ is additionally supported by rigid cross struts, spaced a distance l apart. As before, the rectangular duct axis is the z axis, the wall $x=0$, $x=a$ and $y=b$ are rigid and the boundary at $y=0$ is a membrane of mass per unit area under tension T, supported rigidly along the lines $x=0$ and $x=a$ and also along the lines $y=0$, $z=ml$, where m is any integer, positive or negative. We then can use modifications of the GREEN'S functions of Sect. 40 for our calculations.

We assume, analogously to Sect. 46, that the phase difference from period to period along z is lk_z, where $k_z^2=(\omega/c)^2-(\alpha/a)^2$ and where the value of α is to be determined for free propagation along the duct. The GREEN'S function for periodically supported membrane is then

$$g(x_0, z_0|x_1, z_1) = \sum_{\nu=1}^{\infty} \frac{2}{\delta a c_p^2} \sin\left(\frac{\pi\nu x_0}{a}\right) \sin\left(\frac{\pi\nu x_1}{a}\right) f_\nu(z_0|z_1) \tag{47.1}$$

where f_ν is obviously related to the function of Eqs. (40.2) and (40.3) (in the present case the supports are rigid, so $z_p \to \infty$),

$$\left.\begin{aligned} f_\nu(z_0|z_1) &= \frac{ilc_p}{2\omega} \frac{\cos[k_{p\nu}(z_0+z_1-l)] - \cos[k_{p\nu}(|z_0-z_1|-l)]}{\sin(k_{p\nu}l)} \\ &= \sum_m \frac{e^{ik_m(z_0-z_1)}}{k_m^2-k_{p\nu}^2}\left\{1+\frac{2ik_{p\nu}}{l}\left[\frac{\cos(k_z l)-\cos(k_{p\nu}l)}{\sin(k_{p\nu}l)}\right]\times\right. \\ &\quad \left.\times \sum_q \frac{e^{ik_m z_0 - ik_q z_1}}{k_q^2-k_{p\nu}^2}\right\} \end{aligned}\right\} \tag{47.2}$$

where the integers m and q run from $-\infty$ to $+\infty$, where $k_{p\nu}^2=(\omega/c_p)^2-(\pi\nu/a)^2$ and where $k_m=k_z+(2\pi m/l)$, $k_z^2=(\omega/c)^2-\alpha^2$.

The GREEN'S function for the medium is related to that given in Eq. (40.6), except that, in order to "uncover" the parameter α, so its value can be computed easily, we use series expansions for the y and z factors and use the closed, discontinuous form for the x factor;

$$\left.\begin{aligned} G(x,y,z|x_0,y_0,z_0) &= \sum_{m,n} \frac{\varepsilon_n a}{bl} \cos\left(\frac{\pi n y}{b}\right) \cos\left(\frac{\pi n y_0}{b}\right) \frac{e^{ik_m(z-z_0)}}{\alpha_{mn}\sin\alpha_{mn}} \times \\ &\times \begin{cases} \cos\left(\frac{\alpha_{mn}x}{a}\right)\cos\left[\frac{\alpha_{mn}}{a}(a-x_0)\right] & (0\leqq x\leqq x_0\leqq a), \\ \cos\left[\frac{\alpha_{mn}}{a}(a-x)\right]\cos\left(\frac{\alpha_{mn}x_0}{a}\right) & (0\leqq x_0\leqq x\leqq a) \end{cases} \end{aligned}\right\} \tag{47.3}$$

where $\alpha_{mn}^2=(\omega a/c)^2-(\pi n a/b)^2-(k_m a)^2$ and where k_m is the same as it is in Eq. (47.2). The summation is over n from 0 to ∞ and over m from $-\infty$ to $+\infty$.

As with Eq. (46.7), the pressure on the inner surface of the membrane (for simplicity we neglect p_2 in our discussion of this case; it can be added if need be) must satisfy the homogeneous integral equation for travelling waves

$$
\left.\begin{aligned}
p_1(x,0,z) &= -\varrho\,\omega^2 \int_0^l dz_1 \int_0^a dx_1\, p(x_1,0,z_1)\times \\
&\quad\times \int_0^l dz_0 \int_0^a dx_0\, g(x_0,z_0|x_1,z_1)\, G(x,0,z|x_0,0,z_0) \\
&= -\frac{2\varrho\omega^2 a}{b\,c_p^2} \int_0^l dz_1 \int_0^a dx_1\, p(x_1,0,z_1) \sum_{m,n,\nu} \frac{\varepsilon_n}{\pi^2\nu^2-\alpha_{mn}^2}\, \frac{\sin(\pi\nu x_1/a)}{\alpha_{mn}\sin\alpha_{mn}} \times \\
&\quad\times \left\{\pi\nu\left[\cos\frac{\alpha_{mn}}{a}(a-x) - (-1)^\nu\cos\left(\frac{\alpha_{mn}x}{a}\right)\right] - \right. \\
&\quad \left. -\,\alpha_{mn}\sin\alpha_{mn}\sin\left(\frac{\pi\nu x}{a}\right)\right\} \frac{e^{i k_m(z-z_1)}}{k_m^2-k_{p\nu}^2} \times \\
&\quad\times\left\{1+\frac{2ik_{p\nu}}{l}\,\frac{\cos(k_z l)-\cos(k_{p\nu}l)}{\sin(k_{p\nu}l)} \sum_q \frac{e^{ik_m z - ik_q z_1}}{k_q^2-k_{p\nu}^2}\right\}.
\end{aligned}\right\}\quad (47.4)
$$

To determine the approximate value of the parameter α, we set $p_1(x,0,z)\approx P_0\,e^{ik_z z}$ on both sides of this equation, multiply both sides by $e^{-ik_z z}$ and integrate over x and z. This results in the equation to determine α,

$$
\left.\begin{aligned}
1 &\approx -\frac{8\varrho\omega^2 a^4}{\delta\, b\, c_p^2}\left(\frac{1}{\alpha^2}-\frac{b^2}{3a^2}\right)\sum_{\nu\ \mathrm{odd}} \frac{(1/\pi\nu)^2}{\pi^2\nu^2-(k_p^2-k_z^2)\,a^2}\times \\
&\quad\times\left\{\frac{(2ik_{p\nu}a^2/l)}{\pi^2\nu^2-(k_p^2-k_z^2)\,a^2}\,\frac{\cos(k_z l)-\cos(k_{p\nu}l)}{\sin(k_{p\nu}l)}\right\}
\end{aligned}\right\}\quad (47.5)
$$

where $k_z^2=(\omega/c)^2-(\alpha/a)^2$, $k_p^2=(\omega/c_p)^2$, $k_{p\nu}^2=k_p^2-(\pi\nu/a)^2$ and where the summation is over $\nu=1,3,5,\ldots$.

For the longer wavelengths $k_p a\ll\pi$, so that $k_{p\nu}$ is imaginary for all values of ν and is practically equal to $(i\pi\nu/a)$. In this case the series over ν can be summed and the equation for α becomes

$$
1\approx-\frac{\varrho\omega^2 a^4}{12\delta\, b\, c_p^2}\left(\frac{1}{\alpha^2}-\frac{b^2}{3a^2}\right)\left(1+i\,\frac{192\,a}{\pi^5 l}\right)\qquad(\omega a\ll\pi c_p)\qquad(47.6)
$$

which is to be compared with Eq. (46.13) for $\beta\to 0$. Here, as in the previous case, α is imaginary for the long wavelengths.

For shorter wavelengths we must use Eq. (47.5). This exhibits the various possible resonances of the sequence of rectangular membranes which form the boundary at $y=0$. The purely transverse resonances correspond to one of the denominators $(\pi\nu)^2-k_p^2a^2+k_z^2a^2=(\pi\nu)^2+(\omega a/c)^2-(\omega a/c_p)^2-\alpha^2$ going to zero, whereas the longitudinal resonances correspond to $\sin(k_{p\nu}l)$ going to zero. There are close analogies between this system and the acoustic filters of Sect. 24.

This example completes our outline of the problems of coupled acoustical systems. Details of many other applications can be found in the voluminous literature or, what may be more satisfying, can be worked out by the reader for himself.

Bibliography.

It is manifestly impossible to make this bibliography exhaustive. The writers have consequently included only references to articles, or portions of books, which will, in their opinion, most effectively aid the reader in understanding the subject under discussion. Thus usually the more recent treatments of a topic, particularly those which review the advances to date or which present a unified treatment or which themselves include fairly complete bibliographies, have been chosen, rather than a sequence of "first appearances".

[1] Blokhintzev, D.: The Acoustics of an Inhomogeneous Moving Medium, transl. by R.T. Beyer and D. Mintzer. Providence, Rh. I.: Brown University 1952. See also J. Acoust. Soc. Amer. **18**, 322 (1946).
[2] Baker, B.B., and E.T. Copson: The Mathematical Theory of Huygens' Principle, 2nd. ed. London: Oxford University Press 1950.
[3] Borgnis, F.E.: Rev. Mod. Phys. **25**, 653 (1953).
[4] Bouwkamp, C.J.: Thesis, Groeningen, 1941.
[5] Bouwkamp, C.J.: Rep. Progr. Phys. **17**, 35 (1954).
[6] Brekhovskikh, L.M.: Wave Propagation in Layered Media. Moscow 1957.
[7] Brillouin, L.: Wave Propagation in Periodic Structures. New York-Toronto-London: McGraw-Hill Book Co., Inc. 1946.
[8] Chernov, L.A.: Dokl. Acad Nauk USSR. **98**, No. 6, 953 (1954).
[9] Cook, R.K.: J. Acoust. Soc. Amer. **29**, 324 (1957).
[10] Cremer, L.: Die wissenschaftlichen Grundlagen der Raumakustik, Vol. III. Leipzig: Hirzel 1950.
[11] Cremer, L.: Acustica **5**, 245 (1955).
[12] Curle, N.: Proc. Roy. Soc. Lond., Ser. A **231**, 505 (1955).
[13] Dryden, H.L., F.D. Murnaghan and H. Bateman: Hydrodynamics. New York: Dover Publications 1956.
[14] Ford, G.W., and W.C. Meecham: J. Acoust. Soc. Amer. (to be published).
[15] Gierke, H.E. v.: Aircraft Noise Sources, Chap. 33. Handbook of Noise Control (C. Harris, editor). New York-Toronto-London: McGraw-Hill Book Company, Inc. 1957.
[16] Goldstein, S.: Modern Developments of Fluid Dynamics, Chaps. I, II. Oxford 1938.
[17] Groves, G.V.: J. Atmosph. Terr. Phys. **7**, 113 (1955).
[18] Ingard, U.: J. Acoust. Soc. Amer. **19**, 348 (1948).
[19] Ingard, U.: J. Acoust. Soc. Amer. **31**, 1035 (1959).
[20] Ingard, U., and D. Pridmore-Brown: J. Acoust. Soc. Amer. **23**, 689 (1951).
[21] Isakovich, M. A.: Soviet Phys.-Acoust. (transl. of J. of Acoustics, USSR.) **2**, 149 (1956).
[22] Kirchhoff, G.: Ann. Physik **136**, 177 (1868).
[23] Kneser, H.: J. Acoust. Soc. Amer. **5**, 122 (1933).
[24] Knudsen, V.O.: J. Acoust. Soc. Amer. **3**, 126 (1931).
[25] Konstantinov, B.: J. Tech. Phys. Leningrad **9**, 226, 424 (1939).
[26] Kraichnan, R.H.: J. Acoust. Soc. Amer. **29**, 65 (1957).
[27] Krassilnikov, U.A., and A.M. Obukhov: Soviet Phys.-Acoust. (transl. of J. of Acoustics, USSR.) **2**, 103 (1956).
[28] Lamb, G.: J. Acoust. Soc. Amer. **29**, 1091 (1957).
[29] Lamb, H.: Hydrodynamics, 6th ed. Cambridge, England: Cambridge University Press 1953.
[30] Lighthill, M.J.: Proc. Cambridge Phil. Soc. **49** (1), 531 (1952).
[31] Lighthill, M.J.: Proc. Roy. Soc. Lond., Ser. A **211**, 564 (1952).
[32] Lighthill, M.J.: Proc. Roy. Soc. Lond., Ser. A **222**, 1 (1954).
[33] Lin, T.C., and G.W. Morgan: J. Acoust. Soc. Amer. **28**, 1165 (1956).
[34] Lysanov, Iu. P.: Soviet Phys.-Acoust. (transl. of J. of Acoustics, USSR.) **4**, 1 (1958).
[35] Markham, J.: Phys. Rev. **89**, 972 (1953).
[36] Markham, J., R. Lindsay and R. Beyer: Rev. Mod. Phys. **23**, 353 (1951).
[37] Meecham, W.C., and G.W. Ford: J. Acoust. Soc. Amer. **30**, 318 (1958).
[38] Miles, J.W.: J. Acoust. Soc. Amer. **29**, 226 (1957).
[39] Mintzer, D.: J. Acoust. Soc. Amer. **25**, 922, 1107 (1953); **26**, 186 (1954).
[40] Morse, P.M.: J. Acoust. Soc. Amer. **11**, 56 (1939).
[41] Morse, P.M.: J. Acoust. Soc. Amer. **11**, 205 (1939).
[42] Morse, P.M.: Vibration and Sound, 2nd ed. New York-Toronto-London: McGraw-Hill Book Co., Inc. 1948.
[43] Morse, P.M., and R.H. Bolt: Rev. Mod. Phys. **16**, 141 (1944).
[44] Morse, P.M., and H. Feshbach: Methods of Theoretical Physics, Chap. 7. New York-Toronto-London: McGraw-Hill Book Co., Inc. 1953.

[45] MORSE, P.M., and H. FESHBACH: Methods of Theoretical Physics, Chap. 8. New York-Toronto-London: McGraw-Hill Book Co., Inc. 1953.
[46] MORSE, P.M., and H. FESHBACH: Methods of Theoretical Physics, Chap. 9. New York-Toronto-London: McGraw-Hill Book Co., Inc. 1953.
[47] MORSE, P.M., and H. FESHBACH: Methods of Theoretical Physics, Sect. 11.3. New York-Toronto-London: McGraw-Hill Book Co., Inc. 1953.
[48] MORSE, P.M., and H. FESHBACH: Methods of Theoretical Physics, Sect. 11.4. New York-Toronto-London: McGraw-Hill Book Co., Inc. 1953.
[49] MORSE, P.M., and H. FESHBACH: Methods of Theoretical Physics, Sect. 12.2. New York-Toronto-London: McGraw-Hill Book Co., Inc. 1953.
[50] MÜLLER, E.A., and K.R. MATSCHAT: Z. Flugwiss. **6**, H. 6, 161 (1958).
[51] MÜLLER, E.A., and K.R. MATSCHAT: The Scattering of Sound by a Single Vortex and by Turbulence. Göttingen: Max-Planck-Institut für Strömungsforschung 1959.
[52] OBUKHOV, A.M.: Dokl. Acad. Nauk USSR. **30**, 611 (1941).
[53] OBUKHOV, A.M.: Izv. Acad. Nauk USSR. Geophys. Ser. No. 2, 1953.
[54] OESTREICHER, H.L.: J. Acoust. Soc. Amer. **29**, 1219 (1957).
[55] PACHNER, J.: J. Acoust. Soc. Amer. **23**, 185, 198, 481 (1951).
[56] PEKERIS, C.L.: J. Acoust. Soc. Amer. **18**, 295 (1946).
[57] PRIDMORE-BROWN, D.C., and U. INGARD: National Advisory Committee for Aeronautics Techn. Note 3494 (1955). See also J. Acoust. Soc. Amer. **27**, 36 (1955).
[58] PROUD, J.M., P. TAMARKIN and W.C. MEECHAM: J. Appl. Phys. **28**, 1298 (1957).
[59] PROUDMAN, I.: Proc. Roy. Soc. Lond., Ser. A **214**, 119 (1952).
[60] RAYLEIGH, Lord: Theory of Sound. London: MacMillan & Co., Ltd. 1937.
[61] RIBNER, H.S.: J. Acoust. Soc. Amer. **29**, 435 (1957).
[62] RUDNICK, I.: J. Acoust. Soc. Amer. **19**, 348 (1948).
[63] SCHOCH, A.: Schallreflexion, Schallbrechung und Schallbeugung. In: Ergebnisse der exakten Naturwissenschaften, Bd. XXII, Sect. 33. Berlin: Springer 1950.
[64] SCHOCH, A.: Schallreflexion, Schallbrechung und Schallbeugung. In: Ergebnisse der exakten Naturwissenschaften, Bd. XXII, Sect. 34, 37. Berlin: Springer 1950.
[65] SCHOCH, A.: Acustica **3**, 181 (1953).
[66] SCHOCH, A.: Acustica **2**, 1 (1952); **4**, 289 (1954).
[67] SCHUSTER, K.: Akust. Z. **4**, 335 (1939).
[68] SCOTT, R.: Proc. Phys. Soc. Lond. **58**, 358 (1946).
[69] SECKLER, B.D., and J.B. KELLER: J. Acoust. Soc. Amer. **31**, 192 (1959).
[70] SKUDRZYK, E.: Grundlagen der Akustik. Berlin: Springer 1952.
[71] SKUDRZYK, E.: J. Acoust. Soc. Amer. **29**, 50 (1957).
[72] SOMMERFELD, A.: Partial Differential Equations in Physics (Lectures on Theoretical Physics, Vol. I). New York: Academic Press 1949.
[73] SOMMERFELD, A.: Mechanics of Deformable Bodies (Lectures on Theoretical Physics, Vol. II). New York: Academic Press 1950.
[74] STENZEL, H.: Ann. Physik **43**, 1 (1943).
[75] STENZEL, H.: Leitfaden zur Berechnung von Schallgängen. Berlin: Springer 1958.
[76] TWERSKY, V.: J. Acoust. Soc. Amer. **19**, 209 (1957).
[77] WALTER, A.G.: Proc. Cambridge Phil. Soc. **47**, 109 (1951).
[78] ZWIKKER, E., and C.W. KOSTEN: Sound Absorbing Materials. New York: Elsevier 1949.

Schallabsorption und -dispersion in Gasen.

Von

H. O. KNESER.

Mit 30 Figuren im Text.

A. Übersicht über das Gesamtgebiet[1].

1. Allgemeines. Vor etwa 30 Jahren galt die Theorie der Schallausbreitung in Gasen für abgeschlossen. Sie sagte aus, daß die Schallabsorption infolge der bekannten Transporterscheinungen monoton mit der Frequenz ansteigen müsse, die Schallgeschwindigkeit davon aber praktisch nicht berührt würde, also — wie von NEWTON und LAPLACE postuliert — frequenzunabhängig sei. Durch das Experiment wurde Letzteres vollauf bestätigt. Messungen der Schallgeschwindigkeit — zwar von hoher Präzision, aber ausschließlich im Bereich hörbarer Frequenzen — wurden nur ausgeführt, um „zuverlässige" Werte für C_p/C_v zu gewinnen. Messungen der Schallabsorption — ebenfalls nur im Hörbereich — stießen auf außerordentliche experimentelle Schwierigkeiten. Man begnügte sich hier aber um so leichter mit den recht fragwürdigen Resultaten, als man von ihnen nicht mehr als eine Bestätigung der Theorie erwartete, nach der die Schallabsorption nur durch Wärmeleitfähigkeit und Viskosität bestimmt sein sollte, also durch Materialkonstanten, die man auf direktem Wege sehr viel genauer und einzeln bestimmen konnte.

Seither hat sich die Situation völlig gewandelt: Fast gleichzeitig mit der Erschließung des Ultraschallgebietes — wenige Jahre nach LANGEVINs Entdeckung

[1] Über dies Gebiet sind seit 1950 folgende zusammenfassende Darstellungen erschienen:

1. P. VIGOUREUX: Ultrasonics. London: Chapman & Hall 1950.

2. J. G. MARKHAM, R. T. BEYER u. R. B. LINDSAY: Rev. Mod. Phys. **33**, 353 (1951); umfassender Bericht mit besonderer Betonung aller damals diskutierten Theorien der Schalldisperion.

3. S. PETRALIA: Velocità e assorbimento di ultrasuoni nei gas. Nuovo Cim. **9** Suppl. 1—58 (1952); mit besonderer Betonung der experimentellen Ergebnisse und Angabe von Schallgeschwindigkeitswerten für 43 Gase und Dämpfe.

4. C. TRUESDELL: J. Rational. Mech. Anal. **2**, 643—741 (1953); ausführliche Analyse der kontinuumsmechanischen Grundlagen der Schallausbreitung.

5. L. BERGMANN: Der Ultraschall, Teil II, S. 50—546; Darstellung des Gesamtgebiets im Rahmen der „Anwendung des Ultraschalls". Stuttgart: S. Hirzel 1954.

6. W. T. RICHARDS: Absorption and Velocity of Sound in Vapors. Rev. Mod. Phys. **27**, 25 (1955); Weiterführung und Ergänzung von Nummer 2.

7. K. F. HERZFELD: High Speed Aerodynamics and Jet Propulsion (Hrsg. F. D. ROSSINI), Bd. 1: Thermodynamics and Physics of Matter; Abschnitt H, S. 646—735: Relaxation Phenomena in Gases. Verl.: Princeton: Princeton University Press 1955; *auf diese vorzügliche Darstellung wird im vorliegenden Artikel mehrfach zurückgegriffen; zit. als „H..." mit Nummer des Paragraphen.*

8. O. NOMOTO: Klassifizierung der akustischen Relaxationstheorien. J. Phys. Soc. Japan **12**, 85—99 (1957).

9. K.F. HERZFELD and T.A. LITOVITZ: Absorption and Dispersion of Ultrasonic Waves. New York und London: Academic Press 1959. Enthält das unter 7. genannte Kapitel teils wörtlich, teils dem Inhalt nach.

(1917) wurde bereits die 100 MHz-Grenze erreicht — brach das alte Theorem von der Frequenzunabhängigkeit der Schallgeschwindigkeit zusammen, erwies sich das Studium der Schalldispersion in Gasen als höchst aufschlußreich, und fast noch mehr das der mit ihr zwangsläufig verknüpften Schallabsorption, für deren Messung die Elektronik bald — und vor allem nach dem zweiten Weltkrieg — neue, wirkungsvolle Methoden zur Verfügung stellte.

Für die technische, physiologische und musikalische Akustik, die sich naturgemäß fast nur für Wasser- und Luftschall interessieren, sind diese Forschungszweige ziemlich irrelevant, abgesehen vielleicht davon, daß in gewissen seltenen Spezialfällen nach der Schallabsorption in Luft gefragt wird.

Um so wichtiger sind Schalldisperions- und -absorptionsmessungen für die Bestimmung von Einstellzeiten thermischer Gleichgewichte, d.h. von Relaxationszeiten, geworden und damit für die Erforschung der Energieübertragung bei Zusammenstößen zwischen gleich- und verschiedenartigen Molekülen. Für diesen Problemkreis spielt heute die Schallausbreitung eine ganz ähnliche Rolle wie die Transportphänomene, denen die Relaxationserscheinungen nahe verwandt sind, für die Ermittlung von Stoßzeiten und freien Weglängen.

Den Messungen zugänglich ist heute der Frequenzbereich von etwa 100 Hz bis fast 100 MHz. Wegen der bei Gasen ziemlich einheitlichen Schallgeschwindigkeit von einigen 100 m/sec werden nämlich unterhalb von 100 Hz die Wellenlängen und damit die Apparaturabmessungen zu groß; oberhalb von 100 MHz werden die Anforderungen, die — wegen der Kleinheit der Wellenlänge und der starken Absorption — an die Genauigkeit und Empfindlichkeit der Meßapparatur gestellt werden müssen, unüberwindbar hoch. In Flüssigkeiten und Festkörpern sind Messungen mit künstlich erzeugten Schallwellen von fast 1000 MHz möglich; außerdem in dem engen Frequenzbereich (um 10^{10} Hz), wo die Schallwellenlänge von der Größenordnung derjenigen Lichtwellen ist, für welche Spektralapparate von höchstem Auflösungsvermögen zur Verfügung stehen (λ etwa 0,7 bis 0,2 μ), und zwar mit Hilfe des Brillouin-Effektes (Aufspaltung von Spektrallinien bei Streuung an Wärmewellen).

Die Grenze 10^9 Hz, bis zu welcher man heute Schallwellen erzeugen — allerdings in Gasen noch nicht nachweisen — kann, fällt unter Normalbedingungen ungefähr zusammen mit der gaskinetischen Grenzfrequenz $1/\bar{\tau}$ ($\bar{\tau}$ = mittlere Stoßzeit), die für Gase eine ähnliche Rolle spielt wie die Debyesche Grenzfrequenz für Festkörper. Bei vermindertem Druck jedoch sind Messungen gelungen, bei denen diese Grenzfrequenz weit unterhalb der Meßfrequenz lag (vgl. Ziff. 18). Von Schallwellen kann dann freilich kaum mehr die Rede sein, und die theoretische Behandlung bietet schwierige — noch nicht völlig gelöste — kinetische Probleme.

Es ist klar, daß in unbegrenzten Medien — und nur von solchen wird in diesem Beitrag gehandelt — unterhalb von 10^9 Hz keinerlei innermolekulare Resonanzeffekte für die Absorption und Dispersion der Schallwellen verantwortlich gemacht werden können, sondern nur Relaxationsphänomene im weitesten Sinn des Wortes.

2. Gültigkeit der Laplaceschen Formel. Die Laplacesche Formel für die Phasengeschwindigkeit (c) einer ebenen Welle von geringer Amplitude in einem Medium, dessen Schubmodul gleich Null ist, lautet:

$$c^2 = \frac{K_{\text{ad}}}{\varrho_0}, \tag{2.1}$$

wobei K_{ad} den adiabatischen Kompressionsmodul und ϱ_0 die Dichte im Ruhezustand bedeutet. Auf ideale Gase angewandt, nimmt sie die Form an:

$$c^2 = \gamma \cdot \frac{P_0}{\varrho_0} \tag{2.2}$$

mit $\gamma = C_p/C_v$ und P_0 = Druck im Ruhezustand. Ihr liegt wesentlich die Annahme[1] zugrunde, daß durch die Begrenzung eines — klein gegen die Wellenlänge, aber groß gegen den Molekülabstand zu wählenden — Materieteilchens von den benachbarten keine andere Wirkungen ausgehen als die der Normalspannungen.

Nach (2.1) hängt c nicht von der Frequenz und bei idealen Gasen (2.2) auch nicht vom Druck ab. Wegen der Reversibilität adiabatischer Zustandsänderungen geht der Schallwelle auch keine Energie verloren, und es tritt keine Schallabsorption auf.

Formel (2.2) gilt also streng unter folgenden Voraussetzungen:

1. Kleine Amplituden.
2. Idealer Gaszustand.
3. Verschwindender Einfluß der Ausgleichsvorgänge (Diffusion, Wärmeleitung und Viskosität).

Alle drei Voraussetzungen sind experimentell gleichzeitig erfüllbar. Dann — aber auch nur dann! — lassen sich aus der Schallgeschwindigkeit sehr genaue Werte für das Verhältnis der spezifischen Wärmen ermitteln. Dies Verfahren ist bekanntlich seit KUNDT, der so unter anderen die Einatomigkeit des Hg-Dampfes nachwies[2], oft angewandt worden; teils mit ausgezeichnetem Erfolg, teils mit von vorneherein unglaubwürdigen Ergebnissen, obwohl in allen Fällen alle drei Voraussetzungen durchaus erfüllt zu sein schienen. Die Ursache hierfür ist, daß eines der Ausgleichsphänomene damals unbekannt war, nämlich die durch Relaxationseffekte bedingte Druckviskosität. Sie tritt, im Gegensatz zu allen anderen Ausgleichsphänomenen, bei stationären Experimenten nicht in Erscheinung und ist daher im Voraus nicht abschätzbar. Nur soviel steht fest, daß einatomige Gase keine Druckviskosität besitzen.

Von den drei genannten Voraussetzungen wird hier zunächst die letzte fallen gelassen und in Ziff. 9 bis 12 die Dispersion und Absorption behandelt, die durch die Ausgleichsphänomene bewirkt wird. Wesentlich kürzer werden die Abweichungen vom idealen Gaszustand in Ziff. 17 beschrieben werden. Die Voraussetzung kleiner Amplituden wird in Ziff. 8 präzisiert und in diesem Artikel durchweg beibehalten.

3. Phasenverschiebung zwischen Dichte und Druck. Die Ausgleichsphänomene Diffusion, Wärmeleitung, Schub- und Druckviskosität bewirken primär eine Phasenverschiebung zwischen Druck und Dichte. Dies soll am Beispiel der Wärmeleitung plausibel gemacht werden: Einem Materieteilchen wird in der Schallwelle durch Volumverkleinerung und -vergrößerung periodisch wechselnd Energie zugeführt und entzogen. Ohne Wärmeleitung steigt und fällt die Temperatur konphas mit der Volumänderung. Unter dem Einfluß der Wärmeleitung aber sinkt die Temperatur im Moment des Erreichens des kleinsten Volumens, wo ja keine Kompressionsarbeit mehr zugeführt wird, bereits wieder ab. Das Temperaturmaximum wird also vor dem Zeitpunkt größter Verdichtung erreicht, und Entsprechendes gilt für das Temperaturminimum. Nun sind aber Temperatur

[1] Lord RAYLEIGH bezeichnet sie als ein "subject of misapprehension among students" und als "stumbling block". (Theory of Sound II, S. 23, 1896.)

[2] A. KUNDT: Pogg. Ann. **127**, 497 (1866).

und Druck durch die gleiche kinetische Größe — nämlich die Molekulargeschwindigkeit — bestimmt, daher notwendig konphas. Deswegen muß die Wärmeleitung ein Voreilen des Druckes vor der Verdichtung zur Folge haben. Im P, V-Diagramm ergibt sich eine entgegen dem Uhrzeigersinn durchlaufene geschlossene Kurve. Es wird also bei jedem Zyklus ein durch den Flächeninhalt der Ellipse bestimmter Bruchteil der Kompressionsarbeit in Wärme verwandelt, d. h. pro Periode ein gewisser Anteil der Schallenergie absorbiert. Die gleiche Überlegung läßt sich für die anderen Ausgleichsphänomene anstellen.

Der relative Energieverlust pro Periode ist aber nichts anderes als der auf die Energie bezogene Absorptionsindex (Absorptionskoeffizient je Wellenlänge); denn der gleiche Bruchteil der Gesamtenergie der an einem Materieteilchen während einer Periode $2\pi/\omega$ verlorengeht, wird der Welle auf dem Weg, den sie während dieser Zeit zurücklegt, d. h. auf einer Wellenlänge entzogen. Er hängt also eng mit der Phasenverschiebung φ zusammen. Und zwar gilt für den Absorptionsindex μ (der Amplitude!)[1]:

$$\mu = \pi \varphi. \tag{3.1}$$

Die Tatsache, daß eine Phasenverschiebung zwischen Druck und Verdichtung auftritt, ist ein Fremdkörper im Gebäude der klassischen Mechanik der Kontinua und der klassischen Thermodynamik und weist darauf hin, daß Schallabsorption und -dispersion in den Bereich der Thermodynamik der unvollständigen Gleichgewichte, mit anderen Worten der irreversiblen Prozesse gehören.

Analytisch wird dieser Zusammenhang zwischen Druck und Verdichtung für periodische Vorgänge wie erwähnt durch deren Quotienten, d. h. einen komplexen elastischen Modul dargestellt oder durch den — natürlich ebenfalls komplexen — „Schallwellenwiderstand", d. h. den Quotienten Überdruck/Verformungsgeschwindigkeit.

Alle diese Größen — Phasenwinkel, Modul und Schallwellenwiderstand — sind frequenzabhängig. Für die Frequenz Null wird der Phasenwinkel zu Null, und die beiden anderen Größen werden reell.

4. Beschreibung der Schallabsorption und -dispersion durch die Materialkonstanten der Diffusion, Wärmeleitung und Viskosität. Alle Ausgleichsvorgänge — mit Ausnahme des Wärmeaustausches durch Strahlung, der aber bei der Schallausbreitung keine wesentliche Rolle spielt — werden bekanntlich normalerweise beschrieben durch Materialkonstanten, nämlich durch die

Diffusionskonstante = Materietransport/Konzentrationsgefälle,
Wärmeleitungskonstante = Wärmetransport/Temperaturgefälle,
Viskositätskonstante = Impulstransport/Geschwindigkeitsgefälle.

Tatsächlich erweist sich in allen drei Fällen bei quasistatisch geführten Experimenten die Proportionalität zwischen Transport und Gefälle normalerweise als erfüllt. *Bei hinreichend kleinen* Frequenzen muß sich daher die Schallausbreitung durch diese Ausgleichskonstanten beschreiben lassen. Das ist in der Tat der Fall und wird in den folgenden Abschnitten ausführlich dargestellt. Alle drei Einflüsse bewirken einen frequenzproportionalen Anstieg des Absorptionsindex (μ), und im Zusammenwirken einen dem Quadrat der Frequenz proportionalen Anstieg der Phasengeschwindigkeit (c). Zwischen beiden besteht ein einfacher Zusammenhang [vgl. (8.12)]:

$$\frac{c - c_0}{c_0} = \frac{\mu^2}{8\pi^2}. \tag{4.1}$$

[1] Diese Gleichung wird in Ziff. 7 bewiesen.

($c_0 = c$ für $\omega = 0$.) Die Dispersion wird also schwerlich beobachtbar, da mit $\mu = 0{,}3$, also bei extrem starker Dämpfung, c erst um etwa $1^0/_{00}$ angewachsen ist.

Alles dies gilt — wie gesagt — nur für „hinreichend kleine" Frequenz; eine Bedingung die bei mehratomigen Gasen unter Umständen schon im hörbaren Frequenzbereich nicht mehr erfüllt ist. Dies wird in den folgenden Abschnitten näher erläutert.

5. Einstell- oder Relaxationszeit der „klassischen" Ausgleichserscheinungen. Läßt man in einem Gas ein Konzentrations-, Temperatur- oder Geschwindigkeitsgefälle plötzlich entstehen und dann zeitkonstant bleiben, so wird eine gewisse Zeit verstreichen, ehe der Materie-, Wärme- oder Impulsstrom merklich konstant wird. In einer Schallwelle, deren Schwingungsdauer vergleichbar ist mit jener Einstellzeit oder gar kleiner als sie, können die Ausgleichsphänomene nicht voll zur Wirkung kommen. Damit ist die einschränkende Bedingung „hinreichend kleine Frequenz" präzisiert: Schallabsorption und -dispersion lassen sich nur so lange durch die genannten Materialkonstanten beschreiben, als

$$\omega \cdot \text{Einstellzeit} \ll 1$$

ist.

Entscheidend für die Theorie der Schallabsorption und -dispersion ist also die Frage nach der Einstellzeit der Ausgleichs- oder Transportphänomene. Sie ist relativ einfach abzuschätzen für den Vorgang der Diffusion, der Wärmeleitung und der *Schub*viskosität, womit das sonst schlechthin als Viskosität bezeichnete Phänomen gemeint ist, bei dem die Bewegung der Materie *senkrecht* zum Geschwindigkeitsgefälle und Impulstransport erfolgt (s. Ziff. 6). In Gasen ist der Mechanismus dieser drei Transportphänomene laut kinetischer Gastheorie der gleiche und die Transportgeschwindigkeit durch die mittlere freie Weglänge und die mittlere Molekulargeschwindigkeit bestimmt, genauer durch deren Quotienten, d.h. die mittlere Stoßzeit ($\bar{\tau}$). Daher ist die Gültigkeit der sog. klassischen Theorie der Schallabsorption und -dispersion, die nur die genannten drei Ausgleichsphänomene berücksichtigt, durch die Bedingung eingeschränkt:

$$\omega \bar{\tau} \ll 1 . \qquad (5.1)$$

6. Die Druckviskosität und ihre Einstellzeit. Die oben postulierte Proportionalität zwischen Impulstransport und Geschwindigkeitsgefälle ist bekanntlich

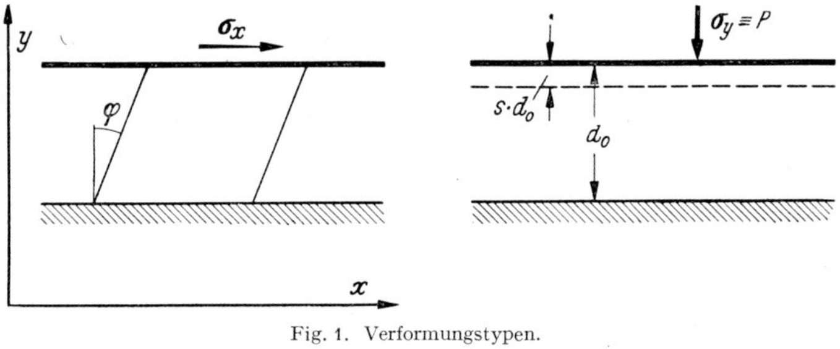

Fig. 1. Verformungstypen.

mit dem Newtonschen Ansatz für den Zusammenhang zwischen Schubspannung (σ_x) und Schubverformungsgeschwindigkeit identisch:

$$\text{Schubviskosität} = \eta = \sigma_x \Big/ \frac{\partial \varphi}{\partial t} \qquad (6.1)$$

(vgl. Fig. 1). Da Gase einer Schubverformung keinen elastischen Widerstand entgegensetzen, treten bei einer solcher *nur* die geschwindigkeitsproportionalen Reibungskräfte auf.

Anders als bei der schub- oder volumenerhaltenden Verformung liegen die Dinge bei dem korrespondierenden Verformungstyp: Der isotropen oder winkelerhaltenden (Ähnlichkeits-) Verformung, die durch Fig. 1 (rechts) eindimensional dargestellt ist. Ihr setzen Gase sowohl einen der Verformung selbst, als auch einen der Verformungsgeschwindigkeit proportionalen Widerstand entgegen[1]. Der letztere wird nur bei hoher Verformungsgeschwindigkeit mit dem ersteren vergleichbar und macht sich daher nur in Schallwellen genügend hoher Frequenz bemerkbar[2]. Analog zur Schubviskosität kann man also eine Druckviskosität ζ definieren:

$$\zeta = P \Big/ \frac{\partial s}{\partial t}\bigg|_{s\to 0}, \qquad (6.2)$$

wobei P den Druck und s die Verdichtung $\left(= \frac{V - V_0}{V_0}\right)$ bedeutet.

Die Analogie zwischen η und ζ legt es nahe, auch die Druckviskosität als Transport- oder Ausgleichsphänomen zu deuten. Aus Dimensionsgründen muß die transportierte Größe in beiden Fällen der Impuls sein[3]. Im Gegensatz zur Schubviskosität ist hier aber der Transport und das Geschwindigkeitsgefälle *parallel* zur Geschwindigkeit gerichtet (Fig. 1). Das bedingt einen wesentlichen Unterschied hinsichtlich der molekular-kinetischen Deutung: Bei der Schubverformung erhalten die an die bewegte Wand prallenden Moleküle zwar alle einen Zuwachs der x-Komponente des Impulses, der Gesamtimpuls wird aber in erster Näherung nicht erhöht. Daher wird auch die Gesamtenergie nur in zweiter Näherung erhöht. Bei einer isotropen Verformung dagegen wird gleichzeitig mit dem Impuls dauernd auch Energie zugeführt und in y-Richtung abtransportiert. Das ändert an der Transportgeschwindigkeit solange nichts, als alle Zusammenstöße elastisch ablaufen. Sowie aber die Möglichkeit der Umwandlung von Energie in innere, d.h. nicht-translatorische Energie besteht, wird das Anlaufen des Energie- und damit des Impulstransportes verzögert[4]; um so mehr, je länger die innere Energie als solche bei ihrem Träger verweilt. Daher gilt für die Druckviskosität unter Umständen eine viel längere Einstellzeit[5]. Sie ist gleich $Z \cdot \bar{\tau}$, wenn zwischen der Aufnahme von innerer Energie aus der translatorischen und der Rückverwandlung in diese Z Stöße erfolgen. Mit einer konstanten, d. h. frequenzunabhängigen Druckviskosität kann also nur gerechnet werden, solange die Bedingung $\omega \cdot Z \cdot \bar{\tau} \ll 1$ erfüllt ist, und das ist z.B. für O_2 von 1 atm ($Z \approx 10^6$) bei 1 kHz bereits nicht mehr der Fall[6].

Das Studium der Ausbreitung ebener Schallwellen ist heute fast der einzige Weg zur Ermittlung der Druckviskosität von Gasen. Dabei ist sie aber untrennbar mit der Schubviskosität verknüpft, denn die Verformung, die ein Volumelement in einer ebenen Schallwelle erfährt, ist weder eine isotrope (winkel-

---

[1] Näheres hierzu in Ziff. 20.

[2] Nachgewiesen auch bei nicht-periodischer Verformung; vgl. A. CARRELLI u. F. CENNAMO, Nuovo Cim. **11**, 429 (1954).

[3] In der Tatsache, daß bei der Viskosität die transportierte Größe Vektorcharakter hat, ist der prinzipielle Unterschied gegenüber den anderen Transportphänomenen begründet. — Die kinetische Bedeutung der Druckviskosität wurde zuerst erkannt von L. J. MANDELSTAM u. M. A. LEONTOVITSCH, J. Exp. Theor. Phys. USSR. **7**, 438 (1937).

[4] Näheres hierzu s. Ziff. 20.

[5] Dies „Latentwerden" der translatorischen Energie wirkt sich auch — aber viel weniger einschneidend — auf den Vorgang der Wärmeleitung aus; vgl. J. MEIXNER: Z. phys. Chem. (B) **53**, 235 (1943).

[6] Während $\bar{\tau}$ praktisch immer größenordnungsmäßig bekannt ist, hängt Z von theoretisch schwer übersehbaren Faktoren — z.B. dem zwischen zwei Molekülen beim Zusammenstoß auftretenden Potential — ab. Außerdem wird Z und damit auch ζ selbst durch geringe Fremdgaszusätze stark herabgesetzt.

erhaltende), noch eine reine (volumerhaltende) Schubdeformation, sondern aus beiden Typen zusammengesetzt (vgl. Ziff. 11).

Da der Frequenzbereich, innerhalb dessen mit den beiden derart verkoppelten Größen als frequenzunabhängigen Konstanten gerechnet werden darf, so außerordentlich verschieden und hinsichtlich der Druckviskosität meist von vornherein nicht anzugeben ist, hat sich der Brauch eingebürgert, den Einfluß der letzteren als ein gesondertes Phänomen[1] zu behandeln — so wird auch in den nachstehenden Abschnitten verfahren — und zwar als Relaxationseffekt, der sich den anderen, den „klassischen" Ausgleichsphänomenen in der Schallwelle additiv überlagert (vgl. Ziff. 16). Dies hat um so mehr Berechtigung, als Frequenzen, für die $\omega \cdot Z \cdot \bar{\tau} \geqq 1$ ist, durchaus erreichbar und besonders aufschlußreich sind, während die Bedingung $\omega\bar{\tau} < 1$ außer bei extrem hohen Frequenzen und tiefen Drucken immer eingehalten ist.

B. Theorie der Schallabsorption und -dispersion auf Grund der Mechanik der Kontinua.

7. Allgemeines zur Darstellung. In den folgenden Abschnitten wird das Problem der Schallabsorption soweit als möglich auf Grund der Mechanik der Kontinua behandelt, zunächst ohne Rücksicht auf Transportphänomene, anschließend (Ziff. 8 bis 12) unter Einbeziehung jeweils eines derselben und endlich unter Berücksichtigung aller (Ziff. 16). Alle Abweichungen vom dämpfungs- und dispersionsfreien Fall werden als klein — in einem gleich zu definierenden Sinn — angesehen, was meist den physikalischen Gegebenheiten entspricht[2].

Nach den Überlegungen der vorstehenden Ziff. 3 bis 6 haben alle Transport- und Relaxationserscheinungen zur Folge, daß eine frequenzabhängige Phasenverschiebung (φ) besteht zwischen dem Überdruck π, definiert durch $p = p_0(1+\pi)$ und der Verdichtung s, definiert durch $\varrho = \varrho_0(1+s)$. φ verschwindet mit $\omega \to 0$. Außerdem wird auch das Verhältnis der Verdichtung zum Überdruck frequenzabhängig (vgl. die folgenden Ziffern). Bezeichnet man dies Verhältnis — den Kompressionsmodul — mit K, so gilt also:

$$\pi = K \cdot s; \qquad K(\omega) = K' + jK''; \qquad \varphi = \operatorname{arc\,tan} \frac{K''}{K'}. \tag{7.1}$$

Ferner gilt für die Bewegung fluider Medien allein auf Grund des Kräftegleichgewichts am Volumelement und des Kontinuitätssatzes im eindimensionalen Fall

$$p_0 \frac{\partial^2 \pi}{\partial x^2} - \varrho_0 \frac{\partial^2 s}{\partial t^2} = 0. \tag{7.2}$$

Wird nun dem Medium durch eine Schallquelle eine harmonische Bewegung von der (reellen) Kreisfrequenz ω aufgezwungen, so lautet die Lösung von (7.2):

$$s = s_0 \cdot e^{j\omega t} \cdot e^{\pm jkx}, \tag{7.3}$$

wobei k die komplexe Ausbreitungskonstante bedeutet:

$$k = k' - jk'' = \omega \sqrt{\frac{\varrho}{K}} = \omega \sqrt{\frac{\varrho}{K'}} \left(1 + j\,\frac{K''}{K'}\right)^{-\frac{1}{2}}. \tag{7.4}$$

[1] Oft unter dem wenig charakteristischen Namen „molekulare Schallabsorption und -dispersion".

[2] Auch hierbei kann auf eine umfassende Darstellung von letzter mathematischer Strenge verwiesen werden, wobei dann freilich die Grenzen des physikalischen Realisier- oder Verifizierbaren gelegentlich überschritten werden. C. Truesdell: J. Rational Mech. Anal. **2**, 643—741 (1953); ferner F. V. Hunt: J. Acoust. Soc. Amer. **27**, 1019—1039 (1955).

Wenn φ und somit wegen (7.1) auch $K''/K' \ll 1$ ist[1], wird demnach:

$$k \approx \omega \sqrt{\frac{\varrho}{K'}}\left(1 - j\,\frac{\varphi}{2}\right).$$

Einsetzen in (7.3) ergibt für

die Wellenlänge $$\lambda = \frac{2\pi}{k'} = \frac{2\pi}{\omega}\sqrt{\frac{K'}{\varrho}}, \tag{7.5}$$

die Phasengeschwindigkeit $$c = \lambda \cdot \frac{\omega}{2\pi} = \sqrt{\frac{K'}{\varrho}}, \tag{7.6}$$

den Absorptionskoeffizienten $$\alpha \equiv k'' = \omega \sqrt{\frac{\varrho}{K'}} \cdot \frac{\varphi}{2}, \tag{7.7}$$

den Absorptionsindex $$\mu \equiv \alpha \lambda = \pi \varphi. \tag{7.8}$$

Wird dagegen das Medium zwischen zwei starren Wänden, die im Abstand L senkrecht zur x-Richtung angeordnet sind, zu stehenden Wellen erregt, was einer Axialresonanz im Zylinderresonator entspricht, so lautet die Lösung von (7.2) zwar wieder wie (7.3), jetzt aber, um die gegebenen Grenzbedingungen zu erfüllen, mit (reellem) $k = n\pi/L$, wobei $n = 1, 2, 3, \ldots$. Dann wird (7.2) nur durch ein komplexes

$$\omega = \omega' + j\omega'' = \frac{n\pi}{L}\sqrt{\frac{K}{\varrho}} \approx \frac{n\pi}{L}\sqrt{\frac{K'}{\varrho}}\left(1 + j\,\frac{\varphi}{2}\right) \tag{7.9}$$

befriedigt. Demnach besitzt die stehende Welle

die Eigenfrequenz $$= \omega' = \frac{n\pi}{L}\sqrt{\frac{K'}{\varrho}}, \tag{7.10}$$

das Dekrement $$\vartheta = \pi\varphi. \tag{7.11}$$

Ist φ nicht mehr $\ll 1$, so werden die Zusammenhänge wesentlich komplizierter[2].

In den folgenden Ziffern wird unter Berücksichtigung der verschiedenen Transport- und Relaxationsphänomene die Größe $\left(\frac{\omega}{k}\right)^2 = \frac{1}{\varrho}(K' + jK'')$ [vgl. (7.4)] berechnet. Sie hängt mit den experimentell zugänglichen Größen Phasengeschwindigkeit und Absorptionsindex gemäß (7.1), (7.6) und (7.8) wie folgt zusammen:

$$\frac{\omega^2}{k^2} = c^2\left(1 + j\,\frac{\mu}{2\pi}\right)^{-2}. \tag{7.12}$$

8. Die ungedämpfte ebene Schallwelle im idealen Gas. Wir behandeln zunächst die Ausbreitung einer ebenen Schallwelle in einem idealen Gas in Abwesenheit aller Transport- und Relaxationsphänomene. Da unter diesen Umständen alle Zustandsänderungen streng reversibel erfolgen, kann keine Absorption auftreten. Wir nehmen ferner alle Abweichungen vom Ruhezustand als klein an; d. h. wenn

$$\left.\begin{aligned} p &= p_0(1+\pi) \text{ den Druck,} \\ \varrho &= \varrho_0(1+s) \text{ die Dichte,} \\ T &= T_0(1+\vartheta) \text{ die Temperatur} \end{aligned}\right\} \tag{8.1}$$

[1] Wieweit das in idealen Gasen der Fall ist, wird in Ziff. 15 behandelt.

[2] Vgl. hierzu R. T. BEYER, R. B. LINDSAY u. J. J. MARKHAM: Rev. Mod. Phys. **23**, 376 (1951).

und u die Schallschnelle bedeuten (p_0, ϱ_0, T_0, sind die Ruhewerte), sollen alle zweiten und höheren Potenzen von π, s, Θ und u und alle Produkte aus ihnen vernachlässigt werden. Während die erste Einschränkung nachher schrittweise abgebaut wird, werden wir die zweite, die „Linearisierung" des Problems beibehalten. Das bedeutet physikalisch, daß in diesem Beitrag nur solche Phänomene behandelt werden, die sich bei Verkleinerung der Schallamplitude nicht verändern.

Die *Zustandsgleichung* für ein ideales Gas lautet

$$p = R\,T\,\varrho\,M\,. \tag{8.2}$$

R bedeutet die universelle Gaskonstante, M das Molekulargewicht. Mit den oben genannten Bezeichnungen nimmt (8.2) die Form

$$\pi = \vartheta + s \tag{8.3}$$

an.

Aus der *Kontinuitätsgleichung*

$$\frac{\partial \varrho}{\partial t} + \frac{\partial}{\partial x}(\varrho u) = 0 \tag{8.4}$$

wird

$$\frac{\partial s}{\partial t} + \frac{\partial u}{\partial x} = 0\,. \tag{8.5}$$

Für die *Bewegungsgleichung*

$$\varrho \frac{\partial u}{\partial t} = -\frac{\partial p}{\partial x} \tag{8.6}$$

erhalten wir

$$\frac{\partial u}{\partial t} = -\frac{p_0}{\varrho_0}\frac{\partial \pi}{\partial x}\,. \tag{8.7}$$

Endlich setzen wir den *1. Hauptsatz* für die hier betrachteten reversiblen Zustandsänderungen an $\left(\text{mit } \Delta V = -\frac{\Delta\varrho}{\varrho^2}\right)$:

$$\Delta U - \frac{p\,\Delta\varrho}{\varrho^2} = 0\,. \tag{8.8}$$

Mit $\Delta U = c_v \cdot \Delta T$ (c_v = spezifische Wärme bei konstantem Volumen) ergibt sich daraus:

$$c_v\,T_0\,\vartheta - \frac{p_0}{\varrho_0}\,s = 0 \tag{8.9}$$

und weiter unter Anwendung von (8.2) und der genannten Vernachlässigungen

$$c_v\,\vartheta - \frac{R}{M}\,s = 0\,. \tag{8.10}$$

Mit den für eine ebene Welle gültigen Ansätzen

$$\left.\begin{aligned} \pi &= \pi_0 \cdot e^{j(\omega t - k x)}, \\ s &= s_0 \cdot e^{j(\omega t - k x)}, \\ \vartheta &= \vartheta_0 \cdot e^{j(\omega t - k x)}, \\ u &= u_0 \cdot e^{j(\omega t - k x)} \end{aligned}\right\} \tag{8.11}$$

wird aus (8.3), (8.5), (8.7) und (8.10), wenn wir die fortan überflüssigen Indices 0 weglassen:

$$\pi - \vartheta - s = 0, \tag{8.12}$$

$$\omega s - k u = 0, \tag{8.13}$$

$$\omega u - \frac{p_0}{\varrho_0} k \pi = 0, \tag{8.14}$$

$$c_v \vartheta - \frac{R}{M} s = 0. \tag{8.15}$$

Diese vier homogenen, linearen Gleichungen haben eine nichttriviale Lösung nur dann, wenn die Determinante ihrer Koeffizientenmatrix verschwindet, d.h. wenn die folgende Gleichung erfüllt ist:

$$k^2 = \frac{1}{\gamma} \frac{\varrho_0}{p_0} \omega^2, \tag{8.16}$$

wobei, wie üblich, $\frac{R}{M c_v} + 1 = \frac{c_p}{c_v} = \gamma$ gesetzt ist.

Der „Wellenvektor" k ist also reell, die Phasengeschwindigkeit $c = \frac{\omega}{k}$ hat den bekannten „Laplaceschen" Wert (2.2)

$$c_0^2 = \gamma \frac{p_0}{\varrho_0}. \tag{8.17}$$

Für den Schallwellenwiderstand w, wie üblich definiert durch

$$w = \frac{u}{\Delta p} = \frac{u}{p_0 \pi}$$

ergibt sich auf demselben Wege:

$$w^2 = \gamma \cdot p_0 \varrho_0, \tag{8.18}$$

d.h. ein reeller, frequenzunabhängiger Wert.

Ebenfalls reell und frequenzunabhängig ist das Verhältnis Überdruck/Verdichtung oder der Kompressionsmodul, definiert durch:

$$K = \frac{\Delta p}{\Delta \varrho / \varrho_0} = \frac{p_0 \pi}{s}. \tag{8.19}$$

Aus (8.12) und (8.15) ergibt sich nämlich:

$$K = \gamma p_0. \tag{8.20}$$

Sobald man, wie das in den folgenden Abschnitten geschieht, Wärmeleitung und -strahlung, Viscositäts- und Relaxationseinflüsse berücksichtigt, werden alle diese charakteristischen Größen — Wellenvektor, Schallwellenwiderstand und Kompressionsmodul — komplex und frequenzabhängig, d.h. es tritt Dispersion und Absorption der Schallwellen ein.

9. Einfluß der Wärmeleitung und Diffusion. In der Schallwelle existieren dauernd Temperaturgradienten, die bei endlicher Wärmeleitfähigkeit (λ) Wärmeströme auslösen und die Zustandsänderungen irreversibel machen. Die Energiebilanz, wie sie in (8.8) angesetzt wurde, stimmt nun nicht mehr, sondern lautet, nach der Zeit differenziert und unter Einführung von $\Delta U = c_v \cdot \Delta T$:

$$c_v \frac{\partial T}{\partial t} - \frac{p_0}{\varrho_0^2} \frac{\partial \varrho}{\partial t} = \frac{\partial Q}{\partial t}, \tag{9.1}$$

wobei $\partial Q/\partial t$ die Wärmemenge angibt, die der Masseneinheit je Zeiteinheit aus der Umgebung zugeleitet wird. Sie ergibt sich aus der Differentialgleichung der Wärmeleitung zu:

$$\frac{\partial Q}{\partial t} = \frac{\lambda}{\varrho_0} \frac{\partial^2 T}{\partial x^2}, \tag{9.2}$$

wobei wir uns von vorneherein auf ebene Wellen, die sich in x-Richtung ausbreiten, beschränken. Damit tritt an die Stelle von (8.15)

$$j\omega\, c_v \vartheta - j\omega \frac{R}{M} s = -k^2 \frac{\lambda}{\varrho_0} \vartheta. \tag{9.3}$$

Aus (8.12) bis (8.14), die erhalten bleiben, und (9.3) ergibt sich dann für den Wellenvektor:

$$k^2 = \frac{1}{\gamma} \frac{1 - j\beta_1}{1 - j\beta_1/\gamma} \cdot \frac{\varrho_0}{p_0} \cdot \omega^2 \tag{9.4}$$

mit der Abkürzung:

$$\beta_1 = \frac{\lambda}{c_v \cdot \varrho_0} \frac{k^2}{\omega}. \tag{9.5}$$

Über die Größe des Korrektionsgliedes β_1 gibt die kinetische Gastheorie Auskunft. Danach ist nämlich

$$\frac{\lambda}{c_v \cdot \varrho_0} \approx \frac{1}{3} \cdot c^2 \bar{\tau}, \tag{9.6}$$

wobei $\bar{\tau}$ die mittlere Stoßzeit und $\bar{c}$ die mittlere Molekulargeschwindigkeit bedeutet, die mit der Schallgeschwindigkeit (c_0) in folgendem Zusammenhang steht[1]:

$$\bar{c}^2 = \frac{3}{\gamma} \cdot c_0^2. \tag{9.7}$$

Da nun k/ω nicht wesentlich von $1/c$ abweicht, wird

$$\beta_1 \approx \frac{1}{\gamma} \omega \bar{\tau} \tag{9.8}$$

also sicher $\ll 1$, solange man mit der Schallfrequenz weit unterhalb der Stoßfrequenz bleibt, wie das hier zunächst angenommen wird.

Für extrem hohe Frequenzen ($\omega \gg 1/\bar{\tau}$) wird $\beta_1 \gg 1$, und die Phasengeschwindigkeit strebt wegen (9.4) dem Wert $\sqrt{p_0/\varrho_0}$ zu; d.h. sie sinkt auf den isothermen Wert ab. Tatsächlich überwiegt dann aber der Einfluß der Viskosität. Auch die dann einsetzenden Abweichungen von der primitiven Gastheorie machen sich insgesamt derart geltend, daß die Phasengeschwindigkeit mit der Frequenz anwächst (vgl. hierzu Ziff. 18).

In einem homogenen Gasgemisch treten weitere Dämpfungsursachen auf: Diffusion und Thermodiffusion[2]. Dies ist so zu verstehen, daß die leichtere Mischungskomponente — dank der größeren Molekulargeschwindigkeit — sich schneller in Richtung eines Druck- bzw. Temperaturgefälles bewegt als die schwerere. In der Schallwelle geht also periodisch eine partielle Entmischung vor sich, der die Diffusion irreversibel entgegenwirkt. So entsteht eine zusätzliche Phasenverschiebung zwischen Druck und Verdichtung, und dadurch zusätzliche Absorption, die von Frequenz und Druck ebenso abhängt wie die durch Wärmeleitung bedingte. Formal wirkt sich dieser Effekt also wie eine erhöhte Wärmeleitfähigkeit aus. Die Konzentrationsabhängigkeit ist komplizierter, weil auch die Änderung der Molwärme mit der Konzentration berücksichtigt werden

[1] Vgl. z.B. J. H. Jeans: Dynamical Theory of Gases, 4. Aufl., Cambridge 1925.

[2] Dies wurde wohl zuerst erkannt von S. Chapman [Trans. Roy. Soc. Lond. A **217**, 115 (1918)].

muß[1]. In Luft, wo die Molekulargewichte sich nur wenig unterscheiden ist der Effekt sehr gering, in He-Kr-Gemischen überwiegt er unter Umständen alle anderen Einflüsse bei weitem (vgl. Ziff. 32).

10. Einfluß der Wärmestrahlung. Prinzipiell anders als der Temperaturausgleich durch Wärmeleitung wirkt sich derjenige durch Wärmestrahlung[2] aus, der nur deswegen hier diskutiert werden soll.

Legt man das Newtonsche Abkühlungsgesetz zugrunde, so trägt zur Temperaturänderung $\partial\vartheta/\partial t$ auch ein Glied $(-q\cdot\vartheta)$ bei, das zu dem durch die Dichteänderung bewirkten $\frac{R}{Mc_v}\frac{\partial s}{\partial t}$ [vgl. (8.10)] hinzutritt:

$$\frac{\partial\vartheta}{\partial t}=\frac{\mathsf{R}}{Mc_v}\frac{\partial s}{\partial t}-q\cdot\vartheta. \tag{10.1}$$

Diese Gleichung ersetzt jetzt (8.10) bzw. (8.15); (8.12) bis (8.14) bleiben unverändert. Mit den Ansätzen (8.11) und mit $Mc_v=C_v$ wird aus (10.1):

$$C_v\cdot\left(1+\frac{q}{j\omega}\right)\vartheta-\mathsf{R}s=0, \tag{10.2}$$

d.h. an die Stelle von C_v ist jetzt $C_v\left(1+\frac{q}{j\omega}\right)$ getreten. Die Korrektur kann also nur mit abnehmender Frequenz bemerkbar werden und wirkt sich dann aus wie eine Verkleinerung von γ und somit der Phasengeschwindigkeit [vgl. (8.17)], die sich ja dem isothermen Wert nähern muß.

Eine Abschätzung des Strahlungseinflusses aus der kinetischen Gastheorie ist natürlich unmöglich. Jedoch beweisen alle experimentellen Befunde[3], daß er unerheblich ist, insofern nämlich als Messungen der Schallgeschwindigkeit immer bessere Übereinstimmung mit dem adiabatischen Wert zeigen, je tiefer die Frequenz.

Anders liegen die Verhältnisse bei Stoßwellen, wo extreme Temperaturen und Temperaturgradienten auftreten und das Newtonsche Abkühlungsgesetz sicher nicht mehr gilt. Hier kann der Strahlungseinfluß alle anderen überwiegen[4].

11. Einfluß der Schubviskosität[5]. Um ihn zu berücksichtigen, bedarf es einer Abänderung der „Bewegungsgleichung" (8.7), während jetzt Zustands-, Kontinuitäts- und Energiegleichung (8.3), (8.4), (8.10) wie im dämpfungsfreien Fall erhalten bleiben.

Daß auch in einer unendlich ausgedehnten, ebenen Schallwelle Schubverformung auftritt und die ihr entsprechenden Reibungskräfte mitspielen, lehrt folgende Überlegung: Ein nach den Achsen (x, y, z) eines rechtwinkligen Koordinatensystems angeordnetes, kubisches Raumelement des — natürlich isotrop an-

[1] Y. ROCARD: J. de Phys. **1** (7), 426 (1930) und "Propagation et absorption du son", Paris: Hermann 1935; ferner J. MEIXNER: Ann. Phys. **43**, 470 (1943) und M. KOHLER: Z. Physik **127**, 40 (1949).

[2] Zuerst — vor der Wärmeleitung! — diskutiert von G. E. STOKES: Phil. Mag. (4), **1**, 305 (1851). Weitere Überlegungen zu diesem Problem: Y. ROCARD: Act. Sci. Ind. Nr. 222 (1935); J. G. MARKHAM: R. T. BEYER u. R. B. LINDSAY: Rev. Mod. Phys. **23**, 353 (1951); A. B. BHATIA: J. Acoust. Soc. Amer. **29**, 823 (1957).

[3] Quantitative Abschätzung für Luft bei Lord RAYLEIGH: Theory of Sound, Bd. 2, S. 24ff. London 1896.

[4] Die Selektivität der Wärmeabsorption berücksichtigt eine Rechnung von P. W. SMITH: J. Acoust. Soc. Amer. **29**, 693 (1957). Zum Einfluß der Strahlung auf die Relaxation vgl. S. J. LUKASIK: J. Acoust. Soc. Amer. **28**, 455 (1956) und Ziff. 20.

[5] Unter der „Schubviskosität" η (englisch: shearing viscosity) verstehen wir die früher schlechthin als Viskosität, Zähigkeit oder Koeffizient der inneren Reibung bezeichnete Materialkonstante.

genommenen — Mediums wird durch eine in x-Richtung fortschreitende Schallwelle vorübergehend zu einem Quader deformiert, unter Beibehaltung seiner Abmessungen in der y- und z-Richtung. Dieser Deformationstyp läßt sich, wie in Fig. 2 dargestellt, in drei Schritten durchführen. Der erste besteht in einer isotropen oder Ähnlichkeitsdeformation, der zweite und dritte in je einer volumerhaltenden oder Schubdeformation, wie man an der Verformung eines von den Würfelkantenmitten gebildeten Quadrats leicht erkennt[1]. Dem ersten Schritt setzt das Material elastische Kräfte entgegen, die in (8.6) durch das rechts stehende Glied berücksichtigt sind; dem zweiten und dritten Schritt wirken — in fluiden Medien nur — Viskositätskräfte entgegen, und zwar, wie sich zeigen läßt[1], je von der Größe $-\frac{2}{3}\eta\frac{\partial^2 u}{\partial x^2}$ (bezogen auf die Volumeneinheit). Somit lautet jetzt die Bewegungsgleichung:

$$\varrho\frac{\partial u}{\partial t} = -\frac{\partial p}{\partial x} + \frac{4}{3}\eta\frac{\partial^2 u}{\partial x^2}. \tag{11.1}$$

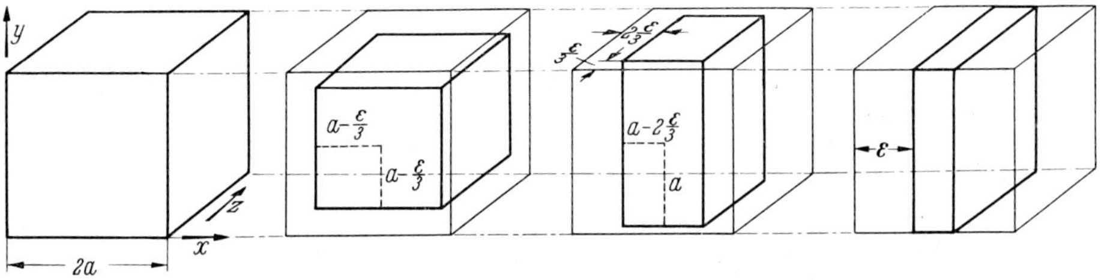

Fig. 2. Verformung eines kubischen Volumelements in einer ebenen Schallwelle.

Mit den für eine ebene Welle kleiner Amplitude gültigen Ansätzen (8.11) folgt dann

$$\omega u = \frac{p_0}{\varrho_0} k\pi + j\frac{4}{3}\frac{\eta}{\varrho_0} k^2 u. \tag{11.2}$$

Dies im Verein mit (8.12), (8.13) und (8.15) ergibt:

$$\frac{k^2}{\omega^2} = \frac{1}{\gamma}\frac{\varrho_0}{p_0}\frac{1}{1+j\beta_2}, \tag{11.3}$$

worin

$$\beta_2 = \frac{4}{3}\frac{\eta}{\gamma p_0}\omega = \frac{4}{3}\frac{\eta}{\varrho c_0^2}\omega. \tag{11.4}$$

Die Schubviskosität der idealen Gase berechnet die kinetische Theorie zu:

$$\eta = \frac{1}{3}\varrho\bar{c}^2\bar{\tau}. \tag{11.5}$$

Somit wird

$$\beta_2 = \frac{4}{9}\frac{\bar{c}^2}{c_0^2}\omega\bar{\tau} \approx \frac{4}{3\gamma}\omega\bar{\tau}, \tag{11.6}$$

wobei (9.7) angewandt wurde. Solange wieder mit Frequenzen gearbeitet wird, für die $\omega\bar{\tau} \ll 1$, ist also auch $\beta_2 \ll 1$.

Wegen (7.4) ist

$$\frac{k^2}{\omega^2} = \frac{\varrho_0}{K'}\cdot\frac{1}{1+j\,K''/K'}$$

[1] S. Timoshenko: Theory of Elasticity. New York 1934. — C. Kittel: Phys. Soc. Rep. Progr. Phys. **11**, 205 (1948).

Durch Vergleich mit (11.3) erkennt man, daß hier

$$\beta_2 = \frac{K'}{K''}, \tag{11.7}$$

und ebenfalls aus (11.3):

$$\frac{\omega^2}{k^2} = c_0^2 (1 + j\beta_2), \tag{11.8}$$

daß die Phasengeschwindigkeit mit steigendem β_2, d.h. mit steigender Frequenz [vgl. (11.6)] anwächst.

12. Einfluß der Relaxation eines Reaktionsgleichgewichtes. Als letzter der dämpfungsbewirkenden Einflüsse sei die Tatsache diskutiert, daß sich ein Reaktionsgleichgewicht nicht unendlich schnell einstellen kann. Da sich in der Schallwelle Druck und Temperatur ändern, wechselt auch die Lage des Gleichgewichtes periodisch. Infolge der endlichen Einstellzeit folgt die Reaktion diesen Änderungen mit einer Phasenverschiebung, und dies führt zu einer Energiedissipation. Unter „Reaktion" sollen nicht nur chemische Reaktionen verstanden werden, sondern auch die Anregung eines Moleküls in einen Zustand höherer Energie eines inneren Freiheitsgrades — z.B. der Molekülschwingung — und die Rückkehr aus einem solchen.

Findet eine Reaktion in der einen oder umgekehrten Richtung statt, so kann sich dabei die innere Energie U und die Molzahl n ändern. Dies bedeutet, daß der erste Hauptsatz (8.8) und die Zustandsgleichung (8.2) eine weitere unabhängige Variable enthalten müssen, die die Lage der Reaktion beschreibt, die Reaktionslaufzahl ξ.

Bewegungsgleichung (8.6) und Kontinuitätsgleichung (8.4) bleiben unverändert. Die Reaktionslaufzahl ist die Molkonzentration einer Komponente, die auf der rechten Seite der Reaktionsgleichung mit dem stöchiometrischen Faktor 1 steht, multipliziert mit dem Molvolumen. Zur Lösung des Problems benötigt man nun noch eine Beziehung, die ξ mit den bisherigen Variablen p, T und ϱ in Verbindung bringt. Man findet sie in der Relaxationsgleichung.

Zu deren Herleitung[1] macht man folgenden phänomenologischen Ansatz: Nach den Vorstellungen der irreversiblen Thermodynamik ist die Einstellgeschwindigkeit des Gleichgewichtes nur von der Affinität A abhängig. Bei kleinen Auslenkungen aus dem Gleichgewicht kann man sich mit dem linearen Ansatz

$$\frac{d\xi}{dt} = a \cdot A \tag{12.1}$$

begnügen. Eine konstante, von A unabhängige Reaktionsgeschwindigkeit ist dabei nicht zu erwarten, denn bei verschwindender Affinität ist das Gleichgewicht erreicht. A ist eine Funktion von zwei unabhängigen äußeren Zustandsvariablen X und Y und der Reaktionslaufzahl ξ. Sie wird aus der Gibbsschen Fundamentalbeziehung gewonnen:

$$T\,dS = dU + p\,dV + A\,d\xi. \tag{12.2}$$

a ist eine von X, Y und ξ abhängige positive Größe, die in erster Näherung als konstant angesehen werden kann. Weitere Angaben kann die phänomenologische Theorie hierzu nicht machen.

Um nun aus (12.1) die Einstellzeit des Gleichgewichtes zu erhalten, muß die Abhängigkeit der Affinität A von der Auslenkung aus dem Gleichgewicht spezifiziert werden. Zunächst hält man die äußeren Variablen X und Y konstant und entwickelt um den Gleichgewichtswert der Reaktionslaufzahl $\bar{\xi}(X, Y)$, wobei

[1] J. MEIXNER: Sonderausgabe der Kolloid-Z. **134**, 3 (1953).

im Rahmen der linearen Näherung nach dem zweiten Glied abgebrochen werden kann. Man erhält, da das konstante Glied $A(X, Y, \bar{\xi}(X, Y))$ verschwindet:

$$A(X, Y, \xi) = \left(\frac{\partial A}{\partial \xi}\right)_{X,Y} \left(\xi - \bar{\xi}(X, Y)\right). \tag{12.3}$$

Durch Einsetzen dieser Gleichung in (12.1) ergibt sich

$$\frac{d\xi}{dt} = a \left(\frac{\partial A}{\partial \xi}\right)_{X,Y} \left(\xi - \bar{\xi}(X, Y)\right). \tag{12.4}$$

Eine Lösung ist sofort möglich, da $\bar{\xi}$ bei konstantem X und Y ebenfalls konstant ist:

$$\xi = \bar{\xi}(X, Y) + C \cdot \exp \frac{t}{\frac{1}{a}\left(\frac{\partial \xi}{\partial A}\right)_{X,Y}}. \tag{12.5}$$

Die im Nenner des Exponenten auftretende Zeitkonstante

$$\tau_{XY} = -\frac{1}{a}\left(\frac{\partial \xi}{\partial A}\right)_{X,Y} \tag{12.6}$$

ist die Relaxationszeit bei konstantem X und Y. Hält man andere Zustandsvariablen konstant, so ergibt sich naturgemäß eine andere Relaxationszeit. Die verschiedenen Relaxationszeiten lassen sich jedoch einfach ineinander umrechnen.

$$\left.\begin{aligned} \frac{\tau_{XZ}}{\tau_{XY}} &= \frac{a(X, Z(X, Y))}{a(X, Y)} \frac{\left(\frac{\partial \xi}{\partial A}\right)_{X,Z}}{\left(\frac{\partial \xi}{\partial A}\right)_{X,Y}} = \frac{\left(\frac{\partial \xi}{\partial A}\right)_{X,Z}}{\left(\frac{\partial \xi}{\partial A}\right)_{X,Y}} \\ &= 1 - \left(\frac{\partial Z}{\partial \xi}\right)_{X,Y} \left(\frac{\partial \xi}{\partial Z}\right)_{A,X} = \left(\frac{\partial Y}{\partial Z}\right)_{A,X} \left(\frac{\partial Z}{\partial Y}\right)_{\xi,X}. \end{aligned}\right\} \tag{12.7}$$

In einem Bereich, in dem eine lineare Abhängigkeit der Affinität von ξ, X, Y und Z genügend gewährleistet ist, kann man die Differentiation bei konstant gehaltenem A ersetzen durch die Differentiation für $A = 0$, d.h. bei währendem Gleichgewicht (Frequenz Null).

Man erhält so für die wichtigsten Relaxationszeiten folgende Beziehungen:

$$\frac{\tau_{pT}}{\tau_{VT}} = \frac{K_T^\infty}{K_T^0}; \qquad \frac{\tau_{pV}}{\tau_{VT}} = \frac{\beta^\infty}{\beta^0}; \qquad \frac{\tau_{pV}}{\tau_{pT}} = \frac{\alpha^\infty}{\alpha^0}, \tag{12.8a}$$

$$\frac{\tau_{VS}}{\tau_{VT}} = \frac{c_v^\infty}{c_v^0}; \qquad \frac{\tau_{pS}}{\tau_{pT}} = \frac{c_p^\infty}{c_p^0}; \qquad \frac{\tau_{pS}}{\tau_{VS}} = \frac{K_S^\infty}{K_S^0}. \tag{12.8b}$$

K_S ist der adiabatische, K_T der isotherme Kompressionsmodul, β der isochore Spannungskoeffizient, α der isobare Ausdehnungskoeffizient. Der Index 0 bedeutet den quasistatischen, der Index ∞ den instantanen („eingefrorenen") Wert.

Die Gln. (12.8a) enthalten auf der rechten Seite nur Differentialquotienten der statischen Zustandsgleichung. Für den Fall, daß diese die Reaktionslaufzahl ξ nicht enthält (Reaktionen mit konstanter Gesamtmolzahl), werden die rechten Seiten von (12.8a) gleich 1 und damit alle isothermen Relaxationszeiten einander gleich.

Nun muß man jedoch eine Änderung der äußeren Variablen zulassen, um eine Verknüpfung zwischen ihnen und der Reaktionslaufzahl zu erhalten. Dazu muß die Entwicklung (12.3) auch auf X und Y ausgedehnt werden. Entwickelt man um X_0, Y_0 und $\xi_0 = \bar{\xi}(X_0, Y_0)$, so erhält man nach Anwendung von (12.1)

$$\frac{1}{a}\frac{d\xi}{dt} = \left(\frac{\partial A}{\partial \xi}\right)_{X,Y}(\xi - \xi_0) + \left(\frac{\partial A}{\partial X}\right)_{\xi,Y}(X - X_0) + \left(\frac{\partial \xi}{\partial Y}\right)_{\xi,X}(Y - Y_0). \quad (12.9)$$

Dies läßt sich mit den Beziehungen

$$\left(\frac{\partial A}{\partial X}\right)_{\xi,Y} = -\left(\frac{\partial A}{\partial \xi}\right)_{X,Y}\left(\frac{\partial \xi}{\partial x}\right)_{A,Y}, \qquad \left(\frac{\partial A}{\partial Y}\right)_{\xi,X} = -\left(\frac{\partial A}{\partial \xi}\right)_{X,Y}\left(\frac{\partial \xi}{\partial X}\right)_{A,Y} \quad (12.10)$$

noch in eine andere Form bringen:

$$\frac{1}{a}\frac{d\xi}{dt} = \left(\frac{\partial A}{\partial \xi}\right)_{X,Y}\left[\xi - \xi_0 - \left(\frac{\partial \xi}{\partial X}\right)_{A,Y}(X - X_0) - \left(\frac{\partial \xi}{\partial Y}\right)_{A,X}(Y - Y_0)\right] \quad (12.11)$$

oder, da

$$\left(\frac{\partial \xi}{\partial X}\right)_{A,Y} = \left(\frac{\partial \bar{\xi}}{\partial X}\right)_Y \quad \text{und} \quad \xi_0 = \bar{\xi}(X_0, Y_0)$$

ist,

$$\frac{d\xi}{dt} = a\left(\frac{\partial A}{\partial \xi}\right)_{X,Y}[\xi - \bar{\xi}(X, Y)]. \quad (12.12)$$

Wie man sieht, gilt dieselbe Relaxationsgleichung (12.4) auch für leicht variiertes X und Y.

Man kann nun für $X = T$, $Y = p$ mit (12.11) die Variable ξ aus der Zustandsgleichung und Energiegleichung eliminieren und damit das Problem lösen. Wesentlich einfacher ist jedoch ein anderes Verfahren. Für die in der Schallwelle vorliegenden adiabatischen Zustandsänderungen ist die Entropie in erster Näherung konstant[1], man benützt sie deswegen zweckmäßig als Variable X. Nimmt man als Variable Y den Druck p, so vereinfacht sich (12.11) wegen $S = \text{const}$ zu

$$\tau_{pS}\frac{d\xi}{dt} + \xi - \xi_0 - \left(\frac{\partial \xi}{\partial p}\right)_{A,S}(p - p_0) = 0. \quad (12.13)$$

Da die Bedingung $S = \text{const}$ schon die Aussage des ersten Hauptsatzes enthält, muß nun nur noch die Zustandsgleichung um p_0, ξ_0 entwickelt werden:

$$\varrho - \varrho_0 = \left(\frac{\partial \varrho}{\partial p}\right)_{\xi,S}(p - p_0) + \left(\frac{\partial \varrho}{\partial \xi}\right)_{p,S}(\xi - \xi_0). \quad (12.14)$$

Aus (12.13) und (12.14) kann man $(\xi - \xi_0)$ und $d\xi/dt$ eliminieren und erhält die sog. *akustische Zustandsgleichung*

$$\tau_{pS}\frac{d\varrho}{dt} + \varrho - \varrho_0 = \tau_{pS}\left(\frac{\partial \varrho}{\partial p}\right)_{\xi,S}\frac{dp}{dt} - \left(\frac{\partial \varrho}{\partial p}\right)_{A,S}(p - p_0). \quad (12.15)$$

Mit den Beziehungen

$$\left(\frac{d\varrho}{dp}\right)_{A,S} = \frac{\varrho}{K_S^0}; \qquad \left(\frac{\partial \varrho}{\partial p}\right)_{\xi,S} = \frac{\varrho}{K_S^\infty} \quad (12.16)$$

und den Ansätzen (8.1) und (8.11) ergibt sich schließlich

$$s(1 + j\omega\tau_{pS}) = \pi \cdot p_0\left(\frac{1}{K_S^0} + \frac{1}{K_S^\infty}j\omega\tau_{pS}\right). \quad (12.17)$$

Für das Quadrat des komplexen Ausbreitungsvektors k findet man

$$\frac{k^2}{\omega^2} = \frac{\varrho_0}{p_0}\cdot\frac{s}{\pi} = \frac{\varrho_0}{K_S^0}\,\frac{1 + \frac{K_S^0}{K_S^\infty}j\omega\tau_{pS}}{1 + j\omega\tau_{pS}} \quad (12.18)$$

[1] J. MEIXNER: Acustica 2, 101 (1952).

13. Diskussion der Relaxationsfunktion. Gl. (12.18) bestimmt die Schallausbreitung in jedem Medium, für welches die Relaxationsgleichung (12.4) und — selbstverständlich — die Kontinuitäts- und Bewegungsgleichung (8.13) und (8.14). Aus (12.18) soll nunmehr die Frequenzabhängigkeit der experimentell zugänglichen Größen abgeleitet werden, nämlich der Phasengeschwindigkeit c, des Absorptionskoeffizienten und -index' [α bzw. μ definiert durch (7.7) bzw. (7.8)], sowie der häufig benützten Größe α/f^2 (f = Frequenz der Schallwelle).

Zunächst werde (12.18) mit Hilfe der allgemeingültigen Beziehung für die Phasengeschwindigkeit bei hinreichend kleiner Frequenz:

$$c_0^2 = \frac{K_0}{\varrho_0} \tag{13.1}$$

umgeformt, wobei einfachheitshalber τ_{pS} durch τ' und K_S durch K ersetzt wird

$$\frac{k^2}{\omega^2} c_0^2 = \frac{1 + \frac{K_0}{K_\infty} j\omega\tau'}{1 + j\omega\tau'}. \tag{13.2}$$

Führt man den „Relaxationsbetrag" ε ein:

$$\varepsilon = 1 - \frac{K_0}{K_\infty} = \frac{c_\infty^2 - c_0^2}{c_\infty^2} \tag{13.3}$$

und ersetzt k durch $k_0 - j\alpha$, so erhält man durch Gleichsetzen der beiderseitigen Real- und Imaginärteile:

$$\frac{c_0^2}{\omega^2}(k_0^2 - \alpha^2) = 1 - \varepsilon \frac{\omega^2\tau'^2}{1 + \omega^2\tau'^2}, \tag{13.4}$$

$$\frac{c_0^2}{\omega^2} \cdot 2k_0\alpha = \frac{\varepsilon\omega\tau'}{1 + \omega^2\tau'^2}. \tag{13.5}$$

Die Auflösung dieser Gleichungen nach k_0 bzw. $c = \omega/k_0$ und α bzw. μ führt auf sehr unübersichtliche Ausdrücke. Daher sei hier die Annahme

$$\alpha^2 \ll k_0^2 \tag{13.6}$$

gemacht und α^2 gegen k_0^2 vernachlässigt, was praktisch immer zulässig ist[1]. Damit ergibt sich aus (13.4) die Dispersionsformel:

$$\frac{c_0^2}{c^2} = 1 - \varepsilon \frac{\omega^2\tau'^2}{1 + \omega^2\tau'^2}. \tag{13.7}$$

Aus (13.5) folgt:

$$\frac{\alpha}{k_0} = \frac{c^2}{c_0^2} \cdot \frac{\varepsilon}{2} \cdot \frac{\omega\tau'}{1 + \omega^2\tau'^2}. \tag{13.8}$$

$1/k_0$ ist aber nichts anderes als der 2π-te Teil der Wellenlänge λ, und so erhält man für den Absorptionsindex ($\mu = \alpha\lambda$) unter Verwendung von (13.8)

$$\mu = \varepsilon\pi \frac{\omega\tau'}{1 + (1-\varepsilon)\,\omega^2\tau'^2} \tag{13.9}$$

mit einem Maximum der Größe

$$\mu_{\max} = \frac{\pi}{2} \frac{\varepsilon}{\sqrt{1-\varepsilon}} \text{ bei } (\omega\tau')_{\max} = \frac{1}{\sqrt{1-\varepsilon}} \tag{13.10}$$

bei $\omega\tau' \cdot \sqrt{1-\varepsilon} = \omega\tau_m = 1$ mit $\tau_m = \sqrt{\tau_{VS} \cdot \tau_{pS}}$.

---

[1] Für den Spezialfall der idealen Gase wird dies in Ziff. 15 zahlenmäßig begründet.

Mit der Abkürzung $\omega\tau' = x$ wird dann:

$$\mu = 2\mu_{\max} \cdot \frac{x/x_{\max}}{1 + (x/x_{\max})^2}. \tag{13.11}$$

Den Absorptionskoeffizienten α erhält man in ganz ähnlicher Weise aus (13.4) und (13.6) zu:

$$\alpha = \frac{\varepsilon}{2c_0} \cdot \frac{\omega^2 \tau'}{\sqrt{[1 + (1-\varepsilon)\,\omega^2 \tau'^2]\,(1 + \omega^2 \tau'^2)}}. \tag{13.12}$$

Die Größen $\frac{c^2}{c_0^2}$, μ, α sind gemäß Formel (13.7), (13.9) und (13.12) in Fig. 3 als Funktionen von $\log \omega\tau'$ dargestellt; dazu die Größe α/f^2, die für $\omega\tau' \ll 1$ frequenzunabhängig wird mit dem Wert:

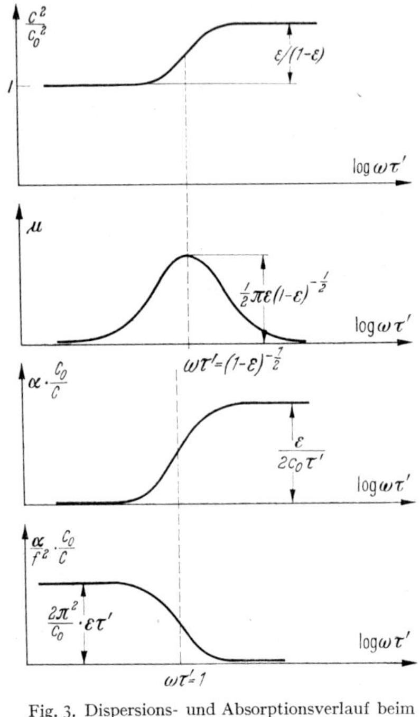

Fig. 3. Dispersions- und Absorptionsverlauf beim einfachen Relaxationskörper.

$$\left.\frac{\alpha}{f^2}\right|_{\omega\to 0} = \frac{2\pi^2}{c_0} \cdot \varepsilon\tau'. \tag{13.13}$$

Aus (12.18) gewinnt man — immer unter der Vernachlässigung (13.6) — folgende Aussagen über die experimentell zugänglichen Größen:

$$\frac{c_\infty^2}{c^2} = \frac{1}{1-\varepsilon} - \frac{\varepsilon}{1-\varepsilon}\,\frac{\omega^2\tau'^2}{1+\omega^2\tau'^2}, \tag{13.14}$$

$$\frac{c^2}{c_0^2} = 1 + \frac{\varepsilon}{1-\varepsilon}\,\frac{\omega^2\tau_m^2}{1+\omega^2\tau_m^2}, \tag{13.15}$$

$$\frac{c^2}{c_\infty^2} = 1 - \varepsilon + \varepsilon\,\frac{\omega^2\tau_m^2}{1+\omega^2\tau_m^2}, \tag{13.16}$$

$$\mu = \alpha\cdot\lambda = \frac{\pi\,\varepsilon}{\sqrt{1-\varepsilon}}\,\frac{\omega\,\tau_m}{1+\omega^2\tau_m^2}, \tag{13.17}$$

$$\mu\,\frac{c_0^2}{c^2} = \pi\,\varepsilon\,\frac{\omega\,\tau'}{1+\omega^2\tau'^2}, \tag{13.18}$$

$$\alpha\,\frac{c_0}{c} = \frac{\varepsilon}{2c_0}\,\frac{\omega^2\tau'}{1+\omega^2\tau'^2}. \tag{13.19}$$

14. Das „Cole-Diagramm" des einfachen Relaxationskörpers. Der einfache Relaxationskörper ist durch die „akustische Zustandsgleichung" (12.15) allgemein, und durch (12.17) für periodische Zustandsänderungen definiert. Sein makroskopisches Verhalten wird am besten durch ein Zeigerdiagramm illustriert, d.h. indem man etwa die Amplitude des Überdruckes [$\Delta p = p_0\pi_0$ vgl. (8.1) und (8.11)] durch den in die Abszissen verlegten Einheitsvektor darstellt und die Verdichtung s durch einen Vektor, dessen Betrag gleich der Verdichtungsamplitude s_0 und dessen Richtung durch seine Phasenverschiebung φ gegen den Überdruckvektor bestimmt ist[1]. Der Verdichtungsvektor ist dann einfach durch den komplexen Ausdruck $s/p_0\pi$ gegeben. Durch Multiplikation mit K_0 macht man ihn zweckmäßig dimensionslos:

$$\mathfrak{S} = K_0\,\frac{s}{p_0\,\pi}. \tag{14.1}$$

[1] In genauer Analogie zu den in der Elektrotechnik üblichen Strom- und Spannungszeigerdiagrammen.

In der komplexen Ebene dargestellt, kennzeichnet $\mathfrak{S}$ also durch Betrag und Richtung die Verdichtung, die eintritt, wenn der Körper einer periodischen Druckschwankung von derjenigen Größe unterworfen würde, die bei quasistatischer Versuchsführung die Verdichtung 1 hervorruft[1].

Die Spur des Vektors $\mathfrak{S}$ bei Variation von $\omega\tau'$ wird häufig als „Cole-Diagramm“ bezeichnet[2].

Aus (12.17) ergibt sich mit der in (13.3) definierten Abkürzung ε:

$$\mathfrak{S} = \frac{1 + (1-\varepsilon)\, j\,\omega\,\tau'}{1 + j\,\omega\,\tau'}. \tag{14.2}$$

Zerlegung in Real- und Imaginärteil ($\mathfrak{S} = \mathfrak{S}_1 + j\,\mathfrak{S}_2$) liefert

$$\mathfrak{S}_1 = \frac{1 + (1-\varepsilon)\,\omega^2\tau'^2}{1+\omega^2\tau'^2}, \quad \mathfrak{S}_2 = \frac{-\varepsilon\,\omega\,\tau'}{1+\omega^2\tau'^2}. \tag{14.3}$$

Eine kurze Rechnung ergibt:

$$\left.\begin{aligned} \mathfrak{S}_1' &= \mathfrak{S}_1 - \left(1 - \frac{\varepsilon}{2}\right) \\ &= \frac{\varepsilon}{2} \cdot \frac{1-\omega^2\tau'^2}{1+\omega^2\tau'^2} \end{aligned}\right\} \tag{14.4}$$

und man erkennt sofort, daß

$$\mathfrak{S}_1'^2 + \mathfrak{S}_2^2 = \frac{\varepsilon^2}{4} \tag{14.5}$$

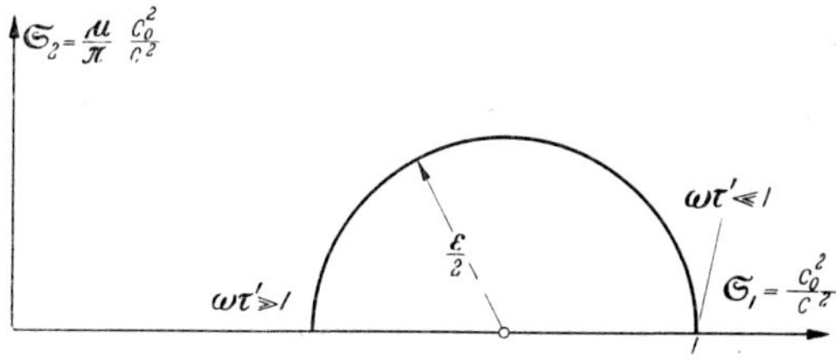

Fig. 4. Cole-Diagramm.

also unabhängig von $\omega\tau'$ ist, d.h.: Bei Variation von $\omega\tau'$ wandert der Endpunkt des Vektors $\mathfrak{S}$ auf einem Kreis mit dem Radius $\varepsilon/2$, um den Punkt $\left(1 - \frac{\varepsilon}{2}\right)$ auf der reellen Achse (vgl. Fig. 4); selbstverständlich nur beim einfachen Relaxationskörper!

Für die Phasendifferenz φ zwischen Überdruck und Verdichtung gilt:

$$\tan\varphi = \mathfrak{S}_2/\mathfrak{S}_1 = -\frac{\varepsilon\,\omega\,\tau'}{1 + (1-\varepsilon)\,\omega^2\tau'^2} \tag{14.6}$$

In idealen Gasen kann die Phasendifferenz höchstens den Wert:

$$\varphi_{\max} = \operatorname{arc\,tan} 0{,}2 = 11^\circ\, 16' \tag{14.7}$$

erreichen (vgl. Ziff. 15).

Wie man aus (13.7) und (13.9) ersieht, ist

$$\mathfrak{S}_1 = \frac{c_0^2}{c^2}, \tag{14.8}$$

$$\mathfrak{S}_2 = -\frac{\mu}{\pi} \cdot \frac{c_0^2}{c^2}. \tag{14.9}$$

Trägt man also an der gleichen Substanz gemessene Wertepaare μ und c in dieser Weise auf [c_0 ist meist bekannt oder nach (8.7) berechenbar], so müssen, wenn es sich um einen einfachen Relaxationskörper handelt, alle Punkte auf einem Kreis liegen, unabhängig von Frequenz und Relaxationszeit τ'.

---

[1] Mit anderen Worten: $\mathfrak{S} = K_0/K$ ist die komplexe relative Kompressibilität.

[2] Diese Darstellung wurde zuerst zur Wiedergabe von dielektrischen Messungen verwendet von K. S. Cole: J. Chem. Phys. **9**, 341 (1941). Zur Darstellung paramagnetischer Relaxationserscheinungen wurde das Verfahren zuerst angewandt von H. B. G. Casimir, D. Bijl u. F. K. du Pré: Physica **8**, 449 (1941); auf das Problem der Schallausbreitung von H. O. Kneser: Ann. d .Phys. **43**, 465 (1943).

Diese Art der Darstellung ist nützlich, wenn — wie bei manchen Gasen — τ' so stark von Verunreinigungen abhängt, daß seine Konstanz von Probe zu Probe nicht garantiert werden kann. Bei der beschriebenen Darstellung kann dann immerhin entschieden werden, ob die Substanz sich wie ein einfacher Relaxationskörper verhält, und — aus der Lage des Punktes auf dem Kreis — welche Relaxationszeit der einzelnen Probe zukommt.

15. Relaxation im idealen Gas. Die auf den sehr einfachen allgemein-thermodynamischen Voraussetzungen (12.1) und (12.3) fußenden Absorptions- und Dispersionsformeln (13.14) bis (13.19) sollen nun auf den Spezialfall der idealen Gase angewandt werden. Die Größen τ_m und τ', die man mit (13.14) bis (13.19) dem Experiment entnimmt, werden — wie üblich — mit (12.8) auf die isotherme Relaxationszeit umgerechnet und hier und im Abschnitt E mit τ bezeichnet.

Da wir von den „klassischen" Ausgleichsphänomenen in dieser und den drei vorangehenden Ziffern absehen, erfolgen langsame Zustandsänderungen des Gases adiabatisch. Unter diesen Umständen läßt sich der Kompressionsmodul K_0 durch die Molwärme bei konstantem Volumen (C_v) wie folgt ausdrücken

$$K_0 = \frac{\mathsf{R} + C_v}{C_v} \cdot p_0 \,. \tag{15.1}$$

Bei der Berechnung von K_∞ ist zu beachten, daß die Existenz einer energetisch ausgezeichneten Komponente, deren Konzentration (ξ) natürlich mit der Temperatur anwächst, eine erhöhte Molwärme bedeutet. Dementsprechend kann man C_v in zwei Anteile aufspalten, nämlich in einen, den man erhalten würde, wenn man ξ bei einer Temperatursteigerung konstant halten könnte, er sei als äußere Molwärme bezeichnet:

$$C_a = C_v(\xi = \text{const}) \tag{15.2}$$

und einen anderen, der allein den Beitrag der ausgezeichneten Komponente angibt:

$$C_i = C_v - C_a \tag{15.3}$$

Der ausgezeichneten Komponente hatten wir eine endliche Einstellzeit τ zugeschrieben. Bei Zustandsänderungen, die hieran gemessen sehr schnell verlaufen — z.B. bei periodischen Vorgängen, für die $\omega\tau \gg 1$ ist — wird ξ also praktisch konstant bleiben und die Molwärme den Wert C_a zeigen. Nun wird aber auch der Kompressionsmodul durch die Molwärme mitbestimmt. Man wird also den Kompressionsmodul für „unendlich schnelle" Zustandsänderungen erhalten, wenn man in (15.3) C_v durch C_a ersetzt[1]:

$$K_\infty = \frac{\mathsf{R} + C_a}{C_a} \cdot p_0 \,. \tag{15.4}$$

Somit nimmt der Relaxationsbetrag $\varepsilon = 1 - \frac{K_0}{K_\infty}$ [vgl. (13.3)] für ideale Gase den Wert an:

$$\begin{aligned} \varepsilon &= 1 - \frac{\mathsf{R} + C_v}{C_v} \cdot \frac{C_a}{\mathsf{R} + C_a} \\ &= \frac{\mathsf{R} \cdot C_i}{C_v(\mathsf{R} + C_a)} \end{aligned} \tag{15.5}$$

[1] Der nicht ganz einfache exakte Beweis findet sich bei J. MEIXNER, a.a.O. Dabei ergibt sich, wie zuerst von J. J. MARKHAM, R. T. BEYER u. R. B. LINDSAY [Rev. Mod. Phys. **23**, 353 (1951)] bemerkt wurde, daß C_i bei konstantem Druck nicht gleich C_i bei konstantem Volumen ist.

Den größtmöglichen Wert wird ε in idealen Gasen dann erreichen, wenn die nur mit Translationsenergie behafteten Moleküle als „Normalkomponente" und alle anderen als „energetisch ausgezeichnete Komponente" zu gelten haben. Die ersteren tragen dann zur Molwärme $C_a = \frac{3}{2}R$ bei, die letzteren ein C_i, dessen Größe von der Temperatur und der Anzahl der übrigen Freiheitsgrade abhängt, so daß $C_v = \frac{3}{2}R + C_i$ zu setzen ist. Daher wird:

$$\varepsilon = \frac{R\,C_i}{\left(\frac{3}{2}R + C_i\right)\frac{5}{2}R} \leqq \frac{2}{5}. \tag{15.6}$$

Für die Schallausbreitungsdaten folgt daraus

$$\text{mittels (13.7)} \qquad c_\infty \leqq c_0\sqrt{\tfrac{5}{3}} \approx 1{,}3\,c_0, \tag{15.7}$$

$$\text{mittels (13.10)} \qquad \mu_{\max} \leqq \frac{\pi}{\sqrt{15}} \approx 0{,}8. \tag{15.8}$$

Im idealen Gas kann also die Phasenverschiebung, zwischen Druck und Verdichtung den Wert 15° [vgl. (7.8)], die Differenz zwischen τ_p und τ_V 40% [vgl. (12.8b)] niemals übersteigen.

Endlich ist bemerkenswert, daß für ideale Gase sich hiermit die früher (13.6) gemachte Vernachlässigung präzisieren läßt; denn nach (13.5), wenn man dort ω/k_0 durch c ersetzt, ist:

$$\left.\begin{aligned} \frac{\alpha}{k_0} &= \varepsilon\cdot\frac{\omega\tau}{1+\omega^2\tau^2}\cdot\frac{1}{2}\frac{c^2}{c_0^2} \\ &\leqq \frac{2}{5}\cdot\frac{1}{2}\cdot\frac{1}{2}\cdot\frac{5}{3} = \frac{1}{6}, \\ \alpha^2 &\leqq \frac{1}{36}k_0^2. \end{aligned}\right\} \tag{15.9}$$

Der Fehler, den die Vernachlässigung (13.5) in die Berechnung der Dispersionskurve hineinträgt, kann also höchstens 1,3% betragen, und auch das nur, wenn $C_i \gg R$ ist. Außerdem kann sich der Fehler in diesem Maße nur im Frequenzbereich $\omega \approx 1/\tau$ auswirken, wo wegen der starken Absorption ohnehin meist keine sehr genauen Messungen der Phasengeschwindigkeit möglich sind.

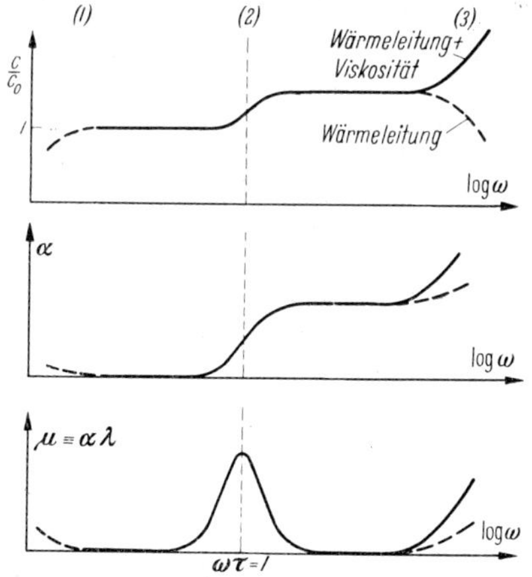

Fig. 5. Dispersions- und Absorptionskurve schematisch unter der Einwirkung von „klassischen" und Relaxationseffekten.

16. Zusammenwirken mehrerer Einflüsse[1]. *α) Übersicht.* In Tabelle 1, Spalte 3—6 sind nochmals die Gleichungen zusammengestellt, von denen wir in Ziff. 9—12 ausgingen, um jeweils *einen* der energiedissipierenden Einflüsse zu berücksichtigen. Spalte 7 gibt die reziproke „komplexe Schallgeschwindigkeit" an in vereinheitlichter Form, so daß die Abhängigkeit von der mittleren Stoßzeit ($\bar{\tau}$) bzw. der Relaxationszeit (τ) und der Frequenz (ω) deutlich wird.

Die daraus resultierende Frequenzabhängigkeit der Dispersion und Absorption ist in Fig. 5 auch dargestellt (qualitativ), und zwar für den Fall, daß die Frequenzbereiche hinreichend weit getrennt sind, in denen sich der Einfluß

[1] Vgl. hierzu die historisch kritischen Bemerkungen von H. Deresiewicz u. M. Greenspan; J. Acoust. Soc. Amer. **29**, 1375 (1957).

Tabelle 1.

Nr.	Energiedissipation	Zustandsgleichung	Energiegleichung	Bewegungsgleichung	Kontinuitätsgleichung	$\frac{k^2}{\omega^2} =$
	Keine	$\boldsymbol{\pi} = \vartheta + s$ (8.3)	$C_v \vartheta - \mathsf{R}\, s = 0$ (8.10)	$\dot{u} = -\frac{p_0}{\varrho_0} \boldsymbol{\pi}'$ (8.7)	$\dot{s} + u' = 0$ (8.5)	$\frac{1}{\gamma} \frac{\varrho_0}{p_0} = \frac{1}{c_0^2}$ (8.16)
3	Durch Wärmeleitung	$\boldsymbol{\pi} = \vartheta + s$ (8.3)	$C_v \dot{\vartheta} - \mathsf{R}\, \dot{s} = \frac{\lambda \mu}{\varrho_0} \vartheta''$ (9.1) bis (9.3)	$\dot{u} = -\frac{p_0}{\varrho_0} \boldsymbol{\pi}'$ (8.7)	$\dot{s} + u' = 0$ (8.5)	$\frac{1}{c_0^2} \cdot \frac{1 - j\omega\overline{\tau}/\gamma}{1 - j\omega\overline{\tau}/\gamma^2}$ (9.4), (9.8)
1	Durch Wärmestrahlung	$\boldsymbol{\pi} = \vartheta + s$ (8.3)	$C_v \dot{\vartheta} - \mathsf{R}\, \dot{s} = -q\,\vartheta$ (10.1)	$\dot{u} = -\frac{p_0}{\varrho_0} \boldsymbol{\pi}'$ (8.7)	$\dot{s} + u' = 0$ (8.5)	$\frac{1}{c_0^2} \cdot \frac{1}{1 + (\gamma - 1)/(1 + q/j\omega)}$ (10.2)
3	Durch Schubviskosität	$\boldsymbol{\pi} = \vartheta + s$ (8.3)	$C_v \vartheta - \mathsf{R}\, s = 0$ (8.10)	$\varrho_0 \dot{u} = -p_0 \boldsymbol{\pi}' + \frac{4}{3} \eta u''$ (11.1)	$\dot{s} + u' = 0$ (8.5)	$\frac{1}{c_0^2} \cdot \frac{1}{1 + j\omega\overline{\tau} \cdot 4/3\gamma}$ (11.3), (11.6)
2	Durch Druckviskosität (Relaxation)	$s + \tau \dot{s} = \frac{1}{\gamma} (\pi - (1 - \varepsilon)\, \tau \dot{\pi})$ (12.16), (15.2), (15.4), (15.5)		$\dot{u} = -\frac{p_0}{\varrho_0} \pi'$ (8.7)	$\dot{s} + u' = 0$ (8.5)	$\frac{1}{c_0^2} \cdot \frac{1 + (1 - \varepsilon)\, j\omega\tau}{1 + j\omega\tau}$ (12.18), (13.3)

1. (vgl. Spalte 1 der Tabelle 1) der Wärmestrahlung, 2. der Druckviskosität oder Relaxation und 3. der Schubviskosität und Wärmeleitung auswirkt. (Die beiden unter 3. genannten fallen ja immer zusammen.) Dann überlagern sie sich in erster Näherung additiv.

β) Die „klassische“ Absorption und Dispersion. Für das Zusammenwirken der beiden „klassischen“ Einflüsse, Wärmeleitung und Schubviskosität findet man auf dem in Ziff. 9 und 11 beschrittenen Wege aus (8.12), (8.13), (9.3) und (11.2):

$$\frac{k^2}{\omega^2} = \frac{1}{\gamma}\,\frac{\varrho_0}{p_0}\,\frac{1 - j\beta_1}{1 - j\left(\frac{\beta_1}{\gamma} - \beta_2\right) + \beta_1\beta_2}. \tag{16.1}$$

Die exakte Lösung der Gl. (16.1) führt auf einen außerordentlich komplizierten Ausdruck für k^2/ω^2, wovon Ziff. 18 handeln wird.

Wesentlich einfacher wird er für ein sog. „Becker-Gas“, d.h. wenn $\beta_1/\gamma = \beta_2$ ist[1], was wegen $\beta_1 = \frac{\lambda}{c_v \cdot \varrho_0}\,\frac{k^2}{\omega}$ [vgl. (9.5)] und $\beta_2 = \frac{4}{3}\,\frac{\eta}{\varrho_0 c_0^2}\,\omega$ [vgl. (11.4)] gleichbedeutend ist mit:

$$\frac{\lambda}{\eta\, c_v} = \frac{4}{3}\gamma\,\frac{1}{c_0^2}\,\frac{\omega^2}{k^2} \approx \frac{4}{3}\gamma. \tag{16.2}$$

Abgesehen von einatomigen Gasen ($\gamma = \frac{5}{3}$) ist die Beziehung (16.2) meist leidlich erfüllt und liefert dann — wofern nicht Relaxationseinflüsse hineinspielen — eine brauchbare Näherung auch für Frequenzen, für die $\omega\bar{\tau}$ nicht mehr $\ll 1$ ist.

Im allgemeinen wird man, wenn $\omega\bar{\tau}$ und somit auch β_1 und $\beta_2 \ll 1$ ist, Gl. (16.1) entwickeln und erhält dann:

$$\frac{k^2}{\omega^2} = \frac{1}{c_0^2}\left[1 - j\left(\beta_1\,\frac{\gamma-1}{\gamma} + \beta_2\right)\right] \tag{16.3}$$

oder nach Rückgängigmachen der Abkürzungen β_1 und β_2 (9.5) und (11.4)

$$\frac{k^2}{\omega^2} = \frac{1}{c_0^2}\left[1 - j(\gamma - 1)\,\frac{\lambda}{c_p \cdot \varrho_0}\,\frac{k^2}{\omega^2}\,\omega - j\,\frac{4}{3}\,\frac{\eta}{\gamma p_0}\,\omega\right]. \tag{16.4}$$

Die beiden imaginären Terme sind $\ll 1$ und $\frac{k^2}{\omega^2} \approx c_0^{-2}$. Für den Imaginärteil von k, d.h. [wegen (7.3)] für den „klassischen“ Absorptionskoeffizienten ergibt sich daher:

$$\alpha_{kl} = \frac{\omega^2}{2c_0}\left[(\gamma - 1)\,\frac{\lambda}{c_0^2\, c_p \cdot \varrho_0} + \frac{4}{3}\,\frac{\eta}{\gamma p_0}\right] = \frac{2\pi^2}{\varrho_0\, c_0^3}\left[(\gamma - 1)\,\frac{\lambda}{c_p} + \frac{4}{3}\eta\right] \cdot f^2. \tag{16.5}$$

Diese unter dem Namen „Stokes-Kirchhoffsche Absorptionsformel“ bekannte Gleichung[2] beschreibt die Schallabsorption ohne eigentliche Relaxationseffekte zutreffend, solange $\omega\bar{\tau} \ll 1$.

Führen wir noch einmal für λ und η die gaskinetischen Werte von (9.6) und (11.5) ein, so wird:

$$\alpha_{kl} \approx \frac{\omega^2}{2c_0}\left(\frac{\gamma-1}{\gamma^2} + \frac{4}{3\gamma}\right)\bar{\tau}. \tag{16.6}$$

Für den Absorptionskoeffizienten je Wellenlänge [vgl. (7.8)] folgt daraus:

$$\mu_{kl} \approx \frac{\pi}{\gamma}\left(\frac{\gamma-1}{\gamma} + \frac{4}{3}\right)\omega\,\bar{\tau} \tag{16.7}$$

[1] R. Becker [Z. Physik **8**, 321 (1922)] hat nämlich gezeigt, daß für ein Gas, dessen Konstanten dieser Beziehung genügen, die Stoß-Wellengleichung explizit lösbar ist. Vgl. hierzu ferner M. Greenspan: J. Acoust. Soc. Amer. **26**, 70 (1954).

[2] Gelegentlich auch nach „Navier und Stokes“ benannt.

oder, wenn wir vorübergehend das Verhältnis der mittleren freien Weglänge zur Schallwellenlänge mit z bezeichnen, unter Beachtung von (9.7)

$$\left.\begin{aligned} \mu_{kl} &\approx \frac{2\pi^2}{\sqrt{3\gamma}}\left(\frac{\gamma-1}{\gamma}+\frac{4}{3}\right)z \\ &\approx 16\cdot z. \end{aligned}\right\} \qquad (16.8)$$

Der Beitrag der Wärmeleitung ist, wie (16.7) erkennen läßt, geringer als derjenige der Schubviskosität. (Dies gilt in noch höherem Maße für Flüssigkeiten mit Ausnahme geschmolzener Metalle.) Ferner zeigt (16.5), daß die klassische Absorption sich umgekehrt proportional zur Dichte ändert, was das Arbeiten mit verdünnten Gasen sehr erschwert. Der Temperatureinfluß ist durch den Faktor $\bar{c}/c_0$ gegeben. Die klassische Absorption steigt etwa proportional $T^{\frac{3}{2}}$ an.

Die durch die „klassischen" Einflüsse bewirkte *Dispersion* ergibt sich ebenfalls mit meist genügender Genauigkeit aus Gl. (16.4), die wir mittels (16.5) umformen:

$$\frac{k^2}{\omega^2} = \frac{1}{c_0^2}\left[1 - j\,\alpha_{kl}\,\frac{2c_0}{\omega}\right] = \frac{1}{c_0^2}\left[1 - j\,\mu_{kl}/\pi\right]. \qquad (16.9)$$

Daraus erhält man

$$c \approx c_0\left[1 + \mu_{kl}^2/8\pi^2\right]. \qquad (16.10)$$

Demnach findet man bei einer Schallwellenlänge, die noch 100 mittlere freie Weglängen enthält ($z = 0{,}01$), nach (16.8) $\mu \approx 0{,}16$, d. h. eine sehr starke Absorption, gleichzeitig aber nur eine Dispersion von der Größenordnung $\frac{c-c_0}{c_0} \approx 10^{-3}$!

γ) „Klassische" und Relaxationseinflüsse. Wenn ein Relaxationseinfluß zu den beiden klassischen derart hinzutritt, daß alle im gleichen Frequenzbereich merkliche Beiträge zur Dispersion und Absorption liefern, so treten komplizierte Wechselwirkungen auf. Die Theorie ist von J. MEIXNER[1] vollständig durchgeführt mit dem Ergebnis, daß jetzt an die Stelle von (16.4) tritt:

$$\frac{k^2}{\omega^2} = \left\{\frac{k^2}{\omega^2}\right\}\cdot\left[1 - j\,a(\omega)\,\frac{\varrho}{T^2}\left(\frac{\partial T}{\partial p}\right)^2_{S,\omega} - j\,\frac{4}{3}\,\frac{\eta}{\varrho}\left\{\frac{k^2}{\omega^2}\right\}\omega\right]. \qquad (16.11)$$

Darin bedeutet $\{k^2/\omega^2\}$ den durch den Relaxationseinfluß modifizierten, frequenzabhängigen Wert von k^2/ω^2, wie er aus (12.18) zu entnehmen ist. Auch $\left.\frac{\partial T}{\partial p}\right|_S$ ist unter Berücksichtigung der Relaxation zu bilden und daher frequenzabhängig. $a(\omega)$ ist definiert durch einen phänomenologischen Ansatz für den Energiefluß:

$$\vec{W} = -\frac{a}{T}\,\mathrm{grad}\,T + bT\,\mathrm{grad}\,\frac{A}{T}, \qquad (16.12)$$

wobei A wie in (12.2) die Affinität darstellt. In Abwesenheit von Relaxationsprozessen ($A = 0$) wird also $\frac{a}{T\varrho}$ gleich der Wärmeleitfähigkeit λ und $\left.\frac{\partial T}{\partial p}\right|_S = \frac{1}{\varrho c_p}$, womit dann (16.11) in (16.4) übergeht.

Die Auswertung einer experimentell gewonnenen Dispersions- oder Absorptionskurve auf Grund dieser letzten Formel stößt allerdings auf große Schwierigkeiten. Immerhin bietet sie die Möglichkeit abzuschätzen, ob die Annahme einer additiven Überlagerung der Relaxations- und der klassischen Einflüsse noch erlaubt ist[2].

---

[1] J. MEIXNER: Acustica **2**, 101 (1952) und F. V. HUNT: J. Acoust. Soc. Amer. **27**, 1019 (1955).

[2] Vgl. J. MEIXNER, a. a. O.

In praxi ergibt das Experiment häufig ein konstantes α/f^2, dessen Zahlenwert aber wesentlich größer ist als der aus Schubviscosität und Wärmeleitung etwa nach (16.5) berechnete. Das deutet dann auf einen Relaxationseffekt hin, dessen Relaxationszeit τ noch wesentlich kleiner ist als der Reziprokwert der höchsten Meßfrequenz.

Auch dies läßt aber bei idealen Gasen schon gewisse Schlüsse auf den Relaxationsvorgang zu. Sein Beitrag zu α/f^2 ist ja wegen (13.13) und (15.5):

$$\left.\frac{\alpha}{f^2}\right|_{\omega\tau \ll 1}^{\mathrm{Rel}} = \frac{2\pi^2}{c_0} \frac{\mathsf{R} \cdot C_i}{C_v(\mathsf{R} + C_a)} \tau . \tag{16.13}$$

Der Beitrag der Schubviskosität und Wärmeleitung ergibt sich aus (16.6) zu:

$$\left.\frac{\alpha}{f^2}\right|_{\omega\bar{\tau} \ll 1}^{\mathrm{kl}} = \frac{2\pi^2}{c_0}\left(\frac{\gamma-1}{\gamma^2} + \frac{4}{3\gamma}\right)\bar{\tau} . \tag{16.14}$$

Wenn also nur wenige Absorptionsmessungen bei tiefen Frequenzen vorliegen, so kann durch Vergleich mit dem berechenbaren „klassischen" Wert von α/f^2 immerhin schon $C_i \frac{\tau}{\bar{\tau}}$ ermittelt und, da C_i meist ungefähr bekannt ist, $\frac{\tau}{\bar{\tau}}$ abgeschätzt werden. Dieser Quotient gibt an, wieviel gaskinetische Zusammenstöße zur Einstellung des thermischen Gleichgewichts erforderlich sind, und bestimmt somit den Relaxationsvorgang entscheidend (vgl. Ziff. 21).

17. Schallausbreitung im realen Gas. Die bisherigen Ableitungen bezogen sich auf ideale Gase, d. h. ihnen lag die Annahme zugrunde, daß bei konstanter Temperatur das Produkt $p \cdot V$ unabhängig von p sei. Dies ist, wie aus Fig. 6 zu ersehen, nur für geringe Drucke und hohe Temperaturen näherungsweise erfüllt.

Für etwas höhere Drucke und geringere Temperaturen genügt die Berthelotsche Zustandsgleichung

$$\left.\begin{aligned} p \cdot V &= A + Bp \\ (T &= \mathrm{const}), \end{aligned}\right\} \tag{17.1}$$

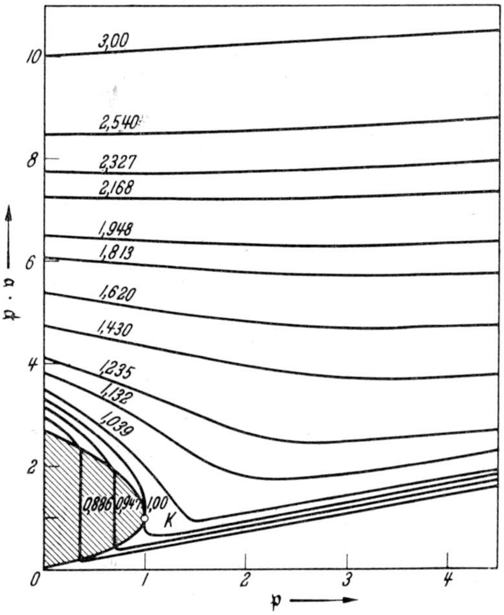

Fig. 6. Schallabsorption und -dispersion bei extremer Verdünnung berechnet für ein einatomiges Gas. Parameter: T/T_{krit} · K kritischer Punkt.

wo $A = \mathsf{R}T\varrho/M$ und B den (temperaturabhängigen) „zweiten Virialkoeffizienten" bedeutet. Mit Hilfe der allgemein gültigen thermodynamischen Beziehungen:

$$c^2 = K_{\mathrm{ad}}/\varrho \tag{17.2}$$

und

$$K_{\mathrm{ad}} = \gamma \cdot K_{is} = \gamma \cdot - V \left.\frac{\partial P}{\partial V}\right|_T ,$$

ergibt sich aus (17.1)

$$c^2 = \frac{\gamma A}{M}\left(1 + \frac{B}{A} p\right)^2 , \tag{17.3}$$

Jetzt hängt aber auch noch γ vom Druck ab, und zwar[1] folgendermaßen:

$$\gamma = \gamma_0 \cdot \left[1 + \frac{4}{3R}\left(\frac{\partial B}{\partial T} + \frac{T}{5}\frac{d^2 B}{d T^2}\right) \cdot p\right]. \tag{17.4}$$

Aus (17.3) und (17.4) folgt:

$$c = c_0(1 + \alpha p) \tag{17.5}$$

mit

$$\alpha = \frac{1}{R}\left(\frac{B}{T} + \frac{2}{3}\frac{dB}{dT} + \frac{2}{15} T \frac{d^2 B}{d T^2}\right). \tag{17.6}$$

Stärkere Abweichungen vom idealen Gaszustand können natürlich durch höhere Glieder in (17.1) (weitere Virialkoeffizienten) berücksichtigt werden. Dies führt dann auf nicht lineare Druckabhängigkeit der Schallgeschwindigkeit:

$$c = c_0(1 + \alpha p + \beta p^2 + \cdots), \tag{17.6}$$

wobei dann aber die Zuordnung von α, β, usw. zu den Virialkoeffizienten sehr kompliziert und die Berechnung der letzteren aus ersteren praktisch unmöglich wird.

Da eine für alle Drucke und Temperaturen hinreichend genau zutreffende Zustandsgleichung nicht existiert, ist es unmöglich einen analytischen Ausdruck von allgemeiner Gültigkeit für die Schallgeschwindigkeit in realen Gasen anzugeben[2]. Durch graphische Differentiation des p, V, τ-Diagramms in Richtung konstanter Entropie [vgl. Gl. (17.2)] ist die Ermittlung der Schallgeschwindigkeit für alle Zustände natürlich prinzipiell durchführbar, allerdings nur mit geringer Genauigkeit[3].

Umgekehrt erweist sich aber die Schallgeschwindigkeit zur Bestimmung der Molwärme C_v realer Gase als brauchbar, und zwar auf Grund folgender Überlegung[4]: Wir schreiben vorübergehend v statt $1/\varrho$ und erhalten anstelle von (17.2):

$$c^2 = -v^2 \left.\frac{\partial p}{\partial v}\right|_S,$$

ersetzen den Differentialquotienten durch den identischen Ausdruck

$$\left.\frac{\partial p}{\partial v}\right|_T + \left.\frac{\partial p}{\partial T}\right|_v \left.\frac{\partial T}{\partial v}\right|_S$$

und benützen die allgemein gültigen Beziehungen:

$$\left.\frac{\partial C_v}{\partial v}\right|_T = T \left.\frac{\partial^2 p}{\partial^2 T}\right|_v \quad \text{und} \quad \left.\frac{\partial T}{\partial v}\right|_s = -\frac{T}{C_v}\left.\frac{\partial p}{\partial T}\right|_v.$$

---

[1] Vgl. z.B. W. H. KEESOM: Helium, S. 95. Amsterdam 1942.

[2] Durch eine empirische Erweiterung der van der Waals-Gleichung [J. HIMPAN, Z. Physik **141**, 566 (1955)] gelingt es allerdings, die Druckabhängigkeit der Schallgeschwindigkeit nahe beim kritischen Punkt der Kohlensäure recht befriedigend darzustellen.

[3] Durchgeführt für Luft und $N_2 - H_2$-Mischungen bei tiefer Temperatur von A. VAN ITTERBECK u. W. VAN DONINCK: Ann. d. Phys. **19**, 88 (1944); vgl. ferner A. MICHELS u. S. R. DE GROOT: Appl. Sci. Res. A **1**, 94 (1947).

[4] H. TIELSCH u. H. TANNENBERGER: Z. Physik **137**, 256 (1954). Deren Messungen an CO_2 am kritischen Punkt zeigen, daß C_v beim kritischen Volumen (2,18 cm^3/g) und bei der kritischen Temperatur (31,04° C) ein Maximum von der dreifachen Höhe des für den idealen Zustand ($V \to \infty$) gültigen Wertes erreicht (21 cal/Grad Mol). — Ähnlich haben A. VAN ITTERBECK und W. DE LAET die spezifischen Wärmen von He-Gas zwischen 1,0 und 3,9° K bestimmt. Physica **24**, 59 (1958).

So ergibt sich

$$C_v = T \cdot \frac{\partial p}{\partial T}\Big|_v^2 \cdot \left(\frac{c^2}{v^2} + \frac{\partial p}{\partial v}\Big|_T\right)^{-1}, \tag{17.7}$$

worin nur experimentell direkt zugängliche Größen auftreten.

Die Ausführungen dieser Ziffer basieren auf rein thermodynamischen Ansätzen, gelten also nur unter der Voraussetzung, daß bei Zustandsänderung stets Gleichgewichtszustände durchlaufen werden. Dann darf natürlich die Schallgeschwindigkeit nicht von der Frequenz abhängen und keine Absorption auftreten[1]. Tatsächlich wird gelegentlich aber Dispersion gefunden; von diesen Resultaten und ihrer Deutung handelt Ziff. 42.

18. Schallausbreitung in hoch verdünnten Gasen. Die Experimentiertechnik ist heute derart fortgeschritten, daß Schallwellen noch bis zu so geringen Drucken vermessen werden können, daß ihre Wellenlänge vergleichbar wird mit der freien Weglänge bzw. ihre Frequenz vergleichbar mit $1/\bar{\tau}\,(\omega\bar{\tau} \gtrsim 1)$. Dies bisher unter der Annahme $\omega\bar{\tau} \ll 1$ abgeleiteten Ausbreitungsformeln reichen dann nicht mehr aus.

Im folgenden soll von Relaxationserscheinungen der bisher diskutierten Art abgesehen, d.h. praktisch nur von Edelgasen die Rede sein. Schon dabei erweist sich die Theorie als sehr kompliziert und besteht keine volle Übereinstimmung mit dem Experiment[2].

Die „klassische" Ausbreitungsformel (16.1)

$$c_0^2 \frac{k^2}{\omega^2}\left[1 - j\left(\frac{\beta_1}{\gamma} - \beta_2\right) + \beta_1\beta_2\right] = 1 - j\beta_1 \tag{18.1}$$

enthält, wenn man für β_1 und β_2 wieder die ursprünglichen Werte (9.5) und (11.4) einsetzt, Glieder der zweiten und vierten Potenz von $c_0 \frac{k}{\omega}$. Nach diesen geordnet lautet sie:

$$\frac{\lambda}{c_v\varrho_0}\frac{\omega}{c_0^2}\left[\frac{-j}{\gamma} + \frac{4}{3}\frac{\omega\eta}{\varrho c_0^2}\right]\left(c_0\frac{k}{\omega}\right)^4 + \left[1 + \frac{j\omega}{c_0^2}\left(\frac{4}{3}\frac{\eta}{\varrho_0} + \frac{\lambda}{c_v\varrho_0}\right)\right]\left(c_0\frac{k}{\omega}\right)^2 - 1 = 0. \tag{18.2}$$

Nun empfiehlt es sich, die Viskosität η durch eine dimensionslose Größe

$$Re = \frac{c_0^2\varrho}{\omega\eta} \tag{18.3}$$

zu ersetzen[3], die den Charakter einer Reynoldsschen Zahl trägt, oder durch

$$r = Re/\gamma. \tag{18.4}$$

$1/r$ hat eine anschauliche Bedeutung: Wegen $c_0^2 = \gamma\frac{p_0}{\varrho_0}$ und $\eta = \frac{\varrho c_0^2}{\gamma}\cdot\bar{\tau}$ [vgl. (11.5) und (9.7)] — welche Beziehungen allerdings nur für Maxwell-Moleküle (s. unten) streng gelten — ist

$$r = \frac{1}{\gamma}\frac{c_0^2\varrho}{\omega\eta} \approx \frac{1}{\omega\bar{\tau}}, \tag{18.5}$$

also $1/r$ ein gerade für „Translations-Relaxation" sehr geeignetes Frequenzmaß.

---

[1] Die Abweichungen vom idealen Gaszustand erschweren unter Umständen die Analyse eines gleichzeitig auftretenden Relaxationseffektes, können aber bei Kenntnis der Zustandsgrößen weitgehend berücksichtigt werden. Vgl. z.B. E. Sittig: Acustica **10**, 81 (1960).

[2] Die grundlegenden experimentellen und theoretischen Arbeiten stammen von M. Greenspan: J. Acoust. Soc. Amer. **26**, 70 (1954); **28**, 644 (1956), sowie von E. Meyer u. G. Sessler: Z. Physik **149**, 15 (1957). Dieser Arbeit folgt die Darstellung im wesentlichen.

[3] H. S. Tsien u. R. Schomberg: J. Acoust. Soc. Amer. **18**, 334 (1946).

Um (18.2) allgemein diskutieren zu können, bedient man sich der folgenden, experimentell gut bestätigten Beziehungen zwischen den Stoffkonstanten η, λ, γ und C_v:

$$\frac{\lambda}{\eta\, c_v} \approx \begin{cases} (9\gamma - 5)/4 & \text{für einatomige Gase}^1, \\ 4\gamma/3 & \text{für mehratomige Gase}^2. \end{cases} \tag{18.6}$$

Führt man (18.5) und (18.6) in (18.2) ein und löst nach $(c_0 k/\omega)^2$ auf, so ergibt sich als reelle Lösung:

$$\left(\frac{c_0 k}{\omega}\right)^2 \begin{cases} \approx \left(1 + j\,\dfrac{7}{5r}\right)^{-1} & \text{für einatomige Gase}^3, \\ = \left(1 + j\,\dfrac{4}{3r}\right)^{-1} & \text{für mehratomige Gase.} \end{cases} \tag{18.7}$$

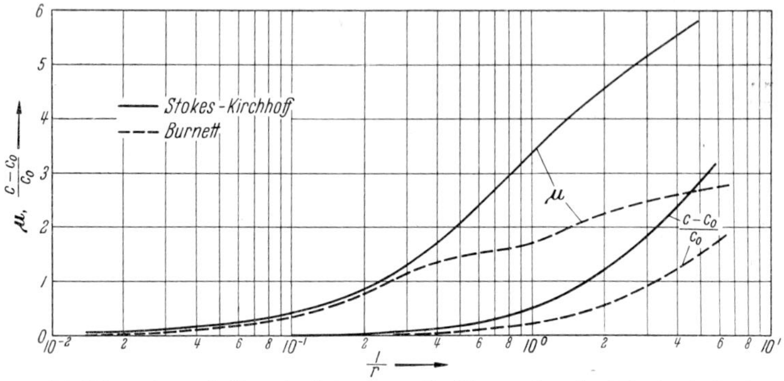

Fig. 7. Schallabsorption und -dispersion bei extremer Verdünnung; berechnet für ein einatomiges Gas.

Die andere, rein imaginäre Lösung von (18.2) gilt für die Wärmewelle und interessiert hier nicht.

Da in (18.7) die Imaginärteile nicht mehr klein sind gegenüber den Realteilen, lassen sich die experimentell bestimmbaren Größen c und μ nicht mehr so einfach angeben wie nach (7.6) und (7.8), sondern man muß hier auf (7.4) zurückgreifen. Dann ergibt sich

$$\left(\frac{c}{c_0}\right)^2 = \frac{2x^2}{x+1}, \tag{18.8}$$

$$\mu = 2\pi \sqrt{\frac{x-1}{2x^2}} \tag{18.9}$$

mit $x^2 = 1 + \left(\frac{7}{5r}\right)^2$ für einatomige Gase und mit $x^2 = 1 + \left(\frac{4}{3r}\right)^2$ für mehratomige Gase (Fig. 7). Zum Vergleich mit Experimenten ist es sinnvoll und üblich, die direkt meßbare, dimensionslose Absorptionsgröße α/β_0 anzugeben, wobei α den Absorptionskoeffizienten je Längeneinheit angibt und $\beta_0 = \omega/c_0$ ist:

$$\frac{\alpha}{\beta_0} = \sqrt{\frac{x-1}{2x^2}}. \tag{18.10}$$

Diese bis hierher „klassisch" durchgeführte Rechnung muß nun bei extrem hohen Frequenzen (genauer: $1/r$-Werten) in zwei Richtungen modifiziert werden:

---

[1] Nach A. EUCKEN; vgl. S. CHAPMAN u. T. G. COWLING: Math. Theory of Nonuniform Gases. Cambridge 1952; vgl. ferner W. F. SCHOTTKY: Z. Elektrochem. **58**, 442 (1956).

[2] Nach R. BECKER: vgl. Ziff. 16β.

[3] M. GREENSPAN [J. Acoust. Soc. Amer. **26**, 70 (1854)] hat gezeigt, daß dieser einfache Ausdruck eine gute Näherung für die recht komplizierte exakte Lösung darstellt.

1. Die Schubspannungen — vermöge der Viscositätskonstanten — und der Wärmestrom — vermöge der Wärmeleitfähigkeit — dürfen nicht mehr der mittleren freien Weglänge Λ proportional angenommen werden. Das erfordert eine Verfeinerung der gaskinetischen Grundlagen[1], wie sie von BURNETT[2] eingeführt und von WANG CHANG und UHLENBECK[3] auf das Schallproblem angewandt wurde, und die Einführung neuer Konstanten, die wesentlich vom Molekülmodell abhängen. Das Ergebnis dieser Rechnungen, denen das Modell von DE BOER und MICHELS[4] zugrunde liegt, ist ebenfalls in Fig. 7 eingetragen (schwach ausgezogene Kurve). Berücksichtigung höherer Näherungsglieder („Super-Burnett-Theorie") führt zu schlechterer Übereinstimmung mit den Experimenten (vgl. Ziff. 31).

2. Wenn bei extrem großen $1/r$-Werten Λ sogar groß wird gegen die ganze Meßstrecke, so daß die Zahl der Molekülzusammenstöße ganz vernachlässigt werden kann, dann besteht die Wirkung eines (ebenen) Schallgebers lediglich darin, den Molekülen einen periodisch wechselnden Impuls in Richtung der Schallwelle zu verleihen, der sich dem statistisch verteilten thermischen Impuls überlagert. Die Schallwelle wird mit zunehmendem Abstand vom Sender mehr und mehr „verlaufen", also scheinbar eine zusätzliche Absorption erleiden, die Schallgeschwindigkeit mehr und mehr durch die Molekulargeschwindigkeit bestimmt werden[5].

Die Meßwerte zeigen bis $1/r \approx 0{,}1$ ausgezeichnete Übereinstimmung mit der „klassischen", bis $1/r \approx 2$ mit der „Burnett-Theorie" und nähern sich bei $1/r \approx 100$ ($\lambda_0 \approx 100\Lambda$!) dem für zusammenstoßfreie Ausbreitung erwarteten Wert.

C. Kinetische Theorie der molekularen Absorption und Dispersion.

19. Allgemeines. Während in den vorangehenden Abschnitten das Problem der Schallabsorption und -dispersion kontinuumsmechanisch behandelt wurde — die mittlere Stoßzeit wurde nur einbezogen, um den Gültigkeitsbereich der Überlegungen festzulegen —, soll nunmehr eine kinetische Behandlung folgen, und zwar in erster Linie des Einflusses der Druckviskosität, den man, da er nur in mehratomigen Gasen wirksam ist, in diesem Zusammenhang folgerichtiger als molekulare Schallabsorption und -dispersion[6] bezeichnet. Die Relaxationszeit, zu der diese Phänomene den Zugang eröffnet haben, gewinnt erst in kinetischer Behandlungsweise ein Interesse für die Molekularphysik.

20. Kinetische Deutung der Schub- und Druckviskosität. Zur Schubverformung einer unendlich ausgedehnten, planparallelen Gasschicht ist eine der Verformungsgeschwindigkeit proportionale Schubspannung erforderlich [vgl. Ziff. 6]. Dies deutet die kinetische Gastheorie bekanntlich damit, daß die an die bewegte Grenzfläche anprallenden Moleküle einen zusätzlichen Impuls in Richtung von

[1] Vgl. S. CHAPMAN u. T. G. COWLING: The mathematical Theory of nonuniform Gases, S. 265ff. London 1939, und M. GREENSPAN: J. Acoust. Soc. Amer. **28**, 644 (1956).

[2] D. BURNETT: Proc. London. Math. Soc. **39**, 385 (1935).

[3] C. S. WANG CHANG u. G. E. UHLENBECK: Eng. Res. Inst. Univ. Michigan Rep. CM 681 (1951). Weitere Überlegungen zu diesem Problem bei P.-L. BHATNAGER: Phys. Rev. **94**, 511 (1954).

[4] J. DE BOER u. A. MICHELS: Physica, Haag **5**, 945 (1938); **6**, 409 (1939).

[5] Vgl. hierzu die Rechnungen von R. K. COOK, M. GREENSPAN u. M. C. THOMPSON: J. Acoust. Soc. Amer. **25**, 192 (1953) und E. MEYER u. G. SESSLER: Z. Physik **149**, 21 (1957).

[6] Dieser etwas farblose Ausdruck ist immerhin noch zutreffender als die Bezeichnung „Relaxationsabsorption ...", da auch die „klassischen" Absorptionseinflüsse, Wärmeleitung und Schubviskosität durchaus als Relaxationserscheinungen gedeutet werden können.

deren Bewegung davontragen und an die andere Grenzfläche transportieren. Bei gleicher Dichte ist die Schubviskosität allein durch die Geschwindigkeit des Impulstransportes bestimmt und ihr proportional. Dem Gas wird bei Schubverformung, bei welcher also sein Volumen erhalten bleibt, in erster Näherung keine Energie zugeführt, da die zusätzlichen Impulsbeträge bei ebensovielen Molekülen die Energie hinauf- wie herabsetzen.

Anders, wenn die Gasschicht einer Normalspannung, also einer Dickenänderung unterworfen wird. Dann werden gleichzeitig mit den jetzt senkrecht zur Wand gerichteten Impulsbeträgen auch Energiebeträge transportiert, d.h. es tritt Wärmeleitung auf, die ebenfalls proportional zur Transportgeschwindigkeit ist. Schubviskosität und Wärmeleitfähigkeit sind also durch die gleiche Zeitkonstante, nämlich die mittlere Stoßzeit $\bar{\tau}$ bestimmt [vgl. (9.6) und (11.5)].

Diese einfachen Überlegungen gelten jedoch nur unter der Voraussetzung, daß sich die Moleküle beim Zusammenstoß wie elastische, glatte Kugel verhalten[1], d.h. daß dabei die gesamte Translationsenergie als solche erhalten bleibt[2]. Sind die Zusammenstöße unelastisch, so wird ein Teil von ihr in „innere Energie", d.h. meist in Kernschwingungsenergie verwandelt; sind die Moleküle „rauh", so wird ein Teil in Rotationsenergie überführt[3].

Da nun sowohl Rotations- wie Schwingungsenergie nur quantenhaft aufgenommen und abgegeben werden, kommt jeder von beiden eine Verweilzeit zu, d.h. sie haften mehr oder weniger lange an ihrem Träger, sicherlich länger als die Translationsenergie, die bei jedem Zusammenstoß unter die Partner aufgeteilt wird. Daher wird die letztere mit einer Geschwindigkeit transportiert, die nicht wesentlich kleiner ist als die mittlere Molekulargeschwindigkeit $\bar{c}$, die ersteren aber wesentlich langsamer; im Grenzfall unendlich langer Verweilzeit sogar nur mit der Geschwindigkeit des Materietransports, d.h. mit der Selbstdiffusionsgeschwindigkeit. So kommt es daß bei Gasen, deren Moleküle „unelastisch und rauh" sind, d.h. innere Freiheitsgrade besitzen, gleichzeitig mit den senkrecht zur Grenzfläche gerichteten Impulsbeträgen Energie transportiert wird, und zwar nicht nur als Translationsenergie oder Wärme — dies geschieht auch bei elastischen, glatten Molekülen — sondern auch als „innere" Energie, und dieser Anteil viel langsamer[4]. Die Verformung durch Normalkräfte erfordert daher wiederum einen der Verformungsgeschwindigkeit proportionalen Normaldruck; d.h. es tritt jetzt eine Druckviskosität auf[5]. Diese ist um so größer, je langsamer

[1] Moleküle verhalten sich dann wie glatte Kugeln, wenn sie nur Zentralkräfte aufeinander ausüben.

[2] Vgl. hierzu Sir JAMES JEANS: An Introduction to the Kinetic Theory of Gases. Cambridge 1940. Die erste bedeutende Arbeit über die molekularkinetische Behandlung der Schallausbreitung stammt von H. A. LORENZ: Arch. néerl. Phys. **16**, 1 (1880).

[3] Dies Modell wurde von M. KOHLER [Z. Physik **125**, 715 (1949)] durchgerechnet. — Edelgasatome verhalten sich also deswegen wie glatte Kugeln, weil sie wegen ihres zu kleinen Trägheitsmomentes keine Rotationsenergie aufnehmen können.

[4] Es sei daran erinnert, daß beim *elastischen* Stoß eines Massenpunktes auf einen gleichen, anfangs ruhenden der Impuls voll auf den letzteren übertragen und mit der Anfangsgeschwindigkeit weiter geleitet wird. Beim *unelastischen* Stoß dagegen verteilt sich der Impuls auf beide Massenpunkte, deren jeder sich mit einer geringeren als der Anfangsgeschwindigkeit fortbewegt, so daß auch der Impulstransport langsamer erfolgt.

[5] Während G. G. STOKES [Trans. Cambridge Phil. Soc. **8**, 287 (1849)] postulierte, daß die Druckviskosität $=0$ sei, konnte R. E. NETTLETON [J. Appl. Phys. **29**, 204 (1958)] zeigen, daß sie auch in einatomigen Gasen $\neq 0$, wenn auch nur von der Größenordnung einiger μ Poise sei. Andrerseits hat J. M. KHALATNIKOV [J. Exp. Theor. Phys. USSR. **29**, 253 (1953) und Sow. Phys. **2**, 169 (1956) übers. von R. T. BEYER] bewiesen, daß die „zweite Viskosität" in idealen Gasen, gleichgültig welcher Statistik sie gehorchen, verschwindet, wenn die Teilchenenergie $\varepsilon = a \cdot p^n$ ist ($p =$ Impuls), wobei $n = 3 \cdot \left.\frac{\delta \ln T}{\delta \ln \varrho}\right|_S$ ist.

der Normalimpuls transportiert wird, d.h. je größer die Verweilzeiten der inneren Energie sind.

Als Materialkonstante verliert die Schubviskosität ihren Sinn, sobald sich die Schubspannung innerhalb eines Zeitintervalls merklich ändert, das vergleichbar ist mit der mittleren Stoßzeit $\bar{\tau}$, weil sich dann ein Impulsstrom überhaupt nicht mehr ausbilden kann. Genau Analoges gilt für die Druckviskosität: Sie verliert ihren Sinn, sobald der Normaldruck sich innerhalb der Verweilzeit τ merklich ändert, also z.B. für Schallwellen, bei denen $\omega\tau \approx 1$. Für $\omega\tau \gg 1$ kann sich der Vorgang überhaupt nicht mehr auswirken, d.h. die Druckviskosität verschwindet[1].

21. Relaxations- und Verweilzeit. In Ziff. 12 wurden die in der „akustischen Zustandsgleichung" auftretenden Größen τ_p und τ_V als Einstell- oder Relaxationszeiten interpretiert und auf ihren statistischen Charakter hingewiesen. Um die Verbindung zwischen diesen und der in Ziff. 20 eingeführten mittleren Verweilzeit τ herzustellen, müssen wir die letztere zunächst genauer definieren.

Diese Größe τ soll angeben, wie lange ein Quantum innerer Energie, d.h. irgendeiner Energieform außer der Translationsenergie, im Mittel als solches erhalten bleibt. Da bei einem Zusammenstoß das Quantum als solches übertragen werden kann, also nur seinen Träger wechselt, ist τ offenbar nicht identisch mit der Verweilzeit eines Moleküls im angeregten Zustand, sondern stellt vielmehr die Verweilzeit oder besser die Lebensdauer eines Quantums innerer Energie dar. Wenn also das thermodynamische Gleichgewicht zwischen innerer und äußerer (d.h. translatorischer) Energie gestört ist, so wird die Störung in der Zeit τ auf den e-ten Teil abgebaut werden.

Die Verweilzeit der inneren Energie muß also mindestens größenordnungsmäßig gleich der isothermen Relaxationszeit τ sein, welche sich zufolge (12.8b) und (15.6) in idealen Gasen nicht wesentlich von der adiabatischen unterscheidet.

In Flüssigkeiten befindet sich jedes Molekül in fortwährendem Kontakt mit einem anderen und daher ist jederzeit die Möglichkeit gegeben, daß sich innere Energie in translatorische verwandelt. In realen Gasen besteht diese Möglichkeit innerhalb der — schwer angebbaren — Zeiträume, die das Molekül in Reichweite der Van der Waals-Kräfte eines anderen verbringt. Nur in idealen Gasen findet ein unmittelbarer Kontakt lediglich während der leidlich definierten, relativ kurzen „Stoßdauern" statt.

Daher ist es bei idealen Gasen sinnvoll und zweckmäßig, die Relaxationszeit in Vielfachen der mittleren Stoßzeit zu messen:

$$\tau = Z\bar{\tau} \tag{21.1}$$

Z bedeutet demnach die Anzahl der „gaskinetischen" Zusammenstöße, die ein Quantum innerer Energie übersteht, ehe sich diese in translatorische verwandelt.

In dem Produkt $Z\bar{\tau}$ sind offenbar beide Faktoren von der *Temperatur* abhängig, und zwar Z in nicht unmittelbar ersichtlicher Weise. Dagegen ist *dichteabhängig* nur der Faktor Z, und zwar bei idealen Gasen umgekehrt proportional zur Dichte[2].

---

[1] H.O. Kneser: Proc. Roy. Soc. Lond., Ser. A **226**, 40 (1954). Weiteres zur Druckviskosität bei H.F. Lu: Scientia Sinica **5**, 33 (1956).

[2] Dies gilt nicht mehr, wenn Dreierstöße in Betracht gezogen werden, deren Wahrscheinlichkeit proportional $1/p^2$ ist, und wenn das Molekül seine innere Energie durch Strahlung abgibt. Den ersteren Fall diskutiert K.F. Herzfeld [H-11], den letzteren S. J. Lukasik [J. Acoust. Soc. Amer. **28**, 355 (1956)] und schätzt ab, daß nur bei extrem tiefen Drucken (etwa 10^{-4} atm) die — druckunabhängige — Strahlungslebensdauer τ_{Str} kleiner wird als $\tau_{\text{Stoß}}$ und damit bestimmend für die Relaxation. Dasselbe wäre auch für tiefe Temperaturen zu erwarten, wenn dort nicht die Relaxationsbeträge verschwindend klein würden. — Vgl. auch R. J. Rubin u. K. E. Shuler: J. Chem. Phys. **26**, 137 (1957).

Schalldispersion und -absorptionsindex hängen wie die vorstehenden Rechnungen zeigen, stets nur vom Produkt $\omega\bar{\tau}$ bzw. $\omega\tau = \omega Z\bar{\tau}$ ab, wofür man in idealen Gasen setzen kann: Materialkonstante · Frequenz/Druck. Daher lassen sich — abgesehen von gewissen Sonderfällen[1] — Absorptions- und Dispersionskurven für ideale Gase genau so gut durch Variation des Druckes, wie der Frequenz ermitteln. Es hat sich auch ganz allgemein eingebürgert, gemessene Schallgeschwindigkeits- und -absorptionsdaten als Funktion von f/p anzugeben[2].

22. Relaxationszeit und Übergangswahrscheinlichkeit. Die mehr qualitativen Überlegungen der letzten Ziffern sollen nunmehr durch quantitative kinetische Ansätze unterbaut werden, wodurch dann die molekularkinetische Bedeutung der Relaxationszeit schärfer hervortritt.

Jedes Molekül (A) möge — außer der sich beliebig rasch einstellenden Translations- (und eventuell Rotations-) Energie — nur zweier Energiezustände fähig sein, z.B. des Grund- und des ersten Anregungszustandes einer Kernschwingung. Sie seien durch die Indices i und j gekennzeichnet. Diesen Zuständen sollen die Energien ε_i und ε_j zukommen, ε_j soll größer als ε_i sein. (Im obigen Beispiel wäre $\varepsilon_i = 0$.) Vom i-Zustand in den j-Zustand können die Moleküle, wenn man von Strahlung absieht, nur anläßlich eines Zusammenstoßes mit einem anderen Molekül (M) übergehen, wenn dieser heftig genug ist. Dieser Energieaustausch läßt sich durch die Reaktion

$$M + A_i \leftrightarrow A_j + M \tag{22.1}$$

beschreiben, auf die man die bekannten Überlegungen der Reaktionskinetik anwenden kann. Bezeichnen c_{A_i} und c_{A_j} die molaren Konzentrationen der Reaktionspartner A_i und A_j, c_M die Gesamtkonzentration, so wird die zeitliche Änderung der Konzentration c_{A_j}

$$\frac{d c_{Aj}}{dt} = (r - r_0) - (r' - r'_0). \tag{22.2}$$

Hierin bezeichnen $(r - r_0)$ und $(r' - r'_0)$ die Auslenkungen der Reaktionsgeschwindigkeiten

$$r = k\, c_M\, c_{A_i} \quad \text{und} \quad r' = k'\, c_M\, c_{A_j} \tag{22.3}$$

aus den Gleichgewichtswerten r_0 und r'_0. k und k' sind Geschwindigkeitskonstanten für hin- und rücklaufende Reaktion. Da beide Teilreaktionen (22.1) bimolekular verlaufen, sind die Reaktionsgeschwindigkeiten r und r' von zweiter Ordnung.

Bleiben die Auslenkungen aus dem Gleichgewicht klein, was bei einer Schallwelle stets erfüllt ist, so genügt in der Entwicklung der Reaktionsgeschwindigkeiten um den Gleichgewichtswert bei konstanter Temperatur und Volumen das erste Glied:

$$\left.\begin{aligned} r - r_0 &= \left(\frac{\partial r}{\partial c_{A_i}}\right)_T (c_{A_i} - c^0_{A_i}) = k\, c_M\, (c_{A_i} - c^0_{A_i}); \\ r' - r'_0 &= \left(\frac{\partial r'}{\partial c_{A_j}}\right)_T (c_{A_j} - c^0_{A_j}) = k'\, c_M\, (c_{A_j} - c^0_{A_j}). \end{aligned}\right\} \tag{22.4}$$

Da bei der Reaktion (22.1) die Gesamtmolzahl konstant bleibt, ist

$$(c_{A_i} - c_{A_{i0}}) = -(c_{A_j} - c^0_{A_j}). \tag{22.5}$$

[1] Siehe Fußnote 2, S. 159.

[2] Messungen von M. C. HENDERSON u. L. PESELNIK [J. Acoust. Soc. Amer. **29**, 1074 (1957)] an CO_2 nahe beim kritischen Punkt zeigen, daß auch dort noch $1/\tau$ linear mit der Dichte ansteigt, die dann allerdings nicht mehr druckproportional ist.

Die Gl. (22.2) erhält mit (22.4) und (22.5) die Form

$$\frac{d c_{A_j}}{d t} = c_M (k + k') (c_{A_j} - c^0_{A_j}). \tag{22.6}$$

Da die Änderungen der molaren Konzentrationen proportional zu den Änderungen der Reaktionslaufzahl ξ (s. Ziff. 12, S. 142) sind, liefert der Vergleich der Gln. (12.4) und (12.6) mit (22.6) im Rahmen der obigen Vernachlässigungen direkt den Zusammenhang zwischen der Relaxationszeit und den Geschwindigkeitskonstanten[1]

$$\tau_{VT} = \frac{1}{c_M (k + k')}. \tag{22.7}$$

Die Gl. (22.7) gestattet, die Geschwindigkeitskonstanten k und k' einzeln zu ermitteln; denn im thermischen Gleichgewicht gilt die Boltzmann-Verteilung und somit wegen (22.3):

$$\frac{k}{k'} = \frac{r_0}{r'_0} \cdot \frac{c^0_{A_j}}{c^0_{A_i}} = \frac{c^0_{A_j}}{c^0_{A_i}} = e^{-\frac{\varepsilon_j - \varepsilon_i}{\varkappa T}}. \tag{22.8}$$

Die Konstanten k und k' sind nichts anderes als die Übergangswahrscheinlichkeiten eines Moleküls A pro Zeiteinheit bei der Konzentration (c_M) von einem Mol pro Volumeneinheit[2].

Man schreibt deswegen

$$k = \frac{1}{Z} N_{\text{Stoß}}, \tag{22.9}$$

wobei $N_{\text{Stoß}}$ die mittlere Zahl der Stöße pro Zeiteinheit bei einer Gesamtkonzentration von einem Mol pro Volumeneinheit ist.

Damit ergibt (22.7) einen Zusammenhang zwischen der Relaxationszeit und den quantenmechanisch zu berechnenden Übergangswahrscheinlichkeiten (vgl. Ziff. 44).

23. Kompliziertere Relaxationsprozesse. In den bisherigen Ausführungen wurde durchweg angenommen, daß in der die Schallwelle tragenden Materie nur *eine* „energetisch ausgezeichnete Komponente" existiere (vgl. Ziff. 12), bzw. ihre Moleküle nur *eines* angeregten Zustandes fähig seien und demnach sich das Gleichgewicht nach einer Störung nach einer einfachen Exponentialfunktion mit der Zeit wieder einstelle. Diese Annahme ist in der Tat oft gerechtfertigt.

In völliger Allgemeinheit, also unter Einbeziehung beliebig vieler Anregungs-, Ionisations-, Dissoziationszustände usw., ist das Problem von MEIXNER thermodynamisch behandelt worden[3]. Naturgemäß ergeben sich dann keine Formeln die unmittelbar am Experiment geprüft werden können.

Schon die Berücksichtigung nur zweier Zustände bringt wesentliche Komplikationen. Der Gang der Rechnung[4] sei im folgenden nur angedeutet.

Es werde angenommen, daß zwei angeregte Zustände existieren, die zur Molwärme die Beiträge C_{i1} bzw. C_{i2} beisteuern, so daß

$$C_v = C_a + C_{i1} + C_{i2} \tag{23.1}$$

ist.

---

[1] H.O. KNESER: Ann. Phys. **11**, 761 (1931); **16**, 360 (1937). Berichtigung der erstgenannten Arbeit durch A. J. RUTGERS: Ann. Phys. **16**, 350 (1933).

[2] Ausführliche Rechnung bei R. J. RUBIN u. K.E. SHULER: J. Chem. Phys. **26**, 454 (1957).

[3] J. MEIXNER: Sonderausgabe der Z. Kolloidchemie. **134**, 3 (1952).

[4] Vgl. K. F. HERZFELD (H 8 und 9); ferner R. BROUT: J. Chem. Phys. **22**, 1500 (1954).

Die Indices a, $i1$ und $i2$ kennzeichnen also drei verschiedene Formen molekularer Energie[1]. Der Relaxationsvorgang besteht dann im Ausgleich zwischen ihnen. Dieser kann nun auf zwei verschiedenen Wegen vor sich gehen:

$$\alpha\text{: Parallelausgleich}\quad a \begin{matrix} \nearrow\!\swarrow\; i1 \\ \searrow\!\nwarrow\; i2 \end{matrix}$$
$$\beta\text{: Serienausgleich}\quad a \overset{\tau_1}{\longleftrightarrow} i1 \overset{\tau_2}{\longleftrightarrow} i2\,^{2}. \tag{23.2}$$

τ_1 und τ_2 bedeuten die Relaxationszeiten der parallel bzw. in Serie verlaufenden Teilprozesse[3].

Hinsichtlich der Relaxationsgleichung (12.4) unterscheiden sich die beiden Fälle:

$$\text{Fall } \alpha\text{:}\quad -\frac{\partial \xi_1}{\partial t} = \frac{1}{\tau_1}(\xi_1 - \xi_{10}), \tag{23.3}$$

$$-\frac{\partial \xi_2}{\partial t} = \frac{1}{\tau_2}(\xi_2 - \xi_{20}); \tag{23.4}$$

$$\text{Fall } \beta\text{:}\quad -\frac{\partial \xi_1}{\partial t} = \frac{1}{\tau_1}(\xi_1 - \xi_{10}) - \frac{1}{\tau_2}[(\xi_2 - \xi_{20}) - (\xi_1 - \xi_{10})], \tag{23.5}$$

$$-\frac{\partial \xi_2}{\partial t} = \frac{1}{\tau_2}(\xi_2 - \xi_{20}). \tag{23.6}$$

Für periodische Störungen des Gleichgewichts kann die Differentation nach t durch Multiplikation mit $j\omega$ ersetzt werden, und (23.3) und (23.4) bzw. (23.5) und (23.6) lassen sich nach ξ_1 und ξ_2 auflösen. Es zeigt sich, daß beide Größen in fast genau gleicher Weise von der Frequenz und je zwei Zeitkonstanten τ' und τ'' abhängen, die allerdings nicht mit τ_1 und τ_2 identisch, sondern komplizierte Linearkombinationen sind[4]. Da aber von vorneherein keine der Relaxationszeiten τ_1 und τ_2 bekannt ist, sondern beide aus der Frequenzabhängigkeit der Dispersion oder Absorption ermittelt werden müßten, so ist es praktisch unmöglich, experimentell zwischen Fall α und β zu unterscheiden.

Auch die Messung der Druckabhängigkeit führt nicht — wie gelegentlich vermutet wurde — weiter, da man annehmen muß, daß alle Relaxationszeiten umgekehrt proportional zum Druck sind[5] und daher wie bei der einfachen Relaxation ξ_1 und ξ_2 und somit die Schallabsorption und -dispersion stets von ω/p abhängt.

Demnach sollen hier nur die dem Fall α entsprechenden Schallausbreitungsformeln diskutiert werden; und zwar auf Grund einer abgekürzten — und daher nicht allgemein gültigen — Ableitung. Gln. (23.5) und (23.6), auf periodische Vorgänge angewandt, lauten:

$$\xi_1 = \frac{\xi_{10}}{1 + j\omega\tau_1}, \qquad \xi_2 = \frac{\xi_{20}}{1 + j\omega\tau_2}. \tag{23.7}$$

---

[1] Der häufigste Fall wird der sein, daß a die Summe der translatorischen und rotatorischen Energie ist und $i1$ und $i2$ die Energie zweier verschiedener Schwingungstypen.

[2] Der 3 mögliche Fall, der bei Vertauschung von 1 und 2 entsteht, bringt prinzipiell nichts Neues.

[3] In Ziff. 46 werden Gründe dafür geltend gemacht werden, daß für alle Anregungszustände ein und derselben Molekülschwingung die gleiche Relaxationszeit gilt.

[4] Vgl. H 8, Formel (8—6).

[5] Dies erscheint zunächst nicht zwingend für τ_2 im Fall β, d.h. für die Relaxationszeit bei Übergängen zwischen zwei angeregten Zuständen desselben Moleküls. Quantentheoretisch kann aber auch ein solcher Vorgang nur unter Beteiligung eines weiteren Moleküls, das die Energiedifferenz liefert, bzw. abführt erfolgen, so daß auch $\tau_2(\beta) \sim 1/p$ wird. Dies wurde von R. N. SCHWARTZ u. Z. J. SLAWSKY (unveröff. Nav. Ord. Lab. Tech. Rep. und H) ausführlich diskutiert.

Der Betrag, den die ausgezeichneten Komponente zur Molwärme C_v im Gleichgewicht liefert, sei jetzt mit C_{i0} bezeichnet (früher C_i). Bei gestörtem Gleichgewicht sei er C_i. Dann gilt

$$C_{i1} : C_{i10} = \xi_1 : \xi_{10} \quad \text{und} \quad C_{i2} : C_{i20} = \xi_2 : \xi_{20}. \tag{23.8}$$

Demnach

$$C_i = C_{i1} + C_{i2} = \frac{C_{i10}}{1 + j\,\omega\,\tau_1} + \frac{C_{i20}}{1 + j\,\omega\,\tau_2}. \tag{23.9}$$

Für das Verhältnis der spezifischen Wärmen idealer Gase im Gleichgewicht

$$\gamma_0 = \frac{C_p}{C_v} = \frac{R + C_a + C_{i0}}{C_a + C_{i0}}$$

gilt demnach bei periodisch gestörtem Gleichgewicht

$$\gamma = \frac{R + C_a + C_i}{C_a + C_i}. \tag{23.10}$$

Wir wenden nun (8.16): $\omega^2/k^2 = \gamma p_0/\varrho_0$ auf den vorliegenden Fall an und auf den Fall ungestörten Gleichgewichts: $c_0^2 = \gamma_0 p_0/\varrho_0$ und erhalten:

$$\frac{1}{c_0^2}\,\frac{\omega^2}{k^2} \approx \frac{\gamma}{\gamma_0} = \frac{C_v}{C_p}\,\frac{R + C_a + C_i}{C_a + C_i}, \tag{23.11}$$

worin für C_i der durch (23.9) gegebene Wert zu setzen ist.

Die Diskussion[1] dieser Relaxationsfunktion ist wesentlich umständlicher als die in Ziff. 13 für den Fall einfacher Relaxation durchgeführte. Nach Trennung von Real- und Imaginärteil ergeben sich mit Hilfe von (7.12) folgende Dispersions- und Absorptionsformeln:

$$\frac{c^2}{c_0^2} = 1 + \frac{R}{C_p \cdot C_a} \cdot \left[\frac{C_1' \omega^2 \tau_1'^2}{1 + \omega^2 \tau_1'^2} + \frac{C_2' \omega^2 \tau_2'^2}{1 + \omega^2 \tau_2'^2}\right], \tag{23.12}$$

$$\mu = \pi \frac{c^2}{c_0^2} \cdot \frac{R}{C_p \cdot C_a} \cdot \left[\frac{C_1' \omega \tau_1'}{1 + \omega^2 \tau_1'^2} + \frac{C_2' \omega \tau_2'}{1 + \omega^2 \tau_2'^2}\right]. \tag{23.13}$$

Darin bedeuten:

$$C_a = C_v - C_{i10} - C_{i20}, \tag{23.14}$$

$$\left.\begin{aligned} \left.\begin{matrix} 2\tau_1' \\ 2\tau_2' \end{matrix}\right\} &= \tau_1 \left(1 - \frac{C_{i10}}{C_v}\right) + \tau_2 \left(1 - \frac{C_{i20}}{C_v}\right) \pm \left(D + \frac{C_{i10} \cdot C_{i20}}{C_v^2 \cdot D}\,\tau_1\,\tau_2\right) \\ D &= \tau_1 \left(1 - \frac{C_{i10}}{C_v}\right) - \tau_2 \left(1 - \frac{C_{i20}}{C_v}\right), \end{aligned}\right\} \tag{23.15}$$

$$\left.\begin{aligned} C_2' + C_2' &= C_1 + C_2, \\ C_1' \tau_1' + C_2' \tau_2' &= \frac{C_a}{C_v} [C_1 \tau_1 + C_2 \tau_2]. \end{aligned}\right\} \tag{23.16}$$

Sind die beiden Relaxationszeiten sehr verschieden ($\tau_1/\tau_2 \gg 1$ oder $\ll 1$), so zeigt die Dispersionskurve — über log ω aufgetragen — laut (23.12) zwei Wendepunkte, nämlich bei $\omega_1 = 1/\tau_1'$ und $\omega_2 = 1/\tau_2'$, und bei denselben Frequenzen[2] treten Maxima des Absorptionsindex μ auf. Wie man aus (23.15) sieht, sind ω_1 und ω_2 etwas verschoben gegenüber denjenigen Wendepunkts- und Maximumsfrequenzen, die sich ergeben würden, wenn nur der eine oder nur der andere Relaxationsprozeß wirksam wäre; in völliger Analogie zum „Auseinanderstreben“ der Eigenfrequenzen zweier Oszillatoren beim Einschalten einer Kopplung.

---

[1] Vgl. H 8.

[2] Der geringfügige Unterschied zwischen der Wendepunkts- und der Maximumfrequenz, der sich bei der einfachen Relaxation herausstellte [vgl. (13.6) und (13.11)], ist hier infolge der nicht ganz exakten Ableitung entfallen.

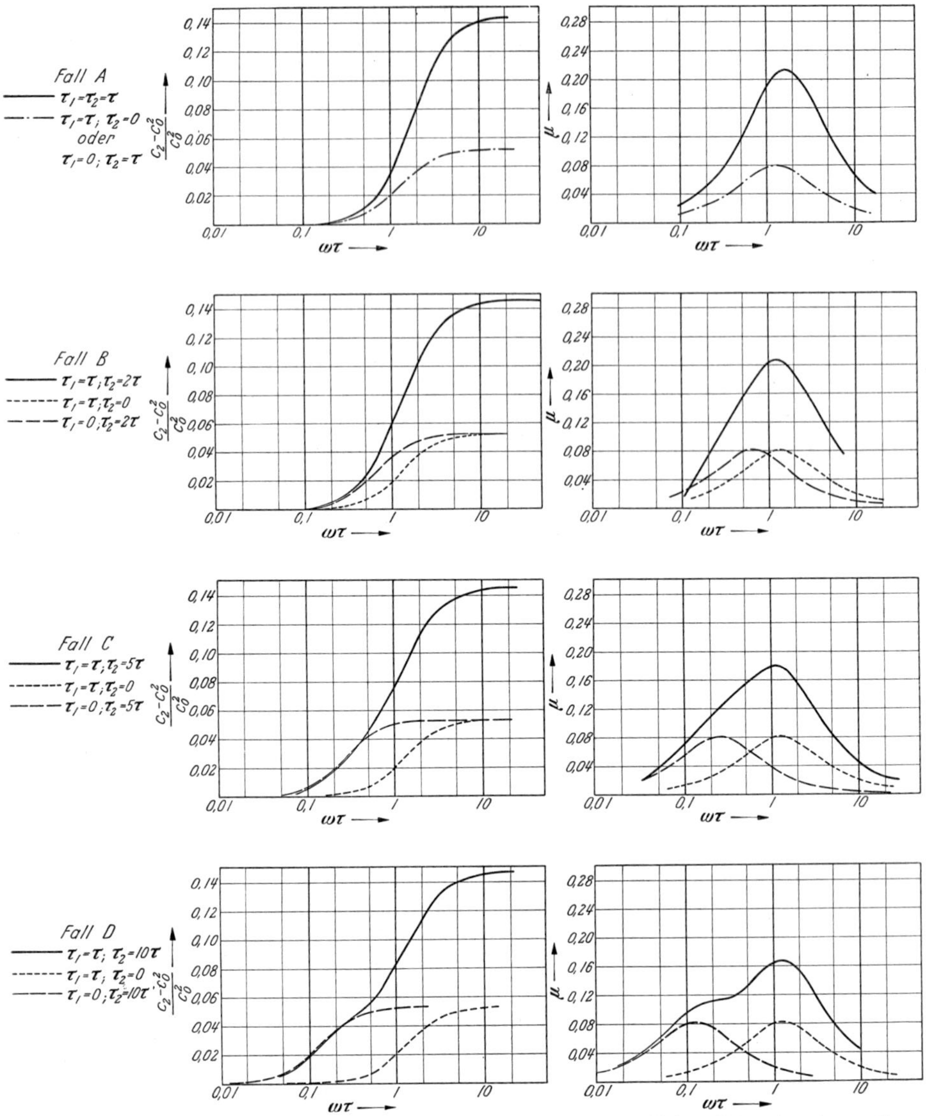

Fig. 8. Absorptions- und Dispersionsverlauf, wenn zwei Relaxationsprozesse mit verschiedenen Relaxationszeiten vorliegen.

Für $\tau_1/\tau_2 \approx 1$ werden die Verhältnisse viel komplizierter und sollen durch einige Beispiele[1] mit folgenden Zahlenwerten veranschaulicht werden:

$$C_v = \frac{9}{2} R; \qquad C_{i10} = C_{i20} = R;$$

$$A: \ \tau_1 = \tau_2 = \tau;$$

$$B: \ \tau_1 = \tau_2/2;$$

$$C: \ \tau_1 = \tau_2/5;$$

$$D: \ \tau_1 = \tau_2/10.$$

[1] Ein weiteres Beispiel — die Schallausbreitung in teilweise dissoziiertem Jod-Dampf — wurde durchgerechnet von H. O. KNESER u. O. GAULER: Phys. Z. **37**, 677 (1936). — Vgl. ferner R. T. BEYER: J. Acoust. Soc. Amer. **29**, 243 (1957).

Die Dispersions- und Absorptionskurven für diese vier Fälle sind in Fig. 7 wiedergegeben[1]. Bemerkenswert ist die Nicht-Additivität der Maximalwerte des Absorptionsindex und die geringfügige Abweichung von der normalen Dispersionskurve (Fig. 8), die eine sehr hohe Meßgenauigkeit erforderlich macht, wenn aus einer Dispersionskurve zwei nicht allzu verschiedene Relaxationsprozesse herausanalysiert werden sollen.

Wenn mehr als zwei Relaxationsprozesse gleichzeitig ablaufen, so können Gl. (23.12) und (23.13) unmittelbar verallgemeinert werden. (23.15) und (23.16) werden algebraisch von höherer Ordnung.

Die Absorption und Dispersion harmonischer Schallwellen erweist sich also als ein verhältnismäßig ungeeignetes Mittel zur Analyse komplizierterer Relaxationsvorgänge. Ein anderer Weg, der sich anbietet, ist der, die Verformung von Rechteckimpulsen oder nicht harmonischer Wellen beim Durchgang durch ein relaxationsbehaftetes Medium zu studieren. Dies ist an elektrischen Modellen versucht worden[2] mit dem Ergebnis, daß mit mäßigem apparativen Aufwand Relaxationsprozesse, deren Relaxationszeiten sich um einen Faktor $\geqq 5$ differieren (bei gleichem Relaxationsbetrag), noch unterscheidbar sind, was keinen wesentlichen Fortschritt gegenüber sinusförmiger Anregung bedeutet.

D. Experimentelle Methoden.

24. Allgemeines. Bis etwa 1920 war das Interesse der experimentierenden Physiker ganz überwiegend auf Messung der Schall*geschwindigkeit* gerichtet, gelegentlich aus praktischen Gesichtspunkten (z.B. für Zwecke der Schallortung[3]) und dann auf Luft beschränkt, meistens aber mit dem Ziel, vermeintlich besonders genaue Werte für C_p/C_v zu gewinnen. Abgesehen von den Freiluft-Messungen[4] wurde dabei fast immer das höchst elegante Verfahren der Kundtschen Staubfiguren in mancherlei Abwandlungen verwendet. Die Schall*absorptions*messungen waren damals — ohne elektronische Methoden! — außerordentlich schwierig und unsicher[5].

Mit der Entdeckung der piezoelektrischen Schwingquarze durch Langevin (1918) und dem Aufkommen elektronischer Methoden wurden dem Experiment ganz neue Wege eröffnet. Grüneisen erkannte wohl als erster die außerordentlichen meßtechnischen Möglichkeiten, die die Herstellung variabler und genau meßbarer Frequenzen mittels des „Röhrensenders" bietet. Seit Pierce sein Interferometer entwickelt hatte, wurden Präzisionsmessungen der Schallgeschwindigkeit — und später in den Händen von Hubbard auch der Schallabsorption — auch im Ultraschallgebiet möglich.

Mit diesem Instrument fand Pierce die ersten Andeutungen von Schalldispersion. Nachdem sie als Relaxationseffekt gedeutet und ihre notwendige Verknüpfung mit Schallabsorption erkannt war, wandte sich das Interesse dieser in steigendem Maße zu. Beim Studium der Relaxationserscheinungen werden heute oft Absorptions- den Dispersionsmessungen vorgezogen, weil erstere nur schwach temperaturabhängig ist, während Präzisionsmessungen der Schallge-

[1] Kurve A mit $\tau_1 = 1$; B mit $\tau_1 = 1{,}343$; C mit $\tau_1 = 1{,}522$, damit die Dispersionsmittelpunkte zusammenfallen.

[2] K. Walter: Acustica **6**, 245 (1956). Dort auch ältere Literatur zur rechnerischen Analyse eines Relaxationsspektrums aus Meßdaten bei sinusförmiger Anregung.

[3] E. von Angerer u. R. Ladenburg: Ann. Phys. **66**, 293 (1921).

[4] Zum Beispiel T. C. Hebb: Phys. Rev. **14**, 74 (1919) und E. Esclangon: C. R. Acad. Sci., Paris **168**, 165 (1919).

[5] N. Neklepajev: Ann. Phys. **25**, 175 (1911).

schwindigkeit sehr genaue Temperaturmessung [oder eine gleichzeitige Messung bei extrem tiefen Frequenzen (c_0)] verlangen.

Seit dem Aufkommen der Funkmeß- oder Radar-Technik finden Impulsverfahren in steigendem Maße Verwendung, allerdings nur für Frequenzen oberhalb etwa 1 MHz. Aus Laufzeit und räumlicher Abklingung eines hochfrequenten Schallimpulses können Schallgeschwindigkeit und -absorption unter Umständen gleichzeitig mit hoher Präzision ermittelt werden. Bei Gasen sind wegen der ungünstigen Anpassungsverhältnisse gewisse experimentelle Schwierigkeiten erst in jüngster Zeit überwunden worden.

Als *Schallquellen* werden im niederfrequenten Bereich (bis etwa 10^5 Hz) ganz überwiegend Membransender in Gestalt von Membranen, Platten oder Bändchen verwandt; bei hohen Frequenzen (oberhalb 10^5 Hz) fast ausschließlich piezoelektrische Schallgeber.

Die experimentellen Methoden lassen sich in zwei prinzipiell verschiedene Gruppen aufteilen:

1. Solche, die sich der Interferenz der Schallwellen bedienen, wo also die Schallgeschwindigkeit aus Frequenz und Wellenlänge bzw. Resonatorabmessung erschlossen wird und die Schallabsorption aus der zeitlichen Abklingung oder der Resonanzbreite; ihr besonderer Vorzug liegt darin, daß die immer sehr genau meßbare Frequenz als wesentliche Meßgröße eingeht.

2. Solche, die mit fortlaufenden Wellen arbeiten unter Vermeidung von Interferenz- und Beugungseffekten (Hallraum- und Laufzeitmessungen; räumliche Abklingung); sie seien als Ausbreitungsmethoden bezeichnet.

Diesen Gruppen sind die nächsten beiden Ziffern gewidmet; ein weiterer der Lichtbeugungsmethode, die in gewissem Sinne beiden Gruppen angehört. Angesichts der eingehenden Darstellung in anderen Artikeln dieses Bandes wird keine erschöpfende Darstellung angestrebt, sondern für jeden Verfahrenstyp eine Ausführungsform repräsentativ beschrieben oder mindestens zitiert.

25. Interferenz-Methoden. *α) Zylinder-Resonatoren*[1] sind nur bis zu mäßig hohen Frequenzen ($\lesssim 10$ kHz) verwendbar. Bei geringem Durchmesser steigt die Wanddämpfung mit der Frequenz stark an, bei großem Durchmesser überlagern sich die Radialresonanzen dem „axialen Spektrum" zu dicht.

Zufuhr und Abnahme der Schallenergie geschieht immer durch zentrale Öffnungen in den Stirnflächen, deren Einfluß auf Resonanzfrequenz und Dämpfung sorgfältig berücksichtigt werden müssen.

Bei den ersten, noch heute nicht übertroffenen Präzisionsmessungen der Schallgeschwindigkeit, die Grüneisen[2] an Luft und Wasserstoff ausführte, wurde noch das Ohr zum Nachweis der Resonanz benützt; später das Mikrophon[3], wodurch die Form des Resonanzmaximums meßbar wurde. Seine Halbwertsbreite ergibt die Dämpfung, die mit steigender Frequenz und abnehmendem Druck immer stärker durch Reibung und Wärmeleitung an den Rohrwänden bestimmt ist, was die Messung der Gasabsorption erschwert. Auch die Radialresonanzen können für Absorptionsmessungen herangezogen werden[4].

---

[1] Die Theorie des Zylinderresonators, die seit Helmholtz (1863) immer wieder behandelt wurde, ist durch L. Fritsche (Diss. Stuttgart 1958; erscheint in Acustica) zu einem gewissen Abschluß gebracht und durch sehr genaue Messungen bestätigt worden. Dort auch ältere Literaturangaben.

[2] E. Grüneisen u. E. Merkel: Ann. Phys. **66**, 344 (1921).

[3] H. Oberst: Akust. Z. **2**, 76 (1937). — H. Knötzel: Akust. Z. **5**, 245 (1940). — L. Fritsche: Diss. Stuttgart 1958; erscheint in Acustica.

[4] L. Fritsche: Vgl. Fußnote 1.

β) Kugelresonatoren sind zwar mit der erforderlichen Genauigkeit sehr viel schwieriger herzustellen, haben aber den großen Vorteil, daß die Wandreibung entfällt, sofern man mit Radialresonanzen arbeitet. Diese sind dann unter Umständen so schwach gedämpft, daß Absorptionsmessungen zweckmäßig mit Hilfe der zeitlichen Abklingung ausgeführt werden[1]. Für Schallgeschwindigkeitsmessungen wurde das Verfahren noch nicht benutzt, weil Hohlkugeln mit so konstantem Radius, wie es Präzisionsmessungen erfordern, sich nicht anfertigen lassen.

γ) Das Interferometer[2] wurde von PIERCE[3] anfangs nur für Schallwellenlängen und damit -geschwindigkeitsmessungen entwickelt. Im Prinzip ähnelt es dem Zylinderresonator bei Anwendung von axsialen Resonanzen hoher Ordnung. Als variable Meßgröße wird aber nicht die Frequenz benützt[4], sondern meist der Abstand vom Schallgeber zum Reflektor, also die Resonanzlänge, oder die Temperatur[5]. Da keine Wandreibung, sondern nur geringe Reflexionsverluste auftreten, ist das Instrument für höhere Frequenz (0,2 bis einige MHz[6]) als der Zylinderresonator anwendbar. Gegenüber diesem hat das Interferometer aber den — oft schwerwiegenden — Nachteil, daß die Wellenflächen nicht notwendig eben sind, wodurch die Äquidistanz der Knotenebenen in Frage gestellt ist.

Für *Absorptions*messungen brauchbar wurde das Interferometer durch HUBBARDS[7] Theorie, die der Theorie verlustbehafteter elektrischer Leitungen nachgebildet ist: Der Piezokristall mit seinen Elektroden und der angekoppelten, durch den Reflektor begrenzten Gassäule wird als Vierpol aufgefaßt. Seine Stromaufnahme, als Funktion des Abstandes Schallquelle—Reflektor aufgetragen, zeigt Extrema, aus deren Breite oder Höhe — je nach dem wie stark das Gas absorbiert — der Absorptionskoeffizient auf ziemlich komplizierte Weise ermittelt wird.

Die Genauigkeit interferometrischer Schallgeschwindigkeitsmessung bei schwach absorbierenden Gasen wird durch die Güte der Spindel begrenzt, mit der der Reflektor verschoben wird, ferner durch die Stabilität der Schallfrequenz und die Konstanz der Temperatur. Unter besonders günstigen Umständen kann die Schallgeschwindigkeit auf $\pm \frac{1}{10}$‰ genau bestimmt werden. Für Absorptionsmessungen muß eine Genauigkeit von $\pm 5\%$ als sehr günstig betrachtet werden.

Beim *Doppel-Kristall-Interferometer* besteht auch der Reflektor aus einem Piezokristall. Das Eintreten der Resonanz wird dann nicht an der Rückwirkung auf den Sender, also als Differenzeffekt konstatiert, sondern durch direkten Empfang am Reflektorkristall. Das Instrument ist auch — und sogar vorzugsweise — dann noch brauchbar, wenn infolge von starker Absorption oder absichtlich herabgesetzter Reflexion am Empfänger keine Resonanz mehr auftritt. Es wird daher im nächsten Paragraphen behandelt.

---

[1] H. O. KNESER: Phys. Bl. **5**, 519 (1949) und HORIUCHI: J.C.A.-Kongreß, Cambridge/Mass. 1956.

[2] Kritik der Möglichkeiten dieses Instrument bei H 13, S. 681—683 und bei E. G. RICHARDSON: Research **9**, 249 (1956). Vollständige Theorie des Interferometers bei F. E. BORGNIS: Acustica **7**, 151—174 (1957).

[3] G. W. PIERCE: Proc. Amer. Acad. **60**, 271 (1925).

[4] Das ist bisher nur bei Flüssigkeitsinterferometern durchgeführt. H. J. LEON: J. Acoust. Soc. Amer. **27**, 1107 (1955).

[5] D. BENDER: Ann. Phys. (5) **38**, 93 (1940) und J. F. W. BELL: J. Acoust. Soc. Amer. **25**, 96 (1953).

[6] Ein „Mikro-Interferometer" bis 300 MHz wurde angegeben von R. A. MCCONNELL: J. Acoust. Soc. Amer. **27**, 672 (1955); ein für geringe Drucke und hohe Frequenzen (11 MHz) brauchbares Interferometer von M. GREENSPAN u. M. C. THOMPSON jr.: J. Acoust. Soc. Amer. **25**, 92 (1953).

[7] J. C. HUBBARD: Phys. Rev. **59**, 934 (1941) und frühere Arbeiten.

Schallmessungen bei Drucken von weniger als 10^{-3} mm Hg haben sich mit einer ähnlichen Anordnung durchführen lassen, bei der anstelle der piezoelektrischen Wandler Kondensatorwandler mit festem Dielectricum („Sellsche Schwinger") verwandt wurden[1]. Sie bewähren sich am besten zwischen 100 und 600 kHz, wobei ihr Radius zwecks guter Richtwirkung groß gegen die Wellenlänge gemacht wird.

26. Ausbreitungsmethoden. Bei diesen Methoden wirken Resonanzen, Interferenz- und Beugungseffekte störend und müssen vermieden werden.

α) Beim Hallraumverfahren (reverberation method) wird die Schallwelle in einem Raum mit hochreflektierenden, möglichst nicht parallelen Wänden erzeugt, dessen Abmessungen groß gegen die Wellenlänge sein sollen. Resonanz wird vermieden entweder durch rotierende Schaufelräder, die das Schallfeld verwirbeln[2] oder durch Frequenzwobbelung[3]. Gemessen wird der zeitliche Abfall der Schallintensität nach Abschalten der Quelle, oder die mittlere Schallintensität, die sich im Dauerbetrieb einstellt[4]. Die Wandverluste müssen durch besondere Versuche, z.B. in einer geometrisch ähnlichen Kammer ermittelt werden.

Das Verfahren liefert natürlich *nur* Absorptionswerte. Außer bei Luft von Atmosphärendruck wird man die Kammerabmessungen kaum größer als etwa 1 m wählen können, wodurch das Verfahren auf Frequenzen zwischen etwa 10 und 30 kHz beschränkt ist.

β) Räumliche Abnahme von Kugelwellen[5] kann nur im Freien oder in „schalltoten" Räumen zur Messung der Absorption herangezogen werden. Außerdem muß die Schallwellenlänge groß sein im Vergleich zu den Abmessungen der Schallquelle, wodurch dem Verfahren eine ziemlich niedrige obere Frequenzgrenze gesetzt ist ($\approx$100 kHz). Dem exponentiellen, durch die Gasabsorption bedingten Intensitätsabfall überlagert sich der geometrisch bedingte quadratische. Ersterer überwiegt erst in größerem Abstand von der Schallquelle, so daß die Apparatur bei nicht sehr stark absorbierenden Gasen sehr große Abmessungen haben muß[6].

γ) Mittels der räumlichen Abnahme von ebenen Wellen sind sowohl im nieder- wie im hochfrequenten Bereich (2 bis 10 kHz[7] bzw. 1 bis 10 MHz[8]) vorzügliche Absorptionsmessungen durchgeführt worden.

Im niederfrequenten Bereich wird die Ebenheit der Wellen dadurch erzwungen, daß die Schallwelle in einem Rohr mit vollkommen absorbierendem Abschluß verläuft. Der Rohrdurchmesser ist so klein gewählt, daß bei den Meßfrequenzen noch keine Radialresonanzen auftreten. Der Schallgeber, ein Bändchen-Lautsprecher ist verschiebbar angeordnet; der Empfänger, ein Kondensatormikrofon ortsfest. Der exponentielle Abfall ist durch Wandverluste, „klassische" und Relaxationsabsorption bestimmt. Die letztere konnte ANGONA so mit einer bislang nicht erreichten Genauigkeit bestimmen.

Das hochfrequente Verfahren bedient sich eines Doppelkristall-„Interferometers". Dank der geringen Wellenlänge (<1 mm) sind die Wellen ohne weitere Vorkehrungen eben. Bei geeigneter Dicke und Einbettung des Empfangskristalls[9] kann sein Reflexionsvermögen zu Null gemacht und dadurch jede störende Inter-

---

[1] E. MEYER u. G. SESSLER: Z. Physik **149**, 15 (1957).
[2] V. O. KNUDSEN: J. Acoust. Soc. Amer. **5**, 112 (1933).
[3] E. J. EVANS u. E. N. BAZLEY: Acustica **6**, 238 (1956).
[4] H. O. KNESER u. V. O. KNUDSEN: Ann. Phys. (5) **21**, 687 (1934).
[5] N. SCHMIDTMÜLLER: Akust. Z. **3**, 115 (1938).
[6] Vgl. hierzu H. O. KNESER: Ergebn. exakt. Naturw. **22**, 143 (1949).
[7] F. A. ANGONA: J. Acoust. Soc. Amer. **25**, 1111 (1953).
[8] M. GREENSPAN u. M. C. THOMPSON jr.: J. Acoust. Soc. Amer. **25**, 92 (1953).
[9] D. M. TOWLE: J. Acoust. Soc. Amer. **27**, 530 (1955).

ferenz vermieden werden. Bei niedrigen Drucken treten solche wegen der enorm anwachsenden Absorption nicht merklich auf. GREENSPAN konnte mit 11 MHz noch bei Drucken unterhalb 1 mm Hg messen! (>800 MHz/atm). Die Messungen können dann nur noch über eine Wellenlänge ($\approx 1\frac{1}{2}$ freie Weglängen) erstreckt werden. Durch eine raffinierte mechanische Konstruktion wird die Übertragung von Körperschall ("mechanical crosstalk") auf dem Empfangskristall völlig unterdrückt.

Bei den beiden letztgenannten Anordnungen wird gleichzeitig mit der Absorption auch die Schallwellenlänge gemessen, und zwar durch Vergleich der akustisch empfangenen, mit der Entfernung Sender—Empfänger variierenden Phase mit der elektrisch zugeführten nicht verzögerten Phase des Senders.

δ) Das Impulsverfahren[1] ist schon aus schaltungstechnischen Gründen nur im MHz-Bereich anwendbar. Bei ihm werden Störungen durch Interferenz und Reflexion gewissermaßen durch zeitliche Distanzierung vermieden. Dadurch können auch bei geringer Absorption mit dem einfachen wie mit dem Doppel-Kristall-„Interferometer" gleichzeitig Laufzeit- (d.h. Geschwindigkeits-) und Abkling- (d.h. Absorptions-)messungen ausgeführt werden[2].

Läßt man den am Empfänger eintreffenden Impuls am Sender wieder einen neuen auslösen, so ergibt sich ein periodischer Vorgang, dessen Frequenz durch die Laufzeit bestimmt ist. Dies sog. „sing-around-Verfahren" ermöglicht sehr genaue Relativmessungen der Schallgeschwindigkeit (vorzugsweise in Flüssigkeiten[3]).

ε) Der sogenannte Quarzwind, der sonst oft als störend sorgfältig unterdrückt werden muß, bietet eine weitere Möglichkeit zur Absorptionsmessung[4]. Ein Schallstrahl der Intensität I führt Bewegungsgröße im Betrage I/c mit sich (je Zeit und Flächeneinheit). Wenn in eine Mediumschicht vom Querschnitt 1 und der Dicke Δx während der Zeit τ die Energie $\alpha \Delta x \tau$ absorbiert wird (α = Absorptionskoeffizient), so ist die je Zeiteinheit übertragene Bewegungsgröße gleich $\alpha \Delta x \tau/c$. Dies ist gleichbedeutend mit einer Volum-Kraft, die je nach den experimentellen Bedingungen eine Strömung oder Druckdifferenz erzeugt.

27. Lichtbeugungsmethode. Dies Verfahren[5] kann sowohl mit stehenden wie mit laufenden Wellen im MHz-Bereich ausgeführt werden. Die Wellenlänge wird aus dem Winkelabstand zwischen nullter und erster Ordnung erschlossen, die Absorption — wenn stehende Wellen vermieden werden — aus der Abnahme der Intensität der ersten Ordnung mit wachsendem Abstand von der Quelle. Das Verfahren erfordert sehr große Schallintensitäten, wodurch das Gas unkontrollierbar erwärmt werden kann. Aus demselben Grunde ist das Verfahren nur für Schallabsorptionsmessungen bei hohen Drucken angewandt worden.

28. Vergleich der experimentellen Methoden. Abgesehen von den Effekten, die durch Abweichung vom idealen Gaszustand veranlaßt werden (vgl. Ziff. 17), sind alle Absorptions- und Dispersionserscheinungen auf Transporterscheinungen zurückzuführen, also bei Gasen immer durch das Produkt Frequenz · mittlere

---

[1] J.H. ANDREAE, R. BASS, E.L. HEASELL u. J. LAMB: Acustica **8**, 131 (1958).

[2] H. M. WIGHT: J. Acoust. Soc. Amer. **28**, 459 (1956).

[3] Zuerst angegeben von E. A. HIEDEMANN 1945; ausgebaut von G. W. FICKEN u. E. A. HIEDEMANN, J. Acoust. Soc. Amer. **28**, 921 (1956).

[4] H 13, S. 683. — Theorie von C. ECKART: Phys. Rev. **73**, 68 (1948) und F. E. FOX u. K. F. HERZFELD: Phys. Rev. **78**, 156 (1950); ferner J. J. MARKHAM: Phys. Rev. **86**, 497 (1952) und W. NYBORG: J. Acoust. Soc. Amer. **25**, 68 (1953); Experimente von H. MEDWIN: J. Acoust. Soc. Amer. **26**, 332 (1954).

[5] H. GROBE: Phys. Z. **39**, 333 (1938). — O. PETERSEN: Phys. Z. **41**, 29 (1940). — H. BÖMMEL: Helv. phys. Acta **18**, 3 (1945).

Stoßzeit bestimmt. Bei idealen Gasen ist es daher sinnvoll, die Wirksamkeit eines experimentellen Verfahrens danach zu beurteilen, in welchem Bereich von $\omega\tau$ es verwendet worden ist; oder, da $\omega = 2\pi f$ und $\tau \sim 1/p$, in welchem Bereich von f/p[1]. Das ist aus Fig. 9 zu ersehen[2]. Durch die Strichdicke soll ganz ungefähr die Genauigkeit des Verfahrens angedeutet werden.

Mit Ausnahme des Kugelresonators und des Hallraums sind alle sowohl für Absorptions- wie für Schallgeschwindigkeitsmessungen benützt worden. Die größte Genauigkeit dürfte mit dem Zylinderresonator erzielt worden sein. Bei sehr hohen f/p-Werten streuen die Meßwerte naturgemäß am stärksten. Die Schraffur in Fig. 9 soll andeuten, wo bei 0° C etwa die „Debyesche Grenzfrequenz" liegt, d. h. wo die Schwingungsdauer gleich der mittleren Stoßzeit wird. Bei den Messungen von GREENSPAN wird sie erreicht, bei denen von MEYER und SESSLER, die in Fig. 9 noch nicht berücksichtigt sind, weit überschritten.

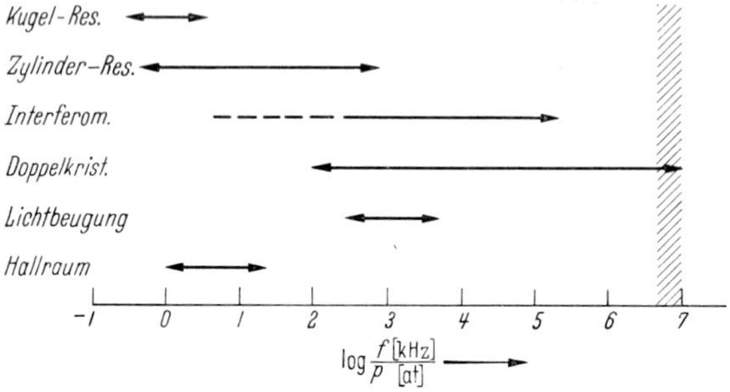

Fig. 9. Anwendungsbereich verschiedener Meßmethoden.

29. Verfahren zur direkten Bestimmung von Relaxationszeiten[3]. α) In der Schallwelle wird die Schwankung der Konzentration angeregter Zustände durch Druck- und Temperaturschwankungen verursacht. Das gleiche kann bei optisch aktiven Molekülen durch periodisch schwankende Einstrahlung derjenigen (ultraroten) Wellenlänge erreicht werden, die die Moleküle absorbieren. Die absorbierte Anregungsenergie wird je nach Länge der Relaxationszeit langsamer oder schneller in Translationsenergie umgesetzt und als periodische Erwärmung oder Druckerhöhung gemessen. Aus der Phasenverschiebung zwischen Licht- und Druckschwankung kann die Relaxationszeit ermittelt werden[4].

β) Beim Ausströmen aus einer Düse entnehmen die Moleküle ihre Translationsenergie der inneren, wobei Abkühlung eintritt. Trifft der Strahl senkrecht auf eine starre Wand, so wird er plötzlich abgebremst. Die zugehörige Erwärmung geht aber, wenn die Relaxationszeit groß ist, relativ langsam vor sich. Mißt man nun mittels einer Art Pitot-Rohr den Stau-Druck im ausströmenden Gas unmittelbar vor der Düse, so ist dieser im „relaxierenden" Gas kleiner als beispielsweise in einem Edelgas. Aus der Abhängigkeit der Druckdifferenz von der Ausströmungsgeschwindigkeit kann die Relaxationszeit berechnet werden[5].

---

[1] Für die Umrechnung von f/p auf $\omega\tau$ gilt angenähert: $\omega\tau = q\sqrt{\frac{T}{273}}\,\frac{f}{p}$ wobei, wenn f/p in MHz/atm eingesetzt wird, für He $q = 9{,}3 \cdot 10^{-4}$ für Ar $q = 10{,}6 \cdot 10^{-4}$, für H_2 $q = 4{,}1 \cdot 10^{-4}$, für $O_2 = 9{,}7 \cdot 10^{-4}$ und für $CO_2 = 6{,}9 \cdot 10^{-4}$. Wegen $\omega_{\max} = \frac{1}{\tau}$ wird dann $Z \equiv \frac{\tau}{\bar{\tau}} = (\omega\bar{\tau})^{-1}$.

[2] Demnach stehen Methoden zur Verfügung, die einen Bereich von $1:3 \cdot 10^7$ überdecken. Dem entspräche in der „Optik" ein Bereich, der von Röntgenstrahlen bis zu den cm-Wellen reicht.

[3] Diese werden hier nur summarisch behandelt, da sie nur indirekt zum Studium der Schallausbreitung beitragen. Eine eingehendere Darstellung findet man bei H 15, S. 684ff.

[4] G. GORELIK: C. R. Acad. Sci. USSR. **54**, 779 (1946). — P. v. SLOBODSKAYA: Izv. Acad. Nauk. SSSR. **12**, 656 (1948). — T. J. COTTRELL: Trans. Faraday. Soc. **46**, 1025 (1950).

[5] A. KANTROWITZ: J. Chem. Phys. **14**, 150 (1946). — Theorie bei W. GRIFFITH: J. Appl. Phys. **21**, 1319 (1950).

Die derart an N_2, H_2O und CCl_2F_2 gewonnenen Werte[1] stimmen bemerkenswert gut mit akustisch bestimmten überein.

γ) Noch schnellere, unperiodische Zustandsänderungen treten in *Stoßwellen* auf, die daher ebenfalls zur Ermittlung von Relaxationszeiten dienen können, und zwar auf zwei verschiedenen Wegen: Entweder man untersucht — etwa mit Hilfe des Mach-Zehnder-Interferometers — hinter der Stoßwellenfront den Verlauf der Dichte[2], die bereits bei mittleren Relaxationszeiten viel langsamer abfällt als nach der Rankine-Hugoniot-Gleichung zu erwarten: oder man mißt das Reflexionsvermögen der Stoßwellenfront für Licht in Abhängigkeit vom Einfallswinkel[3], ein experimentell sehr schwieriges Verfahren.

E. Experimentelle Ergebnisse.

30. Allgemeines. Wie in Kapitel B und C dargelegt, treten Abweichungen von der Laplaceschen Formel aus verschiedenen Gründen auf: Bei zu hohen Drucken machen sich die Abweichungen vom idealen Gaszustand bemerkbar, bei niedrigen Drucken — genauer gesagt: bei großen f/p — kommen Relaxationserscheinungen ins Spiel. Die Laplacesche Formel darf also nur in einem Druck- und Frequenzbereich, der nicht a priori anzugeben ist, als gültig angenommen werden. Daher wird im folgenden auf Angabe von C_p/C_v-Werten mit wenigen Ausnahmen verzichtet[4].

Tabelle 2.

	c_0 (0° C) m/sec	α/f^2 (20° C) · 10^{13} cm^{-1} sec^2 Wärmeleitung	+ Schubviscosität	= Summe
He . . .	971	0,216	0,309	0,525
Ne . . .	433,4	0,75	1,07	1,82
Ar . . .	308,5	0,77	1,08	1,85
H_2 . . .	1261	0,052	0,117	0,169
D_2 . . .	890	0,22	0,25	0,47
N_2 . . .	337,5	0,39	0,94	1,33
O_2 . . .	315,5	0,49	1,16	1,65
Luft . .	331,6	0,38	0,99	1,37
CO_2 . .	258,3	0,31	1,09	1,40
SO_2 . .	209	0,27	1,10	1,37
NH_3 . .	415	0,11	0,45	1,40

Eine Zusammenstellung einiger Werte von c_0, *berechnet* nach der Laplaceschen Formel (für 0° C), und von α/f^2, *berechnet* nach der Kirchhoff-Stokeschen Formel (für 20° C und 760 Torr) gibt Tabelle 2.

Im folgenden (Ziff. 31 bis 40) werden zunächst nur Messungen an hinreichend idealen Gasen im Hinblick auf ihre Relaxationserscheinungen einschließlich der als Translationsrelaxation aufzufassenden „klassischen" Absorption und Dispersion behandelt. Anschließend wird in Ziff. 41 und 42 die Schallausbreitung in teilweise dissoziierten und in realen Gasen, insbesondere in der Nähe des kritischen Punktes behandelt. Wo sich beide Komplexe überschneiden — was sich durch

[1] P. W. Huber u. A. Kantrowitz: J. Chem. Phys. **15**, 275 (1947).

[2] W. Griffith, D. Brickl u. V. Blackman: Phys. Rev. **102**, 1209 (1956).

[3] E. F. Greene, G. R. Cowan u. D. F. Hornig: J. Chem. Phys. **19**, 427 (1951) und H. B. Palmer u. D. F. Hornig: J. Chem. Phys. **26**, 98 (1957).

[4] Eine sehr vollständige Zusammenstellung der bis 1952 gemessenen Schallgeschwindigkeit in 46 Gasen und Dämpfen findet man bei S. Petralia: Nuovo Cim. 9 Suppl. Nr. 1, 1—58 (1952). — Niederfrequente Schallgeschwindigkeitsmessungen in H_2, N_2, Luft, O_2 und CO_2 bei V. Hovi. Ann. Acad. Sci. Fenn. A VI, Nr. 18, 18 (1959).

geeignete Wahl der Versuchsbedingungen vermeiden läßt — treten Komplikationen auf[1], die allerdings quantitativ nicht sehr ins Gewicht fallen[2].

Bei den Relaxationserscheinungen interessiert vor allem die molekularkinetisch wichtigste Größe $Z = \tau/\bar{\tau}$ (vgl. Ziff. 21). Aus der Lage des Absorptionsmaximums über der f/p-Achse ($f/p|_{max}$) läßt sich Z auf Grund folgender Überlegungen berechnen: Wegen (13.10) gilt:

$$2\pi f/p|_{max} = (\tau p \sqrt{1-\varepsilon})^{-1}. \tag{30.1}$$

$\bar{\tau}$ ist nur definiert für „harte Kugeln" (vgl. Ziff. 21). Für dies Molekülmodell gilt aber nach KOHLER[3]: $\bar{\tau} = \eta/1{,}271 p$. Damit wird aus (30.1)

$$2\pi \left.\frac{f}{p}\right|_{max} = \frac{1{,}271}{\eta\sqrt{1-\varepsilon}} \cdot \frac{\bar{\tau}}{\tau}.$$

Daher, wenn $\varepsilon \ll 1$:

$$Z \approx \text{const} \Big/ \left.\frac{f}{p}\right|_{max}. \tag{30.2}$$

Bei Zimmertemperatur hat „const" den Wert (in MHz/atm) 2433 für H_2, 1031 für O_2, 1199 für N_2, 1112 für NO, 984 Cl_2 und 1439 für CO_2.

31. Schallausbreitung in reinen Edelgasen. Für He, Ne, Ar, Kr und Xe liegen Messungen[4] vor, die im Hinblick auf die zu erwartenden Abweichungen von der Stokes-Kirchhoffschen Theorie bis zu den höchsten bisher erreichten Werten von f/p ausgedehnt worden sind. Stellt man die Schallausbreitungsdaten in Abhängigkeit von $\omega\bar{\tau}$ dar[5], so liegen die Meßpunkte für jedes der genannten Edelgase ganz eng um ein und dieselbe Dispersions- bzw. Absorptionskurve, wie theoretisch zu erwarten ist. Diese stimmt bis $\omega\bar{\tau} \approx 0{,}2$ vollkommen mit der Stokes-Kirchhoff-Theorie, darüber hinaus aber weder mit dieser noch mit der Burnett-Theorie (vgl. Ziff. 18) überein. Die Theorie der Schallausbreitung in hochverdünnten Gasen kann demnach noch nicht als endgültig geklärt angesehen werden. In Fig. 10 sind die Ergebnisse für He als einem Repräsentanten der Edelgase wiedergegeben; die durchgezogene und die punktierte Kurve sind dieselben, die schon in Fig. 8 gezeigt wurden[6]. Die Schallgeschwindigkeit steigt also tatsächlich bei den höchsten $\omega\bar{\tau}$-Werten auf das dreifache von c_0 an!

Sehr genaue Messungen der Absorption in He bei kleinen f/p-Werten[7] zeigen ebenfalls sehr befriedigende Übereinstimmung mit der „klassischen" Theorie. In der Nähe des Siedepunktes dominieren natürlich die Abweichungen vom idealen Gaszustand[8].

Für Argon liegen besonders viele und genaue Absorptionsmessungen vor. Sie sind in Fig. 11 zusammengestellt, und zwar ist der Quotient $\alpha p/f^2$, der nach (16.5) frequenz- und druckunabhängig sein soll, als Funktion von f/p aufgetragen. Er hat unterhalb von 50 MHz/atm sehr genau den „klassischen" Wert; darüber sinkt er merklich ab, wie nach Fig. 8 zu erwarten.

---

[1] O. NOMOTO: Bull. Kobayaski Inst. **1**, 162 (1952).

[2] R. T. BEYER: J. Acoust. Soc. Amer. **24**, 714 (1952).

[3] M. KOHLER: Z. Physik **125**, 715 (1949); vgl. auch H 5, S. 661. Die früher zur Abschätzung des Viskositätseinflusses benützte Gl. (11.5) ergibt: $\bar{\tau} \approx \eta/p$.

[4] M. GREENSPAN: J. Acoust. Soc. Amer. **28**, 64 (1956).

[5] Vgl. Ziff. 28.

[6] Daß die in He bei 1 MHz gemessenen Absorptionswerte etwas höher liegen als die bei 11 MHz, hält GREENSPAN nicht für experimentell gesichert. Die neueren Messungen von E. MEYER u. G. SESSLER (Z. Physik **149**, 15 (1957)] konnten in Fig. 10 und 11 noch nicht aufgenommen werden.

[7] A. VAN ITTERBECK u. L. VERHAEGEN: Nature, Lond. **167**, 477 (1951).

[8] A. VAN ITTERBECK u. W. DE LAET: Physica, Haag **24**, 59 (1958). — W. G. SCHNEIDER u. G. J. THIESSEN: Canad. J. Res. A **28**, 509 (1950) (He).

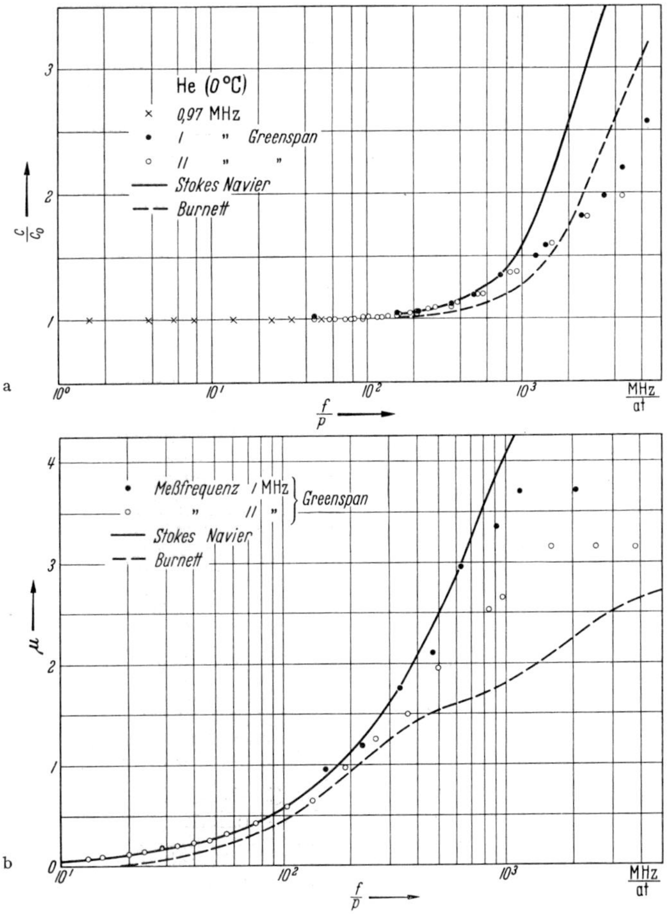

Fig. 10a u. b. Schallgeschwindigkeit in Helium nach M. Greenspan.

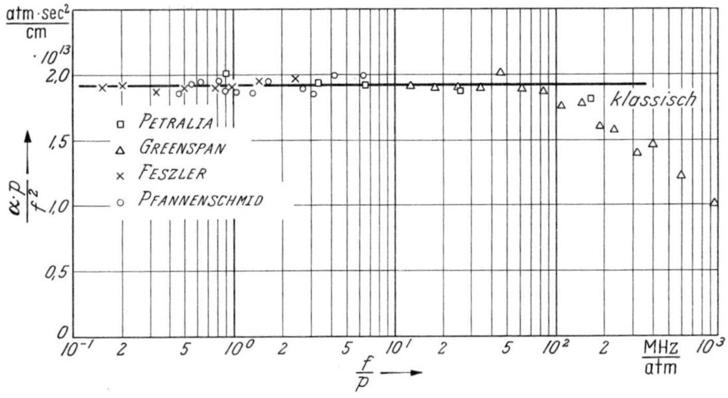

Fig. 11. Schalldispersion in Argon; $\alpha p/f^2$ in Abhängigkeit von f/p.

32. Mischungen von Edelgasen. Solche Mischungen interessieren im Hinblick auf den Diffusionseffekt, der hier unverdeckt zu Tage tritt. Die in Ziff. 9

umrissenen Überlegungen führen auf folgende Absorptionsformel[1]:

$$\left.\begin{aligned}\frac{\alpha}{f^2} = \frac{2\pi^2}{c_0^3}\Big[\frac{4}{3}\frac{\eta}{\varrho} + \frac{\gamma-1}{\gamma}\frac{\lambda}{c_v\varrho} + \\ + \frac{\gamma-1}{\gamma}\frac{\nu_{12}'\nu_{12}}{c_v\varrho} + \gamma D_{12}C_1C_2\widetilde{M}^2 + 2(\gamma-1)\,\nu_{12}C_1C_2\widetilde{M}\Big].\end{aligned}\right\} \quad (32.1)$$

Darin bedeutet

C_1 und C_2 = Molkonzentrationen der Mischungspartner,
D_{12} = Diffusionskonstante,
ν_{12} = Thermodiffusionskonstante,
$\nu_{12}' = \nu_{12} D_{12} T_0/C_1 C_2 p$,
$\widetilde{M}$ = relative Differenz der Molekulargewichte M_1 und M_2,
$= (M_2 - M_1)/(C_1 M_1 + C_2 M_2)$.

Die ersten beiden Terme sind die „Stokes-Kirchhoffschen" Glieder, genau wie in (16.5). Ihre Konzentrationsabhängigkeit für das Gemisch Kr—He ist in Fig. 12 punktiert eingetragen, diejenige der Summe aller fünf Terme ausgezogen. Die letzten drei Terme geben den Einfluß der Diffusion und Thermodiffusion an[2]. Bei 50%iger Mischung ist der Diffusionseinfluß demnach $3\frac{1}{2}$ mal so groß wie die Summe der beiden anderen. Die Messungen[3] bestätigen dies.

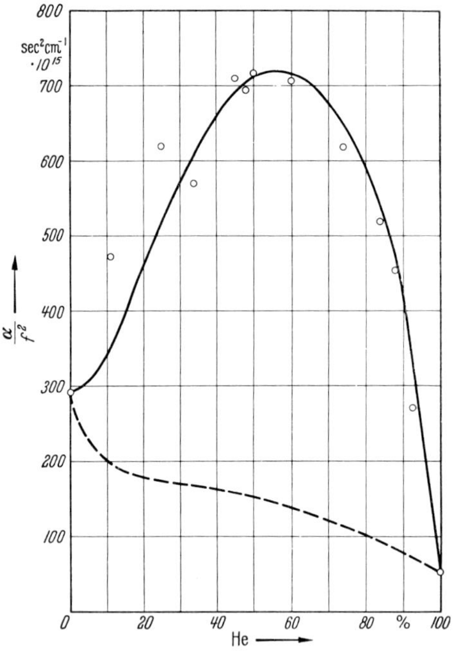

Fig. 12. Schallabsorption in Edelgasmischungen abhängig von der Konzentration.

Der Einfluß der Diffusion auf die Schalldispersion bleibt wegen (16.10) in allen Fällen geringfügig. Daher gilt in Edelgasgemischen weitgehend die Laplace-Beziehung (2.2), wenn man ϱ_1 nach der Mischungsregel berechnet[4].

33. Allgemeines über mehratomige Gase. Wir sehen zunächst wieder von den Erscheinungen ab, die durch Abweichungen vom idealen Gaszustand bedingt sind, und betrachten nur die Relaxationsphänomene: Während den einatomigen Gasen mit ihren drei translatorischen Freiheitsgraden nur *eine* Relaxationszeit zukommt, die weitgehend identisch ist mit der mittleren Stoßzeit $\bar{\tau}$ und daher etwa proportional $T^{-\frac{1}{2}}$, hat man bei den mehratomigen Gasen mindestens eine Relaxationszeit für die rotatorischen Freiheitsgrade, die etwa von der Größenordnung $10\bar{\tau}$ ist, und eine weitere, um zwei bis vier Zehnerpotenzen längere für die Schwingungsfreiheitsgrade. Über die Temperaturabhängigkeit der ersteren

[1] M. KOHLER: Ann. Phys. **39**, 209 (1941) und Phys. Z. **127**, 40 (1949).

[2] Die in ihnen enthaltenen Konstanten sind entnommen aus J. O. HIRSCHFELDER, C. F. CURTISS u. R. B. BIRD: Molecular Theory of Gases and Liquids. New York 1954.

[3] S. PETRALIA: Nuovo Cim. **1**, 351 (1955).

[4] A. VAN ITTERBECK u. J. NIHOUE [Acustica **5**, 142 (1955), **7**, 180 (1957)] konnten daher aus der zeitlichen Änderung der Schallgeschwindigkeit während des Diffusionsvorganges den Diffusionskoeffizienten ermitteln.

ist wenig bekannt; die letztere nimmt mit steigender Temperatur sehr viel stärker ab als $\bar{\tau}$. Die Maxima des Absorptionsindex und die Dispersionsstufen nehmen an Höhe mit der Temperatur im gleichen Maße zu wie die Beiträge der zugehörigen Freiheitsgrade zur Molwärme. Der daraus resultierende Absorptions- und Dispersionsverlauf für mehratomige Gase ist qualitativ in Fig. 13 wiedergegeben. Negative Temperaturkoeffizienten sind demnach durchaus möglich.

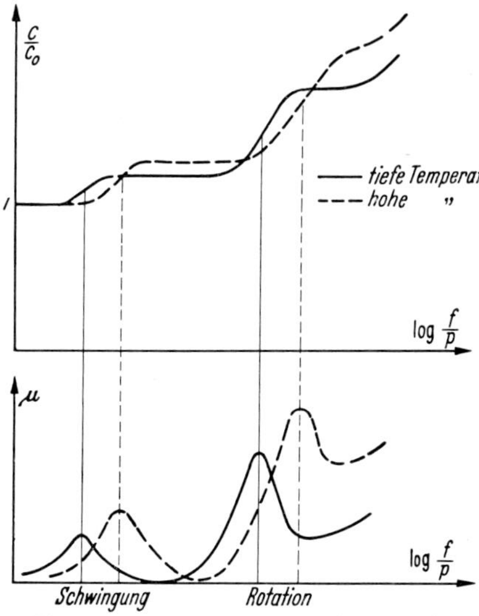

Fig. 13. Temperaturabhängigkeit der Relaxationsdispersion und -absorption; qualitativ.

Wie stark die Relaxationsprozesse sich bemerkbar machen und in welchem f/p-Bereich, d.h. mit welcher Relaxationszeit, hängt überwiegend vom Quotienten $\frac{\Theta}{T}$ ab, wobei $\Theta = \frac{\varepsilon_j - \varepsilon_i}{k}$ (vgl. 22.7). Die tiefsten Θ-Werte sind für einige gängige Gase in Fig. 14 zusammengestellt; und zwar für H_2 die Rotationsquanten Θ_{rot} (für die H_2-Schwingung gilt $\Theta_{\text{Osz.}} = 5958°$ K, für D_2 4211° K) für alle übrigen Gase nur $\Theta_{\text{Osz.}}$[1].

$\Theta/T \cong 10$ gibt so geringe Effekte, daß sie mit den heutigen experimentellen Mitteln kaum mehr nachzuweisen sind. $\Theta/T \cong 1$ gibt meist so kurze Relaxationszeiten, daß die zugehörigen Absorptions- und Dispersionseffekte mit den „klassischen" nahezu verfließen. Da die Rotationsquanten umgekehrt proportional dem Trägheitsmoment der Moleküle und somit bei allen anderen Gasen sehr viel kleiner sind als bei Wasserstoff, ist ein ausgeprägtes Absorptionsmaximum der Rotationsrelaxation bei Zimmertemperatur nur in H_2, HD, D_2, HCl, HBr zu erwarten.

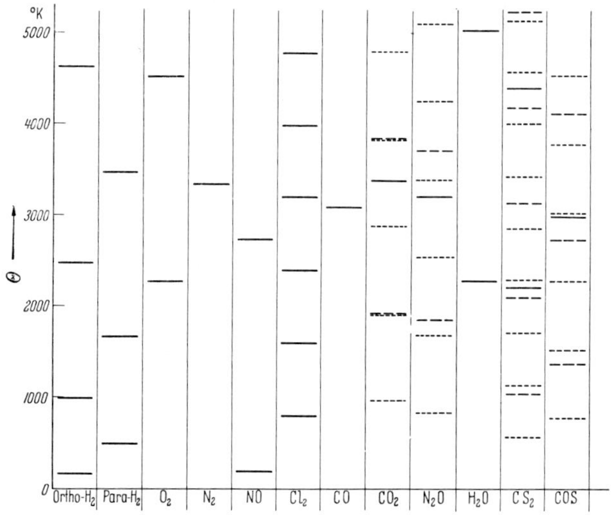

Fig. 14. Termschemata der inneren Energie für einige zwei- und dreiatomige Gase; ausgezogene und gestrichelte Linien bedeuten Valenzschwingungen, punktierte Linien Deformationsschwingungen.

Im Bereich $2 < \Theta/T < 8$ läßt sich die Höhe des Relaxationsmaximums recht genau bestimmen und daraus der Beitrag des betreffenden Freiheitsgrades zur Molwärme berechnen. Einer direkten Bestimmung aus der Molwärme ist er meist längst nicht mehr zugänglich.

[1] Der für NO eingetragene Wert $\Theta = 2720°$ K deutet an, daß der Grundzustand dieses Moleküls infolge der 2 möglichen Spinorientierung aufgespalten ist; vgl. hierzu Ziff. 35.

34. Wasserstoff. In der oben benütztenSchreibweise gilt für H_2:

$$\Theta = 82{,}6 \cdot j\,(j+1)\ {}^\circ\mathrm{K}, \quad j = 1, 2, 3, \ldots$$

Bei Normal-Wasserstoff von Zimmertemperatur tragen daher etwa vier Rotationszustände zur Rotationswärme wesentlich bei, während der Beitrag der Schwingungszustände verschwindend gering ist.

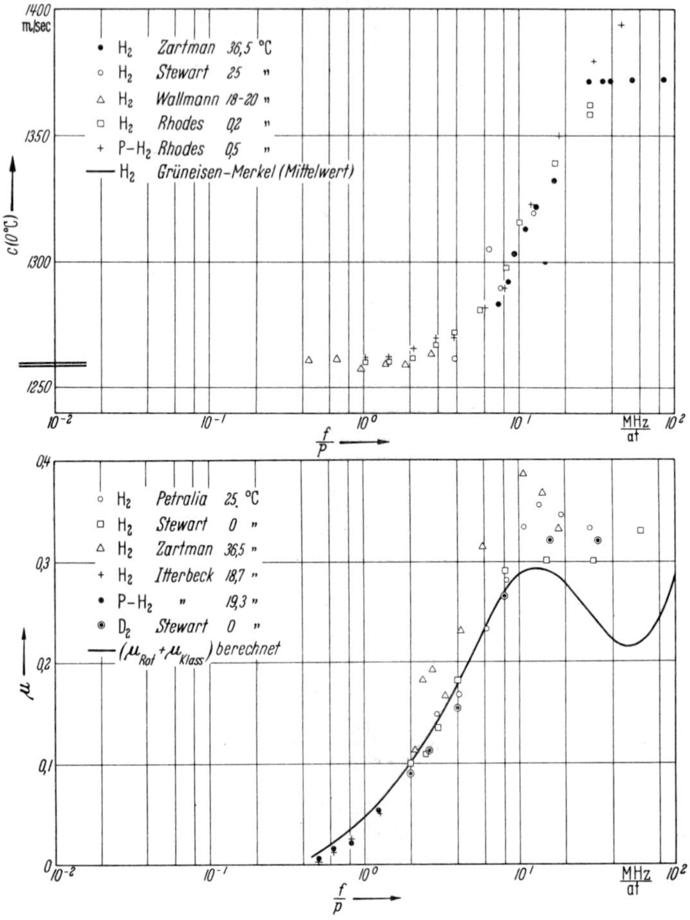

Fig. 15. Dispersion und Absorption in H_2.

Fig. 15 zeigt den Dispersions- und Absorptionsverlauf für Wasserstoffgas; ersteren (reduziert auf 0° C) über vier Zehnerpotenzen von f/p. Eine genauere Analyse ist beim Para-Wasserstoff versucht worden[1], wo nur Rotationszustände mit geraden j-Werten vorkommen, also bei Zimmertemperatur nur $j=2$ und $j=4$ merklich zu C_i beitragen. Unter diesen Umständen läßt sich die Dispersionskurve tatsächlich — wenn auch nicht unbedingt zwingend — durch einen zwei-

[1] Die Rotationsdispersion wurde erstmals nachgewiesen von E. S. STEWART: Phys. Rev. **69**, 632 (1946). Die niederfrequenten Schallgeschwindigkeitswerte stammen von E. GRÜNEISEN u. E. MERKEL, Ann. d. Phys. **66**, 344 (1921) und M. WALLMANN, Ann. d. Phys. **21**, 671 (1934). Alle neueren Messungen an Wasserstoff findet man zitiert bei H.D. PARBROK u. W. TEMPEST: J. Acoust Soc. Amer. **30**, 985 (1958). Deren Meßergebnisse konnten in Fig. 15 nicht mehr aufgenommen werden.

fachen Relaxationsprozeß darstellen mit den Relaxationzeiten 1,7 und $0{,}8 \cdot 10^{-9}$ sec. Durch Division mit $\bar{\tau}$ ergibt sich daraus:

$$Z\,(2 \to 0) \approx 250 \quad \text{und} \quad Z(4 \to 2) \approx 110\,.$$

In der gleichen Größenordnung bewegen sich die (mittleren) Z-Werte für Normal-Wasserstoff: bei 288° K $Z = 260$, bei 197° K $Z = 350$[1]. Z ändert sich demnach wesentlich stärker als $T^{-\frac{1}{2}}$.

Messungen in D_2 führen auf etwa halb so große Z-Werte[2].

35. Stickstoff, Stickoxyd, Sauerstoff. Außer den „klassischen" Einflüssen und der Rotationsrelaxation[3] tragen hier die Schwingungsfreiheitsgrade und — beim NO — die Aufspaltung des Grundzustandes ($^2\Pi_{\frac{3}{2}}$ und $^2\Pi_{\frac{1}{2}}$; infolge der zwei möglichen Einstellungen des Elektronenspins zum Bahndrehimpuls) zur Absorption bei.

Tabelle 3.

	N_2	NO	O_2
$C_{\text{klass}} \cdot 10^9$ [atm/Hz]	4,61	4,9	5,53
$\mu_{\max}$ (Rot)[4]	0,275	0,275	0,275
$f/p\|_{\max}$ (Rot) [Hz/atm]	$3{,}4 \cdot 10^8$ [5]	$4{,}0 \cdot 10^8$ [6]	$4{,}6 \cdot 10^8$ [5]
$\mu_{\max}$ (Osz)[7]	$2{,}8 \cdot 10^{-4}$	$1{,}41 \cdot 10^{-3}$	$5{,}6 \cdot 10^{-3}$
$f/p\|_{\max}$ (Osz) [Hz/atm]	≈ 10 [8]	$4 \cdot 10^5$ [3]	50 [9]
$\mu_{\max}$ (Spin)[7]	—	$15{,}2 \cdot 10^{-3}$	—
$f/p\|_{\max}$ (Spin) [Hz/atm]	—	$6{,}8 \cdot 10^7$ [6]	—
Z_{Rot}	5,2	$\sim 4{,}2$ [6]	3,3 [5]
Z_{Osz}	$\approx 10^8$ [5]	$2{,}7 \cdot 10^3$	$2 \cdot 10^7$
Z_{Spin}		16	

Diese drei bzw. vier Beiträge ($\mu_{\text{klass}}, \mu_{\text{Rot}}, \mu_{\text{Osz}}, \mu_{\text{Spin}}$) dürften mit guter Annäherung additiv sein, und alle drei Gase können für diejenigen Temperaturen und Drucke, bei denen Messungen angestellt wurden, als ideal angesehen werden. Daher kann man μ allgemein als Funktion von f/p angeben; d.h. wegen (16.5) und (13.11)

$$\mu = C_{\text{klass}} \frac{f}{p} + \sum_n 2\mu_{n,\max} \frac{x/x_{n,\max}}{1 + (x/x_{n,\max})^2}\,,$$

wobei n bzw. für „Rot", „Osz" und „Spin" steht, und $x : x_{\max}$ durch $f/p : f/p|_{\max}$ ersetzt werden kann, da im idealen Gas τ immer proportional $1/p$ ist. Tabelle 3 gibt die Konstanten an, die für die drei Gase einzusetzen sind (für 20° C).

Den gesamten Verlauf des „Absorptionsspektrums" in doppelt-logarithmischer Darstellung gibt Fig. 15a wieder; zum Teil unmittelbar den Messungen ent-

---

[1] Mit der Strahlmethode (vgl. Ziff. 29β) wurde bei etwa den gleichen Temperaturen $Z \approx 160$ bzw. 205 ermittelt.

[2] A. VAN ITTERBECK u. P. MARIENS: Nature, Lond. **167**, 477 (1951). Argumente gegen diese Deutung bei R. HERMAN und K. E. SHULER: J. Chem. Phys. **29**, 366 (1958).

[3] Kritische Literaturzusammenstellung bei H. D. PARBROCK u. W. TEMPEST, Acustica **8**, 345 (1958).

[4] Vgl. (15.5) mit $C_i = R$, $C_v = \frac{5}{2} R$, $C_a = \frac{3}{2} R$.

[5] G. SESSLER: Acustica **8**, 395 (1958); dort auch ältere Literatur.

[6] H. J. BAUER, H. O. KNESER u. E. SITTIG: J. Chem. Phys. **30**, 1119 (1959).

[7] Aus spektroskopischen Daten berechnet.

[8] S. J. LUKASIK u. J. E. YOUNG: J. Chem. Phys. **27**, 1149 (1957) (extrapoliert). G. R. COWAN, E. F. GREENE u. D. F. HORNIG: J. Chem. Phys. **19**, 427 (1951); (Stoßwellen in N_2).

[9] H. u. L. KNÖTZEL: Ann. Phys. (6) **2**, 393 (1948).

nommen (insbesondere bei $f/p < 10^8$ Hz/atm), zum Teil durch Extrapolation gewonnen. Es fällt auf, daß die Gesamtabsorption bei den höchsten f/p-Werten den „klassischen" Betrag unterschreitet, wie auch in Ar (vgl. Fig. 11); daß die Rotationsmaxima bei allen drei Gasen fast gleich liegen, die Schwingungsmaxima aber in O_2 und N_2 bei viel niedrigerem f/p als in NO, was auf dessen elektrisches Dipolmoment zurückzuführen ist (vgl. Ziff. 46). Dies drückt sich auch sehr deutlich in den

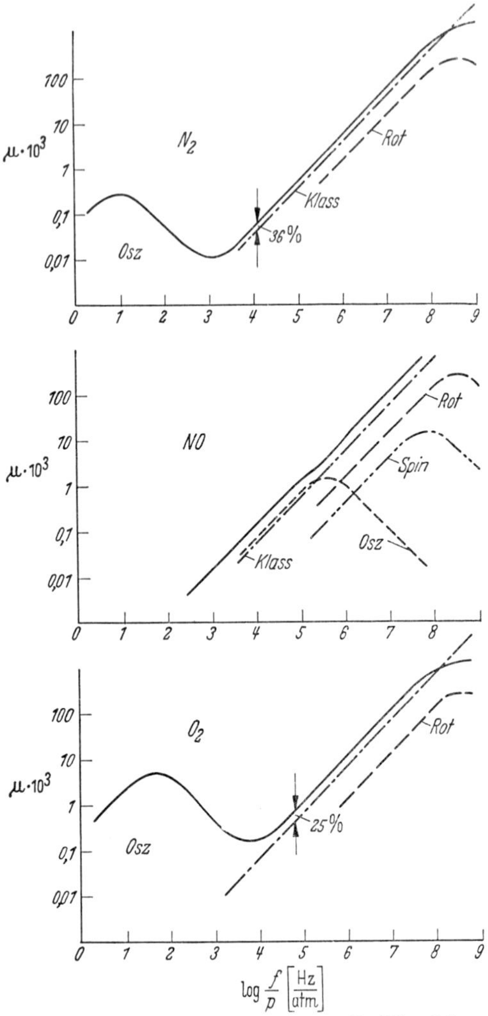

Fig. 15a. Absorptionsindex von N_2, NO und O_2; doppelt-logarithmisch.

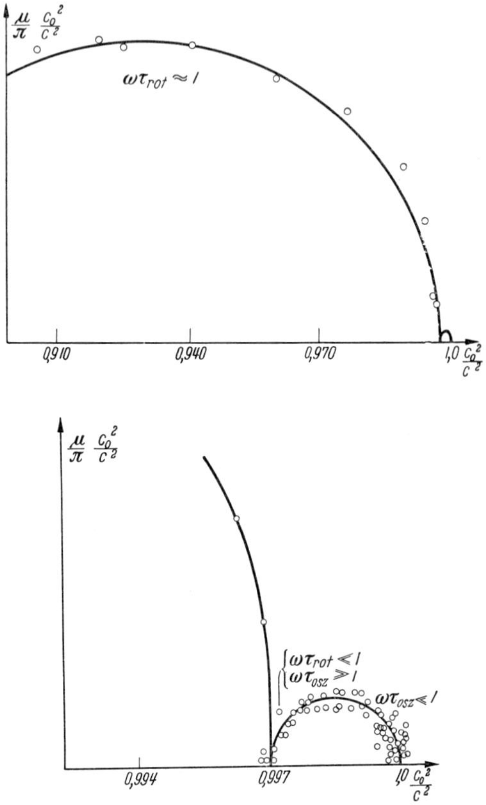

Fig. 16. Cole-Diagramm für O_2.

Z_{Osz}-Werten aus, die sich um fast drei Zehnerpotenzen unterscheiden (vgl. Tabelle 3) Daß die Z_{Rot}-Werte durchweg viel kleiner sind als bei H_2 liegt an den kleineren Rotationsquanten der schwereren Moleküle.

Im Bereich niedriger und mittlerer f/p-Werte liegen für O_2 genügend zusammengehörige Dispersions- und Absorptionsmessungen vor, so daß das „Cole-Diagramm" (vgl. (14.8) und (14.9)) konstruiert werden kann (Fig. 16). Von $C_0^2/C^2 = 1$ beginnend gruppieren sich die Punkte zunächst um einen kleinen Halbkreis, der der Schwingungsrelaxation entspricht, und dann um einen viel größeren, der den Beginn der Rotationsrelaxation darstellt.

36. Weitere zweiatomige Gase. Die Schallgeschwindigkeit in CO wurde mehrfach gemessen[1] [bei 0° C (337,6 ± 0,3) m/sec]; Dispersion wurde bisher nur bei hohen Temperaturen festgestellt[2]. Die Diskussion der Resultate verschiedener Autoren hinsichtlich der Rotations- und Schwingungsrelaxation führt auf ziemlich differierende Werte für Z_{rot} und Z_{Osz}[3]. Immerhin liegen sie, wie zu erwarten, etwa in der gleichen Größenordnung wie bei NO ($Z_{rot} \approx 4$; $Z_{Osz} \approx 10^3$).

Cl_2 ist sehr genau vermessen[4]. Das Absorptionsmaximum der Schwingungsrelaxation hat — nach Korrektur auf den idealen Gaszustand genau die (für $\Theta = 806°$ K) zu erwartende Größe $\mu_{max} = 8{,}3 \cdot 10^{-2}$ bis 20° C, die Relaxationszeit erweist sich auch hier noch, ja sogar bis in den flüssigen Zustand hinein als umgekehrt proportional zur Dichte und führt auf den Wert $Z_{Osz} = 4{,}2 \cdot 10^4$ bei 20° C.

HCl zeigt wegen des großen Θ-Wertes und kleinen Trägheitsmomentes nur Rotationsrelaxation[6]. Der auffallend niedrige Wert $Z_{rot} = 7$ (bei Zimmertemperatur) deutet auf einen erheblichen Einfluß des Dipolmomentes hin; vgl. Ziff. 46.

37. CO_2, COS, CS_2 und N_2O. Unter den dreiatomigen Gasen sind diese durch geradlinige Anordnung der Atome im Molekül ausgezeichnet.

Die *Rotations*zustände liegen hier energetisch meist etwas tiefer als bei zweiatomigen Gasen. Daher ist auch hier bestenfalls der Beginn des Rotationsdispersionsgebiets erfaßbar. Z_{rot} kann nur roh abgeschätzt werden und ist wahrscheinlich immer < 10.

Der niedrigste *Schwingungs*zustand gehört der Biegeschwingung an und liegt bei allen untersuchten dreiatomigen Gasen im günstigen Bereich:

$$500°\,\text{K} < \Theta < 1000°\,\text{K}.$$

Sie zeigen daher alle Relaxation in gut meßbarer Stärke im Bereich $f/p \approx 50$ bis 500 kHz/atm.

Als Beispiel seien die Absorptions- und Dispersionskurve für CO_2-Gas wiedergegeben (Fig. 17), das am häufigsten und genauesten vermessen wurde[5]. Die Kurven sind durch geeignete Wahl von ε und τ nach (13.6) bzw. (13.8) den Meßwerten angepaßt.

Die Übereinstimmung der aus spektroskopischen Daten berechneten μ_{max}-Werte mit den akustisch gemessenen stellt eine glänzende Bestätigung der Relaxationstheorie dar. Allerdings liegen die besonders genau gemessenen Werte für μ_{max} bei CO_2, CS_2 und N_2O um einige Prozente, aber unverkennbar unterhalb der berechneten (vgl. Tab. 4). Dies ist darauf zurückzuführen, daß nicht alle Beiträge, die die Schwingungsfreiheitsgrade zu C_i liefern, mit der gleichen Relaxationszeit behaftet sind. Bei CO_2 gilt der angegebene τ_{Osz}-Wert sicher für den tiefsten Zustand der Biegeschwingung; wahrscheinlich auch für die höheren Zustände *dieses* Schwingungszustandes (vgl. hierzu Ziff. 45). Vermutlich gelten für

---

[1] A. Wüllner: Wied. Ann. **4**, 321 (1878). — G. Schweikart: Ann. Phys. **48**, 593 (1915). — A. van Itterbeck u. P. Mariens: Physics **4**, 609 (1937).

[2] G. G. Sherratt u. E. Griffiths: Proc. Roy. Soc. Lond., Ser. A **147**, 292 (1934) und D. Bender: Ann. Phys. **38**, 199 (1940).

[3] Vgl. H 22, S. 699.

[4] F.D. Shields: J. Acoust. Soc. Amer. **32**, 180 (1959), und E. Sittig: Acustica **10**, 81 (1960); dort auch ältere Literatur. Cl_2 erweist sich geradezu als Schulfall für die Schallausbreitung in einem nichtidealen Gas mit Relaxation.

[5] Erstmals von H. O. Kneser: Ann. Phys. **11**, 777 (1931). Genaueste Messungen und ältere Literatur bei M. C. Henderson u. J. Z. Klose: J. Acoust. Soc. Amer. **31**, 29 (1959) und H. O. Kneser u. H. Roesler: Acustica **9**, 224 (1959).

[6] M.A. Breazeale u. H.C. Kneser: J. Acoust. Soc. Amer. 1960 (z. z. im Druck).

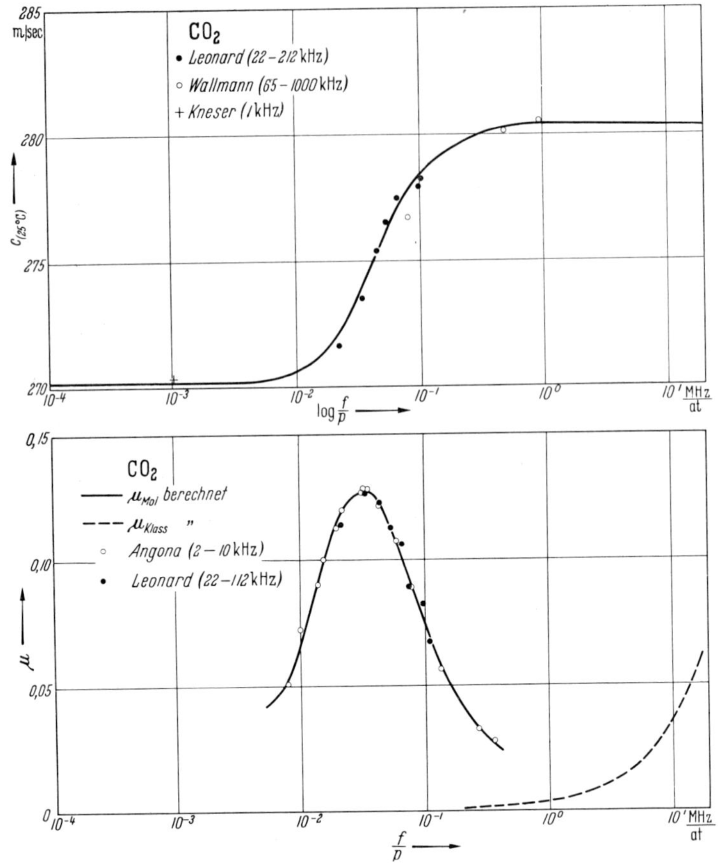

Fig. 17. Dispersion und Absorption in CO_2.

Tabelle 4.

Gas		CO_2	COS	CS_2	N_2O
Molekulargewicht		44	60	76	44
Θ (°K)[1]	Biegeschwingung	959	758	570	847
	symmetrische Valenzschwingung	1920	1370	1043	1850
	asymmetrische Valenzschwingung	3380	2988	2190	3200
C_i/R (300° K)[1]	Biegeschwingung	0,454 · 2	0,602 · 2	0,747 · 2	0,563 · 2
	symmetrische Valenzschwingung	0,069	0,221	0,397	0,082
	asymmetrische Valenzschwingung	0,002	0,005	0,040	0,003
Gesamt C_i/R (300° K)		0,978	1,430	1,931	1,211
μ_{max} berechnet		0,132	0,163	0,199	0,146
μ_{max} gemessen		0,127[2]	(0,17)[4]	0,193[2]	0,153[5]
$(c_\infty - c_0)/c_0$ berechnet		0,045	0,058	0,071	0,0515
$f/p\|_{max}$ (kHz/atm)		35[2]	287[3]	379[2]	153[3]
τ_{Osz} (μsec) bei 1 atm		6,2	0,56	0,42	1,0
Z_{Osz}[1]		86000	9600	8700	11800

[1] Entnommen aus H 23.
[2] F. ANGONA: J. Acoust. Soc. Amer. **25**, 116 (1953).
[3] V. O. KNUDSEN u. E. FRICKE: J. Acoust. Soc. Amer. **12**, 255 (1940).
[4] E. F. FRICKE: J. Acoust. Soc. Amer. **12**, 245 (1940) (extrapoliert).
[5] H. M. WIGHT: J. Acoust Soc. Amer. **28**, 459 (1956).

die anderen (höheren) Schwingungszustände größere Relaxationszeiten[1]. Ob hier Parallel- oder Serienrelaxation vorliegt (vgl. Ziff. 23) läßt sich noch nicht entscheiden[2].

τ_{Osz} erweist sich in weiten Grenzen proportional zur reziproken Dichte; sogar noch in der Nähe des kritischen Zustandes[3].

Mit steigender Temperatur sinkt τ_{Osz} stark ab; zwischen 0° C und 200° C annähernd linear auf etwa die Hälfte[4].

38. Weitere anorganische Gase. Die wesentlichsten Resultate über Gase mit nichtlinearen Molekülen — außer organischen Dämpfen (s. Ziff. 39) — sind in Tabelle 5 zusammengestellt. Bemerkenswert ist, daß sich nur in einem

Tabelle 5

Gas	Temperatur °C	Z_{Osz}	Methode	Autor
H_2O	213	400	Strahl	P. W. HUBER u. A. KANTROWITZ: J. Chem. Phys. **15**, 275 (1947)
	313	280		
	433	190		
	20—80		Absorption	D. BRICKL u. W. L. NYBORG: J. Acoust. Soc. Amer **28**, 151 (1956)
SO_2[5]	27	1900	Absorption	E. F. FRICKE: J. Acoust. Soc. Amer. **12**, 245 (1950)
	27	1900	Strahl	W. GRIFFITH: J. Appl. Phys. **21**, 1319 (1950)
	20	1850	Absorption und Dispersion	S. PETRALIA: Nuovo Cim. **9**, 818 (1952)
NH_3	40	1700 und 13600	Dispersion	K. F. BUSCHMANN u. K. SCHÄFER: Z. phys. Chem. B **50**, 73 (1941).
	100	620 und 2500	Dispersion	
	20	1300	Strahlung	W. GRIFFITH, s. oben
	20	$Z_{\mathrm{rot}} \approx 10$	Absorption und Dispersion	S. PETRALIA: Nuovo Cim. **10**, 817 (1953)
CF_4	22	6000	Absorption und Dispersion	W. H. BYERS: J. Chem. Phys. **11**, 348 (1943)
SF_6	36,1	4680	Dispersion	C. L. O'CONNOR: J. Acoust. Soc. Amer. **26**, 361 (1954)

Fall (NH_3) Abweichungen vom „einfachen" Relaxationsverlauf andeutungsweise gezeigt haben. Bei SF_6 dagegen, wo 15 Schwingungstypen merklich zur Schwingungswärme beitragen, hat die sehr sorgfältig untersuchte Dispersion keine Anzeichen für eine Verbreiterung des Relaxationsgebietes erbracht.

[1] Am genauesten läßt sich die Frage, ob ein einfacher Relationsprozeß vorliegt, mit Hilfe der Cole-Darstellung (vgl. Ziff. 14) prüfen, die dann einen Kreis ergeben müßte. Tatsächlich zeigen die Experimente Abweichungen hiervon, insbesondere bei tiefen Frequenzen [H. O. KNESER u. H. ROESLER, erscheint in Z. Physik].

[2] Rechnungen hierzu bei K. F. BUSCHMANN u. K. SCHÄFER [Z. phys. Chem. B **50**, 73 (1841)] sind außer für CO_2 auch für N_2O durchgeführt worden.

[3] M. C. HENDERSON u. J. Z. KLOSE: J. Acoust. Soc. Amer. **31**, 29 (1959). Daraus kann man schließen, daß hier das Eigenvolumen der Moleküle noch klein ist gegen das Gesamtvolumen. Bei Cl_2 gilt dies sogar bis in den flüssigen Zustand hinein; vgl. Ziff. 36.

[4] F. D. SHIELDS: J. Acoust. Soc. Amer. **29**, 450 (1957).

[5] Die Untersuchung von J. D. LAMBERT u. R. SALTER [Proc. Roy. Soc. Lond., A **243**, 78 (1957)] konnten noch nicht in Tabelle 5 aufgenommen werden. Danach treten in SO_2 zwei um den Faktor 10 unterschiedene Schwingungs-Relaxationszeiten auf, die bei Temperaturvariation ein Maximum durchlaufen. Theoretische Überlegungen machen dies verständlich; vgl. P. G. DICKENS u. J. W. LINNETT: Proc. Roy. Soc. Lond. Ser. A **243**, 84 (1957).

Auffallend sind ferner die niedrigen Z-Werte für H_2O und NH_3. Die extrem schweren, als „Freons" bezeichneten Gase (CCl_2F_2, CF_2Cl, $CHClF_2$, ...) zeigen ebenfalls Schwingungsrelaxation[1].

39. Organische Gase und Dämpfe. In dem Maße, wie die Relaxationszeit τ_{Osz} oder die „Abregungszahl" Z_{Osz} für die physikalische Chemie interessant wurde, häufen sich die Messungen der Schallausbreitungsgrößen auch in Gasen mit komplizierter gebauten Molekülen[2]. Meist beschränken sich dabei die Autoren auf eine Abschätzung von τ_{Osz} oder Z_{Osz}, die bei Kenntnis der Schwingungswärme auch dann möglich ist, wenn nur ein Anstieg der Schallgeschwindigkeit oder -absorption in beschränktem f/p-Bereich gemessen wurde. Darüber hinaus sind Präzisionsmessungen der Absorption in C_2H_4O [3] und der Dispersion in einer Reihe von chlorierten Methanderivaten durchgeführt worden[4].

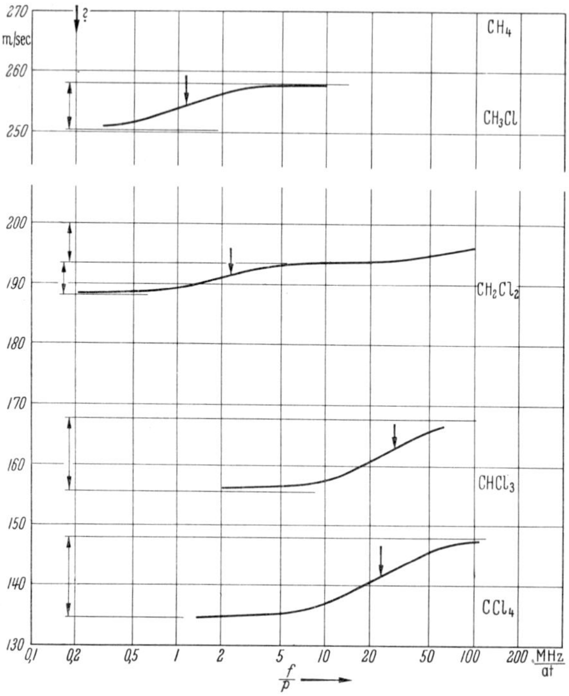

Fig. 18. Dispersion in chlorierten Methanderivaten.

Das Ergebnis der letzteren ist in Fig. 18 zusammengefaßt. Hier zeigt sich, daß in der Reihe (CH_4), CH_3Cl, ..., CCl_4 die Frequenz des Wendepunkts nicht monoton ansteigt, bzw. Z_{Osz} nicht monoton absinkt, obwohl die zugehörigen Θ-Werte (für das kleinste Schwingungsquant) sich so verhalten; ferner, daß anscheinend CH_2Cl als einziges Glied in dieser Reihe zwei deutlich getrennte Relaxationsgebiete aufweist. Diese Befunde haben sich bisher noch nicht deuten lassen.

Abgesehen vom anomalen Verhalten des CH_2Cl wird jedoch auch bei diesen und vielen anderen komplizierten Molekülen stets eine einfache Relaxation beobachtet. Dies und die Tatsache, daß Z_{Osz} in einfacher Weise von der Größe des kleinsten Schwingungsquants abzuhängen scheint, bestärkt die Vermutung[5], daß

[1] Y. MIYAHARA u. E. G. RICHARDSON: J. Acoust. Soc. Amer. **28**, 1016 (1956).

[2] Zusammengestellt von E. G. RICHARDSON: Rev. Mod. Phys. **27**, 15 (1955); ferner P. G. T. FOGG u. J. D. LAMBERT: Proc. Roy. Soc. Lond., Ser. A **232**, 537 (1955) mit umfassendem Literaturverzeichnis. Eine neuere Zusammenstellung von Relaxationszeiten für acht organische Gase findet man bei K. F. HERZFELD: J. Acoust. Soc. Amer. **29**, 1180 (1957); für weitere neun bei P. D. EDMONDS u. J. LAMB: Proc. Phys. Soc. Lond. **72**, 940 (1957).

[3] F. ANGONA: J. Acoust. Soc. Amer. **25**, 1116 (1953).

[4] D. SETTE, A. BUSALA u. J. C. HUBBARD: J. Chem. Phys. **23**, 787 (1955) und T. D. ROSSING u. S. LEGVOLD: J. Chem. Phys. **23**, 1118 (1955). Theoretische Deutung dieser Befunde bei F. L. TANCZOS: J. Chem. Phys. **25**, 439 (1954). Auch im flüssigen Methylenchlorid treten zwei Dispersionsgebiete auf; J. H. ANDREAE: Proc. Phys. Soc. Lond. B **70**, 71 (1957).

[5] J. D. LAMBERT u. J. S. ROWLINSON: Proc. Roy. Soc. Lond., Ser. A **204**, 424 (1950/51) und P. G. T. FOGG, P. A. HANKS u. J. D. LAMBERT: Proc. Roy. Soc. Lond., Ser. A **219**, 490 (1953).

meistens eine Serienrelaxation vorliegt, und zwar derart, daß Schwingungsenergie zunächst mit großer Relaxationszeit vom tiefsten Schwingungszustände aufgenommen und dann sehr rasch auf alle anderen übertragen wird.

Bei CH_4 liegt die Schwingungsrelaxation so tief — bei etwa 0,2 MHz/atm[1] —, daß sie sich der Rotationsrelaxation nicht überlagert. Messungen im Bereich 10 bis 100 MHz/atm[2] ergaben für Z_{rot} den Wert 14 bis 17.

Der Vergleich von Cis- und Trans-Dichloräthylen[3] ($C_2H_2Cl_2$) ergibt für das letztere Gas eine wesentlich höhere Relaxationsfrequenz.

Auch in n-Hexan-Dampf wird überklassische Schallabsorption und Dispersion beobachtet, die sich durch eine Relaxationszeit, d.h. durch sehr rasch aufeinanderfolgende „Serienanregung" der verschiedenen Schwingungsfreiheitsgrade deuten läßt[4]. Bei hohen Drucken nahe dem kritischen Punkt macht sich anscheinend ein Assoziationsprozeß zusätzlich bemerkbar[5].

40. Gasmischungen. Die in Ziff. 32 behandelten Mischungen von Edelgasen zeigen den Einfluß der (Thermo-) Diffusion, der sich etwa beim Mischungsverhältnis 1:1 als eine kräftige Erhöhung der Absorption auswirkt, unterhalb 1:100 aber kaum nachweisbar ist.

Völlig anders verhalten sich Gase mit Schwingungsrelaxation, wenn ihnen Fremdgase beigemischt werden. So verschwindet z.B. in CO_2 bei 100 kHz die Dispersion und die nicht-klassische Absorption fast völlig, sobald man nur Bruchteile eines Mol-Prozents Wasserdampf zusetzt. Ältere Schallmessungen, bei denen auf extreme Reinheit des Versuchsgases meist nicht besonders geachtet wurde, sind daher oft nicht verläßlich.

Die Deutung dieser und ähnlicher Erscheinungen ist die folgende[6]: Die Relaxationszeit wird durch Verunreinigungen in sehr verschiedenem Maße, meist außerordentlich stark verkürzt. Verkürzung der Relaxationszeit bedeutet aber Verkleinerung von Z_{Osz}, d.h. das schwingende Molekül wird „empfindlicher" gegen Zusammenstöße, oder: Zusammenstöße mit Fremdmolekülen führen viel häufiger als solche mit gleichartigen zur Umwandlung von Schwingungs- in Translationsenergie. Damit eröffnet sich ein Zugang zum Studium gaskinetischer Zusammenstöße zwischen ungleichen Molekülen.

Am genauesten ist das Phänomen untersucht am O_2 mit kleinen Zusätzen von H_2O und NH_3. Zwischen 0,6 und 4,7 kHz wurde bei 1 atm Absorption und Dispersion im Zylinderresonater gemessen. Das Ergebnis zeigt Fig. 19[7]. Als Dispersionsgröße wurde $\gamma^0 = c^2 \frac{\varrho_0}{p_0}$ aufgetragen, also die Zahl, die im dispersionsfreiem Gas das Verhältnis der Molwärmen angibt. Diese Größe strebt oberhalb des Dispersionsgebiets dem Wert 1,4000 ($=\frac{7}{5}$) zu, wie er einem nicht schwingungsfähigen Hantel-Molekül zukommt. Der Absorptionsindex für 1 kHz liegt bei 0 und 4 Molekülprozent NH_3 unterhalb 10^{-3}, bei Zwischenwerten der NH_3-Konzentration über 10^{-2}.

Quantitativ ergibt sich für die Abhängigkeit der Relaxationsfrequenz ($\approx f_{max}$) ein *linearer* Anstieg mit der Konzentration bei NH_3 (Fig. 20). Dasselbe gilt für CO_2 bei Zusatz von H_2S, H_2, CH_3OH, C_3H_7OH, C_7H_8 und H_2O, und zwar in

[1] A. EUCKEN u. S. AYBAR: Z. phys. Chem., Abt. B **46**, 195 (1940) und W. GRIFFITH: J. Appl. Phys. **21**, 1319 (1950). Vgl. auch Fig. 18.

[2] B. T. KOLLY: J. Acoust. Soc. Amer. **29**, 1005 (1957).

[3] D. SETTE, A. BUSALA u. J. C. HUBBARD: J. Chem. Phys. **20**, 1899 (1952).

[4] J. Z. KLOSE: J. Acoust. Soc. Amer. **7**, 605 (1958).

[5] V. F. NOSDREV: Dokl. Akad. Nauk. USSR **85**, 1005 (1952).

[6] W. T. RICHARDS u. J. A. REID: Nature, Lond. **130**, 739 (1932). — A. EUCKEN u. R. BECKER: Z. phys. Chem., Abt. B **20**, 467 (1933).

[7] H. u. L. KNÖTZEL: Ann. Phys. (6) **2**, 393 (1948). In reinem O_2 ist $f_{max} \lesssim 0{,}06$ kHz

dieser Reihenfolge anwachsend[1], so daß 1% H_2O in CO_2 die Relaxationsfrequenz bereits verzehnfacht (Fig. 21).

Nicht linear wächst dagegen die Relaxationsfrequenz des O_2 mit der H_2O-Konzentration an (vgl. Fig. 20). Dies ist der einzige derartige Fall, der bisher beobachtet wurde.

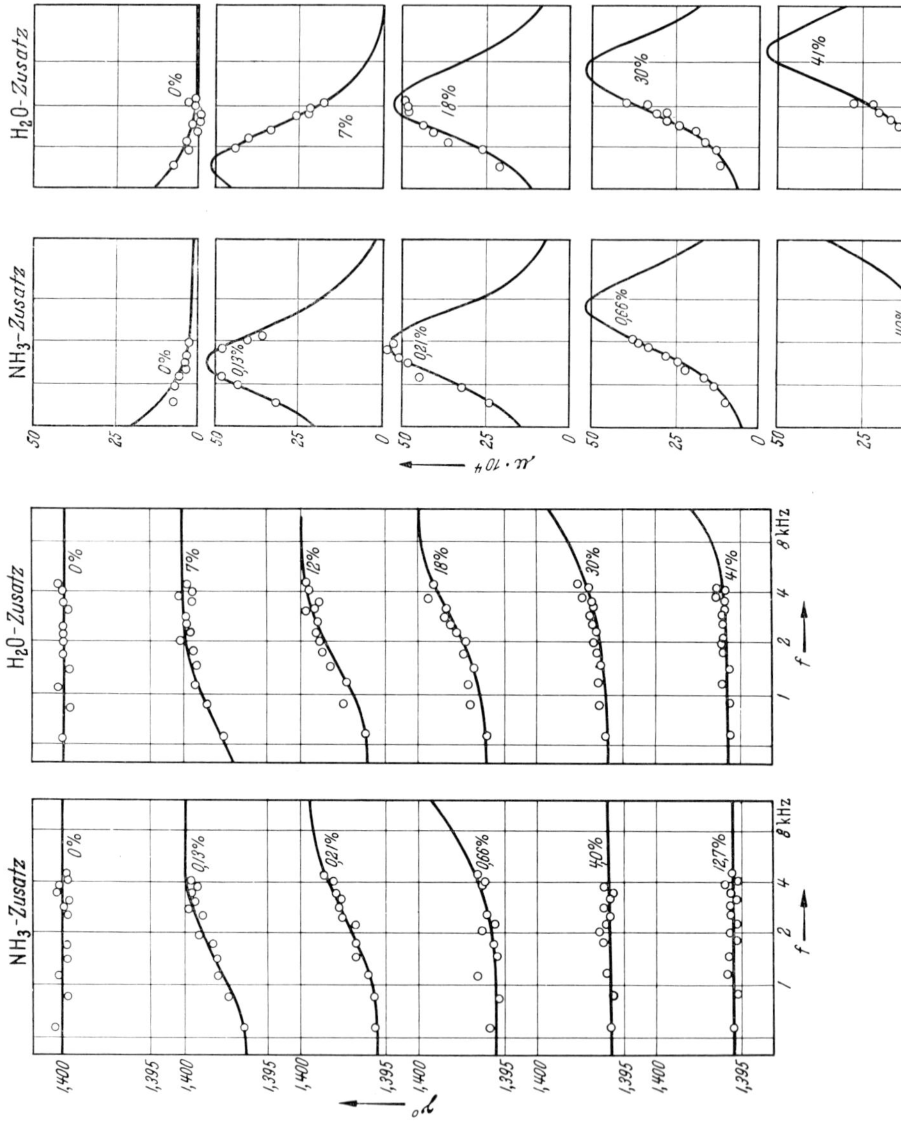

Fig. 19. Verschiebung des Absorptionsmaximums von O_2 durch NH_3-Zusatz (in Molprozenten) und H_2O-Zusatz (in relativer Feuchte); $\tau = 19$°C.

Einen Überblick über alle Gasgemische, in denen Relaxationsfrequenzen gemessen wurden, gibt Tabelle 6.

Eine eingehende Analyse aller dieser Daten — insbesondere solche verschiedener Autoren — wird eben dadurch sehr erschwert, daß die Z-Werte so außer-

[1] V. O. KNUDSEN u. E. F. FRICKE: J. Acoust. Soc. Amer. **12**, 255 (1940).

ordentlich empfindlich sind gegen geringste, oft kaum vermeidbare Verunreinigungen des Grundgases. Immerhin lassen Ergebnisse, die unter vergleichbaren Umständen[1] oder gar mit der gleichen Apparatur gewonnen werden, gewisse Vergleiche und allgemeine Aussagen zu. Daher sind in Tabelle 7[2] einige Werte für Z' in Gasmischungen wiedergegeben, wobei Z' jetzt diejenige Zahl bedeutet, die angibt, wieviel Zusammenstöße *mit einem Fremdmolekül* ein schwingendes Molekül des Grundgases übersteht, ehe es seine Schwingungsenergie in Rotations- und Translationsenergie verwandelt. M bedeutet das Molekulargewicht (vgl. hierzu Ziff. 47).

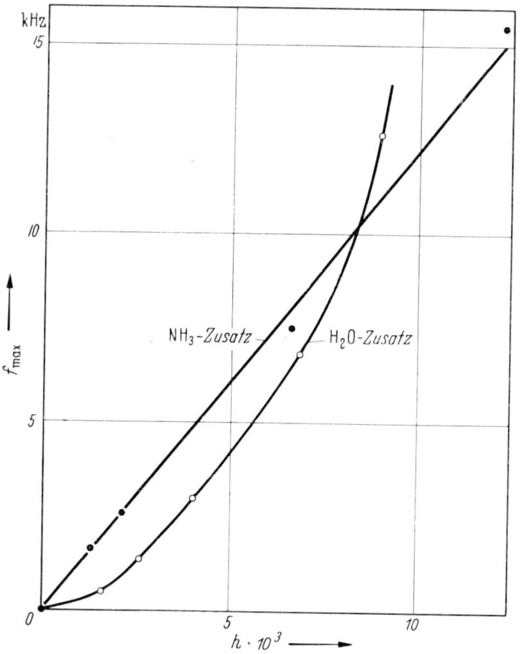

Fig. 20. Verschiebung der Relaxationsfrequenz von O_2 durch H_2O- und NH_3-Zusatz.

Ähnliche Versuche wurden mit N_2O und C_2H_4 als Grundgasen und verschiedenen organischen Dämpfen als Zusätzen durchgeführt[3].

Aus diesen Zahlen geht hervor:

1. Das Massenverhältnis der Stoßpartner, das nach den Gesetzen des makroskopischen Stoßes die „Unelastizität" bestimmen sollte, ist für die Umwandlung von Schwingungs- in andere Energieformen offenbar *nicht* von entscheidendem Einfluß; denn sonst müßte der Zusammenstoß eines schweren Moleküls (z. B. Cl_2) mit einem leichten (z. B. H_2) weniger wirksam sein, d. h. größeres Z' aufweisen, als derjenige mit einem schweren (z. B. N_2 oder Ar). In Wirklichkeit ist es umgekehrt. Das gleiche geht aus der Verschiedenheit nebeneinander stehender Zahlen der

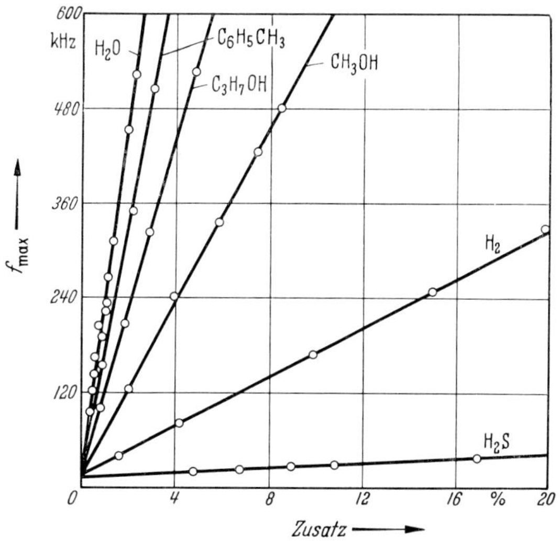

Fig. 21. Verschiebung der Relaxationsfrequenz von CO_2 durch Zusatzgase.

---

[1] Die in Tabelle 7 wiedergegebenen Zahlen entstammen fast ausnahmslos Dispersionsmessungen, die in den Jahren 1932—1935 im Physikalisch-Chemischen Institut der Universität Göttingen unter Leitung von A. EUCKEN ausgeführt wurden.

[2] Entnommen aus A. EUCKEN, Öst. Chem.-Ztg. Nr. **20**, 1 (1935).

[3] J. W. ARNOLD, J. C. MCCOUBREY u. A. R. UBBELOHDE: Proc. Roy. Soc. Lond. **248**, 445 (1958); hier auch ältere Literaturangaben.

Tabelle 6.

Zusatz	Grundgas										
	N_2	O_2	Cl_2	CO_2	COS	CS_2	N_2O	CH_4	C_2H_4O	C_2H_4	Luft
He . . .		9	4, 10, 18, 23	4, 10, 18, 23, 30	21		18, 21, 23			24	
Ne . . .		19		4, 10, 19							
Ar . . .			4, 10, 18, 23	4, 10, 18, 23, 30	21		18, 23			24	
H_2 . . .		9	4, 10, 18, 23	2, 3, 4, 10, 13, 18, 23	13, 21	13	13, 18, 22, 23	21		24	
N_2 . . .			10, 18, 23	7, 12, 30	21				24		
O_2 . . .	14, 15			7, 12	21						
CO . . .		9	10, 18, 23		21		18, 22, 23				
HCl . .			4, 10, 18, 23	4, 10, 18, 23							
CO_2 . .	7, 11, 12	7, 9, 12				1		21	1		
COS . .	11										
CS_2 . .	7, 11, 12	7, 9, 12		1, 7, 12					1		12
N_2O . .	11										
H_2O . .	6	5, 6, 8, 19, 21		2, 4, 7, 10, 12, 13, 17, 18, 19, 20, 23, 26, 29	13	13	13, 18, 22, 23, 25				6, 28
SO_2 . .	11										
NH_3 . .		5, 8					18, 22, 23				
O_3 . . .		9									
H_2S . .		9		13							
D_2O . .				19, 20			22, 25				
CH_4 . .			4, 10, 18, 23	4, 10, 18, 23			18, 21, 23				
C_2H_4O .			1			1					
CH_3OH .		7, 12		2, 7, 12, 13	13	13	13				
C_3H_7OH		7, 12		2, 7, 12, 13	13	13	13				
C_2H_5OH		7, 9, 12		7, 12							
C_2H_2 . .		9									
C_6H_6 . .		9									
$HCCl_3$.		9									
CCl_4 . .		9									
$C_6H_5CH_3$				13		13	13				

Legende zu Tabelle 6

[1] F. ANGONA: J. Acoust. Soc. Amer. **25**, 116 (1953).
[2] V. O. KNUDSEN u. E. F. FRICKE: J. Acoust. Soc. Amer. **12**, 255 (1940).
[3] W. H. PIELEMEIER u. W. H. BEYER: J. Acoust. Soc. Amer. **15**, 17 (1943).

Legende zu Tabelle 6 (Forts.).

[4] A. Eucken u. R. Becker: Z. phys. Chem. B **20**, 467 (1933).
[5] H. Knötzel u. L. Knötzel: Ann. d. Physik **2**, 393 (1948).
[6] V. O. Knudsen: J. Acoust. Soc. Amer. **5**, 112 (1933).
[7] R. S. Alleman: J. Acoust. Soc. Amer. **10**, 88 (1938).
[8] V. O. Knudsen u. L. Orbert: J. Acoust. Soc. Amer. **7**, 249 (1936).
[9] H. O. Kneser u. V. O. Knudsen: Ann. d. Physik **21**, 682 (1934).
[10] A. Eucken u. R. Becker: Z. phys. Chem. B **27**, 235 (1935).
[11] E. F. Fricke: J. Acoust. Soc. Amer. **12**, 245 (1940).
[12] V. O. Knudsen u. E. F. Fricke: J. Acoust. Soc. Amer. **10**, 89 (1938).
[13] V. O. Knudsen u. E. F. Fricke: J. Acoust. Soc. Amer. **12**, 257 (1940).
[14] C. Ener, F. Gabrysh u. I. C. Hubbard: J. Acoust. Soc. Amer. **24**, 474 (1952).
[15] I. F. Zartman: J. Acoust. Soc. Amer. **21**, 171 (1949).
[16] I. C. Hubbard: Phys. Rev. **41**, 523 (1932).
[17] W. H. Pielemeier, H. L. Sexton u. D. Telfair: J. Chem. Phys. **8**, 106 (1940).
[18] A. Eucken u. L. Kuchler: Phys. Z. **39**, 831 (1938).
[19] A. van Itterbeck u. P. Mariens: Physica **7**, 125 (1940).
[20] D. Sette u. I. C. Hubbard: J. Acoust. Soc. Amer. **25**, 994 (1953).
[21] A. Eucken u. S. Aybar: Z. phys. Chem. B **46**, 195 (1940).
[22] A. Eucken u. H. Jaaks: Z. phys. Chem. B **30**, 85 (1935).
[23] F. Patat u. E. Bartholomé: Z. phys. Chem. B **32**, 396 (1936).
[24] W. T. Richards u. J. A. Reid: J. Chem. Phys. **2**, 206 (1934).
[25] H. M. Wright: J. Acoust. Soc. Amer. **28**, 459 (1956).
[26] F. A. Gutowski: J. Acoust. Soc. Amer. **28**, 478 (1956).
[27] S. Sinnes u. W. E. Roseveare: J. Chem. Phys. **4**, 427 (1936).
[28] E. J. Evans u. E. N. Bazley: Acustica **6**, 238 (1956).
[29] B. Widom u. S. H. Bauer: J. Chem. Phys. **31**, 1670 (1953).
[30] H. O. Kneser u. H. Roesler: Proc. 3 rd ICA-Congr. 1960.

Spalten 3 und 4 (Tab. 6) hervor. Nur der Unterschied zwischen H_2 und D_2 dürfte rein stoßmechanisch zu verstehen sein.

2. Molekülpaare, die chemisch miteinander reagieren können (ohne es unter den herrschenden Bedingungen zu tun), zeigen in der Regel auffallend kleine Z'-Werte, d.h. das Schwingungsquant geht beim Zusammenstoß mit hoher Wahrscheinlichkeit verloren. Dies zeigt sich besonders auffallend, wenn man Stoßpartner mit paarweise gleichen Massen vergleicht, beim Vergleich von Cl_2+N_2 mit Cl_2+CO (= Phosgen!) und von N_2O+He mit N_2O+D_2. Auch die außerordentliche Empfindlichkeit des Z' in O_2 gegenüber allen Partnern, die H enthalten[2], dürfte die gleiche Ursache haben.

Tabelle 7.

Zusatzgas	M	Grundgase		
		Cl_2 $M=71$	NO_2 $M=44$	CO_2 $M=44$[1]
H_2 . . .	2	780	630	480
D_2 . . .	4		440	
He . . .	4	900	1700	1700
CH_4 . .	16	190	840	2400
NH_3 . .	17		450	
H_2O . .	18		60	40
N_2 . . .	28	43000		
CO . . .	28	230	3600	
HCl . .	36	120		
Ar . . .	40	~32000		4700

Ein erschöpfendes Verständnis solcher Stoßprozesse ist freilich nicht auf Grund so einfacher Vorstellungen zu erwarten, sondern nur vom Standpunkt der Quantenmechanik (vgl. hierzu Ziff. 47).

Bei einigen Mischungen — z.B. Cl_2 mit N_2 und CO_2 mit He, Ar und N_2 — ergibt sich Z' größer als Z. Die Relaxationszeit wird also durch das zugesetzte Fremdgas vergrößert, d.h. die Relaxationsfrequenz verkleinert; und zwar, wie

[1] Die Absolutwerte stimmen aus den vorgenannten Gründen nicht mit Tabelle 3 überein.
[2] H. O. Kneser u. V. O. Knudsen: Ann. Phys. **21**, 682 (1934).

sich bei den CO_2-Gemischen gezeigt hat[1] nicht proportional der Konzentration des Fremdgases. Mit der Annahme von Zweierstößen allein ist dieser Befund nicht zu deuten.

In Mischungen von Gasen, deren jedes ein ausgeprägtes Relaxationsverhalten zeigt, und deren Relaxationszeiten weit auseinander liegen, treten trotzdem auch beim Mischungsverhältnis $\approx 1:1$ keine zwei Relaxationsgebiete auf[2]. Absorptions- und Dispersionsverlauf sind stets innerhalb der Fehlergrenze durch „einfache Relaxationsfunktionen" darstellbar.

41. Teilweise dissoziierte Gase. Die endliche, wenn auch bei Gasen sehr hohe Einstellgeschwindigkeit des Dissoziationsgleichgewichts stellt einen Relaxationsprozeß komplizierterer Art dar als die bisher behandelten. NERNST erkannte bereits 1910[3], daß dies Einfluß auf die Schallausbreitung haben müsse. EINSTEIN[4] rechnete das Problem für eine einfache Reaktion vom Typus $A_2 \rightleftharpoons 2A$ durch. Da aber der Molekülzerfall zweifellos aus einem angeregten Zustand heraus stattfindet, ist der Prozeß sicher immer von einer Anregungs-, meist wohl Schwingungsrelaxation begleitet, von der nicht feststeht, ob sie parallel oder in Serie erfolgt. Immerhin läßt sich das Problem ziemlich allgemein durchrechnen[5], auch für eine Reaktion, die nach dem Schema $aA + bB \cdots \rightleftharpoons qQ + rR + \cdots$, gegebenenfalls über Zwischenstufen verläuft[6].

Experimentell ist die Dissoziationsrelaxation in N_2O_4, dem einfachsten bei Zimmertemperatur merklich dissoziierten Gas häufig untersucht[7] und in jüngster Zeit nachgewiesen worden[8]. Bei Zimmertemperatur tritt das Absorptionsmaximum bei $f/p = 2 \cdot 10^6$ Hz/atm auf. Es verlagert sich bei 50° C nicht wesentlich, woraus man schließen muß, daß die Reaktionsgeschwindigkeit wesentlich durch die Verweilzeit im angeregten Zustand bestimmt ist, aus dem heraus dann das Molekül dissoziiert.

Verdünnt man das dissoziierende Gas mit einem inerten, z.B. 5% N_2O_4 in 95% Ar, so wächst die maximale Absorption auf etwa das Doppelte an. Der überraschende Effekt erklärt sich wie folgt: Der Anteil, den der Dissoziationsvorgang zur Molwärme beiträgt, also C_i [vgl. (15.3)] wird sehr groß gegen C_a, so daß $C_i \approx C_v$ wird. Dies in (15.5) eingesetzt macht $\varepsilon = R/(R + C_a)$, und $\mu_{\max}$ wird wegen (13.10) gleich $R/\sqrt{C_a(R + C_a)}$, also in Ar, wo C_a nur $\frac{3}{2}R$ beträgt, wesentlich größer als im N_2O_4.

In Azetonitril und Azetaldehyd, welche Gase ebenfalls bei Zimmertemperatur merklich dissoziiert sind, konnte keine Dispersion nachgewiesen werden[9].

42. Reale Gase, kritischer Zustand. Messungen der Schallgeschwindigkeit in He bei hohen Drucken und tiefen Temperaturen[10] zeigen den nach (17.5) zu er-

---

[1] H. O. KNESER u. H. ROESLER: Proc. 3 rd ICA-Congr. 1960.

[2] Untersucht von F. ANGONA [J. Acoust. Soc. Amer. **25**, 1116 (1953)] an Mischungen von CO_2 mit CS_2 und C_2H_4O und von J.D. ROSSING und S. LEGVOLD [J. Chem. Phys. **23**, 1118 (1955)] an Mischungen von $CHClF_2$ mit CF_4 und $CHCl_2F$ mit $CClF_3$.

[3] Veröffentlicht von F. KEUTEL: Diss. Berlin 1910.

[4] A. EINSTEIN: Ber. Preuss. Akad. Wiss. 1920, S. 380.

[5] H. O. KNESER u. O. GAULER: Phys. Z. **37**, 677 (1936).

[6] D. TABUCHI: J. Chem. Phys. **23**, 2033 (1955).

[7] H. SELLE: Z. phys. Chem. **104**, 1 (1923). — E. GRÜNEISEN u. E. GOENS: Ann. Phys. **72**, 193 (1923). — G. B. KISTIAKOWSKY u. W. T. RICHARDS: J. Amer. Chem. Soc. **52**, 4661 (1930). — D. G. C. LUCK: Phys. Rev. **40**, 440 (1932). — W. T. RICHARDS u. E. A. REID: J. Chem. Phys. **1**, 114, 737 (1933). — C. E. TEETER: J. Chem. Phys. **1**, 251 (1933).

[8] H. J. BAUER, H. O. KNESER u. E. SITTIG: Acustica **9**, 181 (1959), und G. SESSLER: Acustica **9**, 119 (1959).

[9] J. D. LAMBERT u. J. E. ROWLINSON: Proc. Roy. Soc. Lond., Ser. A **204**, 424 (1950).

[10] W. G. SCHNEIDER u. G. J. THIESEN: Canad. J. Res. A **28**, 509 (1950) und A. VAN ITTERBECK u. W. DE LAET: Physica, Haag **24**, 59 (1958).

wartenden linearen Anstieg mit dem Druck; und zwar um so stärker, je tiefer die Temperatur (bei 200° C etwa 0,026% je Atmosphäre, bei −78° C etwa 0,07% je Atmosphäre). Aus solchen Messungen kann nach (17.6) der zweite Virialkoeffizient mit einer Genauigkeit ermittelt werden, die der des üblichen Verfahrens — der Berechnung aus der Kompressibilität — nicht nachsteht.

Wesentlich problematischer ist die Schallausbreitung in Gasen, für die die Berthelotsche Zustandsgleichung (17.1) nicht mehr ausreicht und im allgemeinen auch durch keine andere ersetzt werden kann, insbesondere also in unmittelbarer Nachbarschaft des kritischen Punktes. Dort haben die Isentropen einen Wendepunkt. Die Schallgeschwindigkeit muß dort mit steigendem Druck — wegen (2.1): $c^2 = -\frac{V}{\varrho}\frac{dp}{dV}\Big|_s$ — ein Minimum durchlaufen, das um so tiefer ist, je genauer man die kritische Temperatur einhält. Bei höheren Temperaturen wird das Minimum flacher und verschwindet schließlich ganz, bis endlich der oben beschriebene monotone Anstieg mit dem Druck einsetzt[1]. Bei Temperaturen unterhalb der kritischen tritt mit Erreichen des Dampfdrucks Kondensation ein, und die Schallgeschwindigkeit steigt abrupt auf den Wert, der der Flüssigkeit entspricht.

Genau dies Verhalten zeigen die sehr sorgfältigen Messungen an CO_2 [2] (vgl. Fig. 22). Die kleinste erreichte Schallgeschwindigkeit beträgt 135 m/sec, ist also nur halb so groß wie diejenige unter Normalbedingungen! Innerhalb der Meßgenauigkeit ($\pm 0{,}2$%) war im Bereich 0,4 bis 1,2 MHz keine Frequenzabhängigkeit festzustellen[3].

Qualitativ die gleichen Ergebnisse wurden erzielt bei Schallgeschwindigkeitsmessungen am kritischen Punkt in NO_2 [4], SF_6 [5], einer Anzahl organischer Dämpfe[6] und — besonders genau untersucht — Xe[7]. Ob die hier gemessene Dispersion (vgl. Fig. 23) reell ist, bedarf wohl noch der Bestätigung. Sie tritt nur im Bereich 1,5° ober- und unterhalb der kritischen Temperatur auf, wo die Meßfehlergrenzen besonders weit sind. In keinem der sonst untersuchten Gase konnte Dispersion nachgewiesen werden.

Im gleichen Temperaturintervall wächst der Absorptionsindex in Xe[7] (gemessen bei 0,25 MHz) plötzlich von 0,05 auf mehr als das 10fache und sinkt steil wieder ab[8]. Ein noch schärferes Maximum zeigt — über der Temperatur aufgetragen — der Absorptionsindex in SF_6, der innerhalb von 1° C von 0,02 auf

[1] Dasselbe ist auch aus Fig. 6 zu ersehen: Nahe der kritischen Temperatur ($\mathfrak{T} \gtrsim 1$) ist B zunächst negativ, und die Schallgeschwindigkeit nimmt mit steigendem Druck ab, vgl. (17.1) und (17.3). Erst bei $\mathfrak{T} \approx 2{,}5$ setzt der monotone Anstieg ein.

[2] H. Tielsch u. H. Tanneberger: Z. Physik **137**, 256 (1954) und H. Tanneberger: Z. Physik **153**, 445 (1959). Die Messungen erfordern äußerste Konstanz des Druckes und der Temperatur, höchste Reinheit des Gases und Vermeidung eines Dichtegradienten, der sich am kritischen Punkt wegen der dort extrem großen Kompressibilität einstellen kann. Vgl. auch C. M. Herget: J. Chim. Phys. **8**, 537 (1940) (0,27 MHz); J. Noury: C. R. Acad. Sci., Paris **223**, 377 (1946); **233**, 516 (1951); **234**, 1036 (1952) (0.96 MHz); N. S. Anderson u. L. P. Delsasso: J. Acoust. Soc. Amer. **24**, 423 (1951) (0,57 MHz); H. D. Parbrock: Acustica **3**, 49 (1953) (0,5 bis 2 MHz).

[3] Das Dispersionsgebiet, das der Schwingungsrelaxation entspricht, liegt beim kritischen Druck weit oberhalb dieses Frequenzbereichs.

[4] J. Noury: C.R. Acad. Sci., Paris **233**, 516 (1951) (0,96 MHz).

[5] W. G. Schneider: J. Chem. Phys. **18**, 1300 (1950); **20**, 795 (1952) (0,6 MHz).

[6] C. M. Herget, s. oben; H. Tanneberger, s. oben; und vor allem V. F. Nozdrew: J. Acad. USSR. **1**, 235 (1955) [Sowj. Phys.-Acoustics **1**, 249 (1957)].

[7] A. G. Chynoweth u. W. G. Schneider: J. Chem. Phys. **20**, 1777 (1952) (0,25 bis 2,25 MHz).

[8] Ganz ähnliches wird beobachtet in Flüssigkeiten bei der kritischen Löslichkeitstemperatur vgl. A. G. Chynoweth u. W. G. Schneider: J. Chem. Phys. **19**, 1566 (1951) und M. Cevolani u. S. Petralia: Nuovo Cim. (X) **2**, 495 (1955).

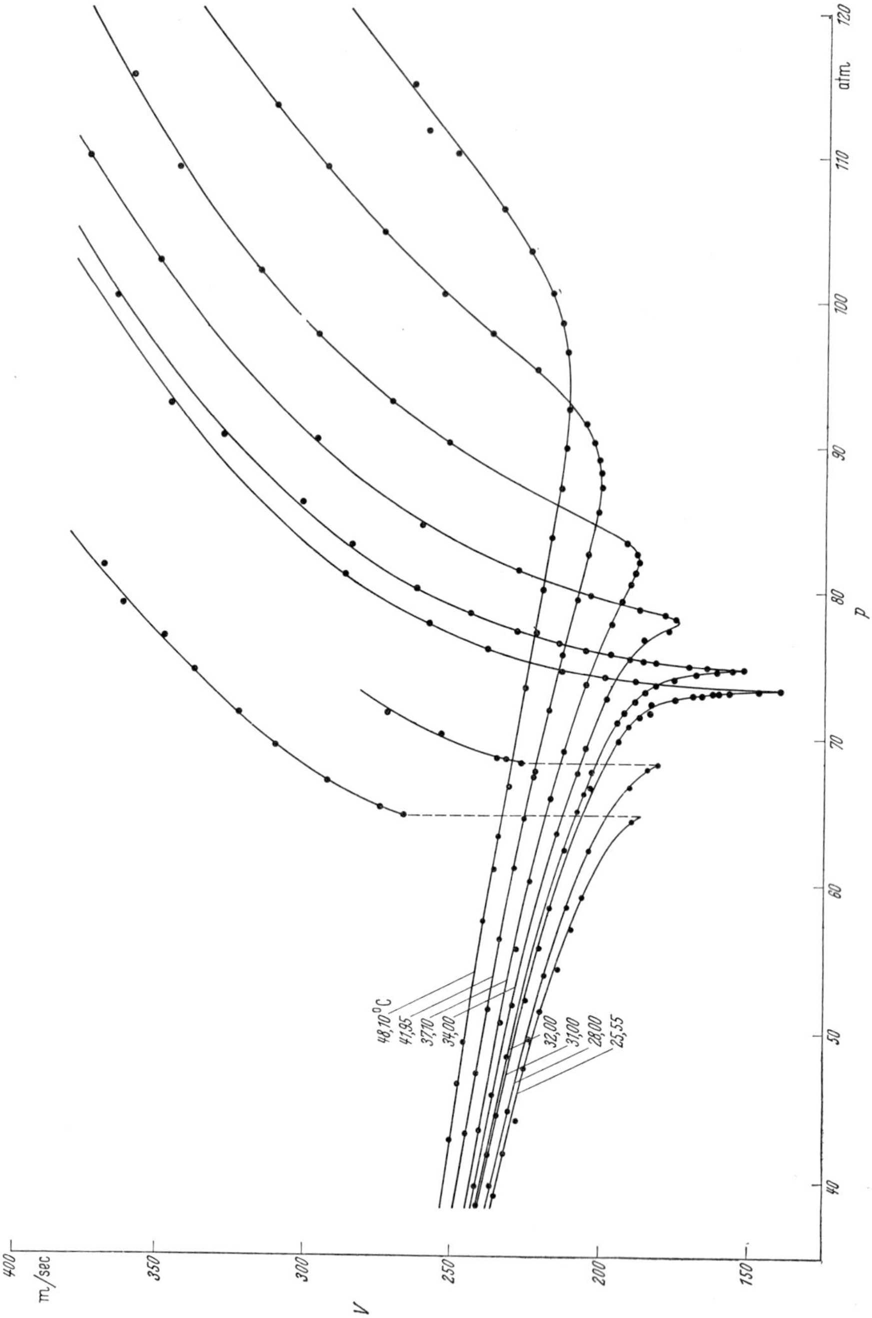

Fig. 22. Schallgeschwindigkeit in CO_2 als Funktion des Druckes bei konstanter Temperatur.

0,27 und wieder zurück springt (bei 0,6 MHz), und in Äthan (von 0,012 auf 0,6; bei 0,3 und 0,9 MHz)[1]. Über die Abhängigkeit des Absorptionsindex von der Frequenz ist bisher nichts bekannt.

---

[1] H. TANNEBERGER: Z. Physik **153**, 445 (1959).

Da weder die Viscosität am kritischen Punkt ein anormales Verhalten zeigt[1], noch auch eine eventuelle Streuung an den sich doch bildenden Atom- oder Molekülschwärmen zur Deutung der extrem hohen Absorptionsspitzen ausreicht[2], so können die Beobachtungen kaum anders als durch einen Relaxationsvorgang erklärt werden. Folgende Deutung[2] erscheint plausibel: Im kritischen Zustand bilden sich bekanntlich — erkennbar an der Opaleszenz — Schwärme von locker, durch Van der Waals-Kräfte zusammengehaltenen Molekülen. Ihre mittlere Anzahl und Größe, die die Größenordnung 10^{-3} cm erreichen mag, hängt sehr stark von der Dichte ab. Bei einer noch so kleinen Verdichtung, wie sie etwa in der Schallwelle auftritt, müssen sich also sehr erhebliche Umlagerungen in den

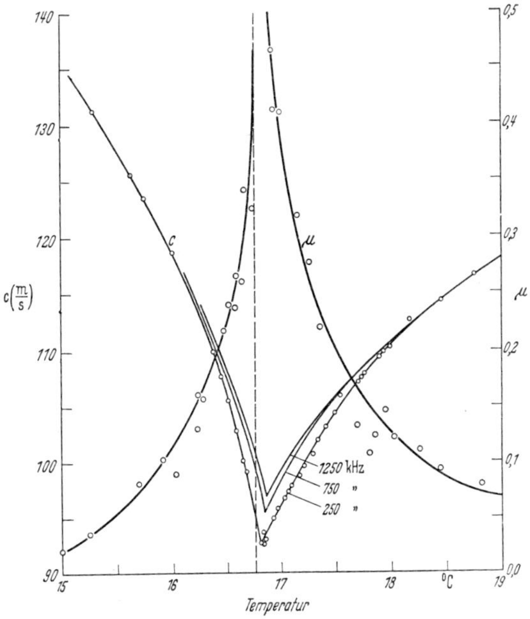

Fig. 23. Schallgeschwindigkeit in Xenon als Funktion der Temperatur bei 0,25, 0,75 und 1,25 MHz. Meßpunkte der Deutlichkeit wegen nur für 0,25 MHz eingetragen.

Schwärmen vollziehen, ehe das Gleichgewicht und damit der endgültige Druck sich einstellt. Das bedeutet Phasenverschiebung zwischen Druck und Verdichtung und somit Schallabsorption und -dispersion (vgl. Ziff. 3). Allerdings darf man kaum erwarten, daß sich der Vorgang mit *einer* wohldefinierten Relaxationszeit abspielt, sondern man wird ein breites Relaxationszeitspektrum (und demnach breites Absorptions- und Dispersionsgebiet) annehmen müssen, das sich mit Annäherung an den kritischen Punkt immer stärker nach längeren Relaxationszeiten (tieferen Frequenzen) verschiebt und immer mehr verbreitert. Die Dispersionskurven für verschiedene Temperaturen (T_1 bis T_6), die sich der kritischen T_c nähern (gleichgültig, ob von höheren oder niederen Temperaturen kommend), müßten dann den in Fig. 24 skizzierten Verlauf haben. Mißt man nun die Dispersion $\left(\frac{d \log c}{d f}\right)$ im Frequenzbereich *A-B*, so wächst sie bis zum kritischen Punkt monoton an, während sie im Bereich *B-C* einen Maximalwert

[1] S. N. Naldrett u. O. Maass: Canad. J. Res. B **18**, 322 (1940).
[2] A. G. Chynoweth u. W. G. Schneider: J. Chem. Phys. **20**, 1777 (1952), insbesondere S. 1780.

vor T_c überschreitet. Dasselbe gilt für den Absorptionsindex. Danach bleibt allerdings unverständlich, warum in CO_2 zwar eine Absorptionsspitze von ähnlicher Größe wie in Xe auftritt, aber keine meßbare Dispersion[1].

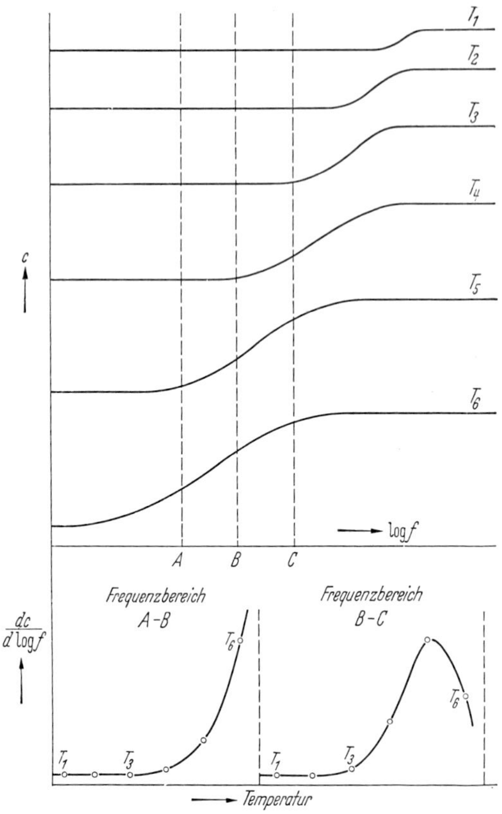

Fig. 24. Hypothetischer Verlauf der Dispersion im kritischen Zustand infolge Relaxation der Schwarmbildung.

43. Schallausbreitung in feuchter Luft und in der freien Atmosphäre. Das technisch besonders wichtige Problem der Schall*absorption* in Luft mit H_2O-Beimengungen wurde erfolgreich zum erstenmal von V. O. KNUDSEN[2] in Angriff genommen mit dem überraschenden Ergebnis, daß im hörbaren Frequenzbereich die Absorptionswerte bis zu 20mal höher lagen, als man auf Grund der klassischen Theorie erwarten sollte. Im Anschluß an diese Arbeit konnte das Phänomen als Relaxation allein des atmosphärischen Sauerstoffs gedeutet werden[3]. Die bahnbre-

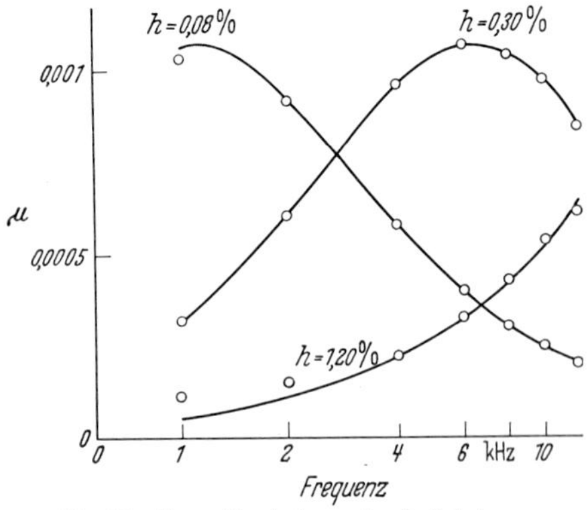

Fig. 25. Absorptionsindex μ der Luft bei verschiedenen Feuchtigkeiten.

chenden Untersuchungen von KNUDSEN wurden erst 23 Jahre später übertroffen durch Messungen die im Hallraum des National Physical Laboratory, Teddington, durchgeführt wurden[4], die eine sonst bisher unerreichte Genauigkeit erzielten und den folgenden Ausführungen im wesentlichen zugrunde liegen.

Die physikalische Interpretation ist in diesem Fall besonders schwierig, weil mindestens drei verschiedene Partner am Relaxationsvorgang beteiligt sind.

Der Absorptionsindex μ ist bis hinauf zu Frequenzen von etwa 10 kHz überwiegend durch die Relaxations-Absorption bestimmt und zeigt die für den ein-

[1] Mathematisch unterbauen lassen sich diese Vorstellungen durch Einführung eines komplexen, dichteabhängigen „Stokes-Koeffizienten" nach dem Vorgang von L. TISZA, Phys. Rev. **61**, 531 (1942). Danach läßt sich das Auftreten des steilen Absorptionsmaximums formal erklären, das allerdings notwendig von Dispersion begleitet sein müßte; vgl. L. GALATRY u. J. NOURY: J. Phys. Radium **17**, 375 (1956).

[2] V. O. KNUDSEN: J. Acoust. Soc. Amer. **5**, 112 (1933).

[3] H. O. KNESER: J. Acoust. Soc. Amer. **5**, 122 (1933).

[4] E. J. EVANS u. E. N. BAZLEY: Acustica **6**, 238 (1956). Die Methode der Schallabklingung in Hallräumen, die groß gegen die Wellenlänge sind, erweist sich als besonders günstig. Sie dürfte jedoch auf andere Gase als Luft kaum anwendbar sein.

fachen Relaxationstyp zu erwartende „glockenförmige" Frequenzabhängigkeit mit $\mu_m = 1{,}1 \cdot 10^{-3}$ (Fig. 25; man beachte die Unterschrift). Für Sauerstoff ergibt sich mit $\Theta = 2235^\circ$ K (vgl. Fig. 14) $\mu_m = 5{,}6 \cdot 10^{-3}$, was für Luft gerade auf den obigen Wert führt. Die Frequenz maximaler Absorption wird mit zunehmendem H_2O-Gehalt außerordentlich stark erhöht, und zwar wiederum deutlich nichtlinear (vgl. Ziff. 40, Fig. 20). Die daraus zu berechnende Abhängigkeit der Relaxationszeit τ von der Feuchte $\left(h = 100 \cdot \frac{\text{Partialdruck des Wasserdampfes}}{\text{Gesamtdruck}}\right)$ läßt sich mit sehr guter Näherung darstellen durch

$$1/\tau = 1{,}92 \cdot h^{1{,}30} \cdot 10^5\,[\sec^{-1}], \qquad (43.1)$$

was sich physikalisch bisher nicht interpretieren läßt; jedoch geht daraus mit Sicherheit hervor, daß nicht allein Zweierstöße für die Umwandlung von Schwingungs- in Translationsenergie verantwortlich zu machen sind. Geht man mit den empirischen Werten der Formel (43.1) für (h) in die Formel (13.10) ein, so ergeben sich für den Absorptionskoeffizienten in Abhängigkeit von Frequenz und Feuchte die in Fig. 26 ausgezogenen Kurven. Die zahllosen im Hallraum durchgeführten Messungen[1] stimmen mit diesen Kurven durchweg besser als $\pm 5\%$ überein! Der „klassische" Absorptionskoeffizient[2] beträgt:

$$\alpha_{kl} \approx (11{,}7 + 0{,}1t)\, f^2 \cdot 10^{-12}\,[\mathrm{m}^{-1}] \qquad (43.2)$$

(f = Frequenz in Hz; t = Temperatur in °C) und ist daher selbst bei 12 kHz ($\alpha \approx 0{,}005$ [m^{-1}]) unwesentlich[3]. Eine systematische Abweichung nach höheren Werten — angedeutet durch die gestrichelten Kurvenstücke — zeigen die Messungen nur bei den 1 und 2 kHz-Kurven und hohem Wasserdampfgehalt ($h > 0{,}7\%$; entsprechend etwa 30% relative Feuchte[4]).

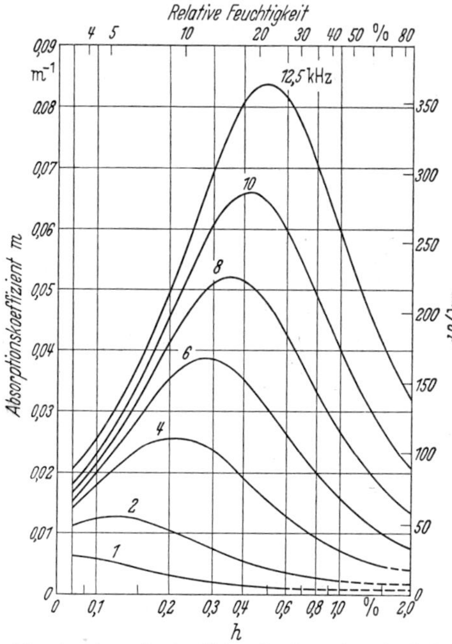

Fig. 26. Absorptionskoeffizient der Intensität der Luft in Abhängigkeit von der Feuchte.

Für Ultraschallfrequenzen ist der Verlauf der Absorption in feuchter Luft wesentlich weniger genau gemessen worden[5] und zeigt den quadratischen Anstieg mit der Frequenz, wie er nach der — dort prädominierenden — klassischen Absorptionsformel (43.2) zu erwarten ist.

Man kann demnach behaupten, daß der Absorptionskoeffizient bei Atmosphärendruck für alle Frequenzen (abgesehen von den extrem hohen, bei denen Rotationsrelaxation bemerkbar wird) sich additiv aus zwei Anteilen zusammensetzt: dem klassischen und dem von der Schwingungsrelaxation des Sauerstoffs herrührenden. Mit einer für technische Zwecke ausreichenden Genauigkeit läßt

[1] S. Fußnote 4, p. 192.

[2] Auf die Amplituden bezogen, wie in diesem ganzen Artikel.

[3] Auch wenn man eine vielleicht nicht unerhebliche Abhängigkeit der Viskosität der Luft von der Feuchte in Betracht zieht. W. Paeschke: Phys. Z. **36**, 564 (1935).

[4] Die vielleicht vorhandene Relaxationsabsorption des Stickstoffs reicht nicht aus, um die Diskrepanz zu deuten.

[5] L. G. Sivian: J. Acoust. Soc. Amer. **19**, 914 (1947).

sich daher der Absorptionskoeffizient feuchter Luft und Temperaturen (t) zwischen 0 und $+30°$ C bei Atmosphärendruck durch folgende Formel darstellen

$$m = (11{,}7 + 0{,}1\,t)\,f^2 \cdot 10^{-12} + \frac{(0{,}81 + 0{,}022\,t) \cdot 10^{-5} \cdot 2\pi\tau f^2}{1 + 4\pi^2\tau^2 f^2}, \tag{43.3}$$

wobei τ nach (43.1) zu berechnen ist[1].

Messungen der *Schallgeschwindigkeit* in Luft sind sehr häufig und mit großer Sorgfalt durchgeführt. Für die Schallgeschwindigkeit ($c(0)$) unter Normalbedingungen, d.h. für trockne, CO_2-freie Luft bei 0° C und 760 Torr, ergeben sich Werte zwischen 331,4 und 331,6 m/sec. Die Ursache für diese verhältnismäßig starke Streuung ist vorwiegend in der Dispersion zu suchen, die durch die Schwingungsrelaxation des O_2 mit seiner stark variablen Relaxationszeit herrührt (vgl. Ziff. 40)[2]. Unter Berücksichtigung der besten Messungen und nach Korrektur aller denkbaren Fehlerquellen[3] ergibt sich für die Schallgeschwindigkeit in Luft unter Normalbedingungen

$$c(0) = (331{,}45 \pm 0{,}05)\ \text{m/sec.}$$

Dieser Wert ist als unterer Grenzwert in ausgezeichneter Übereinstimmung mit den aus den Stoffkonstanten der Luft berechneten Wert anzusehen ($\omega\tau_{\text{Osz}} \ll 1$)[4]. Für hohe Frequenzen kann er bis 331,57 m/sec ansteigen.

Wäre Luft ein ideales Gas und ihre spezifischen Wärmen temperatur- und frequenzunabhängig, so würde die Schallgeschwindigkeit vom Druck gar nicht abhängen und von der Temperatur gemäß:

$$c_{\text{id}}(t) = c(0) \cdot \sqrt{1 + t/273{,}13}\,. \tag{43.4}$$

Die Abweichungen von diesem Idealverhalten seien durch einen Korrektionsfaktor x gekennzeichnet, definiert durch:

$$c = c_{\text{id}}(1 + x)\,. \tag{43.5}$$

Aus (16.10) und Tabelle 2 geht hervor, daß die klassischen Dispersionseinflüsse bei Atmosphärendruck praktisch nichts zu x beitragen ($x \approx 3 \cdot 10^{-19} \cdot f$). Viel größer ist der Einfluß der Abweichungen vom idealen Gaszustand und der Temperatur- und eventuellen Frequenzabhängigkeit der spezifischen Wärmen. Er ist *berechnet* worden[5] unter der Annahme, daß die Luft sich aus 78,09 (Volumen-)% N_2, 20,95% O_2, 0,93 % Ar und 0,03% CO_2 zusammensetzt, und zwar einmal für den Fall, daß die Frequenz weit unterhalb aller vorkommenden Relaxationsfrequenzen liegt, also mit den statischen Werten der spezifischen Wärmen (Fig. 27a) und einmal für den Fall, daß die Frequenz weit oberhalb aller Schwingungs-, aber unterhalb aller Rotations-Relaxationsfrequenzen liegt, also unter Weglassung aller Schwingungswärmen (Fig. 27b). Welcher von beiden Fällen vorliegt, wird weitgehend vom Feuchtigkeitsgehalt abhängen und an der Größe der Absorption zu erkennen sein.

[1] Eine für praktische Zwecke meist ausreichende Tabelle zur Berechnung der Schallabsorption in geschlossenen Räumen findet man bei R. W. YOUNG, J. Acoust. Soc. Amer. **29**, 311 (1957).

[2] H. O. KNESER: Ann. Phys. **34**, 665 (1939).

[3] Vgl. H. C. HARDY, D. TELFAIR u. W. H. PIELEMEYER: J. Acoust. Soc. Amer. **13**, 226 (1942). — Neuere Messungen bei tiefen Temperaturen und bis 20 atm bei A. VAN ITTERBECK u. W. DE ROSS, Appl. Sci. Res. A **6**, 21 (1956).

[4] Die Bedingung dürfte bei ganz trockner Luft nur mit extrem tiefen Meßfrequenzen zu erfüllen sein (vgl. S. 183, Fußnote 7).

[5] P. W. SMITH jr., Computation of the Velocity of Sound in Gases. Techn. Mem. 29, Ac. Res. Lab., Harvard University.

Messungen in der freien Atmosphäre werden naturgemäß stark durch räumliche und zeitliche Inkonstanz der Temperatur, des Druckes und der Zusammensetzung der Atmosphäre beeinflußt. Allein die letzteren können bereits Schwankungen der Schallgeschwindigkeit um 0,05 m/sec bewirken. Dazu kommt der Einfluß des Windes, der in jüngster Zeit genauer studiert worden ist[1].

Großräumige Inhomogenitäten der Temperatur bewirken natürlich Brechung der Schallwellen. Durch Inversionsschichten entstehen in der weiteren Umgebung der Schallquelle „Zonen des Schweigens"[2] und nachweisbare Echos sogar in unmittelbarer Nähe[3].

Übrigens tritt bei einer vertikal nach oben, d.h. entlang einem exponentiellen Druckgefälle verlaufenden ebenen Schallwelle ein weiterer „klassischer" Effekt auf, weil — bei konstant bleibender Energie — die Schallschnelle mit abnehmendem Druck anwachsen muß und dann nicht mehr als klein im Sinne von Ziff. 8 betrachtet werden darf[4]. Die daraus resultierende Dispersion beträgt:

$$c = c_0 \cdot \left(1 + \frac{1}{32\pi^2} \cdot \frac{\lambda^2}{H}\right), \qquad (43.6)$$

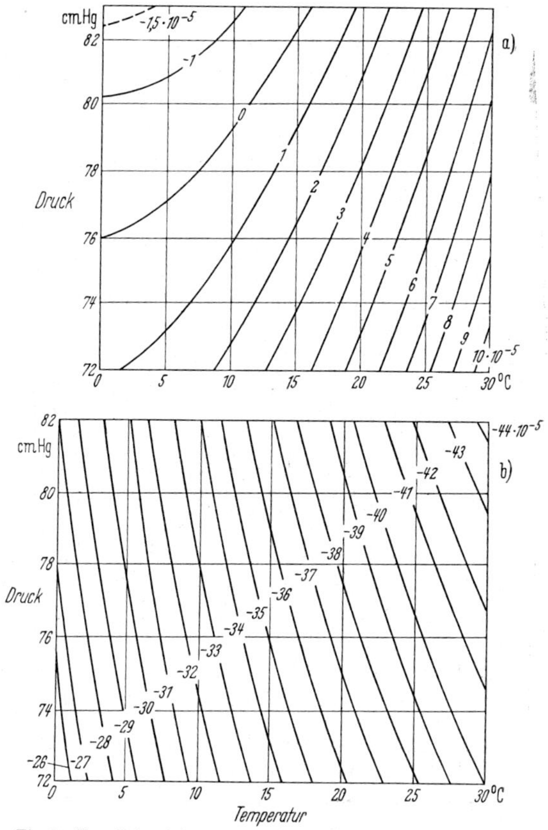

Fig. 27. Korrektionsfaktor zur Berechnung der Schallgeschwindigkeit in Luft für verschiedene Drucke und Temperaturen. (Nach P. W. SMITH.)

wobei H die virtuelle Höhe der isotherm angenommenen Atmosphäre (≈ 8 km) und λ die Wellenlänge bedeutet. Danach wächst die Schallgeschwindigkeit mit abnehmender Frequenz; allerdings um unmeßbar kleine Beträge.

F. Theorie der Relaxationszeiten.

44. Allgemeines und Qualitatives über die Größe Z. Die klassische Theorie der Schallausbreitung, wie sie von LAPLACE, STOKES und KIRCHHOFF entwickelt wurde, beschreibt alle Eigenschaften elastischer Wellen im unbegrenzten Gasraum in völliger Übereinstimmung mit dem Experiment, sofern keine „molekularen" Relaxationseffekte auftreten. Unter dieser Bedingung sind von ihr — abgesehen

[1] P. ROTHWELL: J. Acoust. Soc. Amer. **19**, 205 (1947); **28**, 656 (1957).

[2] F. RITTER: Z. techn. Phys. **7**, 182 (1926). — H. HERGESELL u. P. DUCKERT: Preuß. Aeronaut. Obs. Lindenberg 16 D, 1930. — E. F. COX, B. L. ATANASOFT, H. SNAVELY, D.W. BEECHER u. J. BROWN: J. Meteorology **6**, 303 (1949). — P. ROTHWELL: l. c.

[3] G. W. GILMAN, H. B. COXHEAD u. F. H. WILLIS: J. Acoust. Soc. Amer. **18**, 247 (1946).

[4] E. SCHRÖDINGER: Phys. Z., **18**, 445 (1917) und H. LAMB: Hydrodynamics. Cambridge 1932.

von den Verhältnissen bei extrem geringen Drucken — keine wesentlich neuen Erkenntnisse oder Daten zu erwarten.

Anders in Gasen mit Relaxation, d.h. praktisch in allen mehr als einatomigen Gasen. Hier tritt als neue, sonst kaum zugängliche Eigenschaft die Relaxationszeit auf[1]. Das Verhältnis Relaxationszeit zu mittlere Stoßzeit gibt die Zahl (Z) der Zusammenstöße an, die ein angeregtes Molekül — genauer: ein Quantum innerer Energie — durchschnittlich übersteht, ehe sich seine Energie in Translationsenergie verwandelt [vgl. Gl. (21.1)]. $1/Z$ ist also die Wahrscheinlichkeit, daß die quantisierte Energie sich bei einem Zusammenstoß in translatorische verwandelt.

Z ist die neue, für die Kenntnis des An- und „Abregungs-"mechanismus interessante Größe, die sich aus Schallausbreitungsuntersuchungen ergibt.

Das Problem, Z aus anderen Eigenschaften des Einzelmoleküls abzuleiten, oder das umgekehrte erweist sich als außerordentlich kompliziert. Es kann heute insofern als gelöst gelten, als es möglich ist, die Größenordnung von Z voraus zu berechnen[2]. Diese Rechnungen in vollem Umfang wiederzugeben, ist hier nicht der Ort. Es sollen im folgenden nur einige der grundlegenden Überlegungen umrissen werden, die eine gewisse Systematik in das experimentelle Material hineinbringen.

Wenn beim Zusammenstoß eines Moleküls, das sich in einem angeregten Quantenzustand befindet, mit einem anderen die quantisierte Energie in translatorische verwandelt wird, so muß während der Zeit, in der der Quantensprung erfolgt, die Relativgeschwindigkeit der beiden Stoßpartner sprunghaft anwachsen. Die Wahrscheinlichkeit dieses Vorgangs — also die Größe $1/Z$ — wird um so größer sein je kleiner das Energiequant ist. Ceteris paribus muß Z daher mit wachsendem Energiequant zunehmen. So erklärt sich qualitativ, daß Z_{Rot} immer viel kleiner ist als Z_{Osz}. Auch der niedrige Wert von Z für die „Elektronenwärme" des NO (vgl. Ziff. 35) ist hiermit in Einklang.

45. Grundzüge der Theorie des Energieaustausches zwischen Rotations- und Translationsfreiheitsgraden. Zur Berechnung von Z_{Rot} bedarf es eines mathematisch zu behandelnden „Modells" für den Vorgang des Molekülzusammenstoßes, das den wirklichen Verhältnissen einigermaßen entspricht; insbesondere also eines Potentialansatzes. Hieraus muß ein Ausdruck $P_{mm'}(w, w')$ entwickelt werden, der die Wahrscheinlichkeit eines Übergangs zwischen den Rotationsniveaus m und m' angibt, als Funktion der Relativgeschwindigkeiten vor und nach einem Zusammenstoß (w bzw. w'), welche durch den Energiesatz verknüpft sind. $P_{mm'}(w, w')$ ist dann über die Geschwindigkeitsverteilung der Moleküle zu mitteln. So ergibt sich die Wahrscheinlichkeit $\mathfrak{P}_{mm'}$ der Umwandlung von Rotationsenergie des Übergangs $m - m'$ in Translationsenergie für das Gas, und daraus

$$Z_{\mathrm{Rot}} = (\mathfrak{P}_{mm'} + \mathfrak{P}_{m'm})^{-1} \tag{45.1}$$

[analog zu Gl. (22.7)].

Bei der quantenmechanischen Behandlung[3] wird das Potential mit

$$V(x, \varphi) = V_0 \, e^{-x/a} \, \mathfrak{Cof}\,(b \cos \varphi) \tag{45.2}$$

[1] In Flüssigkeiten und Festkörpern gewinnt man aus Relaxationsuntersuchungen darüber hinaus Kenntnisse über die Aufteilung der Molwärme, über Umlagerung von Gitterbausteinen u.a.m.

[2] Die wichtigsten der einschlägigen theoretischen Arbeiten sind unter Führung oder Mitwirkung von K. F. Herzfeld entstanden und von ihm zusammenfassend dargestellt; vgl. S. 129, Fußnote 1, Nr. 9.

[3] Vgl. J. C. Beckerle: J. Chem. Phys. **21**, 2034 (1951); dort findet man auch eine Übersicht über ältere theoretische Arbeiten.

angenommen (x = Abstand der Stoßpartner, φ = Winkel der Achse des einen gegen die Verbindungslinie), dessen Konstanten durch Anpassung an den Potentialansatz von LENNARD-JONES (vgl. Ziff. 46) bestimmt werden. Einsetzen von $V(x, \varphi)$ in die — eindimensionale — Schrödinger-Gleichung führt dann nach ziemlich umfangreichen Rechenoperationen zur Berechnung von $\mathfrak{P}_{mm'}$. Daraus ergeben sich Z-Werte, die auf den in Ziff. 34 angegebenen experimentellen hinsichtlich der Temperaturabhängigkeit und in der Größenordnung übereinstimmen[1].

46. Grundzüge des Energieaustauschs zwischen Schwingungs- und Translationsfreiheitsgraden. Wird ein schwingendes System, z. B. ein mit einem Schwingungsquant behaftetes Molekül einer Störung ausgesetzt, die „adiabatisch", d. h. im Vergleich zur Schwingung langsam verläuft, so ändert sich sein Quantenzustand nicht[2]. Ein Maß für die Adiabasie ist offenbar das Verhältnis der Zeit, während welcher die Störung andauert, zur Schwingungsdauer $(1/\nu)$ des ungestörten Systems. Setzt man die Dauer der Störung mit l/w an, wobei w die Relativgeschwindigkeit zwischen zwei Stoßpartnern und l eine für die Wirkungssphäre des Moleküls charakteristische Länge bedeutet, so kann man

$$x = \frac{l\nu}{w} \tag{46.1}$$

als Adiabasiefaktor bezeichnen. Je „adiabatischer" nun ein Zusammenstoß verläuft, desto geringer ist die Wahrscheinlichkeit, daß der Schwingungszustand sich ändert. Daher muß $Z = Z_{\text{Osz}}$ (der Index ist fortan entbehrlich) wesentlich durch x bestimmt sein, und zwar mit zunehmendem x anwachsen[3].

Bei nur geringen Abweichungen vom thermischen Gleichgewicht kann man w durch die mittlere Molekulargeschwindigkeit $\overline{w} \approx \sqrt{3\,\mathbf{k}T/m}$ ersetzen und erhält dann:

$$x = \frac{l\nu}{\sqrt{3\,\mathbf{k}T/m'}} = \frac{l}{[l]} \cdot \sqrt{\frac{\Theta}{T}}, \tag{46.2}$$

worin m die (reduzierte) Masse der Stoßpartner $[l] = (2h/\nu m)^{\frac{1}{2}}$ eine für die Molekülschwingung charakteristische Länge bedeutet[4].

---

[1] Weiterentwicklung der Theorie bei K. TAKAYANGI: Proc. Phys. Soc. Lond. **70**, 348 (1957).

[2] Der „Adiabatensatz" wurde von EHRENFEST in die Quantentheorie eingeführt und von L. LANDAU u. E. TELLER auf das vorliegende Problem angewandt [Phys. Z. Sowjet. **10**, 34 (1936)]. Zu den nachstehenden Überlegungen vgl. H. O. KNESER, Propriétés Optiques et Acoustiques des Fluides Comptrimés, Colloques Internationaux du C.N.R.S. Paris 1959.

[3] Auf die fast gleiche Aussage führt eine quantenmechanische Abschätzung: Betrachtet man das schwingende Molekül als ruhend und den anlaufenden Stoßpartner als Materiewelle der Wellenlänge $\lambda = h/mw$, so kann das schwingende Molekül nur dann eine Veränderung erfahren, wenn die Welle an ihm gestreut wird. Ob und wie das geschieht, hängt vom Verhältnis $x' = l/\lambda$ ab. Demnach ist

$$x' = \frac{l\,m\,w}{h} = \frac{l\nu}{w}\,\frac{2E_{\text{kin}}}{h\nu}.$$

Ersetzt man nun $h\nu$ durch $\mathbf{k}\Theta$ [vgl. Gl. (22.4) und Ziff. 33] und E_{kin} durch $\frac{3}{2}\,\mathbf{k}T$, so wird

$$x' = x \cdot \frac{3\,T}{\Theta},$$

wobei $3\,T/\Theta$ in allen praktisch vorkommenden Fällen von der Größenordnung 1 ist (vgl. Ziff. 33).

[4] $[l]$ ist das $\sqrt{6}\,\pi$-fache der Amplitude eines Oszillators der Masse m, der Frequenz ν und der Energie $h\nu$.

Setzt man für l den Bindungsradius[1] ein, so ergeben sich für zweiatomige Gase bei mäßigen Temperaturen für x Werte zwischen 2 und 8, d.h. hier erfolgt der Kontakt überwiegend „adiabatisch". In Fig. 28 sind alle an zweiatomigen Gasen gemessenen Z_{Osz}-Werte in Abhängigkeit von x aufgetragen. Sie lassen sich einer stetigen Kurve zuordnen[2] mit alleiniger Ausnahme des CO, wo die Messungen wohl einer Nachprüfung bedürfen, und des NO. Dies Molekül besitzt als einziges ein elektrisches Dipolmoment, dem es vermutlich zuzuschreiben ist, daß die primitive Adiabasieüberlegung hier nicht zutrifft[3].

Nun setzt man die „Abregungswahrscheinlichkeit" Z^{-1} im Einzelfall mit $Z^{-1} = Z_0'^{-1} \cdot e^{-x}$ an[4]. Im statistischen Mittel ist sie aber auch durch die Anzahl der Zusammenstöße und die Verteilung ihrer Relativgeschwindigkeiten mitbestimmt. Berücksichtigt man dies[5], so ergibt sich:

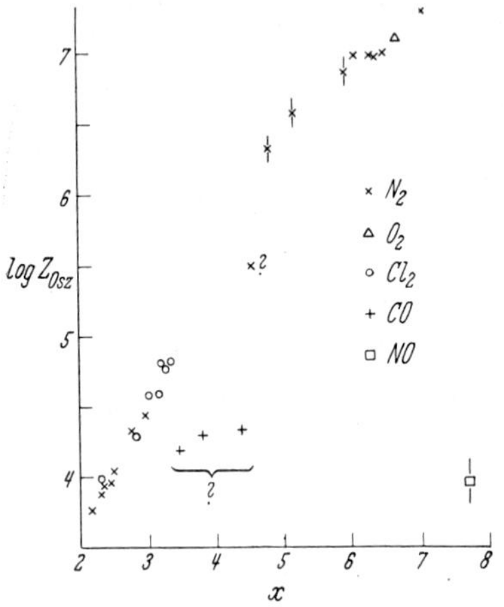

Fig. 28. Z in Abhängigkeit vom Adiabasiefaktor (x) für zweiatomige Gase.

$$Z = a \frac{Z_0'}{x} e^{b x^{\frac{2}{3}}}, \tag{46.3}$$

wobei $a = 2^{-\frac{1}{2}} \pi^{-\frac{4}{3}} \approx 0{,}154$, $b = \frac{3}{2} \cdot (12\pi^2)^{\frac{1}{3}} \approx 7{,}4$. Demnach wächst Z für $x > (\sqrt{12} \cdot \pi)^{-1} \approx 0{,}1$ monoton an; und zwar mit etwa der gleichen Steigung wie die Punktreihe der Fig. 28.

Zur Berechnung des Absolutwertes von Z ist die Kenntnis des Wechselwirkungspotentials (H) erforderlich. Der einfachste Ansatz[6] lautet: $H = H_0 \cdot e^{-X}$, wobei X den Abstand zwischen dem schwingenden und dem „head-on" anlaufenden Stoßpartner bedeutet. Ein nach anderen Erfahrungen besserer Potentialansatz[7], der auch anziehende Kräfte berücksichtigt, lautet:

$$H = -4\varepsilon \left[\left(\frac{r_0}{r}\right)^6 - \left(\frac{r_0}{r}\right)^{12} \right]. \tag{46.4}$$

Auch mit diesem wurde das Problem durchgerechnet[8] und anschließend auf drei Dimensionen erweitert[9], während alle vorherigen Rechnungen nur eindimensional durchgeführt waren. Das Ergebnis lautet[10]:

$$Z = Z_0 \cdot \mathfrak{M} \cdot Z_{\mathrm{Vibr}} \cdot Z_{\mathrm{Tr}}. \tag{46.5}$$

[1] Der Bindungsradius (covalent radius) ist derart definiert, daß die Summe der Radien den Kernabstand zweier kovalent gebundener Atome angibt. Vgl. L. PAULING: Nature of Physical Bond, S. 164. Ithaka, N.Y.: Cornell-Univ. Press 1948. — H. A. SKINNER: Trans. Faraday Soc. **41**, 645 (1945). l ist nahezu gleich dem halben Kernabstand.

[2] Die Zahlenwerte für N_2, die nur zum kleinen Teil aus Schallmessungen stammen, sind entnommen aus: K. LUKASI u. J. E. YOUNG, J. Chem. Phys. **27**, 1149 (1957).

[3] Auch unter den dreiatomigen Molekülen zeichnet sich das mit einem starken elektrischen Dipolmoment behaftete H_2O durch extrem geringe Werte von Z_{Osz} aus. Es ist auch sehr bezeichnend, daß sich das starke magnetische Moment des O_2 hier nicht bemerkbar macht.

[4] L. LANDAU u. E. TELLER: Zit. in Ziff. 45.

[5] Vgl. hierzu Z. SLAWSKY, R. N. SCHWARTZ u. K. F. HERZFELD: J. Chem. Phys. **20**, 1591 (1952); **22**, 767 (1954). — Die obige Darstellung folgt im wesentlichen derjenigen von H 27 bis 35. Den Beweis für (46.3) findet man bei H 27, Formel 7a und 7b und Fußnote 7.

[6] J. M. JACKSON u. N. F. MOTT: Proc. Roy. Soc. Lond., Ser. A **137**, 703 (1932). Vgl. auch H 28 und 29.

[7] J. E. LENNARD-JONES: Proc. Roy. Soc. Lond., Ser. A **106**, 441 (1924).

[8] Z. SLAWSKY, R. N. SCHWARTZ u. K. F. HERZFELD: J. Chem. Phys. **20**, 1591 (1952) und H 30.

[9] R. N. SCHWARTZ u. K. F. HERZFELD: J. Chem. Phys. **22**, 767 (1954) und H 31; ferner T. TAGAYANAGI u. T. KISHIMOTO: Progr. Theor. Phys. Japan **9**, 578 (1953).

[10] Vgl. die Formeln H 31—2 bis 31—5b und 31—8.

Darin bedeutet:

Z_0 einen Zahlenfaktor, der berücksichtigt, daß nicht — wie bei den Rechnungen angenommen — alle Zusammenstöße „head-on" erfolgen; man kann abschätzen, daß $1 < Z_0 < 10$ ist.

$\mathfrak{M} = 2\frac{M_B M_C (M_A + M_B + M_C)}{M_A (M_B^2 + M_C^2)}$, wobei M_B und M_C die Molekulargewichte der beiden Teile des schwingenden (Hantel-)Moleküls und M_A dasjenige des anderen Stoßpartners bezeichnen.

$$Z_{\text{Vibr}} = \frac{1}{2\pi^2}\frac{\Theta'}{\Theta}, \text{ wobei } \Theta' = 16\pi^4 \frac{\nu^2}{k}\left(\frac{1}{M_A} + \frac{1}{M_B} + \frac{1}{M_C}\right)^{-1}\left(\frac{r_0}{17{,}5}\right)^2.$$

$$Z_{\text{Tr}} = \pi^2 \sqrt{\frac{3}{3\pi}} \cdot \left(\frac{\Theta}{\Theta'}\right)^2 \left(\frac{T}{\Theta'}\right)^{\frac{1}{6}} \cdot e^{\frac{3}{2}\left(\frac{\Theta}{T}\right)^{\frac{1}{3}} - \frac{\Theta}{2T} - \frac{\varepsilon}{kT}}.$$

r_0 und ε sind durch (46.2) definiert und für die meisten Moleküle bekannt[1]. Man erkennt übrigens leicht, daß Θ'/T bis auf einen Zahlenfaktor mit dem Adiabasiefaktor x [vgl. (46.2)] übereinstimmt, wenn man dort den „Moleküldurchmesser" l durch den im Potentialansatz (46.4) begründeten Abstand r_0 ersetzt und statt m das reduzierte Molekulargewicht einführt.

Die Leistungsfähigkeit der Formel (45.6) — über mehr als vier Größenordnungen von Z! — wird durch die nachstehende Tabelle illustriert; (berechnet mit $Z_0 = 3$).

Tabelle 8[2].

Stoßpartner	r_0 10^{-8} cm	ε/k °K	Θ °K	Θ' °K	T °K	Z berechnet	Z gemessen	$Z_{\text{ber}} : Z_{\text{gem}}$
N_2-N_2	3,70	91,5	3380	4786000	600	$1{,}5 \cdot 10^9$	$2 \cdot 10^7$	75
N_2-H_2	3,20	55,2	3380	618000	600	$5 \cdot 10^3$		
O_2-O_2	3,24	113,2	2260	2424000	288	$1{,}0 \cdot 10^8$	$2{,}5 \cdot 10^7$	4
O_2-H_2	3,03	61,4	2260	236000	288	1100	$2{,}0 \cdot 10^4$	0,05
Cl_2-Cl_2	3,30	357	810	638000	288	$13 \cdot 10^3$	$34 \cdot 10^3$	0,4
Cl_2-He	3,15	46,6	810	34100	288	75	900	0,08
Cl_2-N_2	3,41	181	810	410000	288	$9{,}5 \cdot 10^3$	$43 \cdot 10^3$	0,2

Wenn das schwingende Molekül mehrerer Zustände des gleichen Schwingungstyps fähig ist (klassisch gesprochen: wenn auch Oberschwingungen merklich angeregt sind), so erhebt sich die Frage, ob allen Übergängen die gleiche Relaxationszeit, mit anderen Worten derselbe Z-Wert zukommt. Die Theorie von LANDAU und TELLER[3] bejaht diese Frage, wie zu erwarten, da sie im wesentlichen auf klassisch-mechanischen Überlegungen basiert. Das Experiment scheint dies zu bestätigen, denn auch in den Fällen, wo höhere Schwingungszustände zum Relaxationsbetrag merklich beitragen, lassen sich die Meßergebnisse — wenigstens bei allen dreiatomigen Gasen (vgl. Tabelle 3) — zwanglos mit *einer* Relaxationszeit darstellen.

Die Theorie von HERZFELD, SCHWARTZ und SLAWSKY ist weiter ausgebaut worden[4], besonders im Hinblick auf die chlorierten Methane. Sie führt dort auf

[1] Sie lassen sich aus der Temperaturabhängigkeit der Konstanten der inneren Reibung und der Diffusion der Gase und Gasmischungen erschließen; vgl. J. O. HIRSCHFELDER, C. F. CURTISS u. R. B. BIRD: Molecular Theory of Gases and Liquids. New York: Wiley 1954.

[2] Entnommen aus H 31, S. 719.

[3] Zit. in Ziff. 45. Allgemeiner behandelt von R. BROUT: J. Chem. Phys. **22**, 1500 (1954).

[4] F. L. TANCZOS: J. Chem. Phys. **25**, 439 (1956).

zwei stark verschiedene Relaxationszeiten, wie sie für CH_2Cl_2 tatsächlich beobachtet wurden (vgl. Ziff. 39).

Die hier umrissenen Überlegungen nehmen an, daß der Austausch zwischen Schwingung und Translation direkt, ohne Mitwirkung der Rotationsfreiheitsgrade abläuft. Diese Annahme wird gestützt durch die Beobachtung, daß Z für CO_2—H_2O und CO_2—D_2O praktisch den gleichen Wert hat[1], obwohl H_2O und D_2O sehr verschiedene Trägheitsmomente (aber fast gleiche Massen) besitzen[2].

47. Schwingungsan- und -abregung zwischen chemisch affinen Partnern. Bereits in Ziff. 40 wurde an Hand der Z-Werte, die sich in Gasmischungen herausgestellt haben, darauf hingewiesen, daß diese auffallend gering sind, wenn dem Grundgas andere Gase beigemischt werden, die im Prinzip mit jenem reagieren können; und zwar auch dann, wenn eine solche Reaktion unter den Versuchsbedingungen überhaupt nicht nachweisbar eintritt. Demnach ist die Wahrscheinlichkeit, daß quantisierte Schwingungsenergie in Translationsenergie verwandelt wird, in denjenigen Fällen besonders groß, wo ein schwingendes Molekül mit einem ihm chemisch „affinen" zusammenstößt[3], wo also chemische Valenzkräfte merklich mitwirken.

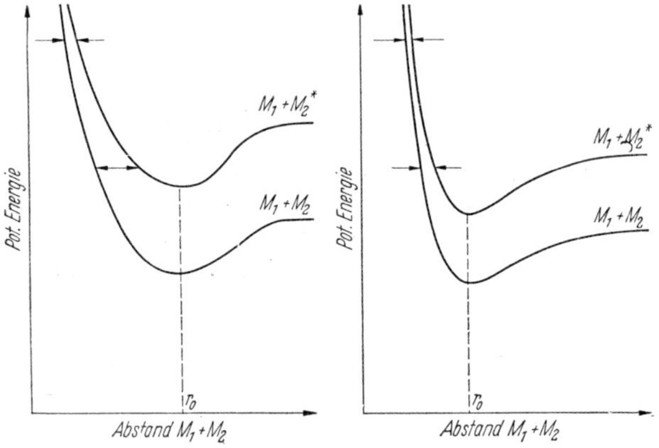

Fig. 29. Potentialkurven für zwei Moleküle, zwischen denen nur van der Waals-Kräfte wirken.

Diesem Befund tragen die in Ziff. 45 dargestellten Überlegungen offenbar nicht in vollem Umfang Rechnung. Das mag daher rühren, daß die Konstanten des dort benützten Potentialansatzes (46.4) abgeleitet sind aus Vorgängen, die sich mehr in der Peripherie des Moleküls abspielen[4], während sich beim Zusammenstoß chemisch affiner Moleküle der Potentialverlauf tiefgreifend ändert.

Dies macht die folgende Überlegung qualitativ verständlich[5]: Die potentielle Energie der beiden Stoßpartner (M_1 und M_2) als Funktion ihres Abstandes (r) dargestellt, zeigt — falls sie nicht miteinander reagieren können — ein durch Van der Waalssche Kräfte bedingtes flaches Minimum im Abstand r_0 (Fig. 29). Wenn ein Partner (M^*) mit einem Schwingungsquant der Energie W behaftet ist, so gilt für die Gesamtenergie des ganzen Systems, vermindert um die relative kinetische Energie, eine um W nach oben verschobene Kurve, vermutlich von fast gleicher Gestalt mit etwa gleichem r_0. Ein strahlungsloser Übergang von der oberen auf die untere Kurve, d. h. Verwandlung des Quantes in Translationsenergie wird dargestellt durch den horizontalen Doppelpfeil. Ein solcher Übergang findet — dem Franck Condon-Prinzip zufolge — vorzugsweise dann statt, wenn

[1] A. VAN ITTERBEEK u. P. MARIENS: Physica, Haag **7**, 125 (1940) und D. SETTE u. J. C. HUBBARD: J. Acoust. Soc. Amer. **25**, 994 (1954).

[2] Theoretische Überlegungen hierzu bei B. WIDOM u. S. H. BAUER: J. Chem. Phys. **21**, 1670 (1953) und Z. DE WETTE u. Z. SLAWSKY: Physica, Haag **20**, 1169 (1954).

[3] Dieser Gedanke wurde zuerst von J. FRANCK u. A. EUCKEN ausgesprochen [Z. phys. Chem. Abt. B **20**, 460 (1933)]; später von A. EUCKEN näher ausgeführt; vgl. insbesondere A. EUCKEN u. L. KÜCHLER: Z. techn. Phys. **19**, 517 (1938).

[4] Nämlich Viskosität und Diffusion, vgl. S. 199, Fußnote 1.

[5] A. EUCKEN u. L. KÜCHLER: l. c.

sich dabei r nur wenig zu ändern braucht, d.h. im linken Teil der Kurven, der nur erreicht wird, wenn der Zusammenstoß mit erheblicher kinetischer Energie (E_k) erfolgt, also bei hoher Temperatur. Z' (vgl. Ziff. 40) muß also mit steigender Temperatur abnehmen und zwar stark, wenn der linke Teil der Potentialkurven flach verläuft, und schwach, wenn er steil ansteigt.

Während also r_0 ein Maß für die Eindringtiefe des Fremdmoleküls und damit für den Absolutwert von Z' darstellt[1], wird dessen Temperaturkoeffizient nur durch den Verlauf der Potentialkurve bei kleinem r bestimmt. Für einen tief eindringenden Stoßpartner wird die Potentialkurve steil ansteigen, d.h. kleine Z'-Werte werden im allgemeinen einen geringen Temperaturkoeffizient zeigen. Dadurch wird in der Tat das Verhalten der Zusatzgase He (verglichen mit Ar) und H_2 (verglichen mit D_2) richtig charakterisiert. Im letzteren Fall bewirkt die um den Faktor $1/\sqrt{2}$ kleinere Molekulargeschwindigkeit einen etwas größeren Z'-Wert (vgl. Ziff. 40, Tabelle 7).

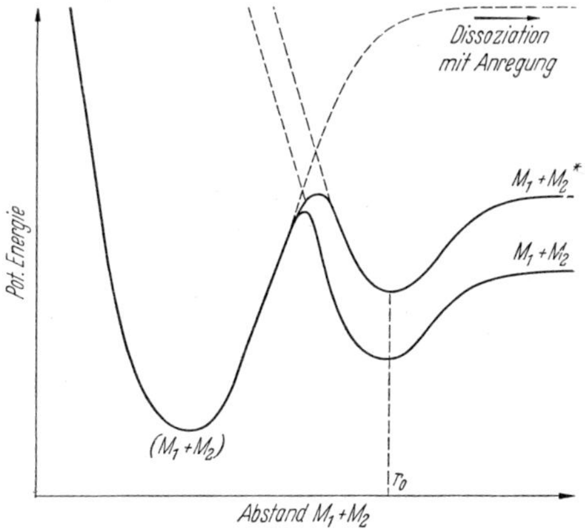

Fig. 30. Potentialkurven für zwei Moleküle, die eine chemische Bindung eingehen können.

Molekülpaare, die chemisch reagieren könnten, zeigen, wie gesagt, auffallend kleine Z'-Werte. Auch diese „chemische" Wirkung findet eine Deutung im Bilde der Potentialkurven. Sie müssen bei solchen Stoßpaaren außer der van der Waalsschen eine tiefe, der vollzogenen Reaktion entsprechende Mulde bei kleinerem r zeigen (Fig. 30). Man kann sie sich entstanden denken aus der Überlagerung einer Kurve vom Typ der Fig. 29 mit einer anderen, deren Asymptote aber wesentlich höher liegt, da die Dissoziation mindestens *ein* angeregtes Produkt liefern wird. Bestimmend für einen Zusammenstoß, bei dem die Reaktion noch nicht eintritt, ist aber der Verlauf der Kurve gerade im Überschneidungsgebiet. Gewisse Überlegungen[2] sprechen dafür, daß gerade hier die für den Zusammenstoß eines schwingenden mit einem Fremdmolekül gültige Potentialkurve flacher verläuft, so daß sich die beiden Kurven — mit und ohne Schwingungsenergie — stark annähern, ja vielleicht überschneiden. Der Übergang von der ersteren auf die letztere, d.h. die Umwandlung des Schwingungsquantes in Translationsenergie würde dann durch das tiefe Potentialminimum erleichtert, selbst wenn dieses beim Zusammenstoß gar nicht erreicht wird.

[1] Tiefes Eindringen bedingt lange Dauer des Zusammenstoßes, und damit wahrscheinlich eine große Chance für die Störung der Schwingung, d.h. kleines Z bzw. Z'.

[2] A. EUCKEN u. L. KÜCHLER: l.c.

Schallabsorption und -dispersion in wäßrigen Elektrolytlösungen.

Von

KONRAD TAMM.

Mit 35 Figuren.

A. Einleitung.

1. Relaxationsvorgänge in Elektrolytlösungen. Es ist aus vielen Messungen bekannt (s. Zusammenstellung bei SETTE [1]), daß die Schallabsorption in Seewasser (Fig. 1) und in vielen anderen wäßrigen Elektrolytlösungen von der in

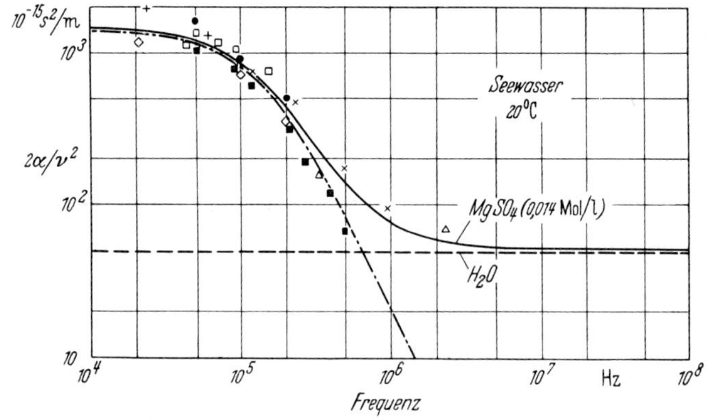

Fig. 1. Schallabsorption ($2\alpha/\nu^2$) in Seewasser in Abhängigkeit von der Frequenz im Vergleich zu der einer 0,014 molaren $MgSO_4$-Lösung. Zusammenstellung der veröffentlichten Meßwerte nach TAMM [17]. ◇ EVEREST, O'NEIL (1946); + Univ. of California (1949); △ THIESSEN, LESLIE, SIMPSON (1948); × LIEBERMANN (1948); □ LEONARD (nat.) (1949); ■ LEONARD (synth.) (1949); ● TAMM (synth.) (1950).

reinem Wasser erheblich mehr abweicht, als durch den Einfluß der Elektrolyt-Ionen auf die Struktur des Lösungsmittels erklärt werden kann[1]. Dieser Einfluß auf die Wasserstruktur besteht darin, daß eine der Strukturformen des Wassers — nach EUCKEN [2] bestimmte Wassermolekül-Aggregate — bei Anwesenheit

[1] Die Schallabsorption des reinen Wassers ist, wie für eine frequenzunabhängige Viscosität zu erwarten, dem Quadrat der Frequenz ν proportional. Ihr Absolutwert $\alpha/\nu^2 = 25 \cdot 10^{-17}\,\mathrm{sec}^2\,\mathrm{cm}^{-1}$, der recht genau gemessen ist, ist jedoch, wie bei den meisten Flüssigkeiten, größer (und zwar um den Faktor 3) als der sich aus der Schubviskosität ergebende Wert. Die Ursache dieser Überschußabsorption ist eine Strukturrelaxation, die nach EUCKEN [2] wie auch HALL [3] in der verzögerten Einstellung des Gleichgewichtes zweier oder mehrerer Strukturformen des Wassers (Kugelpackung und Aggregate bzw. Eisstruktur) besteht. GIERER und WIRTZ [4] vermuten Platzwechselvorgänge als Relaxationsursache. Aufschlüsse über die Art der Strukturänderung und über die zugehörigen Energie-Unterschiede liefern Messungen der Temperatur- und der Druckabhängigkeit von Schallgeschwindigkeit und Absorption, wie sie von FOX und ROCK [5] und von PINKERTON [6] bzw. von LITOVITZ [7] durchgeführt wurden.

von Ionen abgebaut wird. Damit wird das Gleichgewicht zwischen den verschiedenen Strukturformen so verschoben, daß die Schallabsorption des Wassers sich etwas vermindert. Es läßt sich zeigen, daß dieser „Lösungsmittel-Effekt" des Wassers bei den erreichbaren Elektrolytkonzentrationen verhältnismäßig klein ist. Er muß aber grundsätzlich bei allen Elektrolytlösungen auftreten.

Die erwähnte außerordentlich große Absorption in wäßrigen Lösungen einiger Elektrolyte überdeckt den Einfluß auf das Lösungsmittel. Sie ist auf Relaxationserscheinungen zurückzuführen, die auf der Wechselwirkung der Elektrolyt-Ionen untereinander und mit dem Lösungsmittel beruhen. Die Wechselwirkung zwischen den Ionen äußert sich einerseits in der Bildung der Ionenwolken, andererseits in Reaktionen zwischen Ionen entgegengesetzter Polarität, z.B. in der Bildung von undissoziierten Molekülen bzw. Komplexen oder anderen Reaktionsprodukten. Bei diesen Reaktionen ist das Wasser nicht nur als Lösungsmittel beteiligt, sondern unter Umständen nehmen auch Wassermoleküle bzw. Protonen und Hydroxyl-Ionen an den Reaktionen teil. Eine weitere Wechselwirkung der Ionen mit dem unveränderten Lösungsmittel besteht in der Bildung von Hydrathüllen um die Ionen.

Bei allen diesen Vorgängen bzw. Reaktionen erfolgt die Einstellung des Gleichgewichtes zwischen Bildung und Zerfall mit einer endlichen Geschwindigkeit bzw. mit endlicher Zeitkonstante. Damit ist — wie EINSTEIN [*8*] es zuerst für chemische Reaktionen in Gasen gezeigt hat — die Voraussetzung für eine Relaxationsabsorption gegeben, wenn außerdem die Gleichgewichtsverteilung selbst mit den Schallfeldgrößen Druck und Temperatur schwankt, denn nur dann macht sich die verzögerte Gleichgewichtseinstellung bemerkbar. Wegen der nahezu isothermen Schallausbreitung in wäßrigen Lösungen ist bei diesen — im Gegensatz zu anderen Flüssigkeiten — die Druckabhängigkeit des Gleichgewichts allein maßgebend, während seine Temperaturabhängigkeit keinen Beitrag liefert [1].

Grundsätzlich treten alle genannten Relaxationsvorgänge in wäßrigen Elektrolytlösungen gleichzeitig auf, wenn die Voraussetzungen für sie gegeben sind. Ihr Beitrag zur Gesamtabsorption ist jedoch verschieden und hängt von der Art des Elektrolyten und von seiner Konzentration, sowie von der Meßfrequenz ab.

2. Historisches. Absorptionsmessungen an wäßrigen Lösungen von Elektrolyten wurden zunächst verhältnismäßig unsystematisch und wegen der einfacheren Meßverfahren bei verhältnismäßig hohen Frequenzen (über 1 MHz) durchgeführt. Als einer der Ersten fand BAZULIN [*26*] 1938 eine Relaxationsabsorption bei einem Elektrolyten (Zinkacetat). Häufig wurde seiner Bedeutung wegen Seewasser untersucht, für das auch bald Messungen bei tieferen Frequenzen vorlagen, da hier einfache Ausbreitungsmessungen auch bei tiefen Frequenzen, wie sie von EVEREST und O'NEIL [*9*], THIESSEN, LESLIE und SIMPSON [*10*], LIEBERMANN [*11*] u.a. durchgeführt wurden, möglich waren. Sie wurden später von LEONARD [*13*] in synthetischem Seewasser ergänzt. Dabei stellte sich heraus, daß der konstante Wert der auf das Quadrat der Frequenz bezogenen Absorption (α/ν^2) unterhalb 1 MHz erheblich über den Wert des reinen Wassers ansteigt und dann bei dem etwa 30fachen konstant bleibt. Dies Verhalten führte zuerst LIEBERMANN [*12*] auf einen durch Ionen verursachten Relaxationsprozeß zurück; — er vermutete einen Dissoziationsprozeß der stärksten Komponente des Seewasser-Salzgehaltes, des Kochsalzes. Messungen von LEONARD [*14*] an

[1] Dies gilt für große Verdünnung exakt nur für 4° C; der Beitrag bleibt jedoch auch bei Zimmertemperatur und Konzentrationen < 1 Mol/Liter noch klein.

Magnesiumsulfat entsprechender Konzentration bei tieferen Frequenzen ergeben ähnlich hohe Absorption wie Seewasser und führten LIEBERMANN [12] und LEONARD, COMBS und SKIDMORE [14] zu der Erkenntnis, daß die Seewasserabsorption durch das Magnesiumsulfat verursacht wird. Sie befanden sich damit in Übereinstimmung mit den Ergebnissen von TAMM und KURTZE [17], die aus eigenen Messungen an den Komponenten des Seewassers zu diesem Schluß kamen und außerdem einen Einfluß der Kochsalzkomponente fanden.

Die Feststellung, daß die in Seewasser und Magnesiumsulfat beobachtete Absorption mit der Dissoziation des Magnesiumsulfats zusammenhängt, hat eine ganze Reihe von weiteren Untersuchungen ausgelöst, die unter anderem zeigten, daß in anderen Elektrolyten, insbesondere anderen Sulfaten zweiwertiger Metalle, ganz ähnliche Relaxationserscheinungen auftreten. Es ist zwar sicher, daß diese mit der Dissoziation der Elektrolyte zusammenhängen, die Frage, welche der möglichen Reaktionen zwischen den auftretenden Ionen, Ionenkomplexen, Elektrolyt- und Lösungsmittelmolekeln die Relaxation verursacht, ist jedoch nur in einzelnen Fällen vollständig geklärt, z.B. beim Ammoniak und bei der Schwefelsäure und anderen „einfachen" Systemen.

Die oben genannten Messungen an Magnesiumsulfat zusammen mit ergänzenden Messungen des Einflusses von Temperatur und Druck, Konzentration, Fremd-Elektrolytzusatz, Dielektrizitätskonstante von LEONARD und WILSON [15], TAMM, KURTZE und KAISER [17a], BIES [16], CARSTENSEN [20], CONOLLY und FOX [21], BARRETT und BEYER [22], SMITHSON und LITOVITZ [25] sowie theoretische Überlegungen dieser Autoren ([15] bis [25]), HALL [23], BARTHEL [24] und EIGEN [50] haben diese Frage zwar bis zu einem gewissen Grade klären können; eine endgültige Entscheidung über den genauen Reaktionsablauf, der zu der gemessenen Absorption führt, steht jedoch noch aus. Es scheint jetzt aber festzustehen, daß mehrere Reaktionsgleichgewichte ineinander greifen, deren Gesamtheit man wohl am besten als stufenweise Dissoziation bezeichnet. Hier seien auch die Messungen und Untersuchungen von SMITHSON, LITOVITZ [25], BAZULIN [26], RÜFER [27], CLAEYS, ERRERA, SACK [28], STREHLOW, BECKER [29], SMITH, BARRETT, NAMARA, BEYER [30, 30a, 30b], KOR, VERMA, STUEHR, YEAGER, HOVORKA [31, 31a], BUSS [32] und MULDERS [33] an anderen Sulfaten genannt, die ähnliche Ergebnisse und entscheidende Beiträge zur Lösung des Problems brachten.

Die bei den Sulfaten und anderen meist als vollständig dissoziiert angesehenen Elektrolyten gewonnenen Anschauungen finden eine Ergänzung bei den sicher als unvollständig-dissoziiert anzunehmenden schwachen Elektrolyten, von denen viele sehr hohe Absorption zeigen. Neben Ammoniak, bei dem von KURTZE, TAMM [17a] bzw. von EIGEN [50] die Konzentrationsabhängigkeit und von CARNEVALE und LITOVITZ [7a] die Druckabhängigkeit der Relaxation gemessen und gedeuted wurde, sind von BAZULIN [26], v. ITTERBEEK und VERHAEGEN [62] und von BEYER, BARRETT und MCNAMARA [30a] Lanthannitrat und die Acetate besonders eingehend untersucht worden.

Die bei Relaxationsvorgängen außer der Absorption in der Nähe der Relaxationsfrequenz stets auftretende Dispersion der Schallgeschwindigkeit ist bei den wäßrigen Elektrolytlösungen sehr klein und daher außerordentlich schwer zu messen. Die relative Gesamtänderung der Schallgeschwindigkeit beträgt auch in günstigen Fällen (z.B. in 0,1 mol $MnSO_4$) nur 10^{-4}. Aus diesem Grunde hat man erst in den letzten Jahren mit geeigneten Meßmethoden die erwartete Dispersion nachweisen können. CARSTENSEN [20] und FOX und MARION [34] gelang die Dispersionsmessung für $MnSO_4$ und für $MgSO_4$ durch Anwendung von geeigneten Vergleichsverfahren, bei denen Schallgeschwindigkeitsdifferenzen gemessen werden (s. Ziff. 13).

B. Theorie der Relaxationsabsorption in wäßrigen Elektrolytlösungen.

I. Einfache Reaktionen.

3. Zur Druck-Relaxation in Flüssigkeiten. Es ist das Ziel der Theorie, Beziehungen abzuleiten zwischen den Daten der in Elektrolytlösungen auftretenden „Reaktionen" und ihrem akustischen Relaxationsverhalten, das in der verzögerten Einstellung des durch das Schallfeld periodisch gestörten Reaktionsgleichgewichtes besteht und sich in einer Dispersion der Schallgeschwindigkeit und einer frequenzabhängigen Absorption äußert.

Für das Relaxationsverhalten ist einerseits die Einstellgeschwindigkeit (Zeitkonstante) des Reaktionsgleichgewichtes und andererseits die Volumenänderung maßgebend, die mit der durch das Schallfeld (Druck bzw. Temperatur) verursachten Verschiebung des Gleichgewichts verbunden ist und sich als zusätzliche Kompressibilität äußert. Diese beiden Größen sind also für eine Reaktion zu ermitteln. Umgekehrt gestattet die Kenntnis des Relaxationsverhaltens unter Umständen Rückschlüsse auf die Art der erzeugenden Reaktion[1].

Wird in einem (Einphasen-)System, in dem nur eine Reaktion und die zugehörige Rückreaktion auftritt, das Gleichgewicht zwischen Reaktanten und Reaktionsprodukten gestört, so strebt es diesem bei kleinen Abweichungen mit einer Geschwindigkeit zu, die der Abweichung proportional ist. Ist ξ_i eine Größe, die das Fortschreiten der Reaktion bzw. ihren Stand beschreibt (z.B. die Konzentration eines Reaktionsproduktes) und ξ_{ig} ihr Gleichgewichtswert, so ist also

$$\frac{\partial \xi_i}{\partial t} = -\frac{\xi_i - \xi_{ig}}{\tau}, \tag{3.1}$$

wobei τ die Zeitkonstante der sich ergebenden exponentiellen Annäherung an das Gleichgewicht ist; sie ist — wie MANES [*38*] gezeigt hat — für alle zur gleichen Reaktion gehörigen Größen ξ_i die gleiche[2].

Ist nun der Gleichgewichtswert ξ_g abhängig vom Druck bzw. von der Temperatur, so verschiebt er sich in einer Schallwelle mit diesen Größen. In Wasser und wäßrigen Elektrolytlösungen sind die Temperaturänderungen in einer Schallwelle vernachlässigbar klein, so daß ihre Wirkung neben der des Druckes nicht berücksichtigt zu werden braucht. Man erhält in der Nähe einer zeitlich unveränderlichen Ruhelage $\bar{\xi}$, zu der der Ruhedruck $\bar{p}$ gehört

$$\xi_g - \bar{\xi} \approx \left(\frac{\partial \xi_g}{\partial p}\right)_T (p - \bar{p}) \equiv \left(\frac{\partial \xi}{\partial p}\right)_{T,g} (p - \bar{p}). \tag{3.2}$$

Der Index g der Differentialquotienten soll hierbei bedeuten, daß der Wert einzusetzen ist, der sich ergibt, wenn die Druckänderung so langsam erfolgt, daß das System ständig im Gleichgewicht ist. Man erhält durch Einsetzen von (3.2) in (3.1) eine Differentialgleichung für ξ und p:

$$\left(\tau \frac{\partial}{\partial t} + 1\right)(\xi - \bar{\xi}) \approx \left(\frac{\partial \xi}{\partial p}\right)_{T,g} (p - \bar{p}). \tag{3.3}$$

---

[1] Bezüglich allgemeiner theoretischer Betrachtungen sei auf die Arbeiten von KNESER [*35*], MEIXNER [*36*], HIEDEMANN und SPENCE [*37*], MANES [*38*], MARKHAM, BEYER, LINDSAY [*39*] und FRENKEL [*40*] sowie HERZFELD und LITOVITZ [*80*] verwiesen (s. auch den Beitrag von KNESER in diesem Band).

[2] Die an sich geringfügigen Unterschiede in den Relaxationszeiten, die in homogenen Flüssigkeiten bei verschiedenen Reaktionsbedingungen (konstante Temperatur, konstante Entropie usw.) auftreten [*36*], [*37*], spielen bei Lösungsreaktionen keine Rolle. Die gelöste Substanz ist meist so verdünnt, daß der Zustand, der sich einstellt, durch das Lösungsmittel bestimmt ist.

Für zeitlich sinusförmig veränderlichen Schalldruck

$$(p - \bar{p}) = \Delta p \cdot e^{i\omega t}$$

ist auch der Reaktionsstand ξ (d.h. die Konzentration des betrachteten Reaktionspartners) sinusförmig veränderlich,

$$(\xi - \bar{\xi}) = \Delta \xi \cdot e^{i\omega t};$$

er ist gegen den Schalldruck phasenverschoben, wie sich aus der komplexen Darstellung ergibt, die aus (3.3) unmittelbar folgt:

$$(i\omega\tau + 1)\,\Delta\xi \approx \left(\frac{\partial \xi}{\partial p}\right)_{T,g} \Delta p.$$

Für sehr kleine Schalldrucke erhält man für die Abhängigkeit zwischen Reaktionsstand und Schalldruck:

$$\lim_{\Delta p \to 0} \frac{\Delta \xi}{\Delta p} = \left(\frac{\partial \xi}{\partial p}\right)_{T,\omega} = \frac{1}{1 + i\omega\tau} \left(\frac{\partial \xi}{\partial p}\right)_{T,g}. \tag{3.4}$$

Ist der Reaktionsablauf mit einer Volumenänderung verbunden $(\partial v/\partial \xi) \neq 0$, so wirkt sich jede Druckänderung der Schallwelle über die Änderung der Gleichgewichtslage des Reaktionsstandes in einer zusätzlichen Volumenänderung aus. Diese kommt zu der hinzu, die im System (d.h. der Lösung) auch ohne Verschiebung des Reaktionsstandes (also bei sehr schnellen Druckänderungen) auftritt. Man erhält dementsprechend eine zusätzliche Komponente β_r in der Gesamtkompressibilität:

$$\beta = \frac{1}{v}\left(\frac{\partial v}{\partial p}\right)_{T,\omega} = \frac{1}{v}\left(\frac{\partial v}{\partial p}\right)_{\xi} + \frac{1}{v}\left(\frac{\partial v}{\partial \xi}\right)_{T}\left(\frac{\partial \xi}{\partial p}\right)_{T,\omega} = \beta_\infty + \beta_r. \tag{3.5}$$

Für zeitlich sinusförmig verlaufenden Schalldruck, also mit (3.4), ist

$$\beta = \frac{1}{v}\left(\frac{\partial v}{\partial p}\right)_{\xi} + \frac{1}{v}\left(\frac{\partial v}{\partial \xi}\right)_{T} \cdot \left(\frac{\partial \xi}{\partial p}\right)_{T,g} \frac{1}{1 + i\omega\tau} = \beta_\infty + \frac{\beta_i}{1 + i\omega\tau}. \tag{3.6}$$

Der relaxierende Anteil β_i der Kompressibilität läßt sich auf bekannte thermodynamische Größen zurückführen (s. Ziff. 5); das gleiche gilt von der Zeitkonstante τ (s. Ziff. 4).

Das Komplexwerden der Kompressibilität (3.6), das eine Phasenverschiebung zwischen Dichte und Druck bedeutet, ist mit der Umwandlung von Schallenergie in Wärme verbunden, so daß eine Schallabsorption α auftritt. Man kann diese und die Phasengeschwindigkeit u_{Ph} leicht über die komplexe Schallgeschwindigkeit

$$\boldsymbol{u} = (\partial \varrho/\partial p)^{-\frac{1}{2}} = (\varrho\,\beta)^{-\frac{1}{2}}$$

berechnen, die ihrerseits durch die komplexe Kompressibilität β und die Dichte ϱ des Mediums gegeben ist:

$$\frac{1}{\boldsymbol{u}} = \frac{1}{u_{\mathrm{Ph}}} - i\frac{\alpha}{\omega} = \sqrt{\varrho\beta}.$$

Es ergibt sich die bekannte Beziehung für μ, die Absorption pro Wellenlänge [*30*]:

$$\mu \equiv 2\alpha\lambda = 4\pi\frac{\alpha}{\omega}u_{\mathrm{Ph}} \approx 2\pi\frac{\omega\tau}{1 + \omega^2\tau^2}\frac{\beta_i}{\beta_\infty} \approx \frac{2\omega\tau}{1 + \omega^2\tau^2}\mu_m, \tag{3.7}$$

wobei

$$\mu_m \approx \pi\beta_i/\beta_\infty. \tag{3.8}$$

μ steigt linear mit der Frequenz an, erreicht für die Relaxationsfrequenz $\nu_m = \omega_m/2\pi = 1/2\pi\tau$ ein Maximum μ_m und fällt dann umgekehrt proportional zur

Frequenz wieder ab. Der zugehörige Verlauf der Phasengeschwindigkeit

$$u_{\mathrm{Ph}}/u_\infty \approx 1 - \frac{1}{2}\frac{\beta_i}{\beta_\infty}\frac{1}{1+\omega^2\tau^2} \tag{3.9}$$

zeigt eine Dispersion bei der Relaxationsfrequenz $\nu_m = 1/(2\pi\tau)$ mit einer Stufenhöhe d.h. einer relativen Gesamtänderung der Phasengeschwindigkeit zwischen sehr tiefen und sehr hohen Frequenzen (u_0 bzw. u_∞)

$$\frac{u_\infty - u_0}{u_\infty} \approx \frac{1}{2}\frac{\beta_i}{\beta_\infty} \approx \frac{\mu_m}{2\pi}. \tag{3.10}$$

4. Zeitkonstante der Einstellung des Reaktionsgleichgewichtes. Die Zeitkonstante der Einstellung des Gleichgewichtes zwischen Vorwärts- und Rückwärtsreaktion in einem System ist im allgemeinen durch die Reaktionsgeschwindigkeiten in beiden Richtungen gegeben. Sie kann mit Hilfe der Reaktionskinetik bestimmt werden[1].

Es sei zunächst als Beispiel, ohne auf den Reaktionsmechanismus einzugehen, *das einfache Dissoziationsgleichgewicht* $A^+ + B^- \rightleftharpoons AB$ in einem gelösten Elektrolyten behandelt (s. auch Ziff. 37). Dabei sind A^+ und B^- die Assoziationspartner mit den Konzentrationen (Teilchenzahl pro Mengeneinheit) n_A und n_B und AB das Assoziationsprodukt mit der Konzentration n_{AB}. Die Zerfallsreaktion besitzt eine im allgemeinen konzentrationsunabhängige Geschwindigkeitskonstante k_{21}. Die Zahl der je Zeiteinheit zerfallenden Assoziate (Brutto-Zerfallsgeschwindigkeit) ist daher der Assoziat-Konzentration proportional:

$$-(\dot{n}_{AB})_{\mathrm{Zerf}} = k_{21}\, n_{AB}.$$

Die Rekombinationsreaktion, die von der Konzentration beider Reaktionspartner abhängt,

$$+(\dot{n}_{AB})_{\mathrm{Bildg}} = k_{12}\, n_A\, n_B = {}^0k_{12}\, \Pi^f\, n_A\, n_B,$$

hat dagegen in den meisten Fällen eine Geschwindigkeitskonstante k_{12}, die von der Konzentration beider Ionensorten abhängig ist. Man spaltet daher häufig einen konzentrationsunabhängigen Anteil ${}^0k_{12}$ ab, der sich als Grenzwert für verschwindende Konzentrationen ergibt, während die Konzentrationsabhängigkeit einem Faktor $\Pi^f \approx f_A\, f_B$ (dem Aktivitätskoeffizienten-Produkt)[2] zugeschrieben wird, $k_{12} = {}^0k_{12}\,\Pi^f$.

[1] Für den sehr allgemeinen Fall einer Einphasenreaktion vom Typ

$$a\,A + b\,B + \cdots \rightleftharpoons m\,M + n\,N + \cdots$$

d.h. für den Fall, daß sowohl für Hin- als auch für die Rückreaktion mehrere Reaktanten und mehrere Reaktionsprodukte in stöchiometrischen Verhältnissen auftreten, die durch $a, b \ldots m, n \ldots$ gegeben sind, wurde unter Vernachlässigung der Aktivitätskoeffizienten die Beziehung

$$1/\tau = r_f\, z \cdot (d \ln \Pi^n/\partial\xi) \quad \text{mit} \quad \Pi^n = [M]^m \cdot [N]^n \cdots [A]^{-a} \cdot [B]^{-b} \cdots$$

für die Zeitkonstante abgeleitet (s. z.B. Manes [38]), wobei $r_f = (\partial\xi/\partial t)_f$ die Bruttogeschwindigkeit der Vorwärtsreaktion und ξ die Abweichung vom Gleichgewicht ist (r_f und ξ können auf irgendeine Schlüsselkomponente der Reaktion bezogen werden). Die Konzentrationsfunktion Π^n geht für das Gleichgewicht in den Quotienten $K_n = K/\Pi^f$ über [s. Gl. (4.2)]. Da die Koeffizienten $a, b \ldots m, n$ stöchiometrische Angaben sind, die tatsächlich an einer Einzelreaktion beteiligten Mengen aber Vielfache bzw. Bruchteile z davon sind, bleibt im allgemeinen ein Unsicherheitsfaktor z bestehen. z kann immer dann bestimmt werden, bzw. die Gleichung kann so geschrieben werden, daß $z = 1$, wenn die Anzahl der an der Reaktion beteiligten Moleküle bzw. Atome bekannt ist.

[2] Bereits Brönstedt [*41*], Bjerrum [*42*] und später Christiansen [*43*] führten die Aktivitätskoeffizienten f_i in reaktionskinetische Berechnungen ein. Sie erfassen den Einfluß der Ionenwolke. Ihre Einführung ist nur sinnvoll, wenn sich das Verteilungsgleichgewicht in der Ionenwolke schnell gegen die betrachteten Reaktionen einstellt. Bezüglich der Aktivitätsprodukte Π^f vgl. auch Eucken [*44*], Harned und Owen [*45*], Kortüm [*46*], Falkenhagen [*47*] und Wicke und Eigen [*48*]. Hier ist $\Pi^f = f_A f_B/f_{AB} \approx f_A \cdot f_B$, denn da AB keine Ladung trägt, ist $f_{AB} \approx 1$.

Die Gesamtänderung $\dot{n}_{AB}$ der Konzentration n_{AB} des Reaktionsproduktes ist durch die Überlagerung beider Teilreaktionen gegeben, d.h. durch die Summe

$$\dot{n}_{AB} = (\dot{n}_{AB})_{\text{Zerf}} + (\dot{n}_{AB})_{\text{Bildg}} = -k_{21}\, n_{AB} + {}^0k_{12}\, \Pi^f\, n_A\, n_B \tag{4.1}$$

die außer von k_{21} und ${}^0k_{12}$ von Π^f und den Konzentrationen n_{AB}, n_A, n_B abhängig ist. Gleichgewicht ist vorhanden, wenn sie verschwindet ($\dot{n}_{AB}=0$), also für bestimmte Konzentrationswerte n_{ABg}, n_{Ag} und n_{Bg}[1] und dem davon abhängigen Faktor Π^f_g, wobei diese Größen der Bedingung

$$\frac{n_{Ag}\, n_{Bg}}{n_{ABg}} = \frac{k_{21}}{{}^0k_{12}\, \Pi^f_g} = \frac{K_{12}}{\Pi^f_g} = K_{12n} \tag{4.2}$$

genügen. Dabei ist das Verhältnis $k_{21}/{}^0k_{12} = K_{12} = K_D$ die Gleichgewichtskonstante der Dissoziation. Bringt ein äußerer Einfluß das System aus dem Gleichgewicht durch direkte oder indirekte Veränderung einer oder mehrerer der in dieser Beziehung enthaltenen Größen, so tritt eine endliche Konzentrationsänderung entsprechend (4.1) auf, die so gerichtet ist, daß sie zur Wiederherstellung des Gleichgewichtes führt. Bei der vorliegenden Reaktion wird dies leicht erkennbar, wenn man in (4.1) die Gleichgewichtsbedingung (4.2) einsetzt:

$$\dot{n}_{AB} = -k_{21}(n_{AB} - n_{ABg}) + {}^0k_{12}(\Pi^f\, n_A\, n_B - \Pi^f_g\, n_{Ag}\, n_{Bg}),$$

und dann diese Beziehung in der Nähe des Gleichgewichtes linearisiert durch Einführen der Abweichung der Faktoren Π^f, n_A, n_B vom Gleichgewicht $n_i - n_{ig} = \Delta n_i$ und $\Pi^f - \Pi^f_g = \Delta \Pi^f = \sum_{i=A,B,AB} (\partial \Pi^f/\partial n_i)\, \Delta n_i$

$$\dot{n}_{AB} = -k_{21}\, \Delta n_{AB} + {}^0k_{12}\left\{\left[\Pi^f n_B + n_A n_B \left(\frac{\partial \Pi^f}{\partial n_A}\right)\right] \Delta n_A + [\cdots]\, \Delta n_B + [\cdots]\, \Delta n_{AB}\right\}.$$

Man erhält dann mit dem stöchiometrischen Gleichgewicht bzw. mit der Elektroneutralität $\Delta n_A = \Delta n_B = -\Delta n_{AB}$

$$\dot{n}_{AB} = -\left\{k_{21} + {}^0k_{12}\Pi^f\left[n_A + n_B + n_A\, n_B \sum_{i=A,B,-AB} \frac{\partial \ln \Pi^f}{\partial n_i}\right]\right\} \cdot \Delta n_{AB} = -\frac{1}{\tau}\, \Delta n_{AB}. \tag{4.3}$$

Aus dieser Differentialgleichung folgt die bekannte Tatsache, daß sich die Konzentration dem Gleichgewichtswert mit einer Zeitkonstante $\tau = \tau_D$ zeitlich exponentiell[2] nähert:

$$\frac{1}{\tau_D} = -\frac{\dot{n}_{AB}}{\Delta n_{AB}} = k_{21} + {}^0k_{12}\Pi^f\left[n_A + n_B + n_A\, n_B \sum_{i=A,B,-AB} \frac{\partial \ln \Pi^f}{\partial n_i}\right] = k_{21} + k'_{12}.^{3} \tag{4.4}$$

Die Einstellgeschwindigkeit $1/\tau$ des Gleichgewichtes setzt sich aus zwei Anteilen zusammen, einem konzentrationsunabhängigen k_{21} und einem zweiten An-

---

[1] Der Index g bezeichnet den Gleichgewichtswert. Er wird jedoch fortgelassen, wo eine Verwechslung nicht möglich ist.

[2] Das Exponentialgesetz und dementsprechend die Beziehung für die Zeitkonstante gelten allgemein für die Einstellung von Gleichgewichten, wenn nur eine Reaktion auftritt.

[3] Etwas allgemeiner kann man für Gl. (4.4) schreiben

$$\frac{1}{\tau} = k_{21}\, n_{AB} \cdot \sum_{i=A,B,-AB} \frac{\partial \ln K_D}{\partial n_i} = k_{21}\, n_{AB}\left(\frac{1}{n_{AB}} + \frac{1}{n_B} + \frac{1}{n_A} + \sum_i \frac{\partial \ln \Pi^f}{\partial n_i}\right)$$

Man kann statt der Summe der Ableitungen bei Konstanthaltung der anderen Konzentrationen natürlich auch die Ableitung nach einer Konzentration n_i bei konstanter Salzkonzentration $n = n_A + n_{AB}$ einführen, wenn nur ein Ionengleichgewicht vorhanden ist:

$$n \sum_{i=A,B,-AB} \frac{\partial \ln \Pi^f}{\partial n_i} = n\left(\frac{\partial \ln \Pi^f}{\partial n_i}\right)_n = \left(\frac{\partial \ln \Pi^f}{\partial \delta}\right)_n.$$

teil, der mit der Salz- bzw. Elektrolytkonzentration n zunimmt. Dieser zweite Anteil wird mit dem ersten vergleichbar, wenn die Konzentration n_A bzw. n_B mit der Größe $K_{Dn} = K_D/\Pi^f = k_{21}/{}^0k_{21}\,\Pi^f$ vergleichbar wird. Das entspricht einer Konzentration, bei der Dissoziationsgrad δ bereits auf etwa 50% abgesunken ist, wie sich durch Umformen von Gl. (4.4) ergibt. Mit Gl. (4.2) und $n_A = n_B = \delta n$ bzw. $n_{AB} = (1-\delta)\,n$ ist nämlich

$$\left.\begin{aligned} k'_{12} &= k_{21}(1-\delta)\,\frac{2}{\delta^+}, \quad \text{wobei} \quad \frac{2}{\delta^+} = \frac{2}{\delta} + \left(\frac{\partial \ln \Pi^f}{\partial \delta}\right)_n, \\ \text{so daß} \qquad 1/\tau_D &= k_{21} + k'_{12} = k_{21}\left(1 + \frac{2(1-\delta)}{\delta^+}\right). \end{aligned}\right\} \tag{4.5}$$

Die Konzentrationsabhängigkeit des Produkts $\Pi^f \approx f_A f_B = f^2$ kann in bestimmten Fällen aus thermodynamischen Messungen ermittelt werden. Fig. 3 zeigt den Verlauf des mittleren Aktivitätskoeffizienten f für einige Elektrolyte, wie er von WICKE und EIGEN [*51a*], [*55*] ermittelt wurde; er nimmt mit der Konzentration zunächst schnell ab, erreicht aber bei den 2-2-wertigen Elektrolyten einen flachen Verlauf bei Konzentrationen um 0,1 ... 1 Mol/Liter[1].

Für Reaktionen anderen Grades erhält man ähnliche Beziehungen für die Einstellgeschwindigkeit des Gleichgewichtes.

Für die Umwandlungs- (bzw. Anregungs-) Reaktion $A \rightleftharpoons A'$, bei der im allgemeinen beide Geschwindigkeitskonstanten k_{23} und k_{32} konzentrationsunabhängig sind (so daß ihr Verhältnis $k_{32}/k_{23} = K_{23} = K_U$ die Gleichgewichtskonstante der Umwandlung ist), hat die Einstellgeschwindigkeit die besonders einfache Form

$$\frac{1}{\tau} = \frac{1}{\tau_U} = k_{32} + k_{23} = k_{32}\left(1 + \frac{1}{K_U}\right), \quad \text{mit } K_U = k_{32}/k_{23}. \tag{4.5}$$

Sie ist konzentrationsunabhängig und ist von der größeren Geschwindigkeitskonstante bestimmt.

5. Relaxierender Anteil der Kompressibilität. Der relaxierende Anteil β_i der Kompressibilität läßt sich auf bekannte Größen zurückführen. In der Aufspaltung

$$\beta_i = \left[\frac{1}{v}\left(\frac{\partial v}{\partial \xi}\right)_T\right] \cdot \left(\frac{\partial \xi}{\partial p}\right)_{T,g} \tag{5.1}$$

ist unter der Voraussetzung, daß ξ die Konzentration (Teilchen/Volumeneinheit) einer Reaktionskomponente ist, der erste Faktor nichts anderes als die Differenz der Partialvolumina der Reaktionsprodukte und der Reaktanten $\Delta\,{}^*V_n = \Sigma\,{}^*V_{Pn} - \Sigma\,{}^*V_{Rn}$, bezogen auf eine Einzelreaktion[2]

$$\frac{1}{v}\left(\frac{\partial v}{\partial \xi}\right)_T = \frac{1}{N_L}\,\Delta\,{}^*V_n = \frac{1}{N_L}\left(\Sigma\,{}^*V_{Pn} - \Sigma\,{}^*V_{Rn}\right). \tag{5.2}$$

Zur Bestimmung des zweiten Faktors in Gl. (5.1), der die Druckabhängigkeit des Reaktionsgleichgewichts enthält, zerlegt man diesen zweckmäßig in zwei Faktoren, von denen der erste nG nur von den Konzentrationen abhängt, indem man zunächst nach $K_n = K/\Pi^f$, dem Gleichgewichtsverhältnis der Konzentrationen der Reaktanten und der Reaktionsprodukte, differenziert

$$\left(\frac{\partial \xi}{\partial p}\right)_{T,g} = \left(\frac{\partial \xi}{\partial \ln K_n}\right)_{T,g} \cdot \left(\frac{\partial \ln K_n}{\partial p}\right)_{T,g} = n\,G \cdot \left(\frac{\partial \ln K_n}{\partial p}\right)_{T,g}, \tag{5.3}$$

[1] In diesem Bereich kann daher der dritte Summand des zweiten Anteils vernachlässigt werden, wie das von EIGEN, KURTZE und TAMM [*18*] getan wurde.

[2] Man bezieht die Partialvolumina meist auf 1 Mol; da sich die Größe $(\partial v/\partial \xi)/v$ auf eine Einzelreaktion bezieht, sind sie durch die Loschmidtsche Zahl N_L zu dividieren. Der Index n gibt an, daß die Partialvolumina bei der jeweiligen Konzentration zu nehmen sind.

wobei

$$K_n = \frac{K}{\Pi^f} = \frac{k_{\text{rückw.}}}{k_{\text{vorw.}}} = \frac{n_A \cdot n_B \ldots}{n_M \cdot n_N \ldots}. \tag{5.4}$$

α) Bestimmung des Faktors G.

Für die Reaktion $A + B \rightleftharpoons AB$, z.B., ist $K_n = K_{Dn} = n_A n_B / n_{AB}$, wählt man noch $\xi = n_A$, d.h. $\partial n_A/\partial\xi = \partial n_B/\partial\xi = -\partial n_{AB}/\partial\xi = 1$, so ergibt sich

$$G = G_D = \frac{1}{n}\,\frac{\partial\xi}{\partial \ln K_D/\Pi^f} = \left[\frac{n}{n_A} + \frac{n}{n_B} + \frac{n}{n_{AB}}\right]^{-1} \tag{5.5}$$

und bei Einführung des Dissoziationsgrades $\delta = n_A/n$ mit $n_A = n_B = n - n_{AB}$

$$G = G_D = \frac{\delta(1-\delta)}{2(1-\delta)+\delta} \quad \text{mit} \quad K_n = K_{Dn} = \frac{\delta^2}{(1-\delta)}\,n. \tag{5.6}$$

Durch Eliminieren von δ erhält man G_D als Funktion derjenigen Konzentration, die in die Kombination $n/K_n = n\Pi^f/K$ eingeht. Der Verlauf von G_D (s. G_I für $\alpha = 1$ in Fig. 2a) zeigt einen Maximalwert 0,173 bei $n\Pi^f/K \approx 1$, d.h. für Konzentrationen, die zahlenmäßig der Gleichgewichtskonstante nahekommen. In der Umgebung dieser Konzentration ist G_D wenig abhängig von der Konzentration, ein Umstand, der sich bei den Elektrolytlösungen entscheidend auswirkt.

Sind die Konzentrationen $n_A \neq n_B$, so gelten andere Beziehungen für G und K_n. Ist z. B. Na_2SO_4 (s. Ziff. 37) in der ersten Dissoziationsreaktion völlig dissoziiert $[Na_2SO_4 \rightarrow Na^+ + (NaSO_4)^-]$, so sind die Konzentrationen gegeben durch $[Na^+] = n_A = (1+\delta)\,n$, $[SO_4^{--}] = n_B = \delta n$ und $[NaSO_4^-] = (1-\delta)\,n$, und es wird

$$G = G_{D2} = \frac{\delta(1-\delta)(1+\delta)}{2-(1-\delta)^2} \quad \text{mit} \quad K_n = K_{D2n} = \frac{\delta(1+\delta)}{1-\delta}\cdot n. \tag{5.7}$$

Der Maximalwert von G_{D2} beträgt in diesem Falle 0,215 bei $n\Pi^f/K \approx 0{,}6$.

β) Für die Anregungs- bzw. Umwandlungsreaktion $A \rightleftharpoons A'$ ergibt sich unabhängig von der Konzentration für $[A'] = \alpha n$ und $[A] = (1-\alpha)\,n$

$$G = G_U = \frac{K}{(1+K)^2} = \alpha(1-\alpha) \quad \text{mit} \quad K = K_U = \frac{\alpha}{1-\alpha}. \tag{5.8}$$

Die Größe G_U kann also höchstens den Wert 0,25 erreichen, nämlich dann, wenn $\alpha = 0{,}5$ wird.

β) Bestimmung des Faktors $\partial \ln K_n/\partial p$.

Der zweite Faktor in Gl. (5.3), $\partial \ln K_n/\partial p$ ist thermodynamisch bestimmt und durch die Differenz der Partialvolumina $\Delta{}^*V_n$ gegeben (dabei bedeutet der Index n wieder, daß die Partialvolumina bei den vorhandenen Konzentrationen zu nehmen sind):

$$\frac{\partial \ln K_n}{\partial p} = \frac{\partial \ln K_{Dn}}{\partial p} = \frac{\partial \ln (n_A\, n_B/n_{AB})}{\partial p} = \frac{\Delta{}^*V_D}{RT}\cdot\frac{1}{1+G_D\, n\,(\partial \ln \Pi^f/\partial n_A)_n}. \tag{5.9}$$

Den im Nenner auftretenden Korrekturfaktor $[1 + G_D(\partial \ln \Pi^f/\partial\delta)_n]$ erhält man durch folgende Überlegung: Das sich einstellende Konzentrationsverhältnis K_{Dn} ist, wie bereits mehrfach erwähnt, bei Elektrolytlösungen konzentrationsabhängig. Entsprechend Gl. (4.2) $K_{Dn} = K_D/\Pi^f$ wird die Abweichung von seinem Grenzwert K_D für verschwindende Konzentration durch das Produkt Π^f erfaßt (wobei $\Pi^f_{n=0} = 1$, s. auch Ziff. 4 und Fig. 4).

Man kann also auch $\partial \ln K_n/\partial p$ in zwei Faktoren aufspalten, von denen der erste die Verhältnisse bei verschwindender Konzentration (gegeben durch

$\Delta^* V_{D0}$), der zweite[1] die Konzentrationsabhängigkeit erfaßt:

$$\frac{\partial \ln K_{Dn}}{\partial p} = \frac{\partial \ln K_D}{\partial p} - \frac{\partial \ln \Pi^f}{\partial p}, \quad \text{wobei} \quad \frac{\partial \ln K_D}{\partial p} = \frac{\Delta^* V_{D0}}{RT}. \tag{5.10}$$

Bei dem zweiten Glied ist die Druckabhängigkeit der Konzentration zu berücksichtigen

$$\frac{\partial \ln \Pi^f}{\partial p} = \left(\frac{\partial \ln \Pi^f}{\partial p}\right)_\xi + \left(\frac{\partial \ln \Pi^f}{\partial \xi}\right)_p \frac{\partial \xi}{\partial p} \quad \text{wobei} \quad \left(\frac{\partial \ln \Pi^f}{\partial p}\right)_\xi = \frac{\Delta^* V_{D0}}{RT} - \frac{\Delta^* V_D}{RT}. \tag{5.11}$$

Durch Einsetzen von $\partial\xi/\partial p$ nach Gl. (5.3) erhält man mit $\xi = n_A$ die bereits angegebene Gl. (5.9) bzw.

$$\left(\frac{\partial \xi}{\partial p}\right)_{T,g} = \left(\frac{\partial n_A}{\partial p}\right)_{T,g} = n \frac{G_D \cdot \Delta^* V_D}{1 + n G_D (\partial \ln \Pi^f / \partial n_A)_{n,p}} = n G_D^+ \Delta^* V_D, \tag{5.9a}$$

wobei

$$G_D^+ = \left[\frac{1}{G_D} + \left(\frac{\partial \ln \Pi^f}{\partial \delta}\right)_{n,p}\right]^{-1} = \left[\frac{1}{1-\delta} + \frac{2}{\delta^+}\right]^{-1}.$$

Man erhält also G_D^+ aus G_D, indem man in Gl. (5.6) das Glied $2/\delta$ durch $2/\delta^+ = 2/\delta + (\partial \ln \Pi^f/\partial \delta)_{n,p}$ ersetzt. Man kann G_D^+ als speziellere Schreibweise des allgemeiner gültigen Ausdrucks G_{I}^+ nach Gl. (8.9) ansehen.

Bei der Anregungs- bzw. Umwandlungsreaktion sind keine Aktivitätskoeffizienten zu berücksichtigen, so daß $K_n = K = K_U$ und $\Delta^* V_n = \Delta^* V_0 = \Delta^* V_U$ konzentrationsunabhängig werden

$$\frac{\partial \ln K_n}{\partial p} = \frac{\partial \ln K_U}{\partial p} = \frac{\Delta^* V_U}{RT} \tag{5.12}$$

bzw.

$$\left(\frac{\partial \xi}{\partial p}\right)_{T,g} = n G_U \Delta^* V_U. \tag{5.12a}$$

γ) Berechnung der Kompressibilität. Mit den abgeleiteten Beziehungen ergibt sich für den relaxierenden Anteil β_i der Kompressibilität

$$\beta_i = \frac{n}{N_L} \cdot G^+ \frac{(\Delta^* V_n)^2}{RT}, \tag{5.13}$$

wobei für die Dissoziation nach Gl. (5.9a) und (5.11)

$$G^+ = G_D^+ \quad \text{und} \quad \Delta^* V_n = \Delta^* V_D = \Delta^* V_{D0} - RT (\partial \ln \Pi^f / \partial p)_{n_A}$$

und für die Anregung

$$G^+ = G_U \quad \text{und} \quad \Delta^* V_n = \Delta^* V_U.$$

Sie ist somit auf anderweitig meßbare Größen zurückgeführt und kann damit berechnet werden. Der Faktor G^+ ist, wie oben ausgeführt, eine Funktion der relativen Konzentration der beteiligten Reaktanten und der Reaktionsprodukte.

Man erhält damit den Maximalwert der Absorption je Wellenlänge

$$\mu_m = (2\alpha\lambda)_m = \pi G^+ \frac{n}{N_L} \cdot \frac{(\Delta^* V_n)^2}{\beta_\infty \cdot RT}, \tag{5.14}$$

bzw. mit den üblichen Dimensionen

$$\mu_m = 2{,}8 \frac{\beta_{H_2O}}{\beta_\infty} \cdot G^+ \cdot \frac{c}{[\mathrm{Mol/cm^3}]} \cdot \frac{(\Delta^* V_n)^2}{[\mathrm{cm^3/Mol}]^2}; \tag{5.14a}$$

[1] Der hier abgespaltene konzentrationsabhängige Anteil $\partial \ln \Pi^f/\partial p$ wird von einigen Autoren von vornherein in den Faktor G hineingenommen, der dann entsprechend komplizierter wird und genau G_D^+ entspricht

wobei der Zahlenwert 2,8 für $(\Pi^f/RT\,\beta_{H_2O})/[\text{Mol/cm}^3]$ steht und für 20° C mit $RT = 2480\ Nm/\text{Mol}$ und der Kompressibilität von reinem Wasser $\beta_{H_2O} = 0{,}455 \times 10^{-9}\ m^2/N$ berechnet wurde. Der Faktor $\beta_{H_2O}/\beta_\infty$ weicht in wäßrigen Elektrolytlösungen nur wenig von 1 ab.

Bezieht man, wie üblich, die Absorptionswirkung auf ein Molekül des Elektrolyten, so erhält man analog zum Absorptionsquerschnitt $Q = 2\alpha/n = 2\alpha/c\,N_L$ (s. Ziff. 20) einen Maximalwert des „Absorptionsvolumens" $Q\lambda$

$$(Q\lambda)_m = \pi\, G^+ \cdot \frac{(\Delta^* V_n)^2}{N_L\,\beta_\infty\, RT}\,, \tag{5.15}$$

bzw. in den üblichen Dimensionen

$$\frac{(Q\lambda)_m}{[\text{m}^3]} = 4{,}70 \cdot 10^{-30} \cdot G^+ \frac{(\Delta^* V_n)^2}{[\text{cm}^3/\text{Mol}]^2}\,. \tag{5.15a}$$

Eine Abschätzung für den zu erwartenden Wert für $(Q\lambda)_m$ im optimalen Bereich für $G_D^+ \approx G_D \approx 0{,}2$ bei einem „normalen" Wert von $\Delta^* V_n \approx 5$ cm³/Mol ergibt $(Q\lambda)_m \approx 25 \cdot 10^{-30}$ m³. Das entspricht größenordnungsmäßig recht gut den in vielen Fällen beobachteten Werten (s. Fig. 13).

II. Reaktionsfolgen.

6. Absorptionsspektren von Reaktionsfolgen. Reaktionen zwischen gelösten Partikeln lassen sich formal in mehrere Schritte zerlegen[1]: 1. Begegnung der reagierenden Partikel auf Grund ihrer Diffusionsbewegung, d.h. Bildung eines „Begegnungskomplexes", in dem die Partikeln noch völlig ihre Eigenschaften bewahrt haben, aber so nahe gerückt sind, daß der zweite Schritt stattfinden kann. 2. Reaktion der Partikeln im Begegnungskomplex zu dem Reaktionsprodukt bzw. zu mehreren Reaktionsprodukten. Diese Reaktion kann über mehrere Zwischenstufen verlaufen. 3. Auseinanderbewegung der Reaktionsprodukte, wenn mehrere vorhanden sind. Entsprechendes gilt für die Rückreaktion, so daß sich für die Reaktion $A + B \rightleftharpoons M + N$ die folgende formelle Aufteilung der Teilreaktionen ergibt:

$$A + B \rightleftharpoons A, B \rightleftharpoons A\,B \equiv M\,N \rightleftharpoons M, N \rightleftharpoons M + N\,.$$

Dabei bedeuten A, B und M, N Zwischenzustände (Begegnungskomplexe), die in vielen Fällen in sehr kleiner Konzentration auftreten (s. unten).

Bei der bereits behandelten bimolekularen Lösungsreaktion $A + B \rightleftharpoons A\,B$ gibt es den Zerfall in andere Reaktionsprodukte nicht. Sie spaltet daher nur in ein Diffusionsgleichgewicht D und ein Umwandlungsgleichgewicht U nach folgendem Schema auf:

$$A + B \underset{D}{\rightleftharpoons} A, B \underset{U}{\rightleftharpoons} A\,B\,.$$

Dabei kann, wie bereits erwähnt, die Umwandlung über mehrere Zwischenstufen verlaufen. Das Endprodukt $A\,B$ kann ein Molekül oder irgendein Assoziat sein.

Wie im folgenden genauer gezeigt wird, erfolgt die Gleichgewichtseinstellung eines solchen Systems nach einer Zeitfunktion, die durch Überlagerung zweier Exponentialfunktionen gegeben ist. Man kann die zugehörigen Zeitkonstanten zwei Reaktionssystemen (Gleichgewichten) I und II zuordnen, die jedoch nicht mit dem Diffusionsgleichgewicht D bzw. dem Umwandlungsgleichgewicht U identisch sind. Nur dann, wenn die Einstellzeiten der beiden Teilgleichgewichte D

[1] Vgl. CHRISTIANSEN [*49*] und EIGEN [*50*], [*51*], [*51a*]; s. auch die Zusammenfassung bei EUCKEN [*44*].

und U sich stark voneinander unterscheiden, ist eins der neuen Systeme mit einem Diffusionsgleichgewicht, das andere mit einem Umwandlungsgleichgewicht zu identifizieren.

Der schnellere Vorgang (D oder U) verläuft dann so, als ob der langsamere gar nicht vorhanden wäre; das neue System I mit der kleineren Zeitkonstante τ_{I} ist also identisch mit dem sich schneller einstellenden Teilgleichgewicht. Für den langsameren Vorgang befindet sich der schnellere ständig im Gleichgewicht. Am Ausgleichsvorgang II mit der größeren Zeitkonstante τ_{II} nehmen also alle Partikel teil, und er verläuft zwischen allen Partikeln, die zu dem System I mit der kleineren Zeitkonstante gehören, einerseits und dem Rest andererseits.

Ist die Konzentration des Zwischenzustandes A, B klein, dann läuft die Reaktion praktisch zwischen $A + B$ und $A\,B$. Der schnellere Ausgleichsvorgang I, der ja zwischen einem Endzustand und diesem Zwischenzustand A, B läuft, stirbt dann aus, so daß der langsamere Ausgleichsvorgang II allein übrigbleibt und die verbleibende Relaxationsfrequenz bestimmt.

7. Ermittlung der Einstellgeschwindigkeiten (Relaxationsfrequenzen). Nimmt man nun für die Teilvorgänge in der oben behandelten bimolekularen Lösungsreaktion $A^+ + B^- \rightleftharpoons A\,B$ bestimmte Geschwindigkeitskonstanten k_{12}, k_{21} und k_{23}, k_{32} an

$$\underset{(1)}{A^+ + B^-} \underset{\substack{k_{21}\\ D}}{\overset{k_{12}}{\rightleftharpoons}} \underset{(2)}{A, B} \underset{\substack{k_{32}\\ U}}{\overset{k_{23}}{\rightleftharpoons}} \underset{(3)}{AB}, \tag{7.1}$$

so erhält man unter der Voraussetzung (s. Ziff. 4), daß sich das Ionenwolkengleichgewicht vergleichsweise schnell einstellt, für die zeitliche Änderung der Konzentration n_A bzw. n_B und n_{AB} als Differenz der Brutto-Reaktionsgeschwindigkeiten

$$\dot{n}_A = \dot{n}_B = -\,n_A\,n_B\,k_{12} + n_{A,B}\,k_{21} \quad \text{und} \quad \dot{n}_{AB} = n_{A,B}\,k_{23} - n_{AB}\,k_{32}.$$

Für das Gleichgewicht ($\dot{n}_A = \dot{n}_B = 0$; $\dot{n}_{AB} = 0$) gilt also bei Einführung der Gleichgewichtskonstanten K_D und K_U sowie des Aktivitätskoeffizientenproduktes Π^f, welches für die Reaktion U allerdings keine Rolle spielt:

$$\frac{n_{Ag}\,n_{Bg}}{n_{A\,Bg}} = \frac{k_{21}}{k_{12}} = \frac{k_{21}}{{}^0k_{12}\,\Pi^f_g} = \frac{K_D}{\Pi^f_g} \quad \text{und} \quad \frac{n_{A,Bg}}{n_{A\,Bg}} = \frac{k_{32}}{k_{23}} = K_U. \tag{7.2}$$

Aus den linearisierten[1] Gleichungen [s. Ziff. 4, Gl. (4.3)]:

$$\left.\begin{aligned} \Delta\dot{n}_A &= k_{21}\,\Delta n_{A,B} - {}^0k_{12}\,\Pi^f\left[n_A + n_B + n_A n_B\left(\frac{\partial \ln \Pi^f}{\partial n_A} + \frac{\partial \ln \Pi^f}{\partial n_B}\right)\right]\Delta n_A,\\ \Delta\dot{n}_{AB} &= k_{23}\,\Delta n_{A,B} - k_{32}\,\Delta n_{AB} \end{aligned}\right\} \tag{7.3}$$

läßt sich für jedes der beiden Teilgleichgewichte: Diffusion bzw. Umwandlung, wenn es allein vorhanden ist (also für $\Delta n_{A,B} = -\Delta n_A = -\Delta n_B$ bzw. $\Delta n_{A,B} = -\Delta n_{AB}$) in der oben angegebenen Weise eine Einstellgeschwindigkeit bzw. reziproke Zeitkonstante ablesen[2]:

$$\left.\begin{aligned} 1/\tau_D &= k_{21} + k'_{12} = k_{21} + {}^0k_{12}\,\Pi^f\left[n_A + n_B + n_A\,n_B\left(\frac{\partial \ln \Pi^f}{\partial n_A} + \frac{\partial \ln \Pi^f}{\partial n_B}\right)\right],\\ 1/\tau_U &= k_{23} + k_{32}. \end{aligned}\right\} \tag{7.4}$$

Treten beide Reaktionen gleichzeitig auf, dann sind die beiden Differentialgleichungen (7.3) nicht mehr unabhängig voneinander. Die beiden Zeitkonstanten

[1] Unter der Voraussetzung, daß $\Delta n_A = \Delta n_B$ und daß Π^f wenig von n_{AB} abhängt.

[2] Mit den unter Ziff. 4 diskutierten Einschränkungen (s. Anm. 2, S. 207).

τ_{I} und τ_{II}, die nun auftreten, sind also nicht mehr mit τ_D und τ_U identisch, sondern verhältnismäßig komplizierte Kombinationen der Geschwindigkeitskonstanten[1]:

$$\left.\begin{aligned} 1/\tau_{\mathrm{I}} &= \tfrac{1}{2}\left[\Sigma k + \sqrt{(\Sigma k)^2 - 4\varkappa}\right] = \lambda_{\mathrm{I}}, \\ 1/\tau_{\mathrm{II}} &= \tfrac{1}{2}\left[\Sigma k - \sqrt{(\Sigma k)^2 - 4\varkappa}\right] = \lambda_{\mathrm{II}} \\ \text{mit}\quad \Sigma k &= k'_{12} + k_{21} + k_{23} + k_{32} \\ \text{und}\quad \varkappa &= k'_{12} k_{23} + k'_{12} k_{32} + k_{21} k_{32}. \end{aligned}\right\} \tag{7.5}$$

Sie geben die Einstellgeschwindigkeiten der Gleichgewichte zweier voneinander unabhängiger Systeme I und II an, die durch die beiden „Normalvariablen" $\Delta n'_{\mathrm{I}}$ und $\Delta n'_{\mathrm{II}}$ (allgemein $\Delta n'_j$) bestimmt sind, d.h. durch zwei unabhängige Konzentrationsabweichungen vom Gleichgewicht, die ihrerseits lineare Kombinationen der drei ursprünglichen Konzentrationsänderungen $\Delta n_A = \Delta n_B$, $\Delta n_{A,B}$ und Δn_{AB} (allgemein Δn_i) sind.

In tensorieller Schreibweise erhält man für diesen linearen Zusammenhang

$$(\Delta n'_j) = \boldsymbol{M}(\Delta n_i) \quad \text{bzw.} \quad (\Delta n_i) = \boldsymbol{M}^{-1}(\Delta n'_j), \tag{7.6}$$

wobei die Matrix $\boldsymbol{M}$, aus der sich die inverse Matrix $\boldsymbol{M}^{-1}$ nach den bekannten Regeln bestimmen läßt, gegeben ist durch[2]

$$\boldsymbol{M} = \begin{pmatrix} \dfrac{k'_{12}}{k'_{12} - 1/\tau_I} & 1 & \dfrac{k_{32}}{k_{32} - 1/\tau_I} \\ \dfrac{k'_{12}}{k'_{12} - 1/\tau_{II}} & 1 & \dfrac{k_{32}}{k_{32} - 1/\tau_{II}} \\ 1 & 1 & 1 \end{pmatrix} \tag{7.6a}$$

Durch Einsetzen von $1/\tau_I$ und $1/\tau_{II}$ erhält man

$$\left.\begin{aligned} \Delta n'_{\mathrm{I}} &= -\frac{k'_{12}}{2}\left[2(k_{23} + k_{32}) - \Sigma k - \sqrt{\ }\right]\Delta n_A + \\ &\quad + \frac{k_{21}}{2}\left[2k_{32} - \Sigma k - \sqrt{\ }\right]\Delta n_{A,B} + k_{21} k_{32}\,\Delta n_{AB}, \\ \Delta n'_{\mathrm{II}} &= +\frac{k'_{12}}{2}\left[2(k_{23} + k_{32}) - \Sigma k + \sqrt{\ }\right]\Delta n_A - \\ &\quad - \frac{k_{21}}{2}\left[2k_{32} - \Sigma k + \sqrt{\ }\right]\Delta n_{A,B} - k_{21} k_{32}\,\Delta n_{AB}, \\ \Delta n'_{\mathrm{III}} &= +\Delta n_A \qquad + \Delta n_{A,B} \qquad + \Delta n_{AB} = 0, \end{aligned}\right\} \tag{7.6b}$$

wobei

$$\sqrt{\ } = \sqrt{(\Sigma k)^2 - 4\varkappa}.$$

Die beiden unabhängigen Systeme I und II benehmen sich nun genau so wie einfache Systeme, und ihr Relaxationsverhalten kann in gleicher Weise berechnet werden (s. Ziff. 4 und 5). An die Stelle der Größe ξ_i, die das Fortschreiten der Reaktion angibt, treten jetzt die Normalvariablen $\Delta n'_{\mathrm{I}}$ bzw. $\Delta n'_{\mathrm{II}}$. Die Behandlung des hier zunächst betrachteten allgemeinen Falles stößt wegen der komplizierten Ausdrücke für die Normalvariablen auf erhebliche Schwierigkeiten.

---

[1] Eine ausführliche Darstellung dieser Berechnung geben EIGEN [*51*], [*51a*] bzw. EIGEN und TAMM [*81*].

[2] Die Koeffizienten ergeben sich durch die Bedingung, daß die Faktoren λ_{I} und λ_{II}, wie oben angegeben, nur noch Funktionen der „Geschwindigkeitskonstanten" k'_{12}, k_{21}, k_{23}, k_{32} und nicht mehr der veränderlichen Konzentrationen sind:

$$\Delta \dot{n}'_{\mathrm{I}} = -\lambda_{\mathrm{I}} \cdot \Delta n'_{\mathrm{I}}; \qquad \Delta \dot{n}'_{\mathrm{II}} = -\lambda_{\mathrm{II}}\,\Delta n'_{\mathrm{II}}. \tag{7.7}$$

Die bei der Transformation sich ergebende dritte Variable Δn_{III} ist der konstanten Gesamtkonzentration wegen Null. Aus dem gleichen Grunde kann man in den Normalvariablen eine der Konzentrationsänderungen Δn_A, $\Delta n_{A,B}$ oder Δn_{AB} eliminieren.

Im allgemeinen sind nun die beiden Zeitkonstanten der Teilgewichte „Diffusion" und „chemische Umwandlung" nicht von gleicher Größe. Meist ist die Einstellzeit eines der beiden Teilgleichgewichte sogar wesentlich kürzer als die des anderen. Das Gleichgewicht des schnelleren Vorgangs stellt sich dann, wie bereits erwähnt, so ein, als ob der langsamere gar nicht vorhanden wäre. Für den langsameren Vorgang befindet sich dagegen der schnellere immer im Gleichgewicht. In diesen Fällen lassen sich die beiden Zeitkonstanten leicht bestimmen; dann ist nämlich $\varkappa \ll (\Sigma k)^2$, und es ergibt sich als Näherung

$$\left.\begin{aligned} 1/\tau_{\mathrm{I}} &\equiv \lambda_{\mathrm{I}} \approx \Sigma k - \varkappa/\Sigma k, \\ 1/\tau_{\mathrm{II}} &\equiv \lambda_{\mathrm{II}} \approx \varkappa/\Sigma k. \end{aligned}\right\} \tag{7.8}$$

Die beiden möglichen Fälle, daß die Diffusion schnell gegen die Umwandlung ist ($\tau_D \ll \tau_U$), bzw. daß sie sehr langsam gegen diese erfolgt ($\tau_D \gg \tau_U$), seien ihrer Wichtigkeit wegen hier diskutiert.

α) $\tau_D \ll \tau_U$. Die Diffusion ist der schnellere Vorgang, wenn einerseits die Konzentration nicht zu klein ist und wenn außerdem die „chemische" Umwandlung $A, B = AB$ mit einer großen Aktivierungsenergie verbunden ist. (Dieser Fall liegt offenbar beim Natriumsulfat vor; s. Ziff. 37.) Es wird dann mit

$$\left.\begin{aligned} &k_{21} + k'_{12} \gg k_{32} + k_{23}: \\ &\frac{1}{\tau_{\mathrm{I}}} \approx k_{21} + k'_{12} = \frac{1}{\tau_D} \text{ bzw. } \frac{1}{2\tau_{\mathrm{I}}} = k_{21}\left[1 + \frac{2\alpha(1-\delta)}{\delta^+}\right], \\ &\frac{1}{\tau_{\mathrm{II}}} \approx k_{32} + \frac{1}{1 + k_{21}/k'_{12}} k_{23} \lesseqq \frac{1}{\tau_U} \text{ bzw. } \frac{1}{2\tau_{\mathrm{II}}} = k_{32}\left[1 + \frac{2(1-\alpha)(1-\delta)}{2\alpha(1-\delta)+\delta^+}\right]. \end{aligned}\right\} \tag{7.9}$$

Dabei ist $\alpha = n_{A,B}/(n_{A,B} + n_{AB})$ der Umwandlungsgrad und $\delta = n_A/n_0$ der Gesamtdissoziationsgrad, während δ^+ eine Korrektur durch die Konzentrationsabhängigkeit des Aktivitätskoeffizienten enthält (s. Anm. 2, S. 218), so daß wegen Gl. (7.2) und (7.4):

$$\frac{k_{23}}{k_{32}} = \frac{1-\alpha}{\alpha} \quad \text{und} \quad \frac{k'_{12}}{k_{21}} = \frac{2\alpha(1-\delta)}{\delta^+} \quad \text{mit} \quad \delta^+ = \delta\Big/\left[1 + \frac{\delta}{2}\left(\frac{\partial \ln \Pi^f}{\partial \delta}\right)_n\right].$$

Die kleinere Zeitkonstante τ_{I} weicht, wie zu erwarten, nur unwesentlich von τ_D ab, also von derjenigen Zeitkonstante, die sich bei Vorhandensein der Diffusion allein ergibt. Sie ist also auch konzentrationsabhängig, und die zugehörige Relaxationsfrequenz $\nu_{m\mathrm{I}}$ beginnt bei großen Konzentrationen zuzunehmen. Die größere Zeitkonstante τ_{II} ist gegen τ_U vergrößert, d. h. die zugehörige Relaxationsfrequenz $\nu_{m\mathrm{II}}$ verkleinert. Bei kleinen Konzentrationen ist sie durch k_{32}, bei großen durch $k_{23} + k_{32} = 1/\tau_U$ gegeben. Die Änderung der Relaxationsfrequenz mit der Konzentration wird also klein für den Fall großer Konzentration der Zwischenstufe ($[A, B] \gg [AB]$); sie wird groß für den Fall verschwindender Konzentration der Zwischenstufe. Das ist verständlich, denn in diesem Fall geht die Reaktion praktisch direkt von $A + B$ nach AB (s. Fig. 2).

Der Verlauf der Relaxationsfrequenzen mit der Konzentration ist aus Fig. 2 zu ersehen, in der die Relativwerte $\nu_{m\mathrm{I}}/2\pi k_{21}$ und $\nu_{m\mathrm{II}}/2\pi k_{32}$ zusammen mit den zugehörigen G-Werten (s. Ziff. 8) über der konzentrationsabhängigen Variablen $n\Pi^f/K_D = c\Pi^f/{}^cK_D = (1-\delta)/\delta^2$ [1] für verschiedene Umwandlungsgrade α aufgetragen sind. Für hohe Umwandlungsgrade ($\alpha \approx 1$) zeigt $\nu_{m\mathrm{I}}$ den typischen Verlauf für ein binäres Gleichgewicht, nämlich einen starken Anstieg mit der Konzentration, während $\nu_{m\mathrm{II}}$ dem typischen, konstanten Verlauf der Anregungsreaktion folgt.

[1] Dieser Parameter wurde gewählt, weil $\Pi^f/{}^cK_D$ ebenso wie δ aus thermodynamischen Messungen gewonnen wird, wenn man das Gesamtgleichgewicht wie eine einfache Dissoziation behandelt. Die Konzentrationswerte n (Teilchen/Volumeneinheit) und c (Mol/Volumeneinheit) unterscheiden sich nur um einen Faktor, die Loschmidtsche Zahl N_L, ebenso die Gleichgewichtskonstanten $K_{n\to 0} \equiv K$ und $K_{c\to 0} \equiv {}^cK$. (Den Unterschied soll der hochgestellte Index c bei ${}^cK$ bzw. ${}^cK_D = (c_A c_B/c_{A,B})_{c\to 0}$ andeuten.)

Bei kleinen Umwandlungsgraden $\alpha \ll 1$ kehrt sich das Verhalten gerade um. Als Folge der geringen Besetzung des Zustandes A, B schiebt sich nämlich der Frequenzanstieg für $\nu_{m\mathrm{I}}$ zu sehr hohen Konzentrationen hinauf, während die Reaktion II praktisch zwischen den Zuständen $A+B$ und AB als binäres Gleichgewicht verläuft. Bei Dissoziationen über Zwischenstufen können die Relaxationsfrequenzen also ein auf den ersten Blick irreführendes Bild liefern (s. auch Ziff. 8).

Die in Fig. 2 zusätzlich eingetragene Konzentrationsskala gilt für $MgSO_4$-Lösungen und wurde unter Verwendung der von EIGEN und WICKE [55] angegebenen Gleichgewichtskonstante von $5 \cdot 10^{-3}$ Liter/Mol und für die von ihnen ermittelten Aktivitätskoeffizienten (s. Fig. 3) errechnet. Mit Hilfe dieser Werte kann man auch den Einfluß der Aktivitätskoeffizienten im Fall der $MgSO_4$-Lösungen berücksichtigen. Man erkennt, daß die Konzentrationsabhängigkeit der Relaxationsfrequenzen durch diesen Einfluß erheblich verkleinert wird.

β) $\tau_D \gg \tau_U$. Die Einstellung des Umwandlungsgleichgewichtes $A, B \rightleftharpoons AB$ verläuft schneller als die des Diffusionsvorgangs, wenn die Aktivierungsenergie der Umwandlung klein ist. Dieser Fall ist offenbar bei einigen Reaktionen unter Beteiligung von Protonen oder Hydroxylionen auf Grund deren anomaler Beweglichkeit gegeben (s. Ziff. 35 und 36). Es wird dann ganz analog zu dem oben erhaltenen Ergebnis

für[1] $k_{23}+k_{32} \gg k'_{12}+k_{21}$:

$$\left.\begin{aligned} \frac{1}{\tau_{\mathrm{I}}} &\approx k_{23}+k_{32}=\frac{1}{\tau_U}, \\ \frac{1}{\tau_{\mathrm{II}}} &\approx k'_{12}+k_{21}\frac{1}{1+k_{23}/k_{32}} \leq \frac{1}{\tau_D}. \end{aligned}\right\} \qquad (7.10)$$

Die kleinere Zeitkonstante τ_{I} weicht wenig von τ_U ab, sie ist konzentrationsunabhängig und außerordentlich klein, so daß sie kaum beobachtet werden kann. Die größere Zeitkonstante τ_{II} ist konzentrationsabhängig und kann beträchtlich von τ_D abweichen.

Ist die Konzentration des Zwischenzustandes A, B klein, dann gehen die Teilchen schnell durch diesen Zustand hindurch; das Reaktionsgleichgewicht verläuft zwischen $A+B$ und AB. Die Relaxationsfrequenz $\nu_{m\mathrm{II}}$ steigt daher mit zunehmender Elektrolytkonzentration von $k_{21} \cdot k_{32}/k_{23}$ aus mit $k'_{12}=k_{12}[n_A+n_B+n_A n_B(\partial \ln \Pi^f/\partial n_A+\partial \ln \Pi^f/\partial n_B)]$ an. Ist die Konzentration des Zwischenzustandes groß, so ist praktisch nur der Diffusionsvorgang vorhanden. Dieser bestimmt die Relaxationsfrequenz, die von k_{21} aus mit k'_{12}, also nahezu proportional zu der Konzentration, ansteigt [s. Gl. (7.10)].

8. Bestimmung der maximalen Absorptionsvolumina $(Q\lambda)_{m\mathrm{I}}$ und $(Q\lambda)_{m\mathrm{II}}$. Die beiden Volumenänderungen $\Delta^* V_{\mathrm{I}}$ und $\Delta^* V_{\mathrm{II}}$, die zu den zwei Relaxationsfrequenzen $\nu_{m\mathrm{I}}$ und $\nu_{m\mathrm{II}}$ gehören (s. Ziff. 7), und das Absorptionsspektrum einer Dissoziation über eine Zwischenstufe bestimmen,

$$\underset{(1)}{A^+ + B^-} \underset{D}{\overset{\Delta^* V_D}{\rightleftharpoons}} \underset{(2)}{A, B} \underset{U}{\overset{\Delta^* V_U}{\rightleftharpoons}} \underset{(3)}{AB},$$

wobei

$$[A]=[B]=\delta n \qquad [A,B]=(1-\delta)\,\alpha n \qquad [AB]=(1-\delta)(1-\alpha)\,n,$$

lassen sich aus den zugehörigen Volumenänderungen $\Delta^* V_D$ und $\Delta^* V_U$ verhältnismäßig leicht berechnen, wenn man die oben (s. Ziff. 7) bereits benutzte Voraussetzung macht, daß eins der beiden Teilgleichgewichte — entweder das eigentliche Diffusionsgleichgewicht $A+B \rightleftharpoons A, B$ oder das Umwandlungsgleichgewicht $A, B \rightleftharpoons AB$ — sich wesentlich schneller einstellt als das andere.

[1] Bei schwachen Säuren und Basen ist immer zusätzlich $k_{23} \gg k_{32}$.

Es sei hier der Fall betrachtet, daß das Diffusionsgleichgewicht die kleinere Zeitkonstante besitzt: $\tau_D \ll \tau_U$. Unter dieser Bedingung vereinfachen sich die angegebenen Ausdrücke für die Normalvariablen erheblich, insbesondere dann, wenn darüber hinaus *beide* Geschwindigkeitskonstanten der Diffusion größer als die der Umwandlungsreaktion sind: $k'_{12}, k_{21} \gg k_{23}, k_{32}$. Bei gleichzeitiger Weglassung überflüssiger Faktoren erhalten die Normalvariablen die einfache Form:

$$\left.\begin{aligned} \Delta n_{\mathrm{I}} &= -a\,\Delta n_A + b\,\Delta n_{A,B} &\quad \text{mit}\quad a &= \frac{k'_{12}}{k'_{12}+k_{21}},\\ \Delta n_{\mathrm{II}} &= \Delta n_A + \Delta n_{A,B} = -\Delta n_{AB} & b &= \frac{k_{21}}{k'_{12}+k_{21}}. \end{aligned}\right\} \tag{8.1}$$

Umgekehrt lassen sich die ursprünglichen Konzentrationsänderungen der Reaktionspartner durch die Normalvariablen leicht ausdrücken

$$\left.\begin{aligned} \Delta n_A &= b\,\Delta n_{\mathrm{II}} - \Delta n_{\mathrm{I}},\\ \Delta n_{A,B} &= a\,\Delta n_{\mathrm{II}} + \Delta n_{\mathrm{I}},\\ \Delta n_{AB} &= -\Delta n_{\mathrm{II}}. \end{aligned}\right\} \tag{8.2}$$

An diesem Gleichungssystem erkennt man, wie erwartet, daß bei dem Gleichgewicht I ein Austausch nur zwischen den Zuständen $A+B$ und A, B stattfindet, während bei II der Austausch zwischen AB einerseits und den Zuständen A, B und $A+B$ zusammen andererseits zustandekommt.

Die Gesamtabsorption ergibt sich als Überlagerung der beiden relaxierenden Anteile der Kompressibilität:

$$\mu = 2\pi \sum_{j=\mathrm{I},\,\mathrm{II}} \frac{\beta_j}{\beta_\infty}\,\frac{\omega\tau_j}{1+\omega^2\tau_j^2} \quad \text{mit} \quad \beta_j = \frac{1}{v}\left(\frac{\partial v}{\partial \xi_j}\right)_{T,p}\cdot\left(\frac{\partial \xi_j}{\partial p}\right)_{T,g}. \tag{8.3}$$

α) Berechnung der Volumenänderung $1/v\,(\partial v/\partial \xi_j)_T$. Die relative Änderung des Volumens ist durch die Konzentrationsänderungen der drei Zustände $A+B$, A, B und AB gegeben, deren Partialvolumina $^*V_i$ verschieden sind.

$$\frac{\Delta v}{v} = ({}^*V_A + {}^*V_B)\,\Delta n_A + {}^*V_{A,B}\,\Delta n_{A,B} + {}^*V_{AB}\,\Delta n_{AB}. \tag{8.4}$$

Führt man die Normalvariablen ein und verwendet man gleichzeitig die zur Bildung des Begegnungskomplexes gehörige Volumenzunahme[1] $\Delta {}^*V_D = {}^*V_{A,B} - ({}^*V_A + {}^*V_B)$ sowie die zur Bildung des Moleküls (bzw. Komplexes) AB gehörige $\Delta {}^*V_U = {}^*V_{AB} - {}^*V_{A,B}$, so erhält man

$$\frac{\Delta v}{v} = \Delta {}^*V_{\mathrm{I}}\,\Delta n_{\mathrm{I}} + \Delta {}^*V_{\mathrm{II}}\,\Delta n_{\mathrm{II}} \tag{8.5}$$

Es ist demnach

$$\Delta {}^*V_{\mathrm{I}} = \frac{1}{v}\frac{\partial v}{\partial n_{\mathrm{I}}} = \Delta {}^*V_D; \quad \Delta {}^*V_{\mathrm{II}} = \frac{1}{v}\frac{\partial v}{\partial n_{\mathrm{II}}} = \Delta {}^*V_U + \gamma\,\Delta {}^*V_D. \tag{8.6}$$

$$\text{mit} \quad \gamma = \frac{k_{21}}{k'_{12}+k_{21}} \ \text{bzw.} = {}^2\gamma = \frac{\delta^+}{2\alpha(1-\delta)+\delta^+}.$$

Während also die Volumenänderung bei dem Gleichgewicht I nur durch die bei der Begegnungskomplex-Bildung auftretende Volumenänderung $\Delta {}^*V_D$ bestimmt ist, kommt bei dem Gleichgewicht II zu dem Betrag $\Delta {}^*V_U$ durch die Umwandlung noch ein Anteil $\gamma\,\Delta {}^*V_D = k_{21}/(k'_{12}+k_{21})\cdot\Delta {}^*V_D$ aus der Diffusionsstufe hinzu. Er kommt dadurch zustande, daß ein Teil der Partikel nach der Umwandlung

[1] Hier ist die Differenz der Partialvolumina bei der jeweiligen Konzentration n bzw. c einzusetzen.

$AB \to A, B$ sofort nach $A + B$ übergeht. Der Faktor γ entspricht ungefähr der Gleichgewichtsverteilung der Partikel auf die beiden Stufen $A + B$ und A, B.

β) Berechnung von $(\partial \xi_j/\partial p)_{T,g}$. Da für das Auftreten der Konzentrationsänderungen die Druckabhängigkeit der beiden Gleichgewichtskonstanten K_U und K_D bzw. K_D/Π^f [s. Gl. (7.2)][1] maßgebend ist und da diese beiden Größen als Funktionen des Dissoziationsgrades bzw. des Anregungsgrades aufgefaßt werden können,

$$K_U = \frac{\alpha}{1-\alpha}; \quad K_{Dn} = \frac{K_D}{\Pi^f} = \frac{\delta^2 n}{\alpha(1-\delta)} = \frac{\delta^2 n}{(1-\delta)}\left(1 + \frac{1}{K_U}\right), \tag{8.7}$$

ist es zweckmäßig, die Konzentrationen ξ_j, d.h. die Normalvariablen Δn_{I} und Δn_{II} auf die ursprünglichen Konzentrationen $n_A = \delta n$, $n_{A,B} = \alpha(1-\delta)\, n$, $n_{AB} = (1-\alpha)(1-\delta)\, n$ zurückzuführen und die Differentiation über δ und α zu führen:

$$\left.\begin{aligned} &\frac{\partial n_{\mathrm{I}}}{\partial p} = \lim_{\Delta p \to 0}\left(-a\frac{\Delta n_A}{\Delta p} + b\frac{\Delta n_{A,B}}{\Delta p}\right)\\ &\text{mit}\\ &\qquad \lim_{\Delta p\to 0}\frac{\Delta n_A}{\Delta p} = \left[\frac{\partial n_A}{\partial \alpha}\cdot\frac{\partial\alpha}{\partial \ln K_U}\cdot\frac{\partial \ln K_U}{\partial p} + \frac{\partial n_A}{\partial \delta}\,\frac{\partial \delta}{\partial \ln K_{Dn\alpha}}\times\right.\\ &\qquad\qquad \left.\times\left(\frac{\partial \ln K_{Dn}}{\partial p} + \frac{1}{1+K_U}\cdot\frac{\partial \ln K_U}{\partial p}\right)\right]. \end{aligned}\right\} \tag{8.8}$$

Man erhält dann für die beiden gesuchten Größen Ergebnisse, die sich in der üblichen Weise (s. Ziff. 5) in einen nur von α und δ bzw. δ^+ abhängigen Anteil[2] G_{I}^+ bzw. G_{II}^+ und eine Differenz von Partialvolumina $\Delta^* V_{\mathrm{II}}/RT$ bzw. $\Delta^* V_{\mathrm{I}}/RT$, die jeweils mit einer der oben [s. Gl. (8.6)] ermittelten identisch ist, aufspalten lassen

$$\left.\begin{aligned} &\frac{\partial n_{\mathrm{I}}}{\partial p} = n\, G_{\mathrm{I}}^+ \frac{\Delta^* V_{\mathrm{I}}}{RT} \quad \text{wobei } \Delta^* V_{\mathrm{I}} = \Delta^* V_D\\ &\qquad G_{\mathrm{I}}^+ = \frac{G_{\mathrm{I}}}{1 + G_{\mathrm{I}}(\partial \ln \Pi^f/\partial\delta)_n} = \frac{\delta^+}{2}\cdot\frac{k'_{12}}{k_{21}}\cdot\frac{1}{1 + k'_{12}/k_{21}}\\ &\qquad \text{bzw. } {}^2G_{\mathrm{I}}^+ = \frac{\alpha(1-\delta)\,\delta^+}{2\alpha(1-\delta)+\delta^+}\\ &\frac{\partial n_{\mathrm{II}}}{\partial p} = n\, G_{\mathrm{II}}^+ \frac{\Delta^* V_{\mathrm{II}}}{RT} \quad \text{wobei } \Delta^* V_{\mathrm{II}} = \Delta^* V_U + \gamma\,\Delta^* V_D \text{ mit } \gamma \text{ [s. Gl. (8.6)]}\\ &\qquad G_{\mathrm{II}}^+ = \frac{\delta^+}{2}\cdot\frac{k'_{12}k_{23}}{k_{21}k_{32}}\cdot\frac{1}{1 + k'_{23}/k_{32}}\\ &\qquad \text{bzw. } {}^2G_{\mathrm{II}}^+ = (1-\delta)(1-\alpha)\left[\alpha + (1-\alpha)\frac{\delta^+}{2(1-\delta)+\delta^+}\right]\\ &\qquad\qquad = \frac{1 + k'_{12}/k_{21}}{1 + K_{23}}\, G_D^+ . \end{aligned}\right\} \tag{8.9}$$ [2]

Mit den gewonnenen Größen $1/v \cdot \partial v/\partial n$ und $\partial n_j/\partial p$ kann man nun die gesuchten maximalen Absorptionsvolumina angeben[3]:

$$\left.\begin{aligned} (Q\lambda)_{m\,\mathrm{I}} &= \frac{\pi}{N_L\cdot\beta_\infty\cdot RT}\cdot G_{\mathrm{I}}^+\cdot(\Delta^* V_{\mathrm{I}})^2\\ &\quad \text{mit } G_{\mathrm{I}}^+ \text{ und } \Delta^* V_{\mathrm{I}} \text{ n. (8.9)}\\ (Q\lambda)_{m\,\mathrm{II}} &= \frac{\pi}{N_L\cdot\beta_\infty\cdot RT}\cdot G_{\mathrm{II}}^+\cdot(\Delta^* V_{\mathrm{II}})^2\\ &\quad \text{mit } G_{\mathrm{II}}^+ \text{ und } \Delta^* V_{\mathrm{II}} \text{ n. (8.9)}. \end{aligned}\right\} \tag{8.10}$$

[1] Die Berücksichtigung der Aktivitätskoeffizienten ist bei schnellen Reaktionen etwas problematisch (s. Ziff. 10α).

[2] Die Einführung von $(1-\delta)$ und α verwandelt die auch für mehrstufige Gleichgewichte gültige Form G_{I}^+ bzw. G_{II}^+ in die speziellere ${}^2G_{\mathrm{I}}^+$ bzw. ${}^2G_{\mathrm{II}}^+$, die nur für das 2-stufige gilt.

[3] Der Verlauf dieser Größen G_{I}, G_{II} und $\Delta^* V_{\mathrm{I}}$, $\Delta^* V_{\mathrm{II}}$ läßt sich wenigstens näherungsweise schon durch die Betrachtung der Gleichgewichtsverhältnisse verstehen. Behandelt man das Gleichgewicht I als binäres Gleichgewicht mit einem Teil-Dissoziationsgrad $\delta' = n_A/(n_A + n_{A,B})$, der sich also nur auf die Zahl $n_A + n_{A,B}$ der an der Reaktion teilnehmenden Partikel

In Fig. 2a ist der Verlauf der Größen G_{I} und G_{II}, die man aus G_{I}^{+} und G_{II}^{+} erhält, wenn man die Konzentrationsabhängigkeit des Aktivitätskoeffizienten-Produkts Π^f vernachlässigt, d.h. für $\delta^+ \to \delta$ einsetzt, für verschiedene Umwandlungsgrade $\alpha = n_{A,B}/(n_{A,B} + n_{AB})$ in Abhängigkeit von dem dimensionslosen Konzentrationsparameter $n\,\Pi^f/K = c\,\Pi^f/{}^cK$ aufgetragen[1] (s. Anm. Ziff. 7). Es zeigt sich, daß die Größen G_{I} und G_{II} in weiten Konzentrationsbereichen ähnlich wie G sehr flach verlaufen[2]. Der Verlauf von G_{I} unterscheidet sich für große α (d.h. für den Fall, daß der Zustand A, B weit überwiegt) nicht sehr von dem der Größe G, die aus $c\Pi^f/{}^cK$ bzw. δ so bestimmt wird, als ob es sich bei dem Gesamtgleichgewicht um eine einfache Dissoziation handelt. Ihr Maximalwert ist jedoch kleiner, und er ist zu etwas höheren Konzentrationen verschoben.

Der Wert G_{II} verläuft bei großen α dagegen grundsätzlich anders und nähert sich — im Gegensatz zu G_{I} — gerade erst für kleine α dem Verlauf von G. Der Maximalwert von G_{II} ist für $\alpha \leqq 0{,}5$ immer 0,25 und liegt für $\alpha \approx 0{,}5$ bei sehr hohen Konzentrationen; erst bei sehr kleinen Werten von α rückt das Maximum in die Nähe des Maximums von G. Für Werte $\alpha > 0{,}5$ wird mit zunehmendem α das Maximum kleiner, und G_{II} fällt im mittleren Konzentrationsbereich stark ab. Ebenso wie bei den Relaxationsfrequenzen ist also auch bei den G-Werten der Verlauf mit der Konzentration von dem Umwandlungsgrad α abhängig. Die Zusammendrängung der Konzentrationsskala auf Grund der Konzentrationsabhängigkeit der Aktivitäten bewirkt, daß die Konzentrationsabhängigkeit der G-Werte sehr klein werden kann.

Betrag und Konzentrationsabhängigkeit des Absorptionsvolumens sind außer durch die Faktoren G_{I} bzw. G_{II} im wesentlichen durch die zugehörigen Differenzen der Partialvolumina gegeben. Während jedoch für den Fall, daß die Diffusion der schnellere Vorgang ist, $\Delta^*V_{\mathrm{I}} (= \Delta^*V_D)$ nur den geringfügigen Gang von Δ^*V_D mit der Konzentration aufweist, ist Δ^*V_{II} $(= \Delta^*V_U + \gamma\,\Delta^*V_D)$ auf Grund der Konzentrationsabhängigkeit des Faktors γ stark konzentrationsabhängig. Das ist besonders dann der Fall, wenn die Partialvolumina-Differenzen Δ^*V_U und Δ^*V_D entgegengesetzte Vorzeichen haben, weil dann bei einer bestimmten Konzentration Δ^*V_{II} Null wird, so daß die Absorption bei dieser verschwinden muß. Fig. 2b zeigt für eine Reihe von Werten Δ^*V_D/Δ^*V_U den Verlauf von Δ^*V_{II} für verschiedene α. Es können sehr starke Konzentrationsabhängigkeiten auftreten.

Haben Δ^*V_U und Δ^*V_D entgegengesetzte Vorzeichen, so treten nur für sehr große und sehr kleine Umwandlungsgrade α geringfügige oder wenigstens monotone

---

bezieht, dann kann man den G'-Faktor und das zugehörige Absorptionsvolumen $(Q\,\lambda)_m$ ganz formal nach Gl. (5.6) angeben. Man braucht diese Größen dann nur noch auf die Gesamtzahl n der Partikel umzurechnen, und erhält mit der oben gewählten Definition die gleichen Werte wie bei der genauen Rechnung

$$\left.\begin{aligned} G_{\mathrm{I}G} &= G'\,\frac{n_A + n_{A,B}}{n} = \frac{\alpha\,\delta\,(1-\delta)}{2\,\alpha\,(1-\delta) + \delta} = G_{\mathrm{I}} \\ \Delta^*V_{\mathrm{I}G} &= \Delta^*V_D = \Delta^*V_{\mathrm{I}}\,. \end{aligned}\right\} \tag{8.11a}$$

Das gleiche Verfahren liefert für das Gleichgewicht II allerdings ein etwas von der exakten Rechnung abweichendes Ergebnis, das jedoch den grundsätzlichen Verlauf gut wiedergibt.

$$\left.\begin{aligned} G_{\mathrm{II}G} &= G'' = (1-\alpha)\,(1-\delta)\,[\alpha\,(1-\delta) + \delta] = (G_{\mathrm{II}}^{+})_{\delta^+\to 2\delta} \neq G_{\mathrm{II}} \\ \Delta^*V_{\mathrm{II}G} &= \Delta^*V_U + \frac{n_A + n_{A,B}}{n}\,\Delta^*V_D = \\ &\Delta^*V_U + \frac{\delta}{\alpha\,(1-\delta) + \delta}\,\Delta^*V_D = (\Delta^*V_{\mathrm{II}})_{\delta^+\to 2\delta} \neq \Delta^*V_{\mathrm{II}}\,. \end{aligned}\right\} \tag{8.11b}$$

[1] Der hochgestellte Index c soll andeuten, daß die Gleichgewichtskonstante ${}^cK$ sich auf Konzentrationen c bezieht, die in Mol/Volumeneinheit gemessen sind.

[2] G ist identisch mit G_{I} für $\alpha = 1$ bzw. mit G_{II} für $\alpha = 0$.

Fig. 2a. Konzentrationsabhängigkeit der Relaxationsfrequenzen $\nu_{m\,\mathrm{I}}$ und $\nu_{m\,\mathrm{II}}$ (Relativwerte $2\pi\nu_{m\,\mathrm{I}}/k_{21}$ und $2\pi\nu_{m\,\mathrm{II}}/k_{32}$) und der Faktoren G_{I} und G_{II}, berechnet für eine „Dissoziation über eine Zwischenstufe" (mit schneller Einstellung des Diffusionsgewichtes und langsamer Einstellung des Umwandlungsgleichgewichtes) für verschiedene Umwandlungsgrade α. ——— ohne und – – – mit Berücksichtigung der Änderung der Aktivitätskoeffizienten mit der Konzentration. $c\Pi^f/{}^cK$-Skala gültig für alle 2-2-wertigen Elektrolyte, c-Skala für $MgSO_4$.

Fig. 2b. Konzentrationsabhängigkeit der Volumenänderung $\Delta^* V_{\mathrm{II}}$ (Relativwert $\Delta^* V_{\mathrm{II}}/\Delta^* V_U$) berechnet für die langsame Relaxation eines „Gleichgewichtes über eine Zwischenstufe" (Diffusion: schnell, Umwandlung: langsam) für verschiedene Umwandlungsgrade α und für verschiedene Verhältnisse $\Delta^* V_D/\Delta^* V_U$. Die Konzentrationsabhängigkeit der Aktivitätskoeffizienten und der Partialvolumendifferenz $\Delta^* V_D$ ist nicht berücksichtigt.

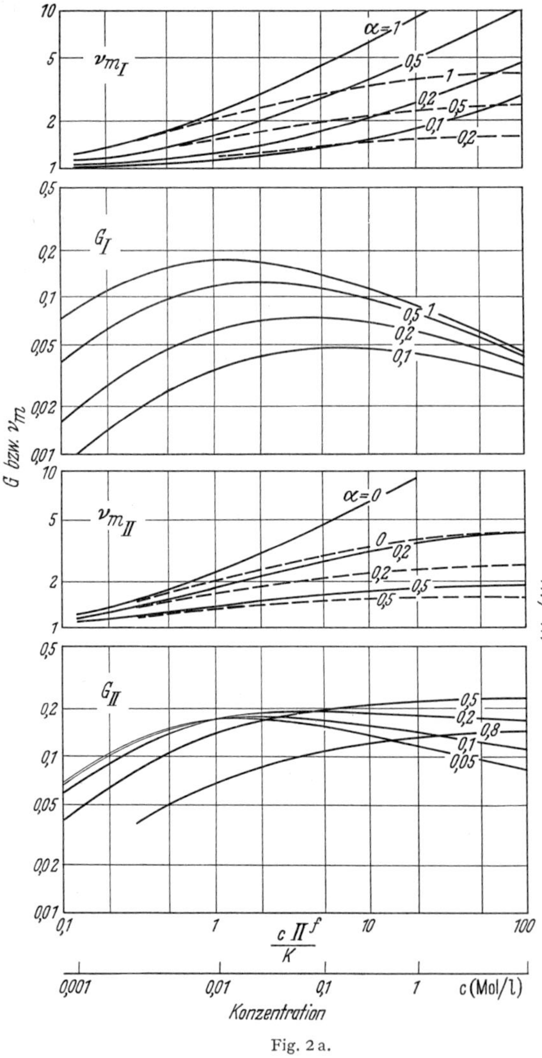

Fig. 2a.

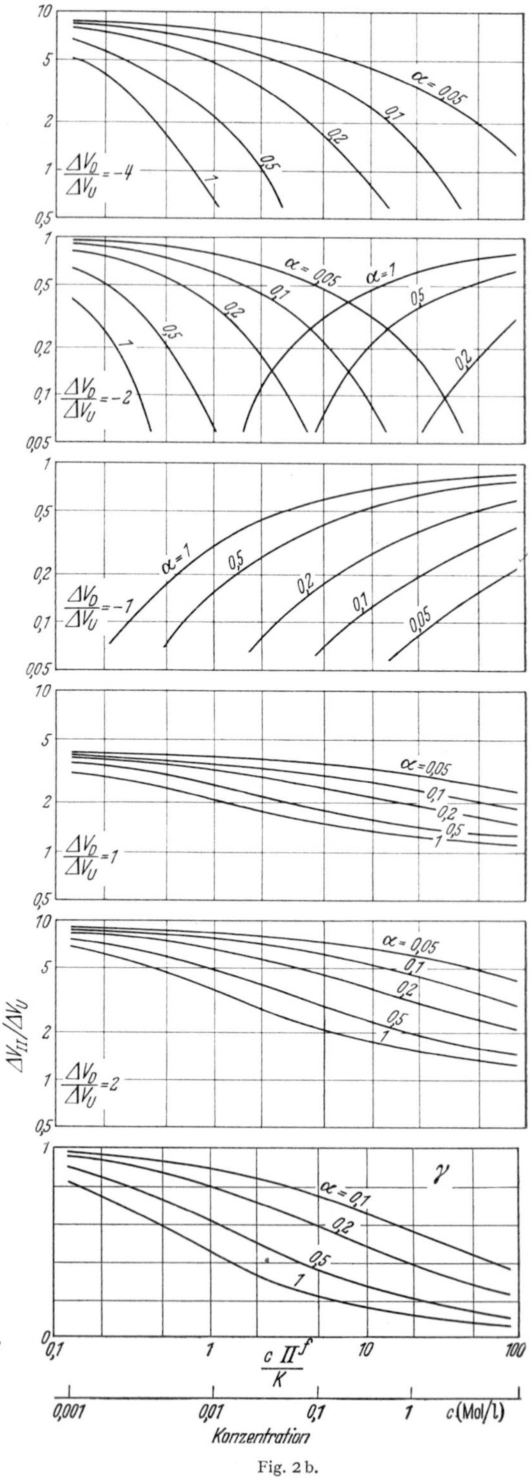

Fig. 2b.

Konzentrationsabhängigkeiten auf, die möglicherweise von einer entgegengesetzten Konzentrationsabhängigkeit des G-Faktors kompensiert werden können. Nur diese können dann die vielfach gemessene geringe Konzentrationsabhängigkeit des Absorptionsvolumens liefern.

9. Dissoziation über mehr als eine Zwischenstufe. Es ist durchaus möglich, daß die Dissoziation über mehr als eine Zwischenstufe verläuft. Speziell der Übergang vom Begegnungskomplex zum Aquokomplex bzw. Molekül kann natürlich über Zwischenstufen erfolgen. Sehr wahrscheinlich ist bei einigen Elektrolyten nach dem Diffusionsschritt das Ineinanderschieben der Hydrathülle zur Bildung eines Hydratkomplexes $A \cdot B$, welches eine beträchtliche Volumenänderung bewirkt, außerdem mit einer Aktivierungsenergie verbunden, deren Überwindung einer Zwischen-Umwandlungsreaktion U gleichkommt. Dieser folgt dann ein weiterer Umwandlungsschritt U^* vom Hydratkomplex zum Aquokomplex, in dem A und B unmittelbar benachbart sind:

$$\underbrace{A + B \underset{D}{\rightleftharpoons} A, B \underset{U}{\rightleftharpoons} A \cdot B}_{D^*} \underset{U^*}{\rightleftharpoons} AB \tag{9.1}$$

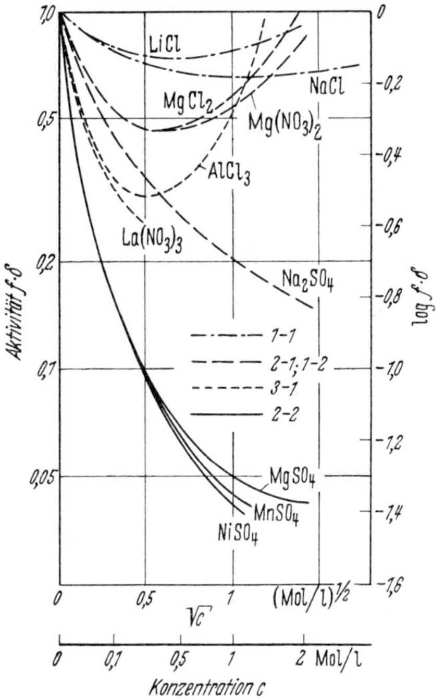

Fig. 3. Konzentrationsabhängigkeit der Aktivität ($f\delta$) für verschiedenwertige Elektrolyte nach EIGEN [51 a].

Bei der Betrachtung dieser Reaktionsfolge sind nun ganz ähnliche Überlegungen auszuführen, wie bei der Dissoziation über nur eine Zwischenstufe. Man kann sofort folgern, daß die Zwischen-Umwandlung U nur beobachtbar wird, wenn sie verhältnismäßig langsam gegen die Diffusion erfolgt und wenn weder die Konzentration des Hydratkomplexes $A \cdot B$ noch die des Begegnungskomplexes A, B verschwindend klein ist. Sie macht sich dadurch bemerkbar, daß sie — wie andere Umwandlungsreaktionen — eine Einstellgeschwindigkeit (Relaxationsfrequenz) liefert, die nur wenig von der Konzentration abhängt. Es liegen Anzeichen dafür vor, daß diese Zwischen-Umwandlung U bei einigen Elektrolyten eine Rolle spielt. Sie beeinflußt möglicherweise den oberen Anstieg des Absorptionsvolumens bei den Sulfaten (s. Ziff. 37), während wahrscheinlich der Umwandlungsschritt U^* von $A \cdot B$ nach AB die untere Relaxation der 2-2-wertigen Elektrolyte verursacht.

Solange die Konzentration der freien Ionen einen wesentlichen Teil der Elektrolytkonzentration ausmacht, hat das Gleichgewicht D^* immer den Charakter eines binären Gleichgewichtes, insbesondere benimmt sich die stärker ausgeprägte der beiden zugehörigen Relaxationen wie die eines Diffusionsgleichgewichtes (s. Ziff. 6). Für den Grenzfall, daß die Konzentration der Begegnungskomplexe A, B klein ist, geht das Gleichgewicht D^* in das der reinen Diffusion über.

Die im allgemeinen Fall sehr komplizierte Lösung läßt sich in Sonderfällen als geschlossener Ausdruck darstellen, z. B. dann, wenn ein Reaktions-Teilschritt jeweils schnell gegen den nächsten erfolgt. Das dann aus weit getrennten Relaxationsfrequenzen bestehende Relaxationsspektrum läßt sich in diesem Fall sukzessiv berechnen in ähnlicher Weise wie es beim Übergang vom ein- zum zweistufigen Mechanismus möglich war.

Für ein *dreistufiges Gleichgewicht* mit den Bezeichnungen

$$\overset{1}{A} + B \underset{k_{21}}{\overset{k_{12}}{\rightleftharpoons}} \overset{2}{AB_2} \underset{k_{32}}{\overset{k_{23}}{\rightleftharpoons}} \overset{3}{AB_3} \underset{k_{43}}{\overset{k_{34}}{\rightleftharpoons}} \overset{4}{AB_4} \tag{9.2a}$$

bedeutet die oben genannte etwas erweiterte Bedingung

$$k_{12},\ k_{21} \gg k_{23},\ k_{32} \gg k_{34},\ k_{43}, \tag{9.3}$$

daß die Konzentration von AB_4 während der Einstellung der beiden vorgelagerten Gleichgewichte praktisch unverändert bleibt. τ_{I} und τ_{II} sind also mit denen für das zweistufige Gleichgewicht identisch. τ_{III} folgt analog zu τ_{II}.

$$\left.\begin{aligned} \frac{1}{\tau_{\mathrm{I}}} &= k_{21} + k'_{12} \quad \text{mit } k'_{12} \text{ nach Gl. (4.4)},\\ \frac{1}{\tau_{\mathrm{II}}} &= k_{32} + \frac{k'_{12}}{k'_{12} + k_{21}} \cdot k_{23} = k_{32} + k'_{23},\\ \frac{1}{\tau_{\mathrm{III}}} &= k_{43} + \frac{k'_{23}}{k'_{23} + k_{32}} \cdot k_{34} = k_{43} + k'_{34}. \end{aligned}\right\} \tag{9.4}$$

In ähnlicher Weise erhält man die Kompressibilitätsanteile β_j bzw. die zugehörigen maximalen Absorptionsvolumina $(Q\lambda)_{mj}$:

$$\left.\begin{aligned} (Q\lambda)_{mj} &= \frac{\pi}{c}\,\frac{\beta_j}{\beta_\infty} = \frac{\pi}{N_L \beta_\infty R T} \cdot G_j^+ \cdot (\varDelta {}^*V_j)^2 \\ \text{mit} \quad {}^3G_{\mathrm{I}}^+ &= \frac{1}{\left[\frac{\delta^+}{2}\right]^{-1} + [(1-\delta)\,\alpha]^{-1}} = {}^2G_{\mathrm{I}}^+ \quad \text{nach Gl. (8.9)}; \quad \varDelta {}^*V_{\mathrm{I}} = \varDelta {}^*V_{12};\\ {}^3G_{\mathrm{II}}^+ &= \frac{(1-\delta)}{\left[\frac{\delta^+}{2(1-\delta)} + \alpha\right]^{-1} + [(1-\alpha)\,\beta]^{-1}} \quad \text{bezügl. } G_{\mathrm{II}}^+ \text{ s. Gl. (8.9).}\\ &= \frac{1 + k'_{12}/k_{21}}{1 + K_{23}} \cdot G_{D3}^+; \qquad \varDelta {}^*V_{\mathrm{II}} = \varDelta {}^*V_{23} + \gamma\, \varDelta {}^*V_{12};\\ {}^3G_{\mathrm{III}}^+ &= \frac{(1-\delta)(1-\alpha)}{\left[\frac{\delta^+}{2(1-\delta)(1-\alpha)} + \frac{\alpha}{1-\alpha} + \beta\right]^{-1} + [1-\beta]^{-1}}\\ &= \frac{1 + \frac{k'_{12}}{k_{21}} \cdot \left(1 + \frac{1}{K_{23}}\right)}{1 + K_{34}(1 + K_{23})} \cdot G_D^+; \qquad \varDelta {}^*V_{\mathrm{III}} = \varDelta {}^*V_{34} + \frac{k'_{23}}{k'_{23} + k_{32}}\, \varDelta {}^*V_{\mathrm{II}}, \end{aligned}\right\} \tag{9.5a}$$

wobei $K_{23} = k_{32}/k_{23}$; $K_{34} = k_{43}/k_{34}$; $\beta = n_3/(n_3 + n_4)$. k'_{23} s. Gl. (9.4). G_{D3}^+ entsteht aus G_D^+, wenn $\delta = n_1/n$ durch $\delta_3 = n_1/(n - n_4)$ ersetzt wird.

Das Gleichungssystem (9.5) läßt sich für höherstufige Gleichgewichte erweitern, wenn für alle Stufen die Bedingungen

$$k_{n-1,n},\ k_{n,n-1} \gg k_{n,n+1},\ k_{n+1,n} \tag{9.3a}$$

erfüllt sind.

Die Berechnung des dreistufigen Gleichgewichts ist auch dann noch in geschlossener Form möglich, wenn die Einstellgeschwindigkeiten der beiden oberen Stufen vergleichbar sind, wenn also nur

$$k'_{12},\ k_{21},\ k_{23},\ k_{32} \gg k_{34},\ k_{43}. \tag{9.6}$$

Man hat dann für die beiden schnelleren Relaxationen die allgemeineren Lösungen Gl. (7.5) einzusetzen, während für die langsamere Stufe der in Gl. (9.4) gegebene Ausdruck der Form nach erhalten bleibt. Dieser Fall spielt eine große Rolle bei den „starken" Elektrolyten, da sich bei diesen die höheren Dissoziationsstufen bzw. der Ionenwolkeneffekt dicht überlagern (s. Ziff. 38 δ).

III. Geschwindigkeitskonstanten bestimmter Teilreaktionen.

10. Diffusionsvorgänge. Für das Relaxationsverhalten von Elektrolyt-Lösungen sind Wechselwirkungs-Reaktionen sowohl zwischen den Ionen untereinander als auch zwischen den Ionen und den Lösungsmittel-Molekülen (Hydratation) von Bedeutung. Während bei der ersten Gruppe Diffusionsvorgänge eine Rolle spielen, verhalten sich die Reaktionen der zweiten Gruppe wie reine Umwandlungsvorgänge (Vor- und Rückwärts-Reaktion von erster Ordnung), da die Ionen ständig von Lösungsmittel-Molekülen umgeben sind.

Begegnung und Entfernung der Reaktionspartner bei Assoziations- bzw. Dissoziations-Reaktionen sind in ihrer Geschwindigkeit durch die Diffusion der Reaktionspartner in dem Lösungsmittel gegeben.

α) Begegnungsvorgang. Als Begegnungsvorgang ist derjenige Teil der Annäherung der Ionen anzusehen, der allein durch die Diffusion und die elektrostatische Anziehung bestimmt ist. Er endet formal bei einem Abstand $r=a$, in dem eine weitere Annäherung durch andere Erscheinungen (wie Abtrennung von Hydratwassermolekeln, Auftreten chemischer Bindungen usw.) beeinflußt ist. Der zugehörige Zustand der Ionen, der als Begegnungskomplex A, B bezeichnet werden kann, ist also als Teilzustand der Ionenwolke aufzufassen (s. EIGEN [*50*]).

Die Geschwindigkeitskonstante k_{12} des Begegnungsvorgangs kann nach EIGEN [*50*] auf dem von DEBYE [*52*] angegebenen Wege aus dem Diffusionsstrom $I_{Ba}=k_{12}\cdot n_{B\infty}$ der Ionen B durch eine Kugelfläche F_a im Abstand $r=a$ um ein Ion A errechnet werden

$$k_{12}=I_{Ba}\frac{1}{n_{B\infty}}=4\pi\cdot\overline{D}\,\Pi_1^f\,\frac{z_A z_B\cdot e_0^2}{\varepsilon kT}\cdot\left[\exp\left(\frac{z_A z_B e_0^2}{a\,\varepsilon kT}\right)-1\right]^{-1}. \qquad (10.2)$$

Dabei ist k die Boltzmann-Konstante, ε die Dielektrizitätskonstante des Lösungsmittels, $z_A e_0$ und $z_B e_0$ die Ionenladungen, $\overline{D}=D_A+D_B$ der Diffusionskoeffizient für die Relativbewegung des Ions B zum fixiert gedachten Ion A [1].

β) Entfernungsvorgang. Bisher wurde nur der Begegnungsvorgang betrachtet; dieser kann natürlich nur ständig in der angegebenen Weise verlaufen, wenn die angenommene Konzentrationsverteilung durch eine Rückreaktion aufrechterhalten wird, d.h. durch einen Vorgang, der die Ionen B ständig wieder vom Zentralion A wegbefördert. Man zerlegt den Diffusionsvorgang also in zwei Vorgänge, die völlig getrennt voneinander betrachtet werden können.

Man erhält die Geschwindigkeitskonstante k_{21} des Entfernungsvorganges in ähnlicher Weise wie die der Begegnung, wenn man die Randbedingungen durch diejenigen für die aus dem Komplex A, B stammenden Ionen B' ersetzt, nämlich $n_{B'}\to 0$ für $r\to\infty$ und $n_{B'}=1/\Delta v_k$ für $r\to a$, (dabei gibt die zweite Bedingung nur an, daß sich im Komplex A, B d.h. in der Kugelschale vom Volumen Δv_k an der Oberfläche des Zentralions A eben gerade *ein* Teilchen befindet):

$$k_{21}=\frac{4\pi\,\overline{D}\exp\left(z_B e_0\psi/kT\right)}{\Delta v_k\cdot\int\limits_a^\infty\exp\left(z e_0\psi/kT\right)dr/r^2}\approx\frac{4\pi}{\Delta v_k}\cdot\overline{D}\,\Pi_2^f\,\frac{z_A z_B e_0^2}{\varepsilon kT}\cdot\left[1-\exp\left(\frac{-z_A z_B e_0^2}{a\,\varepsilon kT}\right)\right]^{-1}. \qquad (10.3)^2$$

γ) Einstellgeschwindigkeit der Begegnungskomplexe. Mit Hilfe der Geschwindigkeitskonstanten von Begegnung und Entfernung (s. Ziff. 10α und β) kann man die Einstellgeschwindigkeit der Begegnungskomplexe nach Gl. (4.4) sofort angeben. Wenn man zunächst ganz formal den Effekt der Ionenwolke nur durch

[1] Der Faktor Π_1^f ist nach EIGEN [*51*] nicht mit dem bei langsameren Vorgängen wirksamen Aktivitätskoeffizientenprodukt identisch, da dessen Anwendung eine im Gleichgewicht befindliche Ionenwolke zur Voraussetzung hat. Gerade das ist aber bei Vorgängen mit Diffusionsgeschwindigkeit nicht der Fall, denn die Gleichgewichtseinstellung der Ionenwolke ist selbst ein Diffusionsvorgang. Eine hinreichend exakte Anwendung der angegebenen Gl. (10.2) ist also nur möglich bei verhältnismäßig kleinen Ionenkonzentrationen. Bei großen Konzentrationen ist unter Umständen die Relaxation der Ionenwolke mit zu berücksichtigen.

[2] Auch hier können bei großen Konzentrationen auf Grund der Ausbildung der Ionenwolke Abweichungen auftreten. Ihr Vorhandensein soll auch hier wieder rein formal durch den Faktor Π_2^f angedeutet werden.

das (aus dem Gleichgewicht der Ionenwolke definierte) Aktivitätskoeffizienten-Produkt Π^f berücksichtigt, erhält man als Näherung für die Einstellgeschwindigkeit[1]:

$$\frac{1}{\tau_D} = k_{21} + k_{12}(n_A + \cdots) = 4\pi \cdot \overline{D} \cdot \frac{z_A z_B \cdot e_0^2}{\varepsilon \mathrm{k} T} \left[\exp \frac{z_A z_B e_0^2}{a \varepsilon \cdot \mathrm{k} T} - 1\right]^{-1} \times \\ \times \left[\frac{1}{\Delta v_k} \exp \frac{z_A z_B e_0^2}{a \varepsilon \mathrm{k} T} + \Pi^f \left(n_A + n_B + n_A n_B \sum \frac{\partial \ln \Pi^f}{\partial n_i}\right)\right]. \tag{10.4}$$

Die Einstellgeschwindigkeit ist konzentrationsabhängig. Ein Teil dieser Abhängigkeit wird durch das bekannte Verhalten der Aktivitätskoeffizienten mit der Konzentration jedoch kompensiert (s. Ziff. 38).

δ) Einstellgeschwindigkeit der Ionenwolke. Für die zeitliche Einstellung der Ionenwolke in verdünnten Lösungen erhalten DEBYE und FALKENHAGEN [*54*] aus der Kontinuitätsgleichung eine Relaxationszeit, die in der Schreibweise, die EIGEN [*50*] gibt, den Zusammenhang mit k_{12} und k_{21} erkennen läßt

$$\frac{1}{\tau_W} = 4\pi \frac{z_A z_B e_0^2 (n_B D_A + n_A D_B)}{\varepsilon \mathrm{k} T}. \tag{10.5}$$

Die Umordnung der Ionenwolke ist unter Umständen mit einer beträchtlichen Volumenänderung verbunden, die sich auf den veränderten Einfluß der Ionenladungen auf die umgebenden Wassermoleküle bei Annäherung der Ionen zurückführen läßt.

ε) Häufigkeit der Begegnungskomplexe A, B. Aus den Geschwindigkeitskonstanten für Begegnungs- und Entfernungsvorgang läßt sich eine Gleichgewichtskonstante bestimmen:

$$\frac{1}{{}^cK_D} = N_L \frac{k_{12}}{k_{21}} = N_L \Delta v_k \exp\left(\frac{z_A z_B e_0^2}{a \varepsilon \mathrm{k} T}\right) \cdot \Pi^f. \tag{10.6}$$

Sie entspricht dem thermodynamisch ableitbaren Wert und ist natürlich unabhängig von der Diffusionskonstante $\overline{D}$. Der bei der Quotientenbildung auftretende Faktor Π^f entspricht genau dem thermodynamisch definierten Aktivitätskoeffizienten-Produkt.

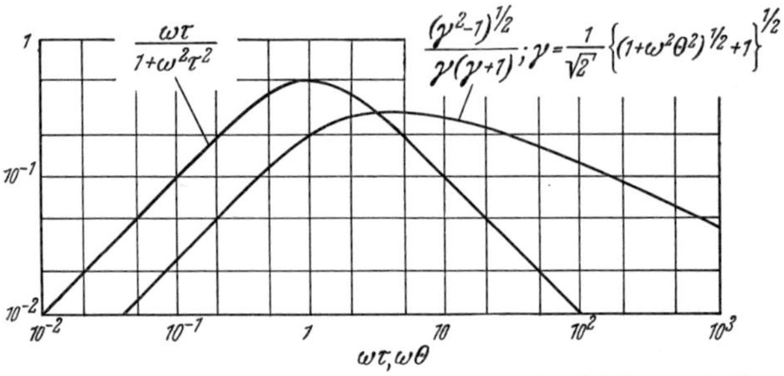

Fig. 4. Frequenzabhängigkeit der Ionenwolken-Absorption ($Q\lambda$) (rechts), im Vergleich zu einer „einstufigen" Relaxations-Absorption (links), nach EIGEN [*51 a*].

Die Kenntnis der Gleichgewichtskonstante ermöglicht eine Abschätzung der Häufigkeit der A, B-Komplexe („Begegnungs-Komplexe"), die dann von Bedeutung ist, wenn eine Weiterreaktion zu stabilen AB-Aggregaten stattfindet. Ohne diese Weiterreaktion ist der A, B-Begegnungs-Komplex nur eine der Lagen, die die in elektrostatischer Wechselwirkung stehenden hydratisierten Ionen A und B zueinander einnehmen können und die insgesamt durch den Begriff der Ionenwolke [*50*] erfaßt werden. Wenn dagegen die Weiterreaktion wesentlich überwiegt, können die Ionenwolkeneffekte

[1] Eine genauere Betrachtung (s. EIGEN [*51*]) zeigt, daß diese Rechnung wegen der nur vergleichbar schnellen Einstellung der Ionenwolke nur eine Näherung ist. Durch den Einfluß der Ionenwolke erhält man statt einer exponentiell verlaufenden Zeitfunktion, d.h. einer einzigen Zeitkonstante eine Überlagerung von Einstellfunktionen mit vielen benachbarten Zeitkonstanten, so daß man dementsprechend eine andere Frequenzabhängigkeit bekommt (s. Fig. 4). Es ist daher sicher nicht berechtigt, in der Einstellgeschwindigkeit auch die Änderung der Aktivitätskoeffizienten in der angegebenen Weise zu berücksichtigen. Ihr Einfluß ist wahrscheinlich wesentlich kleiner.

in erster Näherung vernachlässigt werden, wie das bei den sehr schwachen Elektrolyten der Fall ist.

Während der A, B-Begegnungs-Komplex als Teilzustand der Ionenwolke erscheint, bei dem die beiden hydratisierten Ionen gerade den kleinsten Abstand a haben, der noch ohne eine Veränderung ihrer Eigenschaften möglich ist [*51a*], tritt bei Unterschreitung dieses Mindestabstandes eine teilweise Auflösung der Hydrathülle ein. Außerdem werden spezielle chemische Einflüsse wirksam, die sich in entsprechenden Anteilen der Zustandsgrößen (Entropie, Enthalpie) äußern. Solche Zustände ($r < a$), hier mit AB bzw. $A \cdot B$ gekennzeichnet, sind also als „undissoziiert“ anzusehen und sind von den Ionenwolkeneffekten getrennt zu behandeln. Es ist selbstverständlich, daß auch die elektrostatischen Wechselwirkungskräfte bei diesen kleinen Ionenabständen nicht mehr mit der für große Abstände geltenden Dielektrizitätskonstante des Wassers berechnet werden können.

11. Umwandlungsvorgänge. *α) Chemische Umsetzungen, Assoziatbildung.* Die Berechnung der chemischen Umwandlungen, — zu denen insbesondere auch der Übergang von Begegnungskomplex A, B zum Hydratkomplex $A \cdot B$ oder zur Molekel bzw. zu einem Komplex AB ($A, B \rightleftharpoons AB$) und der Auf- und Abbau von Hydrathüllen ($A \rightleftharpoons A'$) gehört, — ist wesentlich verwickelter als die der Diffusionsvorgänge. Das hat seinen Grund darin, daß für die chemischen Umwandlungen Nahwirkungskräfte entscheidend sind, deren theoretische Erfassung einige Schwierigkeiten bereitet.

Die Häufigkeit der Übergänge von einem Zustand zum anderen, durch die die Geschwindigkeitskonstanten bestimmt sind, ist entsprechend der Arrheniusschen Beziehung durch einen Stoßfaktor j_0 und durch die bei dem Übergang auftretende Aktivierungsenergie ${}^{A}E$ bestimmt.

$$k_i = j_0 \cdot \exp\left(-{}^{A}E_i/RT\right).\text{[1]} \tag{11.1}$$

Der Stoßfaktor j_0, der die Häufigkeit der Stöße zwischen den reagierenden Partikeln erfaßt, ist eine nur schwer bestimmbare Größe. Er kann Höchstwerte bis zur Größenordnung $10^{13}\,\mathrm{sec}^{-1}$ annehmen. Die Temperaturabhängigkeit des Stoßfaktors ist meist gering, so daß sie gegen die der Exponentialfunktion vernachlässigt werden kann. Man kann aus diesem Grunde die Aktivierungsenergie ${}^{A}E_i$ ermitteln, wenn die Temperaturabhängigkeit der Geschwindigkeitskonstanten bzw. Relaxationsfrequenz z.B. auf akustischem Wege ermittelt wurde:

$$\ln k_i = \ln j_0 - {}^{A}E_i \cdot \frac{1}{RT}. \tag{11.1a}$$

In vielen Fällen, vor allem dann, wenn Protonen oder Hydroxylionen beteiligt sind, z.B. [*50*] im Falle $H^+ + OH^- = H_2O$ sind diese Umwandlungsvorgänge wesentlich schneller als die Diffusionsvorgänge, die dann geschwindigkeitsbestimmend sind, während von der chemischen Umwandlung nur die Gleichgewichtskonstante eingeht. In anderen Fällen z.B. bei den Sulfaten zweiwertiger Metalle sind die Umwandlungsvorgänge der großen Aktivierungsenergie wegen jedoch so langsam, daß sie geschwindigkeitsbestimmend werden.

β) Hydratationsgleichgewicht. Änderungen des Hydratationszustandes allein, die sich wie monomolekulare Reaktionen ($A \rightleftharpoons A'$) verhalten, und die isoliert z.B. in vollständig dissoziierten 1-1-wertigen starken Elektrolyten auftreten, ver-

[1] Eyring [*56*] leitete anstelle von Gl. (11.1) folgende Formel ab

$$k_i = \boldsymbol{k}T/h \cdot \exp\left(-\Delta^* F_i/RT\right), \tag{11.2}$$

die die Geschwindigkeitskonstante mit einer freien Aktivierungsenergie $\Delta^* F_i$ verknüpft. Dabei ist $\boldsymbol{k}$ die Boltzmann-Konstante, h die Plancksche Konstante und T die absolute Temperatur.

laufen sehr schnell und können nur bei sehr hohen Frequenzen akustisch wirksam werden. Auf eine Berechnung ihrer Geschwindigkeitskonstanten im einzelnen soll hier verzichtet werden. Bei der Bestimmung der freien Energie dieses Vorganges ist es von Bedeutung, ob die Hydratwassermolekel aus einfachen Lösungsmittel-Molekeln oder aus Lösungsmittel-Aggregaten stammen.

Der Auf- bzw. Abbau der Hydrathüllen, der nicht nur bei der einfachen Hydratation sondern natürlich auch bei der Umwandlung $A, B \rightleftharpoons AB$ auftritt, ist mit einer verhältnismäßig großen Volumenänderung verbunden. Diese Volumenänderung ist zusammen mit der der Ionenwolke eine Voraussetzung für die starke Druckabhängigkeit des Dissoziationsgleichgewichtes in Elektrolytlösungen und damit für die Relaxationseffekte beim Durchgang von Schall durch solche Lösungen. Da bei ungeladenen Teilchen diese Vorgänge gar nicht oder in stark vermindertem Maße auftreten, beobachtet man Absorption auf Grund dieser Vorgänge im wesentlichen nur in wäßrigen Elektrolyt-Lösungen.

C. Meßverfahren[1].

I. Messung von Absorption und Dispersion.

12. Absorptionsmessung. An die Meßverfahren zur Bestimmung der Elektrolyt-Absorption sowie der Dispersion in Elektrolytlösungen werden hohe Genauigkeitsanforderungen gestellt, denn beide Effekte sind besonders bei geringen Elektrolytkonzentrationen sehr klein. Ein möglichst weiter Konzentrationsbereich ist aber für die Deutung der Meßresultate notwendig.

Daneben verlangt die verschiedene Lage der Relaxationsfrequenzen verschiedener Elektrolyte und das Auftreten mehrerer Relaxationsvorgänge in Elektrolyten einen weiten Frequenzbereich, in dem Messungen gemacht werden können. Dies ist nicht mit einem einzigen Meßverfahren möglich, vielmehr gibt es in jedem Abschnitt des Frequenzbereiches optimal geeignete Verfahren.

Während zu Absorptionsmessungen bei hohen Frequenzen (>3 MHz) die üblichen Ausbreitungsmethoden (stationäre fortschreitende Wellen mit optischer Intensitätsmessung mittels Debye-Sears-Effekt, Impulsmethoden mit elektroakustischen Empfängern) angewendet werden, bedingt die kleine Dämpfung unterhalb dieser Grenze die Verwendung von Resonanz- bzw. Nachhallverfahren. Bei der Messung von Elektrolytabsorptionen kommt es weniger auf absolute Genauigkeit als vielmehr darauf an, die Differenz zwischen der Absorption der Elektrolytlösung und der des reinen Lösungsmittels möglichst genau zu bestimmen; man führt daher immer solche Vergleichsmessungen unmittelbar nacheinander aus. Durch die Differenzbildung (zur Ermittlung der Überschußdämpfung) fallen zusätzliche Energieverluste durch Wandungen und Apparatur heraus.

13. Dispersionsmessung. Die Messung der Dispersion in Elektrolytlösungen ist praktisch nur möglich durch Zurückführung der Messung auf den unmittelbaren Vergleich zweier wenig abweichender Schallgeschwindigkeiten. FOX und MARION [*34*] vergleichen die Schallgeschwindigkeiten in der Lösung bei einer Frequenz unterhalb des Dispersionsfrequenzgebietes und einer Frequenz oberhalb desselben. Zu diesem Zweck werden zwei exakt harmonisch zueinander liegende Frequenzen gleichzeitig in das Medium abgestrahlt und die langsame Verschiebung der Phasenebenen in der fortschreitenden Welle gegeneinander elektrisch

[1] Auf eine vollständige Darstellung der Meßverfahren kann hier verzichtet werden, da diese an anderer Stelle des Handbuches gegeben wird.

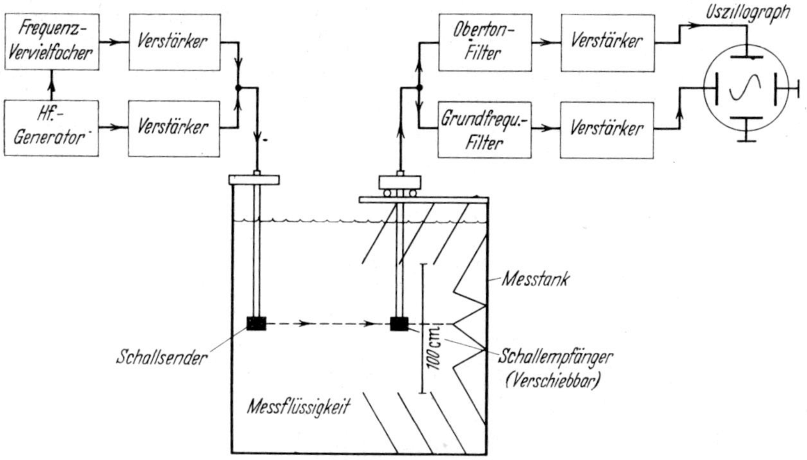

Fig. 5. Schema einer Apparatur zur Messung der Schalldispersion in Elektrolytlösungen durch Phasenvergleich zweier harmonisch liegender Meßfrequenzen nach Fox und Marion [34] (Frequenzbereich 0,1 bis 1 MHz).

abgetastet (Fig. 5). Carstensen [20] gelingt es, Vergleichsmessungen in fortschreitenden Wellen bis zu einigen 100 kHz herunter auszuführen, indem er die konstante Gesamtweglänge zwischen Sender und Empfänger durch Verschieben einer Trennmembran veränderlich aufteilt in einen Teilweg in der Lösung und einen in dem Lösungsmittel (s. Fig. 6). Ein Phasenvergleich zwischen Sender- und Empfänger-Spannung liefert beim Verschieben der Trennfläche direkt die Differenz der Schallgeschwindigkeiten.

II. Meßapparaturen.

14. Resonanzverfahren. Bei diesem Meßverfahren, welches speziell für tiefe Frequenzen (5 bis 50 kHz) geeignet ist, wird die Resonanzschärfe bzw. die Abklingzeit einer einzigen Eigenschwingung des in dem Resonator eingeschlossenen Flüssigkeitsvolumens gemessen und aus dieser die Elektrolyt-

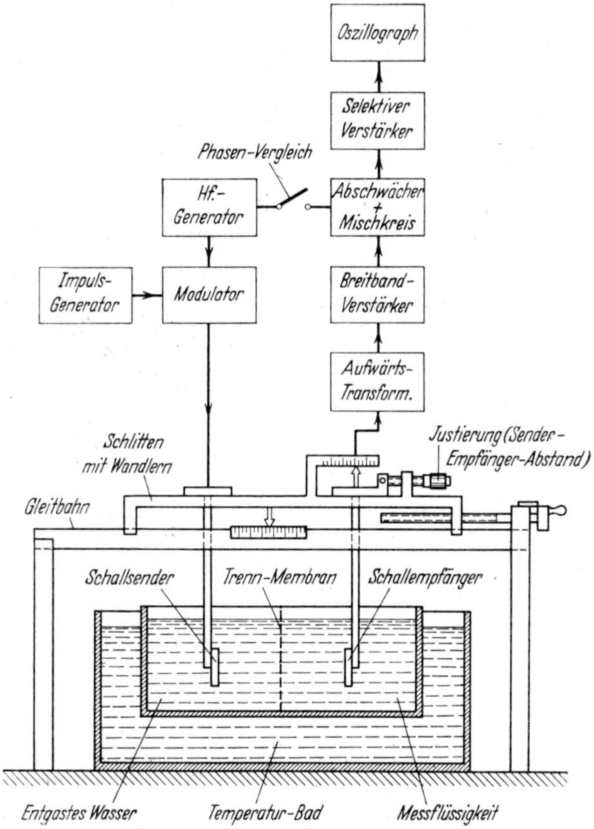

Fig. 6. Schema einer Apparatur zur Messung der Schalldispersion in Elektrolytlösungen durch Phasenvergleich bei kontinuierlicher Substitution des Elektrolyten durch das Lösungsmittel nach Carstensen [20] (Frequenzbereich 0,1 bis 10 MHz).

Absorption bestimmt. Die Energieverluste durch Deformation der Gefäßwand und Flüssigkeitsreibung an dieser bestimmen die Meßgenauigkeit. Man hält sie dadurch klein, daß man Resonatorgefäße mit dünnen Wandungen aus Materialien mit kleinen inneren Verlusten, also Aluminium, Glas, Quarz, verwendet. Besonders kleine Wandverluste erhält man bei Anregung radial symmetrischer Pulsationsschwin-

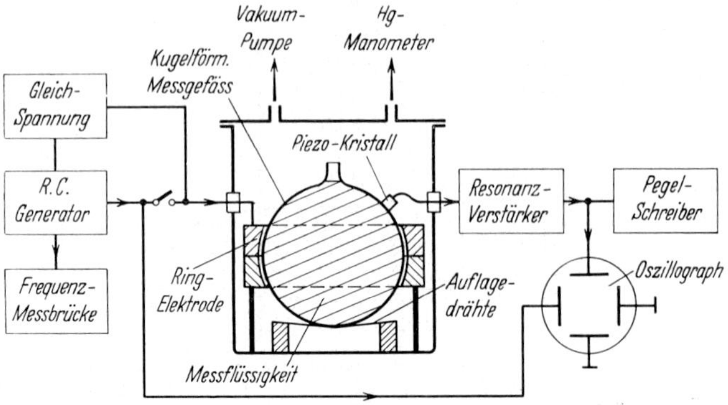

Fig. 7. Schema des Resonanzverfahrens zur Schallabsorptionsmessung unter Verwendung einzelner kugelsymmetrischer Eigenschwingungen eines Flüssigkeitsvolumens nach LEONARD und WILSON [*14*], [*15*] bzw. TAMM [*17*] (Frequenzbereich 4 bis 50 kHz).

gungen in kugelförmigen Resonatoren (Fig. 7). Regt man mit einem Frequenzband an, so bleiben im Verlauf des Nachhallvorgangs, der nach dem Abschalten der Anregung einsetzt, diese Eigenfrequenzen schließlich übrig (s. LEONARD und WILSON [*14*], [*15*] und MOEN [*59*]). Sie können jedoch auch von vornherein bevorzugt angeregt werden (TAMM und NAAKE [*17*], [*60*]). Zur Verminderung der Strahlungsdämpfung wird das Meßgerät in einem Rezipienten untergebracht, der bei der Messung auf wenige mm Hg evakuiert wird. Anregung und Abnahme des Schwingungsvorgangs erfolgen meist über die Gefäßwand von außen. Man verwendet dazu fast immer piezoelektrische Systeme. Zur Bevorzugung der radialsymmetrischen Eigenschwingungen benutzten TAMM und NAAKE ein elektrostatisches Verfahren unter Verwendung einer ringförmigen Elektrode, die das Gefäß umfaßt.

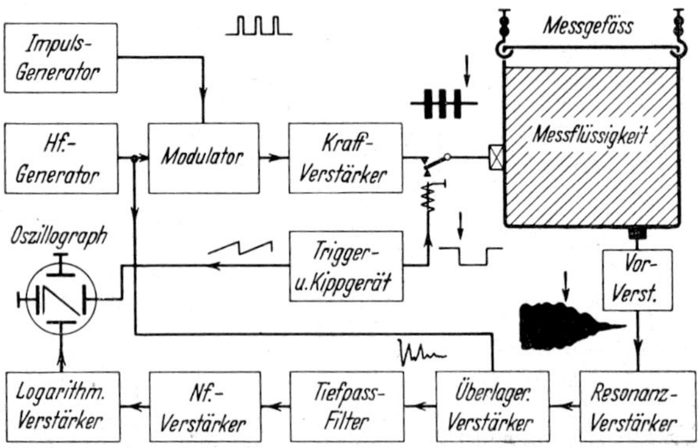

Fig. 8. Schema des Nachhallverfahrens zur Messung der Schallabsorption unter Benutzung des Abklingens eines Frequenzbandes in einem flüssigkeitsgefüllten zylindrischen Gefäß (Frequenzbereich 0,05 bis 1 MHz) nach TAMM und NAAKE [*17*], [*60*].

15. Nachhallverfahren. Im Frequenzbereich oberhalb 50 kHz liegen die Eigenfrequenzen in einem flüssigkeitsgefüllten Resonatorgefäß sehr dicht, wenn dieses eine Mindestgröße besitzt, die sich aus der Forderung genügend kleinen Wandeinflusses ergibt. Es lassen sich dann die Eigenschwingungen nicht mehr diskret anregen. SKUDRZYK und MEYER [*61*], später auch MULDERS [*33*] und TAMM [*17*] gingen daher zu einem Nachhallverfahren über (Fig. 8), bei dem eine große Anzahl von Eigenschwingungen in einem schmalen Frequenzband durch Schwingungsimpulse oder Rauschbänder gleichzeitig angeregt wird. Um auswertbare (im logarithmischen Amplitudenmaßstab) gerade Nachhallkurven, d.h. gleiche Abklingzeit aller Eigenschwingungen, zu erhalten, sorgt man durch Resonatorformen möglichst geringer Symmetrie dafür, daß jede Eigenschwingung mit möglichst verschiedenen Einfallswinkeln an der Wand verbunden ist. Bei automatischer periodischer Aufzeichnung der Nachhallkurve mit einer Wiederholungszeit, die etwas länger als die Nachhallzeit ist [*17*], lassen sich auch schnelle Änderungen der Absorption verfolgen. Zur Ermittlung der Elektrolytabsorption wird der Dämpfungswert der Elektrolytlösung um den des Lösungsmittels reduziert.

16. Ausbreitungsverfahren. Bei Frequenzen über 1 MHz wird die Absorption in Wasser und Elektrolytlösungen so groß, daß man sie durch die Intensitätsabnahme in einem fortschreitenden Schallbündel längs einer sehr begrenzten Meßstrecke messen kann. Ist der Strahlerquerschnitt sehr groß gegen die Wellen-

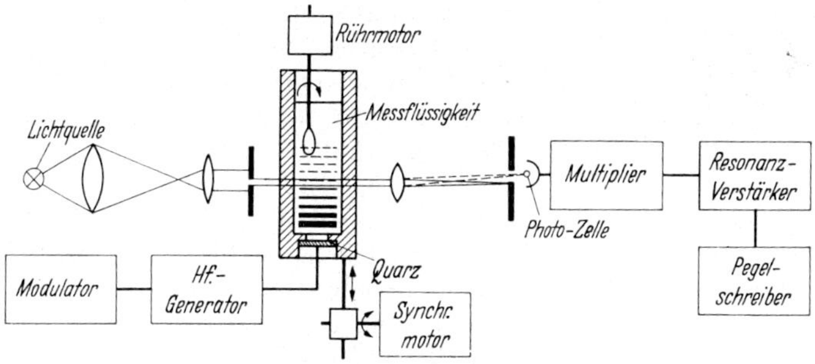

Fig. 9. Schema der Messung der Schallabsorption in fortschreitenden Wellen mit Hilfe der optischen Abtastung (Frequenzbereich (3) 20 bis 100 MHz) nach KURTZE [*17*].

länge, dann erstreckt sich das Nahfeld, innerhalb dessen das Schallbündel einigermaßen parallel bleibt, über die ganze Meßstrecke. Zur Ermittlung der Abahme der Schallenergie verwendet man dementsprechend Empfänger, die über den Querschnitt des Bündels integrieren, also z.B. einen Empfangsquarz mindestens gleicher Größe wie der Sendequarz bzw. ein breites Lichtbündel bei den optischen Methoden oder ausgedehnten Schallstrahlungsdruckmesser.

Obwohl zur Messung ein Vergleich der Schallenergie in zwei verschiedenen Entfernungen vom Sender genügt, werden, der Eliminierung von Schwankungen wegen, meist Meßmethoden vorgezogen, die eine kontinuierliche Registrierung der Energie in Abhängigkeit vom Abstand zwischen Sender und Empfänger in linearem oder (besser) in logarithmischem Maßstab ergeben.

Die *Optische Intensitätsmessung* mit Hilfe des Debye-Sears-Effektes (Fig. 9) liefert eine Integration der Schallintensität, wenn man bei kleinen Schallintensitäten bleibt, bei denen ein linearer Zusammenhang zwischen Schallintensität und Lichtintensität besteht. Dies ist der Fall für die erste Ordnung des Beugungsspektrums, solange die zweite Ordnung nicht nennenswert auftritt. Die Intensität des Beugungslichtes kann direkt photographisch registriert und photometrisch ausgewertet werden. Sie wird aber fast immer photoelektrisch gemessen und elektro-mechanisch aufgezeichnet. Das Verfahren wird speziell im Frequenzbereich 3 bis 100 MHz angewendet. Bei tieferen Frequenzen ist die Trennung der ersten Beugungsordnung von den anderen schwierig; bei höheren ist die Anwendung begrenzt durch das Ansteigen der Schallintensität, die zur Erzeugung genügender Intensität der ersten Ordnung notwendig ist.

Intensitätsmessungen mit Hilfe des *Schallstrahlungsdruckes* wurden mehrfach zur Bestimmung der Absorption angewendet, so z. B. durch v. ITTERBECK und VERHAEGEN [*62*], HSU [*67*] und durch SMITH und BEYER [*30*]. Sie verursachen verhältnismäßig große mechanische Schwierigkeiten und erfordern einigermaßen große Schallintensitäten (Fig. 10).

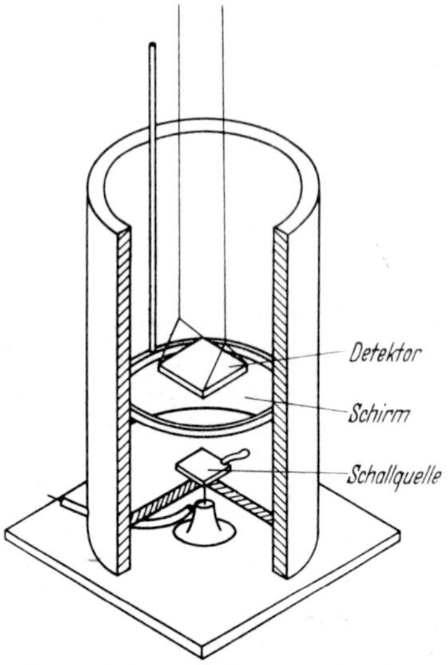

Fig. 10. Schema des Schallstrahlungsdruck-Verfahrens zur Messung der Schallabsorption in fortschreitenden Wellen nach HSU [*67*] bzw. SMITH und BEYER [*30*]. (Frequenzbereich 3 bis 100 MHz).

Die Verwendung *elektroakustischer Empfänger* (z. B. von Quarzplatten) verlangt wegen der auftretenden Integration des Schalldruckes und des damit verbundenen Einflusses der Phase nahezu ebene Phasenflächen und genaue Justierung der Empfängerfläche. Sie hat besondere Bedeutung bei hohen Frequenzen, bei denen die optische Methode nicht mehr arbeitet. Die Gefahr des elektrischen Übersprechens zwischen Sender und Empfänger kann durch Anwendung von Impulsen unschädlich gemacht werden. Solche Impulsverfahren wurden z. B. von PELLAM und GALT [*66*] und von LITOVITZ [*65*] angewendet. Um die notwendige zeitliche Trennung der Impulse bei großer Absorption, d. h. bei kleinen Laufstrecken, zu erreichen, schaltet man Verzögerungsleitungen ein. Man kann dabei mit einem Schallquarz auskommen, der als Sender und Empfänger verwendet wird, wenn man den Schallimpuls am Ende der Meßstrecke in eine Verzögerungsleitung hineinlaufen läßt, an deren Ende er reflektiert wird. Solche Apparaturen (s. Fig. 11, 12) sind geeignet, Messungen bis zu den höchsten in Flüssigkeiten bisher erzeugten Schallfrequenzen (etwa 500 MHz) auszuführen (s. RAPUANO [*64*]). Bei noch höheren Frequenzen macht die Anregung des Schwingquarzes in der erforderlichen hohen Harmonischen Schwierigkeiten.

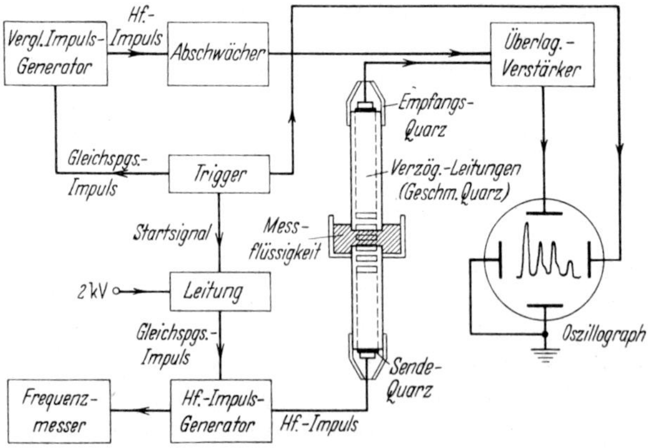

Fig. 11. Schema der Impulsmethode zur Messung der Schallabsorption in fortschreitenden Wellen unter Verwendung von zwei akustischen Verzögerungsleitungen und zwei elektroakustischen Wandlern nach TAMM, KURTZE, KAISER [*17a*] (Frequenzbereich 100 bis 300 MHz).

Neuerdings ist es nach einem von BARANSKI [*68*] angegebenen Verfahren BÖMMEL und DRANSFELD [*68a*] sowie JAKOBSEN [*68b*] gelungen, diese Schwierigkeit zu umgehen, indem sie einen zylindrischen Quarzkristallstab durch Eintauchen in das Feld eines elektromagnetischen Hohlraumresonators von einem Ende her zu sehr hohen Frequenzen (bis zu etwa 20000 MHz) erregen. Die erreichbare Frequenzgrenze ist nur durch die Ausbreitungsdämpfung im Quarzkristall selbst bestimmt, die jedoch sehr klein ist.

Bisher wurden Messungen in wäßrigen Lösungen nur bis zu einer Frequenz von 300 MHz ausgeführt [*17a*]; darüber wird wegen des nahezu quadratischen

Anstieges mit der Frequenz die Dämpfung schon auf Bruchteile von Millimetern so groß, daß Messungen nicht mehr zustande kamen.

Es sei erwähnt, daß bei verhältnismäßig kleiner Absorption, also im Frequenzbereich um 1 MHz, das bereits (unter Ziff. 13) beschriebene Substitutionsverfahren nach CARSTENSEN [20] besonders geeignet ist, auch die Elektrolytabsorption direkt zu bestimmen.

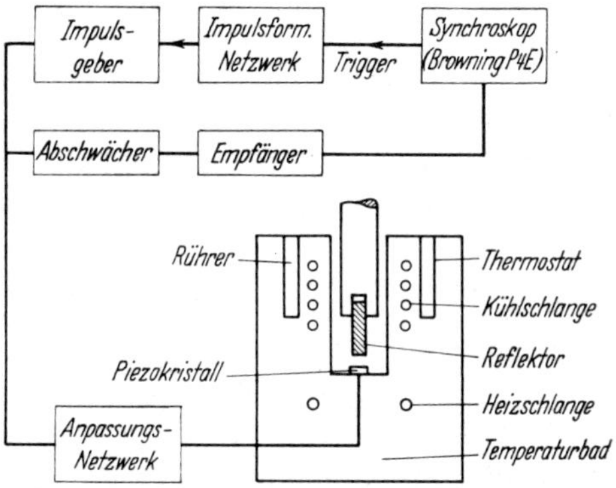

Fig. 12. Schema der Impulsmethode zur Messung der Schallabsorption in fortschreitenden Wellen unter Verwendung einer am Ende reflektierenden akustischen Verzögerungsleitung aus geschmolzenem Quarz. (Frequenzbereich 10 bis 50 MHz) nach PELLAM, GALT [66].

III. Genauigkeit der Ergebnisse.

17. Meßgenauigkeit. Die Meßgenauigkeit ist bei hohen Frequenzen verhältnismäßig hoch; mit Fehlern von mindestens 5% vom Absolutwert der Absorption des Wassers muß aber wohl in jedem Fall gerechnet werden. Bei tiefen Frequenzen nimmt die Genauigkeit erheblich ab, der Fehler erreicht bei 100 kHz etwa 100% des Wertes der Absorption in reinem Wasser.

Da die Elektrolytabsorption durch eine Differenzbildung ermittelt wird, nimmt ihre relative Genauigkeit mit abnehmender Elektrolytabsorption, d. h. mit abnehmender Konzentration, ab. Die relative Genauigkeit eines Absorptionsquerschnittes Q bzw. eines $Q\lambda$-Wertes hängt also nicht nur von seinem Absolutwert, sondern auch von der Konzentration, bei der er bestimmt wurde, ab; mit anderen Worten: Absorptionsquerschnitte, die zu kleinen Absolutwerten der Absorption gehören, haben meist große Fehler. Dies ist bei der Betrachtung der vorliegenden Meßresultate zu berücksichtigen.

18. Reinheit der Elektrolytlösungen. Die meisten der bekannten Messungen wurden mit Elektrolytsalzen großer Reinheit („chemisch rein“ oder pro analysi), die in destilliertem Wasser gelöst waren, vorgenommen. Große Reinheitsgrade sind besonders dann notwendig, wenn kleine Absorptionseffekte zu erwarten sind, die von Absorptionseffekten der Verunreinigungen überdeckt werden können. Gewisse Schwierigkeiten treten bei einigen Lösungen dadurch auf, daß sich, — offenbar durch Einwirkung der im Wasser gelösten Kohlensäure, — Niederschläge bilden [17]. Bei bekanntem Hydratwassergehalt kann man die Konzentration durch Auflösen bestimmter Gewichtsmengen in bestimmten Wasservolumina einstellen. In anderen Fällen wird zweckmäßigerweise eine mittels Areometer bestimmte Grund-Konzentration durch Verdünnen auf die gewünschte Konzentration gebracht.

D. Schallabsorptions-Messungen in Elektrolytlösungen.

I. Ordnung der vorliegenden Meßergebnisse.

19. Meßbereich. Mit den geschilderten Meßverfahren ist im Laufe der Zeit die Absorption einer großen Anzahl von Elektrolyten in wäßrigen Lösungen verschiedener Konzentration, bei verschiedenen Frequenzen und unter verschiedenen Bedingungen (Temperatur, Druck, Anwesenheit anderer Elektrolyten) gemessen worden. Während jedoch bei hohen Frequenzen (3 bis 100 MHz) verhältnismäßig viele und genaue Messungen vorliegen, sind nur wenige Messungen bei tiefen Frequenzen (<3 MHz) gemacht worden, unter 100 kHz bis zu 5 kHz herunter sind sogar nur vereinzelte Messungen verfügbar, wenn man von denen an Seewasser absieht. Hier ist eine Ergänzung notwendig, ebenso bei Frequenzen oberhalb 100 MHz (bis 500 MHz), bei denen auch nur vereinzelte Messungen durchgeführt wurden. Die Messung der Absorption in diesen Grenzgebieten des ganzen Frequenzbereiches von 5 kHz bis 300 MHz hat viel zu dem augenblicklichen Stand der Kenntnis über die Relaxationsvorgänge in Elektrolytlösungen beigetragen.

20. Systematische Darstellung der Meßergebnisse. Bei der großen Zahl der vorliegenden Meßergebnisse für die Elektrolytabsorption[1] ist es zweckmäßig, diese nach bestimmten Gesichtspunkten (Frequenzabhängigkeit, Konzentrationsabhängigkeit, Temperatur- und Druckabhängigkeit) geordnet darzustellen. Darüber hinaus erweist es sich als sehr fruchtbringend, eine Ordnung des außerordentlich unterschiedlichen Verhaltens der verschiedenen Elektrolyte zu versuchen, indem man eine Gruppierung nach Wertigkeit von An- und Kation und nach der Ionenstärke[2] vornimmt. Sehr aufschlußreich sind dann die Ergebnisse, die bei Zusatz anderer Elektrolyte ermittelt wurden.

Aus der Fülle der vorliegenden Meßergebnisse ([*11*] bis [*33*], [*59*], [*62*] bis [*65*]) werden hier nur wenige herausgegriffen, die für die Auswertung geeignet sind und deren Genauigkeit ausreichend ist.

Bei der Auswertung erweist es sich als vorteilhaft, nicht den gemessenen Absolutwert der Elektrolytabsorption, sondern den Absorptionsquerschnitt $Q = 2\alpha/c N_L$ aufzutragen, d. h. diejenige Energie-Absorption, die einem einzigen Elektrolytmolekül zugeordnet werden kann ohne Rücksicht darauf, in welcher Form (Ionen, Assoziate, Moleküle) dieses in der Lösung auftritt[3]. Dabei ist c die Konzentration in Mol/Volumeneinheit und N_L die Zahl der Moleküle je Mol (Loschmidtsche Zahl). Mit den üblichen Einheiten erhält man

$$\frac{Q}{[\mathrm{m}^2]} = 1.60 \cdot 10^{-25} \frac{2\alpha}{[\mathrm{cm}^{-1}]} \cdot \frac{[\mathrm{Mol/Liter}]}{c} . \qquad (20.1)$$

Soweit erforderlich wurde zur leichteren Erkennbarkeit der Relaxationsfrequenzen für die Darstellung der Ergebnisse, insbesondere der Frequenzabhängigkeit, einheitlich das Absorptionsvolumen je Periode ($Q\lambda$) oder die Absorption je Wellenlänge ($\alpha\lambda$) gewählt[4].

II. Meßergebnisse.

21. Frequenzabhängigkeit. Der Frequenzgang der Elektrolytabsorption läßt sich bei allen untersuchten Elektrolytlösungen ebenso wie bei Seewasser (s. Fig. 1) als Relaxationskurve bzw. als Überlagerung zweier oder mehrerer Relaxationskurven deuten. Dies wird besonders deutlich in einer Zusammenstellung (s. Fig. 13)

---

[1] Mit Elektrolytabsorption ist hier und künftig die durch den Elektrolyten hervorgerufene Vergrößerung der Absorption bezeichnet, d. h. die Differenz der Absorptionen von Elektrolytlösung und Lösungsmittel. Sie kann auch negativ werden.

[2] Die Ionenstärke ist definiert als $\Sigma z_i^2 c_i$, wobei z_i die Wertigkeiten sind und c_i die Konzentrationen bedeuten.

[3] Der Absorptionsquerschnitt ist also diejenige Fläche senkrecht zur Fortpflanzungsrichtung einer ebenen Schallwelle, durch die gerade die von einem Molekül absorbierte Schallleistung hindurchgeht.

[4] Bei dieser Form der Darstellung sind bekanntlich den Relaxationsfrequenzen Maxima zugeordnet. In doppelt logarithmischem Maßstab werden bei einem einzigen Relaxationsvorgang Anstieg und Abfall asymptotisch linear und die Form der Kurve vom Absolutwert der Absorption und von der Lage der Relaxationsfrequenz unabhängig. Das erleichtert Erkennbarkeit und Extrapolation wesentlich. Zu beachten ist, daß wegen der linearen Superposition der Relaxationsvorgänge die Absorption in linearem Maßstab addiert werden muß.

von Meßergebnissen an verschiedenen Elektrolytlösungen (s. Fig. 14), die alle den typischen Verlauf von Relaxationskurven bzw. Überlagerungen mehrer Relaxationskurven haben (s. Anm. 4, S. 232). In keinem Fall wurde bisher bei Elektrolytlösungen einwandfrei ein anderer Kurvenverlauf gemessen.

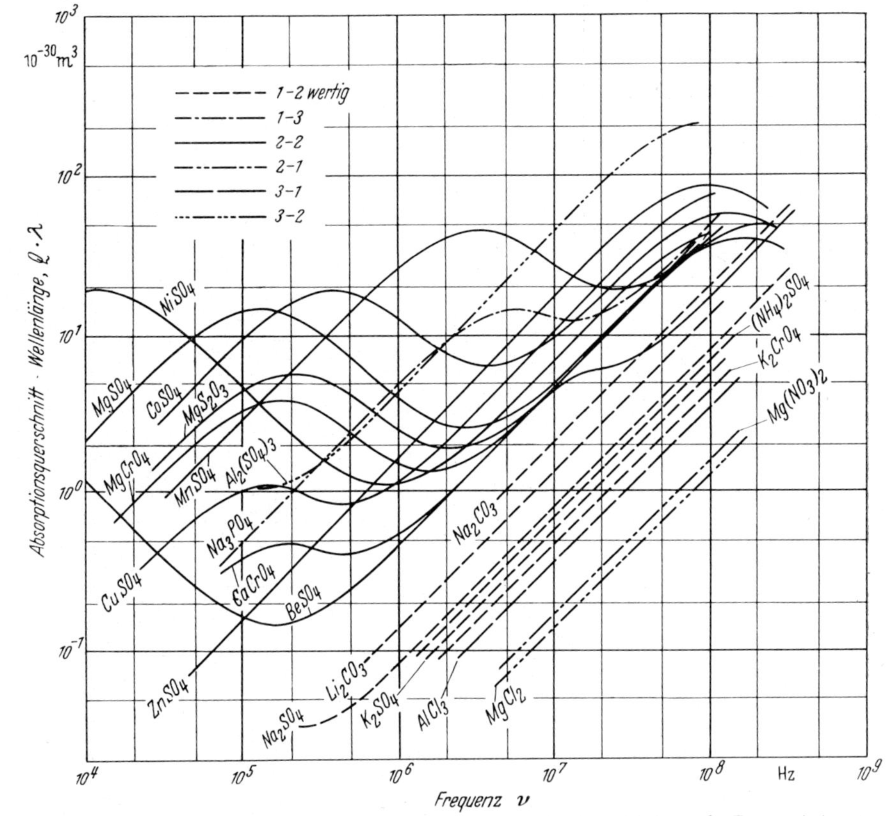

Fig. 13. Übersicht über die Relaxationskurven (Absorptionsvolumen $Q\lambda$ in Abhängigkeit von der Frequenz) einer Anzahl von Elektrolyten in wäßriger Lösung (bezogen auf 20° C) nach Tamm, Kurtze, Kaiser [*17*], [*17 a*]. Die Kurven ohne Konzentrationsangabe sind Mittelwerte bei wenig konzentrationsabhängigem Absorptionsquerschnitt. (Meßpunkte und Korrekturen s. Fig. 14 a—c bzw. Anm. 1, S. 234.)

22. Einfluß der Wertigkeit. Alle untersuchten starken *1-1-wertigen* Elektrolyte (Alkalihalogenide, ihre Säuren und ihre Basen) zeigen im ganzen tieferen Frequenzbereich keine meßbare Elektrolytabsorption. Bei höheren Frequenzen (>3 MHz), bei denen die Meßgenauigkeit größer ist, ergibt sich sogar eine gewisse Verminderung der Gesamtabsorption der Elektrolytlösung gegenüber Wasser; sie steigt mit der Konzentration. Dies ist — wie vorweggenommen werden soll — in Übereinstimmung mit dem zu erwartenden Einfluß des Elektrolyten auf die Strukturverteilung im Lösungsmittel (s. Ziff. 1). Als Beispiele zeigt Fig. 16 je eine Meßreihe [*17*] an NaBr bei 64 und bei 83 MHz. Bei der höchsten gemessenen Konzentration von 5 Mol/Liter beträgt die Gesamtabsorption noch 70% des Wertes von reinem Wasser. Ähnliche Ergebnisse [*17*] erhält man für NaJ.

Eine Ausnahme von dieser Regel bilden offenbar die eindeutig als schwache Elektrolyte bekannten 1-1-wertigen Verbindungen wie $NH_3 \cdot H_2O$, die eine erhebliche Absorption zeigen. Für $NH_3 \cdot H_2O$ liegen Absorptionsmessungen von Tamm und Kurtze [*17*a] sowie von Carnevale und Litovitz [*7a*] vor (Fig. 15), die eine Relaxationsfrequenz zwischen 20 und 50 MHz ergeben.

1-2- und 1-3-wertige „starke" Elektrolyte (z.B Na_2SO_4 bzw. Na_3PO_4) zeigen ausnahmslos unmeßbar kleine Elektrolytabsorption bei tiefen Frequenzen, erst

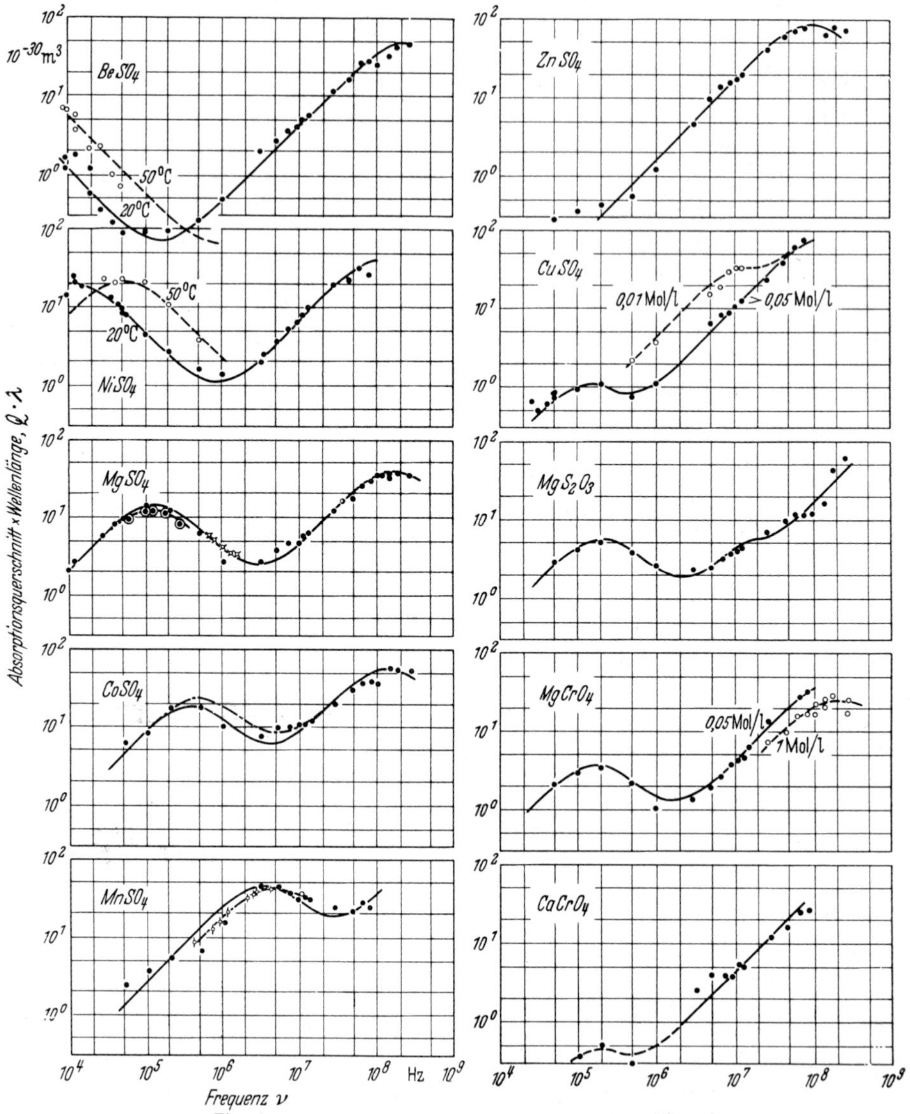

Fig. 14a. Fig. 14b.

Fig. 14a—c. Frequenzabhängigkeit des Absorptionsvolumens $Q\lambda$ einiger „starker" Elektrolyten in wäßriger Lösung. Meßergebnisse von TAMM, KURTZE, KAISER [*17*], [*17a*] bei 20° C ergänzt durch Messungen an $MgSO_4$ von WILSON [*15*] (⊙); MULDERS [*33*] (☿); SMITH, BARRETT, BEYER [*31*] (◑); $MnSO_4$ von CARSTENSEN [*20*] (ϕ). $CoSO_4$ von CARSTENSEN [*20*] bei 35° C, verwendet zu einer Korrektur (—·—·—) der Kurven nach [*17*].
(Korrektur für Na_2CO_3 und Na_3PO_4 s. Anm. 1, S. 234).

oberhalb 10 MHz wird wegen der dort größeren Meßgenauigkeit eine Elektrolytabsorption meßbar. α/ν^2 ist unabhängig von der Frequenz und entspricht einem linear mit der Frequenz ansteigenden Wert $\alpha\lambda$, also einem Verlauf[1], den man mit

[1] Nach neueren Messungen von EIGEN u. SCHWARZ [*51b*] ist die beim Na_2CO_3 sich andeutende Stufe bei etwa 10^7 Hz als real anzusehen und ähnlich wie das beim Na_3PO_4 ($c =$ 0,01 Mol/Liter) sehr ausgeprägte Maximum auf Hydrolyse zurückzuführen (s. Ziff. 36β).

einer sehr hoch liegenden Relaxationsfrequenz erklären kann. Als Beispiele dafür zeigen Fig. 13 u. 14 das Verhalten von K_2SO_4, Na_2SO_4, Li_2CO_3, K_2CrO_4, Na_3PO_4 und einiger anderer Elektrolyte (s. Anm. S. 234). Einen ähnlichen Verlauf erkennt man bei H_2SO_4 (Fig. 14).

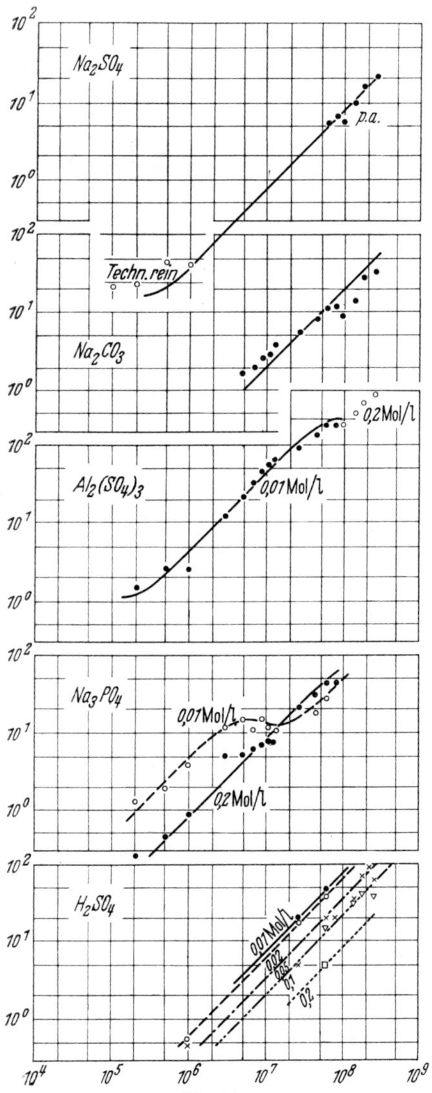

Fig. 14c.

Ein etwas anderes Ergebnis liefern offenbar auch hier die schwachen Elektrolyte. Als Beispiel [*17a*] ist in Fig. 15 der Frequenzverlauf des Wertes $Q\lambda$ für $La(NO_3)_3$ angegeben. Er zeigt die größten Werte zwischen 50 und 100 MHz. Möglicherweise ist der Kurvenverlauf als Überlagerung zweier Relaxationsvorgänge zu deuten (s. Ziff. 6). Die Absolutwerte $(Q\lambda)_m = 100 \cdot 10^{-30}\,\mathrm{m}^3$ gehören zu den größten, die bei Elektrolytlösungen gemessen wurden.

Bei *2-1- und 3-1-wertigen* „starken" Elektrolyten (z. B. $MgCl_2$) findet man bei hohen Frequenzen im Gegensatz zu den Ergebnissen bei den 1-2- und 1-3-wertigen als „stark" angesehenen Elektrolyten nur sehr kleine Werte der Elektrolytabsorption. Auch bei den tiefen Frequenzen ist keine meßbare Elektrolytabsorption vorhanden. Eine Ausnahme bildet $FeCl_3$, das nach Kurtze und Tamm [*17*] eine sehr erhebliche Absorption aufweist. Bei der Messung bereitete jedoch das Ausfallen von $Fe(OH)_3$ Schwierigkeiten.

Auch hier treten bei vielen der eindeutig „schwachen" Elektrolyte gut meßbare Absorptionswerte auf. Sehr gut auswertbare Meßreihen von Bazulin [*26*], v. Itterbeck [*62*] und Barrett, Beyer und McNamara [*30a*], [*33*] liegen besonders für Salze der Essigsäure vor. Für Kupfer- und Zinkacetat findet man die Relaxationsfrequenz mitten im Meßbereich während Calciumacetat nach Tamm und Kurtze[1] für $Q\lambda$ einen gradlinigen Anstieg bis zu sehr hohen Frequenzen zeigt.

Von den *2-2-wertigen Elektrolyten* zeigen auch die gewöhnlich als „stark" bezeichneten dagegen stets erhebliche Absorption fast im ganzen Frequenzbereich, der untersucht wurde (s. Fig. 14). Messungen liegen für eine große Anzahl von Salzen vor, insbesondere von Sulfaten, die wegen ihrer guten Löslichkeit bevorzugt untersucht wurden. Zu diesen gehören Be-, Ni-, Mg-, Co-, Mn-, Zn- und $CuSO_4$ (s. Fig. 14). Darüber hinaus wurden Messungen an Thiosulfaten und Chromaten (MgS_2O_3 und $MgCrO_4$) durchgeführt. Ergebnisse für Wolframate,

[1] Bisher unveröffentlichte Messungen.

die ebenfalls in Frage kommen, sind nicht bekannt. Bei den genannten Elektrolyten tritt außer dem frequenzproportionalen Anstieg der Größen $\alpha\lambda$ bzw. $Q\lambda$, der für die 1-2-wertigen Elektrolyte charakteristisch ist, ein Relaxationsmaximum

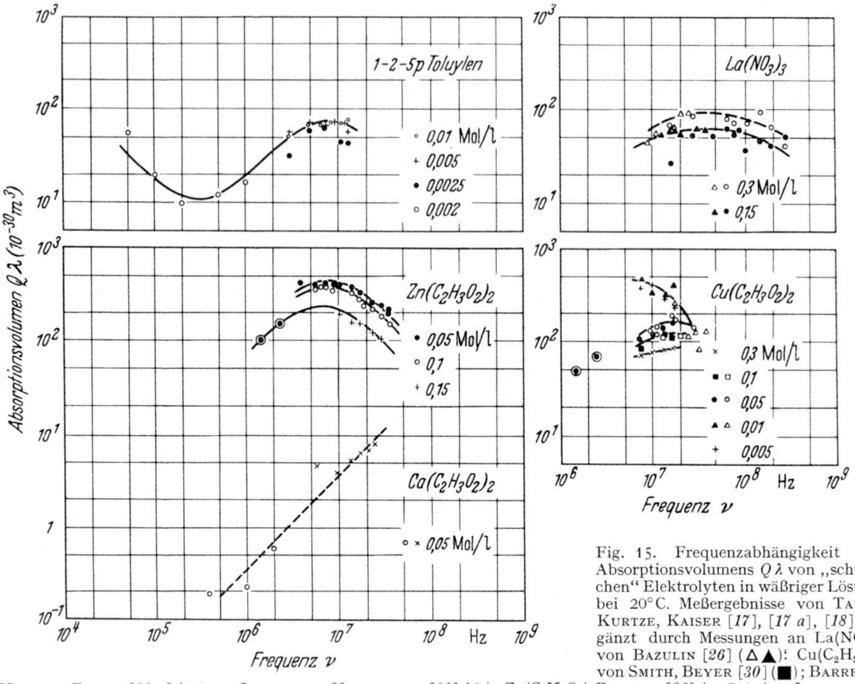

Fig. 15. Frequenzabhängigkeit des Absorptionsvolumens $Q\lambda$ von „schwachen" Elektrolyten in wäßriger Lösung bei 20° C. Meßergebnisse von TAMM, KURTZE, KAISER [17], [17 a], [18] ergänzt durch Messungen an $La(NO_3)_3$ von BAZULIN [26] (△▲): $Cu(C_2H_3O_2)_2$ von SMITH, BEYER [30] (■); BARRETT, McNAMARA, BEYER [30 a] (□); v. ITTERBEEK, VERHAEGEN [62] (⊙); $Zn(C_2H_3O_2)_2$ BAZULIN [26] (● ○ +;) v. ITTERBEEK, VERHAEGEN [62] (⊙).

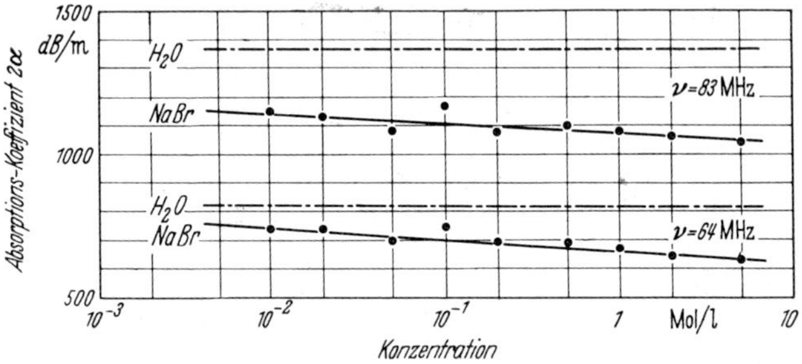

Fig. 16. Konzentrationsabhängigkeit des Absorptionskoeffizienten 2α einer wäßrigen NaBr-Lösung (———) im Vergleich zu dem des reinen Wassers (—·—·—) für 64 und 83 MHz bei 20° C nach KURTZE [17].

im Frequenzbereich zwischen einigen kHz und einigen MHz auf (s. auch Ziff. 24). Nach sehr genauen Messungen vom SMITHSON und LITOVITZ [25] findet sich bei $MnSO_4$ eine schwache Andeutung eines weiteren Relaxationsmaximums dicht oberhalb des starken Maximums bei etwa 5 MHz. $CaCrO_4$ weist nach neueren Messungen oberhalb 10^7 Hz (wie es sich in Fig. 14b andeutet) ebenfalls ein Maximum auf[1].

[1] Es entspricht dem „unteren" Maximum der anderen 2-2-wertigen Elektrolyte, während das Maximum bei $2 \cdot 10^5$ Hz offenbar der Hydrolyse $CrO_4^{--} + H_2O \rightleftharpoons HCrO_4^- + OH^-$ zuzuordnen ist (nach EIGEN, private Mitteilung).

Von *höher-wertigen* Elektrolyten wurde nur das 3-2-wertige $Al_2(SO_4)_3$ untersucht (s. Fig. 14). Es zeigt bei ähnlichem Verlauf wie die 2-2-wertigen Elektrolyte den größten der bekannten $Q\lambda$-Werte.

23. Konzentrationsabhängigkeit. Ganz allgemein ist festzustellen, daß die Elektrolytabsorption mit der Konzentration zunimmt. Diese Zunahme verläuft in einigen Fällen proportional zur Konzentration, so daß sich ein konstanter Absorptionsquerschnitt (je Elektrolytmolekül) ergibt. In anderen Fällen ist die Zunahme jedoch größer oder kleiner als linear. Man gewinnt auch hier eine gewisse Übersicht, wenn man die Elektrolyten in Gruppen betrachtet, die nach den Wertigkeiten beider Ionen geordnet sind.

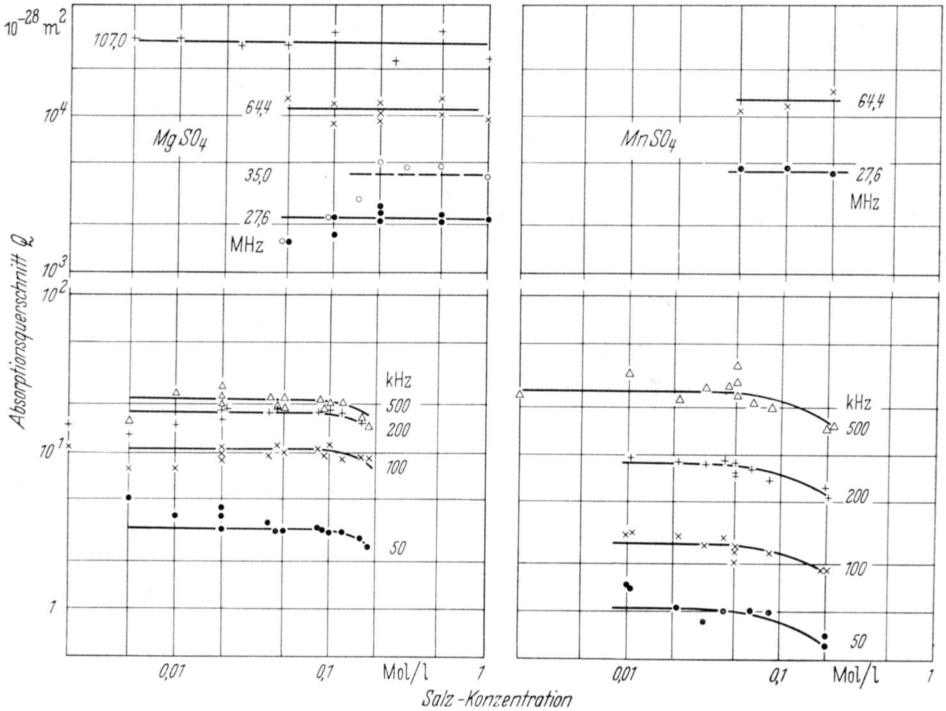

Fig. 17. Konzentrationsabhängigkeit des Absorptionsquerschnitts Q einiger Sulfate zweiwertiger Metalle bei verschiedenen Frequenzen. Messungen von KURTZE und TAMM [*17*], [*18*] bei 20° C ergänzt durch Meßwerte an $MgSO_4$ von SMITH, BARRETT, BEYER [*30b*] (○--○).

Es wurde bereits erwähnt, daß bei *1-1-wertigen Elektrolyten*, soweit sich überhaupt eine Abweichung von der Absorption des Lösungsmittels zeigt, eine negative Elektrolytabsorption gemessen wird. Diese nimmt mit der Konzentration ungefähr linear zu (Fig. 16) und erklärt sich durch den Lösungsmitteleffekt.

Bei den untersuchten *2-2-wertigen Elektrolyten* ergibt sich für alle Frequenzen, d.h. für beide Absorptionsgebiete (charakterisiert durch das Relaxationsmaximum bzw. durch den linearen Anstieg von $\alpha\lambda$), in einem Konzentrationsbereich von 10^{-3} bis 10^{-1} Mol/Liter ein nahezu linearer Anstieg der Absorption mit der Konzentration. Dies bedeutet einen nahezu konstanten Absorptionsquerschnitt Q. Fig. 17 zeigt als Beispiele für die Konzentrationsabhängigkeit die Absoprtionsquerschnitte von $MgSO_4$ und $MnSO_4$ im ganzen untersuchten Frequenzbereich[1].

[1] Bei der Betrachtung der Figuren, insbesondere Fig. 17, ist zu beachten, daß die relativen Meßfehler mit abnehmender Konzentration größer werden, so daß die Streuungen um den Mittelwert des Absorptionsquerschnitts immer größer werden müssen.

Im unteren Frequenzbereich (100 bis 500 kHz) nimmt der Absorptionsquerschnitt bei Konzentrationen oberhalb 0,1 Mol/Liter langsam ab. Im oberen Frequenzbereich tritt eine solche Abnahme ebenfalls auf, jedoch erst bei etwas höheren Konzentrationen, nämlich oberhalb 1 Mol/Liter, wie aus der Zusammenstellung (Fig. 18) der Meßergebnisse von KURTZE [17] in Übereinstimmung mit Messungen von CONNOLLY, FOX [21] an $MgSO_4$ und SMITHSON, LITOVITZ [25] sowie KOR, VERMA [31] an $MnSO_4$ (s. auch Fig. 17 oben), hervorgeht. Eine Abnahme ergibt sich auch für geringere Konzentrationen als 10^{-3} Mol/Liter, wie Messungen von WILSON [15] an $MgSO_4$ zeigen. Aus der im mittleren Konzentrationsbereich für alle Frequenzen festgestellten Konzentrationsunabhängigkeit des Absorptionsquerschnitts folgt, daß im gleichen Konzentrationsbereich auch die Relaxationsfrequenzen konstant sind.

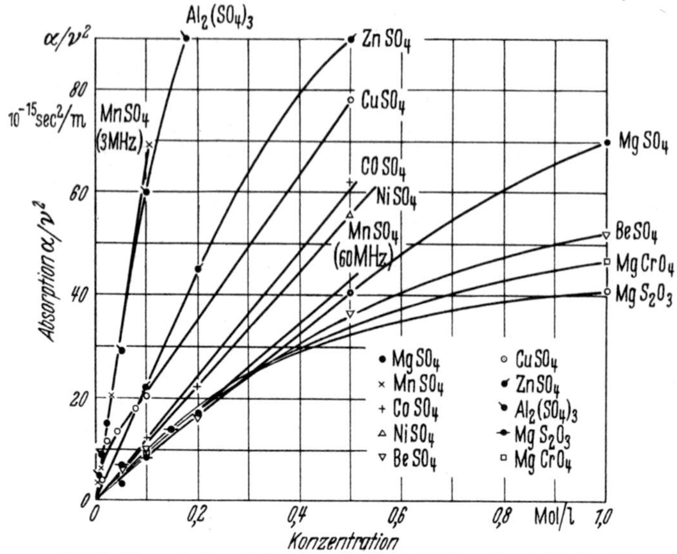

Fig. 18. Konzentrationsabhängigkeit der Elektrolytabsorption (α/ν^2) für einige 2-2-wertige Elektrolyte. Die Messungen sind soweit möglich über mehrere Frequenzen im Bereich 5 bis 100 MHz gemittelt. Nach KURTZE [17.]

Auch viele der *1-2- und 1-3-wertigen Elektrolyten*, z. B. Li_2SO_4 (s. Fig. 19), zeigen, ebenso wie die 2-2-wertigen Elektrolyte, nahezu linearen Anstieg der Absorption mit der Konzentration. Bei allen Natrium-Salzen, z. B. bei Na_2SO_4, wird jedoch nach KURTZE [17] ein flacherer Anstieg bei kleineren Konzentrationen beobachtet, der durch eine (in diesem Konzentrationsbereich wirksame) Abnahme der Eigenabsorption des Lösungsmittels auf Grund des Einflusses der Na^+-Ionen verursacht sein kann.

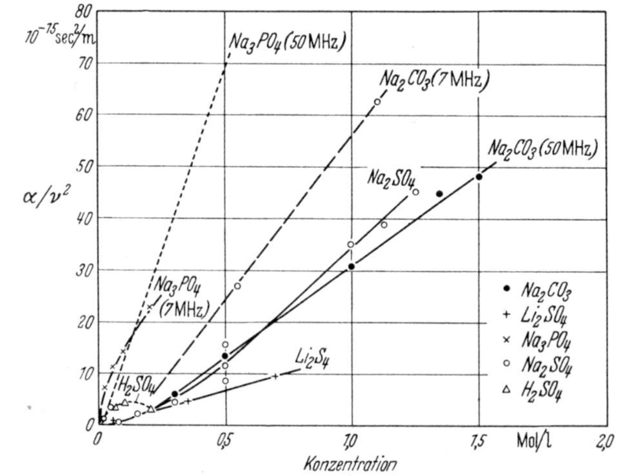

Fig. 19. Konzentrationsabhängigkeit der Elektrolytabsorption (α/ν^2) für einige 1-2-wertige Elektrolyte nach KURTZE [17] (s. auch Fig. 18).

Eine Ausnahme von dieser Konzentrationsunabhängigkeit des Absorptionsquerschnitts macht z. B. die Schwefelsäure. Bei dieser wächst die Absorption über einen weiten Konzentrationsbereich weniger als linear mit der Konzentration, so daß der Absorptionsquerschnitt mit steigender Konzentration abnimmt (Fig. 19 u. 29). Da hier das Relaxationsmaximum nicht im untersuchten Frequenzbereich liegt, kann nur durch andere Überlegungen entschieden werden, ob dies eine Folge einer Erhöhung der Relaxationsfrequenz oder einer Verminderung des Maximums des Absorptionsquerschnitts bzw. des Absorptionsbetrages ist (s. Ziff. 35).

Ebenso findet man auch für den 1-1-wertigen schwachen Elektrolyt $NH_3 \cdot H_2O$ eine starke Abhängigkeit des Absorptionsquerschnitts von der Konzentration (Fig. 31, S. 255). Glücklicherweise liegt hier das Maximum im Meßbereich, nämlich zwischen 20 und 50 MHz. Mit zunehmender Konzentration verschiebt sich die Relaxationsfrequenz nach oben, während der Absorptionsquerschnitt abnimmt.

Für *2-1- und 3-1-wertige „starke" Elektrolyte* können wegen der Kleinheit der Absorption wenig Aussagen über ihre Konzentrationsabhängigkeit gemacht werden. Die Meßschwierigkeiten bei der ausnahmsweise großen Elektrolytabsorption von $Fe(Cl)_3$ erlauben auch bei diesem Salz keine absolut zuverlässige Aussage über die Konzentrationsabhängigkeit.

Bei dem 3-1-wertigen schwachen Elektrolyt $La(NO_3)_3$ ist nur ein begrenzter Frequenzbereich für zwei Konzentrationswerte gemessen (Fig. 15). Eine Auswertung in bezug auf die Konzentrationsabhängigkeit des Absorptionsquerschnittes ist wegen des komplizierten Frequenzverlaufs, der auf zwei Relaxationsfrequenzen hindeutet, noch nicht möglich.

Die 2-1-wertigen schwachen Elektrolyte Kupfer- und Zinkacetat sowie andere Acetate zeigen nach v. ITTERBECK [*62*] und BARRETT, MCNAMARA und BEYER [*30a*] einen wenig konzentrationsabhängigen Absorptionsquerschnitt. Dabei bildet allerdings das Bleiacetat eine Ausnahme; sein Absorptionsquerschnitt nimmt nach v. ITTERBECK und VERHAEGEN [*62*] bei Konzentrationen oberhalb 0,01 Mol/Liter schnell ab.

Für *Elektrolyte höherer Wertigkeiten* liegen nicht genügend Messungen vor, um eine Systematik erkennen zu lassen. Bei dem als einzigen untersuchten 3-2-wertigen Elektrolyten $Al_2(SO_4)_3$ ist der Absorptionsquerschnitt im untersuchten Konzentrationsbereich (0,002 bis 0,5 Mol/Liter) stark konzentrationsabhängig. Der Maximalwert $(Q\lambda)_m$ liegt sehr hoch. Bei sehr großen Konzentrationen macht die auftretende Hydrolyse genaue Messungen unmöglich.

24. Abhängigkeit der Relaxationsfrequenz von der Ionenart. Die bei den 2-2-wertigen Elektrolyten in einem großen Konzentrationsbereich festgestellte Konzentrationsunabhängigkeit des maximalen Absorptionsquerschnitts und der

Tabelle 1. *„Untere" Relaxationsfrequenz ν_m sowie zugehöriges maximales Absorptionsvolumen $(Q\lambda)_m$ und zugehörige Aktivierungsenergie ${}^AE$ wäßriger Lösungen von Sulfaten zweiwertiger Metalle.* (Nach EIGEN, KURTZE und TAMM [*18*], [*81*]).

Elektrolyt	$BeSO_4$	$NiSO_4$	$MgSO_4$	$CoSO_4$	$MnSO_4$	$CuSO_4$	$ZnSO_4$
ν_m [MHz]	0,001	0,01	0,12	0,4	3	10?	>10?
$(Q\lambda)_m$ [10^{-30} m³]	5	20	15	20	50	20	?
${}^AE$ [kcal/Mol]		7,8	6,5/7,5	6,0	6,8/7,8		

Relaxationsfrequenz ermöglicht es, die letzte unabhängig vom maximalen Absorptionsquerschnitt zu behandeln. Die Zusammenstellung der Frequenzabhängigkeiten der Größe $Q\lambda$ für 2-2-wertige Elektrolyte (Fig. 13) zeigt, daß die Relaxationsfrequenz des unteren Maximums vornehmlich vom Kation (vgl. die Sulfate verschiedener Metalle), dagegen kaum von der Art des Anions (vgl. $MgSO_4$, MgS_2O_3, $MgCrO_4$) beeinflußt ist, wenn auch der Relaxationsbetrag $(Q\lambda)_m$ von diesem abhängt. Für die Relaxationsfrequenzen findet man etwa die gleiche Reihenfolge (s. Tabelle 1) wie für die Ionenradien nach GOLDSCHMIDT und PAULING (s. Tabelle 9).

Der Anstieg des Wertes $Q\lambda$ bei hohen Frequenzen ist nur wenig abhängig vom Kation. Er tritt bemerkenswerterweise auch bei 1-2-wertigen Elektrolyten auf, wenn auch mit kleinerem Absolutbetrag, und steht demnach offenbar in Zusammenhang mit den großen zweiwertigen Anionen, hier mit dem SO_4^{--} Ion.

25. Temperatur- und Druckabhängigkeit der Absorption. *α) Temperaturabhängigkeit, Aktivierungsenergie.* An einzelnen Elektrolyten ($MgSO_4$, $CoSO_4$, $NiSO_4$, $MnSO_4$) wurde die Temperaturabhängigkeit der Absorption speziell im Frequenzbereich des unteren Relaxationsmaximums eingehend untersucht. Fig. 20a zeigt als Beispiel für diese Abhängigkeit das Meßergebnis von TAMM [*17*] an $MgSO_4$, welches recht genau mit dem von WILSON [*15*] übereinstimmt (s. Fig. 20b). Bei Temperaturen über 60° C, bei denen einige Schwierigkeiten auftreten, ist die Meßgenauigkeit etwas geringer als bei tiefen Temperaturen. Mit wachsender Temperatur T verschiebt sich das Maximum der Absorption, d. h. die „untere" Relaxationsfrequenz ν_m nach höheren Frequenzen zu (s. auch Fig. 20a oben). Die Verschiebung entspricht einer Aktivierungsenergie von ungefähr 6,5 bzw. 7,5 kcal/Mol[1]. Man erhält diesen Wert als Neigung der Geraden, die sich bei der Auftragung der Meßwerte in der Form (ν_m/T) über $1/T$ ergibt (s. Fig. 20b). In dieser Abbildung sind auch die Ergebnisse von TAMM [*17*] für $CoSO_4$ und $NiSO_4$ eingetragen, aus denen Aktivierungsenergien von 6,0 bzw. 8,7 kcal/Mol resultieren, sowie die Messungen von CARSTENSEN [*20*] und SMITHSON, LITOVITZ [*25*] für $MnSO_4$, die etwas abweichend voneinander 6,8 bzw. 7,85 kcal/Mol ergeben (s. Tabelle 1).

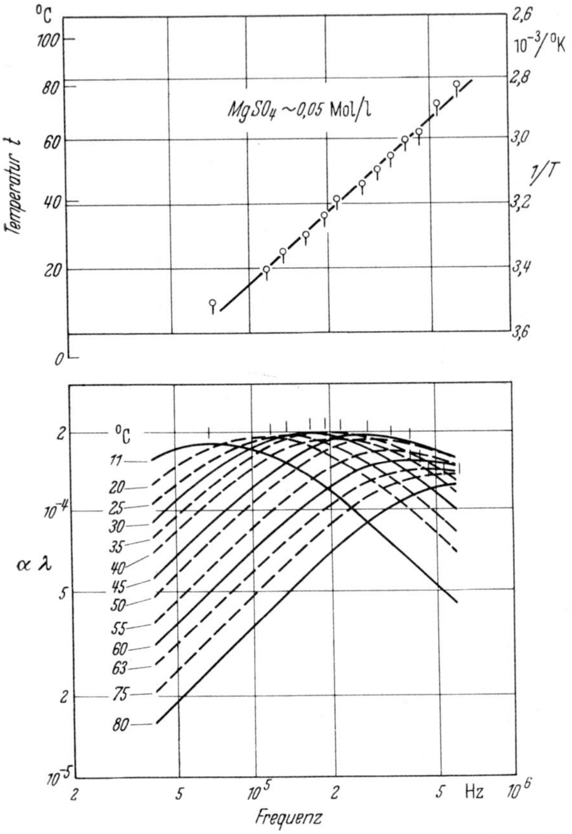

Fig. 20a. Unten: Verschiebung der Relaxationskurven (α λ in Abhängigkeit von der Frequenz) von $MgSO_4$ mit der Temperatur. Oben: Temperaturabhängigkeit der zugehörigen Relaxationsfrequenz nach TAMM [*17*].

Auch der stetige Anstieg von $Q\lambda$ bei hohen Frequenzen verschiebt sich mit der Temperatur nach hohen Frequenzen zu, wie KURTZE [*17*] und CONNOLLY u. FOX [*21*] gezeigt haben. Eine Aktivierungsenergie kann daraus nur ermittelt werden, wenn die Verschiebung des Relaxationsmaximums selbst festgestellt werden kann. Diese ist aber nicht mit Sicherheit zu ermitteln, da die Relaxationsfrequenz außerhalb des Meßbereichs liegt. Nimmt man nun zunächst an,

[1] WILSON [*15*] gibt den etwas höheren Wert, nämlich 7,5 kcal/Mol, für die Aktivierungsenergie von $MgSO_4$ an, aber nur zwei seiner sieben Meßpunkte stimmen nicht mit den Messungen von TAMM [*17*] überein.

daß das maximale Absorptionsvolumen $(Q\lambda)_m$ sich mit der Temperatur wenig ändert, was die Messungen zu bestätigen scheinen, so ist die Verschiebung der Flanken identisch mit einer Verschiebung der Relaxationsfrequenz. Die Auswertung der Messungen von KURTZE liefert dann eine Aktivierungsenergie zwischen 2 und 3 kcal/Mol, während CONNOLLY, FOX einen größeren Wert finden.

β) Druckabhängigkeit. Da im allgemeinen die Partialvolumina, die Geschwindigkeitskonstanten, die Aktivitäten und damit auch die Gleichgewichtskonstante und der Dissoziationsgrad druckabhängig sind, muß sich auch die Absorption und die Relaxationsfrequenz mit dem Druck ändern[1].

CARNEVALE und LITOVITZ [*7a*] haben (bei 45° C) die Druckabhängigkeit der Absorption bei einer 0,1-molaren wäßrigen Lösung von Ammoniak, also einem schwachen Elektrolyten, gemessen. Sie fanden bei Druckerhöhung von 1 auf 1117 bzw. auf 2030 kp/cm² eine Erhöhung der Relaxationsfrequenz ν_m von 20,6 MHz auf 38,7 bzw. 52,9 MHz und eine Verminderung des Absolutwertes von $\alpha_{\mathrm{El}}/\nu^2$ von 47,6 auf

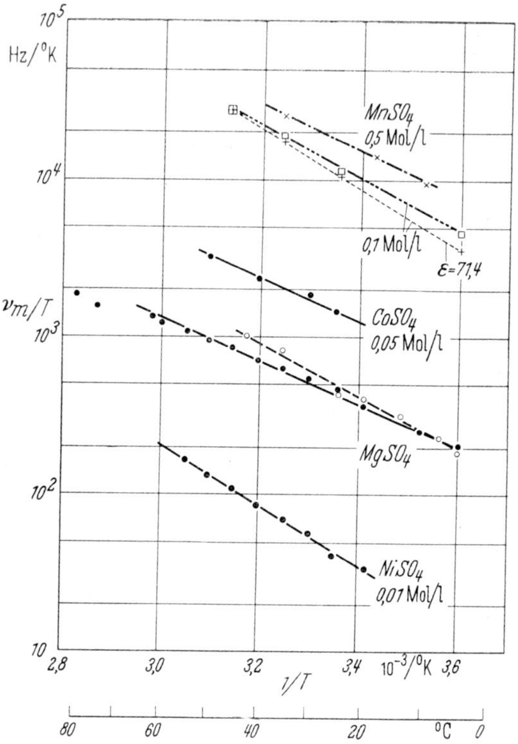

Fig. 20b. Ermittlung der Aktivierungsenergie für einige Sulfate zweiwertiger Metalle aus der Neigung der Geraden $\log \nu_m/T$ über $1/T$. Messungen von KURTZE und TAMM [*17*] ergänzt durch Meßwerte von WILSON [*15*] an $MgSO_4$ (○--○); CARSTENSEN [*20*] an $MnSO_4$ (×···×); SMITHSON und LITOVITZ [*25*] an $MnSO_4$ (in Wasser und in Wasser-Methylalkohol $\varepsilon = 71{,}4$) (□···□, +···+).

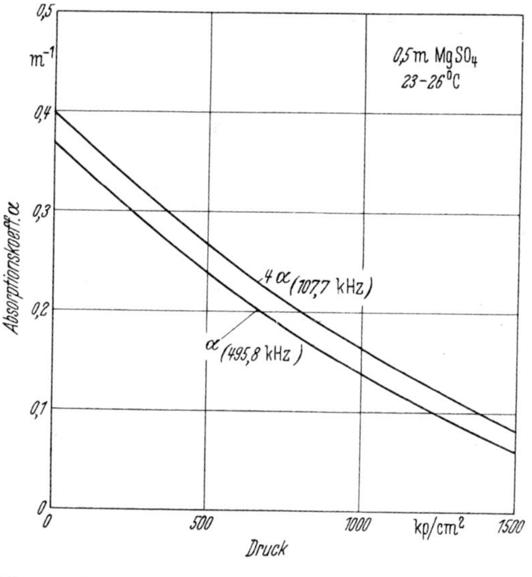

Fig. 21. Druckabhängigkeit der Absorption in einer 0,5-molaren $MgSO_4$-Lösung (ca. 25° C, 107,7 bzw. 495,8 kHz) nach FISHER [*19*].

[1] Die Größenordnung der Druckänderung Δp, die eine gut merkbare Änderung der Gleichgewichtskonstante K bzw. des Dissoziationsgrades δ bewirkt, läßt sich leicht aus der Differenz der Partialvolumina $\Delta^* V_0$ abschätzen. Wegen Gl. (5.10) ist

$$\Delta \ln K \approx \left(-\frac{\Delta^* V_0}{RT}\right) \Delta p .$$

$\Delta \ln K$ wird gleich 1, d.h. K nimmt um den Faktor e = 2,72 zu, wenn $\Delta p = (-RT/\Delta^* V_0)$. Liegt $\Delta^* V_0$ um 25 cm³, so ergibt sich für Δp die Größenordnung von 1000 kp/cm². Bei schwacher Dissoziation nimmt dabei $\delta \approx \sqrt{K/c}$ um den Faktor 1,65 zu. Bisher liegen jedoch nur wenige Messungen der Druckabhängigkeit dieser Größen vor.

31,8 bzw. 26,3 · 10^{-17} sec^2/cm (s. Tabelle 4, Ziff. 36α) bei Frequenzen unterhalb ν_m, während der Wert $(\alpha\lambda)_m$ sich nur wenig ändert.

In einem starken Elektrolyten, nämlich 0,5-molarer wäßriger $MgSO_4$-Lösung hat nur F. FISCHER [19] die Druckabhängigkeit bei 107,7 und 495,8 kHz gemessen. Er ermittelte bei 25° C eine konstante Relaxationsfrequenz von 200 kHz, die der angegebenen Konzentration bei Atmosphärendruck entspricht, und eine Abnahme der Absorption mit dem Druck (s. Fig. 21).

26. Einfluß von Fremdelektrolyt-Zusätzen. *α) Mischungen aus 2-2-wertigen Elektrolyten.* Einen entscheidenden Beitrag zur Klärung der Relaxationsvorgänge in Elektrolytlösungen lieferte die Untersuchung des Einflusses von Fremdelektrolyten.

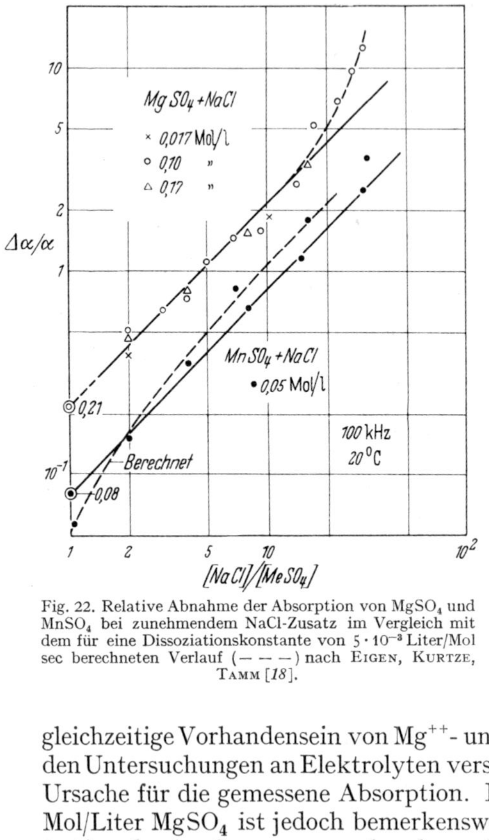

Fig. 22. Relative Abnahme der Absorption von $MgSO_4$ und $MnSO_4$ bei zunehmendem NaCl-Zusatz im Vergleich mit dem für eine Dissoziationskonstante von 5 · 10^{-3} Liter/Mol sec berechneten Verlauf (— — —) nach EIGEN, KURTZE, TAMM [18].

Während sich bei Mischungen von 2-2-wertigen Elektrolyten die Absorption beider Bestandteile im Rahmen der Meßgenauigkeit addiert, — wie von TAMM und KURTZE [17] für die Beispiele $BeSO_4+MnSO_4$ (je 0,025 Mol/Liter) und $MgSO_4+MnSO_4$ (je 0,01 Mol/Liter) gezeigt werden konnte, — treten bei Mischungen von Elektrolyten verschiedener Wertigkeit andere Verhältnisse auf.

β) Zusatz von NaCl zu $MgSO_4$-Lösungen. Die Absorption von Seewasser, welches eine ganze Reihe von Bestandteilen (0,454 Mol/Liter Na^+, 0,010 K^+, 0,052 Mg^{++}, 0,010 Ca^{++} und 0,530 Cl^-, 0,001 Br^-, 0,0275 SO_4^{--}, 0,0025 CO_3^{--}) [1] enthält, ist in ihrem Frequenzverlauf (s. Fig. 1) gut bekannt. Er ergibt eine Relaxationskurve, die sowohl in der Relaxationsfrequenz als auch im Absolutwert sehr genau einer 0,014 molaren $MgSO_4$-Lösung entspricht. Das gleichzeitige Vorhandensein von Mg^{++}- und SO_4^{--}-Ionen ist also offenbar, wie es nach den Untersuchungen an Elektrolyten verschiedener Wertigkeit zu erwarten war, die Ursache für die gemessene Absorption. Die äquivalente Konzentration von 0,014 Mol/Liter $MgSO_4$ ist jedoch bemerkenswerterweise kleiner als die Gesamtkonzentration der im Seewasser vorhandenen Mg-Atome bzw. SO_4-Gruppen[1]. Dies ist eine Folge der Anwesenheit anderer Bestandteile, und zwar der Na^+-Ionen, wie genauere Untersuchungen von TAMM, KURTZE [17] an $MgSO_4$-Lösungen mit NaCl-Zusätzen zeigen. Sind c_{NaCl} und c_{MgSO_4} die jeweiligen Gesamtkonzentrationen der gelösten Salze, so wird die Verminderung der Absorption α_0 der reinen $MgSO_4$-Lösung auf den Wert α quantitativ durch eine von TAMM [17] empirisch gefundene Mischungsregel (s. Fig. 22) angegeben:

$$\frac{\alpha}{\alpha_0} = \frac{1}{1+\varphi\,\frac{c_{NaCl}}{c_{MgSO_4}}} \quad \text{bzw.} \quad \frac{\Delta\alpha}{\alpha} = \frac{\alpha_0-\alpha}{\alpha} = \varphi\,\frac{c_{NaCl}}{c_{MgSO_4}}, \tag{26.1}$$

[1] Hier ist ganz abgesehen von der Form (Ionen, Komplexe, Moleküle), in der die Bestandteile auftreten.

wobei $\varphi = 0,21$ ein konstanter Faktor ist. Eine entsprechende Beziehung gilt auch für NaCl-Zusätze zu $MnSO_4$-Lösungen; jedoch ist der Faktor in diesem Fall $\varphi = 0,08$. Anschaulich ausgedrückt bedeutet die Mischungsregel, daß ein Zusatz von NaCl die Absorption in gleicher Weise verringert, wie eine (um den Faktor φ) kleinere Verminderung der $MgSO_4$-Konzentration. Bei diesem Ergebnis bleibt natürlich zunächst die Frage offen, ob beide Bestandteile des NaCl oder nur einer und welcher für die Absorptionsverminderung verantwortlich sind[1].

γ) Zusatz von $MgCl_2$ bzw. Na_2SO_4 zu $MgSO_4$-Lösungen. Bei den oben (s. Ziff. 22) geschilderten Untersuchungen hatte sich herausgestellt, daß bei den bisher als „stark" angesehenen Elektrolyten eine große Absorption immer dann auftritt, wenn beide Ionenpartner des Elektrolyten mindestens zweiwertig sind. Besonders bemerkenswert ist die lineare Abhängigkeit der Absorption von der Elektrolyt-Konzentration, die hier mit der Konzentration jedes der beiden Bestandteile in einem weiten Konzentrationsbereich übereinstimmt.

Einen wertvollen zusätzlichen Aufschluß liefern nun Untersuchungen des Einflusses von $MgCl_2$- bzw. Na_2SO_4-Zusätzen zu $MgSO_4$-Lösungen, durch welche die Konzentration nur eines Partners verändert wird. Der absorptionsvermindernde Einfluß der Cl^-- bzw. Na^+-Ionen sollte dabei nach den Erfahrungen mit NaCl-Zusätzen [Mischungsregel Gl. (26.1)] wesentlich kleiner als der absorptionserhöhende Einfluß der zusätzlichen Mg^{++}- bzw. SO_4^{--}-Ionen sein, so daß er deren Effekt nicht verdecken kann. Bei beiden Zusätzen ($MgCl_2$ und Na_2SO_4) tritt tatsächlich eine Erhöhung der Absorption (s. Fig. 23b) ein; sie läuft mit steigendem Zusatz einem Grenzwert zu [*17*]. Der Grenzwert der Erhöhung beläuft sich bei einer Anfangskonzentration von 0,01 Mol/Liter $MgSO_4$ auf etwa 100% und bei 0,04 Mol/Liter auf 20%, während bei 0,1 Mol/Liter keine Erhöhung meßbar ist. Praktisch wird der Grenzwert bereits bei gleicher Konzentration beider Mischungspartner erreicht.

δ) Zusatz von Säuren und Laugen zu $MgSO_4$-Lösungen, Einfluß des p_H-Wertes. Durch *Zusatz von Säuren* (Verringerung des p_H-Wertes) wird die Absorption der 2-2-wertigen Elektrolyte vermindert [*17*]; jedoch tritt die Verminderung in nennenswertem Maße erst bei Erreichen von Konzentrationen ein, die mit der des Elektrolyten vergleichbar sind. Die Abnahme der Absorption ist bei Zusatz von H_2SO_4 schwächer als bei HCl (s. Fig. 23a und c), insbesondere gilt das im Frequenzgebiet der oberen Relaxationsfrequenz. Das letzte Ergebnis ist offenbar eine Folge der bei Zusatz von H_2SO_4 sich erhöhenden SO_4^{--}-Konzentration. Der Vergleich des Einflusses von Na_2SO_4 und H_2SO_4 zeigt, daß die Absorptions-Verminderung bei Anwesenheit von H^+-Ionen größer ist als bei der gleichen Konzentration Na^+-Ionen.

Zusatz von Laugen (Vergrößerung des p_H-Wertes) bewirkt eine Erhöhung der Absorption (s. Fig. 23c). Wegen der geringen Löslichkeit der Hydroxyde der in Frage kommenden zweiwertigen Metalle kann hier jedoch nur bis zu einer geringen Konzentration des Zusatzes gemessen werden, die im allgemeinen mit der Ausgangskonzentration des Elektrolyten noch nicht vergleichbar ist.

Setzt man einer $MgCl_2$-Lösung, die an sich keine meßbare Absorption zeigt, eine Lauge (NaOH) zu, so tritt Absorption auf, die bei günstiger Wahl des Mischungsverhältnisses nahezu der einer $MgSO_4$-Lösung gleicher Mg-Konzentration gleichkommt. Wegen der geringen Löslichkeit von $Mg(OH)_2$ muß dabei mit sehr kleinen Konzentrationen gearbeitet werden, so daß beim augenblicklichen Stande die Meßgenauigkeit nicht mehr ausreicht, um die Frequenzabhängigkeit der Absorption genau bestimmen zu können.

[1] Untersuchungen mit „Puffer"-Elektrolyten wurden auch von STUEHR, VERMA, YEAGER, HOVORKA [*31a*] ausgeführt.

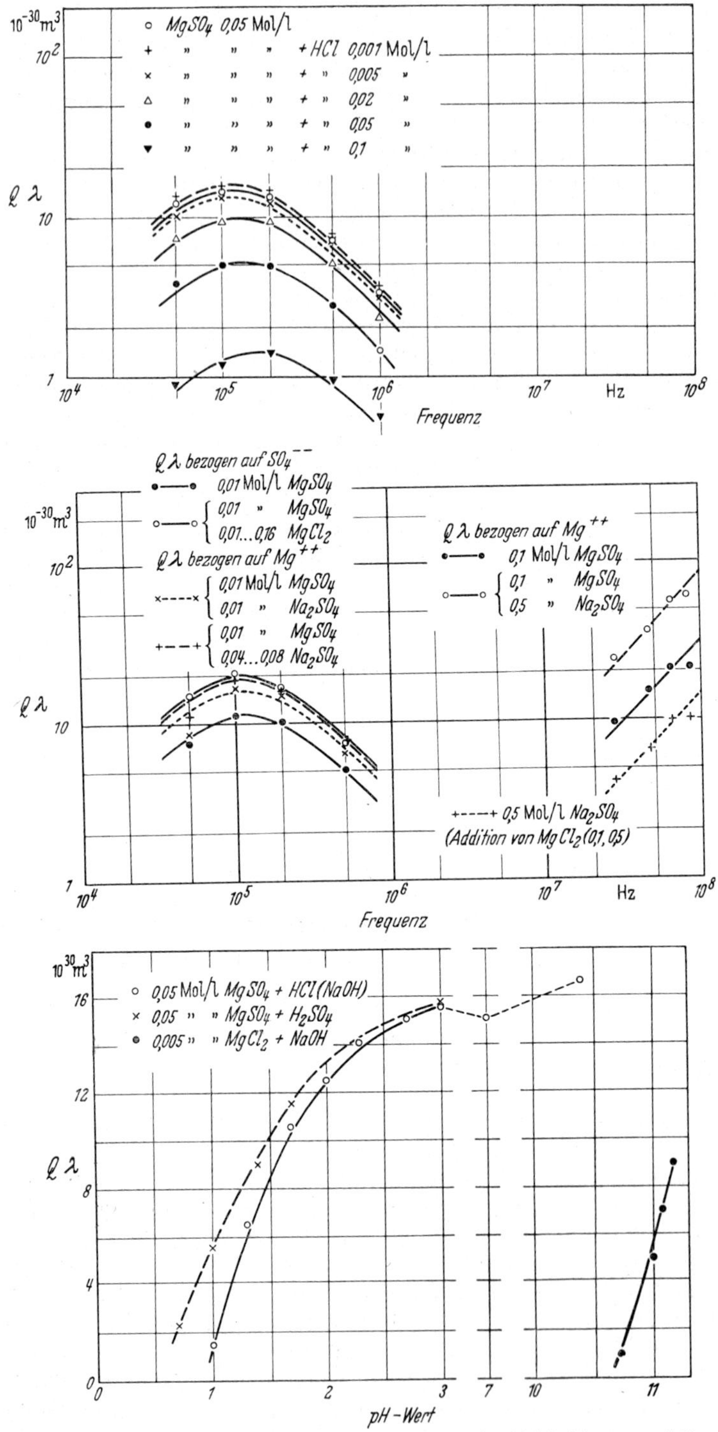

Fig. 23. Einfluß von Fremdelektrolyt-Zusätzen auf die Absorption wäßriger $MgSO_4$-Lösungen nach KURTZE und TAMM [17]. Oben: Absorptionsvolumen $Q\lambda$ in Abhängigkeit von der Frequenz bei Zusätzen von HCl. Mitte: Absorptionsvolumen $Q\lambda$ in Abhängigkeit von der Frequenz bei Zusätzen von Na_2SO_4 bzw. $MgCl_2$. Unten: Absorptionsvolumen $Q\lambda$ von $MgSO_4$- und $MgCl_2$-Lösungen in Abhängigkeit vom pH-Wert.

Die Ergebnisse der vorliegenden Untersuchungen an Mischungen sind in kurzer Form in der Tabelle 2 zusammengestellt.

Tabelle 2. *Einfluß von Fremdelektrolyt-Zusätzen auf die Absorption von wäßrigen $MgSO_4$- bzw. $MgCl_2$-Lösungen.* (Nach EIGEN, KURTZE und TAMM [*18*].)

Mischung Lösung + Zusatz	Elektrolytabsorption bei unterer Relaxationsfrequenz	 im oberen Anstieg
$MgSO_4 + MnSO_4$	Addition	Addition
$MgSO_4 + NaCl$	proportionale Abnahme	proportionale Abnahme
$MgSO_4 + MgCl_2$	begrenzte Zunahme	Addition
$MgSO_4 + NaSO_4$	begrenzte Zunahme	Addition
$MgSO_4 + HCl$	progressive Abnahme	progressive Abnahme
$MgSO_4 + H_2SO_4$	progressive Abnahme (schwächer als bei HCl)	erst bei hoher H_2SO_4-Konzentration progressive Abnahme (schwächer als bei HCl)
$MgSO_4 + NaOH$	geringe Zunahme	keine meßbare Änderung
$MgCl_2 + NaOH$	auftretende Absorption	keine Absorption meßbar

27. Zusatz von Lösungsmitteln kleiner Dielektrizitätskonstante. Durch Zusetzen von Lösungsmitteln mit kleiner Dielektrizitätskonstante, die mit Wasser beliebig mischbar sind (Dioxan, Alkohole) wird die Relaxationsfrequenz und der

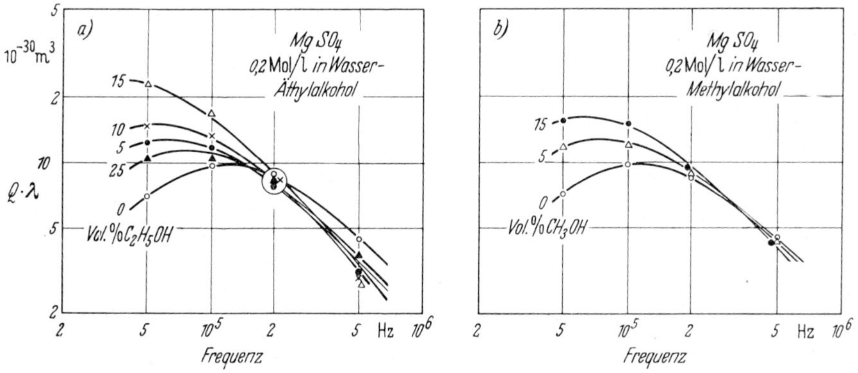

Fig. 24 a u. b. Einfluß von Alkoholzusätzen auf die Absorption (Absorptionsvolumen $Q\lambda$ in Abhängigkeit von der Frequenz) von wäßrigen $MgSO_4$-Lösungen nach TAMM, KURTZE, KAISER [*17a*].

$(Q\lambda)_m$-Wert verändert. Meßreihen von KURTZE, TAMM und KAISER [*17a*] mit Methyl- und Äthylalkohol zeigen bei konstanter $MgSO_4$-Konzentration (0,2 Mol $MgSO_4$ je Liter) eine Abnahme der Relaxationsfrequenz bei gleichzeitiger Zunahme der $(Q\lambda)_m$-Wertes mit zunehmendem Alkoholzusatz (s. Fig. 24). SMITHSON und LITOVITZ finden ein völlig analoges Verhalten — zunehmendes Absorptionsvolumen und abnehmende Relaxationsfrequenz — des unteren Relaxationsmaximums bei $MnSO_4$ für steigenden Zusatz von Methylalkohol, d.h. abnehmender Dielektrizitätskonstante (s. Tabelle 3). Die bei verschiedenen Mischungsverhältnissen mit einer gleichbleibenden Dielektrizitätskonstante von $\varepsilon = 71{,}4$ gemessene Temperaturabhängigkeit der Relaxationsfrequenz (s. Fig. 20b) ergibt eine größere Aktivierungsenergie als bei reinem Wasser, dessen Dielektrizitätskonstante sich mit der Temperatur ändert. Nach den Meßergebnissen der beiden Autoren steigt dagegen die Relaxationsfrequenz des Nebenmaximums bei 30 MHz mit abnehmender Dielektrizitätskonstante an.

Ein etwas anderes Ergebnis zeigen Meßreihen von BIES [*16*], der bei zwei konstanten Mischungsverhältnissen von Wasser und Dioxan mit den Dielektrizitätskonstanten 56,5 und 67,0 (Wasser: 78,5) Messungen bei zunehmender $MgSO_4$-

Tabelle 3. *„Untere" Relaxationsfrequenz in 0,1 molarer $MnSO_3$-Lösung in Abhängigkeit von der Temperatur und der Dielektrizitätskonstante ε des Lösungsmittels (Wasser-Methylalkohol).* (Nach SMITHSON und LITOVITZ [*25*].)

ε	Relaxationsfrequenz in MHz bei			
	5° C	25° C	35° C	45° C
86,0	1,24			
78,5		3,32		
74,8			5,95	
71,4	0,97	3,11	5,55	8,80
64,6		2,84		
61,1			4,84	
58,0				7,60

Konzentration ausführte (s. Fig. 25a). Mit abnehmender Dielektrizitätskonstante (wachsender Dioxankonzentration) steigt die Relaxationsfrequenz erst an und fällt dann wieder ab. Der Verlauf hängt von der Salzkonzentration ab.

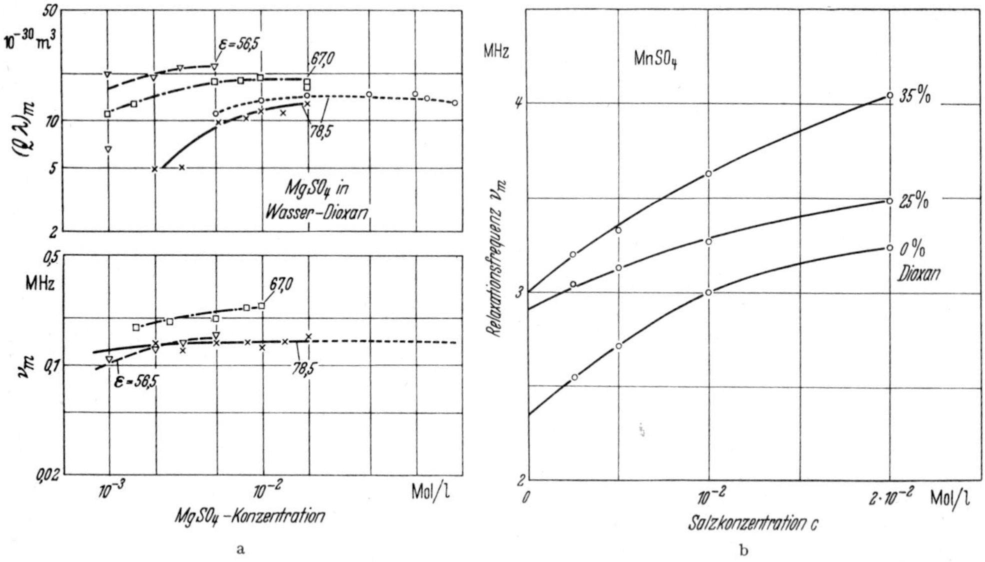

Fig. 25. a Konzentrationsabhängigkeit von Relaxationsfrequenz und maximalem Absorptionsvolumen des unteren Relaxationsmaximums von $MgSO_4$-Lösungen mit Wasser und Wasser-Dioxan-Mischungen bei verschiedener Dielektrizitätskonstante ε nach Messungen von WILSON [*15*] und BIES [*16*] für $MgSO_4$ in Wasser-Dioxan, und KURTZE und TAMM [*17*] für $MgSO_4$ in Wasser. b Konzentrationsabhängigkeit der Relaxationsfrequenz ν_m in wäßrigen $MnSO_4$-Lösungen mit Dioxan-Zusatz nach KOR, VERMA [*31a*].

Ein noch mehr abweichendes Resultat erhalten KOR und VERMA [*31a*] in $MnSO_4$-Lösungen bei Dioxan-Zusätzen. Mit abnehmender Dielektrizitätskonstante steigt dabei die Relaxationsfrequenz des Hauptmaximums stetig an (s. Fig. 25b).

28. Elektrolytlösungen mit schwerem Wasser. Bisher sind nur wenige Messungen an Lösungen in schwerem Wasser ausgeführt worden. SMITHSON und

LITOVITZ [25] fanden, daß sich beim Ersetzen des Wassers in einer 0,1 molaren $MnSO_4$-Lösung durch schweres Wasser das max. Absorptionsvolumen $(Q\lambda)_m$ um 23% vergrößerte während die Relaxationsfrequenz unverändert blieb (Fig. 26).

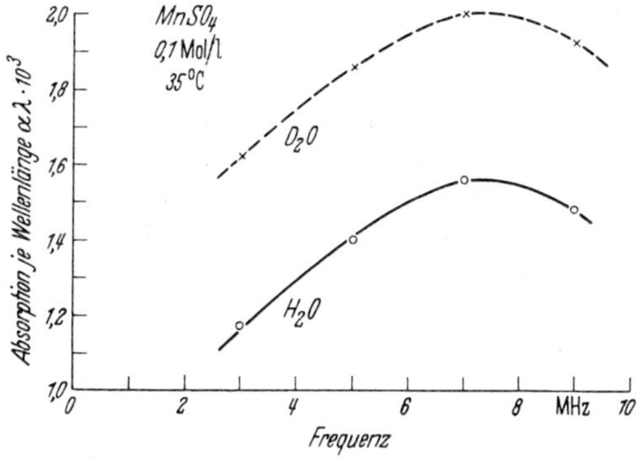

Fig. 26. Elektrolytabsorption je Wellenlänge $(\alpha\lambda)$ in Abhängigkeit von der Frequenz in einer 0,1 molaren $MnSO_4$-Lösung in H_2O bzw. D_2O nach SMITHSON und LITOVITZ [25].

III. Zusammenfassung der Meßergebnisse.

29. Wichtigste Meßergebnisse. Einige der wesentlichen Meßergebnisse seien noch einmal zusammengefaßt.

1. Alle untersuchten schwachen Elektrolyte weisen in wäßrigen Lösungen Schallabsorption durch chemische Relaxationseffekte auf. Bei einigen werden sehr große $(Q\lambda)_m$-Werte erreicht.

2. Außer den als ,,schwach" bekannten Elektrolyten zeigen auch viele der meist als ,,stark" bezeichneten Elektrolyte Relaxationsabsorption, insbesondere die 2-2-wertigen Salze.

3. Wäßrige Lösungen von $MgSO_4$ (und einer Reihe weiterer 3-2- und 2-2-wertiger Salze) weisen eine verhältnismäßig große Schallabsoprtion auf, die sich auf mindestens zwei Relaxationseffekte zurückführen läßt.

4. Im Gegensatz hierzu zeigen Lösungen 2-1-wertiger ,,starker" Elektrolyte, z.B. $MgCl_2$-Lösungen, keinen wesentlichen Unterschied gegenüber reinem Wasser.

5. Relaxationszeit und Absorptionsquerschnitt sind bei 2-2-wertigen Elektrolyten in einem großen Konzentrationsbereich nahezu konstant. Beim Zusatz von Fremdelektrolyten ändert sich zwar meist der Absorptionsquerschnitt, die Relaxationszeit des ,,unteren" Maximums zeigt jedoch keine meßbare Änderung.

6. Die Veränderung des Absorptionsquerschnittes bei Zusatz anderer Elektrolyte (insbesondere der Abfall bei NaCl- und Säurezugabe bzw. der Anstieg bei $MgCl_2$-, Na_2SO_4- und Basenzugabe) erfolgt für beide Absorptionsbereiche nahezu gleichlaufend.

7. Das untere Relaxationsmaximum liegt bei allen Mg-Salzlösungen mit zweiwertigem Anion (SO_4^{--}, CrO_4^{--}, $S_2O_3^{--}$) nahezu bei der gleichen Frequenz. Der obere Anstieg ist auch bei 1-2-wertigen Elektrolyten insbesondere auch in H_2SO_4-Lösungen zu finden. Die übrigen 2-2- und 3-2-wertigen Salze (mit den Kationen Be, Ni, Co, Mn, Cu, Zn, Al) verhalten sich — soweit sie untersucht wurden — ähnlich wie die entsprechenden Mg-Salze. Ihre ,,unteren" Relaxationsfrequenzen unterscheiden sich jedoch voneinander erheblich.

E. Deutung der Absorption in Elektrolytlösungen.

I. Stand der Kenntnisse.

30. Neuere Deutungsversuche, Übersicht. Im Laufe der letzten Jahre sind eine ganze Reihe von Versuchen unternommen worden, auf Grund der jeweils vorliegenden Meßergebnisse die Schallabsorption in Elektrolytlösungen ganz bestimmten relaxierenden Vorgängen in Elektrolyten zuzuordnen. Wegen der gegenseitigen Beeinflussung aller Ionen- und Hydratgleichgewichte in Elektrolyten ist die Deutung der Zusammenhänge verhältnismäßig schwierig. Es ist daher nicht erstaunlich, daß eine ins einzelne gehende Deutung erst in jüngster Zeit gegeben werden konnte.

Die zur Erklärung herangezogenen Vorgänge lassen sich einigermaßen unter den Begriffen Dissoziation bzw. Hydrolyse und Hydratation einordnen. Da die Verhältnisse bei den verschiedenen Elektrolyten stark voneinander abweichen, lassen sich allgemeiner geltende Erklärungen nur für begrenzte Gruppen von Elektrolyten angeben.

Bei den „schwachen" Elektrolyten scheint es festzustehen, daß die Dissoziation der Elektrolytmoleküle Ursache für ein Relaxationsverhalten bildet. Quantitativ ins Einzelne gehende Deutungen liegen für Ammoniak vor [*50*], [*7a*], bei dem die anomale Beweglichkeit der Protonen und Hydroxylionen eine entscheidende Rolle spielt. Zu dieser Gruppe von Elektrolyten muß man sicher auch HSO_4^- rechnen, für das ebenfalls eine quantitative Auswertung Erfolg hatte. In beiden Fällen wird die Reaktion durch die Diffusion beherrscht. Eine lohnende Aufgabe stellen Lanthannitrat und besonders die Acetate dar, für die zwar eine große Reihe von Messungen, jedoch bisher nicht eine quantitative Deutung vorliegt.

Bei den sog. starken Elektrolyten stellen die Salze der Sauerstoffsäuren offenbar eine besondere Gruppe dar. Zu diesen gehört das vielfach untersuchte Magnesiumsulfat und die anderen Sulfate der 2-wertigen Metalle. Man muß annehmen, daß hier molekülähnliche chemische Verbindungen der verschiedenen Ionen auftreten, deren Zerfalls-Bildungsgleichgewicht eine Relaxation verursacht.

Im wesentlichen beruhen die Deutungen auf der Annahme entweder eines Dissoziationsgleichgewichts zwischen undissoziiertem $MeSO_4$, das wahrscheinlich als Aquokomplex $(MeSO_4)_{aq}$ auftritt, und den beiden Ionensorten:

$$MeSO_4 \rightleftharpoons Me^{++} + SO_4^{--} \tag{30.1}$$

oder eines Hydrolysegleichgewichtes (s. BARTHEL [*24*]):

$$Me^{++} + H_2O \rightleftharpoons MeOH^+ + H^+. \tag{30.2}$$

Eine Synthese beider Ansichten haben EIGEN, KURTZE und TAMM [*19*] versucht, indem sie die Eigenschaft des SO_4^{--}-Ions als Protonenfänger berücksichtigten und die gleichzeitige Bildung von HSO_4^- annahmen; dabei blieb die Frage offen, ob $MeOH^+$- und HSO_4^--Ion auseinander diffundieren oder bis zum Zerfall in (hydratisierte) Me^{++}- und SO_4^{--}-Ionen in einem Komplex vereinigt bleiben:

$$MeSO_4 \cdot H_2O \rightleftharpoons MeOH^+ \cdot HSO_4^- \rightleftharpoons Me^{++} \cdot H_2O + SO_4^{--}. \tag{30.3}$$

Sie vermuteten also das Vorhandensein eines „Hydrat-Komplexes" $MeOH^+ \cdot HSO_4^-$, der entweder direkt unter gleichzeitiger Anlagerung von weiteren Hydratwasser in Me^{++}-Ionen und SO_4^{--}-Ionen oder in die Zwischenstufen $MeOH^+$ und HSO_4^- zerfällt. Sie schrieben der Abdissoziation des Metallions bzw. der Trennung der $MeOH^+$-Bindung die tiefere Relaxationsfrequenz zu, ließen aber offen, ob die höhere Relaxationsfrequenz der Auftrennung der HSO_4^--Bindung oder der Bildung des Hydratkomplexes selbst zukäme. Bei diesen Vorgängen spielt das

Hydratwasser eine entscheidende Rolle, denn eine Dissoziation ohne gleichzeitige Wasseranlagerung ist sehr unwahrscheinlich [*51*].

Neuerdings haben SMITHSON und LITOVITZ [*25*] die Rolle des Hydratwassers eingehend behandelt; sie deuten die Absorption im tiefen Frequenzbereich als Ersatz des Sulfat-Ions im $MeSO_4$ durch ein Hydratwasser:

$$MeSO_4 + H_2O \rightleftharpoons Me \cdot H_2O^{++} + SO_4^{--} \qquad (30.4)$$

Dieser Vorgang entspricht wegen des Wasserüberschusses einem binären Dissoziationsgleichgewicht, er verhält sich damit in bezug auf die Konzentrationsabhängigkeit ebenso wie der angenommene Bruttovorgang (30.1). Darüber hinaus ist er geeignet, den Einfluß von Lösungsmitteln, die die Elektrizitätskonstante vermindern, zu erklären.

Auf Grund der Vorstellung [*50*], daß die Dissoziation von Elektrolyten über Zwischenstufen vor sich geht, die durch den Diffusionsschritt und die eigentliche chemische Umwandlung gegeben sind, ergibt sich eine zwanglose Erklärung für das Auftreten mehrerer Relaxationsfrequenzen in einem Elektrolyten. Die nacheinander verlaufenden Reaktionen zeigen mehr oder weniger die typischen Eigenschaften, die durch das binäre Gleichgewicht des Diffusionsschrittes gegeben sind.

Während im Fall der 2-2- und 3-2-wertigen Elektrolyten die Zwischenstufe der Dissoziation auch akustisch wirksam ist, kommt es bei anderen Elektrolyten vor, daß die Zwischenstufe praktisch übersprungen bzw. sehr schnell durchlaufen wird. In diesem Fall tritt im untersuchten Frequenzbereich nur eine Relaxationsfrequenz auf. Möglicherweise ist das bei allen Reaktionen mit Protonen und Hydroxylionen der Fall. Bei anderen Elektrolyten endet die Reaktion auf einer Stufe, die der Zwischenstufe der 2-2-wertigen Elektrolyte ähnlich ist; auch dann tritt nur eine Relaxationsfrequenz auf.

Die Deutung der Relaxationsabsorption der Elektrolyte als Dissoziation über Zwischenstufen schließt also einen großen Teil der bisher von verschiedenen Autoren gegebenen Erklärungen ein. Sie ist in Übereinstimmung mit allen vorliegenden Meßergebnissen und hat damit erhebliche Wahrscheinlichkeit für sich, zumal ähnliche Übereinstimmung für andere, weniger umfassende, Deutungsversuche nur bei einer begrenzten Zahl von Versuchsergebnissen besteht. Dies zeigt sich bei der folgenden Betrachtung der für die Deutung der Absorption in Frage kommenden Vorgänge.

II. Relaxationsvorgänge in Elektrolytlösungen.

31. Anregung von Schwingungszuständen. Die Konzentrationsunabhängigkeit von Relaxationsfrequenz und Absorptionsquerschnitt, die z.B. bei den 2-2-wertigen Elektrolyten für beide Relaxationsmaxima in einem weiten Konzentrationsbereich auftritt, läßt zunächst zwei unabhängige Reaktionen erster Ordnung vermuten. Der nächstliegende Fall einer derartigen „Reaktion", nämlich die Anregung von Schwingungsfreiheitsgraden, scheidet hier aus. Diese wäre nur über eine Temperaturänderung in der Schallwelle möglich, die ja im Wasser kaum auftritt. Abgesehen davon liefert sie keine Erklärung für die gemessenen Fremdioneneinflüsse (s. Ziff. 26).

32. Hydratation. Die Anlagerung von Hydratwassermolekülen an eine Ionenart bzw. ihre Abtrennung verhält sich wie eine Reaktion erster Ordnung, denn sie ist wegen des Überschusses an H_2O-Molekülen nur von der Konzentration der betreffenden Ionensorte abhängig. Man hat daran gedacht, die bei den 2-2-wertigen Elektrolyten auftretenden zwei Relaxationsfrequenzen der Hydratation der beiden Ionensorten zuzuordnen, da jede Hydrathüllen bildet. Ist die Hydratation die einzige Reaktion, die auftritt, dann sollten sich — zumindest bei kleinen Konzentrationen bis zu 0,1 n, — die $MgSO_4$- und die $MgCl_2$-Lösungen in bezug auf das untere Relaxationsmaximum gleichartig verhalten, da die Mg-Ionenkonzentration, die dafür verantwortlich ist, bei gleicher Salzkonzentration in beiden gleich groß ist. Das widerspricht aber der Erfahrung im Konzentrationsbereich 0,01 bis 0,1 n. Eine gegenseitige Beeinflussung der Hydrathüllen ist in diesem Konzentrationsbereich nicht anzunehmen, so daß auch der Fremdelektrolyt-Einfluß unerklärt bleibt. Zudem ergibt eine Abschätzung der Zeitkonstante für die Gleichgewichtseinstellung der Hydrathülle wesentlich kürzere Zeiten als den hier gemessenen Relaxationsfrequenzen entspricht. In dieser einfachen Form ist die Hydratation also sicher nicht die Ursache der gemessenen Relaxationsabsorption.

33. Ionenwolke. Der gemessene Fremdelektrolyt-Einfluß ist nur mit Wechselwirkungseffekten zwischen den Ionensorten zu erklären. Ein einfacher Relaxationseffekt durch Auf- und Abbau der Ionenwolke um das Zentralion anderer Polarität (Debye-Falkenhagen-Effekt) scheidet als alleinige Ursache der gemessenen großen Absorption jedoch von vornherein aus, da dieser (nach HALL [*23*]) sehr kleine Absorptionsquerschnitte ergibt. Außerdem ist die Relaxationszeit der Ionenwolke (s. Ziff. 10) umgekehrt proportional zur Elektrolytkonzentration, so daß keine konstante Relaxationszeit auftreten kann. Vor allem müßte ein Ionenwolkeneffekt bei allen Elektrolyten zu beobachten sein und kann nicht die gefundenen starken individuellen Abweichungen zeigen.

Aus diesen Gründen ist zu erwarten, daß die Absorption durch die Ionenwolke im Bereich der Meßfrequenzen klein ist, so daß sie von meist vorhandenen anderen Absorptionseffekten verdeckt wird. Erst bei hohen Frequenzen (>100 MHz) und großen Konzentrationen kann sie eine Rolle spielen. Es ist wahrscheinlich, daß die bei $MgCl_2$ gefundene Absorption, die erst bei sehr hohen Frequenzen meßbar wird (s. Fig. 13), ein Ionenwolkeneffekt ist.

34. Ionenreaktionen. Bei einer Reihe von Relaxationsvergängen ist es sehr wahrscheinlich, daß sie auf spezielle Ionenreaktionen zurückzuführen sind, die sich als Dissoziations- und deren Rückreaktionen darstellen lassen. Solche Reaktionen sind immer dann zu erwarten, wenn im Gleichgewicht mit den freien Ionen des gelösten Elektrolyten noch undissoziierte oder nur teilweise dissoziierte Bestandteile des Elektrolyten auftreten, wie es in besonderem Maße bei den schwachen Elektrolyten der Fall ist[1]. Nach neueren Erkenntnissen ist, abweichend von der ursprünglichen Deutung, neben den "schwachen" auch eine ganze Reihe sogenannter "starker" Elektrolyte im Wasser nur unvollständig dissoziiert. Dies zeigt eine genauere Analyse der thermodynamischen, insbesondere kalorischen Eigenschaften von Elektrolytlösungen[2]. Der undissoziierte Anteil ist zwar im allgemeinen sehr klein, er kann jedoch bei den Salzen der Sauerstoffsäuren, z.B. bei $MgSO_4$[3] auch recht beträchtlich werden[4]. Da sich die partiellen Volumina

---

[1] Bei den schwachen Elektrolyten ist die Reaktionsarbeit (freie Energie), die bei der Dissoziation aufgebracht werden muß so viel größer als die bei der gleichzeitigen Hydratation gewonnene Hydratationsarbeit (freie Energie), daß das Gleichgewicht stark auf Seiten der undissoziierten Bestandteile liegt.

[2] Ähnliche Folgerungen zog bereits W. NERNST [*69*] aus dem Konzentrationsverlauf der Verdünnungswärmen.

[3] Beim $MgSO_4$ und einigen anderen Elektrolyten wird die Dissoziationswärme negativ (s. [*58*]), d.h. es wird bei der Dissoziation Wärme frei. Diesem Entalpieanteil wirkt allerdings ein so großer Entropieanteil entgegen, daß sich nur noch eine relativ unvollständige Dissoziation ergibt.

[4] Der Dissoziationsgrad einiger Elektrolyte wurde von WICKE und EIGEN [*48*] aus den Aktivitätskoeffizienten, Verdünnungswärmen und den scheinbaren Molwärmen auf Grund neuerer Erkenntnisse bestimmt.

der beiden Zustände „dissoziiert" und „undissoziiert" auf Grund der Hydratation der Ionen merklich unterscheiden, muß eine beträchtliche Absorption erwartet werden, wenn der Dissoziationsvorgang in der vermuteten Weise auftritt. Gerade bei solchen als unvollständig-dissoziiert erkannten Elektrolyten wurden auch besondere Absorptionseffekte beobachtet.

Über den Zustand, in dem sich die undissoziierten Bestandteile befinden (Molekeln, Ionenkomplexe) können bisher nur Vermutungen ausgesprochen werden. Komplexe mit Lösungsmittelmolekeln (Aquokomplexe) sind in einigen Fällen (z.B. bei $MgSO_4$) wahrscheinlich.

Das Vorhandensein von Hydrolyseprodukten, die auf Reaktionen mit den "lösungsmitteleigenen" H^+- oder OH^--Ionen zurückzuführen sind, ist in ähnlicher Weise Ursache von Relaxationserscheinungen. Wegen der Vielfalt der möglichen Reaktionsformen sind eindeutige Zuordnungen zu den gemessenen Relaxationserscheinungen oft schwierig.

Eine besondere Gruppe stellen die Säuren und Basen dar, bei denen ein Ionenpartner mit einer „lösungsmitteleigenen" Ionensorte übereinstimmt. Hier ist die Zahl der verschiedenen Reaktionsmöglichkeiten stark eingeschränkt. Eine weitere Besonderheit besteht darin, daß die H^+- und OH^--Ionen anomal große Beweglichkeit besitzen, die auf Protonensprüngen in Wasserstoffbrückenbindungen beruht (s. Fig. 27).

III. Diskussion spezieller Ionenreaktionen.

35. Ionenreaktionen unter Beteiligung von Protonen. Das am besten bekannte Beispiel für eine Ionenreaktion unter Beteiligung von Protonen liefert die Schwefelsäure. Es wurde von EIGEN [*50*] eingehend diskutiert. Schwefelsäure ist zwar in der ersten Stufe vollständig dissoziiert, nicht aber in der zweiten, deren Dissoziationsgleichgewicht formal durch die Reaktion

$$HSO_4^- \rightleftharpoons H^+ + SO_4^{--} \qquad (35.1)$$

beschrieben wird. Der Übergang ist mit einer akustisch wirksamen Volumenänderung verbunden, denn u.a. ist die Zahl der Ionen vorher und nachher verschieden; außerdem besitzen die auftretenden Ionen verschieden ausgebildete Hydrathüllen.

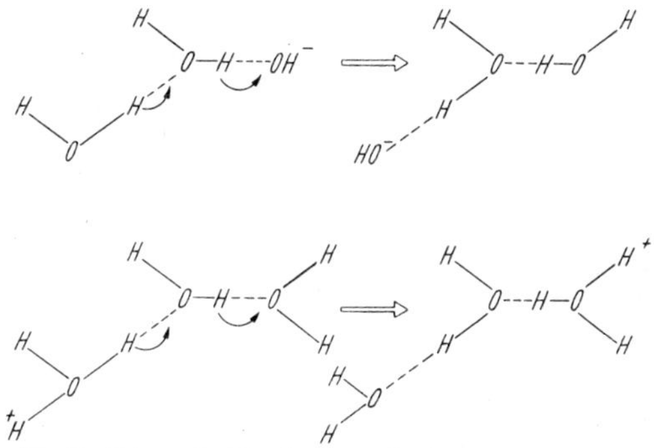

Fig. 27. Schema des Wanderungsmechanismus von Hydroxylionen (oben) und Protonen (unten) in Wasser.

Bei der hier auftretenden Bildungsreaktion (Rekombination), die sich aus der Annäherung (Diffusion) der Ionen auf einen kritischen Abstand und dem Übergang zur Verbindung HSO_4^- zusammensetzt (s. Ziff. 6 und 9), ist der erste Schritt weniger schnell als der zweite, so daß er die Reaktionsgeschwindigkeit k_{Bildg} bestimmt. Dies ist eine Folge der anomalen Beweglichkeit der Protonen, die nach der Annäherung an das SO_4^{--}-Ion bis auf einen kritischen Radius ($a \approx 5$ Å), die Hydrathülle des Ions nahezu ohne Behinderung durchwandern, so daß der Übergang zur Verbindung sehr schnell erfolgt.

Die anomale Beweglichkeit der Protonen, wie auch der Hydroxylionen, erklärt sich mit der gut gesicherten Annahme der Existenz von H_3O^+-Ionen [*55*], [*70*] und der Fluktuation des Überschuß-Protons in Wasserstoffbrückenbindungen entsprechend dem in Fig. 27 dargestellten Schema. Eins der drei Protonen dieser

H_3O^+-Ionen wird dabei an eine benachbarte Wassermolekel abgegeben, welche dann selbst ein Proton weitergeben kann. Geschieht dieser Vorgang mit einer der Hydratwassermolekeln, die in der Umgebung bzw. in der Hydrathülle des Gegenions für das „Anspringen" eines Protons gerade passend ausgerichtet sind, so wird sie damit aus der Hydrathülle herausgelöst und durch ein Proton ersetzt (s. Fig. 28). Dies ist aber mit der Bildung von HSO_4^- identisch [Weg III in Schema (35.2)].

Da die Bildung des HSO_4^--Ions auch erfolgen kann, indem sich spontan eine Bindung verschiebt — dies entspricht einer Abdissoziation eines OH^--Ions (Weg II) — gibt es also zwei Möglichkeiten für den Verlauf der Reaktion:

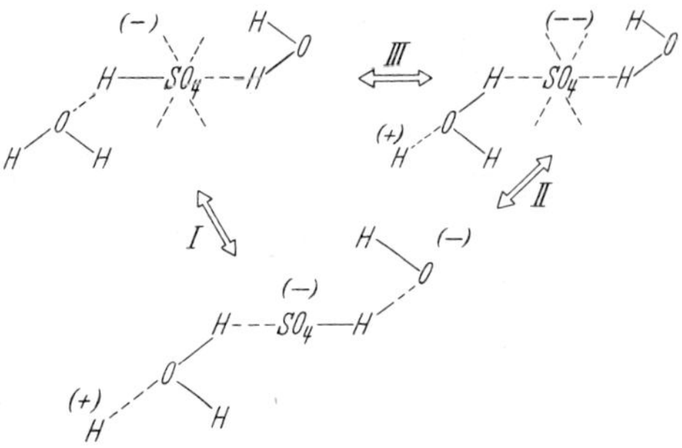

Fig. 28. Schema der Dissoziation von HSO_4^- in wäßriger Lösung. (Der Weg I bis II ist ohne praktische Bedeutung. —— Chemische Bindungen. ····· elektrostatische Kräfte.

$$\begin{array}{ccc} H^+ + SO_4^{--}\cdot H_2O & \overset{III}{\rightleftharpoons} & HSO_4^- + H_2O \\ {\scriptstyle II}\ \nwarrow\!\!\searrow & & \swarrow\!\!\nearrow\ {\scriptstyle I} \\ & H^+ + HSO_4^- + OH^- & \end{array} \tag{35.2}$$

Die Reaktion II entspricht einer Hydrolyse von Hydratwasser durch SO_4^{--}-Ionen, die auch in Lösungen anderer Sulfate auftreten müßte. Die Hydrolyse durch SO_4^{--}-Ionen ist jedoch so gering, daß der Weg II/I keine Rolle gegen III spielt. Dies gilt sicher, solange die H^+-Ionenkonzentration genügend groß ist. Man kann die Dissoziation demnach so behandeln, als ob sie nur auf dem Weg III verliefe. Bei anderen stärker hydrolysierenden Substanzen (z. B. Ammoniak) ist der Weg II/I nicht vernachlässigbar. Ob III oder II/I häufiger ist, hängt vom p_H-Wert ab.

Das zugehörige Reaktionsgleichgewicht ist durch die Dissoziationskonstante ${}^cK_{HSO_4^-} \approx 10^{-2}$ Mol/Liter bestimmt [58]:

$$\frac{[H^+]\,[SO_4^{--}]}{[HSO_4^-]}\,\Pi^f_{H^+,\,SO_4^{--}} = {}^cK_{HSO_4^-}. \tag{35.3}$$

Dabei ist die Konzentration der H^+-Ionen wegen der vorausgegangenen ersten Dissoziationsreaktion wesentlich größer als die der SO_4^{-}-Ionen. Für nicht sehr kleine[1] Elektrolytkonzentrationen ($c > 10^{-6}$ Mol/Liter) sind die Ionenkonzentrationen $[H^+] = (1+\delta)\,c$ bzw. $[SO_4^{-}] = \delta c$ aus der Dissoziation der Schwefelsäure (35.3) allein bestimmt, und der Dissoziationsgrad δ der zweiten Stufe kann nach Gl. (5.7) ermittelt werden.

---

[1] Bei sehr kleinen Konzentrationen macht sich das Dissoziationsgleichgewicht des Wassers

$$H_2O \rightleftharpoons H^+ + OH^- \tag{35.4}$$

bemerkbar. Es liefert zusätzlich H^+-Ionen und bestimmt deren Konzentration für kleine Elektrolytkonzentrationen. Wegen der kleinen Dissoziationskonstante des Wassers

$$\frac{[H^+]\,[OH^-]}{[H_2O]}\,\Pi^f_{H^+,\,OH^-} = {}^cK_{H_2O} \approx 2\cdot 10^{-16}\ \text{Mol/Liter} \tag{35.5}$$

genügen aber schon verhältnismäßig geringe Elektrolytkonzentrationen ($c > 10^{-6}$ Mol/Liter), die ja H^+-Ionenkonzentrationen der gleichen Größenordnung hervorrufen, um die OH^--Ionenkonzentrationen praktisch zum Verschwinden zu bringen und damit die Dissoziation des Wassers völlig zu unterdrücken.

Wie oben erläutert (s. Ziff. 5) ist für $\Pi^f \approx 0{,}5 \ldots 1$ ein maximaler wenig konzentrationsabhängiger Wert $G \approx 0{,}2$ in der Umgebung von $c = 0{,}6 \cdot {}^cK/\Pi^f \approx 10^{-2}$ Mol/Liter zu erwarten, also in dem Bereich, in dem Messungen vorliegen (s. Fig. 29).

Wegen der geringen Konzentrationsabhängigkeit der Differenz der partiellen Volumina, die im übrigen hinreichend genau bekannt ist, ($\Delta^* V \approx 23$ cm³/Mol), wird auch die Größe $(Q\lambda)_m$ nach Gl. (5.13) wenig abhängig von der Konzentration. Die Verschiebung der Absorptionskurve der Schwefelsäure mit der Konzentration kann also hauptsächlich auf eine Konzentrationsabhängigkeit der Relaxationsfrequenz zurückgeführt werden. Unter den obengenannten Voraussetzungen ($\Pi^f \approx 1$) ist (s. Ziff. 4) die Relaxationsfrequenz gegeben durch

$$2\pi\nu_m \approx k_{\text{Zerf}} + k_{\text{Bildg}}([\text{H}^+] + [\text{SO}_4^{--}])$$
$$\approx k_{21} + k_{12}(1 + 2\delta)\,c\,.$$

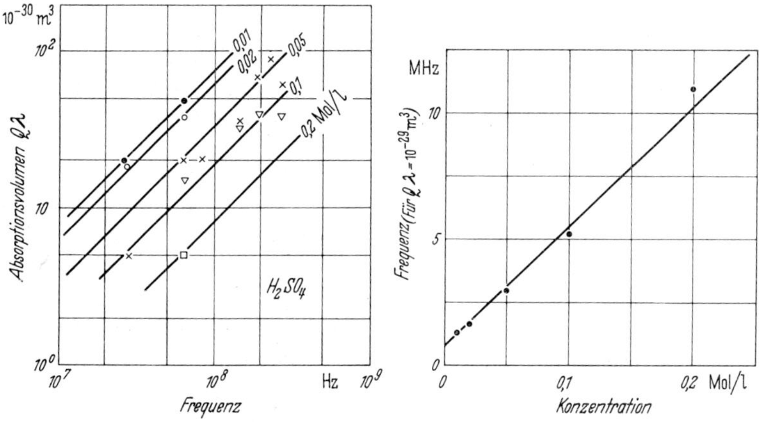

a b

Fig. 29 a u. b. Konzentrationsabhängigkeit der Relaxationsabsorption von wäßrigen H_2SO_4-Lösungen nach Eigen, Kurtze und Tamm [*18*]. a Frequenzgang des Absorptionsvolumens bei verschiedenen Konzentrationen. b Frequenzverschiebung (Frequenz für konstanten Absorptionsquerschnitt) in Abhängigkeit von der Konzentration.

Sie muß demnach von einem Anfangswert, der durch k_{21} bestimmt ist, nahezu linear mit der Konzentration zunehmen, wobei die Steilheit der Zunahme durch k_{12} gegeben ist. In Fig. 29b ist die Verschiebung der Absorptionskurve aufgetragen; sie folgt recht gut dem zu erwartenden Verlauf und liefert ${}^cK_{\text{HSO}_4^-} = k_{\text{Zerf}}/k_{\text{Bildg}} = 1{,}5 \cdot 10^{-2}$ Mol/Liter in guter Übereinstimmung mit dem aus Leitfähigkeits- und EMK-Messungen bekannten Literaturwert [*58*]. Die Dissoziationsgeschwindigkeit ergibt sich in $10^{-2} \ldots 10^{-1}$ molarer Lösung mit den obigen Annahmen zu $k_{\text{Zerf}} = 3 \cdot 10^9\ \text{sec}^{-1}$ die Rekombinationsgeschwindigkeit[1] zu $k_{\text{Bildg}} = 10^{11}$ Liter/Molsec, so daß man eine Relaxationsfrequenz von $5 \cdot 10^8$ Hz zu erwarten hat, was in Übereinstimmung mit den Meßergebnissen ist.

Die Größe der gefundenen Geschwindigkeitskonstante der Rekombination $k_{\text{Bildg}} = 10^{11}$ Liter/Molsec läßt darauf schließen, daß die Begegnungshäufigkeit auf Grund der Diffusion geschwindigkeitsbestimmend ist. Molekular-kinetische Betrachtungen zeigen nun, daß dieser eine Aktivierungsenergie von höchstens 2 bis 3 kcal/Mol zugeschrieben werden kann. Dieser Betrag liegt aber weit unter dem Wert $-5{,}2$ kcal/Mol, der von Davies, Jones und Monk [*58*] für die gesamte

[1] Die gefundene Geschwindigkeitskonstante k_{Bildg} entspricht in ihrer Größenordnung den auch für andere protolytische Reaktionen aus elektrischen Dispersionsmessungen gefundenen Werten, die z.B. für Essigsäure ($H^+ + Ac^- \rightarrow HAc$): $4{,}5 \cdot 10^{10}$ Liter/Molsec [*73*] und für Wasser ($H^+ + OH^- \rightarrow H_2O$): $1{,}3 \cdot 10^{11}$ Liter/Molsec [*72*] betragen.

Dissoziationswärme von HSO_4^- gemessen wurde. Dies ist eine gute Bestätigung für die Annahme zweier Teilvorgänge bei der Rekombination. Die oben aus der Geschwindigkeitskonstante errechnete Energie enthält nur die zum Diffusionsvorgang der Protonen gehörende Aktivierungsenergie von 2 bis 3 kcal/Mol. Der Restbetrag mindestens gleicher Größe (mit umgekehrtem Vorzeichen) bestimmt das sich sehr schnell einstellende Gleichgewicht $A, B \rightleftharpoons AB$ und tritt in der Geschwindigkeitskonstante $k_{\text{Zerf}} = (k_{32}/k_{23})\, k_{21}$ der Rückreaktion $AB \rightarrow A + B$ als Wärmetönung auf.

Die beschriebene Reaktion muß nun auch in Lösungen von Salzen der genannten Säuren mit starken Basen auftreten, also z.B. bei Na_2SO_4 und ähnlichen Elektrolyten. Es wird nämlich ein Teil der freien H^+-Ionen im Wasser zur Bildung von HSO_4^--Ionen verbraucht. Dabei steigt die OH^--Konzentration entsprechend einer schwachen Hydrolyse etwas an. Abgesehen von dem Fall sehr kleiner Salzkonzentration ist die HSO_4^--Ionenkonzentration jedoch immer gegen die der auftretenden $NaSO_4^-$-Ionen sehr klein, so daß die Dissoziationsreaktion $HSO_4^- \rightleftharpoons H^+ + SO_4^{--}$ sicher völlig verdeckt wird durch die Dissoziationsreaktion $NaSO_4^- \rightleftharpoons Na^+ + SO_4^{--}$ (s. auch Ziff. 37).

Ähnliche Verhältnisse wie bei der Schwefelsäure sind mit einiger Sicherheit auch bei den anderen Sauerstoffsäuren also bei der Dissoziation von $HS_2O_3^-$, $HCrO_4^-$ u. a. zu erwarten.

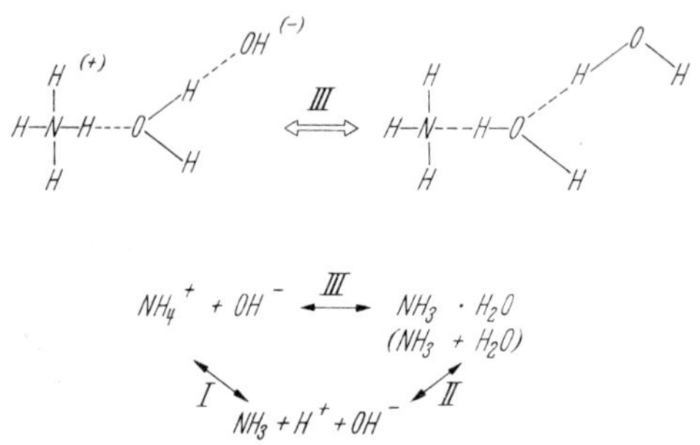

Fig. 30. Dissoziationsschema für Ammoniak ($NH_3 \cdot H_2O$) in wäßriger Lösung. (Der Weg I bis II ist ohne praktische Bedeutung.)

36. Reaktionen unter Beteiligung von Hydroxylionen. Die Hydroxylionen besitzen wie die Protonen eine erhöhte Beweglichkeit, die man wieder einem Wanderungsmechanismus zuschreibt, der in der Verschiebung von Wasserstoffbrückenbindungen besteht (s. Fig. 27 oben). Sind also OH^--Ionen an einer Assoziations-Reaktion beteiligt, so ist wie bei Protonenbeteiligung nach der Begegnung der Ionen ein sehr schneller Übergang zur Verbindung zu erwarten. Die Geschwindigkeitskonstante der Assoziation ist also durch die der Diffusion bestimmt.

α) Dissoziation von Ammoniak. Ein verhältnismäßig übersichtliches Beispiel für eine solche Reaktion liefert die Dissoziation des Ammoniaks in wäßriger Lösung. Die Meßergebnisse (s. Fig. 31 links) zeigen ein Relaxationsmaximum, das sich mit der Konzentration verschiebt von 20 MHz in 0,5 molarer Lösung auf etwa 70 MHz bei 5-molarer Lösung, und das dabei gleichzeitig abnimmt. Wie EIGEN [*50*] gezeigt hat, läßt sich die gemessene Absorption in basischer Lösung nur auf die Gleichgewichtseinstellung (s. Fig. 30).

$$NH_4^+ + OH^- \rightleftharpoons NH_3\,(\dot{+})\,H_2O \tag{36.1}$$

zurückführen. Relaxationseffekte der Ionenwolke und der Hydratation liefern wesentlich zu kleine Absorptionsquerschnitte. Darüber hinaus würde im Gegensatz zu den Meßergebnissen ein Ionenwolkeneffekt eine Zunahme des Absorptionsquerschnitts mit der Konzentration, die Hydratation eine konzentrationsunabhängige Relaxationsfrequenz bedingen.

Zur Prüfung dieser Annahme hat EIGEN [*50*] den zu erwartenden Absorptionsquerschnitt berechnet, indem er die für die Dissoziation der Schwefelsäure gültigen Überlegungen hier sinngemäß anwandte. Berücksichtigt man, daß, abgesehen von sehr kleinen Elektrolytkonzentrationen, die Konzentrationen $[NH_4^+]$ und

$[OH^-]$ gleich werden, dann ist das Gleichgewicht bestimmt durch

$$\frac{\delta^2 c}{1-\delta}\Pi^f = \frac{[NH_4^+][OH^-]}{[NH_3 \cdot H_2O]}\Pi^f_{NH_4^+, OH^-} = {}^cK_{NH_3 \cdot H_2O}. \tag{36.2}$$

Dabei ist die Gleichgewichtskonstante ${}^cK_{NH_3 \cdot H_2O} \approx 1{,}5 \cdot 10^{-5}$ Mol/Liter (bei 25° C) aus Messungen von W. A. ROTH [77] wieder relativ genau bekannt. Sie ist verhältnismäßig klein, so daß der Dissoziationsgrad ebenfalls klein wird (für $c = 1$ Mol/Liter: $\delta \approx 4 \cdot 10^{-3}$) und kann für jede Elektrolytkonzentration c mit Hilfe einer Näherungsformel

$$\delta \approx \sqrt{{}^cK/\Pi^f c} \tag{36.3}$$

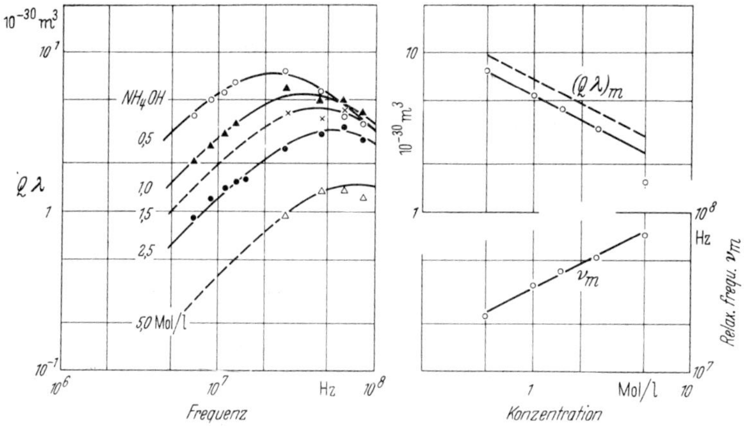

Fig. 31. Konzentrationsabhängigkeit der Relaxationsabsorption wäßriger Ammoniak-Lösungen nach EIGEN, KURTZE, KAISER, TAMM [17a], [50]. Links: Frequenzabhängigkeit des Absorptionsvolumens $Q\lambda$ bei verschiedenen Konzentrationen. Rechts: Maximales Absorptionsvolumen $(Q\lambda)_m$ (oben) und Relaxationsfrequenz ν_m (unten) in Abhängigkeit von der Konzentration.

leicht berechnet werden kann, da das Aktivitätskoeffizienten-Produkt nur wenig von 1 abweicht.

Mit Hilfe des Dissoziationsgrades läßt sich sofort auch der Faktor G berechnen, der für eine einfache Dissoziation der unter Ziff. 5 abgeleiteten Beziehung folgt.

$$G = G_D = \frac{\delta(1-\delta)}{1+(1-\delta)}; \quad \text{und für } \delta \ll 1: \quad G_D \approx \frac{\delta}{2}.$$

Entnimmt man den Messungen die Relaxationszeit $\tau = 1/(2\pi\nu_m)$ (s. Fig. 31 unten), so erhält man mit der bekannten[1] wenig konzentrationsabhängigen Differenz der partiellen Volumina $\Delta^* V_D \approx \Delta^* V_{D_0} = 28\,(\pm 2)$ cm³/Mol den in Fig. 31 oben aufgetragenen Absorptionsquerschnitt, der mit den Meßwerten sehr gut übereinstimmt.

Auf Grund der gemessenen Konzentrationsabhängigkeit der Relaxationsfrequenz läßt sich entscheiden, daß die Reaktion im wesentlichen in der angegebenen Form über die Anlagerung eines Hydroxyl-Ions (Weg III in Abb. 30) verläuft. Ebenfalls möglich wäre der Umweg über die Abdissoziation eines Protons (Weg I) aus dem NH_4^+-Ion, welches sich dann mit einem Hydroxyl-Ion zu Wasser

[1] Die Differenz der partiellen Volumina läßt sich aus denen der Reaktionspartner $\Delta^* V = {}^*V_{NH_4} + {}^*V_{OH} - {}^*V_{NH_3} - {}^*V_{H_2O} = 15 - 2 - 23 - 18 = -28$ cm³/Mol errechnen. Sie wurde von SASLAWSKY [71] auch direkt bei der Neutralisation gemessen. Ein eventuell vorhandener Einfluß der NH_3-Molekeln auf die Struktur des Lösungsmittels in Form eines Abbaus von Wasseraggregaten sollte nach Abschätzungen von EIGEN [50] höchstens eine Abweichung von 10 bis 20% in den Absolutwerten des Absorptionsquerschnitts ausmachen und innerhalb der Meßgenauigkeit liegen.

vereinigt (Weg II). Bei dem „Umweg" (I/II) ist die Dissoziation des Wassers mit der Geschwindigkeitskonstante $k_{\mathrm{Zerf\,H_2O}} = 3 \cdot 10^{-5}\,\mathrm{sec}^{-1}$ (nach einer Abschätzung von EIGEN [*50*]) der langsamste Schritt in der Rückreaktion und bestimmt deren Geschwindigkeitskonstante. Existiert dagegen ein Komplex $NH_3 \cdot H_2O$, so kann die Dissoziation des Wassers aus diesem Komplex heraus (Weg III) sehr viel schneller erfolgen, so daß sich eine größere Geschwindigkeitskonstante der zugehörigen Rückreaktion ergibt.

Bei der hier gerechtfertigten Vernachlässigung der Aktivitätskoeffizienten erhält man für die Relaxationsfrequenz einer einfachen Dissoziationsreaktion [s. Ziff. 4, Gl. (4.4)] bei kleinem Dissoziationsgrad

$$2\pi\nu_m \approx k_{\mathrm{Zerf}} + k_{\mathrm{Bildg}} \cdot 2\delta c \approx k_{\mathrm{Zerf}} + k_{\mathrm{Bildg}}\, 2\sqrt{{}^{c}K\,c}\,, \tag{36.4}$$

wenn der Dissoziationsgrad $\delta \approx \sqrt{{}^{c}K/c}$ entsprechend Gl. (5.6) eingesetzt wird. Trägt man die gemessenen Relaxationsfrequenzen über $\sqrt{{}^{c}Kc}$ auf, so erhält man eine Gerade, deren Neigung

$$k_{\mathrm{Bildg}} \approx 3 \cdot 10^{10}\ \mathrm{Liter/Mol\,sec}$$

liefert (Fig. 31). Dieser Wert ist in guter Übereinstimmung mit dem aus der Debyeschen Formel für die Diffusion von NH_4^+- und OH^--Ionen auf den kritischen Abstand von 3 bis 5 Å errechneten Wert. Das bestätigt die Annahme, daß die Bildungsgeschwindigkeit diffusionsbestimmt ist. Der Wert k_{Zerf} kann nicht direkt aus der Auftragung entnommen werden; er ergibt sich aber aus der Gleichgewichtskonstanten

$$k_{\mathrm{Zerf}} = K \cdot k_{\mathrm{Bildg}} = 5 \cdot 10^5\,\mathrm{sec}^{-1}.$$

Dieser Wert ist wesentlich größer als die Zerfallsgeschwindigkeitskonstante des reinen Wassers (etwa $3 \cdot 10^{-5}\,\mathrm{sec}^{-1}$ nach EIGEN und DEMAEYER [*72*]), so daß die Existenz von $NH_3 \cdot H_2O$-Komplexen erwiesen scheint und die Reaktion dem Weg III nach dem Schema der Fig. 30 entspricht.

Diese Ergebnisse werden von CARNEVALE und LITOVITZ [*7a*] durch Auswertung der von ihnen bis zu Drucken von 2000 kp/cm² gemessenen Druckabhängigkeit der Absorption in 0,1-normaler wäßriger $NH_3 \cdot H_2O$-Lösung (s. Ziff. 25β) bestätigt. Die Auswertung (s. Tabelle 4) zeigt nämlich, daß mit zunehmendem Druck die gemessene Relaxationsfrequenz ν_m proportional zum Dissoziationsgrad δ ansteigt, dessen Druckabhängigkeit bekannt ist bzw. sich näherungsweise aus der Partialvolumen-Differenz $\Delta^* V$ ergibt (denn $\delta \approx \sqrt{K}$ und $\partial \ln K/\partial p = -\Delta^* V_0/RT$). Da bei den vorhandenen kleinen Dissoziationsgraden

$$\delta \ll 1:\quad \nu_m \approx \frac{1}{\pi}\, {}^{0}k_{12}\,\Pi^{f} \cdot c\,\delta$$

ist, folgt aus diesem Befund, daß das Produkt ${}^{0}k_{12}\,\Pi^{f}$ nahezu druckunabhängig ist und damit auch ${}^{0}k_{12}$; denn Π^{f} ist, wie ebenfalls bekannt, nur sehr wenig vom Druck abhängig. Es ergibt sich[1] bei 45°C ${}^{0}k_{12} \approx 5 \cdot 10^{10}$ l/Molsec.

Die Zerfallskonstante k_{21} steigt — im Gegensatz zu ${}^{0}k_{12}$ — stark mit dem Druck an, da die Gleichgewichtskonstante $k_{21}/{}^{0}k_{12} = K = K_D$ wie das Quadrat des Dissoziationsgrades δ ansteigen müßte. Die Druckunabhängigkeit von ${}^{0}k_{12}\,\Pi^{f}$ bewirkt, daß die Absorption bei tiefen Frequenzen

$$\nu \ll \nu_m \text{ und } \delta \ll 1:\quad \frac{\alpha}{\nu^2} = \frac{\pi^2}{2}\,\varrho\, u \cdot \frac{1}{{}^{0}k_{12}\,\Pi^{f}}\, \frac{(\Delta^* V)^2}{RT}$$

wie die Tabelle 4 zeigt, praktisch nur durch die Abnahme von $(\Delta^* V)^2$ mit dem Druck bestimmt ist.

[1] Die Differenz gegenüber dem oben angegebenen Wert ist quantitativ auf die verschiedenen Meßtemperaturen zurückzuführen.

Die auf Grund der Schallabsorption gefundenen Ergebnisse konnten auf einem unabhängigen Wege mit Hilfe des Dissoziations-Feldeffektes[1] von EIGEN und SCHOEN [*73*] bestätigt werden (Fig. 32).

Ähnliche Ergebnisse wurden neuerdings von EIGEN, TAMM und TJADEN[2] an Aminosäuren und von EIGEN und SCHWARZ [*51b*] an substituierten Aminen gefunden und im gleichen Sinne quantitativ gedeutet.

Tabelle 4. *Auswertungsergebnisse der Druckabhängigkeit der Absorption in 0,1 n-$NH_3 \cdot H_2O$-Lösung.*

p kp/cm²	c Mol/l	Πf	δ 10^{-2}	$\Delta^* V$ cm³/Mol	$(\Delta^* V)^2$ $\left(\frac{cm^3}{Mol}\right)^2$	α/ν^2_{exp} 10^{-17} sec²/cm	ν_m exp MHz	k_{12} 10^{10} l/Molsec	K_D 10^{-5} Mol/l	k_{21} 10^5 sec⁻¹
1	0,1	0,986	1,39	28,5	810	47,6	20,6	4,6	1,9	9,1
1117	0,104	0,914	2,32	24,3	590	31,8	38,7	5,5	5,2	28,6
2030	0,107	0,883	3,40	21,3	493	26,3	52,9	5,3	10,6	55,5

β) Dissoziation anderer schwacher Basen, Hydrolyse. Ähnliche Verhältnisse wie beim Ammoniak sind bei der Dissoziation anderer schwacher Basen zu erwarten,

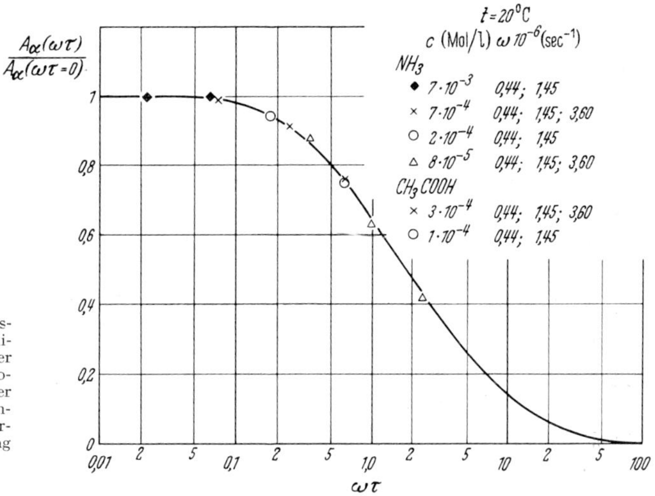

Fig. 32. Dispersion des Dissoziationsfeldeffektes (Abnahme der Amplitude von $\Delta\alpha$ in Abhängigkeit von der normierten Frequenz ω für Ammoniak und Essigsäure. Vergleich der Meßwerte bei verschiedenen Konzentrationen mit dem theoretischen Verlauf für einen Relaxationsvorgang nach EIGEN und SCHOEN [*73*].

zu denen sinngemäß auch die Produkte $(MeOH)^+$ der ersten Dissoziationsstufe der Hydroxyde zweiwertiger Metalle gehören. Ihre zweite Dissoziationsstufe besteht formal in der Abdissoziation des OH^--Ions

$$MeOH^+ \rightleftharpoons Me^{++} + OH^- \tag{36.5}$$

Die Ionen $MeOH^+$ und Me^{++} besitzen verschieden ausgebildete Hydrathüllen, so daß mit dem Übergang sicher eine beträchtliche Volumenänderung verbunden ist, die sich akustisch bemerkbar macht. Die Reaktion geht mit großer Wahrscheinlichkeit nach dem in (36.6) gegebenen Schema vor sich. Bei der Rückreaktion geht also eine Wassermolekel — durch Verschieben einer Wasserstoffbrückenbindung auf eine weiter außen liegende lose Bindung — in ein OH^--Ion

[1] Das Dissoziationsgleichgewicht von NH_3 in wäßriger Lösung hängt von der elektrischen Feldstärke ab (Dissoziations-Feldeffekt). Auf Grund der endlichen Einstellgeschwindigkeit des Gleichgewichts zeigt dieser Dissoziations-Feldeffekt bei kurzen Feldimpulsen eine Dispersion analog dem Schalldispersions-Effekt. Die Abnahme des Feldeffektes mit steigender Frequenz bzw. abnehmender Impulsdauer ist in Fig. 32 aufgetragen. Aus dieser entnimmt man eine Geschwindigkeitskonstante für die Bildung $k_{Bildg} = 3 \cdot 10^{10}$ Liter/Molsec in voller Übereinstimmung mit dem aus der Schalldispersion gefundem Wert.

[2] Veröffentlichung in Vorbereitung.

über, das an das Metallion fest gebunden wird. Die Verschiebung der Bindung kann der Abdiffusion eines Protons entsprechen (Weg II) oder durch die Begegnung mit einem Hydroxylion (Weg I) hervorgerufen sein. Mit der entsprechenden Hinreaktion, bei der das Umgekehrte geschieht, erhält man das Reaktionsschema

$$\begin{array}{ccc} Me^{++}\cdot H_2O + OH^- & \overset{\text{I}}{\rightleftharpoons} & MeOH^+ + H_2O \\ \text{II} \nwarrow\!\!\searrow & & \nearrow\!\!\swarrow \text{III} \\ & MeOH^+ + H^+ + OH^- & \end{array} \tag{36.6}$$

Dabei sind die übrigen wahrscheinlich unverändert bleibenden Hydratwasser der inneren Hülle nicht besonders angegeben. Aus diesem Schema wird die Übereinstimmung der Reaktion mit der Hydrolysereaktion ersichtlich, die ja in mehr oder weniger starkem Maße bei allen zweiwertigen Metallen auftritt.

Berücksichtigt man, daß sich das Reaktionsgleichgewicht III sehr schnell einstellt, so sind zwei Reaktionswege möglich, von denen jeder eine Dissoziation mit anschließender Diffusion und in der anderen Richtung eine Begegnung mit anschließender Assoziation enthält. Die Reaktion folgt dem Weg mit der größeren Reaktionsgeschwindigkeit.

Bei stark hydrolysierenden Metallionen ist der Weg II, der ja einer Hydrolyse des Hydratwassers entspricht, der schnellere; es zeigt sich eine große $MeOH^+$-Konzentration. Bei schwach hydrolisierenden Metallionen (z.B. Mg^{++}) ist der Weg I der bestimmende, solange genügende OH^--Ionen-Konzentration vorhanden ist; dies äußert sich in kleiner $MeOH^+$-Konzentration. Leider liegen nur wenige Absorptionsmessungen an Lösungen von Metallhydroxyden vor. An Magnesiumhydroxyd wurden einige Messungen von KURTZE und TAMM [*17*] durchgeführt. Allerdings ist wegen der geringen Löslichkeit von $Mg(OH)_2$ die erreichbare $MgOH^+$-Konzentration sehr klein, so daß auch der Absolutwert der Absorption klein ist. Durch Zusetzen kleiner Mengen NaOH zu $MgCl_2$-Lösungen haben KURTZE und TAMM die $MgOH^+$-Konzentration soweit als möglich gesteigert. Sie erhielten eine gerade noch feststellbare Absorption (s. Ziff. 2δ) mit einer Relaxationsfrequenz um 120 kHz, die sie dem Dissoziationsgleichgewicht von $MgOH^+$ zuordneten (Weg I). Sehr wahrscheinlich wird die Absorption aber durch Überlagerung verschiedener Hydrolyse-Gleichgewichte verursacht, die schließlich zur Ausfällung von $Mg(OH)_2$ führen. Dafür spricht das starke Ansteigen der Absorption in übersättigten Lösungen.

Die Übereinstimmung der unteren Relaxationsfrequenzen aller Mg-Salze und der $MgCl_2$-NaOH-Mischung läßt darauf schließen, daß bei allen diesen Salzen ein ähnlicher Vorgang die Relaxationsfrequenz bestimmt. Allerdings kann die Größe des Absorptionsquerschnitts der Mg-Salze mit zweiwertigem Anion nicht unmittelbar mit dem beschriebenen Reaktionsvorgang erklärt werden, wenn auch die Reihenfolge der Relaxationsfrequenzen der zweiwertigen Metalle (Al[1], Be, Ni, Mg, Co, Mn, Zn) durchaus der abnehmenden Neigung, MeOH-Ionen zu bilden, bzw. abnehmender Hydrolysewirkung entspricht.

In $FeCl_3$ ist die Konzentration der $FeOH^{++}$-Ionen erheblich höher als die der MgOH-Ionen in $MgCl_2$. Es ist eine größere Absorptionswirkung zu erwarten, wie es die Experimente bestätigen.

37. Dissoziation nicht hydrolisierender Salze. Bei allen schwachen Elektrolyten ist eine unvollständige Dissoziation zu erwarten, so daß ein druckempfindliches Reaktionsgleichgewicht auftritt. Zu den nicht vollständig dissozierten Elektrolyten gehören jedoch auch die ersten Dissoziationsstufen einiger 1-2-

[1] Al weist möglicherweise eine „untere" Relaxationsfrequenz bei noch tieferen Frequenzen als Be auf, also unterhalb aller bisher angewendeten Meßfrequenzen.

wertiger Salze wie $NaSO_4^-$, $LiSO_4^-$, usw[1]. Das wird auch durch das Auftreten einer Absorption bei diesen Salzen bestätigt (s. Fig. 13 und 14). Die 2-1-wertigen Salze wie $MgCl_2$ sind dagegen sehr weitgehend dissoziert. Mit dieser Anschauung ist das Ausbleiben einer großen Relaxationsabsorption in Übereinstimmung. Besonders einfache Verhältnisse erhält man, wenn keine nennenswerte Hydrolyse auftritt, wie es für die meisten Sulfate durch die Neutralität ihrer Lösungen erwiesen ist. In diesem Falle tritt nur ein einziges Reaktionsgleichgewicht auf, wenn die Konzentration genügend groß ist, so daß die H^+-Ionenkonzentration aus dem Wasserdissoziationsgleichgewicht keine Rolle spielt. Für ein solches 1-2-wertiges Salz mit einwertigem Metallion Me^+ und zweiwertigem Anion R^{--} ist das Reaktionsgleichgewicht zwischen Dissoziation und Rekombination

$$Me^+ + R^{--} \rightleftharpoons Me\,R^- \tag{37.1}$$

unter Berücksichtigung der Aktivitätskoeffizienten in der Form des Produktes Π^f durch die Gleichgewichtskonstante K gegeben. Beachtet man, daß die Konzentration der Me^+-Ionen durch die vorangegangene erste Dissoziationsstufe $[Me^+] = (1+\delta)\,c$ die der R^{--}-Ionen aber nur $[R^{--}] = \delta c$ ist, so ist damit der Dissoziationsgrad δ für jede Elektrolytkonzentration c gegeben.

$$\frac{[Me^+]\,[R^{--}]}{[MeR^-]}\,\Pi^f = \frac{(1+\delta)\delta}{1-\delta}\,c\,\Pi^f = {}^cK_D. \tag{37.2}$$

Der Einfluß der Aktivitäten ist bei den 1-2-wertigen Salzen, z.B. bei Na_2SO_4 im allgemeinen nicht zu vernachlässigen. Leider ist ihre Größe und Konzentrationsabhängigkeit nicht genau bekannt[2]. Nur eine sehr grobe Abschätzung auf Grund von Annahmen von Eigen und Wicke [*48*] ist die Annahme eines Dissoziationsgrades $\delta \approx 0{,}4$ und eines Aktivitätsproduktes $\Pi^f \approx 0{,}25$ bei einer Elektrolytkonzentration $c_0 = 0{,}5$ Mol/Liter. Sie liefert aber wahrscheinlich die richtige Größenordnung und entspricht einer Gleichgewichtskonstante (${}^cK_D =$ 0,2 Liter/Molsec) plausibler Größe. Der zugehörige Faktor $G_D \approx 0{,}2$ liegt nahe bei seinem Maximum und ist daher wenig konzentrationsabhängig, so daß sich bei Annahme einer ebenfalls wenig konzentrationsabhängigen Differenz der Partialvolumina $\Delta^* V$ in der Größenordnung 5 bis 10 cm³/Mol ein ebenso konstanter Absorptionsbetrag $(Q\lambda)_m = 25$ bis $100 \cdot 10^{-30}$ m³ ergibt.

Die Absorptionsmessungen [*17a*] an 0,5 und 1,0 molaren Na_2SO_4-Lösungen (s. Fig. 13) zeigen, daß $Q\lambda$ bei 300 MHz bereits den Wert $30 \cdot 10^{-30}$ m³ erreicht hat, aber offenbar noch weiter anwächst. Es ist also sicher $(Q\lambda)_m > 30 \cdot 10^{-30}$ m³; das entspricht einer Differenz in den Partialvolumina von $\Delta^* V \gtrapprox 5$ cm³/Mol. Die Tatsache, daß die Relaxationsfrequenz oberhalb 300 MHz liegt (wie bei der Schwefelsäure), bedeutet, daß die Reaktion sehr schnell abläuft. Nimmt man, wie es naheliegt, eine Dissoziation als Reaktion an, dann werden bei der optimalen Konzentration — in deren Nähe die Messungen gemacht wurden, — die beiden Anteile der Reaktionsgeschwindigkeit $k_{Zerf} + k_{Bildg}\, 2\delta^+ c$ ungefähr gleich. Daraus folgt sofort, daß die Geschwindigkeitskonstante der Dissoziation $k_{Zerf} \geqq 2 \cdot 10^9$ sec^{-1} ist und die freie Aktivierungsenergie $\Delta^* F \lessapprox 6$ kcal/Mol sein muß. Dieser

[1] Mit der unvollständigen Dissoziation erklären z.B. Eigen und Wicke [*48*] den Verlauf des Produktes $\delta \cdot f$ dieser Elektrolyte mit der Konzentration (s. Fig., 4), der — ebenso wie bei den 2-2-wertigen Elektrolyten — von dem der vollständig dissoziierten 1-1-wertigen Elektrolyte stark abweicht.

[2] Eigen und Wicke [*48*] haben vermutet, daß ganz allgemein die Aktivitätskoeffizienten ähnlich wie in vollständig dissoziierten Elektrolyten ($MgCl_2$) mit steigender Konzentration auf einen Minimalwert von 0,5 bei etwa 0,5 Mol/Liter abnehmen und dann ansteigen, und daß in diesem Konzentrationsbereich der Dissoziationsgrad bereits erheblich abgenommen hat. Diese Annahme erklärt die vorhandenen Meßergebnisse an Elektrolytlösungen verschiedener Wertigkeit (s. Landolt-Börnstein [*77*]).

verhältnismäßig kleine Wert läßt vermuten, daß es sich bei der auftretenden Dissoziation offenbar um ein wenig behindertes Ineinanderschieben (bzw. Trennen) der Hydrathüllen der beiden Partner $(Na^+) + (SO_4^{--}) \rightleftharpoons (Na^+) \cdot (SO_4^{--})$ [1] handelt.

Dieses Ineinanderschieben der Hydrathüllen ist eine befriedigende Erklärung für die Volumendifferenz, die (wie aus den gemessenen Schallabsorptionswerten geschlossen werden kann) offenbar speziell bei unvollständig dissoziierten nicht aber bei vollständig dissoziierten Elektrolyten, wie $MgCl_2$, auftritt.

Für die Annahme der Bildung eines Ionen-Komplexes der geschilderten Art spricht auch das Verhalten der Relaxationsfrequenz. Während bei kleinen Konzentrationen die Dissoziationsreaktion die schnellste und damit geschwindigkeitsbestimmende werden muß, ist bei größeren die Rückreaktion entscheidend. Ist (wie bei HSO_4^-) die Übergangsreaktion sehr schnell, so bestimmt die langsamere Diffusion die Relaxationsfrequenz, die deswegen mit der Konzentration ansteigt, wie es bei HSO_4^- gemessen wurde (Fig. 29). Erfolgt jedoch der Übergang mit geringerer Geschwindigkeit, — und dies ist bei $NaSO_4^-$ der Fall, weil die Na^+-Ionen nur normale Beweglichkeit besitzen, — so begrenzt dessen Zeitkonstante die Geschwindigkeit der Assoziation; die Relaxationsfrequenz steigt dann nicht beliebig mit der Konzentration an, sondern nur bis zu einer Grenze. Möglicherweise liegt dieser Fall bei $NaSO_4^-$ vor, da sich die Relaxationsfrequenz für die Konzentrationen 0,5 und 1 Mol/Liter nicht verschiebt. Darüber, wie man sich das Ineinanderschieben der Hydrathüllen, der hydratisierten Ionen zu einem Ionenpaar vorzustellen hat, sagt natürlich die akustische Messung nichts aus.

Es liegt nahe, solche Effekte auch bei anderen Elektrolyten zu suchen. Daß der Verlauf der Absorption der Salze der Sauerstoffsäuren mit einwertigen Metallen dem von Na_2SO_4 gleicht, spricht dafür, daß bei diesen Salzen der gleiche Prozeß vorhanden ist. Bei $MgCl_2$ tritt dieser Prozeß jedoch offenbar nicht auf, hier fehlt wegen der „starren" Hydratation des Mg^{++}-Ions einerseits und der im Vergleich zu H_2O oder SO_4^{--} geringen Wechselwirkung von Cl^- mit Mg^{++} andererseits die Bereitschaft zur Bildung von Komplexen, die beim SO_4^{--} besteht. Dagegen scheinen ähnliche Vorgänge auch bei den Sulfaten der zweiwertigen Metalle (s. Ziff. 38) stattzufinden, da diese alle wie Na_2SO_4 einen „oberen" Anstieg des Absorptionseffektes $Q\lambda$ aufweisen.

38. Stufenweise Dissoziation der 2-2-wertigen Elektrolyte[2]. *α) Deutungsversuche mit einstufiger Dissoziation.* Es ist mehrfach versucht worden — z.B. von LIEBERMANN [*12*], WILSON [*15*] und BIES [*16*] — das Relaxationsverhalten von 2-2-wertigen Elektrolyten durch Annahme eines einstufigen binären Dissoziationsgleichgewichtes zu erklären. Das führt bei dem „unteren" Relaxationsmaximum ($\nu_m \approx 130$ kHz bei $MgSO_4$) auch zu einem gewissen Erfolg.

Aus den bekannten[3] Aktivitäten $(\delta \cdot f)$ läßt sich — ohne weitere theoretische Voraussetzungen bezüglich der Natur der Aktivitätskoeffizienten f — der Dissoziationsgrad δ mit Hilfe von Gl. (5.6): $1 - \delta = (\delta f)^2\, c/{}^cK$ bei Annahme zunächst willkürlicher Werte für die Gleichgewichtskonstante ${}^cK$ (s. Tabelle 5) berechnen. Man erhält dann auch Π^f und $\delta \cdot (\partial \ln \Pi^f / \partial \delta)$ sowie δ^+, so daß G_D^+ und der Faktor $(1 + k'_{12}/k_{21})$, der für die Konzentrationsabhängigkeit der Relaxationsfrequenz $\nu_m = 1/\tau$ verantwortlich ist, ermittelt werden können. Bei kleinen Werten ${}^cK$

[1] Das entstehende Gebilde wird zweckmäßigerweise als Ionen- bzw. Hydratkomplex bezeichnet. Die Schreibweise soll andeuten, daß die inneren Hydrathüllen dabei wahrscheinlich erhalten bleiben.

[2] Die folgenden Betrachtungen halten sich im wesentlichen an Überlegungen von EIGEN und TAMM [*81*].

[3] Es wurden Meßwerte von ROBINSON und STOKES [*76*] verwendet, die bei unvollständiger Dissoziation dem Produkt $(\delta \cdot f)$ entsprechen.

ist $1/\tau$ konzentrationsabhängig; erst für ${}^cK > 2 \cdot 10^{-2}$ Mol/Liter wird $1/\tau$ konstant, wie es den Meßergebnissen bei Konzentrationen zwischen 10^{-3} und 1 Mol/Liter entspricht.

Paßt man die für die Berechnung der Absorptionswerte $(Q\lambda)_m$ neben G_D^+ erforderlichen Volumendifferenzen $\Delta^* V$ den Meßergebnissen (s. Tabelle 5) an,

Tabelle 5. *Auswertung der Theorie der einstufigen Dissoziation für verschiedene Gleichgewichtskonstanten K zur Anpassung an die Meßergebnisse in $MgSO_4$-Lösungen.*

c	δf	$K = 3 \cdot 10^{-3}$ Mol/l			$7 \cdot 10^{-3}$ Mol/l			$2 \cdot 10^{-2}$ Mol/l			10^{-1} Mol/l		
Mol/l		$\Delta^* V$ cm³/Mol	$(Q\lambda)_m$ 10^{-30} m³	$1/\tau k_{21}$	$\Delta^* V$ cm³/Mol	$(Q\lambda)_m$ 10^{-30} m³	$1/\tau k_{21}$	$\Delta^* V$ cm³/Mol	$(Q\lambda)_m$ 10^{-30} m³	$1/\tau k_{21}$	$\Delta^* V$ cm³/Mol	$(Q\lambda)_m$ 10^{-30} m³	$1/\tau k_{21}$
10^{-3}	0,70	−4	9	1,37	−4	5	1,13	−7	4	1,04	−15	5	1,01
10^{-2}	0,38	−4	13	2,67	−4	12	1,42	−7	15	1,10	−14	13	1,02
10^{-1}	0,15	−4	10	5,66	−4	15	1,70	−6	16	1,14	−12	15	1,02
1	0,05	−2	2	9,9	−2	4	1,69	−2	2	1,12	−5	3	1,02

so erhält man ungefähre Übereinstimmung mit den experimentell gefundenen Werten von $\Delta^* V$ (die bei hoher Verdünnung 10 bis 20 cm³/Mol betragen und bis zur Konzentration 1 Mol/Liter um etwa 10 cm³/Mol abnehmen) wieder erst für ${}^cK > 2 \cdot 10^{-2}$ Mol/Liter. Optimale Übereinstimmung ergibt sich sogar erst für ${}^cK \approx 0{,}1$ Mol/Liter. Für noch größere ${}^cK$-Werte z. B. 1 Mol/Liter werden die notwendigen $\Delta^* V$-Werte schon zu groß (≈ 50 cm³/Mol). Der von Bies [*16*] in Anlehnung an Davies [*58*] verwendete Wert ${}^cK = 6{,}2 \cdot 10^{-3}$ Mol/Liter ist demnach für eine Erklärung der Konzentrationsabhängigkeit mit Hilfe eines einstufigen Gleichgewichts zu klein und liefert außerhalb des von Bies untersuchten Bereiches Konzentrationsabhängigkeit der $(Q\lambda)_m$- und ν_m-Werte, die den Meßergebnissen widerspricht.

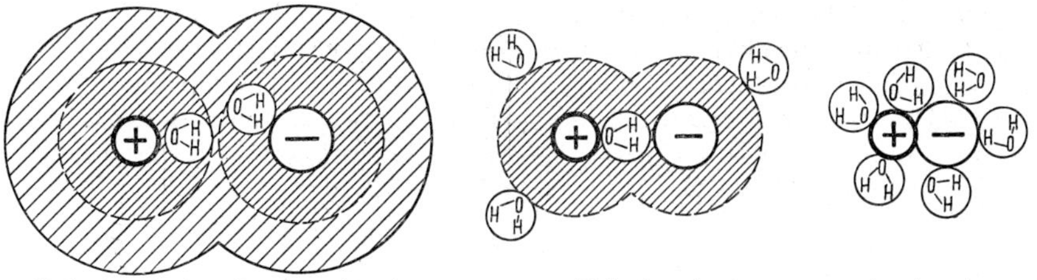

2. Hydratkomplex bzw. Begegnungskomplex 1. Hydratkomplex Aquokomplex

Fig. 33. Schema der stufenweisen Dissoziation eines 2-2-wertigen Elektrolyten nach Eigen [*51*].

Der sich hier ergebende, unwahrscheinlich große Wert ${}^cK \approx 0{,}1$ Mol/Liter steht im scheinbaren Widerspruch zu Angaben von Davies [*58*] und ist ein Argument gegen das Vorhandensein einer einstufigen Dissoziation. Er erklärt sich bei Annahme eines mehrstufigen Gleichgewichts zwanglos als Konstante eines Teilgleichgewichtes (s. Ziff. 38β).

β) Deutung durch mehrstufige Dissoziation. Neben den eben erwähnten Widersprüchen spricht das bereits erwähnte (s. Ziff. 22) Vorhandensein zweier nicht unabhängiger Relaxationsmaxima für ein mindestens zweistufiges Gleichgewicht. Da zur Erklärung beider Maxima die allgemeine Ionenwechselwirkung in Form des Ionenwolkeneffektes ausscheidet (s. Ziff. 33) liegt die Annahme einer stufenweisen Dissoziation (spezifische Wechselwirkung) als Ursache auf der Hand. Diese ist zu erwarten, da bei Unterschreiten eines bestimmten, dem mittleren Durchmesser der hydratisierten Ionen entsprechenden Abstandes die weitere Annäherung der Ionen nur noch stufenweise, nämlich durch schrittweisen Abbau der Hydrathüllen erfolgen kann (s. Fig. 33).

Der Potentialverlauf in der Umgebung eines Ions ist keine monotone Funktion; die Aufenthaltswahrscheinlichkeit eines entgegengesetzt geladenen Ions zeigt entsprechende Maxima. Umgekehrt ist das Auftreten der diskreten Relaxationsmaxima ein direkter Nachweis dieser seit langem bestehenden Vermutung. Das untere Maximum ist demnach einem ersten Dissoziationsschritt z.B. der Einschiebung eines Wassermoleküls zwischen zwei entgegengesetzt geladenen Ionen (Aufbau der inneren Hydrathülle) zuzuschreiben, das obere einem zweiten Dissoziationsschritt, d.h. der Einschiebung eines zweiten Wassermoleküls (Aufbau der äußeren Hydrathülle). Die Vermutung, daß noch weitere diskrete Dissoziationsstufen und damit weitere Relaxationsmaxima durch Einschieben weiterer Wassermoleküle auftreten, läßt sich experimentell schwer prüfen. Wegen der abnehmenden Aktivierungsenergie werden die Relaxationsfrequenzen der weiteren Schritte immer höher, so daß sie in den meisten Fällen oberhalb der bisherigen Frequenzgrenze für die Messung liegen. Sie werden auch immer dichter, so daß die Relaxationskurven verschmieren. Schließlich müssen die Stufen in den allgemeinen Ionenwolkeneffekt (mit breitem Relaxationsspektrum) übergehen. Dieses Verschmieren mit dem Ionenwolkeneffekt ist auch offenbar der Grund, daß bisher nicht mehr als zwei diskrete Maxima beobachtet wurden. Es liegt nahe, auch die Deutung auf zwei diskrete Schritte und einen verschmierten Ionenwolkeneffekt zu beschränken, also im Höchstfall einen dreistufigen Prozeß zu betrachten. Für diesen Fall ist die oben (Abschn. II, Ziff. 9) gegebene theoretische Behandlung geeignet.

Mit der gegebenen Annahme von mindestens zwei Dissoziationsschritten wird das „obere" Maximum der 2-2-wertigen Elektrolyte als zum zweiten Dissoziationsschritt gehörig, praktisch in gleicher Weise erklärt wie die Absorption der 1-2-wertigen Elektrolyte. Die auftretenden Abweichungen zwischen beiden Fällen in bezug auf Relaxationsfrequenz ν_m und Absolutbetrag der Absorption $(Q\lambda)_m$ sind durch Unterschiede in den Dissoziationsgraden, den Partialvolumina und den Aktivierungsenergien leicht erklärbar. So läßt sich der kleinere Wert ν_m (≈ 100 MHz) der 2-2-wertigen Elektrolyte und seine Konzentrationsunabhängigkeit einer langsameren Dissoziation des ersten Hydratkomplexes (mit einem Wassermolekül) zuschreiben.

γ) Quantitative Erklärung der Meßergebnisse für $MgSO_4$. Mit Hilfe der (in Abschn. II entwickelten) Theorie der mehrstufigen Dissoziation ist eine quantitative Behandlung der vermuteten Vorgänge möglich. Die Voraussetzungen der Theorie ($k'_{12}, k_{21} \gg k_{23}, k_{32}$) sind offensichtlich erfüllt, da bei den meisten Elektrolyten sich die beiden Relaxationszeiten um Größenordnungen unterscheiden. Insbesondere gilt das für $MgSO_4$, das hier betrachtet werden soll.

In Tabelle 6 ist ein Beispiel der Auswertung der Gln. (7.10) und (8.10) unter zwei verschiedenen Annahmen (a bzw. b) für die Gesamtgleichgewichtskonstante K aufgeführt. Diese beschreibt das Gleichgewicht zwischen den freien Ionen mit der Konzentration δc einerseits und sämtlichen Assoziatkomplexen mit der Konzentration $(1-\delta)\,c$ andererseits[1].

Die $\Delta^* V$-Werte der beiden Stufen ($\Delta^* V_D = \Delta^* V_{12}$ und $\Delta^* V_U = \Delta^* V_{23}$) wurden so gewählt, daß einerseits eine optimale Anpassung an den gemessenen Konzentrationsverlauf des Absorptionsbetrages $(Q\lambda)_m$ erzielt wurde und andererseits der bekannte Verlauf des Partialvolumens von $MgSO_4$ in wäßriger Lösung (s. Fig. 34b, unten) richtig wiedergegeben wird. Der Konzentrationsverlauf

[1] Hier geht die Voraussetzung ein, daß die Aktivitätskoeffizienten der ungeladenen Komplexe nicht sehr von 1 verschieden sind. Sie ist aber unerheblich, weil die Konzentration $c_{AB_3} \ll c_{AB_2}$.

Tabelle 6. *Auswertung der Theorie der zweistufigen Dissoziation bei zwei verschiedenen Parameterserien (a bzw. b) zur Anpassung an die Meßergebnisse in $MgSO_4$-Lösungen.*

Parameterserie	K 10^{-3} Mol/l	K_{23}	K_{12} 10^{-3} Mol/l	$\Delta^* V_{12}^0$ cm³/Mol	$\Delta^* V_{23}$ cm³/Mol	k_{21} 10^8 sec⁻¹	k_{32} 10^5 sec⁻¹
(a)	5	9	4,5	− 12	− 3	2	8
(b)	20	9	18	− 15	− 5	10	8

c Mol/l	δ (a) (b)	f	$\frac{\partial \ln \Pi f}{\partial \ln \delta}$	$1+\frac{k'_{12}}{k_{21}}$	G_I^+	G_{II}^+	$\Delta^* V_{12}^0 - \Delta^* V_{12}$ exp. cm³/Mol	$\Delta^* V_I$ cm³/Mol	$\Delta^* V_{II}$ cm³/Mol	$(Q\lambda)_{mI}$ 10^{-30} m³	$(Q\lambda)_{mII}$ 10^{-30} m³	$1/\tau_I$ 10^8 s⁻¹	$1/\tau_{II}$ 10^5 s⁻¹
10^{-3}	0,90	0,78	− 0,20	1,20	0,084	0,010	0	− 12	− 13	56	8,0	2,4	8,1
	0,98	0,72	− 0,34	1,04	0,019	0,002	0	− 15	− 19	20	3,4	1,0	8,0
10^{-2}	0,71	0,54	− 0,57	1,59	0,183	0,029	− 1	− 11	− 9,9	103	13,0	3,2	8,3
	0,93	0,41	− 0,70	1,10	0,064	0,007	− 1	− 14	− 18	59	11,0	1,1	8,1
10^{-1}	0,55	0,27	− 0,79	1,98	0,224	0,044	− 3	− 9	− 7,6	85	11,7	4,0	8,4
	0,89	0,17	− 0,90	1,14	0,097	0,011	− 3	− 12	− 16	65	13,2	1,1	8,1
1	0,52	0,10	− 0,97	1,96	0,244	0,048	− 10	− 2	− 4,0	5	3,8	3,9	8,4
	0,88	0,06	− 1,10	1,12	0,108	0,013	− 10	− 5	− 10	13	6,1	1,1	8,1

läßt sich nur befriedigend erklären, wenn man für $\Delta^* V_{12}$ und $\Delta^* V_{23}$ das gleiche Vorzeichen annimmt. Dann folgt aber sofort, daß $\Delta^* V_{II} > \Delta^* V_I$ und — wegen $(Q\lambda)_{mI} \approx 3 \cdot (Q\lambda)_{mII}$ bei $MgSO_4$ — daß $K_{23} > 5$ ist. Verlangt man noch, daß

Tabelle 7. *Parameter zur Berechnung der Kurven in Fig. 34a, b.*

Stufenzahl	K 10^{-3} Mol/l	K_{23}	K_{34}	K_{12} 10^{-3} Mol/l	$\Delta^* V_{12}^0$ cm³/Mol	$\Delta^* V_{23}$ cm³/Mol	$\Delta^* V_{34}$ cm³/Mol	k_{12}^0 1/Molsec	k_{32} sec⁻¹	k_{43} sec⁻¹
2	3	9		3,3	− 12	− 5		$10 \cdot 10^8$	$8 \cdot 10^5$	
2	5	9		5,5	− 12	− 3		$10 \cdot 10^8$	$8 \cdot 10^5$	
2	20	9		22	− 15	− 5		$10 \cdot 10^8$	$8 \cdot 10^5$	
3	7	0,5	7,5	2,4	0	− 14/10	− 3	$4 \cdot 10^{10}$	$10 \cdot 10^8$	$8 \cdot 10^5$
3	20	1	9	40	0	− 18	− 3	$4 \cdot 10^{10}$	$10 \cdot 10^8$	

durch die Konzentrationsabhängigkeit der Partialvolumina der freien Ionen keine Vorzeichenumkehr bei $\Delta^* V_{12}$ entsteht, dann sind die willkürlichen Voraussetzungen schon so weit eingeschränkt, daß praktisch nur die K- und die $\Delta^* V$-Werte der in Tabelle 7 angegebenen Größe in Frage kommen.

Tabelle 8. *Vergleich der (nach* Hall *[24]) berechneten Ionenwolkenrelaxation mit Meßwerten in $MgSO_4$- und $MgCl_2$-Lösungen.*

c Mol/l	Berechnet für Ionenwolke: τ 10^{-9} sec	Berechnet für Ionenwolke: $(Q\lambda)_m$ 10^{-30} m³	Gemessen bei 100 MHz: $(Q\lambda)$ gesamt 10^{-30} m³
10^{-3}	30	0,07	
10^{-2}	4,6	0,2	$MgSO_4$ $MgCl_2$
10^{-1}	0,96	0,7	50 1

In Fig. 34a, b sind die Meßwerte mit den Werten verglichen, die mit Hilfe der in Tabelle 7 angegebenen Parameter berechnet wurden. Für das „untere" Maximum ist die Übereinstimmung bei dem angenommenen zweistufigen Mechanismus mit $K \approx 10^{-2}$ Mol/Liter und $K_{23} = 5 \ldots 10$ quantitativ gut; kleine Abweichungen treten bei hohen Konzentrationen auf. Für das „obere" Maximum ist die Übereinstimmung noch nicht voll befriedigend; der errechnete Verlauf liegt zu hoch und fällt nach hohen Konzentrationen schon zu früh ab. Auch eine Überlagerung der nach Hall [24] berechneten Ionenwolkenrelaxation (s. Tabelle 8) ist nicht in der Lage, diese Diskrepanz zu erklären. Erst die Annahme eines dreistufigen Mechanismus (s. Ziff. 9) mit den in Tabelle 7 angegebenen Parametern liefert eine befriedigende Übereinstimmung zwischen den berechneten Werten $(Q\lambda)_{m\,\mathrm{III}}$ bzw. $(Q\lambda)_{m\,\mathrm{II}}$ und den Meßergebnissen sowohl für das „untere" als auch für das „obere" Maximum (s. Fig. 34). Die der theoretischen Ableitung zugrunde liegende Voraussetzung k'_{12}, $k_{21} \gg k_{23}$, k_{32} dürfte allerdings hier nicht mehr zutreffen, so daß das Ergebnis $(Q\lambda)_{m\,\mathrm{II}}$ für das „obere" Maximum (strichpunktierte Kurve in Fig. 34b) nur eine Näherung ist. Eine Berechnung mit Hilfe der vollständigen Lösungen (s. Ziff. 9)[1] für die dreistufige Dissoziation — ohne die genannte einschränkende Voraussetzung — liefert für $K = 7$ bzw. $20 \cdot 10^{-3}$ Mol/Liter (s. Tabelle 7) die erwähnte gute Übereinstimmung mit den Meßergebnissen (ausgezogene Kurven in Fig. 34b). Beim Vergleich der theoretischen Kurven mit den Meßergebnissen ist zu beachten, daß die im „oberen" Maximum gemessene Absorption bei Annahme von zwei Stufen $(Q\lambda)_{m\,\mathrm{I}}$, bei drei Stufen aber der Überlagerung von $(Q\lambda)_{m\,\mathrm{I}}$ und $(Q\lambda)_{m\,\mathrm{II}}$ entspricht.

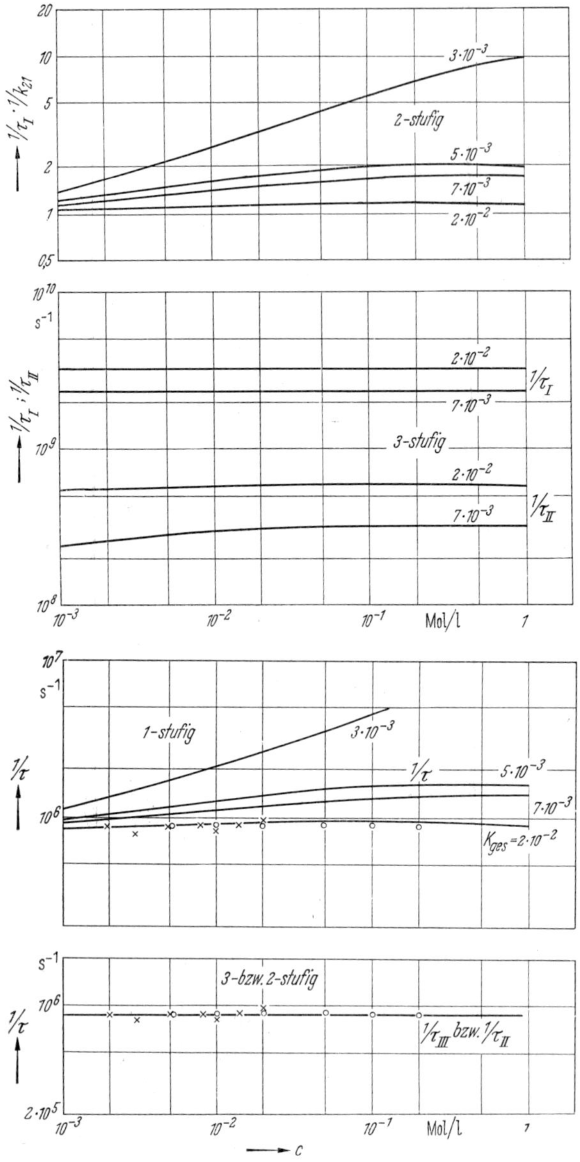

Fig. 34 a.

Fig. 34 a u. b. Konzentrationsabhängigkeit a) der Relaxationsfrequenzen, b) der maximalen Absorptionsvolumina in wäßrigen $MgSO_4$-Lösungen. — mit Parametern nach Tabelle 7 berechnet für 1-, 2- und 3stufige Dissoziation; ○ × ● gemessene Werte.

Ähnliche Ergebnisse liefert die Analyse der Relaxationszeiten. Bei Annahme einer einzigen Stufe wurde die beobachtete Konzentrationsunabhängigkeit der unteren Relaxationsfrequenz erst für $K > 0{,}1$ Mol/Liter erreicht, dann erst wird nämlich $k'_{12}/k_{21} \ll 1$ und $1/\tau$ durch die konstante Dissoziations-Geschwindigkeitskonstante k_{21} bestimmt. Im zweistufigen System ist dieser erste Dissoziationsschritt durch k_{32} charakterisiert, im dreistufigen durch

[1] Streng genommen müßte man sogar ein Gleichungssystem verwenden, das auch den kontinuierlichen Teil der Ionenwolke mit berücksichtigt. Davon wurde hier abgesehen, da die Relaxationsvorgänge, die das „obere" Maximum liefern, sicher noch eine Größenordnung langsamer als die diffusionsbestimmten Vorgänge in der Ionenwolke (s. Tabelle 8) verlaufen.

k_{43}. Bei den angegebenen K-Werten ist diese Dissoziations-Reaktion jeweils schneller als die Rückreaktion, so daß sie die „untere“ Relaxationsfrequenz bestimmt und konzentrationsunabhängig macht. Aus der Relaxationsfrequenz läßt sich umgekehrt die Geschwindigkeitskonstante des ersten Dissoziationsschrittes zu $7{,}5 \cdot 10^5$ sec^{-1} ermitteln. Sie kann eindeutig der Spaltung eines $MgSO_4$-Komplexes zugeordnet werden.

Die sich ergebenden Relaxationsfrequenzen für das „obere“ Maximum bzw. für ein weiteres (bei dreistufiger Dissoziation) lassen sich in bezug auf die Konzentrationsabhängigkeit nicht direkt nachprüfen, da sie bei so hohen Frequenzen liegen, daß die Lage des jeweiligen Maximums nicht einwandfrei meßbar ist. Der Absorptionsanstieg mit der Frequenz zeigt aber, daß sie in der richtigen Größenordnung herauskommen. Die beste Wiedergabe des Relaxationsspektrums und der Absolutwerte der Absorption von $MgSO_4$-Lösungen ergibt sich bei Annahme eines dreistufigen Dissoziationsmechanismus (unter Berücksichtigung eines stets eingestellten Gleichgewichts der Ionenwolke) für $K = 7 \ldots 20 \cdot 10^{-3}$ Mol/Liter, $K_{23} \approx 1$ und $K_{34} = 5 \ldots 10$ sowie den in Tabelle 7 angegebenen Volumenwerten.

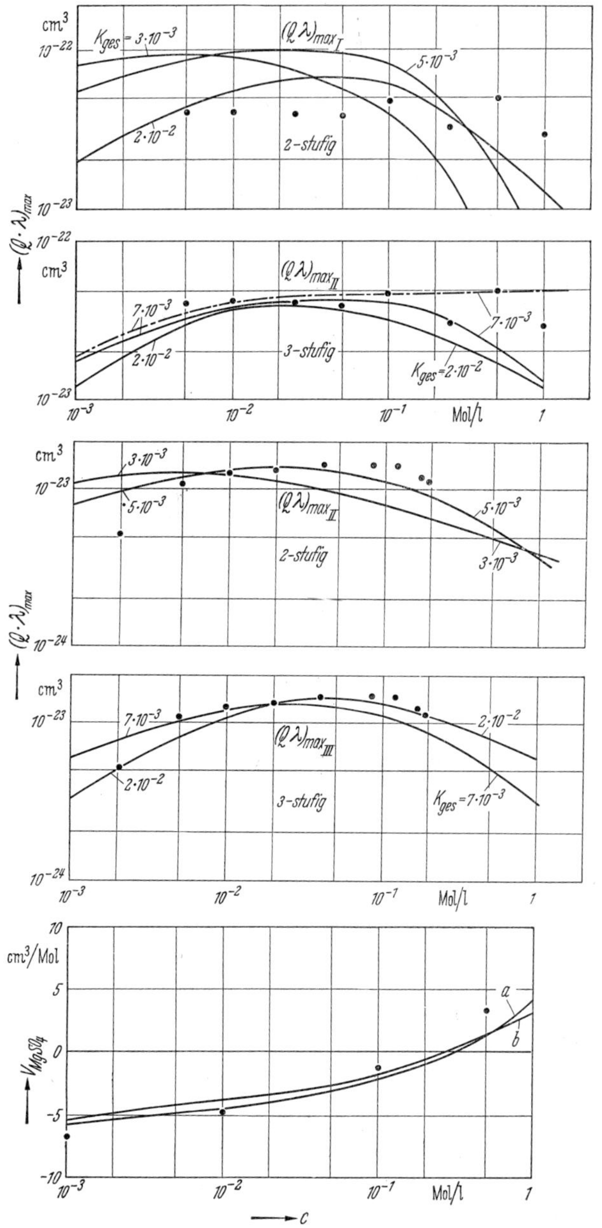

Fig. 34 b.

Für das „untere“ Maximum ist also als langsamster Prozeß der erste Dissoziationsschritt von $MgSO_4$ (Einschieben eines Wassermoleküls) verantwortlich. Für diesen ist es ziemlich gleichgültig, auf welche Weise sich das Gleichgewicht der schnelleren Prozesse einstellt. Bei Annahme einer einstufigen Dissoziation sind alle weiteren Ionenwechselwirkungen in den Aktivitätskoeffizienten zusammengefaßt, die dadurch relativ klein werden. Bei einer Konzentration $c = 0{,}1$ Mol/Liter ergibt sich mit $K = 0{,}1$ Mol/Liter eine Konzentration des undissoziierten Anteils $c_{AB} = 2{,}25 \cdot 10^{-3}$ Mol/Liter. Die Zusammenfassung aller weiteren Schritte in allgemeiner Ionenwechselwirkung liefert (mindestens bei Konzentrationen $c < 10^{-1}$ Mol/Liter) zu kleine Absorption. Die tatsächlich auftretende große Absorption des „oberen" Maximums kann nur durch relativ große spezifische Volumenänderung beim Abbau von Hydrathüllen erklärt werden. Bei Annahme einer zweistufigen Dissoziation erhält man für $K = 10^{-2}$ Mol/Liter und $K_{23} \approx 10$ den gleichen völlig undissoziierten Anteil $c_{AB} = c_3 = 2{,}25 \cdot 10^{-3}$ Mol/Liter wie oben. Es tritt daneben eine zehnfach größere Konzentration $c_{A,B} = c_2$ in einem ersten Dissoziationszustand auf; so daß die Konzentration der freien Ionen vermindert ist und ein größerer Aktivitätskoeffizient resultiert. Von der Ionenwolke ist also ein Anteil $c_{A,B}$ abgespalten. Analog sind die Verhältnisse bei dreistufiger Dissoziation.

δ) Deutung des Verhaltens verschiedener 2-2-wertiger Elektrolyte (Einfluß von Kation und Anion). Als Ergebnis der vorhergehenden Diskussion erhält man eine stufenweise Dissoziation bzw. Komplexbildung der Form:

$$Me^{++}_{aq} + SO^{--}_{4\,aq} \underset{k_{21}}{\overset{k_{12}}{\rightleftharpoons}} (Me^{++}O^{H}_{H}O^{H}_{H}SO_4^{--})_{aq} \underset{k_{32}}{\overset{k_{23}}{\rightleftharpoons}} (Me^{++}O^{H}_{H}SO_4^{--})_{aq} \underset{k_{43}}{\overset{k_{34}}{\rightleftharpoons}} (MeSO_4)_{aq} \qquad (38.1)$$

1	2	3	4
freie hydratisierte Ionen	Begegnungskomplex	Hydratkomplex	Aquokomplex

(Ionenwolkenzustände)

1—2	2—3	3—4
Begegnungsschritt	zweiter Diss.-Schritt	erster Diss.-Schritt
Diffusionsbestimmt	Auf- bzw. Abbau der äußeren Hydrathülle	Auf- bzw. Abbau der inneren Hydrathüllen

Einen Beweis für die Annahme, daß im Zustand 4 die Ionen tatsächlich nicht mehr durch Wassermoleküle getrennt, sondern unmittelbar benachbart sind — wobei sie natürlich noch starke Wechselwirkung mit den Wassermolekülen ihrer Umgebung haben, so daß sie mit diesen Aquokomplexe $(AB)_{aq}$ bilden — liefert die starke Abhängigkeit der „unteren" Relaxationsfrequenz (die ja durch k_{43} bestimmt ist) von der Art des Kations. Sie variiert von Be^{++} zum Mn^{++} bei den Sulfaten um mehr als vier Größenordnungen, wie Tabelle 9 zeigt, in der auch die experimentell gefundenen Aktivierungsenergien und die Ionenradien (nach GOLDSCHMIDT u. PAULING) angegeben sind. Der starke Gang der Relaxationsfrequenz bzw. der Dissoziationsgeschwindigkeit mit dem Radius des unhydratisierten Kations (bei Be^{++} 0,32 Å, bei Mg^{++} 0,70 Å) ist augenfällig. Die Dissoziation erfolgt z.B. bei $BeSO_4$ 1000mal langsamer als bei $MgSO_4$ und $MgCrO_4$ und bei diesen 100mal langsamer als bei $CaCrO_4$. Das beweist, daß der erste Dissoziationsschritt direkt an der Oberfläche des Metallions stattfindet, d.h. daß er von einem nichthydratisierten Komplex ausgeht. Bei dem zweiten Dissoziationsschritt (2—3), bei dem offenbar ein bereits hydratisiertes Metallion vom Sulfation weiter entfernt wird, müssen dagegen die wenig variierenden Radien der hydratisierten Metallionen (bei Be^{++} 2 ... 3 Å) bestimmend sein, so daß die Unterschiede zwischen den verschiedenen Metallionen kleiner werden. Dies gilt natürlich auch für die Bindungskräfte, da im wesentlichen die Bindung zwischen den Wassermolekülen der Hydrathülle des Kations und dem Sulfation gespalten wird. Die Abhängigkeit des ersten Dissoziationsschrittes vom Metallion zeigt sich besonders deutlich bei Komplexen mit den Übergangsmetallen (z.B. Ni und Co). Obwohl das

Tabelle 9. *Zusammenstellung der Geschwindigkeitskonstanten der ersten und zweiten Dissoziationsstufe für die Sulfate verschiedener zweiwertiger Metalle zum Vergleich mit den gemessenen Aktivierungsenergien sowie den Ionenradien.*

$Me^{++}-SO_4^{--}$	Äußere Hydratstufe		Innere Hydratstufe		Aktivierungs-energie A_E	Ionenradius
	Dehydratation k_{23}	Hydratation k_{32}	Dehydratation k_{34}	Hydratation k_{43}		
	sec^{-1}	sec^{-1}	sec^{-1}	sec^{-1}	kcal/Mol	Å
Be^{++}	10^9	10^9	10^2	$1,5 \cdot 10^3$		0,32
$Mg^{++}-SO_4^{--}$			10^5	$8 \cdot 10^5$	6,5/7,5	0,70
$S_2O_3^{--}$	10^9	10^9	10^5	$1,5 \cdot 10^6$		
CrO_4^{--}			10^5	$1,5 \cdot 10^6$		
$Ca^{++}-CrO_4^{--}$	10^9	10^9	(10^7)	$(8 \cdot 10^7)$		1,02
Ni^{++}	10^9	10^9	10^4	10^5	7,8	0,70
Co^{++}	10^9	10^9	$2 \cdot 10^5$	$2,5 \cdot 10^6$	6,0	0,72
Mn^{++}	10^9	10^9	$4 \cdot 10^6$	$2 \cdot 10^7$	6,8/7,8	0,80
Cu^{++}	10^9	10^9	$> 10^7$ *	$> 10^7$ *		0,71
Zn^{++}	10^9	10^9	$> 10^7$ *	$> 10^7$ *		0,72

Ni^{++}-Ion etwa gleichen Radius wie das Mg^{++}-Ion hat, geht der erste Dissoziationsschritt des $NiSO_4$-Komplexes zehnmal langsamer als beim Mg. Ähnliche nicht elektrostatisch erklärbare Unterschiede treten beim Übergang vom Co^{++} zum Cu^{++} auf. Sie haben ihre Ursache offenbar in den Elektronenstrukturen, die für die Bindungsverhältnisse maßgebend sind.

Auch bei den Mg-Komplexen mit verschiedenem Anion treten Unterschiede in den Dissoziations-Geschwindigkeitskonstanten auf; sie sind jedoch geringer, da die Anionen der Sauerstoffsäuren (SO_4^{--}, $S_2O_3^{--}$, CrO_4^{--}) einander sehr ähnlich sind.

Besonders deutlich unterscheiden sich die verschiedenen Metallionen in der Höhe der Absorptionsmaxima $(Q\lambda)_{m\,III}$, die im wesentlichen der Gleichgewichtskonstanten K_{34} umgekehrt proportional ist. Mn^{++}, Ni^{++} und Co^{++} zeigen Werte gleicher Größenordnung, Mn^{++} ergibt einen höheren Wert, Cu^{++} und Zn^{++} einen kleineren, der sich kaum noch aus dem Anstieg zum „oberen" Maximum abhebt*. Das in allen Fällen ermittelte Ergebnis $K_{34} > 1$ besagt, daß alle 2-2-wertigen Elektrolyte den hydratisierten Zustand $A \cdot B$ (hier $= A\,B_3$) vor dem Komplex $A\,B$ (hier $= A\,B_4$) bevorzugen.

Ermittelt man mit Hilfe der recht genau aus $(Q\lambda)_{m\,III}$ bestimmbaren Gleichgewichtskonstante K_{34} die (Dehydratations-) Geschwindigkeitskonstante k_{34} (s. Tabelle 9), so erkennt man auch hier den Einfluß der Elektronenkonfiguration in einer Abweichung zwischen Mg^{++} und Ni^{++}, die durch den Ionenradius nicht zu erklären ist. Besonders kleine k_{34}-Werte ($\approx 10^2\,sec^{-1}$) erhält man[1] für Be^{++}; noch langsamere Dehydratation ist für dreiwertige Ionen, z.B. Al^{+++}, Cr^{+++}, zu erwarten.

Für die Mg-Salze mit verschiedenen Sauerstoffsäuren-Anionen ergeben sich bei dieser Auswertung nahezu gleiche k_{34}-Werte. Das ist zu erwarten, da der Vorgang der Entfernung des letzten Wassermoleküls zwischen Anion und Kation von den großen Sauerstoffsäuren-Anionen (mit ziemlich gleichmäßiger Ladungsverteilung) wenig beeinflußt werden sollte.

* Das „untere" Maximum ist hier nicht genau meßbar, da es sich nur wenig aus dem Absorptionsanstieg zum „oberen" Maximum heraushebt. Die früher für Cu^{++} ermittelten Werte ($k_{43} = 10^6\,sec^{-1}$) gehören wahrscheinlich zu einem Hydrolysevorgang: $Cu^{++} + H_2O \rightleftharpoons CuOH^+ + H^+$, (s. [*51*]).

[1] Das auf Grund akustischer Messungen bei Frequenzen in der Größenordnung von 1 kHz erwartete Relaxationsmaximum wurde inzwischen mit Hilfe der Temperatursprungmethode von EIGEN und DIEBLER [*74*] bei 0,2 kHz gefunden.

Bei der „Dehydratation" handelt es sich wahrscheinlich um eine einfache Verdrängung eines Wassermoleküls aus der Hydrathülle des Metallions durch ein SO_4^{--}-Ion. Die von EIGEN, KURTZE und TAMM [*18*] früher diskutierte Vereinigung über instabile hydrolytische Zwischenstufen in der Form

$$Me^{++}\cdots O\begin{matrix} H \\ \\ H \end{matrix}\cdots SO_4^{--} \rightleftharpoons Me{-}O\begin{matrix} H^+ \\ \\ \end{matrix}\cdots HSO_4^{--} \rightleftharpoons MeSO_4 + H_2O \qquad (38.2)$$

ist (s. auch Ziff. 36) bei den größeren Metallionen (als Mg^{++}) von untergeordneter Bedeutung, da bei diesen die H_2O-Dissoziation im Hydrolyse-Mechanismus sehr langsam erfolgt[1]. Sie ist bei Be^{++}, Fe^{+++} u. a. jedoch nachweisbar.

Beim *„oberen" Relaxationsmaximum* findet man — ganz im Gegensatz zu den großen Variationen in den Relaxationsfrequenzen des unteren Maximums — nur geringe Unterschiede für die Sulfate verschiedener zweiwertiger Metalle. Das ist für die Gleichgewichte von hydratisierten Ionen zu erwarten, weil deren Ionenradien sich nur wenig unterscheiden und weil die Wechselwirkung hauptsächlich elektrostatisch ist. Die durch die Trennung der Ionen gegen diese elektrostatischen Kräfte bestimmte Konstante k_{32} liegt bei allen 2-2-wertigen Elektrolyten in der Größenordnung $10^9\,\text{sec}^{-1}$. Der Abbau der äußeren Hydrathülle bestimmt die Konstante k_{23}, die in der gleichen Größenordnung liegt und damit noch etwas kleiner ist als die „Konstante" k'_{12} des diffusionsbestimmten Schrittes $1\rightarrow 2$ ($k_{12} = 4\cdot 10^{10}$ Liter/Molsec). Die zugehörige Rückreaktion ist durch $k_{21} = 10^9\,\text{sec}^{-1}$ charakterisiert. Der Unterschied der beiden Konstanten ist dabei durch Δv_k und den Einfluß der elektrostatischen Wechselwirkung über den Term $\exp(z_A z_B e^2/\varepsilon a k T) \approx \frac{1}{50}$ gegeben (s. Ziff. 10).

ε) Deutung des Milieueinflusses. Die Annahme einer mehrstufigen Dissoziation als Ursache der Relaxationsabsorption der 2-2-wertigen Elektrolyte erlaubt eine fast restlose Erklärung aller beobachteten Milieueinflüsse (s. Ziff. 26).

Insbesondere läßt sich der *Einfluß von Fremd-Elektrolyten* deuten, die im Bereich des „unteren" Maximums — in dem er bei $MgSO_4$-Lösungen sehr genau untersucht wurde — selbst nicht absorbieren. Zusätze von Fremd-Elektrolyten, die ein Ion mit dem primär vorhandenen $MgSO_4$ gemeinsam haben (z.B. $MgCl_2$ oder Na_2SO_4), erhöhen die Konzentration der Assoziate und verursachen den beobachteten Anstieg der Absorption. Dagegen müssen Fremd-Elektrolyte (z.B. NaCl), die mit $MgSO_4$ kein Ion gemeinsam haben, aber mit einem von dessen Ionen Komplexe[2] (hier $NaSO_4^-$) bilden, die Konzentration der Komplexe und damit die Absorption vermindern. Mittels einfacher Massenwirkungs-Beziehungen konnten EIGEN, KURTZE und TAMM [*18*] die von TAMM [*17*] empirisch gefundene Mischungsregel [s. Gl. (26.1)] quantitativ ableiten:

Mit Hilfe der beiden Gesamt-Gleichgewichtskonstanten für $MgSO_4$ und für $NaSO_4^-$ läßt sich der „Gesamt-Assoziationsgrad" $(1-\delta)$, d.h. das Verhältnis der $MgSO_4$-Komplex-Konzentration zur $MgSO_4$-Salzkonzentration, auch bei Zusatz von NaCl berechnen:

$$\frac{1}{1-\delta} = 1 + \frac{1 + [Na^+]\,\Pi^f/K_{NaSO_4^-}}{[Mg^{++}]\,\Pi^f/K_{MgSO_4}}. \qquad (38.3)$$

Über die aus δ zu bestimmenden G_{II}-Werte (s. Ziff. 5 und 8) läßt sich unter Vernachlässigung der Konzentrationsabhängigkeit von Π^f die relative Abnahme $\Delta\alpha/\alpha$ der Absorption berechnen. Sie entspricht der angeführten Mischungsregel

[1] Bei kleinen Ionen bzw. großen Oberflächenfeldstärken können solche Hydrolysemechanismen allerdings sehr merklich werden und beobachtbare Relaxationsmaxima verursachen, wie EIGEN u. Mitarb. [*75*] gezeigt haben (s. Ziff. 36).

[2] Auf die Existenz der $NaSO_4^-$-Komplexe kann aus der großen Schallabsorption von Na_2SO_4-Lösungen bei hohen Frequenzen (s. Ziff. 37) geschlossen werden.

[s. Gl. (26.1)], welche die in Fig. 22 dargestellten Versuchsergebnisse sehr gut erfaßt und für $MgSO_4$: $\varphi = 0{,}21$, für $MnSO_4$: $\varphi = 0{,}08$ ergibt. Die Auswertung der Gl. (38.1) durch EIGEN [*50*] mit der Vereinfachung $G_{\mathrm{II}}^{+} = G$ (Verlauf s. Fig. 35) ergibt für eine $MgSO_4$-Salzkonzentration $c = 0{,}1$ Mol/Liter und $K_{\mathrm{NaSO}_4^-} = K_{\mathrm{MgSO}_4} = 5 \cdot 10^{-3}$ Mol/Liter den in Fig. 22 eingezeichneten Verlauf, der den Meßwerten gut folgt und $\varphi = 0{,}11$ entspricht.

Auch die p_{H}-Abhängigkeit ist verständlich. Der unterhalb p_{H} 3 auftretende starke Abfall der Absorption beruht auf der Abnahme der $MgSO_4$-Komplexe infolge der Bildung von HSO_4^--Komplexen, deren Dissoziationskonstante etwa 10^{-2} Mol/Liter beträgt (s. Ziff. 36). Der Abfall ist bei Zugabe von HCl größer als bei H_2SO_4, da die Sulfationen der Schwefelsäure, die das Gleichgewicht zugunsten der $MgSO_4$-Komplexe beeinflussen, den Einfluß der H^+-Ionen teilweise kompensieren. Die Relaxation der HSO_4^--Komplexe wird erst bei hohen Frequenzen meßbar und beeinflußt die Absorption im Bereich des unteren Relaxationsmaximums von $MgSO_4$ nicht.

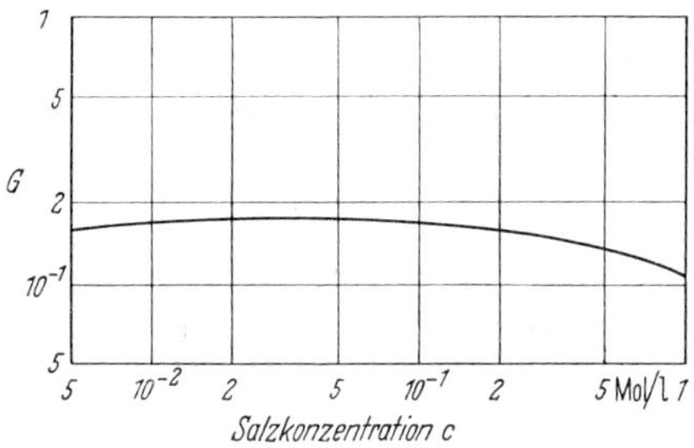

Fig. 35. Konzentrationsabhängigkeit des Faktors G, berechnet für einstufige Dissoziation von $MgSO_4$ nach EIGEN, KURTZE und TAMM [*18*].

Das Verhalten im basischen Bereich bei Zusatz von NaOH ist noch nicht vollständig geklärt, da $Mg(OH)_2$-Ausfällung diesen Zusatz begrenzt. Die geringe Konzentration von $MgOH^+$ kann die Konzentration der $MgSO_4$-Komplexe und damit die Absorption nicht wesentlich vermindern. Der starke Anstieg der Absorption kurz unterhalb der Löslichkeitsgrenze von $Mg(OH)_2$ kann durch Bildung höherer MgOH-Komplexe verursacht sein. Die Relaxation des Gleichgewichts $MeOH^+ \rightleftharpoons Me^{++} + OH^-$ ist bei $Mg(OH)_2$ wegen der geringen Konzentration von $MgOH^+$ kaum beobachtbar, während sie bei anderen Metallionen, wie Be^{++}, nachgewiesen ist (s. EIGEN [*75*]).

Der Fremdelektrolyt-Einfluß tritt beim oberen Relaxationsmaximum von $MgSO_4$ nicht so klar hervor, da sich hier die Relaxationsprozesse der sich neu bildenden Komplexe überlagern. Die Beobachtungen entsprechen aber recht gut den Erwartungen (Ziff. 26, Tabelle 2).

Der Einfluß der *Dielektrizitätskonstante des Lösungsmittels* kann mit Hilfe des mehrstufigen Dissoziationsgleichgewichts ebenfalls befriedigend gedeutet werden. Bei Annahmen einer zweistufigen Dissoziation wird mit abnehmender Dielektrizitätskonstante ε, wie aus analogen Systemen bekannt ist, sowohl k_{32}/k_{23} als auch k_{21}/k_{12} abnehmen. Während also in reinem Wasser als Lösungsmittel (mit $k_{32}/k_{23} = 5 \ldots 10$) wegen $k_{32} \gg k_{23}/(1 + k_{21}/k'_{12})$ die Dissoziations-Geschwindigkeitskonstante k_{32} die Relaxationsfrequenz des „unteren" Maximums bestimmt, wird diese Relaxationsfrequenz mit abnehmender DK schließlich dem Wert k_{23} zustreben. Da sich vermutlich — wegen der auswählenden Solvatation — der Einfluß der DK auf k_{21}/k'_{12} früher als auf k_{32}/k_{23} bemerkbar macht, ist zunächst ein Anstieg von k_{32} auf $k_{32} + k_{23}$ zu erwarten, dann aber ein Abfall auf k_{23}. Berücksichtigt man noch, daß k_{23} selbst mit abnehmender DK ansteigen sollte, so müßte ein weiterer Anstieg der Relaxationsfrequenz auftreten. Je nach Konzentrations- und DK-Bereich sollte also eine Zu- oder eine Abnahme der Relaxationsfrequenz beobachtet werden.

Tatsächlich entspricht der von BIES [*16*] in $MgSO_4$-Lösungen geringer Konzentration ($c < 10^{-2}$ Mol/Liter) bei Dioxan-Zusatz gefundene Verlauf (s. Fig. 25a) dieser Erwartung und zeigt zunächst eine Zunahme, dann eine Abnahme von ν_m

mit abnehmender DK. Das von KOR und VERMA [*31a*] in $MnSO_4$-Lösungen ($c = 0{,}25 \ldots 2 \cdot 10^{-2}$ Mol/Liter) bei Dioxan-Zusatz gemessene stetige Ansteigen der Relaxationsfrequenz entspricht offenbar dem Anfangsanstieg, den BIES bei $MgSO_4$ fand.

Die von TAMM, KURTZE und KAISER [*17a*] in einer 0,2 molaren $MgSO_4$-Lösung bei Zusatz von Alkohol gefundene Abnahme der Relaxationsfrequenz, die auch von SMITHSON und LITOVITZ [*25*] in 0,1 molarer $MnSO_4$-Lösung bestätigt wurde, entspricht offensichtlich der Abnahme auf k_{23}. Daß keine vorübergehende Zunahme von ν_m beobachtet wurde, kann seine Ursache in der höheren Konzentration dieser Lösungen oder in dem andersartigen Zusatz haben, für den die Solvatation anders verlaufen kann als mit Dioxan.

Da der Absolutwert des Absorptionsmaximums (bei wenig verändertem G_{II}^{+}) im wesentlichen der Gleichgewichtskonstante $K_{23} = k_{32}/k_{23}$ umgekehrt proportional sein sollte, muß er mit abnehmender DK erheblich zunehmen. Das entspricht völlig den Meßergebnissen sowohl von BIES [*16*] als auch von TAMM, KURTZE und KAISER [*17a*] (s. Fig. 24).

Die Annahme einer dreistufigen Dissoziation beeinflußt die vorstehenden Überlegungen nur wenig. Die Annahme eines einstufigen Gleichgewichtes ist jedoch nicht in der Lage, die starke Zunahme des Absorptionsmaximums bei abnehmender DK zu erklären.

Das *Ersetzen von H_2O durch D_2O* kann die Geschwindigkeitskonstante k_{43} der Umwandlung der $MgSO_4$-Aquokomplexe in Hydratkomplexe nicht sehr beeinflussen, da dieser Vorgang unmittelbar an der Oberfläche des nichthydratisierten Metallions vor sich geht und da bei der Hydratation die Sauerstoffatome (nicht aber die Wasserstoff- bzw. Deuteriumatome) sich dicht an das Metallion lagern. Dementsprechend sollte die Relaxationsfrequenz des „unteren" Maximums unverändert bleiben. Das ist auch das Ergebnis der Messungen von SMITHSON und LITOVITZ [*25*][1] an $MnSO_4$-Lösungen (s. Fig. 26). Die Zunahme des Absolutwertes der Absorption ist verständlich, da sowohl die $\Delta^* V$-Werte als auch die Gleichgewichtskonstante durch das Lösungsmittel beeinflußt werden.

ζ) Temperatur- und Druck-Einfluß. Die aus der *Temperaturabhängigkeit* der Relaxationsfrequenzen ermittelten Aktivierungsenergien (s. Fig. 20b bzw. Ziff. 24, Tabelle 1) sind in der für den ersten Dissoziationsschritt der Aquokomplexe zu erwartenden Größenordnung und entsprechen in ihrer Reihenfolge den Absolutwerten der Geschwindigkeitskonstanten der Dissoziation bei verschiedenen Metallionen.

Der *statische Druck* beeinflußt die Aktivierungsenergie und damit die Geschwindigkeitskonstante k_{43} der Hydratation des Aquokomplexes ($MeSO_4$) verhältnismäßig wenig, wohl aber die Geschwindigkeitskonstante k_{34} der Rückreaktion. Dem entspricht das von FISHER [*19*] an $MgSO_4$-Lösungen gefundene Ergebnis einer konstanten Relaxationsfrequenz und einer abnehmenden Absorption bei steigendem Druck (s. Fig. 21), denn die erste ist durch k_{43} allein, die letzte durch die druckabhängige Gleichgewichtskonstante K_{34} bestimmt[2].

F. Schlußbemerkungen.

39. Gesicherte Ergebnisse, Ausblick. Auf dem Gebiet der Schallabsorption und -dispersion liegt eine ganze Reihe von Meßergebnissen vor, die zwar wegen der Schwierigkeit von Messungen großer Genauigkeit über einen großen Fre-

[1] Die Autoren vermuten auf Grund ihrer Ergebnisse eine Reaktion vom Typ $MnSO_4 + H_2O = MnH_2O^{++} + SO_4^{--}$.

[2] Die von CARNEVALE und LITOVITZ [*7a*] an Ammoniumhydroxyd, also einem schwachen Elektrolyten (s. Ziff. 36α), gefundene Zunahme der Relaxationsfrequenz (s. Tabelle 4) hat ihren Grund analog in der Zunahme der Dissoziations-Geschwindigkeitskonstante k_{21}, die für die Relaxationsfrequenz bestimmend ist. Die mit dem Druck abnehmende Absorption ist eine Folge der Verminderung von $\Delta^* V$ mit dem Druck.

quenzbereich noch lückenhaft sind, aber ständig ergänzt werden. Für einige Elektrolyte, z.B. Ammoniak, Schwefelsäure, die Acetate und die Sulfate, insbesondere für Magnesiumsulfat, sind sehr ausführliche Untersuchungsreihen vorhanden. Auf diese haben sich auch die theoretischen Untersuchungen bisher konzentriert.

Die Schallabsorption der Elektrolytlösungen läßt sich grundsätzlich durch Relaxationsvorgänge erklären. Annahmen über die Art dieser Relaxationsvorgänge können anhand des beobachteten Verlaufs der Absorption mit der Frequenz, der Konzentration, der Temperatur und des Druckes, sowie in Abhängigkeit von Fremd-Elektrolytzusätzen usw. geprüft werden. Das ist eine verhältnismäßig komplizierte Aufgabe, weil das Verhalten sehr mannigfaltig und zunächst unübersichtlich ist. Man kann das erwarten, weil es ein Abbild der thermodynamischen und kinetischen Eigenschaften der gelösten Elektrolyte ist, die ihrerseits auf der Wechselwirkung der Elektrolyt-Ionen untereinander und mit dem Lösungsmittel beruhen.

Für einige Elektrolyte — speziell die obengenannten — sind bei der Deutung gute Erfolge erzielt worden. So steht fest, daß die Relaxationseffekte in dem Frequenzbereich bis zu einigen 100 MHz auf spezifischen Wechselwirkungen der Ionen des gelösten Elektrolyten beruhen. Bei schwachen Elektrolyten (z.B. Essigsäure und Ammoniak) ist eine einfache Dissoziation der Säure- bzw. Basenmolekel, bei starkem Elektrolyten, insbesondere bei den 2-2-wertigen, eine stufenweise Dissoziation der Aquokomplexe über intermediäre Hydratkomplexe die Ursache der beobachteten Absorption. Während die Aquokomplexe in 2-2-wertigen Elektrolyten (z.B. $MgSO_4$) in einer merklichen Konzentration auftreten, so daß ihre Umwandlung in Hydratkomplexe eine gut beobachtbare Absorption („unteres" Maximum) verursacht, sind bei den 1-2-wertigen Elektrolyten (z.B. Na_2SO_4) solche Aquokomplexe in wesentlich geringerem Maße vorhanden. Die zugehörigen Frequenzen sollten auf Grund der geringeren elektrostatischen Wechselwirkung noch wesentlich höher als bei Cu^{++} liegen. Sie sind deshalb von dem (allein meßbaren) „oberen" Anstieg nicht mehr zu unterscheiden. Bei stark hydrolysierenden Ionen treten außerdem Hydrolysestufen auf. Die allgemeine Wechselwirkung (Ionenwolkeneffekt) liefert erst bei Frequenzen über 100 MHz einen erheblichen Beitrag zur Absorption.

Die Ergebnisse der Deutung haben zum Teil die bestehenden physikalisch-chemischen Vorstellungen bestätigt, gehen aber in einigen Punkten darüber hinaus. Während nämlich die statischen Messungen an Elektrolytlösungen nur Gesamtgleichgewichte erfassen, gehen bei den akustischen Messungen auch die Absolutwerte der Einstellgeschwindigkeiten der einzelnen Teilgleichgewichte ein. Man breitet das thermodynamische Gleichgewicht gewissermaßen auf der Frequenzachse aus und kann somit die einzelnen Anteile der Wechselwirkung getrennt erhalten.

Für die Beurteilung der Leistungsfähigkeit der akustischen Methode ist die Frage entscheidend, ob die Auswertung in bezug auf die Parameter des auftretenden Reaktionsgleichgewichtes eindeutig ist. Bei einem zweistufigen Gleichgewicht sind vier Geschwindigkeitskonstanten k_{12}, k_{21}, k_{23} uns k_{32} (die auch die Teilgleichgewichte und das Gesamtgleichgewicht bestimmen) sowie zwei Partialvolumen-Differenzen $\Delta^* V_{12}$ und $\Delta^* V_{21}$, also sechs Unbekannte, zu bestimmen. Diesen stehen als Meßgrößen die beiden Relaxationsfrequenzen und ihre Konzentrationsabhängigkeiten gegenüber, die zusammen beide Geschwindigkeitskonstanten-Paare zu bestimmen gestatten. Die Absolutwerte der Absorptionsmaxima liefern die Volumendifferenzen. Die Konzentrationsabhängigkeit dieser

Absorptionsmaxima liefert darüber hinaus eine Kontrollmöglichkeit. Allerdings sind nicht in jedem Falle alle numerischen Werte der Messung zugänglich. Durchweg erfordern hinreichend starke Effekte Konzentrationen von mehr als 10^{-3} Mol/Liter. Auch bei mehrstufigen Mechanismen liefert die Messung der Schallabsorption in Abhängigkeit von Frequenz und Konzentration im Prinzip alle den Mechanismus bestimmenden Parameter. Gewisse Komplikationen verursacht die Berücksichtigung der Aktivitätskoeffizienten. Wenn nur geladene Teilchen bezüglich ihrer Aktivitätskoeffizienten berücksichtigt zu werden brauchen, reicht eine zusätzliche Bestimmung des Produktes Π^f aus, um eine willkürfreie Deutung zu ermöglichen.

Die Möglichkeit, mit Hilfe von Schallabsorptions- und -dispersions-Messungen Aussagen über Einstellzeiten von Gleichgewichten mit sehr hohen Reaktionsgeschwindigkeiten zu erhalten, wird in der Zukunft sicher noch weitgehend ausgenützt werden und insbesondere in der chemischen Kinetik von großem Wert sein. Die akustischen Verfahren werden, in Ergänzung zu anderen dynamischen Methoden (wie Temperatursprungmethode, Feldstärkesprungmethode) die Deutung mancher bisher schwer verständlich gebliebenen Eigenschaften von Elektrolytlösungen wesentlich beschleunigen können. Dazu wird es nötig sein, verbesserte Meßmethoden zu schaffen, damit bei erträglichem Zeitaufwand Messungen mit großer Genauigkeit gemacht werden können. Für die akustischen Verfahren gilt das besonders für den Bereich sehr hoher Frequenzen und für den Bereich unter 100 kHz.

Literatur-Verzeichnis.

[*1*] SETTE, D.: Nuovo Cim. **6**, 1 (1949).
[*2*] EUCKEN, A.: Z. Elektrochem. **51**, 6 (1948); **52**, 255 (1948); **53**, 102 (1949).
[*3*] HALL, L.: Phys. Rev. **73**, 775 (1948).
[*4*] GIERER, A., u. K. WIRTZ: Z. Naturforsch. **5**a, 270 (1950).
[*5*] FOX, E.F., and G. ROCK: J. Acoust. Soc. Amer. **12**, 505 (1941). — Phys. Rev. **70**, 68 (1946).
[*6*] PINKERTON, J.M.: Nature, Lond. **160**, 128 (1947).
[*7*] CARNEVALE, E.H., and T.A. LITOVITZ: J. Acoust. Soc. Amer. **27**, 794 (1955).
[*7a*] CARNEVALE, E.H., and T.A. LITOVITZ: J. Acoust. Soc. Amer. **30**, 610 (1958).
[*8*] EINSTEIN, A.: Preuss. Akad. Wiss. Berlin **19**, 380 (1920).
[*9*] EVEREST, F.A., and H.T. O'NEIL: J. Acoust. Soc. Amer. **19**, 255 (1946).
[*10*] THIESSEN, G.J., J.R. LESLIE and F.W. SIMPSON: Canad. J. Res. **26**, 306 (1948). — Appl. Mech. Rev. **1**, 1713 (1948).
[*11*] LIEBERMANN, L.: J. Acoust. Soc. Amer. **20**, 868 (1948).
[*12*] LIEBERMANN, L.: Phys. Rev. **76**, 1520 (1949).
[*13*] LEONARD, R.W.: J. Acoust. Soc. Amer. **18**, 252 (1946).
[*14*] LEONARD, R.W., P.C. COMBS and L.R. SKIDMORE: J. Acoust. Soc. Amer. **21**, 63 (1949).
LEONARD, R.W.: J. Acoust. Soc. Amer. **20**, 224 (1948).
LEONARD, R.W.: Techn. report No. I, U.C.L.A., Phys. Dept. 1950.
[*15*] WILSON, O.B., and R.W. LEONARD: J. Acoust. Soc. Amer. **26**, 223 (1954).
WILSON, O.B.: Phys. Rev. **81**, 657 (1951).
[*16*] BIES, D.A.: J. Chem. Phys. **23**, 428 (1955).
[*17*] TAMM, K., and G. KURTZE: Nature, Lond. **168**, 346 (1951). — Acustica **3**, 33 (1953).
KURTZE, G.: Nachr. Akad. Wiss. Göttingen, math.-phys. Kl. **9**, 57 (1952).
TAMM, K.: Nachr. Akad. Wiss. Göttingen, math.phys. Kl. **10**, 81 (1952).
[*17a*] TAMM, K., G. KURTZE u. R. KAISER: Acustica **4**, 380 (1954).
[*18*] EIGEN, M., G. KURTZE u. K. TAMM: Z. Elektrochem. **57**, 103 (1953).
[*19*] FISHER, F.H.: J. Acoust. Soc. Amer. **30**, 441 (1958).
[*20*] CARSTENSEN, E.L.: J. Acoust. Soc. Amer. **26**, 858 (1954); **26**, 862 (1954.)
[*21*] CONNOLLY, P.L., and F.E. FOX: J. Acoust. Soc. Amer. **25**, 658 (1953).
[*22*] BARRET, R.E., and R.T. BEYER: J. Acoust. Soc. Amer. **25**, 827 (1953).

[23] HALL, L. H.: J. Acoust. Soc. Amer. **24**, 704 (1952).
[24] BARTHEL, R.: J. Acoust. Soc. Amer. **24**, 313 (1952).
[25] SMITHSON, J. R., and T. A. LITOVITZ: J. Acoust. Soc. Amer. **28**, 462 (1956).
[26] BAZULIN, P.: C. R. Acad. Sci. URSS. **19**, 153 (1938). — J. exp. theor. Phys. **9**, 1147 (1939).
[27] RÜFER, W.: Ann. Phys., Lpz. **41**, 301 (1942).
[28] CLAEYS, J., J. ERRERA et H. SACK: C. R. Acad. Sci., Paris **202**, 1493 (1936). — Trans. Faraday Soc. **33**, 136 (1937).
[29] STREHLOW, H., u. M. BECKER: Z. Elektrochem. **63**, 457 (1959).
[30] BEYER, R. T., and M. C. SMITH: J. Acoust. Soc. Amer. **18**, 424 (1946).
[30a] BARRETT, R. E., F. L. MCNAMARA and R. T. BEYER: J. Acoust. Soc. Amer. **23**, 629 (1951); **26**, 966 (1954).
[30b] SMITH, M. C., R. E. BARRETT and R. T. BEYER: J. Acoust. Soc. Amer. **23**, 71 (1951).
[31] KOR, S. K., and G. S. VERMA: J. Chem. Phys. **29**, 9 (1958).
[31a] STUEHR, J., G. S. VERMA, E. YEAGER and F. HOVORKA: J. Acoust. Soc. Amer. **31**, 1586 (1959).
[32] BUSS, W.: Ann. Phys., Lpz. (5) **33**, 143 (1938).
[33] MULDERS, C. E.: Appl. Sci. Res. B **1**, 341 (1949). — Diss. Delft 1950. — Nature, Lond. **164**, 347 (1949).
[34] FOX, F. E., and TH. M. MARION: J. Acoust. Soc. Amer. **25**, 661 (1953).
[35] KNESER, H. O.: Ergebn. exakt. Naturw. **22**, 121 (1949).
[36] MEIXNER, J.: Ann. Phys. **43**, 470 (1943).
[37] HIEDEMANN, E., u. R. D. SPENCE: Z. Physik **43**, 470 (1943).
[38] MANES, M.: J. Chem. Phys. **21**, 1791 (1953).
MANES, M., I. J. E. HOFER and S. WELLER: J. Chem. Phys. **18**, 1355 (1950).
[39] MARKHAM, J. J., R. T. BEYER and R. B. LINDSAY: Rev. Mod. Phys. **23**, 353 (1951).
[40] FRENKEL, J.: Kinetic Theory of Liquids. Oxford 1946.
[41] BRÖNSTEDT, J. N.: Z. phys. Chem. **102**, 169 (1922).
[42] BJERRUM, N.: Z. phys. Chem. **108**, 87 (1924).
[43] CHRISTIANSEN, J. A.: Z. phys. Chem. **113**, 33 (1925).
[44] EUCKEN, A.: Lehrbuch Chemische Physik. Leipzig 1949.
[45] HARNED, H. S., and B. OWEN: The Physical Chemistry of Electrolytic Solutions. New York 1950.
[46] KORTÜM, G.: Elektrolytlösungen. Leipzig 1941.
[47] FALKENHAGEN, H.: Elektrolyte. Leipzig 1953.
[48] WICKE, E., and M. EIGEN: J. Phys. Chem. **58**, 702 (1954).
[49] CHRISTIANSEN, J. A.: J. Coll. Sci. **6**, 3 (1951).
[50] EIGEN, M.: Z. phys. Chem., N. F. **3/4**, 176 (1954).
[51] EIGEN, M.: Chemische Relaxation. Darmstadt (im Druck).
[51a] EIGEN, M.: Disc. Faraday Soc. **24**, 25 (1957).
[51b] EIGEN, M., u. G. SCHWARZ: Z. phys. Chemie (im Druck).
[52] DEBYE, P.: Trans. Electrochem. Soc. **82**, 265 (1952).
[53] DEBYE, P., u. E. HÜCKEL: Phys. Z. **24**, 185 (1923).
[54] DEBYE, P., u. H. FALKENHAGEN: Phys. Z. **29**, 401 (1928).
[55] WICKE, E., M. EIGEN u. TH. ACKERMANN: Z. phys. Chem., N.F. **1**, 340 (1954).
WICKE, E., u. M. EIGEN: Z. Elektrochem. Ber. Bunsenges. **57**, 319 (1953).
[56] GLASSTONE, S., K. J. LAIDLER and H. EYRING: The Theory of Rate Processes. New York 1941.
[57] DAVIES, C. W.: Trans. Faraday Soc. **23**, 351 (1927).
[58] DAVIES, C. W., H. W. JONES and C. B. MONK: Trans. Faraday Soc. **48**, 921 (1952).
[59] MOEN, C. J.: J. Acoust. Soc. Amer. **23**, 62 (1951).
[60] NAAKE, H. J.: DSIR-Report 1951.
[61] SKUDRZYK, E.: Öst. Ing.-Arch. **4**, 408 (1950).
MEYER, E., u. E. SKUDRZYK: Unveröff. Ber. 1943.
[62] ITTERBEEK, A. v., et L. VERHAEGEN: Coll. Ultrason. Trill. Brüssel 1951, S. 220.
[63] ITTERBEEK, A. v., u. P. SLOOTMAKERS: Physica, Haag **17**, 897 (1949).
[64] RAPUANO, R. A.: Phys. Rev. **72**, 78 (1947).
[65] LITOVITZ, T. A.: J. Acoust. Soc. Amer. **23**, 75 (1951).

[*66*] PELLAM, J.R., and J.K. GALT: J. Acoust. Soc. Amer. **18**, 251 (1946). — J. Chem. Phys. **14**, 608 (1946).
[*67*] HSU TSUNG-YUEH, E.: J. Acoust. Soc. Amer. **17**, 127 (1945).
[*68*] BARANSKI, K.N.: Dokl. Akad. Nauk. SSSR. **114**, 517 (1957). — Sov. Res. Phys. (Engl. Transl.) **2**, 237 (1957).
[*68a*] BOEMMEL, H.E., and K. DRANSFELD: Phys. Rev. **1** (7), 234 (1958); **2** (7), 298 (1959); **3**, 83 (1959).
[*68b*] JACOBSEN, E.H.: Phys. Rev. Lett. **2**, 249 (1959). — J. Acoust. Soc. Amer. **32**, 949 (1960).
[*69*] NERNST, W., u. W. ORTHMANN: Berl. akad. Ber. **1926**, 51; **1927**, 156. — Z. phys. Chem. **135**, 199 (1928).
[*70*] SUHRMANN, R., u. R. WIEDERSICH: Z. Elektrochem. Ber. Bunsenges. **57**, 93 (1953).
[*71*] SASLAWSKY, I.I., u. E.G. STANDEL: Z. anorg. Chem. **186**, 1721 (1930).
[*72*] EIGEN, M., u. L.C.M. DE MAEYER: Z. Elektrochem. **59**, 986 (1955).
[*73*] EIGEN, M., u. J. SCHOEN: Z. phys. Chem., N. F. **3**, 126 (1955). — Z. Elektrochem. **59**, 483 (1955).
[*74*] DIEBLER, H., u. M. EIGEN: Z. phys. Chem., N.F. **20**, 299 (1959). — Helv. chim. Acta (in Vorbereitung).
[*75*] CZERLINSKI, G., u. M. EIGEN: Z. Elektrochem. Ber. Bunsenges. **20**, 299 (1959). — CZERLINSKI, G., H. DIEBLER u. M. EIGEN: Z. phys. Chem., N.F. **19**, 246 (1959).
[*76*] ROBINSON, R.A., and R.H. STOKES: Electrolyte Solutions. London 1955.
[*77*] LANDOLT-BÖRNSTEIN, Physikalisch-Chemische Tabellen, EG III (1936), 2816 (nach Messungen von W.A. ROTH).
[*78*] ECKART, C.: Phys. Rev. **58**, 267, 269, 919 (1940); **73**, 373 (1948).
[*79*] HERZFELD, K.F.: J. Acoust. Soc. Amer. **13**, 33 (1941).
[*80*] HERZFELD, K.F., and T.A. LITOVITZ: Absorption and Dispersion of Ultrasonic Waves. New York and London 1959.
[*81*] EIGEN, M., u. K. TAMM: Z. Elektrochem. Ber. Bunsenges. (im Druck).

Dispersion and Absorption of Sound Waves in Liquids and Mixtures of Liquids.

By

DANIELE SETTE.

With 63 Figures.

Introduction. For a long time the more important applications of sound velocity measurement in liquids have been in the evaluations of adiabatic compressibility and of the ratio of specific heats, when the isothermal compressibility had already been found by static measurements. In recent years however the determination of sound velocity and of absorption coefficient has furnished a method for studying molecular and structural properties of liquids. The analysis of the causes of sound dispersion and absorption shows in fact that in many cases the dispersion and a relevant part of the measured absorption coefficient are due to some molecular processes. The measurements of velocity and of sound absorption coefficient have therefore assumed great importance. Usually, however, the sound dispersion in the frequency range of experiment is too small to be detected, and the results of absorption measurements are mainly used.

Moreover, intimate relations between the values of sound velocity and chemical or structural characteristics of the molecules of the liquid have been found. This gives to the sound velocity the properties of a primary quantity in a molecular theory of liquids.

The present review is divided into three parts. In Part A the general theories of sound dispersion and absorption are given. The principal sources of dispersion and absorption are discussed and the methods used at present for representing and explaining the experimental results are indicated and compared, when possible.

Part B examines the more significant experimental results obtained in the various categories of liquids and it integrates, when necessary, the theoretical treatments of Part A, in dealing with specific cases. An accurate description of the methods of measurement is omitted because it can be found in other parts of this book.

In Part C the dependence of the low-frequency velocity on chemical composition and structure of liquids is considered.

The material of this paper covers pure liquids and binary mixtures of liquids and does not include electrolytic solutions which are treated elsewhere[1].

A. General theories of dispersion and absorption of sound waves in liquids.

I. Visco-thermal theory and classical absorption.

1. Hydrodynamical equations. In hydrodynamics we suppose we are dealing with a fluid which is homogeneous, isotropic when at rest, viscous, thermally conducting and chemically inert. The propagation of sound waves in such a

[1] In TAMM's contribution to this volume, p. 202.

fluid is regulated by a system of equations[1] valid for any motion in the fluid and which we briefly state as follows.

α) Continuity equation. This expresses the assumption that during the process matter is neither created nor destroyed. The equation may be written in EULER'S form:

$$\frac{\partial \varrho}{\partial t} + \frac{\partial}{\partial x_i}(u_i \varrho) = \frac{\partial \varrho}{\partial t} + u_i \frac{\partial \varrho}{\partial x_i} + \varrho \frac{\partial u_i}{\partial x_i} = \frac{D\varrho}{Dt} + \varrho \operatorname{div} \boldsymbol{u} = 0 \tag{1.1}$$

where ϱ is the density; x_i and u_i $(i=1, 2, 3)$ are respectively the Cartesian coordinates and the components of the velocity $\boldsymbol{u}$ of a material particle. The summations are to be extended over all the allowable values of the subscript i. Moreover we denote with D/Dt the material derivative

$$\frac{D}{Dt} = \frac{\partial}{\partial t} + u_i \frac{\partial}{\partial x_i}. \tag{1.2}$$

β) Force equation. This can be expressed in CAUCHY'S formulation by

$$\varrho \frac{D u_i}{Dt} = \varrho F_i + \frac{\partial t_{ij}}{\partial x_j} \tag{1.3}$$

where $\boldsymbol{F}$ is the external force on unit mass of the fluid, and t_{ij} is a second-rank stress tensor which gives the net action of contiguous fluid on a volume element of the medium. For an isotropic viscous fluid the stress tensor can be assumed in first approximation to be a linear function of the rate of deformation and given by the Newton-Cauchy-Poisson law

$$t_{ij} = -p\,\delta_{ij} + \eta' d_{kk}\,\delta_{ij} + 2\eta\, d_{ij}; \quad t_{ij} = t_{ji}. \tag{1.4}$$

In this relation:

(a) p is a scalar, or hydrostatic pressure function which can be put equal to thermodynamical pressure p_{th}. p in general is not equal to the mean pressure

$$p_m = \tfrac{1}{3} t_{ii} = -p + (\tfrac{2}{3}\eta + \eta')\, d_{ii}.$$

The minus sign appears in front of p because, unlike what is assumed in elasticity, a tension is considered as a negative pressure in a fluid.

(b) δ_{ij} is the Kronecker symbol which is equal to 1 when $i=j$ and otherwise zero.

(c) d_{ij} is the rate of deformation tensor:

$$d_{ij} = \frac{1}{2}\left(\frac{\partial u_i}{\partial x_j} + \frac{\partial u_j}{\partial x_i}\right). \tag{1.5}$$

(d) η ist the first (shear) coefficient of viscosity and η' the second coefficient of viscosity. The term *bulk viscosity* is usually given to the linear combination $\eta_B = \eta' + \frac{2}{3}\eta$ which, when put equal zero, constitutes the so-called *Stokes' relation*. Substitution of (1.4) and (1.5) in (1.3) gives for the force equation

$$\left.\begin{aligned} \varrho \frac{D\boldsymbol{u}}{Dt} &= \varrho \boldsymbol{F} - \operatorname{grad} p + (\eta' + \eta) \operatorname{grad}(\operatorname{div} \boldsymbol{u}) + \eta\, \nabla^2(\boldsymbol{u}) + \\ &+ (\operatorname{div} \boldsymbol{u}) \operatorname{grad} \eta' + 2(\operatorname{grad} \eta \operatorname{grad})\, \boldsymbol{u} + \operatorname{grad} \eta \operatorname{curl} \boldsymbol{u}. \end{aligned}\right\} \tag{1.6}$$

Assuming η and η' constant and the validity of STOKES' relation, Eq. (1.6) yields the well-known Navier-Stokes equation.

[1] H. LAMB: Hydrodynamics. New York 1945. — RAYLEIGH: Theory of sound. New York 1945. — C. TRUESDELL: J. Rat. Mech. and Analysis 1, 125 (1952). — F. V. HUNT: J. Acoust. Soc. Amer. 27, 1019 (1955).

γ) State equation and energy equation. As already postulated we are dealing with a homogeneous fluid, i.e. a fluid for which exists a caloric equation of state among the *specific internal energy* per unit mass w, and any other two local state variables for which we choose the *specific entropy* per unit mass s, and the specific volume $v = \varrho^{-1}$

$$w = w(s, v). \tag{1.7}$$

The state of the fluid is determined by the knowledge of w, s, v. The following relations hold for thermodynamical pressure p_{th}, temperature and specific heats (for unit mass):

$$p_{\text{th}} = -\left(\frac{\partial w}{\partial v}\right)_s, \quad T = \left(\frac{\partial w}{\partial s}\right)_v, \quad \overline{C}_p = T\left(\frac{\partial s}{\partial T}\right)_p, \quad \overline{C}_v = T\left(\frac{\partial s}{\partial T}\right)_v, \quad \gamma = \frac{\overline{C}_p}{\overline{C}_v}. \tag{1.8}$$

The conservation of energy during a process in such a fluid is expressed in tensorial form by the following Fourier-Kirchhoff-Neumann energy equation

$$\varrho\left(\frac{Dw}{Dt}\right) = t_{ij}\, d_{ij} - \frac{\partial q_i}{\partial x_i} \tag{1.9}$$

where $q_i = (q_i)_{\text{cond}} + (q_i)_{\text{rad}}$ is the total heat flux tensor (mechanical units) whose divergence accounts for the energy which leaves the material element through conduction and radiation. $(q_i)_{\text{cond}}$ is given by the FOURIER's relation:

$$(q_i)_{\text{cond}} = -K_t \frac{\partial T}{\partial x_i} \tag{1.10}$$

where K_t, thermal conductivity, is in general a function of state variables, although it is usually assumed constant. $(q_i)_{\text{rad}}$ can be calculated by means of NEWTON's law of cooling:

$$\frac{\partial (q_i)_{\text{rad}}}{\partial x_i} = \varrho\, \overline{C}_v\, q\, (T - T_0). \tag{1.11}$$

q is a radiation coefficient and $(T - T_0)$ the local excess temperature.

Eq. (1.9) can be transformed using standard thermodynamic relations into:

$$\varrho\, \overline{C}_v \frac{DT}{Dt} + \varrho\, \overline{C}_v \left[\frac{\gamma - 1}{\beta_t}\right] \frac{\partial u_i}{\partial x_i} + \frac{\partial q_i}{\partial x_i} - \Phi_\eta = 0 \tag{1.12}$$

where $\beta_t = \varrho\, (\partial v / \partial T)_p$ is the thermal expansion coefficient and Φ_η is a viscous dissipation function

$$\Phi_\eta = \eta'\, d_{kk}\, d_{ii} + 2\eta\, d_{ij}\, d_{ji}. \tag{1.13}$$

The system of continuity, force and energy equations among the variables ϱ, T and $\boldsymbol{u}$ together with the state equation of the particular fluid, allows, at least in a formal way, the treatment of any problem of fluid motion. The system however is not linear and no general solution has been given. It is necessary to introduce approximations to deal with practical cases.

2. Viscothermal equations for small amplitude sound waves. In the study of the propagation of sound waves in a fluid we are concerned with the deviations of variables from their (equilibrium) values at rest. Considering only first order variations we can put:

$$\varrho = \varrho_0 + \varrho_1, \qquad T = T_0 + \Theta_1, \qquad \boldsymbol{u} = 0 + \boldsymbol{u}_1. \tag{2.1}$$

Assuming that the variations are small, i.e. limiting ourselves to small amplitude sound waves, it is possible, when Eqs. (2.1) are introduced in (1.1), (1.6), (1.12), to neglect powers of small quantities higher than the first and their products.

This procedure of *linearization* yields equations among variational components which are sufficient to describe the propagation of any kind of sound waves according to hydrodynamics taking into account viscosity, heat conduction and radiation. These equations are called: *first order acoustic equations*[1].

In order to review the indications of the *viscothermal theory* on the dispersion and absorption of sound waves in liquids we consider the first order acoustic equation in the particular case of plane sinusoidal waves. In such a case we deal with a one-dimensional problem and we can suppose that all variational components have the form of a damped harmonic oscillation

$$I_0\, e^{j\omega t}\, e^{-\psi x}$$

where $I_0\, e^{j\omega t}$ gives the harmonic oscillation at the source and ψ, the propagation vector, is a complex quantity which depends upon the nature of the medium and the frequency ($f=\omega/2\pi$). Putting

$$\psi=\alpha+j k, \tag{2.2}$$

α is the absorption coefficient per cm (for the amplitude of the wave) and

$$c=\frac{\omega}{k} \tag{2.3}$$

is the phase velocity.

In this case the first order acoustic equations reduce to a system of algebraic equations in ϱ_1, u_1, Θ_1:

$$\left.\begin{aligned} \varrho_0(\alpha+j k)\, u_1-j\omega\,\varrho_1&=0,\\ \left[j\omega\,\varrho_0-\eta\left(2+\frac{\eta'}{\eta}\right)(\alpha+j k)^2\right] u_1-(\alpha+j k)\,\frac{c_0^2}{\gamma}\left[\varrho_1+\beta_{t0}\,\varrho_0\,\Theta_1\right]&=0,\\ -\left[\frac{(\gamma-1)}{\beta_{t0}}\right](\alpha+j k)\, u_1+\left[j\omega-\left(\frac{K_t}{\varrho_0 C_v}\right)(\alpha+j k)^2+q\right]\Theta_1&=0, \end{aligned}\right\} \tag{2.4}$$

where

$$c_0=\frac{\omega}{k_0}=\left(\frac{\partial p}{\partial\varrho}\right)_s^{\frac{1}{2}}$$

is a reference velocity introduced as the velocity of a disturbance in the fluid for an adiabatic process without viscous losses.

The system (2.4) has a non-trivial solution only when the determinant of the coefficients is zero. This condition yields a biquadratic equation in ψ (which reduces to the Kirchhoff-Langevin equation if heat radiation effects are not considered).

This equation can be written in a simpler form using some dimensionless parameters[2]:

$$\gamma=\frac{C_p}{C_v};$$

viscosity number $\quad \mathscr{V}=2+\dfrac{\eta'}{\eta};$

Stokes numbers $\quad \boldsymbol{S}=\dfrac{\omega\eta}{\varrho_0 c_0^2},\qquad \boldsymbol{S}'=\dfrac{\omega}{q};$

thermoviscous number $\quad \boldsymbol{Y}=\dfrac{K_t}{\eta\mathscr{V}C_p};$

frequency number $\quad \boldsymbol{X}=\mathscr{V}\boldsymbol{S}=\dfrac{\omega\eta\mathscr{V}}{\varrho_0 c_0^2}.$

---

[1] In a similar way one can introduce in (2.1) second order variational components and obtain second order acoustic equations, needed to study second order effects.

[2] C. TRUESDELL: J. Rat. Mech. and Analysis **2**, 643 (1953). — F. V. HUNT: J. Acoust. Soc. Amer. **27**, 1019 (1955).

A fluid is entirely determined by the value of the material parameters γ and $\boldsymbol{Y}$ while the propagation of waves in it is described by means of $\boldsymbol{X}$.

The secular equation of the system (2.4) is then written:

$$\left(1-\frac{j}{\boldsymbol{S}'}\right)+\left[\frac{(\alpha+jk)}{k_0}\right]^2\left[1+j\boldsymbol{X}(1+\gamma\boldsymbol{Y})+\frac{\gamma\boldsymbol{X}_t-j}{\gamma\boldsymbol{S}'}\right]+\left[\frac{(\alpha+jk)}{k_0}\right]^4\boldsymbol{X}\boldsymbol{Y}(j-\gamma\boldsymbol{X})=0. \quad (2.5)$$

According to this equation α and k depend on four parameters in a complicated way and it may be shown that the effects of viscosity and heat exchange in general are not linearly additive. In order to simplify the solution of (2.5) it is however usual to make this assumption which is justified a posteriori quantitatively. If one does not consider for the moment heat radiation ($\boldsymbol{S}'\to\infty$), (Eq. 2.5) is written:

$$-2\left[\frac{k_0}{\alpha+jk}\right]^2=1+j\boldsymbol{X}(1+\gamma\boldsymbol{Y})\pm\{[1-\boldsymbol{X}^2(1-\gamma\boldsymbol{Y})^2]+j2\boldsymbol{X}[1-(2-\gamma)\boldsymbol{Y}]\}^{\frac{1}{2}}. \quad (2.6)$$

The solutions of (2.6) have been thoroughly investigated by TRUESDELL recently[1]. Among his results are the following equations which express dispersion (c/c_0) and absorption coefficient according to the viscothermal theory as power series of $\boldsymbol{X}$. These equations are valid for most liquids (weak conductors) with the exception of mercury and helium II (strong conductors) as long as $X<0.1$.

$$\left.\begin{aligned}
\frac{c}{c_0}&=1+\frac{1}{4}\boldsymbol{X}^2[3+10(\gamma-1)\boldsymbol{Y}-(\gamma-1)(7-3\gamma)\boldsymbol{Y}^2]+O(\boldsymbol{X}^4),\\
\frac{\alpha}{k_0}&=\frac{A_0}{2\pi}=\frac{1}{2}\boldsymbol{X}\Big\{1+(\gamma-1)\boldsymbol{Y}-\frac{1}{8}\boldsymbol{X}^2[5+35(\gamma-1)\boldsymbol{Y}+(\gamma-1)\times\\
&\qquad\times(35\gamma-63)\boldsymbol{Y}^2+(\gamma-1)(5\gamma^2-30\gamma+33)\boldsymbol{Y}^3]\Big\}+O(\boldsymbol{X}^5),\\
\frac{\alpha}{k}&=\frac{A}{2\pi}=\frac{1}{2}\boldsymbol{X}\Big\{1+(\gamma-1)\boldsymbol{Y}-\frac{1}{4}\boldsymbol{X}^2[1+11(\gamma-1)\boldsymbol{Y}-(\gamma-1)\times\\
&\qquad\times(23-11\gamma)\boldsymbol{Y}^2+(\gamma-1)(\gamma^2-10\gamma+13)\boldsymbol{Y}^3]\Big\}+O(\boldsymbol{X}^5),
\end{aligned}\right\}\quad (2.7)$$

where $A=\alpha\lambda$ is the absorption coefficient for wavelength λ and $A_0=\alpha\lambda_0$, λ_0 being the reference wavelength.

It is to be observed that neglecting in (2.7) terms in $\boldsymbol{X}^2$ and higher powers, one obtains the Kirchhoff approximation:

$$\left.\begin{aligned}
\frac{c}{c_0}&=1,\\
\alpha_K&=\frac{1}{2}k_0[\boldsymbol{X}+(\gamma-1)\boldsymbol{X}\boldsymbol{Y}]=\frac{\omega^2}{2\varrho_0c_0^3}\left[\eta\mathscr{V}+(\gamma-1)\frac{K_t}{\bar{C}_p}\right],
\end{aligned}\right\}\quad (2.8)$$

yielding no sound dispersion at all.

3. Classical absorption coefficient. Characteristics of dispersion and absorption in the viscothermal theory. If one assumes the validity of the so—called STOKES' relation ($\mathscr{V}=\frac{4}{3}$) one obtains for the absorption coefficient from Eqs. (2.8) the Kirchhoff-Stokes expression, usually referred to as *classical absorption coefficient:*

$$\alpha_c=\frac{\omega^2}{2\varrho_0c_0^3}\left[\frac{4}{3}\eta+(\gamma-1)\frac{K_t}{C_p}\right]. \quad (3.1)$$

The validity of STOKES' relation is justified for monoatomic gases where it expresses that during symmetrical compression no work is done by viscous forces.

The experimental values of α/f^2 are for most liquids larger than those given by (3.1) and frequently they decrease with frequency in some part of the range.

[1] C. TRUESDELL: J. Rat. Mech. and Analysis 2, 643 (1953).

It is conceivable that such behaviour might be explained on the basis of the exact viscothermal theory with a suitable choice of the second viscosity coefficient. TRUESDELL'S analysis of correct solutions of Eq. (2.6) demonstrates however that this is not the case. It is in fact possible to show that if in some cases of highly absorbent fluids, like benzene, carbon disulphide (and many gases) we adjust the second coefficient of viscosity in such a way as to explain with the viscothermal theory the low frequency experimental absorption coefficients, the values of absorption coefficients at the resonance peak and at higher frequencies are much larger than experimental values. Moreover it can be shown that according to the viscothermal theory: (a) the dispersion, at least from a certain frequency, increases with frequency and goes to infinity with $\boldsymbol{X}$; (b) the absorption coefficient for wavelength, A, approaches the limit 2π; (c) A_0 and α/k_0 approach zero at high frequencies and therefore they must experience at least one maximum as function of frequency (visco-thermal resonance). The maximum of A_0 is very broad; it has always about the same magnitude ($\alpha/k_0 \approx \frac{1}{3}$) and it could happen at any frequency by a suitable choice of the viscosity number.

As it will be seen in Part B, there are various experimental results which are in contrast with such behaviour and seem to be in better agreement with the indications of relaxation theories. Unlike the viscothermal effect, the relaxation phenomena produce an increase of velocity with frequency up to a limiting value (c_∞); moreover A_0 shows a maximum whose height and frequency position depend on c_0 and c_∞.

The experimental indications therefore seems to prove that dispersion and absorption of sound waves in fluids and in particular in liquids cannot be accounted for by the viscothermal theory alone. This seems due to the fact that in classical hydrodynamics no consideration is taken of the characteristics of the fluid particles and of their possible existence in various energetic states. As will bee seen in the following sections this is done by the relaxation theories. It could also be done by modifying the theories of hydrodynamics in various ways. A first and formal way would be that of rejecting the hypothesis of constant viscosity coefficients in the stress-strain relation of Eq. (1.4). We will discuss this modification later. A more satisfactory way would be that of considering the fluid as a mixture of two fluids and to develop the hydrodynamics of such a system. This is equivalent to supposing that the viscothermal and relaxation effects exist independently and operate simultaneously. Because both processes are non-linear the results will in general be different from those obtained by adding the two effects. Z. SAKADY[1] and J. MEIXNER[2] started the analysis of the two-fluid mixture theory, considering at the same time internal transformations inside the fluid and transport phenomena (heat conduction, diffusion, thermo-diffusion and viscosity). Although not much progress has been done along these lines, Meixner succeeded in showing that in liquids, especially in those (the majority) for which the relaxation times are of the order of 10^{-11} sec, the effects of internal transformation and those due to viscosity, heat conduction and diffusion are practically additive over the whole frequency range of experiment, and that the losses due to viscosity and heat conduction are well given by the Kirchhoff-Stokes expression of the *classical absorption coefficient.*

MEIXNER finds for the square of the complex velocity an expression similar to the one obtained by KIRCHHOFF for the calculation of classical absorption, with the difference that the factors in the various terms are frequency-dependent

[1] Z. SAKADY: Proc. Phys.-Math. Soc. Japan **23**, 208 (1941).
[2] J. MEIXNER: Acustica **2**, 101 (1952).

in consequence of the presence of relaxation phenomena. It is possible however to see that for a frequency much smaller or larger than the relaxation frequency ($\omega\tau \ll 1$; $\omega\tau \gg 1$; τ = relaxation time) the absorption coefficient is approximately formed of two terms of which the first is due to relaxation and the second to transport phenomena. The latter term is proportional to ω^2 in both regions. although the proportionality factors are different for low and high frequencies. An estimate of MEIXNER shows that in liquids the change of the proportionality factor between the two ranges of very low frequencies ($\omega\tau \ll 1$) and very high frequencies ($\omega\tau \gg 1$) is about 10 to 20 percent.

This is a relatively small variation, and shows that no great error is introduced if the proportionality factor at low frequencies is used for the whole frequency range of experiment, which in liquids generally does not reach the relaxation frequency. Also in the few cases in which experiments can be performed

Table 1. *Values of α/f^2 due to viscosity and heat conductivity in some liquids at room temperature* (P. BIQUARD).

Liquid	$\alpha_\eta/f^2 \cdot 10^{17}$ $\sec^2 cm^{-1}$	$\alpha_{th}/f^2 \cdot 10^{17}$ $\sec^2 cm^{-1}$	$\alpha_c/f^2 \cdot 10^{17}$ $\sec^2 cm^{-1}$
Acetone	6.54	0.5	7.04
Benzene	8.36	0.3	8.66
Chloroform	10.045	0.057	10.1
Ether	8.48	0.49	8.97
Ethyl acetate	7.95	0.31	8.26
Methyl acetate	6.34	0.44	6.78
Toluene	7.56	0.28	7.84
Water	8.5	0.0064	8.5
Xylene (m)	8.13	0.24	8.37

in the relaxation region, considering the losses due to relaxation being much bigger than those due to transport phenomena in this region and the limited precision of measurements, no significant error is introduced by assuming the additivity of absorption coefficients and using the classical expression for the absorption due to viscosity and heat conduction. These considerations based on MEIXNER'S work give confidence in the normal procedure used in analyzing the results of absorption measurements in liquids. It is customary in fact to consider various dissipation effects as additive and to use the classical absorption coefficient (α_c) for the losses due to viscosity and heat conduction. It is to be observed that the losses due to viscosity (α_η) are in general much larger in liquids than those due to heat conductivity (α_{th}). Table 1 gives some values calculated by BIQUARD[1] for the absorption coefficients due to viscosity and to heat conduction, compared with the experimental values. It is evident that except in particular cases, the losses due to heat conduction can be neglected compared to those due to viscosity.

4. Dispersion and absorption due to heat radiation. The effects of heat radiation can be easily evaluated on the assumption that they can be added to those produced by viscosity, heat conduction and relaxation. This approximate procedure is justified by the smallness of losses and dispersion due to heat radiation.

In order to study the effects of viscosity and heat conduction we have supposed $\boldsymbol{S}' = \omega/q = \infty$ in Eq. (2.5) To examine heat radiation, let S' be finite and $\boldsymbol{X}$ and $\boldsymbol{XY}$ go to zero.

[1] P. BIQUARD: Ann. Phys., Paris **6**, 195 (1936).

One finds[1] the solution already given by STOKES:

$$\left.\begin{aligned} \frac{c}{c_0} &= \frac{2}{\gamma}\,\frac{1+\gamma^2 S'^2}{1+\gamma S'^2+\sqrt{1+\gamma^2 S'^2}\sqrt{1+S'^2}},\\ A &= \alpha\cdot\lambda = \frac{2\pi(\gamma-1)\,S'}{1+\gamma S'^2+\sqrt{1+\gamma^2 S'^2}\sqrt{1+S'^2}},\\ A_0^2 &= (\alpha\lambda_0)^2 = 2\pi^2\gamma\,\frac{\sqrt{1+S'^2}\sqrt{1+\gamma^2 S'^2}-1-\gamma S'^2}{1+\gamma^2 S'^2}. \end{aligned}\right\} \quad (4.1)$$

The dispersion curve $(c/c_0)^2$ increases with S' between γ^{-1} and 1 with slope zero for $S'=0$ and $S'=\infty$ and only one inflection point.

The absorption coefficients for wavelengths A and A_0, are zero for $S'=0$ and $S'=\infty$ and have only one maximum:

$$\left.\begin{aligned} A_{\max} &= \frac{2\pi(\sqrt{\gamma}-1)}{\sqrt{\gamma}+1} &&\text{for}\quad S' = \frac{1}{\sqrt{\gamma}},\\ (A_0)_{\max} &= \frac{\pi}{2}(\gamma-1)\sqrt{\frac{2}{\gamma+1}} &&\text{for}\quad S' = \frac{1}{\gamma}\sqrt{\frac{3\gamma+1}{\gamma+3}}. \end{aligned}\right\} \quad (4.2)$$

The dispersion and absorption due to heat radiation in liquids are in general very small (less than for heat conduction) and it is customary to neglect them in calculations. It is important however to observe that the dependence of disperion and absorption on frequency ($S'=\omega/q$) is in this case of the same form as that which we shall find for relaxation processes.

II. Relaxation in liquids.

5. Relaxation processes. In classical hydrodynamics use is made of the normal state equation for the particular fluid, assuming that it is sufficient to determine entirely the state of the fluid when any two (independent) state variables are given. In some cases, however, this procedure gives an inadequate description of reality because it does not take into account the fact that individual particles may be in various energetic states. The particles of the fluid (e.g. molecules) in fact have in general various internal degrees of freedom which could be differently excited; moreover, they may be in different energetic conditions in the relation to neighboring particles. The possibility of fluid particles being in various energetic states brings out the existence of an equilibrium distribution of them for each set of values of independent thermodynamical variables. When these variables are changed the distribution of particles among the allowed energy states passes to a new equilibrium with a mechanism characteristic of the particular case. To reach the new equilibrium, therefore, a finite time (relaxation time), is required during which there is no equilibrium correspondence between the distribution of particles among allowed energy states and independent thermodynamical variables. Relaxation processes are originated in this way. Their existence induces dispersion and absorption of sound waves.

It has been observed that a connection can be found between relaxation processes and viscosity and heat conduction. This is easily seen for monatomic gases, where, according to the kinetic theory, viscosity and heat conduction coefficients are introduced to describe momentary departures from equilibrium (Maxwell) distribution for translational degrees of freedom of molecules. Dispersion and absorption of sound waves described by means of viscosity and heat conduction would be caused by relaxation of translational degrees of freedom;

[1] F. V. HUNT: J. Acoust. Soc. Amer. **27**, 1019 (1955).

the relaxation times would be of the order of the times between collisions. The extension of such interpretations to the cases of polyatomic gases and liquids is however not obvious and somewhat dubious.

Various treatments[1–12] of relaxation processes have been given starting from a phenomenological point of view, or by means of irreversible thermodynamics, statistical thermodynamics, kinetic theory. Some of them have a general character and are useful in showing the common characteristics of relaxation phenomena of different kinds.

All treatments produce the same behavior in dispersion and absorption of sound waves and try to evaluate the parameters of the processes by means of characteristic properties of the fluid. No attempt is here made to give an account of all the treatments which can be found in literature; we will only introduce the more important kinds of relaxation phenomena in liquids trying to stress their physical significance.

Let us therefore, suppose that one mole of our liquid is formed by N particles which can exist in only two different energy states, 1 and 2, and that the transition between these states is regulated by a chemical reaction in a broad sense which, at present, we assume to be of first order:

$$\frac{dN_2}{dt} = N_1 K_{12} - N_2 K_{21} \tag{5.1}$$

where N_1 and N_2 are the numbers of particles in each state per mole and K_{12}, K_{21} are the rate constants.

According to Eq. (5.1) the total number of particles does not vary as a result of the reaction.

The heat of reaction per mole can be introduced as the addition of the change ΔW of internal energy at constant volume and of the work required to produce the isothermal change of volume ΔV:

$$\Delta H = \Delta W + p\,\Delta V = C_v\,\Delta T + p\,\Delta V$$

where p is the pressure according to the definition: $p = T(\partial S/\partial v)_T$; S is the entropy.

In general, during the reaction both ΔW and ΔV are different from zero. When an acoustic wave passes through the liquid, relaxation losses are set up in consequence of the simultaneous variations of temperature and pressure produced by the wave.

6. Thermal relaxation. A special and important case is verified when $\Delta V = 0$; no volume change is associated with the reaction; the isothermal compressibility, $\chi_i = -\frac{1}{V}\left(\frac{\partial V}{\partial p}\right)_T$, is not affected by the reaction. The heat of reaction (5.2) is then equal to the change of internal energy ΔW.

---

[1] A. Einstein: Sitzg. Berlin. Akad. p. 380, 1920.
[2] K. F. Herzfeld and F. O. Rice: Phys. Rev. **31**, 691 (1928) and Herzfeld in [*17*].
[3] H. O. Kneser: Ann. Phys., Lpz. **11**, 761 (1931); **16**, 360 (1933); **32**, 277 (1938). — Phys. Z. **39**, 800 (1938) and [*12*].
[4] A. J. Rutgers: Ann. Phys., Lpz. **16**, 350 (1933).
[5] L. Landau and E. Teller: Phys. Z. Sowjet. **10**, 34 (1936).
[6] L. I. Mandelstam and M. A. Leontovich: J. exp. theor. Phys. URSS. **7**, 438 (1937).
[7] L. Hall: Phys. Rev. **73**, 775 (1948).
[8] S. R. de Groot: Thermodynamics of irreversible processes. New York 1951.
[9] J. J. Markham: J. Acoust. Soc. Amer. **22**, 628 (1950).
[10] J. Meixner: In Ref. [*5*]. — Acustica **2**, 101 (1952). — Z. angew. Phys. **6**, 215 (1953).
[11] See in Ref. [*13*] a systematic review of different treatments.
[12] O. Nomoto: J. Phys. Soc. Japan **11**, 848 (1946).

Such a case is that of relaxation due to the energy partition between external and internal degrees of freedom, and it has importance in polyatomic gases as well as in some types of unassociated liquids. The unassociated liquids (benzene, carbon tetrachloride, etc.) are characterised by the fact that the basic fluid units (particles) are individual molecules: they can be considered at times, in an approximate way, as very dense gases.

When sound waves travel through such a fluid, during compression the energy is taken by the molecules at first as kinetic energy in the direction of the wave and only afterwards it flows into the other degrees of freedom through the collision mechanism. In an analogous way during expansion, energy is taken at first from the translational degree in the direction of the wave. While few collisions are sufficient to reach the energy equipartition among translational degree and, in general, rotational degrees of freedom, many collisions are needed to change the energy distribution in the vibrational degrees: a relaxation time of appreciable value is bound to the energy equilibrium between the degrees which rapidly adjust to changes (translational + rotational), which we call external degrees, and the vibrational (internal) degrees.

The specific heat at constant volume C_v of the system is formed by a first part, C_e due to the external degrees of freedom and a second part, C_i, due to the internal degrees. The latter is a maximum for very slow changes of temperature and vanishes for very fast temperature variations. For slow processes

$$C_v = C_e + C_i. \tag{6.1}$$

Moreover let us distinguish between an external temperature (of translational degrees), T_{tr} and a temperature T_i, of the internal degrees of freedom and let us call $W_i(T_i)$ the energy in the vibrational modes for a temperature T_i; at equilibrium, $T_i = T_{\mathrm{tr}}$.

Let us suppose that only one vibrational mode is of interest in the phenomenon and that only two quantum states (1, 2) are of importance. The molecules are distributed between state 1 (vibration unexcited) and state 2 (vibration excited).

It is then possible to show[1] that for a reaction (5.1)

$$\frac{\partial W}{\partial t} = -\frac{1}{\tau}\left[W_i(T_i) - W_i(T_{\mathrm{tr}})\right] \tag{6.2}$$

where

$$\tau = \frac{1}{K_{12}^0 + K_{21}^0} \tag{6.3}$$

and K_{12}^0, K_{21}^0 are the equilibrium values of K_{12}, K_{21}.

Eq. (6.2) has the characteristic form of a relaxation equation and shows that when a deviation of W_i from the equilibrium value $W_i(T_{\mathrm{tr}})$ occurs, the variation in time of W_i is proportional to the deviation itself.

The time constant in (6.2) is the relaxation time (6.3). If, as is usually the case, for the energy of molecules in the two states (w_1, w_2) there holds the relation:

$$w_2 - w_1 \gg kT,$$

then it follows

$$\frac{K_{12}}{K_{21}} = \exp\left[-\frac{(w_2 - w_1)}{kT}\right] \ll 1,$$

and therefore $\tau \approx \frac{1}{K_{21}}$ (k is the Boltzmann constant); the relaxation time, is practically equal to the time needed for deexcitation of the vibrational mode through molecular collisions.

[1] See, for instance, K. F. HERZFELD's paper in: Thermodynamics and Physics of Matter. Princeton N. J. 1955.

For small temperature variations, it is always possible to write

$$W_1(T_i) - W_i(T_{tr}) = C_i(T_i - T_{tr}). \tag{6.4}$$

By using this relation, Eq. (6.2) gives:

$$\frac{\partial T_i}{\partial t} = -\frac{1}{\tau}(T_i - T_{tr}) \tag{6.5}$$

and for a periodic change of T_{tr}

$$T_i = \frac{T_{tr}}{1 + j\omega\tau}. \tag{6.6}$$

At the frequency $\omega/2\pi$ the contribution of the internal degrees to the specific heat C_v is given by:

$$C_{i\omega} = \frac{\partial W_i}{\partial T_{tr}} = \frac{\partial W_i}{\partial T_i}\frac{\partial T_i}{\partial T_{tr}} = C_i \frac{1}{1 + j\omega\tau}. \tag{6.7}$$

We are now able to calculate the sound velocity in the liquid under the specified conditions, without taking into account viscosity and heat conduction. The general expression, already mentioned (p. 278), for the velocity square in adiabatic processes can be written:

$$\frac{1}{[\boldsymbol{V}]^2} = \left(\frac{\partial p}{\partial \varrho}\right)_S^{-1} = \chi_{is}\,\varrho\,\frac{C_v}{C_p}. \tag{6.8}$$

The effect of relaxation in the energy distribution between internal and external degrees of freedom is shown only in the fact that the specific heat becomes frequency-dependent. According to our assumptions, χ_{is} does not vary during the process.

The velocity has a complex expression

$$\frac{1}{[\boldsymbol{V}]^2} = \left(\frac{1}{c} + j\frac{\alpha}{\omega}\right)^2 = \chi_{is}\,\varrho\,\frac{C_e + C_i\frac{1}{1 + j\omega\tau}}{\varDelta + C_e + C_i\frac{1}{1 + j\omega\tau}} \tag{6.9}$$

where

$$\varDelta = C_p - C_v.$$

7. Relaxation formulae for sound propagation. A detailed discussion of sound dispersion and absorption produced by relaxation phenomena according to Eq. (6.9) can be found in the treatment of these phenomena in gases. We limit ourselves to the main characteristics and give the more important formulae, without spending time in their derivation. The velocity given by Eq. (6.9) becomes real for either $\omega \to 0$ or $\omega \to \infty$

$$\left.\begin{aligned} \frac{1}{\boldsymbol{V}_0^2} &= \frac{1}{c_0^2} = \chi_{is}\,\varrho\,\frac{C_e + C_i}{\varDelta + C_e + C_i}, \\ \frac{1}{\boldsymbol{V}_\infty^2} &= \frac{1}{c_\infty^2} = \chi_{is}\,\varrho\,\frac{C_e}{\varDelta + C_e}. \end{aligned}\right\} \tag{7.1}$$

Let us call with KNESER [*12*]

$$\varepsilon = \frac{c_\infty^2 - c_0^2}{c_\infty^2} = \frac{C_i \varDelta}{C_v(C_e + \varDelta)} \tag{7.2}$$

and

$$\tau' = \tau\,\frac{C_e + \varDelta}{C_v + \varDelta} \tag{7.3}$$

slightly smaller than τ. For the dispersion one gets:

$$\left(\frac{c}{c_0}\right)^2 \approx \frac{1 + \omega^2\tau'^2}{1 + \omega^2\tau'^2(1 + \varepsilon)}. \tag{7.4}$$

Fig. 1a shows the behaviour of $(c/c_0)^2$ as function of $\log \omega$: the curve has an inflection point for

$$\omega_{\text{in}} = \frac{1}{\tau' \sqrt{1-\varepsilon}} \approx \frac{1}{\tau}. \tag{7.5}$$

The absorption coefficient produced by thermal relaxation is given by:

$$\alpha = \frac{1}{2} \frac{c}{c_0^2} \frac{\varepsilon \omega^2 \tau'}{1+\omega^2 \tau'^2}. \tag{7.6}$$

At very high frequencies $\left(\omega^2 \gg \frac{1}{\tau'^2}\right)$, α becomes independent of ω,

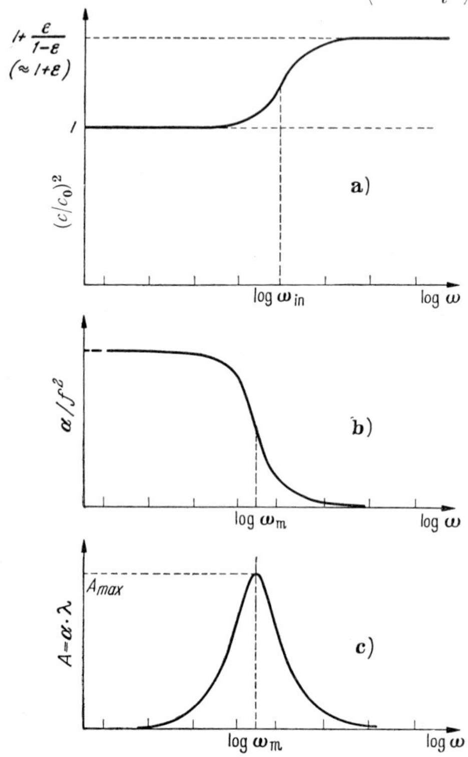

Fig. 1a—c Dispersion and absorption curves for a single relaxation process.

$$\alpha = \frac{1}{2} \frac{c}{c_0^2} \frac{\varepsilon}{\tau'}. \tag{7.7}$$

At low frequencies $\left(\omega^2 \ll \frac{1}{\tau'^2}\right)$:

$$\frac{\alpha}{f^2} = \frac{2\pi^2}{c_0} \varepsilon \tau' \tag{7.8}$$

the absorption coefficient is proportional to the frequency square as it is for the classical absorption coefficient [Eq. (3.1)]. Fig. 1b gives α/f^2 as function of $\log \omega$ through the relaxation frequency.

The absorption coefficient per wave-length is:

$$\left.\begin{aligned} A = \alpha \cdot \lambda = \frac{1}{2} \frac{c^2}{c_0^2} 2\pi \varepsilon \times \\ \times \frac{\omega \tau'}{1+\omega^2 \tau'^2} \approx \frac{\pi \varepsilon \omega \tau'}{1+\omega^2 \tau'^2} \end{aligned}\right\} \tag{7.9}$$

and it reaches a maximum:

$$A_{\max} \approx \frac{\pi \varepsilon}{2} \tag{7.10}$$

at

$$\omega = \omega_m = \frac{1}{\tau'}. \tag{7.11}$$

The height of the maximum of A depends through ε on the increase in velocity $(c_\infty^2 - c_0^2)$ produced by the process (Fig. 1c).

The preceding treatment has been made on the assumption that only one vibrational mode is involved and that only two quantum states are of importance. LANDAU and TELLER[1] have studied the case where more levels of the same mode, considered as a harmonic oscillator, are exited. They have shown that in this case all quantum states have the same relaxation time given by (6.3).

In the molecules, however, various vibrational modes may be present and excited at the same time. Apart from the question concerning the excitation mechanism of various modes (see relaxation in gases), the formulae given for dispersion and absorption have to be modified for the simultaneous presence of several relaxation processes having in general different relaxation times. The resulting formulas are very complex except for the case in which the relaxation times are very different (ratio bigger than 20) because in such a condition it is

[1] L. LANDAU and E. TELLER: Phys. Z. Sowjet. 10, 34 (1936).

possible to assume that each phenomenon happens independently of the others. When the relaxation times of different modes are of the same order of magnitude, the precision of measurement does not allow one to distinguish the small variations of dispersion and absorption curves which the exact formulas cause in comparison with those for a relaxation with only one characteristic time. It is customary in these cases, therefore, to apply the equations for only one relaxation time and derive from the comparison with experiment a mean relaxation time. In such a case the relaxing specific heat is given by the addition of the contributions of all vibration modes.

For diatomic molecules, the specific heat of the single vibrational mode is given by the Einstein relation:

$$C_i = R\left(\frac{\Delta w}{RT}\right)^2 \frac{\exp\left(-\frac{\Delta w}{RT}\right)}{\left[1-\exp\left(-\frac{\Delta w}{RT}\right)\right]^2} \tag{7.12}$$

where $\Delta w = h\nu$ is the quantum jump between levels and ν the fundamental frequency. In polyatomic molecules, the same expression can be used approximately for each mode. If, therefore, various modes are taking part in relaxation phenomena happening with the same (mean) relaxation time, the contribution of internal degrees to the specific heat, to be introduced in the relaxation equation, is

$$C_i = R\sum\left\{\left(\frac{\Delta w_j}{RT}\right)^2 \frac{\exp\left(-\frac{\Delta w_j}{RT}\right)}{\left[1-\exp\left(-\frac{\Delta w_j}{RT}\right)\right]^2}\right\} \tag{7.13}$$

where the summation with respect to the index j is to be extended to all vibration modes involved (independently of degeneracy).

8. Thermal relaxation due to slow chemical processes. The preceding treatment of thermal relaxation which we have given for the case of energy distribution among the degrees of freedom of molecules, remains valid without any alterations for the case in which inside the liquid there exists an equilibrium, as for a slow chemical process, that depends on temperature but whose change does not affect the volume: in this case the pressure variations produced by sound waves do not bear on the reaction and again $\Delta H = \Delta W$.

The formulae for thermal relaxation can be applied using a suitable expression of the equivalent specific heat involved in relaxation. When a slow chemical process is present in the liquid, it produces a measurable increase of the specific heat, because an increase in temperature shifts the equilibrium and this is accomplished with some heat absorption. If the reaction does not affect the number of particles, Eq. (5.1) is valid. At equilibrium

$$\frac{N_2^0}{N_1^0} = \frac{K_{12}^0}{K_{21}^0} = K = \exp\left(-\frac{\Delta H}{RT}\right), \tag{8.1}$$

where K is the equilibrium constant. Because $N_1^0 = N - N_2^0$,

$$\frac{N_2^0}{N} = \frac{K}{1+K}, \tag{8.2}$$

$$\frac{\partial N_2^0}{\partial T} = \frac{K}{(1+K)^2}\frac{\partial \log K}{\partial T} = N\frac{K}{(1+K)^2}\frac{\Delta H}{RT^2}. \tag{8.3}$$

In the last equation use has been made of the Van't Hoff relation

$$\frac{\partial \log K}{\partial T} = \frac{\Delta H}{RT^2}. \tag{8.4}$$

The equivalent specific heat is:

$$C_i' = \frac{\Delta H}{N}\frac{\partial N_2^0}{\partial T} = \mathsf{R}\left(\frac{\Delta H}{\mathsf{R}T}\right)^2 \frac{\exp\left(-\frac{\Delta H}{\mathsf{R}T}\right)}{\left[1-\exp\left(-\frac{\Delta H}{\mathsf{R}T}\right)\right]^2}. \tag{8.5}$$

The general case however is that in which the reaction does not leave the number of particles unchanged. For dissociation of double molecules, Eq. (5.1) is changed into

$$\frac{dN_2}{dt} = K_{12}(N_1+N_2)\,N_1 - K_{21}\,N_2^2 \tag{8.6}$$

where N_1 is the number of double molecules, and N_2 of single molecules. The expression of C_i' is then:

$$C_i' = \mathsf{R}\left(\frac{\Delta H}{2\,\mathsf{R}T}\right)^2 \frac{\exp\left(-\frac{\Delta H}{2\,\mathsf{R}T}\right)}{\left\{1+\left[\frac{1}{2}\exp\left(-\frac{\Delta H}{2\,\mathsf{R}T}\right)\right]^2\right\}^{\frac{3}{2}}}. \tag{8.7}$$

Recently E. FREEDMAN[1] and M. MANES[2] have considered a reaction of general form. According to FREEDMAN let us write the reaction in the following way:

$$\sum_{1=j}^{n} a_j\,A_j = 0, \tag{8.8}$$

where A_j are the components which enter into the reaction with stoichiometric coefficient a_j; a_j is positive if A_j is produced by the reaction and negative in the opposite case. It follows that

$$C_i' = D\,\mathsf{R}\left(\frac{\Delta H}{\mathsf{R}T}\right)^2 \tag{8.9}$$

where ΔH is the heat of reaction and

$$D = \left[\sum\left(\frac{a_j^2}{N_j}\right) - \frac{\sum a_j^2}{N}\right]^{-1}. \tag{8.10}$$

The relaxation time in this case can be expressed by:

$$\tau = \frac{D}{U} \tag{8.11}$$

where U is the equilibrium gross reaction rate which is supposed to be the same in forward and backward directions for small perturbations. FREEDMAN and MANES suggest the use of sound absorption to study the kinetics of very fast chemical reactions.

9. Compressional relaxation. A second and important kind of relaxation happens when the process in the liquid represented by reaction (5.1) is isothermal or unaffected by temperature changes. If the two states (1 and 2) have a different specific volume, pressure variation produced by sound waves becomes important: $\Delta H = p\,\Delta V$ [see Eq. (5.2)].

A characteristic example is that of water at 4° C. In this case the excess of experimental absorption coefficient over the classical one cannot be due to thermal relaxation, because the coefficient of thermal expansion (β_t) is zero and is (for a mole) $\Delta = C_p - C_v = \frac{\beta_t^2 T V}{\chi_{\mathrm{is}}}$: the adiabatic process of sound propagation

---

[1] E. FREEDMAN: J. Chem. Phys. **21**, 1784 (1953).
[2] M. MANES: J. Chem. Phys. **21**, 1791 (1953).

is isothermal at the same time. To explain the excess of absorption in water, P. DEBYE[1] (1939) suggested that structural changes which follow the pressure variations slowly might be present inside the liquid and originate relaxation losses.

L. HALL[2] developed such a theory for water assuming that the molecules can be in two states: (1) an open structure, roughly like the tetrahedral one of ice, with the oxygen atom at the centre and the two hydrogen atoms occupying two corners of the tetrahedron (the other corners being empty); (2) close packed structure.

According to HALL[3], state 1 has larger volume and lower free energy (W_1) and state 2 has smaller volume and higher energy (W_2).

The reaction equation is still (5.1), but the rate constants are functions of pressure. For small changes:

$$K = K^0 + (p - p_0)\frac{\partial K}{\partial p} \tag{9.1}$$

where K^0 is the equilibrium value.

The relaxation equation can be easily written:

$$-\frac{\partial N_2}{\partial t} = \frac{1}{\tau}(N_2 - N_2^0) - \frac{1}{\tau}\frac{\partial N_2^0}{\partial p}(p - p_0) \tag{9.2}$$

where N_2^0 is the equilibrium value of the number of molecules in state 2 and τ is given by:

$$\tau = \frac{1}{K_{12} + K_{21}}. \tag{9.3}$$

For a simple harmonic motion Eq. (9.2) becomes:

$$(N_2 - N_2^0) = \frac{1}{1 + j\omega\tau}\frac{\partial N_2^0}{\partial p}(p - p_0). \tag{9.4}$$

Using Van't Hoff's equation

$$\left[\frac{\partial}{\partial p}(\log K)\right]_T = \frac{\partial}{\partial p}\log\frac{N_2^0}{N_1^0} = -\frac{V_2 - V_1}{RT}, \tag{9.5}$$

one obtains

$$\frac{\partial N_2^0}{\partial p} = \frac{V_1 - V_2}{RT}\frac{N_2^0 N_1^0}{N} \tag{9.6}$$

and Eq. (9.4) is transformed into

$$\left.\begin{aligned}(N_2 - N_2^0) &= \frac{1}{1 + j\omega\tau}\frac{V_1 - V_2}{RT}\frac{N_2^0 N_1^0}{N}(p - p_0)\\ &= \frac{1}{1 + j\omega\tau}\frac{V_1 - V_2}{RT}N\frac{1}{2\left(1 + \operatorname{Cos}\frac{\Delta H}{RT}\right)}(p - p_0).\end{aligned}\right\} \tag{9.7}$$

In the last expression use has been made of

$$\frac{K_{12}^0}{K_{21}^0} = \frac{N_2^0}{N_1^0} = \exp\left(-\frac{\Delta H}{RT}\right). \tag{9.8}$$

[1] P. DEBYE: Z. Elektrochem. **45**, 174 (1939).

[2] L. HALL: Phys. Rev. **73**, 775 (1948).

[3] Recent research on the effect of pressure on sound absorption by T. A. LITOVITZ and E. H. CARNEVALE confirms for water the validity of a two-state theory, but contrary to HALL's assumption it seems to indicate the open structure as the higher energy state. It seems, moreover that the energy difference between the two states (equal to ΔH in the present case) depends on temperature. J. Appl. Phys. **26**, 816 (1955).

Let us now express the mole volume of the liquid as a function of $(p-p_0)$ and of the compressibilities χ_1, χ_2 of the two structural forms. If V_1, V_2 are the molecular volumes of the forms, and V that of the mixture, then

$$N V = N_1 V_1 [1 - \chi_1 (p - p_0)] + N_2 V_2 [1 - \chi_2 (p - p_0)]. \tag{9.9}$$

Neglecting quantities of second order, we find

$$V - V_0 = - V_0 \chi_\infty (p - p_0) + (V_2 - V_1) \frac{N_2 - N_2^0}{N} \tag{9.10}$$

where

$$\left.\begin{aligned} V_0 &= V_1 \frac{N_1^0}{N} + V_2 \frac{N_2^0}{N}, \\ V_0 \chi_\infty &= V_1 \chi_1 \frac{N_1^0}{N} + V_2 \chi_2 \frac{N_2^0}{N}. \end{aligned}\right\} \tag{9.11}$$

In the case of periodic variations of p, Eqs. (9.10) and (9.7) yield

$$(V - V_0) = - \left[V_0 \chi_\infty + \frac{(V_1 - V_2)^2}{RT} \frac{1}{2\left(1 + \operatorname{Cos} \frac{\Delta H}{RT}\right)} \frac{1}{1 + j\omega\tau} \right] (p - p_0). \tag{9.12}$$

The effective adiabatic (and isothermal) compressibility at frequency $\omega/2\pi$ can be written

$$\left.\begin{aligned} \chi_\omega &= - \frac{1}{V_0} \left(\frac{\partial V}{\partial p}\right)_T = \chi_\infty + \frac{\chi_r}{1 + j\omega\tau} \\ &= \chi_0 - \chi_r \frac{j\omega\tau}{1 + j\omega\tau} \end{aligned}\right\} \tag{9.13}$$

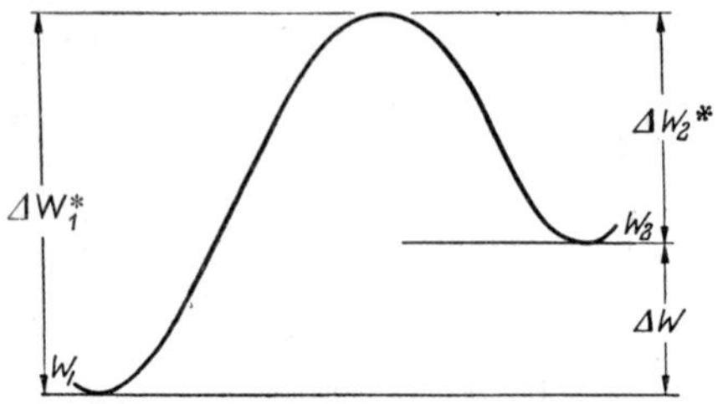

Fig. 2. Energy diagram for a two-state equilibrium.

where

$$\chi_r = \frac{(V_1 - V_2)^2}{V_0 RT} \frac{1}{2\left[1 + \operatorname{Cos} \frac{\Delta H}{RT}\right]} \tag{9.14}$$

is the relaxing component of compressibility and $\chi_0 = \chi_\infty + \chi_r$ the static value of adiabatic compressibility.

Eq. (9.3) for the relaxation time, can be modified using the following relations from the theory of absolute reaction rates

$$\left.\begin{aligned} K_{12} &= \frac{kT}{h} \exp\left(- \frac{\Delta W_1^*}{RT}\right), \\ K_{21} &= \frac{kT}{h} \exp\left(- \frac{\Delta W_2^*}{RT}\right) \end{aligned}\right\} \tag{9.15}$$

where ΔW_1^* and ΔW_2^* (Fig. 2) are the activation energies of the forward and backward reactions. It follows that

$$\tau = \frac{h}{kT} \frac{\exp \frac{\Delta W_1^*}{RT}}{1 + \exp \frac{\Delta H}{RT}}, \tag{9.16}$$

because $\Delta H = \Delta W$ in the present case.

The complex sound velocity in the liquid in which these relaxation process are present is given (neglecting viscosity and heat conduction) by

$$\frac{1}{[V]^2} = \left(\frac{1}{c} - j \frac{\alpha}{\omega}\right)^2 = \varrho \chi_\omega. \tag{9.17}$$

Neglecting α^2/ω^2 in comparison with $1/c^2$, there results the dispersion formula

$$\left(\frac{c}{c_0}\right)^2 \approx \frac{1+\omega^2\tau^2}{1+\omega^2\tau^2\left(1-\frac{\chi_r}{\chi_0}\right)}. \tag{9.18}$$

The absorption coefficient is:

$$\alpha = \frac{c}{2c_0^2}\,\frac{\chi_r}{\chi_0}\,\frac{\omega^2\tau}{1+\omega^2\tau^2}. \tag{9.19}$$

Eqs. (9.18) and (9.19) correspond to the analogous relations (7.4), (7.6) for thermal relaxation.

The relaxation times are usually very short (for water of the order of 10^{-12} sec) so that in general $c \approx c_0$ in the range of experiment and the following approximation is used for α:

$$\frac{\alpha}{f^2} = \frac{2\pi^2}{c_0}\,\frac{\chi_r}{\chi_0}\,\tau = \frac{2\pi^2}{c_0}\left(1-\frac{\chi_\infty}{\chi_0}\right)\tau. \tag{9.20}$$

The preceding treatment is essentially that followed by HALL to explain absorption in water.

A. GIERER and K. WIRTZ[1] have also treated the case of quasi-crystalline liquids where the relaxation phenomena are bound to volume changes. According to them the same disorders (holes) of the lattice which are present in the quasi-crystalline liquid and cause the lack of long distance order, are responsible for relaxation absorption as well as for fluidity.

The possibility that order is produced by compression is bound to a recombination of complementary disorders; this is a second order reaction. If the concentration of disorders is small the probability of recombination is also small and the life of a particular state of disorder as well as the associated relaxation time is large. Because the process which causes sound absorption is the same as that which causes fluidity, the relaxation time can be expressed through the viscosity coefficient. GIERER and WIRTZ give, for a cubic lattice:

$$\tau = \frac{V\eta}{2RT} \tag{9.21}$$

where V is the molecular volume. They calculate

$$\frac{\alpha}{f^2} = \pi^2 \varrho\, c\, \eta \left(\frac{d\ln\eta}{dp}\right)^2 N_H \tag{9.22}$$

where N_H is the concentration of disorders (holes) per particles

$$N_H = \exp\left(-\frac{\Delta W_H^*}{RT}\right) \tag{9.23}$$

and ΔW_H^* is the activation energy necessary to produce a hole.

10. Presence of various relaxation processes. Distribution of relaxation times. We have considered the typical cases of liquids in which the equilibrium originating the relaxation process was altered either by the temperature variations alone or by the pressure variations alone produced by sound waves. The more important cases belong to one of these two categories in the sense that the process of one of the two kinds is by far the more important one. In general however, it may happen that the equilibria existing inside the liquid are sensitive to both temperature and pressure variations; moreover various equilibria might be present which originate different relaxation processes. In the latter case, although, as we have already mentioned, the effects of different dissipative processes are not additive,

[1] A. GIERER and K. WIRTZ: Z. Naturforsch. 5a, 270 (1950).

it is customary to assume, in a first approximation, the validity of the superposition principle, if the characteristic frequencies of the relaxation phenomena are well separated. At times, however, the separation of different relaxation processes is not possible and it is necessary to admit the existence of a distribution of relaxation times. One should then develop formulae noticeably more complicated than the one obtained for a process with only one relaxation time; the advantage of these formulae is however, frequently questionable.

11. Relaxation and second viscosity coefficient. It has already been pointed out that classical hydrodynamics is unable to explain the body of experiments on sound dispersion and absorption in liquids, because it does not consider some aspects of the physical behaviour of particles: in particular it does not take into account the existence of equilibria either inside the molecules or among them which, after a disturbance, require a finite time to be re-established.

Hydrodynamics, however, may be changed to include these processes: we will then have a new way of presenting relaxation phenomena. This can be accomplished in different ways. One of them has already been mentioned and consists of : (1) considering the fluid as a mixture of at least two others, each having its particles in a well defined energy state: (2) developing a two fluid-mixture hydrodynamics.

Another way, simpler although more questionable, takes advantage of the existence of a second viscosity coefficient in the hydrodynamical equations and examines what assumptions are to be made to bring the theory into agreement with the experiment.

We have already discussed the reason why the validity of the superposition of various dissipative effects is assumed to a first approximation and it is costumary to calculate the absorption due to viscosity and heat conduction by means of the *classical* expression of the absorption coefficient, i.e. using the so called STOKES' *relation*

$$3\eta_B = 3\eta' + 2\eta = 0. \tag{11.1}$$

This relation, however, is correct only for monatomic gases, and it is simple to find its meaning in a general fluid. Writing down the equation of motion in hydrodynamics, it has been assumed that the stress tensor was a linear function of the rate of deformation, Eq. (1.4). The mean pressure is given by

$$p_m = -p_0 + (\tfrac{2}{3}\eta + \eta')\,\mathrm{div}\,\boldsymbol{u} \tag{11.2}$$

which, using the continuity equation for a fluid whose density does not vary from point to point, may be written:

$$p_m = -p_0 + \left(\frac{2}{3}\eta + \eta'\right)\frac{1}{\varrho}\frac{d\varrho}{dt}. \tag{11.3}$$

It is evident, therefore ,that the validity of STOKES' relation makes the pressure in the fluid depend only upon the instantaneous value of density through p_0 and not upon its derivative. When relaxation processes are present in a fluid this condition is obviously not satisfied and the pressure may depend on the recent and remote history of the fluid.

Rejection of STOKES' relation yields the Kirchhoff approximation, Eq. (2.8), for dispersion and absorption due to viscosity and heat conduction. There is no dispersion while the absorption coefficient is proportional to the square of the frequency and the formula involves the addition of two terms (neglecting heat conduction):

$$\alpha = \frac{\omega^2}{2\varrho_0 c^3}(2\eta + \eta') = \frac{\omega^2}{2\varrho_0 c^3}\left[\frac{4}{3}\eta + \eta_B\right]. \tag{11.4}$$

The first term is the one given when STOKES' relation is valid. The second term has the same frequency characteristics as the absorption coefficient due to relaxation provided $\omega \ll \frac{1}{\tau}$: Eq. (7.8) and (9.20).

As was pointed out by L. TISZA[1] the hydrodynamical equations are formally able to describe the behaviour of a real fluid if the frequency of the sound waves is much smaller than the relaxation frequency, i.e., in the low frequency range the pressure inside the fluid is sufficiently well determined by the consideration of the recent history of the fluid given by the first derivative of density.

Equating the expression for the absorption coefficient due to η_B according to (11.4) with those given by the relaxation processes [Eqs. (7.8), (9.20)] one could calculate η_B and η'[2]. In liquids η_B would be larger than η from twofold to hundreds of times.

Much discussion has taken place and is still pending on the correctness and the meaning of this calculation as well as on the possibility of the existence of a bulk viscosity independent of relaxation processes.

Unfortunately up to now, no method has been found for an independent measurement of η' in liquids. The coefficient comes into play only in those motions in which div $\boldsymbol{u}$ differs from zero. It enters into acoustical streaming, a second order effect of wave propagation. C. ECKART[3] studied the steady flow caused by the radiation pressure gradient which occurs as a consequence of absorption of plane sound waves into the liquid and from his calculation it was hoped to find an independent way to determine the ratio η'/η by means of streaming measurements in tubes. The measurements performed by L. N. LIEBERMANN[4] and confirmed by A. CARRELLI and F. CENNAMO[5] seemed to indicate an agreement between the values of η' calculated in this way and those obtained assigning to a bulk viscosity coefficient all the excess of the measured absorption coefficient. The interpretation of the results of these measurements was soon questioned. FOX and HERZFELD[6] pointed out from considerations of acoustic momentum that the velocity of streaming depends upon the total absorption in the liquid which produces the radiation pressure gradient and not upon any selected mechanism of absorption as resulted from ECKART's calculations; in consequence, the velocity of streaming depends upon η' only through α and measurements of streaming velocity do not provide an independent determination of η'. The same conclusions were reached in different ways also by W. L. NYBORG[7] and J. E. PIERCY and J. LAMB[8]. It is therefore commonly agreed that the two measurements, acoustical streaming and sound absorption, do not give independent information and that LIEBERMANN's results cannot be used to show the existence of a bulk viscosity which would explain the largest part of the observed sound absorption, apart from relaxation processes. The problems concerning bulk viscosity need much further theoretical work in order to be clarified.

The possibility, however, of a hydrodynamical explanation of the experiments at least in a formal way, by means of a coefficient of bulk viscosity different

[1] L. TISZA: Phys. Rev. **61**, 531 (1942).
[2] Compressional viscosity as introduced in visco-elastic theory is equivalent to η_B.
[3] C. ECKART: Phys. Rev. **73**, 68 (1948).
[4] L. N. LIEBERMANN: Phys. Rev. **75**, 1415 (1949).
[5] A. CARRELLI and F. CENNAMO: Nuovo Cim., Ser. IX **11**, 429 (1954); Ser. IX **12**, 1 (1954); Ser. X **1**, 365 (1955).
[6] F. E. FOX and K. F. HERZFELD: Phys. Rev. **78**, 156 (1950).
[7] W. L. NYBORG: J. Acoust. Soc. Amer. **25**, 68 (1953).
[8] J. E. PIERCY and J. LAMB: Proc. Roy. Soc. Lond., Ser. A **226**, 43 (1954).

from zero (or of a suitable value of η') as suggested by TISZA, only exists if $\omega \ll \frac{1}{\tau}$ without changing the basic assumption of hydrodynamics. For frequencies near that of relaxation, α is no more proportional to ω^2 and dispersion beginns. One could think that in such a case the pressure inside the fluid depends not only on the recent but also on the remote history of the fluid and this circumstance is not sufficiently taken into account by the first derivative of density. According to TISZA one may proceed as in optics and consider η_B as a complex function of frequency. In a formal way this is satisfactory because putting $\eta_B = \eta_{Br} + j\eta_{Bi}$ it is easy to see that, together with an absorption coefficient which depends upon η_{Br}, there is a dispersion depending on η_{Bi}. Equating the expressions obtained for dispersion and absorption coefficient in this way with those given by relaxation theories, one would determine the frequency dependence of η_{Br} and η_{Bi}.

This procedure, however, has received much criticism. One question frequently asked is why one should choose to make η_B complex and frequency dependent instead of both η and η'.

Although many questions still remain to be satisfactorily answered, some authors use the second and bulk viscosity coefficients in discussion of results of sound absorption measurements in liquids. Sometimes a frequency dependence of η is considered together with that of η_B.

In visco-elastic theory the same problems will be considered from a somewhat different point of view.

III. Visco-elasticity.

12. Visco-elastic theory. Theoretical investigation of the liquid state is made extremely difficult by the fact that liquids posses properties which are characteristic of both gases and solids which sometimes seem contradictory. Moreover, contrary to what happens in gases and solids, these properties can vary from case to case in a wide range. It is therefore difficult to give a general definition of a liquid and theoretical treatments sometimes consider liquids as very dense gases, sometimes as solid substances for which the long distance order has been destroyed.

Studying sound propagation in liquids in the preceding sections, we have considered the classical hydrodynamical equations and the modifications needed to account for relaxation. In classical hydrodynamics, liquids are treated in the same way as gases and their viscosity is thought of as originated by processes of dissipation of energy and momentum.

Sometimes, however, as for instance when one investigates sound propagation in liquids in the transition region to amorphous solids, it is necessary to take into account their solid-like nature. This is done by the visco-elastic theories. The fundamental theory was developed by J. FRENKEL[1]. Other contributions were made by W. P. MASON and coworkers[2], HOFF LU[3], R. S. MARVIN, R. ALDRICH and H. S. SACK[4], T. A. LITOVITZ and T. LYON[5]. We start by mentioning that, as can be seen in sound propagation theory in solids, the equation governing the propagation of irrotational waves along the axis x_1 in an ordinary elastic

[1] J. FRENKEL: Kinetic theory of liquids. Oxford 1946.

[2] W. P. MASON, W. O. BAKER, H. J. MCSKIMIN and J. H. HEISS: Phys. Rev. **73**, 1074 (1948).

[3] HOFF LU: J. Acoust. Soc. Amer. **23**, 12 (1951).

[4] R. S. MARVIN, R. A. ALDRICH and H. S. SACK: J. Appl. Phys. **25**, 1213 (1954).

[5] T. A. LITOVITZ and T. LYON: J. Appl. Phys. **27**, 179 (1956).

material, can be put in the form:

$$\varrho \frac{\partial^2 \xi_1}{\partial t^2} = \left(\boldsymbol{K} + \frac{4}{3}\,\boldsymbol{G}\right) \frac{\partial^2 \xi_1}{\partial x_1^2} \tag{12.1}$$

where ξ are the displacements, $\boldsymbol{K}$ and $\boldsymbol{G}$ the bulk and shear moduli defined by means of strain and stress tensors as follows. The strain tensor has components

$$\varepsilon_{ij} = \frac{1}{2}\left(\frac{\partial \xi_i}{\partial x_j} + \frac{\partial \xi_j}{\partial x_i}\right). \tag{12.2}$$

The normal stress, σ, and strain, ε, are given by

$$\left.\begin{aligned} \sigma &= \tfrac{1}{3}\sum_{1}^{3} \sigma_{jj}\,, \\ \varepsilon &= \tfrac{1}{3}\sum_{1}^{3} \varepsilon_{jj} \end{aligned}\right\} \tag{12.3}$$

and the deviatoric stress and strain tensor are:

$$\left.\begin{aligned} \sigma_{ij}^* &= \sigma_{ij} - \delta_{ij}\,\sigma\,, \\ \varepsilon_{ij}^* &= \varepsilon_{ij} - \delta_{ij}\,\varepsilon \end{aligned}\right\} \tag{12.4}$$

where δ is the Kronecker symbol. The definitions for $\boldsymbol{K}$ and $\boldsymbol{G}$ are then:

$$\boldsymbol{K} = \frac{\sigma}{3\,\varepsilon}\,, \tag{12.5}$$

$$\boldsymbol{G} = \frac{\sigma_{ij}^*}{2\,\varepsilon_{ij}^*}\,. \tag{12.6}$$

The propagation velocity of sound waves is given in a material of this kind, according to (12.1), by

$$[\boldsymbol{V}]^2 = \frac{\boldsymbol{K} + \frac{4}{3}\,\boldsymbol{G}}{\varrho}\,. \tag{12.7}$$

13. Visco-elastic liquid under shearing stress. Any theory which considers the liquid state as a solidlike state must furnish a determination of $\boldsymbol{K}$ and $\boldsymbol{G}$ to be introduced in (12.7) to find the expressions for phase velocity and for the absorption coefficient of sound waves. It is therefore necessary to characterize the behaviour of liquids when a compression takes place or a shear stress is applied. We shall consider the second kind of event first.

According to FRENKEL the atoms or the molecules in a liquid body vibrate around equilibrium positions as in solids, although the equilibrium positions are not permanent, in the sense that each atom or molecule during a large number of oscillations can accumulate enough energy to pass into an adjacent equilibrium position momentarily empty. In order to jump, the molecule must have an activation energy to overcome the potential barrier due to the surrounding particles. Each atom or molecule will therefore stay an average time, τ, around the same position to build up the required energy. When no force is applied on the system, the atoms or molecules jump in all directions and no macroscopic flow is observed.

A system of this kind behaves differently when a force is acting upon it according to the duration of the action: if this time is much smaller than the average life-time τ of particles in a position, the body behaves as an elastic solid; if instead it is larger than τ the effect of the force will be to make the jumps of atoms (or molecules) easier in the direction of the applied force and flow is produced. From this point of view it is evident that the system combines the properties of an idealized elastic solid and those of an idealized viscous fluid.

When a shearing stress p_{ij} is applied to a layer of the liquid an elastic strain and a viscous flow (in i direction) are produced. The motion is desribed by the Maxwell phenomenological equation, which express that the velocity $\boldsymbol{u}$ of the molecules of the layer is the sum of the velocity of elastic displacement and of the velocity of viscous flow:

$$\frac{\partial u_i}{\partial x_j} = \frac{1}{G}\frac{d p_{ij}}{dt} + \frac{1}{\eta} p_{ij} \tag{13.1}$$

where G is the rigidity modulus. Eq. (13.1) is a relaxation equation in which viscosity and rigidity are intimately connected. If the velocity variation is suddenly stopped the stress neither stays constant as in solids, nor vanishes at once as in classical fluids, but it goes exponentially to zero with a time constant (Maxwell or shear relaxation time):

$$\tau_S = \eta / G. \tag{13.2}$$

If the shearing stress is alternating the motion is essentially a viscous flow if $\omega \ll \frac{1}{\tau_S}$, or it is an elastic vibration if $\omega \gg \frac{1}{\tau_S}$.

According to this theory, liquids possess a shear elasticity whose effects are masked for most liquids by the low values of η, but become evident when the viscosity is large enough.

Eq. (13.1) may be written in a general form, using the strain (ε^*_{ij}) and stress ($\sigma^*_{ij} = p^*_{ij}$) tensors,

$$p^*_{ij} + \tau_S \dot{p}^*_{ij} = 2G\,\tau_S\,\dot{\varepsilon}^*_{ij}. \tag{13.3}$$

If a sinusoidal stress is applied (13.3) changes into

$$p^*_{ij}(1 + j\,\omega\,\tau_S) = j\,2G\,\tau_S\,\omega\,\varepsilon^*_{ij}. \tag{13.4}$$

According to (12.6) the shear modulus for the case of a solid-like liquid is given by:

$$\boldsymbol{G} = \frac{p^*_{ij}}{2\varepsilon^*_{ij}} = G\frac{1}{1+\dfrac{1}{j\,\omega\,\tau_S}} = G\frac{\omega^2\tau_S^2}{1+\omega^2\tau_S^2} + j\,G\frac{\omega\,\tau_S}{1+\omega^2\tau_S^2} \tag{13.5}$$

and is complex. The coefficient of the imaginary part is the frequency-dependent shear viscosity which at low frequencies reduces to the normal shear viscosity $\eta = G\tau_S$. In the following discussion (Sect. 15) τ_S will be indicated as τ_1.

14. Visco-elastic liquid under compressional stress. Turning now to the determination of the bulk modulus, it has to be observed that when a solid-like liquid is compressed (or expanded) two effects take place which contribute to the value of $\boldsymbol{K}$: (1) the average distances among atoms (or molecules) are slightly and uniformly changed as in solids; (2) the particles may pass to a more closely packed arrangement during compression and to a more open structure during expansion. The former process is relatively rapid and it can be considered instantaneous and in phase with the applied pressure. The latter instead involves jumps of molecules or parts of molecules from one position to another across potential barriers which stabilize the equilibrium configurations and it therefore requires an activation energy and consequently a finite time, so that in general the change of degree of order lags considerably behind the applied pressure. In the case of monatomic liquids the rearrangement of molecules may only consist in their passage from a structure of approximately packed spheres to another more losely packed of the same kind, and the time needed must coincide with the average life-time of molecules in one equilibrium position, i.e. with the time which determines the ordinary viscosity. In other liquids the structures before and after compression may differ widely and the time lag cannot coincide with that which characterizes first viscosity. It is evident that this description of the phenomenon is the same that has been used for the treatment of compressional relaxation (HALL). It is now used in a more general way and, as will be seen, the present treatment may include also those effects which have been previously described by means of thermal relaxation.

In order to find a relation between stress and strain allowing to calculate the bulk modulus let us suppose that a variation of the volume of a liquid mass is produced; as J. FRENKEL shows the corresponding variation of pressure is formed by two parts:

$$p = p_1 + p_2. \tag{14.1}$$

The first part, p_1, is the equilibrium pressure which would be established in the case of very slow variations of volume. It is given by

$$p_1 = -K_1 s \tag{14.2}$$

where K_1 is the static compressional modulus and $s = \frac{\Delta V}{V} = 3\varepsilon$ is the fractional condensation.

The second part, p_2, is the deviation of pressure from the equilibrium value due to the non-equilibrium degree of order. For p_2, FRENKEL establishes the relation:

$$-\frac{ds}{dt} = \frac{1}{K^2}\frac{dp_2}{dt} + \frac{1}{\eta_2} p_2. \tag{14.3}$$

This is a relaxation equation; the relaxation time is:

$$\tau_2 = \frac{1}{K_2}\eta_2. \tag{14.4}$$

K_2 and η_2 respectively have the dimensions of a modulus of compressibility and of a viscosity coefficient which FRENKEL specifies as deviation modulus and deviation volume viscosity. $\eta_2 = \eta_c$ however is usually referred to as volume or compressional viscosity. Its relation to bulk viscosity as introduced in hydrodynamics will soon be seen.

If we consider a periodic variation, Eqs. (14.1), (14.2), (14.3) yield:

$$p = -\left[K_1 + K_2 \frac{1}{1 + \frac{1}{j\omega\tau_2}}\right] s \tag{14.5}$$

and the effective bulk modulus [Eq. (12.5)] is complex:

$$\boldsymbol{K} = \frac{\sigma}{3\varepsilon} = \frac{-p}{s} = K_1 + K_2 \frac{\omega^2\tau_2^2}{1+\omega^2\tau_2^2} + j K_2 \frac{\omega\tau_2}{1+\omega^2\tau_2^2}. \tag{14.6}$$

At very low and very high frequencies the modulus becomes real and equal to $\boldsymbol{K}_0 = K_1$; $\boldsymbol{K}_\infty = K_1 + K_2$.

Although the preceding treatment has been carried out for the case in which the local order which is altered is connected with the existence of structures having different specific volumes, it may be extended to the case in which compression or expansion alters the energy distribution between external and internal degrees of freedom (thermal relaxation). In this case the difference between temperatures of internal and external degrees of freedom of molecules is the parameter which characterizes the deviation of the system from equilibrium. FRENKEL calculated the expression of K_2 to be introduced in (14.6) to obtain the value of $\boldsymbol{K}$, while K_1 is the adiabatic static modulus of compressibility $K_1 = \frac{C_p}{C_v} K_0$ (K_0, isothermal modulus of compressibility). The expression for K_2 is:

$$K_2 = K_0 \frac{C_p - C_v}{C_v} \frac{C_i}{C_e}. \tag{14.7}$$

The associated relaxation time is τ_2 and the corresponding viscosity coefficient $\eta_2 = K_2 \tau_2$.

15. Sound propagation in a visco-elastic liquid. The preceding calculations give the expression of bulk (14.6) and shear (13.5) moduli to be introduced into Eq. (12.7) to find the phase velocity and the absorption coefficient of sound waves in a visco-elastic liquid.

In the general case $\tau_1 \neq \tau_2$. The visco-elastic theory however, has been applied essentially to the study of the behaviour of associated liquids in the region of high viscosity. In these liquids, the process responsible for K_2 is intimately coupled with the flow process and there are many indications in favour of the hypothesis $\tau_1 = \tau_2$. The latter is usually assumed to hold in a first approximation. Then the calculation of velocity and absorption coefficient is simplified.

Putting:

$$\frac{1}{[\boldsymbol{V}]^2} = \left(\frac{1}{c} - j\frac{\alpha}{\omega}\right)^2 \tag{15.1}$$

and assuming $\frac{\omega^2}{c^2} \gg \alpha^2$,

$$[\boldsymbol{V}]^2 \approx c^2 + j\, 2\alpha \frac{c^3}{\omega} = \frac{1}{\varrho}\left[K_1 + \left(K_2 + \frac{4}{3} G\right) \frac{1}{1 + \frac{1}{j\,\omega\,\tau}}\right]. \tag{15.2}$$

The velocity is given by:

$$c^2 = \frac{1}{\varrho}\left[K_1 + \left(K_2 + \frac{4}{3} G\right) \frac{\omega^2 \tau^2}{1 + \omega^2 \tau^2}\right]. \tag{15.3}$$

The low and high frequency velocities are:

$$c_0^2 = \frac{K_1}{\varrho}, \qquad c_\infty^2 = \frac{1}{\varrho}\left[K_1 + K_2 + \frac{4}{3} G\right]. \tag{15.4}$$

The absorption coefficient can be expressed in the form

$$\alpha = \frac{1}{2\varrho c^3}\left(K_2 + \frac{4}{3} G\right) \frac{\omega^2 \tau}{1 + \omega^2 \tau^2}, \tag{15.5}$$

equivalent to (9.19). At low frequencies, $\omega^2 \tau^2 \ll 1$,

$$\alpha = \frac{2\pi^2 f^2}{\varrho c_0^3}\left(\frac{4}{3} G + K_2\right)\tau \tag{15.6}$$

and, using (13.2) and (14.4),

$$\alpha = \frac{2\pi^2 f^2}{\varrho c_0^3}\left(\frac{4}{3}\eta + \eta_c\right). \tag{15.7}$$

This is equivalent to the expression (11.4) given by hydrodynamics, if the STOKES' relation is rejected. Use is here made of the compressional viscosity introduced by the visco-elastic theory. The comparison of (15.7) and (11.4) shows that, in the case where the assumption $\tau_1 = \tau_2$ is valid, the compressional viscosity of the visco-elastic theory, takes the place of the bulk viscosity of the hydrodynamical theories.

Comparison of (15.3) and (15.5) with experiments performed on associated liquids, as will be seen in Part B below (Sect. 25), is not entirely satisfactory. The absorption coefficient per wavelength plotted as function of $\log \omega$ gives a curve whose maximum is smaller than the theoretical value. Moreover the bell-shaped curve is broader than expected in the case of only one relaxation time and it is asymmetrical about the maximum. This disagreement cannot be removed by making $\tau_1 \neq \tau_2$. For this reason, and because there are some indications in favour of it, the assumption $\tau_1 = \tau_2$ is generally maintained.

W. P. MASON and coworkers[1] suggested that in these cases losses of a hysteresis type might exist together with relaxation processes which they assumed to have only one relaxation time. These losses would be produced by a stress-strain curve having the shape of a hysteresis loop. To represent these losses it is necessary to introduce an imaginary component of the elastic constant. The losses per cycle produced by the process are independent of frequency and therefore the absorption coefficient α at high frequencies (or at high viscosities) simply becomes proportional to the frequency. Such a process is able to explain the observed asymmetry of the curve of the absorption coefficient per wavelength. It does not explain, however, the experimental value of the maximum absorption per wavelength which, sometimes, is appreciably smaller than the theoretical one[2].

Another way to explain the experiments is that of assuming the existence of a distribution of relaxation times for both shear and compressional processes. A justification of the presence of a wide distribution of relaxation times can also be found in connection with the mechanism followed by molecules of a solid-like liquid to rearrange themselves when a stress is applied. They have to jump from one position to another across potential barriers which depend on the position of the neighboring molecules. According to FRENKEL the time that a molecule must wait in one position before jumping is coupled with the activation energy required, ΔW^*, by the relation

$$\tau = A \exp\left(\frac{\Delta W^*}{kT}\right), \tag{15.8}$$

where A is a constant related to the oscillation frequency in the potential well. Each molecule in the liquid may find itself in a great variety of configurations with respect to the surrounding molecules; to each configuration there corresponds a stabilizing potential and a value of activation energy. It seems, therefore, obvious that to this distribution of activation energies, there should correspond a wide distribution of relaxation times. T. A. LITOVITZ and T. LYON[3] have derived an expression for the complex modulus assuming a uniform distribution of activitation energies in the liquid between two values ΔW_1 and ΔW_2. The comparison with experiments in n-propyl alcohol seem, however, to suggest that, at least in this case, the distribution of activation energy is actually antisymmetric towards smaller values of ΔW.

IV. Special effects.

16. Shear waves in liquids. In some cases, it is possible to generate transverse, or shear, waves in liquids. The experimental investigation is difficult because they are usually strongly attenuated; when it is possible to do the experiments however they furnish useful information on the properties of liquids.

[1] W. P. MASON, W. O. BARKER, H. J. MCSKIMIN and J. H. HEISS: Phys. Rev. **73**, 1074 (1948).

[2] See for instance T. A. LITOVITZ and T. LYON: J. Appl. Phys. **27**, 179 (1956).

[3] T. A. LITOVITZ and T. LYON: J. Appl. Phys. **27**, 179 (1956).

The characteristics of such type of waves can be easily established by means of visco-elastic theory. The propagation of transverse waves in solids is regulated by the equation:

$$\varrho \frac{\partial^2 \xi}{\partial t^2} = \boldsymbol{G} \frac{\partial^2 \xi}{\partial x_3^2} \tag{16.1}$$

where ξ is the displacement perpendicular to the direction of propagation x_3. The velocity of propagation is:

$$[\boldsymbol{V}_t]^2 = \frac{\boldsymbol{G}}{\varrho}. \tag{16.2}$$

For visco-elastic materials, the same relation holds provided expression (13.5) is used for $\boldsymbol{G}$:

$$[\boldsymbol{V}_t]^2 = \frac{G}{\varrho} \frac{1}{1 + \frac{1}{j\omega\tau_S}}. \tag{16.3}$$

From (16.3) it is possible to calculate the phase velocity c_{tr} and the absorption coefficient α_{tr} putting

$$\frac{1}{[\boldsymbol{V}]^2} = \left(\frac{1}{c_{\mathrm{tr}}} - j\frac{\alpha_{\mathrm{tr}}}{\omega}\right)^2. \tag{16.4}$$

In the present case the absorption coefficient can be very high so that in general it is not possible to neglect α_{tr}^2 with respect to $\omega^2/c_{\mathrm{tr}}^2$. The general formulae therefore are complicated. It may be seen, however that if $\omega\tau_S \ll 1$ (i.e. liquids of low viscosity at moderate frequencies), the absorption coefficient per wavelength is so high that it is hardly possible to speak of propagation. If instead $\omega\tau_S \gg 1$, i.e. in solid-like substances having high viscosity at high frequencies, the absorption coefficient per wavelength may be very low and the velocity to a first approximation is given as in solids by:

$$c_{\mathrm{tr}} = \sqrt{\frac{G}{\varrho}}. \tag{16.5}$$

The last result can be easily obtained assuming that $\alpha_{\mathrm{tr}} \ll \frac{\omega}{c_{\mathrm{tr}}}$. Then

$$c_{\mathrm{tr}}^2 = \frac{G}{\varrho} \frac{\omega^2 \tau_S^2}{1 + \omega^2 \tau_S^2} \tag{16.6}$$

which for $\omega^2 \tau_S^2 \gg 1$ gives (16.5). For the absorption coefficient there holds

$$\alpha_{\mathrm{tr}} = \frac{G}{2\varrho c_{\mathrm{tr}}^3} \frac{\omega^2 \tau_S}{1 + \omega^2 \tau_S^2} \tag{16.7}$$

from which, for $\omega\tau_S \gg 1$,

$$\alpha_{\mathrm{tr}} \cdot \lambda = \frac{\pi}{\omega\tau_S} = \frac{\pi}{\omega} \frac{G}{\eta}. \tag{16.8}$$

According to (16.8) the absorption per wavelength in this case is inversely proportional to the viscosity coefficient.

Transverse or shear waves in liquids may be generated by cylindrical crystal vibrating in a purely torsional mode or by quartz crystals cut in a suitable manner. In ordinary liquids, as has been mentioned, the shear waves are so highly attenuated that it is impossible to investigate the properties of propagation directly; when generated, however, they alter the electric parameters of the source. It is then possible to get information on the properties of the shear waves generated from the measurements of the loading effect, i.e. increase of resonant resistance and decrease of the resonant frequency of the radiator when the medium changes from vacuum to the liquid under examination.

17. Absorption due to other sources. At the end of this theoretical review of the various sources of sound losses it is to be mentioned that in particular cases, other losses are to be considered. It is usually assumed that, to a first approximation, the superposition principle is valid also for the absorption coefficients produced by these processes.

R. LUCAS[1] has calculated the sound absorption coefficient due to energy diffusion (scattering) when volume elements of compressibility χ' are dispersed in a liquid of compressibility χ. If N is the concentration of heterogeneous nuclei, supposed spherical and or radius r,

$$\alpha = \frac{2\pi}{9}\,\omega^4 N \frac{r^6}{c^4}\left(\frac{\chi'-\chi}{\chi}\right)^2, \qquad (17.1)$$

i.e. the absorption coefficient is proportional to the fourth power of the frequency.

P. S. EPSTEIN[2] and his coworker R. R. CARHART[3] have studied the case in which viscous fluid particles are suspended in a liquid taking into account also the losses due to thermal conduction.

The case in which solid particles are suspended has been treated by various authors by assuming the particles either rigid or elastic[4]. The consideration of suspensions exceeds the limits of the present paper. We will only quote a few papers dealing with this subject[5].

In all preceding treatments we have assumed that the sound waves are of small amplitude. Additional losses are present if this condition is not satisfied. Work concerning the propagation of large amplitude sound waves has been done by various authors[6]. R. LUCAS[7] has studied the additional losses due viscosity when there are density fluctuations in the liquid.

B. Experimental results on dispersion and absorption of sound in liquids and liquid mixtures.

I. Outline of experimental methods.

18. Principal methods for sound velocity measurements. A short review of the principal methods used at present for sound velocity and absorption coefficient measurements will be given before dicussing the experimental results.

We shall not describe in detail the various methods because this is done in Part 2 of this volume[8].

---

[1] R. LUCAS: C. R. Acad. Sci., Paris **201**, 1107 (1935); **203**, 459, 611 (1936). — J. Phys. Radium **8**, 41 (1937).

[2] P. S. EPSTEIN and THEODORE VON KARMAN: Anniversary Volume, of the California Inst. Techn., Pasadena 1941.

[3] P. S. EPSTEIN and R. R. CARHART: J. Acoust. Soc. Amer. **25**, 553 (1953).

[4] C. J. T. SEWELL: Phil. Trans. Roy. Soc. Lond., Ser. A **210**, 239 (1910). — H. LAMB: Hydrodynamics. New York 1945. — P. S. EPSTEIN and THEODORE VON KARMAN: Anniversary Volume of the California Inst. Techn., Pasadena 1941.

[5] S. RYTOV, V. VLADIMINSKI and M. GALANIN: Ž. eksp. teor. Fiz. **8**, 614 (1938). — V. VLADIMINSKI and M. GALANIN: Ž. eksp. teor. Fiz. **9**, 233 (1939). — G. K. HARTMANN and A. B. FOCKE: Phys. Rev. teor. Fiz. **57**, 221 (1940). — R. J. URICK: J. Acoust. Soc. Amer. **20**, 283 (1948). — V. J. STAKUTIS, R. W. MORSE, M. DILL and R. T. BEYER: J. Acoust. Soc. Amer. **27**, 539 (1955).

[6] P. BIQUARD: Ann. Phys. Paris **6**, 195 (1936). — F. E. FOX [*8*]. — F. E. FOX and W. A. WALLACE: J. Acoust. Soc. Amer. **26**, 994 (1954). — J. S. MENDOUSSE: J. Acoust. Soc. Amer. **25**, 5 (1953). — S. M. TOWLE and R. B. LINDSAY: J. Acoust. Soc. Amer. **27**, 530 (1955).

[7] R. LUCAS: C. R. Acad. Sci., Paris **203**, 459 (1036).— J. Phys. Radium **8**, 41 (1937).

[8] See also [*1*], [*11*], [*20*] where extensive information and reference to original papers may be found.

The measurements of sound velocity can be done by methods which are based on determination of the remaining quantities which appear in one of the two equations

$$c = \frac{l}{t}, \tag{18.1}$$

$$c = \lambda \cdot f, \tag{18.2}$$

where l is the displacement of the wave front in the time t. The methods of the first category [Eq. (18.1)] are called direct, the others indirect.

The indirect methods give the higher precision and for a long time they have been those exclusively employed: only the use of pulse systems has allowed measurements of satisfactory precision by means of direct methods.

The first indirect method is that of the interferometer in which standing waves are produced in the liquid between the source and a reflector: movements of the reflector by half wavelengths allow the determination of λ. The detection of the positions of the reflector at which the formation or the destruction of standing waves occurs is usually made by means of the current in the high frequency circuit of the source. When the reflector is moved the reaction of the fluid column between source and reflector changes periodically and this can produce periodic variations of the impedance of the source and of the electric current in the high-frequency circuit. Very important for the precision of the method is the parallelism between source and reflector. This method studied by PIERCE[1], HUBBARD[2], FOX[3], HERZFELD[4] and many other has been extensively used with many modifications and gives a precision of the order of $1^0/_{00}$. It is particularly useful for measurements at temperatutes and pressures far from those of the room. The highest frequencies used are in the megacycle range.

The diffraction of light produced by a system of plane sound waves has originated various optical methods for the measurement of velocity. The first one is based on the measurement of the angle of deviation of the light diffracted in the n-th order spectrum:

$$\sin \varphi_n = \frac{n\Lambda}{\lambda}$$

where Λ and λ are the wavelenghts respectively of light and sound. Usually a photograph of the spectra is taken and the distances between the diffraction spectra are measured on it. The precision may reach 1 to $2^0/_{00}$. An advantage of this method is that it may be used also at relatively high frequencies.

Another optical method is that of secondary interference: in this case the optical disposition is such that the image of a standing wave system between source and reflector is observed on a screen as a system of parallel lines whose separation corresponds to $\lambda/2$. By moving the vessel with a micrometer screw it is possible to observe the shift of the lines on the screen and to determine λ. The precision of the method can reach $0{,}1^0/_{00}$.

Such accuracy can be obtained also in an interferometer developed by A. BARONE[5] which can be used with opaque liquids. In this case an auxiliary liquid is used where the interference of two systems of plane waves takes place. The acoustical interference is made visible by means of an optical method; one of the interfering systems of waves has travelled between source and reflector in the liquid under measurement. In this way it is possible to detect movements of the reflector by half wavelengths.

[1] G. W. PIERCE: Proc. Amer. Acad. Arts Sci. **60**, 271 (1925).
[2] J. C. HUBBARD: Phys. Rev. **38**, 1011 (1931); **41**, 523 (1932).
[3] E. F. FOX: Phys. Rev. **52**, 973 (1937).
[4] K. F. HERZFELD: Phys. Rev. **53**, 899 (1938).
[5] A. BARONE [7].

The diffraction of light allows amplitude modulation at high frequency of a light beam, which can be used to make stationary the image of a progressive wave obtained with the secondary interference method. GIACOMINI[1] has developed a high precision method for velocity determination along these lines.

Recently various pulse methods have been used for velocity measurements. It is possible to measure the time which a pulse requires to travel forth and back in the space between source and reflector. The electronic time mark on an oscilloscope can be used for the time measurement. The precision of this method is a few parts per thousand. Some pulse methods which are analogous to the interferometer for continuous waves have been developed, and some times relative velocity measurements have been done by comparing the times required for a pulse to travel between source and reflector in two interferometers of which one is filled with a known liquid. The pulse methods are important however essentially for absorption measurements and the velocity determinations which they allow are not the best possible.

19. Principal methods for sound absorption measurements. The principal methods used for the determination of the sound absorption coefficient are:

1. methods based on the measurement of the radiation pressure of plane progressive waves;
2. methods based on the measurement of the acoustic pressure;
3. interferometer methods;
4. optical methods;
5. pulse methods;
6. reverberation method.

The radiation pressure Π in a system of progressive waves is proportional to the wave intensity and its determination as function of the distance of propagation, x, of plane waves allows the determination of α:

$$\Pi_x = \Pi_0 \exp(-2\alpha x).$$

The radiation pressure on an obstacle can be measured by means of a torsion balance. The precision which can be reached, when suitable procedures are used to avoid the influence of secondary effects such as acoustic streaming and the formation of standing waves between source and obstacle, is of the order of a few percent. This method can be used in the range between about 0.5 Mc/sec and a few megacycles per second and requires considerable amounts of liquid. As already mentioned, it is important to eliminate the influence of the acoustic streaming on the measurement of the radiation pressure. The method which uses the acoustical pressure is independent of this requirement: the measurement may be performed by means of a piezoelectric microphone which uses a quartz crystal as receiver. Special care must be spent to avoid a coupling between the high frequency generator and the receiver which would add a wrong signal to the one produced by the microphone. Various procedures have been studied for this purpose, some of which make use of a frequency- or of an amplitude-modulation of the waves sent from the source.

The interferometer already described for velocity measurements can be used also for absorption coefficient determinations. The theory has been developed by HUBBARD, HERZFELD, FOX and others in order to obtain α from the behaviour of the current in the quartz circuit when the distance between source and reflector is varied. For various reasons, as for instance the importance of the reflection

[1] A. GIACOMINI: Ric. Sci. **18**, 803 (1948).

coefficient at the reflector, the precision of the method is rather low. Richardson[1] has developed an interferometer in which the position of the reflector is not changed and an hot wire detector is used to measure the amplitude of vibration of the standing waves; from these data α is calculated.

Numerous optical methods have been developed which are based on the dependence of the intensity of light diffracted in various spectra from the intensity of ultrasound: for instance the intensity of light of first diffraction order (or of zero order) depends linearly on the intensity of sound provided the latter is small. With this limitation the intensity of the diffracted light can be a measure of the sound intensity. These optical methods have been extensively used in the range 1 to 75 Mc/sec and the precision can reach the order of a few percent. The liquids must be transparent; usually a considerable volume of them is needed and the measurements becomes rather difficult when the temperature is very different from that of the room.

In recent years pulse methods have been developed and have been much used. They allow experiments on small quantities of liquids and it is possible without great difficulties to perform measurements in conditions very different from those of the surrounding room; i.e. at high pressures, at high and very low temperatures. The experimental disposition is similar to that of normal interferometer; the source however is driven by a pulsed generator so that a packet of waves is radiated. The waves are reflected by the reflector and are received by a crystal which usually is the same as the source. On an oscilloscope it is then possible to see a series of echoes due to the traveling back and forth of the wave-packet, whose distances on the calibrated time axis are proportional to the distance between source and reflector. Moving the reflector, the echoes change their position and size on the oscilloscope screen and this allows the determination of α. Various improvements have been developed to eliminate some possible errors, as for instance that due to change in the receiver sensibility with time, and it is possible now to use this method in the range 0.5 to 250 Mc/sec. In the high-frequency range it is customary to use as reflector a fused quartz rod with plane-parallel terminations which works as a delay line so that notwithstanding the very small distance between source and reflector which it is necessary to use, it is possible to observe on the oscilloscope screen an echo, well distinguished from the main pulse and due to the reflection of sound on the second terminal of the quartz rod. The precision of the pulse method is of the order of a few (1 to 2) percent.

For measurement at relatively low frequencies (50 to 100 kc/sec) the reverberation method has been used. In this case, a tank of spherical shape is filled with the liquid and the system is excited with a sound source which is suddenly stopped; the decay of the density of sound energy in the tank is then observed. The experiments are arranged so that the radiation of the tank as well as the energy losses in the material of the sperical shell can be neglected; from the measured decay it is then possible to calculate α for the liquid.

II. Liquids.

20. A classification of liquids. For the purpose of presenting a review of experimental results it is useful to introduce a classification of liquids according to the causes of sound dispersion and absorption which predominate in them. It is to be observed, however, that in the frequency range of experiment the velocity changes, which are to be expected for different causes, in most liquids

[1] E. G. Richardson: Proc. Phys. Soc. Lond. **52**, 480 (1940).

are well below the precision of the measurements and therefore essentially only the results of absorption determinations can be used as a basis for classification.

A possible classification is the following one:

(a) Liquids with classical absorption (monoatomic liquids).

(b) Unassociated liquids (thermal relaxation of internal degrees).

(c) Liquids with temperature-dependent structural effects (thermal relaxation of slow rate chemical equilibria).

(d) Low viscosity liquids with pressure dependent structural effects (compressional relaxation).

(e) Liquids with strong visco-elastic effects (highly viscous liquids).

Of course, as with any classification, it is only partially satisfactory for several reasons; at times for instance, various causes of dispersion and absorption have an importance of the same order of magnitude and it is some what arbitrary to assign the liquid to a group.

We will follows, however, the preceding classification.

21. Liquids with classical absorption. A few low viscosity liquids show an absorption coefficient very close to the classical one, Eq. (3.1), i.e. calculated for viscosity and heat conduction assuming STOKES' relation.

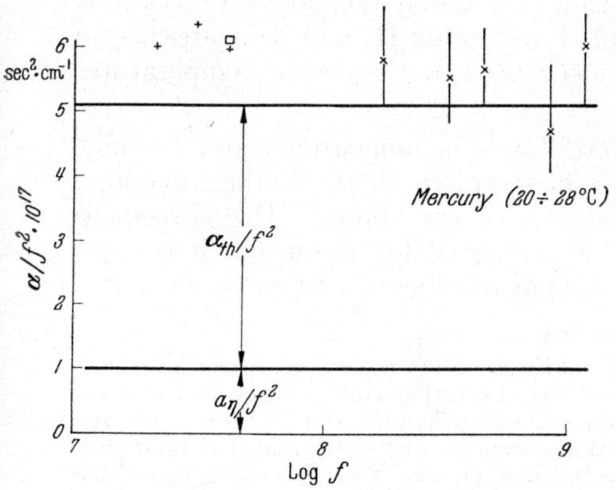

Fig. 3. Sound absorption in mercury (H. O. KNESER [*12*]). Measurements by P. RIECKMANN (+), R. BÄR (□) and RINGO (×).

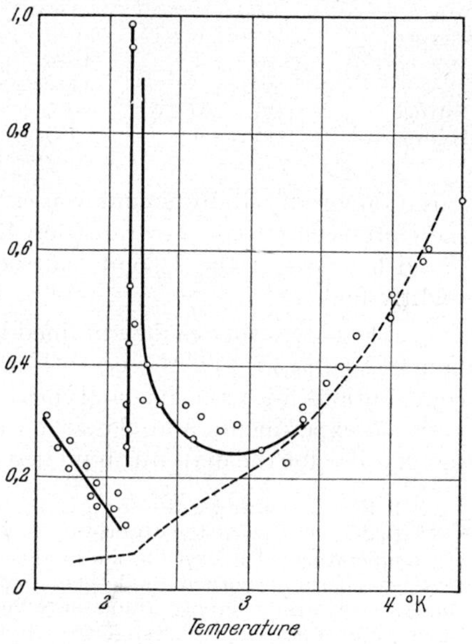

Fig. 4. Sound absorption in liquid helium (PELLAM-SQUIRE).

Mercury is the only monoatomic liquid at ordinary temperatures. It has been studied in the frequency range 20 to 1000 Mc/sec. The deviation of α_{exp} from the classical value is about 25% for the measurements of BÄR[1] and RIECKMANN[2] (20 to 54 Mc/sec) and about 15% for those of RINGO[3] et al. (100 to 1000 Mc/sec) and these seem to be the orders of magnitude of the possible errors. In Fig. 3 these results as well as the classical values and the contributions of viscosity and heat conductivity are shown; mercury is the only case known in which the losses due to heat conductivity are larger than those due to viscosity; the contrary is usually true (see Table 1).

[1] R. BÄR: Helv. phys. Acta **10**, 332 (1937).

[2] P. RIECKMANN: Phys. Z. **40**, 582 (1939).

[3] G. R. RINGO, J. W. FITRGERALD and B. G. HURDLE: Phys. Rev. **72**, 87 (1947).

A second case is that of liquid helium which has been studied below 4.5° K by PELLAM and SQUIRE[1] (Fig. 4). The experimental absorption coefficient agrees with the classical one (dashed line) until the temperature is lowered nearly to the λ point for transformation of helium I in helium II at 2.19° K. The velocity of propagation goes from 180 m/sec at 4.5° K to 230 m/sec at 1.5° K with no marked discontinuity at the λ point. The low values of velocity are bound to the small density. Measurements at 15 Mc/sec and 1.3 Mc/sec show that no dispersion is present in this range. The deviations of the experimental absorption coefficient from the classical curve are due to the structural changes which take place in the liquid. As the temperature is lowered (<3° K) near the λ-point, the absorption increases rapidly to fall as soon as the λ-point is pased. This is a characteristic behaviour when two phases are present and their equilibrium is altered by temperature

Table 2. *Absorption coefficient of liquified gases* (J. K. GALT).

Liquid	T (°K)	Velocity m/sec	$\alpha_\eta/f^2\times 10^{17}$ cm^{-1} sec^2	$\alpha_{th}/f^2\times 10^{17}$ cm^{-1} sec^2	$\alpha_c/f^2\times 10^{17}$ cm^{-1} cm^2	$\alpha_{exp}/f^2\times 10^{17}$ cm^{-1} cm^2
Argon	85.2 ± 0.2	853	7.9	2.6	10.5	10.1
Oxygen	87.0 ± 0.2	952	5.5	1.8	7.3	8.6
	70 ± 1	1094	5.6	1.1	6.7	8.6
	60 ± 5	1119	7.3	1.0	8.3	8.6
Nitrogen	73.9 ± 0.2	962	6.6	2.9	9.5	10.6
Hydrogen	17 ± 1	1187	3.7	2.1	5.8	5.6

variation produced by sound waves, causing a thermal relaxation process. It therefore seems that the transition helium I to helium II, which in absence of sound happens at the λ-point, can be induced by sound waves at temperatures slightly higher[2].

Table 2 gives the results obtained by GALT[3] in some monoatomic and diatomic liquefied gases at 44.4 Mc/sec with a pulse method. In the table the calculated contributions of viscosity and heat conductivity are shown. The agreement between experiments and classical values is very good for argon, but it is satisfactory also for the diatomic liquefied gases if one considers that GALT's estimated

[1] J. R. PELLAM and C. F. SQUIRE: Phys. Rev. **72**, 1245 (1947).

[2] Below the λ-point the absorption coefficient, after a sudden fall, increases with decreasing temperature. The explanation of this part of the absorption curve can be given on the basis of superfluid-normal fluid theory according to which helium II is a mixture of two fluids: a superfluid having atoms in a highly degenerate ground state and a normal fluid having atoms in exited states. TISZA [J. Phys. Radium **11**, 164, 350 (1940)] suggested that sound waves could force a non-adiabatic transition from normal fluid to superfluid; these transitions would be more numerous at low temperatures where superfluid is more easily formed and this would explain the increase of sound losses as the temperature decreases.

The same two-fluid theory explains the thermal waves (second sound) produced in helium II, for instance, by means of a grid of wires in which an alternating current passes. The velocity of these waves is given according to TISZA:

$$c = -\left[\frac{N_n}{N_s}\frac{\partial}{\partial T}\left(\frac{1}{S}\right)\right]^{-\frac{1}{2}}$$

N_n and N_s being the concentration of atoms in normal fluid and in superfluid; S is the entropy of helium II. This velocity is zero at the λ-point, increases with decreasing temperature to a maximum of about 20 m/sec and decreases when 0° K is approached. No dispersion has been detected. The absorption coefficient m of the temperature wave, $T = T_0 \exp(-m x)$, (second sound) is about 0,01 cm^{-1} at 1.65° K; 0.1 cm^{-1} at 2.06° K and increases rapidly as the λ-point is approached.

[3] J. K. GALT: J. Chem. Phys. **16**, 505 (1948). — The value of η_c for hydrogen has been calculated by MARKHAM-BEYER-LINDSAY [*13*].

accuracy for α is 15% for nitrogen and 10% for other liquefied gases. This agreement seems to show that viscosity and heat conductivity are responsible for all sound losses in these liquefied diatomic gases; i.e. the equipartition of energy among the degrees of freedom of molecules does not enter into play because the vibrations are frozen.

22. Unassociated liquids. *α) Nature of relaxation processes.* Unassociated polyatomic liquids are those which have single molecules as basic units. In recent years sound absorption measurements have shown the existence of relaxation processes, with the relaxation frequency in the accessible range for several liquids of the category; however for most of them α/f^2 stays constant over the whole frequency range of experiment and has values many times larger (800 to 1000)

Table 3. *Absorption coefficient in some typical unassociated liquid.*

Liquid	Frequency Mc/sec	Temperature (°C)	$\alpha_{exp}/f^2 \times 10^{17}$ $cm^{-1} sec^2$	$\alpha_c/f^2 \times 10^{17}$ $cm^{-1} sec^2$
Carbon disulphide	1—5	20	6000	5
Carbon tetrachloride	1—100	20	500	20
Benzene	0.2—40	20	850	6.9
Fluorobenzene	30	25	278	8.8
Chlorobenzene	30	25	148	9.7
Bromobenzene	30	25	140	13.1
Iodobenzene	30	25	210	16.7
Methylene chloride	30	25	1100	6.1
Methylene bromide	30	25	567	1.6
Methylene iodide	30	25	250	23.2
Trans-dichloroethylene	30	20	360	8.5
Cis-Dichloroethylene	30	20	540	6.4

than the classical parameter, as is shown in Table 3 where the data for some typical unassociated liquids are given. Much discussion has taken place on the nature of the relaxation processes responsible for absorption: it seems however that the evidence is now in favour of their being of a thermal nature in preference to a structural nature (for instance of the kind suggested by GIERER and WIRTZ). This evidence will appear from the following survey.

According to the thermal explanation unassociated liquids can be considered approximately as very dense gases where energy is exchanged among molecules only during collisions. Therefore, thermal relaxation, as in polyatomic gases, is to be expected together with absorption due to viscosity and heat conduction. While the energy levels of vibrational modes do not vary appreciably for molecules in gaseous and liquid states, the relaxation time is much shorter in liquids because of the larger number of collisions per second: for a gas at room temperature and atmospheric pressure the number of collisions is of the order of 5×10^9 per second, for liquids this number is, to a first approximation, of the order of kT/h, i.e. about 10^{12}. For this reason the relaxation frequencies should be in general beyond the accessible range: there are some cases in which this is not true and the complete relaxation curve can be measured. When the parameter α/f^2 is constant in the frequency range of experiment the only formula of thermal relaxation theory available is (7.8) which may be written:

$$\frac{\alpha}{f^2} = \frac{2\pi^2}{c_0} \frac{\Delta}{C_v C_p} C_i \tau. \tag{22.1}$$

In 1941, HERZFELD[1] used this relation to show that the observed constancy of α/f^2 in unassociated liquids is not in contrast with the attribution of the excess

[1] K. F. HERZFELD: J. Acoust. Soc. Amer. **13**, 33 (1941).

of α over the classical value to relaxation of vibrational modes. HERZFELD assumed C_i equal to the total vibrational specific heat of gaseous molecules and calculated from absorption data the values 1×10^{-10} sec and 3×10^{-10} sec for τ in carbon tetrachloride and benzene respectively. These values are in agreement with the observed behaviour of α/f^2. Measurements in carbon tetrachloride have been extended to 105 Mc/sec and the value of α/f^2 stays constant all over the range. LAMB[1] has investigated benzene up to 250 Mc/sec; while α/f^2 is constant up to 90 Mc/sec, a small decrease is found at higher frequencies; this behaviour indicates a τ of the order of HERZFELD'S calculation. Recently HERZFELD[2] has selected a number of substances for which τ_{gas} has been measured in the vapour state and he has calculated τ_{liq} in the liquid by means of (22.1). Some results are given in Table 4. It turns out that the ratio between relaxation times in gaseous and liquid states does not vary much ($100 \div 600$) and it is about the same as the ratio of densities. This conclusion, although obtained by means of a calculation which does not take in account pecularities of single substances, seems to indicate that the nature of the phenomena does not change when going from gaseous to liquid state and that the main variation is due to the change of time between collisions.

Table 4. *Relaxation times for some substances in vapour (τ_g) and liquid (τ_l) states, and densities* (K. F. HERZFELD).

Substance	$\tau_g\cdot10^8$ sec	$\tau_l\cdot10^{10}$ sec	τ_g/τ_l	ϱ_l/ϱ_g
CH_3Br	7.5	1.26	600	460
CH_2Cl_2 *	5.8	5.3	110	—
$CHCl_3$	1.35	1.3	105	320
CCl_4	2.1	1.26	170	260
$(CH_2Cl)_2$	0.5	0.495	100	320
$(CHCl)_2$	0.62	2.1	350	323
C_6H_6	5	2.7	180	280
CS_2	72.7	28.3	260	420

* Two relaxation processes ($C_1-\tau_1$; $C_2-\tau_2$) have been found in the vapour phase; the relaxation time quoted is $\tau=\dfrac{C_1\tau_1+C_2\tau_2}{C_1+C_2}$.

Another argument in favour of thermal relaxation of internal degrees of freedom as cause of sound losses in unassociated liquids is given by the behaviour of binary mixtures (BAUER, SETTE), which as it will be seen in Sect. 9 agrees with theoretical expectations based on thermal theory.

β) The case of carbon disulphide. Further support to the thermal nature of relaxation processes in unassociated liquids is given by the analysis of results in carbon disulphide.

This liquid has been studied by many authors because it is the low viscosity liquid with the larger absorption in the megacycle range and therefore it appeared soon as the more characteristic representative of the category of unassociated liquids. The results of different researchers often did not agree, probably because small quantities of impurities (see mixtures, Sect. 26) have a tremendous effect on the absorption coefficient of these liquids. Recent research (RAPUANO[3], ANDREAE and LAMB[4], HUDDART[5], SETTE[6], KISHIMOTO and NOMOTO[7]) have furnished more reliable data (Fig. 5[8]) which determine most characteristics of

[1] Communication made in a seminar at Catholic University (Washington D.C.) on May 31, 1955. [See E. L. HEASELL and J. LAMB: Proc. Phys. Soc. Lond. B **69**, 869 (1955) (Note added on proof).]

[2] Communication made in a seminar at Catholic University (Washington D.C.) on May, 31, 1956. [See J. Acoust. Soc. Amer. **29**, 1180 (1957) (Note added on proof).]

[3] R. A. RAPUANO: Phys. Rev. **72**, 78 (1952).

[4] J. H. ANDREAE and J. LAMB: Proc. Phys. Soc. Lond. B, **64**, 1021 (1951).

[5] D. H. A. HUDDART: Diss. London 1950.

[6] D. SETTE: J. Chem. Phys. **19**, 1342 (1951).

[7] T. KISHIMOTO and O. NOMOTO: Bull. Kobayasi Inst. Tokyo **2**, 63 (1952).

[8] The results obtained by BÄR and BAZULIN used in Fig. 5 are contained in the papers: R. BÄR: Helv. phys. Acta **10**, 332 (1937); P. BAZULIN: J. exp. theor. Phys. USSR. **8**, 457 (1938).

the relaxation process involved. The experiment does not extend to the whole frequency range of the relaxation process and at the highest frequency used (200 Mc/sec) α/f^2 has not yet reached its constant value. The data can be fitted to a curve

$$\frac{\alpha}{f^2} = \frac{A}{1+\left(\frac{f}{f_r}\right)^2} + B \tag{22.2}$$

which is the sum of a term produced by a single relaxation process and a constant term; (f_r = relaxation frequency).

Table 5. *Vibrational specific heat in carbon disulphide at 25° C.*

Vibrational frequency (cm^{-1})	657	397	1523	—
Degeneracy	1	2	1	—
Einstein specific heat (cal/mole^{-1} deg^{-1})	0.914	2×1.4755	0.069	—
Total vibrational specific heat (cal/mole^{-1} deg^{-1})	—	—	—	3.934

Table 5 gives the frequencies of the vibrational modes of CS_2 and their contribution to the specific heat at 25° C, calculated by Eq. (7.13) with due consideration for degeneracy.

Lamb and Andreae[1] at first fitted Rapuano's[2] results and theirs with a curve following Eq. (22.2) having $A = 5.385\times10^{-17}$, $B = 428\times\times10^{-17}$ sec^2 cm^{-1} and f_r = 72.1 Mc/sec. According to them (1954) the experiment could be explained by assuming that only the degenerate bending vibration mode was involved. This explanation was not entirely satisfactory and the value of B seemed still too high in comparison with the value of α/f^2 due to viscosity (5×10^{-17} sec^2 cm^{-1}). Recently Andreae, Heasell and Lamb[3] have extended the range of their measurements up to 190 Mc/sec; the experimental results differ slightly from those of Rapuano at the high frequency end of the field tested. These authors have shown that their results at 25° C are fitted by a single relaxation curve obtained assuming that all the vibrational modes relax together; the relaxation frequency would be 78 Mc/sec and the value of B is of the same order of that due to viscosity and heat conductivity.

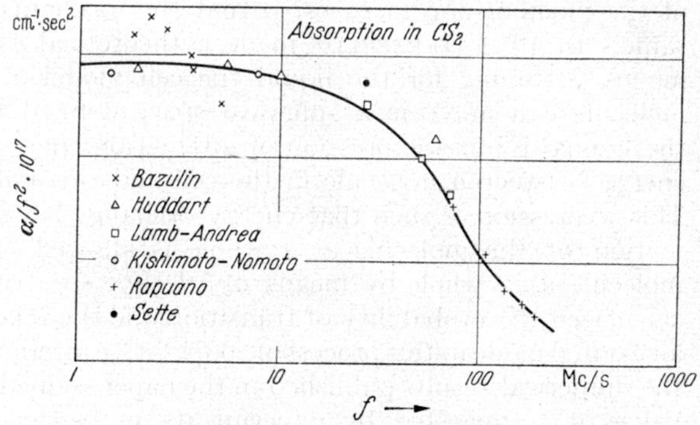

Fig. 5. Sound absorption in carbon disulphide (Bergmann [1]).

Similar results were reached by Kishimoto and Nomoto[4] who made some calculations on CS_2 using essentially the data of Fig. 5. They assume that all vibrational specific heat is relaxing with the same characteristic time and that B is equal to the classical value of α/f^2; the experiment would then be fitted by a curve (22.2) with $A = 5700\times10^{-17}$ sec^2 cm^{-1} and $f_r = 85.6$ Mc/sec.

[1] J. H. Andreae and J. Lamb: Proc. Phys. Soc. Lond. B **64**, 1021 (1951); A **226**, 51 (1954), and Ref. [5].
[2] R. A. Rapuano: Phys. Rev. **72**, 78 (1947).
[3] J. H. Andreae, E. L. Heasell and J. Lamb: Proc. Phys. Soc. Lond. B **69**, 625 (1956).
[4] T. Kishimoto and O. Nomoto: Bull. Kobayasi Inst. Tokio **2**, 63 (1952).

The fact that all vibrational modes seem to relax together, and therefore a relaxation curve for a simple process is observed, is in agreement with what has been observed in relaxation processes in gases. In polyatomic gaseous molecules in fact, although it is not to be excluded that sometimes independent excitation of different modes occurs, the more frequent case is that of series excitation via the mode of lowest frequency, with internal conversion times very short (LAMBERT and ROWLINSON[1], SETTE, BUSALA and HUBBARD[2]): the energy is then exchanged between external degrees and the mode of lowest frequency (smallest excitation quanta); it successively flows into the other modes with very small time delay. In this case one observes a single relaxation process in which the entire vibrational specific heat is involved.

The dispersion of sound velocity in CS_2 can be calculated from the value of the maximum absorption per wavelength and should be of the order of 8%. Some measurements of velocity at different frequencies have been made but no systematic research has been performed.

γ) Calculation of transition probability and of relaxation time in carbon disulphide. The measurements in CS_2 have been used recently by LITOVITZ[3] in a theoretical paper to produce more evidence on the thermal nature of relaxation process in unassociated liquids and on the perfect analogy of its characteristic with that of the phenomenon in gases so that the mechanism may be assumed to be the same. In 1952 HERZFELD[4] made a theoretical calculation of τ for vibrational modes, assuming for the liquid the cell model of LENNARD-JONES in which a molecule can move in a spherical space defined by nearest neighbours. From the Lennard-Jones expression of interaction energy he calculated the interaction energy between a molecule in the cell and the molecules on the wall of the cell. This expression is such that energy exchange between internal vibration and the motion of the molecule as a whole is allowed. Describing the motion of the molecule as a whole by means of a Debye spectrum of elastic waves, HERZFELD calculated the probability of transition and the relaxation time for deactivation of an excited mode in this process of cooperative interaction of the molecules. Although the numerical results published in the paper seemed to show an agreement with the value of τ suggested by experiments in benzene, a mistake has been subsequently found by HERZFELD[5] in the calculation; the correct value shows that this cooperative process of energy exchange between internal and external degrees of freedom, although present, is not usually important because it produces a probability of transfer much smaller than needed to explain the experiments.

Starting from this conclusion, LITOVITZ tried to extend to liquids the hypothesis used in gas theory that binary collisions are essentially the only important process for energy exchange, and to apply the Schwartz and Herzfeld[6] theory to the calculation of transition probabilities.

According to these two authors, the probability in gases that a particle will pass from the first excited state to the ground state upon binary collision is given by

$$P_{1\text{-}0} = 0.716\left(1+\frac{c^*}{T}\right)^{-1}\left(\frac{d_c}{d_0}\right)^2\left(\frac{\pi}{3}\right)^{\frac{1}{2}}\frac{8\pi^3\mu_{12}h\nu}{\beta^* h}\exp\left[-\left(3\,\Phi^*+\frac{h\nu}{2kT}+\frac{\varepsilon}{kT}\right)\right] \tag{22.3}$$

[1] J. D. LAMBERT and J. S. ROWLINSON: Proc. Roy. Soc. Lond., Ser. A **204**, 424 (1950).
[2] D. SETTE, A. BUSALA and J. C. HUBBARD: J. Chem. Phys. **20**, 1899 (1952); **23**, 787 (1955).
[3] T.A. LITOVITZ: J. Chem. Phys. **26**, 469 (1957).
[4] K. F. HERZFELD: J. Chem. Phys. **20**, 288 (1952).
[5] Private communication of Prof. HERZFELD.
[6] R. N. SCHWARTZ and K. HERZFELD: J. Chem. Phys. **22**, 767 (195

where c^* is SUTHERLAND'S constant, d_c is the distance of closest approach, d_0 is the distance corresponding to the zero of the Lennard-Jones potential curve, μ_{12} is the reduced mass of colliding molecules, β^* is the constant in an exponential curve used to approximate the repulsive part of LENNARD-JONES' potential curve, ε is the depth of the minimum of the Lennard-Jones potential curve and Φ^* is given by

$$\Phi^* = \left[\frac{2\pi^2 \mu^2 (h\nu)^2}{\beta^* h^2 kT}\right]^{\frac{1}{3}}. \tag{22.4}$$

The value of P_{1-0} can be estimated by means of quantities obtained by various independent measurements, without the use of any constant.

The knowledge of P_{1-0} permits the calculation of the relaxation time for thermal processes when binary collisions are responsible for energy transitions:

$$\tau = \left\{N P_{1-0}\left[1 - \exp\left(-\frac{h\nu}{kT}\right)\right]\right\}^{-1}, \tag{22.5}$$

N being the number of collisions per second.

Applying to liquids the relations established for gases, one may assume the validity of (22.3) because, as has been already pointed out, if thermal relaxation is responsible for the absorption in liquids, the intimate nature of the process does not vary. In order to calculate τ, it is then necessary to evaluate N. This is not simple because the volume of the molecules themselves cannot be neglected in comparison to the volume occupied by the liquid. LITOVITZ has used three theories of the liquid state for the calculation of N for use in (22.5) and from the comparison of theory and experiment for pressure and temperature variations of τ in CS_2 he has concluded that the cell model of EYRING and HIRSCHFELDER[1] gives the best results.

N can be given by the ratio between an average velocity of molecules, $\bar{v}$, and the mean free path, L_f:

$$N = \frac{\bar{v}}{L_f}. \tag{22.6}$$

For $\bar{v}$ one can take to a first approximation the expression given by the kinetic theory

$$\bar{v} = \sqrt{\frac{8kT}{\pi M}}. \tag{22.7}$$

For L_f the cell model gives

$$L_f = 2\left[\left(\frac{\Omega}{n}\right)^{\frac{1}{3}} - 2r_m\right], \tag{22.8}$$

where Ω is the volume occupied by n molecules and r_m is the radius of a molecule assumed to be a rigid sphere. If one considers the value of τ at different pressures, the only quantity which changes is L_f and therefore:

$$\frac{\tau_p}{\tau_0} = \frac{L_{fp}}{L_{f0}} = \frac{\left(\frac{\Omega_p}{n}\right)^{\frac{1}{3}} - 2r_m}{\left(\frac{\Omega_0}{n}\right)^{\frac{1}{3}} - 2r_m}. \tag{22.9}$$

LITOVITZ has compared this relation with the results of some measurements made in CS_2. Table 6 gives the results. Two values for r_m have been used; the first, 2.22 Å is given by HIRSCHFELDER for CS_2; the second, 2.16 Å gives better agreement and could be the right value to be used because the value of r_m for any

[1] H. EYRING and J. O. HIRSCHFELDER: J. Phys. Chem. **41**, 249 (1937).

given molecule varies according to the experiment used for its determination by as much as 5% and because CS_2 really is not a spherical molecule as assumed. It is possible also to see that using $r_m = 2.16$ Å the value calculated for P_{1-0} at room temperature from experimental ultrasonic data is the same for the gas and the liquid within experimental error.

LITOVITZ has also compared theory and experiment for the temperature variation. In this case P_{1-0} is the quantity which changes with temperature and according to (22.3) the exponential is essentially responsible for this dependence. Introducing a value of Φ^* found for gases and determining the factor (assumed in first approximation independent of temperature) in front of the exponential by comparison with experiment, LITOVITZ calculates P_{1-0} for two more temperatures according to the Schwartz-Herzfeld theory and compares

Table 6. *Pressure dependence of thermal relaxation time of CS_2 at 244° K* (T. A. LITOVITZ).

P (kg/cm²)	τ_p/τ_0 theoretical cell model $2r_m = 4.44$ Å	$2r_m = 4.32$ Å	$\left(\frac{\tau_p}{\tau_0}\right)_{exp}$
1	1.0	1.0	1.0
500	0.67	0.83	0.87
1000	0.33	0.67	0.65

Table 7. *Temperature dependence of P_{1-0} in liquid CS_2* (T. A. LITOVITZ).

T (°K)	f_r (Mc/sec)	$P_{1-0} \times 10^4$ S.H. theory	from acoustic data
298	78.0	1.03	1.03
244	46.4	0.48	0.47
210	31.0	0.26	0.28

them with the experimental data obtained from (22.5), using the cell model of the liquid with $r_m = 2.16$ Å. The results are given in Table 7 and are very satisfactory.

This good agreement between experiment and a theory developed for thermal processes in gases, shows that also in unassociated liquids the dissipative processes are to be ascribed to the time required for deexcitation of internal degrees of freedom by means of binary collisions.

In the Schwartz-Herzfeld theory the transitions are supposed to happen when the molecules, during collisions, are so close that the repulsive part of the potential is concerned; this is equivalent to saying that the short range forces are responsible for the transitions while the long range forces probably have importance in determining the kind of approach of molecules and their orientation during collision. This indication confirms another one already found by studying the two dichlorethylenes in the liquid[1] and gaseous states[2]. While the trans-form has no dipole moment, the cis-dichlorethylene has a strong dipole moment. In both gas and liquid states, however, the deexcitation of molecules is faster in the trans-form.

Conclusions similar to those of LITOVITZ were reached by MIFSUD and NOLLE[3] who have studied the velocity and absorption in carbon tetrachloride, benzene and carbon disulphide at various temperatures and pressures and have tried to explain the experimental results by applying either the structural or the thermal relaxation theory; while their results seem to be in agreement with the approximate predictions of the thermal theory they are in contrast with those of the structural theory.

δ) The case of toluene. Passing now to other liquids which show α/f^2 frequency-dependent, we find toluene. Fig. 6 gives the results obtained by MOEN[4]. Above

[1] D. SETTE: J. Chem. Phys. **19**, 1337 (1951).
[2] D. SETTE, A. BUSALA and J. C. HUBBARD: J. Chem. Phys. **20**, 1899 (1952).
[3] J. F. MIFSUD and A. W. NOLLE: J. Acoust. Soc. Amer. **28**, 469 (1956).
[4] J. MOEN: J. Acoust. Soc. Amer. **23**, 62 (1951).

1 Mc/sec it seems that α/f^2 stays constant[1] at least up to 75 Mc/sec around 78×10^{-17} sec² cm⁻¹. This value is larger than the classical one, 7.8×10^{-17} sec² per cm⁻¹ and it shows that other dissipative causes are operative besides the low frequency relaxation process. ANDREAE and LAMB[2] assign the observed relaxation to the stretching vibration of C—H bonds in the methyl group of toluene. This mode has $\nu = 2.960$ cm⁻¹ and degeneracy 3. ANDREAE and LAMB calculate a value of the maximum absorption per wavelength of 3.2×10^{-5} which is in fairly good agreement with the value (3.8×10^{-5}) obtained from experiment making use of some extrapolations. Recently, however, BEYER[3] has performed experiments between 50 and 400 kc/sec in the temperature range 6 to 40° C obtaining results somewhat different. While the presence of a relaxation process with a characteristic frequency of about 100 kc/sec at 20° C is confirmed the changes of A_{max} with temperature allow the calculation of a reaction heat (5.2 kcal/mole) different from that belonging to the process suggested by ANDREAE and LAMB (8.5 kcal/mole).

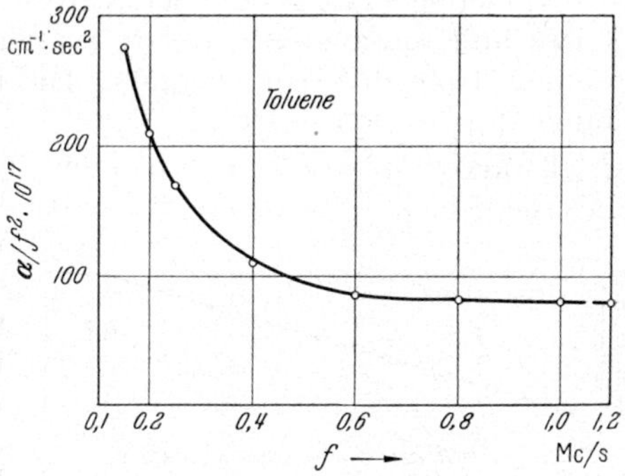

Fig. 6. Sound absorption in toluene (C. J. MOEN).

BEYER finds also evidence of a lower frequency relaxation process.

ε) Rotational isomers. Thermal relaxation in the frequency range from 100 kc/sec to 1 Mc/sec has been found in liquids whose molecules can exist in two forms and pass from one to the other by rotation of part of the molecule around some bonds (rotational isomers). A first class is that of some derivates of cyclohexane by substitution of one or more H atoms with suitable groups. The ring of carbon atoms in cyclohexane can be found in two planar chair configurations and a molecule can pass from the first to the second by rotation around the C—C bound. To each carbon atom in cyclohexane two hydrogen atoms are bound of which one is in the plane of the carbon ring (equatorial) and the other is outside the plane (polar, three from one side and three from the other side of the ring). When rotation around the C—C bond occurs, the equatorial H atoms become polar and vice versa. This has no effect in cyclohexane because the two chair configurations have the same energy; if however an H atom is substituted by suitable groups it may happen that the rotational isomers have different energy. In Fig. 7 the two chair configurations for methylcyclohexane are indicated. The possibility of rotations inside the molecules is equivalent to the presence of one or more internal degrees of freedom. It is to be observed however that in contrast to vibrational modes which are quantised (and therefore the exchange of energy with external degree of freedom must be

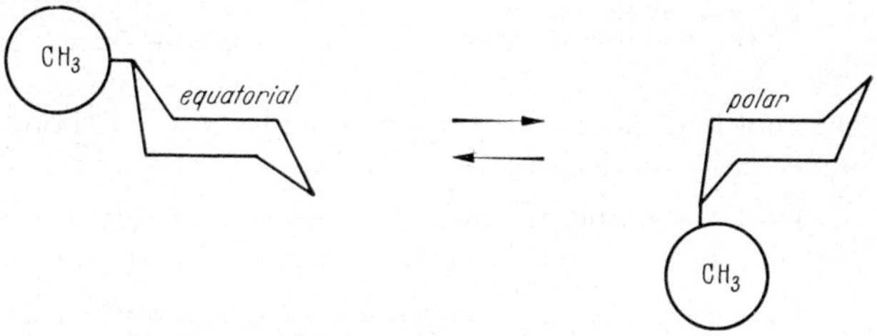

Fig. 7. Configurations of rotational isomers.

[1] G. S. VERMA: J. Chem. Phys. **18**, 1352 (1950) and [*13*].
[2] J. H. ANDREAE and J. LAMB: Proc. Phys. Soc. Lond. B **64**, 1021 (1951).
[3] R. T. BEYER: J. Acoust. Soc. Amer. **27**, 1 (1955).

equal to the quanta) the passage from one isomer to the other is not quantised. The system may be described by means of a two-state potential energy diagram with an activation energy; the passage is possible as for a chemical reaction when energy is given in any amount larger than the activation energy. For this reason these liquids could also be included in the category of low viscosity liquids with temperature-dependent structural effects which are treated in Sect. 23 below.

The equilibrium between rotational isomers with different energies can be perturbed by sound waves, producing relaxation effects.

Numerous cyclohexane derivatives have been studied by KARPOVICH[1] and by LAMB and SHERWOOD[2], and relaxations have been found when the rotational isomers have different energies. The relaxation frequencies are usually in the range 100 to 200 kc/sec.

KARPOVICH observed also a low frequency relaxation (80 kc/sec) in cyclohexane which he attributed to the distrubed equilibrium between rotational isomers which have pseudochair and boat configurations. DE GROOT and LAMB[3] have found relaxation in two aldehyde (crotonaldehyde and cinnamaldehyde) in the range 100 kc/sec to 1 Mc/sec and they assign them to the perturbed equilibrium between two isomer configurations:

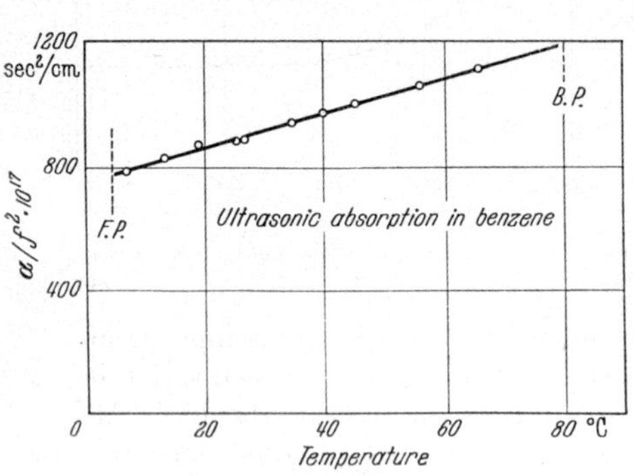

Fig. 8. Temperature dependence of ultrasonic absorption in benzene.

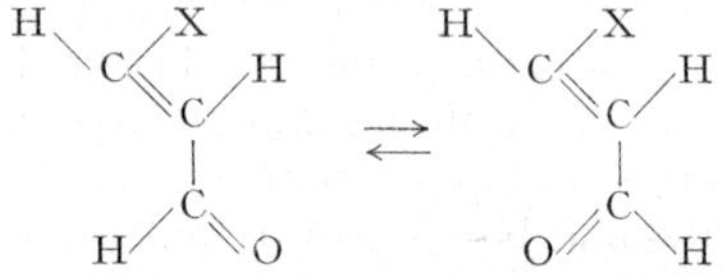

where X is respectively a methyl group or a benzene ring. There would be in the molecule no free rotation around the C—C bond and the lower part of the molecules would be planar.

DE GROOT and LAMB suggest that probably the previously observed relaxation in esters (e.g., ethyl acetate) may be due to some kind of rotational isomerism.

ζ) Variations of absorption coefficient with temperature and pressure. The possibility of applying the Schwartz-Herzfeld theory, used to calculate transition probabilities in binary collisions of gas molecules, to unassociated liquid , as LITOVITZ has shown, is important for the examination of the influence of pressure and temperature on the phenomena. LITOVITZ has applied the theory to the case of CS_2 where the relaxation times can be directly obtained by experiment in the range of relaxation frequencies.

The absorption coefficient of unassociated liquids having a relaxation frequency well beyond the range of experiment usually increases when temperature rises. Fig. 8 gives the results in benzene[4] at 30 Mc/sec between melting and boiling points, and Figs. 9 and 10 refer to chloro-substituted benzene and halogenated methylenes[5]. This behavior could be explained by a theoretical investigation

[1] J. KARPOVICH: J. Chem. Phys. **22**, 1767 (1954).
[2] J. LAMB and J. SHERWOOD: Trans. Faraday Soc. **51**, 1674 (1955a).
[3] M. S. DE GROOT and J. LAMB: Trans Faraday Soc. **51**, 1676 (1955).
[4] D. SETTE: Ref. [5], p. 153.
[5] D. SETTE: J. Chem. Phys. **19**, 1337 (1951).

similar to that used by LITOVITZ, using the Schwartz-Herzfeld theory of transition probabilities in gases.

Some general considerations on the temperature dependence of the absorption coefficient were also made by KITTEL[1] and MARKHEM, BEYER, LINDRAY [*13*]. The coefficient due to a relaxation process (thermal or compressional) is given by a relation

$$\frac{\alpha}{f^2} = A \frac{\tau}{1+\omega^2\tau^2}. \quad (22.10)$$

Considering that $1/\tau$ is the rate of deactivation of molecules and that

$$K_{21} \sim e^{-\frac{\Delta W}{T}}, \quad (22.11)$$

τ has a negative temperature coefficient. The temperature variation of α/f^2 depends on: (1) the sign of the temperature coefficient of $A\tau$; (2) the relative value of ω and $1/\tau$. If A has a large positive temperature coefficient, the same is true for $A\tau$ and variation of α/f^2 with increasing temperature will always be positive. If instead $A\tau$ has a small (negative or positive) temperature coefficient, then the sign of the α/f^2 variation depends on the frequency and it is positive above and negative below the relaxation frequency.

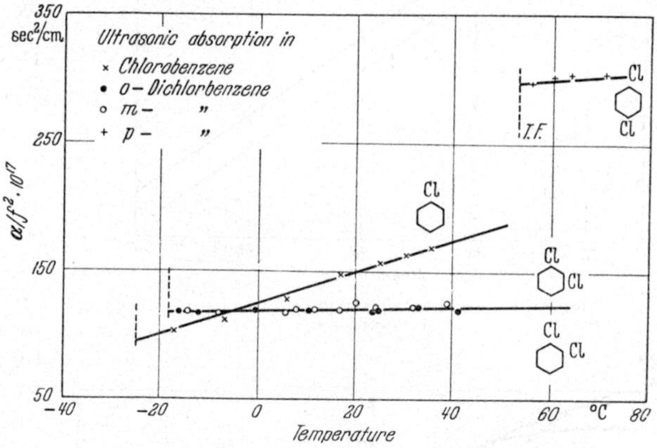

Fig. 9. Temperature dependence of ultrasonic absorption in chloro- and dichloro-benzenes.

According to this analysis, the unassociated liquids are characterised by a large positive temperature coefficient of A in the thermal relaxation processes involved.

23. Liquids with temperature-dependent structural effects. To this category belong those pure liquids whose molecules can be found in different states of aggregation and wherein no variation of volume is associated with the passage from one form to the other. In these liquids the distribution of molecules between 1 and 2 is disturbed by the temperature variations produced by sound waves. The termal relaxation we observe is in many respects equivalent to that originated by the lag in energy distribution between internal and external degrees of freedom and we have already seen how it may be represented by means of a frequency-dependent specific heat.

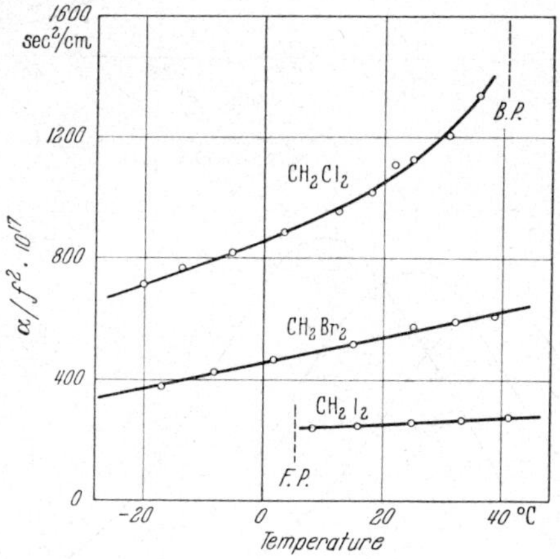

Fig. 10. Temperature dependence of ultrasonic absorption in halogenated methylenes.

The relaxation times for these equilibria are often so large that the whole relaxation range can be investigated.

[1] C. KITTEL: J. Chem. Phys. **14**, 614 (1946).

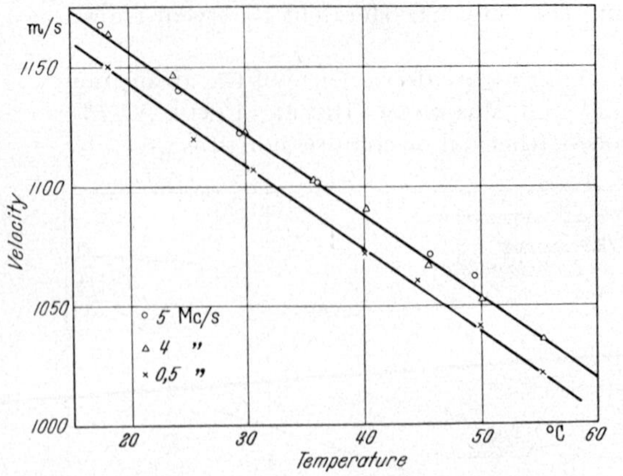

Fig. 11. Dispersion in acetic acid (J. LAMB and J. M. M. PINKERTON).

Table 8. *Temperature dependence of A and B in acetic acid* (J. LAMB and J. M. M. PINKERTON).

Temperature (°C)	$A \times 10^{17}$ $sec^2\ cm^{-1}$	$B \times 10^{17}$ $sec^2\ cm^{-1}$
17	178000	160
20	160000	151
25	132000	140
30	107000	132
35	88700	124
40	72900	118
45	58800	112
50	48400	106
55	41100	100
60	33800	95

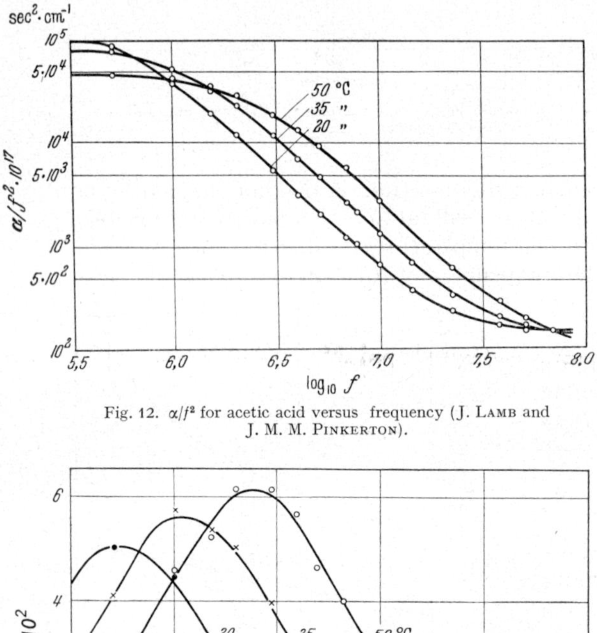

Fig. 12. α/f^2 for acetic acid versus frequency (J. LAMB and J. M. M. PINKERTON).

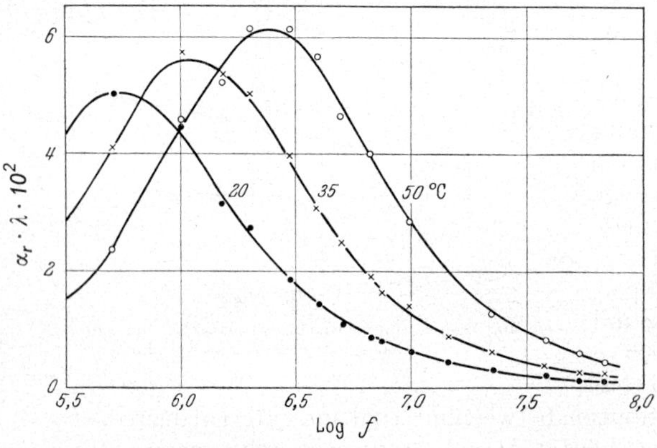

Fig. 13. $\alpha_r \cdot \lambda$, vs. frequency in acetic acid (J. LAMB and J. M. M. PINKERTON).

Dispersion and absorption in acetic acid have been studied by BAZULIN[1] and recently PINKERTON and LAMB[2] have furnished a valuable body of results. Fig. 11 gives the temperature variation of velocity for various frequencies. At frequencies higher than 4 Mc/sec one gets the same line as for 4 Mc/sec, i.e. no further dispersion is detectable. The dispersion between 0.5 und 4 Mc/sec is however evident. Fig. 12 and 13 give PINKERTON and LAMB's results for α/f^2 and $\alpha_r \cdot \lambda$ between 20° C and 50° C. Their results may be represented by Eq. (22.2) with values of A and B given by Table 8.

The dispersion data are in good quantitative agreement with absorption results. The values of B show that the high frequency value of α/f^2 is still higher than the classical one (20×10^{-17} sec^2/cm at 30° C) and this indicates that probably another relaxation phenomenon is present at higher frequencies. The lowfrequency relaxation effect has a relaxation frequency which increases with temperature; also $(\alpha\lambda)_{max}$ increase with T. Acetic acid has been

[1] P. BAZULIN: Dokl. Acad. Nauk. SSSR. **3**, 285 (1936). — P. BAZULIN and J. M. MERSAN: Dokl. Acad. Nauk. SSSR. **24**, 690 (1939).

[2] J. LAMB and J. M. M. PINKERTON: Proc. Roy. Soc. Lond., Ser. A **199**, 114 (1949).

studied in the vapour phase and it is well established that dimerization occurs with two molecules held together by two hydrogen bonds and an equilibrium is present between single and double molecules. Since the first experiment of BAZULIN in acetic acid it was suggested (by SPAKOWSKI[1]) that the observed relaxation was bound to this equilibrium and this was the first opinion of PINKERTON and LAMB. They assumed that: (1) the equilibrium obeys the kinetics of a first order reaction $A \rightleftharpoons B$; (2) K_{21} has a form

$$K_{21} = D\,T^m \exp\left(-\frac{\Delta W_2^*}{RT}\right)$$

with m equal to zero or to a small positive number. This means that

$$f_{rm} = \frac{1}{2\pi\tau} = \frac{K_{21}}{2\pi} = \frac{D}{2\pi}\,T^m \exp\left(-\frac{\Delta W_2^*}{RT}\right). \tag{23.1}$$

The experiment did not allow one to determine the exact value of m but yielded a value of 8.86 kcal/mole for ΔW_2^* for dissociation. This value is very different from the heat of complete dissociation in the gas phase (15.94 kcal/mole at 25° C). For this reason LAMB and PINKERTON suggested that the reaction could proceed in two or more steps and the observed phenomena could be connected with the breaking of only one hydrogen bond[2].

It is to be observed, however, that the formation of dimers is not a firstorder reaction, $2\,CH_3COOH \rightleftharpoons (CH_3COOH)_2$ as assumed by PINKERTON and LAMB: the reaction in the forward direction is of second order while the reverse reaction is of first order. FREEDMANN[3] applied to this case the correct relations and found a value for the heat of reaction of -6.21 kcal/mole. Moreover FREEDMANN has calculated for ΔH a value of -6.5 kcal/mole in pure acetic acid in liquid state from the values recently obtained for association of acetic acid in benzene. The two values compare satisfactorily. This would suggest that the observed relaxation in acetic acid is due to the equilibrium between dimeric and monomeric state[4].

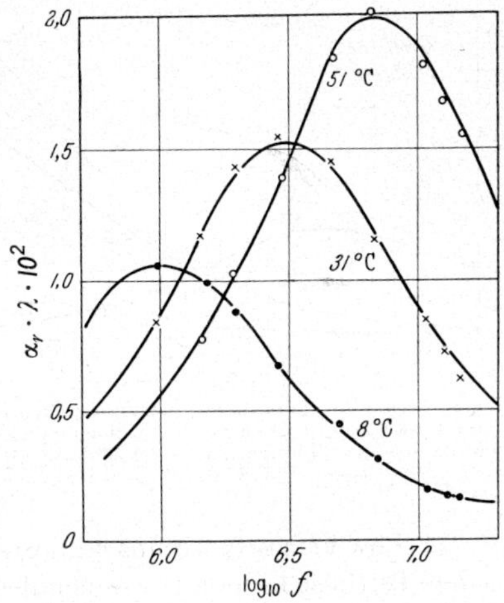

Fig. 14. $\alpha_r\,\lambda$ versus frequency in propionic acid (J. LAMB and H. A. HUDDART).

Fig. 14 gives the results of LAMB and HUDDART[5] for the relaxing part of the absorption coefficient per wavelength $(\alpha_r \cdot \lambda)$ in propionic acid. The dispersion expected from the value of $(\alpha \cdot \lambda)_{max}$ is smaller than in acetic acid and it has not

---

[1] B. SPAKOWSKI: Dokl. Acad. Nauk. SSSR. **18**, 169 (1938).

[2] In a subsequent paper ANDREAE and LAMB have attributed the observed relaxation to excitation of flexural vibrations of the carbon-hydrogen bonds. Proc. Phys. Soc. Lond. B **64**, 1021 (1951).

[3] E. FREEDMANN: J. Chem. Phys. **21**, 1784 (1953).

[4] Recently LAMB has performed measurements of absorption in dilute solutions of acetic acid in n-hexane, nitrobenzene, toluene, and chlorobenzene. He finds a peak of the absorption coefficient at very low concentrations at frequencies of the order of 10 Mc/sec. He suggests that this maximum is bound to dimer-monomer equilibrium, so that the process observed at high concentrations should be different. (Communication in a seminar at Catholic University, Washington D.C., on May 31, 1956). [See J. PIERCY and J. LAMB: Trans. Faraday Soc. **52**, Part 7, 930 (1956) (Note added on proof).]

[5] J. LAMB and H. A. HUDDART: Trans. Faraday Soc. **46**, 540 (1950).

yet been measured[1]. Also in this case it seems that the absorption arises from the perturbation of the equilibrium monomerdimer. FREEDMANN has calculated $\Delta H = -9.33$ kcal/mole and the results seems to be in agreement with other information on this reaction.

Evidence of relaxation processes with a relaxation frequency around 5 Mc/sec has been found in formic acid by BAZULIN[2]; moreover some acetates (methyl, ethyl) and formates (ethyl) have been investigated although not so completely as acetic and propionic acid, showing the existence of relaxation processes in the megacycle region[3]. The Fig. 15 gives the experimental results in ethyl acetate collected by MARKHAM, BEYER and LINDSAY [13] together with the theoretical curves for two relaxation processes and for shear viscosity. The addition of the ordinates of the three theoretical curves (dashed line) seems well to fit the experiments. The possibility of the existence of two relaxation processes in ethyl acetate was first suggested by KNESER [12] and the relaxation frequencies have been adjusted to give the best fit with experiment. Of course this procedure is simply indicative of the possibility that two relaxations could be present.

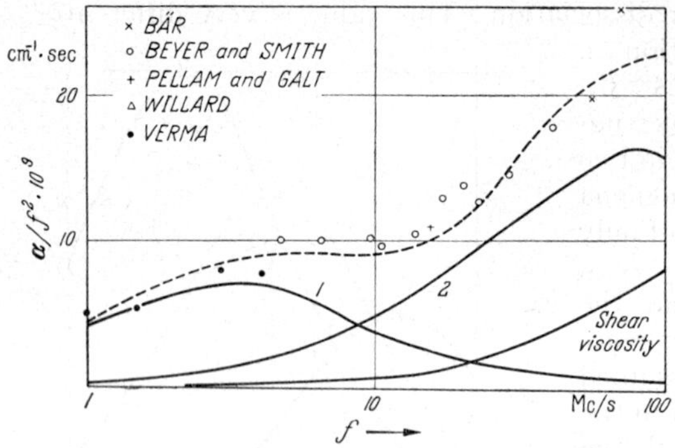

Fig. 15. Sound absorption in ethyl acetate: experimental results; theoretical curves (1, 2) for two relaxation processes, for shear viscsity and their addition (– – –) (J. MARKAM, R. T. BEYER and R. B. LINDSAY).

In formic acid, as well as in these acetates and formates, it seems plausible to admit that at least one of the relaxations present at low frequencies is of a nature similar to those in acetic and propionic acids. We have however already mentioned the suggestion of DE GROOT and LAMB[4] that the relaxation in esters may be due to same kind of rotational isomerism.

24. Low viscosity liquids with pressure-dependent structural effect. α) *The case of water.* In these liquids the molecules can be bound in various structures which have different specific volumes and energies. The pressure variations produced by sound waves alters the equilibrium between the forms and sound energy is lost.

We have already seen how this phenomenon can be treated by means of the theory of compressional relaxation or by visco-elasticity. These treatments are completely equivalent as long as the viscosity of the liquid is low; when the viscosity becomes high it is necessary to take fully into account the elasticity of the liquids and visco-elastic theory must be used.

The characteristic liquid of this class is water. The parameter α/f^2 remains constant over the whole range of experiment and velocity measurements at hyperfrequencies do not indicate dispersion up to 10^{10} cycles/sec[5].

[1] It has been recently measured: A. BARONE, G. PISENT and D. SETTE: Nuovo Cim. **7**, 365 (1958) (Note added on proof).

[2] P. BAZULIN: J. exp. theor. Phys. URSS. **8**, 457 (1938).

[3] See the review article [13].

[4] M. S. DE GROOT and J. LAMB: Trans. Faraday Soc. **51**, 1676 (1955).

[5] Velocity measurement at hyperfrequencies are made by studying the BRAGG reflection of a light beam on thermal waves by which thermal agitation is formed. These waves are elastic waves which have frequencies distributed in a wide range (up to 10^{10} cycles/sec) and propagate in all directions. The values obtained for the velocity of propagation are in some liquids smaller than the low-frequency sound velocity: this seems due to the change of propagation at these high frequencies from adiabatic to isothermal. For more details see [1].

In 1941 HERZFELD[1] showed that Eq. (7.8) of thermal relaxation theory if applied to the case of water would furnish a value of τ of 2×10^{-8} sec which is not in agreement with the observed constancy of α/f^2; this is an indication that thermal relaxation is not the prevalent dissipative process in water.

Further support to this conclusion was given by FOX and ROCK's measurements[2] of α as a function of temperature between 2° C and 40° C. The curve does not show any particular behaviour in the neighbourhood of 4° C where the thermal expansion coefficient of the liquid is zero and the adiabatic wave propagation becomes isothermal. In this case no changes of temperature are produced by sound waves and thermal relaxation ceases to exist because the equilibrium between internal and external degrees of freedom is not perturbed. DEBYE[3] (1939), HERZFELD and others suggested that the losses could be due to structural effects depending on pressure. L. HALL[4] (1948) worked out the theory of compressional relaxation based on a two-state model of the liquid presented in Sect. 9 above. According to BERNAL and FOWLER's[5] indications, water is thought to be a mixture of two structures: (1) an open one similar to the tetrahedral arrangement of molecules in ice and (2) a structure corresponding to close-packed molecules. HALL assigns to state 1 a larger volume and a lower energy, to state 2 a smaller volume and a higher energy. The majority of molecules is in state 1.

The theory of compressional relaxation yields the formulae (9.14), (9.16), (9.20) for the relaxing compressibility, χ_r, the relaxation time and the low-frequency absorption coefficient.

Because for the passage from state 1 to state 2 the molecules must break the same bonds and overcome the same barriers as for shear flow, HALL assumed that the activation energies for shear and compressional flows are of the same order of magnitude. If, moreover, one assumes that the number of molecules in state 1 is much larger than in state 2, then ΔW_1^* can be put equal to the activation energy for shear viscous flow, ΔW_η^*. The latter can be evaluated using the EYRING expression for η:

$$\eta = \frac{h N_A}{V} \exp \frac{\Delta W_\eta^*}{RT} \tag{24.1}$$

where N_A is the AVOGADRO's number and V the molar volume. Eq. (9.16), yields:

$$\tau = \frac{V}{RT[1+\exp(\Delta W_\eta^*/RT)}\,\eta. \tag{24.2}$$

In order to compare theory and experiment it is necessary to evaluate two of the tree quantities, $\Delta W = \Delta H$, $(V_1 - V_2)$, χ_∞ which are to be introduced in the formulae for χ_r, τ, and α.

HALL's estimates of V_1 is between 18 and 19.6 cm³ and of V_2 10.4 cm³. He uses the average value of $(V_2 - V_1)/V_0 = 0.47$. The value for χ_∞ is between 15×10^{-12} and 18×10^{-12} cm²/dyne. Eq. (9.14) yields $\Delta H \approx 0.5$ kcal/mole, a value which seems to indicate that state 1 and 2 differ by one hydrogen bond.

Fig. 16 gives the theoretical curve calculated by HALL for α/f^2 vs. temperature and the experimental results of PINKERTON[6], FOX and ROCK, and SMITH and

[1] K. F. HERZFELD: J. Acoust. Soc. Amer. **13**, 33 (1941).
[2] F. E. FOX and G. D. ROCK: J. Acoust. Soc. Amer. **12**, 505 (1940).
[3] P. DEBYE: Z. Elektrochem. **45**, 174 (1939).
[4] L. HALL: Phys. Rev. **73**, 775 (1948).
[5] J. D. BERNAL and FOWLER: J. Chem. Phys. **1**, 515 (1933).
[6] J. M. M. PINKERTON: Nature, Lond. **160**, 128 (1947).

BEYER[1]. The relaxation times calculated by HALL are 4×10^{-12} sec at 0° C and 0.64×10^{-12} sec at 80° C and they are consistent with the absence of dispersion up to hypersound frequencies and the constancy of α/f^2 in the experimental range.

β) Pressure dependence of absorption in water. Recently LITOVITZ and CARNEVALE[2] have investigated the pressure dependence of absorption in water and they have found valuable information on the compressional losses. In Table 9 are given their results obtained at 0° C (25 Mc/sec) and 30° C (45 Mc/sec) up to 2000 kg/cm². The absorption is expresssed by LITOVITZ and CARNEVALE by means of a relation:

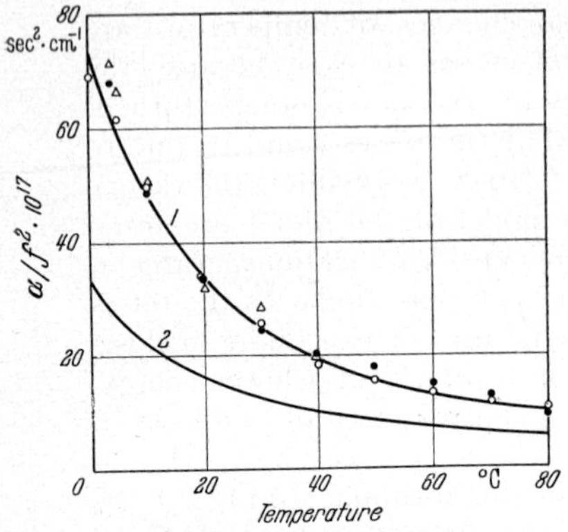

Fig. 16. Sound absorption vs. temperature in water: 1, HALL's treatment; 2, shear viscosity (L. HALL).

$$\alpha_{\exp} = \frac{2\pi f^2}{\varrho c_0^3}\left(\frac{4}{3}\eta + \eta_c\right) \qquad (24.3)$$

according to either (11.4) or (15.7). From this equation they calculate η_c (compressional viscosity) in the last column of Table 9.

If one wishes to apply the HALL theory at various pressures it is necessary to observe that the free energy difference between the two states $\Delta W = W_2 - W_1 = \Delta H$ depends upon pressure and the variation of ΔW is equal to $-p\Delta V$. When the pressure raises, the close-packed arrangement becomes more probable because it has the smaller volume and accordingly ΔW decreases. In order to calculate the variation of ΔW with p it is necessary to make some assumption regarding the dependence of ΔV on p. LITOVITZ and CARNEVALE resonably assume that the ice-like structure is more compressible than the close-packed structure and, because the proportion of the latter state present in the liquid increases with pressure, ΔV should decrease when pressure increases. A resonable calculation indicates a decrease of about 10% in ΔV between 1 and 2000 kg/cm². This corresponds to a decrease of ΔW from 500 cal/mole obtained by HALL at atmospheric pressure to 140 cal/mole at 2000 kg/cm². It is then possible to see that HALL's theory predicts an increase of α/f^2 while the experiment indicates a decrease of this parameter with pressure.

Table 9. *Sound velocity and absorption in water as functions of pressure* (T. A. LITOVITZ and E. H. CARNEVALE).

T °C	P kg/cm²	c m/sec	$\alpha_\eta/f^2\cdot 10^{17}$ sec² cm⁻¹	$\alpha_{\exp}/f^2\cdot 10^{17}$ sec² cm⁻¹	$\alpha_{\exp}/\alpha_\eta$	η_c cpoise
0	1	1404	17.0	57.5	3.40	5.67
0	500	1492	12.9	47.1	3.65	5.94
0	1000	1580	10.6	38.5	3.63	5.69
0	1500	1669	9.0	30.5	3.39	5.30
0	2000	1757	7.7	24.7	3.21	5.12
30	1	1510	6.10	18.5	3.01	2.15
30	500	1595	5.30	15.4	2.91	2.05
30	1000	1677	4.62	12.7	2.75	2.02
30	1500	1756	4.20	11.1	2.64	1.95
30	2000	1830	3.63	9.9	2.75	2.03

[1] M. SMITH and R. BEYER: Phys. Rev. **73**, 654 (1948).

[2] T. A. LITOVITZ and E. H. CARNEVALE: J. Appl. Phys. **26**, 816 (1955).

LITOVITZ and CARNEVALE therefore suggest a modification of HALL's theory assuming that the open-packed state has the higher free energy. Then ΔW would increase by $p\Delta V$ when the pressure rises and α/f^2 would decrease. Fig. 17 gives the pressure dependence of the structural absorption as a function of pressure in water. The curves are calculated assuming that the open-packed structure possesses the higher energy. The agreement between theory and experiment is within 6% in the range of pressure 1 to 2000 kg/cm². LITOVITZ and CARNEVALE also point out that a temperature dependence of ΔW is to be assumed. The pressure data seem to suggest a variation from 500 cal/mole at 0° C to 650 cal per mole at 30° C.

γ) Ratio $\alpha_{\text{exp}}/\alpha_c$ and temperature. An experimental result, already observed by FOX and ROCK, is that in water the ratio $\frac{\alpha_{\text{exp}}}{\alpha_\eta} \approx \frac{\alpha_{\text{exp}}}{\alpha_c}$ remains practically constant with temperature. If one assumes that the origins of the losses are viscosity and the lag of the equilibrium among structural forms with respect to pressure, the absorption is given by the expression (24.3) where the coefficient of viscosity, which appears together with shear viscosity, is the bulk viscosity coefficient of the hydrodynamical theory or the compressional viscosity coefficient of the visco-elastic theory. Therefore

$$\frac{\alpha_{\text{exp}}}{\alpha_\eta} = \frac{\frac{4}{3}\eta + \eta_c}{\frac{4}{3}\eta} = \frac{4\eta + 3\eta_c}{4\eta}. \tag{24.4}$$

Because this ratio is about 3 in water, $\eta_c \approx \frac{8}{3}\eta$.

This result points to a close connection between the processes which are responsible for shear and compressional viscosities in these liquids, as is suggested by the visco-elastic theory.

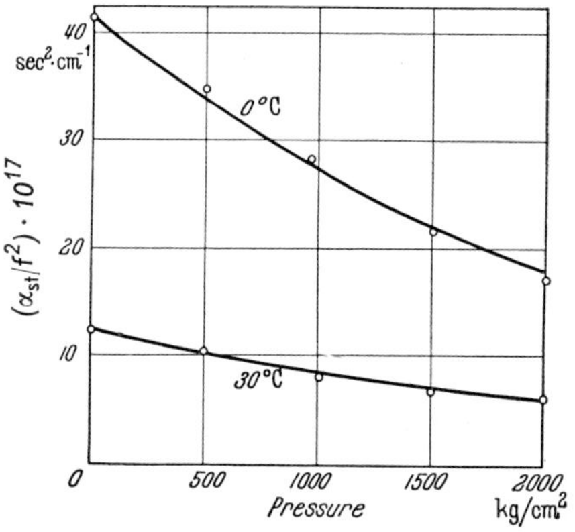

Fig. 17. Pressure dependence of structural absorption in water: theoretical curves and experimental results (T. A. LITOVITZ and E. H. CARNEVALE).

δ) Other liquids. To the category of low viscosity liquids with pressure-dependent structural effects there belong various strongly associated substances like alcohols. These are liquids which are characterized by strong interactions among molecules and seem to have a solidlike structure. In these cases the distribution of energy among the degrees of freedom of single molecules is very fast because of the coupling among molecules so that thermal relaxation loses importance.

As in water, however, the molecules of these liquids can be found in various structural forms whose equilibrium may be altered by a sound wave. In contrast to the case of water at 4° C the propagation is not isothermal so that probably both pressure and temperature variations affect the equilibrium.

In Table 10[1] there are given for various alcohols the experimental values of the ratio $\alpha_{\text{exp}}/\alpha_\eta$ at different temperatures. It stays approximately constant as in water and this can be taken as an argument in favour of the prevalent importance of the pressure-dependent structural effect in these liquids.

[1] Values from J. M. M. PINKERTON: Proc. Roy. Soc. Lond., Ser. B **62**, 129 (1949) and J. R. PELLAM and J. K. GALT: J. Chem. Phys. **14**, 608 (1946).

Table 10. *Ratio α_{exp}/α_c for water and alcohols.*

Liquid	T (°C)	f Mc/sec	$\alpha_{exp}/f^2 \times 10^{17}$ ($cm^{-1} sec^2$)	$\alpha_\eta/f^2 \times 10^{17}$ ($cm^{-1} sec$)	α_{exp}/α_c
Water	0	7.5—67.5	59.6	17.09	3.33
	20		25.3	8.16	3.10
	40		14.6	4.85	3.01
	60		10.15	3.36	3.00
	80		7.89	2.58	3.06
	100		6.87	2.11	3.26
Methyl alcohol	2	15	45	15	3
	19.3		37	14	2.64
Ethyl alcohol	−50	52.4	137.0	68.4	2.00
	−30		93.2	47.6	1.94
	−10		67.6	35.2	1.92
	10		55.9	27.4	2.04
	30		48.7	22.9	2.13
	50		44.9	19.8	2.27
	70		42.4	17.8	2.39
n-propyl alcohol	2	15	87	55	1.58
	27.5		70	36	1.94
n-buthyl alcohol	2	15	106.5	65	1.64
n-amyl alcohol	2.8	15	155	103	1.37
	28.6		106	58	1.82

The characteristic properties of liquids belonging to the category which we are considering are as follows:

1. α/f^2 is constant in the frequency range of experiment and therefore no dispersion is observed.

2. α has a value a few times the classical one and the ratio α/α_c is approximately temperature-independent.

3. α decreases quickly when the temperature is raised.

The last circumstance is essentially due to the destructive effect of thermal agitation on the structures of the liquid.

Table 11. *Absorption coefficient in some typical liquids with pressure depending structural effect.*

Liquid	Frequency Mc/sec	Temperature °C	$\alpha_{exp}/f^2 \times 10^{17}$ $cm^{-1} sec^2$	$\alpha_c/f^2 \times 10^{17}$ $cm^{-1} sec^2$
Methyl alcohol	1—250	20—25	34	14.5
Ethyl alcohol	1—220	20—25	54	22
n-propyl alcohol	15—280	22—28	75	36
n-bythyl alcohol	1—4	25	104	50
n-amyl alcohol	15	29	106	58

In Table 11 the values of α/f^2 are given for some typical liquids of this category.

Fig. 18 gives α/f^2 *vs.* pressure in some primary alcohols, as obtained by CARNEVALE and LITOVITZ[1] at 45 Mc/sec. The absorption coefficient decreases when the pressure increases. The ratio η_c/η decreases with pressure, i.e. η_c increases less than η.

Some attempts to apply to the alcohols the two-state model of compressional losses which has been successful for water have been made without much advantage. SETTE[2] tried to apply HALL's treatment to ethyl alcohol, but he found a value of α/f^2 for structural relaxation much smaller than the difference between experimental and classical values of the parameters.

[1] E. H. CARNEVALE and T. A. LITOVITZ: J. Acoust. Soc. Amer. **27**, 547 (1955).
[2] D. SETTE: Phys. Rev. **78**, 476 (1950).

CARNEVALE and LITOVITZ recently tried to explain the pressure variation of absorption in alcohol on the basis of HALL's treatment and reached the result that no combination of ΔF and ΔV could be found to bring theory in agreement with experiment in the whole range of pressure studied.

It therefore seems that in the case of alcohols a two-state model is inadequate for the description of structural losses and that more than two states are to be considered.

This conclusion is supported by the results in n-propyl alcohol[1] in the region of high viscosity where it is necessary to assume the existence of a distribution of relaxation times, because the relaxation theory with a single relaxation time is inadequate to describe the absorption and dispersion data. This is equivalent to saying that more than two states are present in n-propyl alcohol.

The case of n-propyl-alcohol at low temperature, i.e. in the high viscosity range, will be considered in the next section (subsection γ). It is very important because it is the only simple liquid which has been studied in both low and high viscosity ranges and it clearly shows the gradual increase of importance of viscoelastic properties as the viscosity increases.

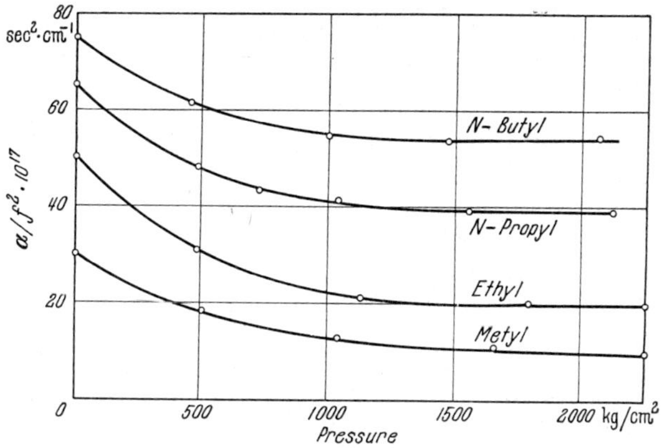

Fig. 18. Sound absorption vs. pressure in some primary alcohols (E. H. CARNEVALE and T. A. LITOVITZ).

25. Liquids with strong visco-elastic effects. *α) High viscosity liquid.* It has been customary to consider the high viscosity liquids as a particular category not because the origins of losses in them were different from those which are manifest in the low viscosity liquids, but because sometimes the high value of viscosity gives a special form to the experimental results.

Early work[2] seemed to indicate for some liquids of this category values of α/f^2 which, in a temperature range around room temperature, were in agrement, with the classical ones, given by (3.1) within the limits of experimental accuracy. Further research has however shown for most of them that α/f^2 is frequency-dependent and that at certain temperatures and frequencies can become lower than the classical value. Discussion is still pending on the possibility of explaining some of the experiments by means of exact solutions of visco-thermal theory. In this respect dispersion measurements have great importance, because, as was pointed out, for the visco-thermal theory the dispersion should increase indefinitely with frequency, while relaxation processes produce a leveling-off of velocity at high frequencies. While doubts exist on the nature of the more important dissipative processes in some viscous liquids, in others the indications are in favour of a visco-elastic behaviour, i.e. the situation is not different from that existing in low viscosity liquids with pressure-dependent structural effects except for the fact that, frequently, the viscosity is sufficiently high that the visco-elastic properties are fully shown in the frequency range of experiment. We will

[1] T. LYON and T. A. LITOVITZ: J. Appl. Phys. **27**, 179 (1956).
[2] J. L. HUNTER: J. Acoust. Soc. Amer. **13**, 36 (1941).

indicate some typical experimental results in liquids of this category, especially in liquids of simple constitution; other examples of high viscosity liquids will be found in the treatment of long-chain polymers.

Among the first measurements on high viscosity liquids are those of MIKHAILOV and GUREVICH[1] on resin, between 0.5 and 5 Mc/sec. They found that the absorption at a fixed frequency increases with viscosity (changing temperature) when the latter is small. If the viscosity is increased to high values a maximum of the absorption coefficient is first reached: afterwards the absorption coefficient decreases with increasing viscosity. MARKHAN, BEYER and LINDSAY [*13*] are in favour of an explanation based on exact solutions of STOKES' equations in which only one viscosity coefficient is present; the lack of dispersion measurements does not allow one to draw sure conclusions on this point.

β) The case of glycerine. Similarly appear the experimental results in glycerine where the existence of a compressional viscosity and the presence of relaxation processes in both viscosities seem to have been established. Figs. 19 and 20 respectively give the results of absorption measurements at 31 Mc/sec (LITOVITZ[2]) and of velocity at 30 Mc/sec (FOX-LITOVITZ[3]) in glycerine having a water content of 5% and a viscosity at 26° C of 3.41 poise. FOX and LITOVITZ have compared these results with those indicated by the exact solution of STOKES' equation according to LUCAS[4] and do not find agreement because the experimental value of maximum absorption is only one third of the theoretical prediction and the velocity seems to level off at high viscosities instead of increasing indefinitely with it.

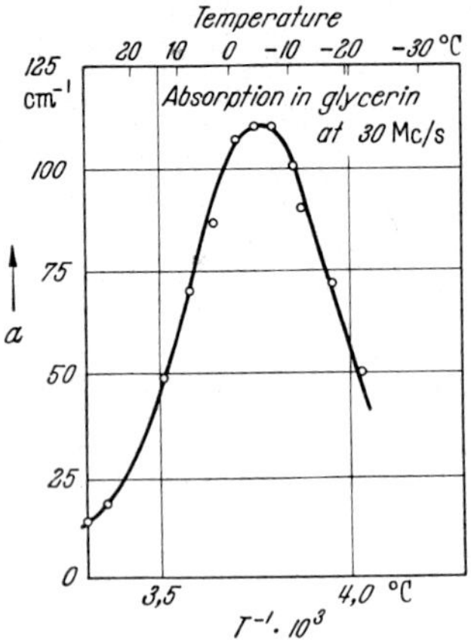

Fig. 19. Sound absorption in glycerin (T. A. LITOVITZ).

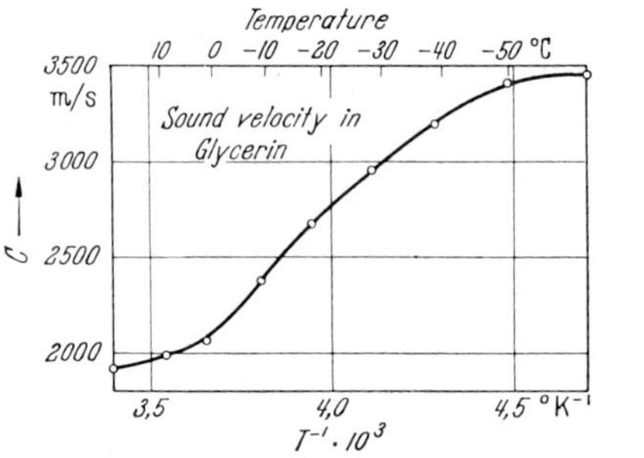

Fig. 20. Sound velocity in glycerin (F. E. FOX and T. A. LITOVITZ).

The results can instead be explained on relaxation processes by means of visco-elastic theory. In the range between about 0° C and 40° C the ratio $\alpha_{\exp}/\alpha_c$ is about 2, where α_c is given by (3.1). This shows that notwithstanding the high values of shear viscosity the situation is similar to that found in associated low viscosity liquids ($\alpha_{\exp}/\alpha_c \approx 1 \div 3$) and can be explained by means of a compressional viscosity. The contribution of the compressional viscosity would be about the same as that of the shear viscosity in the range 20 to 30° C, and the activation energies of the two processes, as may be shown, are of the same order. The ratio $\alpha_{\exp}/\alpha_c$ has fallen below unity at $-10°$ C and it indicates that at these

[1] I. G. MIKHAILOV and S. B. GUREVICH: J. exp. theor. Phys. USSR. **19**, 193 (1949).
[2] T. A. LITOVITZ: J. Acoust. Soc. Amer. **23**, 75 (1951).
[3] See Ref. [*5*], p. 38.
[4] R. LUCAS: C. R. Acad. Sci., Paris **206**, 658 (1938).

temperatures the relaxation times of both viscous processes are so large that the flow does not follow the sound wave at 31 Mc/sec. LITOVITZ assumes that the activation energies for the two viscous processes are equal, and this means that τ_S and τ_2 given by (13.2) and (14.4) are equal:

$$\tau_S = \tau_2 = \tau_0 \exp\left(\frac{\Delta W}{kT}\right). \tag{25.1}$$

This assumption finds support in a fair agreement between experiment and the consequent indications of visco-elastic theory. τ_0 is about 10^{-19} sec. The experimental curves for absorption and dispersion, although they have the general form of those indicated by visco-elastic theory with the assumption of only one relaxation time, show various deviations. The bell-shaped curve of absorption vs. viscosity is broader than the single relaxation time curve and it is asymmetrical towards the high viscosities. Similar deviations are found in the dispersion curves.

It could be supposed either that the relaxation times of the two viscous processes are not equal or that a distribution of relaxation times is present in both processes.

LITOVITZ and SETTE[1] have compared the acoustic and dielectric behaviour of glycerine. They found that reduced dielectric and ultrasonic constants plotted vs. viscosity at 30° C are similar. The imaginary parts of the constants, which represent the losses, have a peak at the same viscosity. In both cases similar deviations from single relaxation time processes have been observed; for instance the bell-shaped curves of losses have a maximum lower than the theoretical and they are asymetric in the same way (Fig. 21).

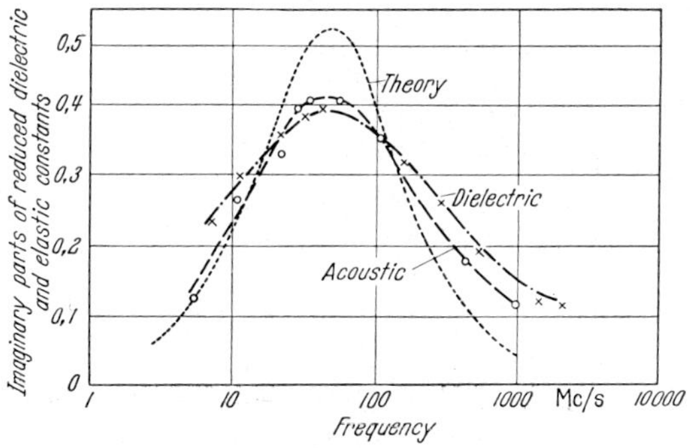

Fig. 21. Acoustic and dielectric losses in glycerin (T. A. LITOVITZ and D. SETTE).

A similarity exists therefore between dielectric and ultrasonic behaviour of the liquid. In the theory of dielectric relaxation a factor of importance is the rate at which rotational jumps of molecules are happening so that the molecules may change orientation; the acoustic behaviour depends on the two viscosities, i.e. upon the rates at which the molecules jump to new positions under a shear or a compressional stress.

The departure of the dielectric phenomena from the theory for a single relaxation time process has been attributed to the presence of a distribution of relaxation times as a consequence of fluctuations of activation energy for rotation of dipoles, due to changes of configuration around a molecule produced by thermal agitation.

In the acoustic case, part of the deviation could be due to a difference of the two times τ_S and τ_2. It seems, however, that as for dielectric relaxation thermal fluctuation must produce a distribution of relaxation times for both viscous processes. The striking similarity of acoustic and dielectric behaviour seems to indicate that a possible difference between τ_S and τ_2 is masked by the very probable existence of a distribution of relaxation times for the two kinds of viscous processes.

[1] T. A. LITOVITZ and D. SETTE: J. Chem. Phys. **21**, 17 (1953).

LITOVITZ' and SETTE's results therefore suggest that the behaviour of glycerine could be explained by means of the visco-elastic theory maintaining the approximation $\tau_S = \tau_2$ and assuming a suitable distribution of relaxation times.

γ) The case of n-propyl-alcohol. Distribution of relaxation times. Recently LYON and LITOVITZ[1] have studied a liquid of simpler constitution, n-propyl-alcohol, which can be cooled to high viscosities before freezing. It has been studied between 2° C and −155° C in the frequency range 1 to 82 Mc/sec; the viscosity goes from about 0.02 poise at 2° C to 2.3×10^6 poise to −155° C. At temperatures where α/f^2 is constant the ratio $\alpha_{\text{exp}}/\alpha_c$ is 1.77. It is an associated liquid where according to (24.3) the compressional viscosity is equal to the shear viscosity within the limit of experimental accuracy.

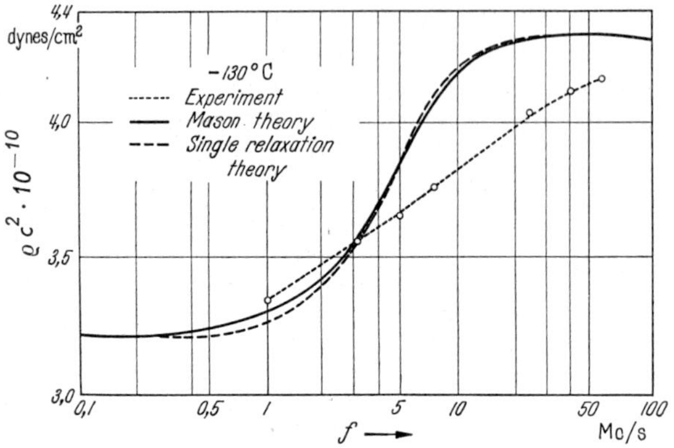

Fig. 22. Velocity dispersion in n-propyl alcohol (T. LYON and T. A. LITOVITZ).

Figs. 22 and 23 give typical results. The dashed lines are calculated by means of visco-elastic theory (15.2) assuming equal shear and compressional relaxation times. The measured absorption per wavelength gives a curve which is broader than the single relaxation curve, and it is asymmetrical. The calculated maximum is about twice the experimental one. The experimental results cannot be explained assuming only two relaxation times.

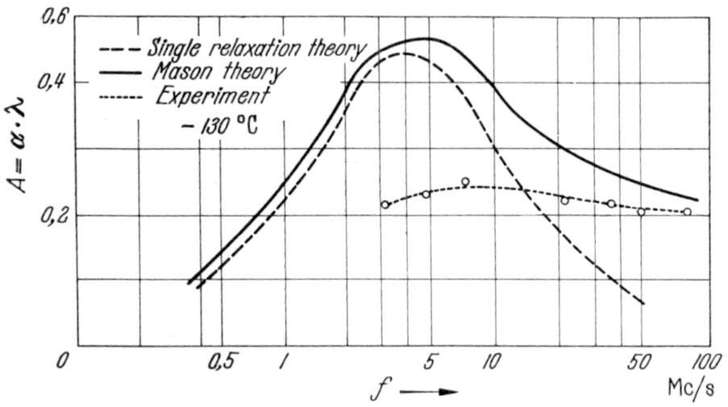

Fig. 23. Absorption per wave length in n-propyl alcohol (T. LYON and T. A. LITOVITZ).

MASON[2], treating similar cases in polymers, has suggested the possibility of an "hysteresis" component of losses in order to explain the almost constant value of absorption coefficient per wavelength at high frequencies.

In Figs. 22 and 23 the full lines indicate the curves obtained from MASON's theory. Although it is possible that hysteresis effects are present, it is evident that the main deviation between experiment and single relaxation time theory must be produced by other causes. LITOVITZ and LYON therefore suggest the existence of a distribution of relaxation times. Their results in n-propyl-alcohol at low temperatures (high shear viscosity) seem to indicate that a distribution of relaxation times is necessary to explain the compressional losses, while they are not sufficient to decide whether such a necessity exists also for shear losses. The shear relaxation time is longer than the relaxation times involved in the compressional relaxation.

[1] T. LYON and T. A. LITOVITZ: J. Appl. Phys. **27**, 179 (1956).

[2] W. P. MASON: Piezoelectric crystals and their application to ultrasonics. New York: Van Nostrand 1950.

δ) Other viscous liquids. Similar results were obtained by LITOVITZ, LYON and PESELNICK[1] in pentachloro-biphenyl whose viscosity strongly depends on temperature. The ratio α_{exp}/α_c is constant and equal to 3.27 at temperatures around 70° C; it falls to about 0.2 at 20° C. Also in this case absorption coefficient and dispersion data deviate from the indications of a single relaxation time theory, and asymmetry of the same type as already mentioned is present. A distribution of relaxation times has to be assumed but in this case it is especially evident that there is a component of the absorption coefficient at very high viscosities which is linearly dependent on frequency and which could be due to some hysteresis effect of MASON's type. Fig. 24 gives the absorption coefficient at 0° C between 7 and 50 Mc/sec.

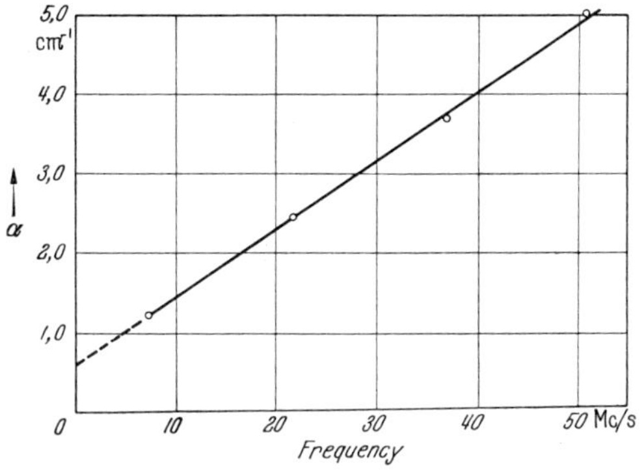

Fig. 24. Sound absorption vs. frequency at 0° C in pentachlorobiphenyl (T. A. LITOVITZ, T. LYON and L. PESELNICK).

Researches on castor oil have been made by NOMOTO, KISHIMOTO and IKEDA[2] and recently by WUENSCH, HUETER and COHEN[3]. Also in this liquid it has been found that at temperatures of about 50° C α_{exp}/α_c is bigger than unity although very close to it, while the ratio decreases to values smaller than unity when the temperature decreases. Fig. 25 gives the results of WUENSCH

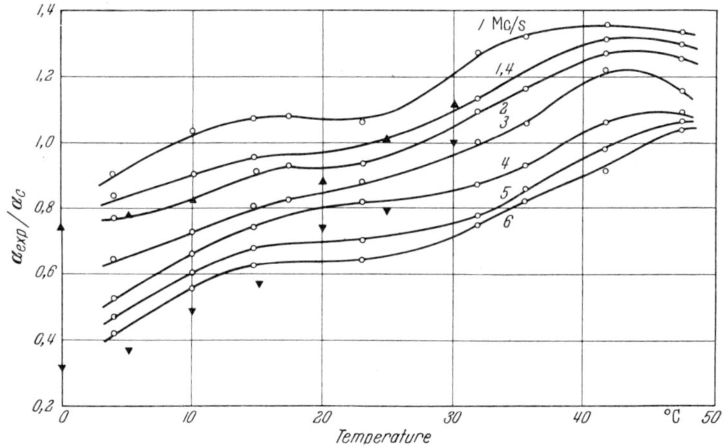

Fig. 25. Sound absorption in castor oil (B. J. WUENSCH, T. F. HUETER and M. S. COHEN).

et al. and some results of NOMOTO et al. It is therefore evident that also in the case of castor oil, a liquid of more complicated nature than the other ones previously examined, the behaviour is that of a visco-elastic liquid.

PRYOR and RICHARDSON[4] studied liquid sulphur between 100 and 250° C particularly in the transition region where polymerization occurs. Their results can be explained by means of a relaxing compressional viscosity.

[1] T. A. LITOVITZ, T. LYON and L. PESELNICH: J. Acoust. Soc. Amer. **26**, 566 (1954).
[2] O. NOMOTO, T. KISHIMOTO and T. IKEDA: Bull. Kahayasi Inst. Tokio **2**, 72 (1952).
[3] B. J. WUENSCH, T. F. HUETER and M. S. COHEN: J. Acoust. Soc. Amer. **28**, 311 (1956).
[4] A. W. PRYOR and E. G. RICHARDSON: J. Phys. Chem. **59**, 14 (1955).

III. Binary mixtures of liquids.

26. Binary mixtures of unassociated liquids. The measurements of sound absorption in mixtures formed by two unassociated liquids have furnished results, which, as has already been mentioned, have given support to the explanation of the excess absorption on the basis of thermal relaxation of vibrational modes.

Figs. 26 and 27 give the results in two typical mixtures of unassociated liquids: in the first case, benzene-toluene, the two components have very different absorption coefficients, in the second, benzene-carbon tetrachloride, the pure liquids have absorption coefficients of the same order: the full lines are given by the theory developed by BAUER[1] for the first type of mixture and extended by SETTE[2].

The theoretical treatment is based on two basic ideas: (1) the excess of sound absorption in these liquids is due to relaxation phenomena in energy distribution between external and internal degrees of freedom of molecules; (2) when two liquids are mixed the deexcitation of a molecule happens faster in collisions with molecules of the different kind than in collision with molecules of the same kind. The reason for this can be seen in the fact that the vibrational levels of the molecules of the two kinds being different, energy exchange during collisions will always involve translational energy, i.e. it is not possible for a vibrational quantum to pass unchanged from one molecule to the other. The efficiency of collisions of molecules of different kinds is therefore higher in producing the equipartition of energy than the efficiency of collisions between similar molecules.

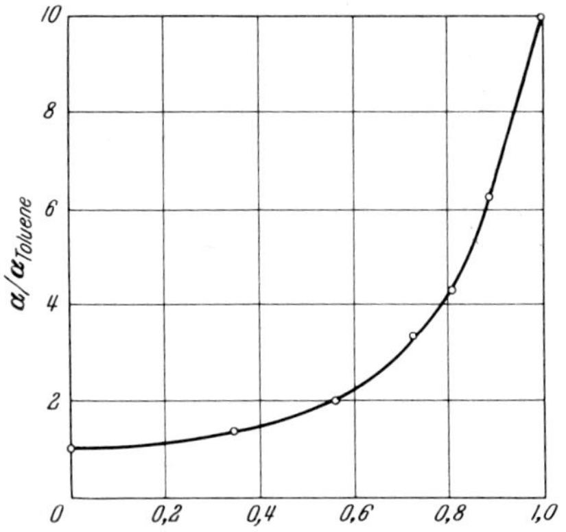

Fig. 26. Sound absorption in benzene-toluene mixtures: theoretical curve and experimental values (o) (E. BAUER).

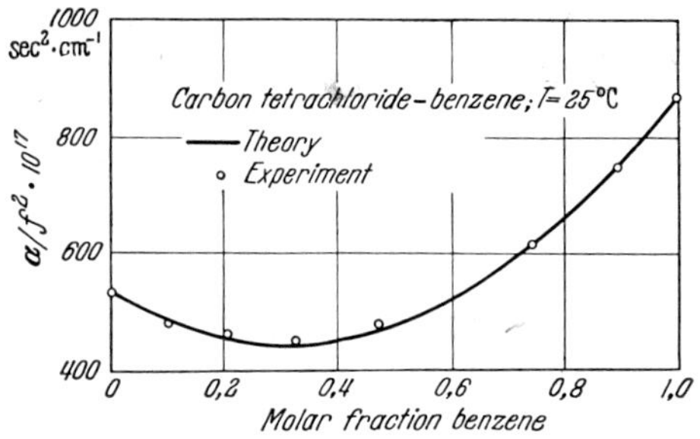

Fig. 27. Sound absorption in carbon tetrachloride—benzene mixtures.

To simplify the treatment it is also assumed that: (1) only binary collisions have importance; (2) collisions between excited molecules can be neglected; (3) the molecules can be found in the ground state (0) or at a single excited level.

Let a and $(1-a)$ be the mole fractions of the two components A the more absorbing and B, and a_0, b_0 the mole fractions of exited A and B molecules. Writing down two equations of detailed balance and applying a perturbation method, the following expression is obtained:

$$\frac{\alpha}{f^2} = 2\pi\left[\frac{\pi c}{c_\infty^2}(\gamma'-1)\frac{1}{C_p'}\right]\left[\frac{a\,C_A}{\Phi_{10}} + \frac{(1-a)\,C_B}{\Psi_{10}}\right] \tag{26.1}$$

where c and c_∞ respectively are the measured velocity of the mixture and the velocity at frequencies much higher than the mean dispersion frequency (f_{rm}); γ' is the ration C_p'/C_v' of the contributions of the external degrees of freedom

[1] E. BAUER: Proc. Phys. Soc. Lond. A **62**, 141 (1949).
[2] D. SETTE: J. Chem. Phys. **18**, 1592 (1950).

to the principal specific heats; C_A and C_B are the equilibrium values of the vibrational specific heats of A and B molecules. Moreover:

$$\left.\begin{aligned}\Phi_{10} &= k_{10}a_0 + g_{10}b_0,\\ \Psi_{10} &= l_{10}a_0 + h_{10}b_0\end{aligned}\right\} \tag{26.2}$$

k, g, l, h being the transition probabilities relating respectively to (AA), (AB), (BA), (BB) collisions. To simplify Eq. (26.1) it has been assumed to a first approximation that the quantity $\left[\frac{2\pi^2 c}{c_\infty^2}(\gamma'-1)\frac{1}{C_p'}\right]$ varies linearly with concentration and therefore can be written:

$$M_B(1-d\,a).$$

Among the transition probabilites the following relations may be written:

$$\left.\begin{aligned}z k_{ij} &= h_{ij},\\ g_{ij} &= t k_{ij} = \frac{t}{z} h_{ij},\\ l_{ij} &= u h_{ij}\end{aligned}\right\}(i,j=0,1). \tag{26.3}$$

Because the A component is more absorbing than B the (AA) collisions are less efficient than (BB) collisions, i.e. z is bigger than unity and it can be put equal to the ratio of the mean dispersion frequencies of B and A molecules, $z=f^B_{rm}/f^A_{rm}$. The coefficients t and u in Eqs. (26.3), according to the assumptions, are also bigger than unity and express how more efficient are collisions of different molecules in deexciting an A or B molecule than collisions of similar molecules. Eq. (26.1) can be written:

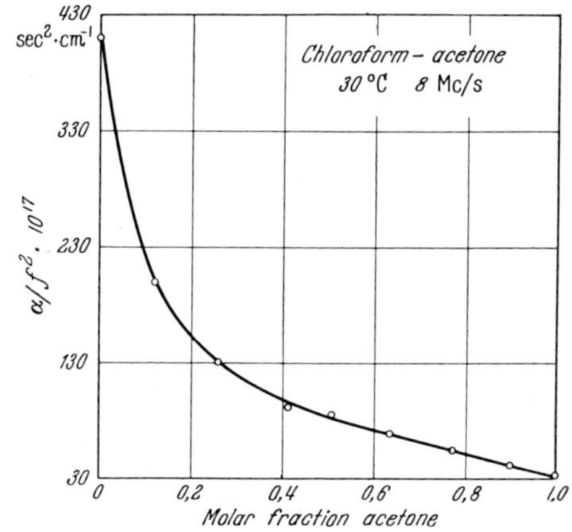

Fig. 28. Sound absorption in chloroform-acetone mixtures.

$$\frac{\alpha}{f^2} = \frac{2M_B}{h_{10}}(1-d\,a)\left[\frac{a\,z\,C_A}{a+t(1-a)} + \frac{(1-a)\,C_B}{1+a\,(u-1)}\right] \tag{26.4}$$

or

$$\frac{(\alpha/f^2)_a}{\alpha_B/f^2} = \frac{\alpha}{\alpha_B} = (1-d\,a)\left[\frac{a\,z}{a+t(1-a)}\,\frac{C_A}{C_B} + \frac{(1-a)}{1+a\,(u-1)}\right]. \tag{26.5}$$

Eq. (26.5) can be easily compared with experiment. The value of d can be determined putting $\alpha=\alpha_A$ for $a=1$.

When the two components have very different absorption coefficients, Eq. (26.5) can be further simplified assuming $g_{ij}=l_{ij}=h_{ij}$, i.e. $t=z$ and $u=1$. The theoretical curve of Fig. 26 has been obtained in this way[1]. Many binary systems shown such a dependence of the absorption coefficient on the composition: chloroform—toluene, carbon tetrachloride—toluene, carbon tetrachloride—acetone[2], benzene—nitrobenzene, chloroform—nitrobenzene[3], chloroform—acetone (Fig. 28). The temperature coefficient of the absorption of these mixtures is positive as it is in normal unassociated liquids and α/f^2 is frequency-independent in the range of experiment. Fig. 29 gives α/f^2 vs. temperature for some mixtures carbon tetrachloride—toluene[4].

[1] E. BAUER: Proc. Phys. Soc. Lond. A **62**, 141 (1949); experimental results by GROBE: Phys. Z. **39**, 333 (1938).
[2] D. SETTE: Ref. [4], p. 318.
[3] D. SETTE: J. Acoust. Soc. Amer. **23**, 359 (1951).
[4] A. MEZ and W. MAIER: Z. Naturforsch. **10**a, 997 (1955).

Fig. 27 refers to a case in which the two components, A benzene and B carbon tetrachloride, have absorption coefficient of the same order. For this mixture $t = 2.4$ and $u = 2.0$.

Of course the theoretical treatment is valid as long as the liquid mixtures behave, like the pure components, as unassociated liquids; the theory fails when the components although unassociated have molecules which can strongly interact when the two liquids mix. In these cases the curve absorption coefficient vs. composition assumes different shapes.

An example of this limitation of the theoretical treatment is obtained considering the systems carbon tetrachloride—chloroform and benzene—chloroform[1]. The chloroform molecules have a dipole with the positive termination of the surface and the negative one inside the molecules. For this reason, notwith-standing the appreciable dipole moment, chloroform molecules do not associate. Carbon tetrachloride has non-polar molecules which have high symmetry. The interactions between chloroform and carbon tetrachloride molecules are small and the mixtures of these two components behave as those of two unassociated liquids according to Eq. (26.5) (Fig. 30). In this case $t = 1$ and $u = 1.92$ if A is the carbon tetrachloride.

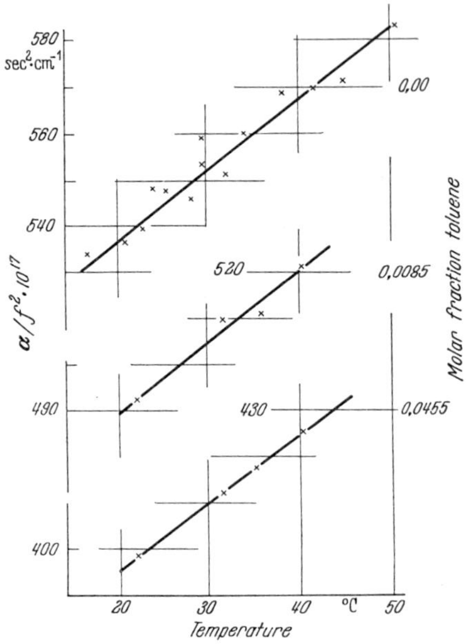

Fig. 29. Sound absorption vs. temperature in some carbon tetrachloride-toluene mixtures (A. MEZ and W. MAIER).

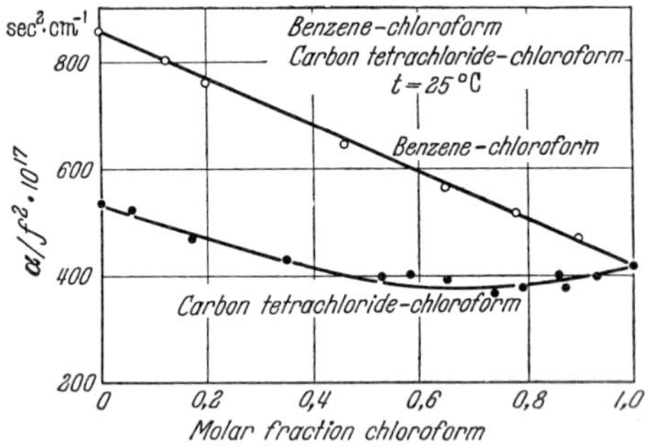

Fig. 30. Sound absorption in benzene—chloroform and carbon tetrachloride—chloroform mixtures.

Benzene molecules, in contrast to carbon tetrachloride molecules, have high polarizability and can interact strongly with chloroform molecules. The absorption curve is given in Fig. 30. If we try to apply Eq. (26.5), A being benzene, we find $t = 1.36$, while u for de-excitation of chloroform molecules in collisions with benzene molecules has a value 0.73 smaller than unity, in contrast with the ideas underlying the theory. This shows that the theory fails when strong interactions between molecules of the two unassociated compounds occur in the mixtures.

27. Binary mixture with structural effects. α) *Systems of an unassociated high absorbing liquid and an associated liquid.* The absorption coefficient of binary systems formed by an unassociated high absorbing liquid and an associated one shows a general behaviour similar to that found in mixtures of two unassociated liquids with very different absorption coefficients, i.e. when the less absorbing

---

[1] See footnote 3, p. 329.

liquid is added to the other the variation of the absorption is essentially due to the fast deexcitation of the molecules of the high absorbing unassociated component during collision with molecules of different kind. In some mixtures of this kind, however, it has been found by MEZ and MAIER[1] that a structural dissipative effect is also present at low concentrations of the associated liquids. This effect seems due to perturbation of equilibria among associations of molecules of the associated component, essentially the monomer—dimer equilibrium. This effect has been found in dilute solutions of phenol, alcohols and acetic acid in carbon tetrachloride, cyclohexane and chlorobenzene. It will be interesting to examine other unassociated solvents to see if this structural effect is always present or if it is limited to some unassociated solvents. It is to be observed in fact that, while the sound velocity of solutions of alcohols in carbon tetrachloride shows minima at molar concentrations of the same order of those for which the structural effects are found (<0.5) in the absorption coefficient and these minima are explained[2] assuming the formation of alcohol associations, the sound velocity of solutions of alcohol in benzene[3] does not show the minima at low alcohol concentration. This fact is believed due to the dissociation effect of benzene molecules which prevents the formation of alcohol associations at low concentrations: accordingly in the case of alcohol—benzene mixtures the increase of sound absorption at a molar concentration of alcohol smaller than 0.1 should not be present and the curve absorption coefficient vs. composition found by SETTE[4] (Fig. 31) which has the general behaviour found in a mixture of two unassociated liquids, should be correct also at mole fractions smaller than 0.07.

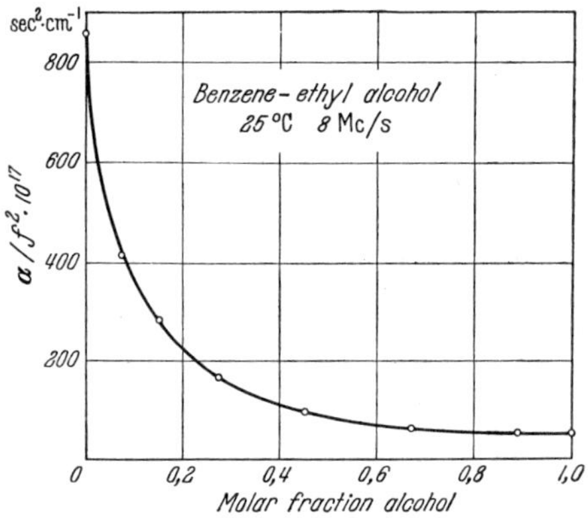

Fig. 31. Sound absorption in benzene—ethyl alcohol mixtures.

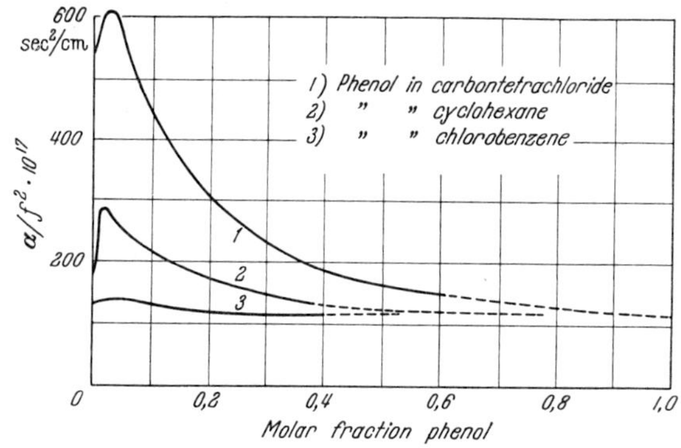

Fig. 32. Sound absorption in some phenol solutions (A. MEZ and W. MAIER).

Fig. 32 gives the results obtained at 20° C and 20 Mc/sec by MEZ and MAYER in solutions of phenol; the dashed curves are extrapolations beyond the solubility range of phenol in the solvent. The presence of maxima at low concentrations is evident. Fig. 33 refers to the low concentration range of phenol — carbon tetrachloride mixtures at different temperatures and Fig. 34 gives the temperature

[1] W. MAIER and A. MEZ: Z. Naturforsch. **7**a, 300 (1952); **10**a, 997 (1955).

[2] T. DERENZINI and A. GIACOMINI: Ric. Sci. **13**, 27 (1942).

[3] P. TUOMIKOSKI and U. NURMI: Comment. Phys. Mat. Helsinki **10**, 11 (1940); see also D. SETTE [*19*].

[4] D. SETTE: Nature Lond. **166**, 114 (1950).

dependence of the absorption coefficient for some mixtures of this system having molar concentrations of phenol between 0 and 0.05.

The excess of sound absorption over its classical value is partly due to thermal relaxation in the energy distribution among the external and vibrational degrees of freedom of the molecules. In the low concentration range, however, the maximum found in the absorption coefficient shows clearly that a new dissipative process is working. Although the dissipative effects of various origins are not strictly additive, we may assume to a first approximation that the superposition principle is valid and try to separate from the others the contribution of the new process to the absorption coefficient in order to investigate its origin.

MEZ and MAIER have used empirical methods to obtain from the experimental results this contribution to the absorption coefficient. They examine the varia-

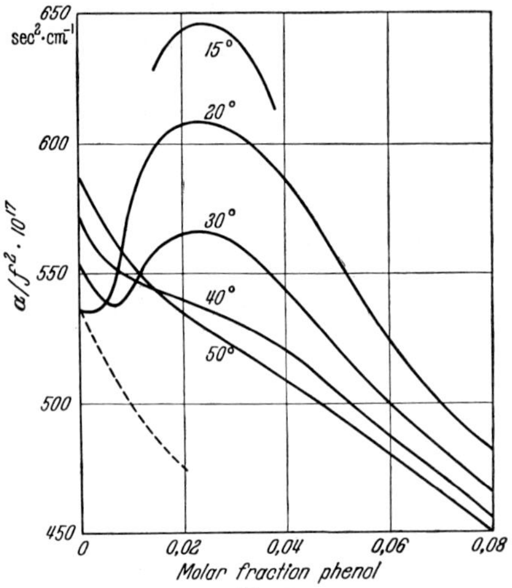

Fig. 33.

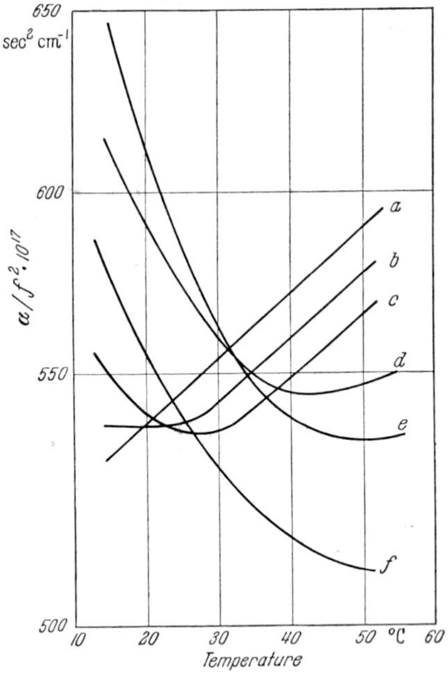

Fig. 34.

Fig. 33. Sound absorption in dilute solutions of phenol in carbon tetrachloride (A. MEZ and W. MAIER).

Fig. 34. Temperature dependence of sound absorption in some dilute solutions of phenol in carbon tetrachloride. Phenol molar fractions: (a) 0.00; (b) 0.0035; (c) 0.0065; (d) 0.0148; (e) 0.0241; (f) 0.0501.

tions of α with temperature for phenol—carbon tetrachloride mixtures (Fig. 34) and for some mixtures formed by two unassociated liquids like toluene and carbon tetrachloride (Fig. 29). In the last case α increases linearly with temperature, while in mixtures phenol—carbon tetrachloride of small phenol mole fractions (Fig. 34 curves for 0.0035 and 0.0065 mole fraction) the absorption coefficient decreases with increasing temperature in a low temperature range and only from a particular temperature it starts to increase with about the same temperature coefficient of the pure solvent. The temperature at which the temperature coefficient of α goes through zero from negative to positive values increases quickly with the phenol content of the mixture.

MEZ and MAIER use the curves α vs. temperature for low phenol concentrations (<0.01 mole fraction) to calculate the contribution to α of the new dissipative process. They extrapolate the linear portion of the curve with positive temperature coefficient to lower temperatures and take as an approximate value for the contribution, the difference of ordinates of the experimental curve and the extrapolated straight line, at the same temperature (Fig. 35).

For mole fractions higher than 0.01 up to 0.05 they use another approximate method. On the diagrams of Fig. 33 they plot the values obtained at low concentrations, with the previous procedure, for the difference of the experimental absorption coefficient and the contribution of the new process (dashed line, at 20° C). This difference is, of course, due to the classical absorption and to that produced by thermal relaxation of vibrational modes. The curve is then extrapolated to higher phenol concentrations. The difference of ordinates between this curve and the experimental one gives the estimated values of the contribution of the new process to α in mixtures of various phenol contents. In this way Mez and Maier calculate the diagram of Fig. 36 whichgives the estimated contribution to α/f^2 of the dissipative processes present at small phenol concentrations.

An explanation of these losses can be given assuming that the phenol molecules associate and that the equilibrium

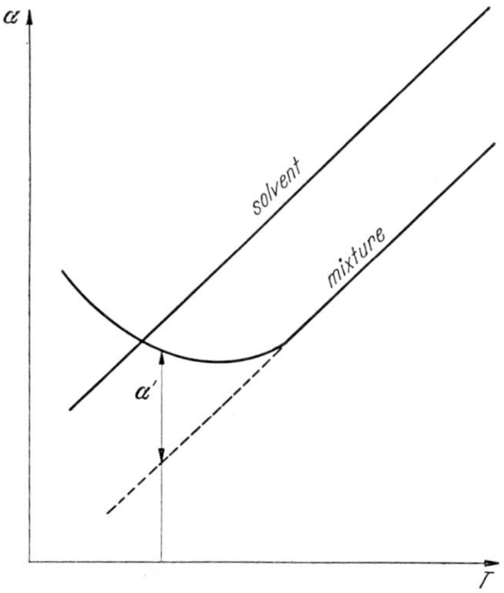

Fig. 35. Calculation of contribution α' of the new dissipative process in very dilute phenol solutions (A. Mez and W. Maier).

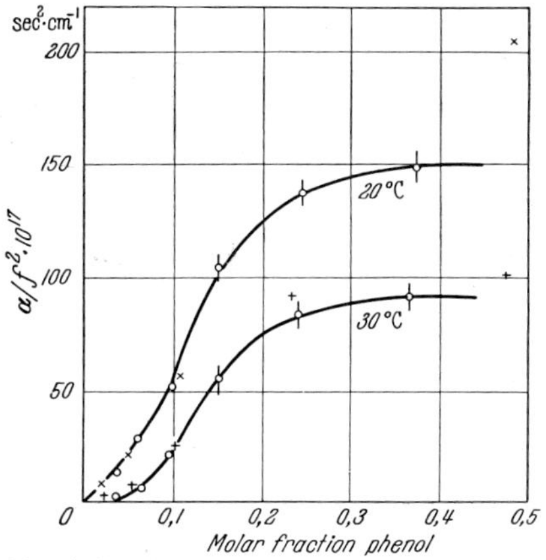

Fig. 36. Contribution to α/f^2 of the new dissipative process in phenol carbon tetrachloride mixtures: o, experimental values; ×, +, calculated values.

of single and associate molecules is altered by the sound wave so that a relaxation process is originated. Phenol molecules associate by hydrogen bonds and of course various associations are possible. At low concentrations, however, one can assume that the molecules associate mainly in pairs. The equilibrium to be considered is then:

$$\mathrm{Ph}_2 \rightleftharpoons 2\,\mathrm{Ph}.$$

Applying the theoretical treatment of relaxation phenomena to this particular case, Mez and Maier succeed in explaining the shape of the diagram of Fig. 36: the crosses in fact indicate values of α/f^2 calculated assuming that the dissipative process is a relaxation phenomenon in the equilibrium monomer—dimer of phenol molecules altered by sound waves.

β) Systems of polar liquids with a maximum in the absorption coefficient curve. Some mixtures formed by two associated liquids, or by an associated liquid and a polar one, show a strong maximum at an intermediate composition. This behaviour has been found in some mixtures of water with alcohols, glycol ethers, acetone[1], in mixtures of ether and alcohol[2], of nitrobenzene and alcohols[3], of

[1] G. W. Willard: J. Acoust. Soc. Amer. **12**, 438 (1941). — F. H. Willis: J. Acoust. Soc. Amer. **19**, 242 (1947). — C. J. Burton: J. Acoust. Soc. Amer. **20**, 186 (1948).
[2] D. Sette: Nuovo Cim., Ser. X **1**, 800 (1955).
[3] D. Sette: J. Acoust. Soc. Amer. **23**, 359 (1951)

ethyl methyl ketone and dioxane[1]. Fig. 37 gives BURTON's results in mixtures of water and some alcohols at room temperature. The system water—methyl alcohol which does not show the maximum at room temperatures, behaves like the other mixtures at lower temperatures[2] (Fig. 38).

The absorption of these mixtures strongly depends on temperature and frequency. Figs. 39 and 40 gives STOREY's[3] results in water—ethyl alcohol mixtures respectively at various temperatures (at 22 Mc/sec) and for various frequencies at 0° C. Figs. 41 and 42 instead gives the temperature and frequency variation of absorption coefficient of mixtures having compositions in the proximity to the absorption maxima of some other systems.

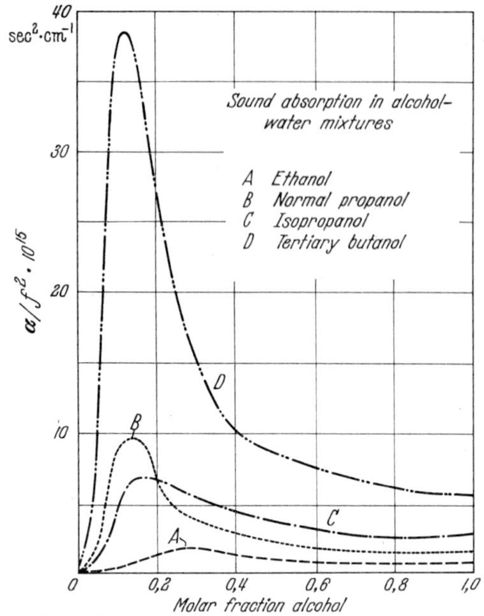

Fig. 37. Sound absorption in some alcohol-water mixtures (C. J. BURTON).

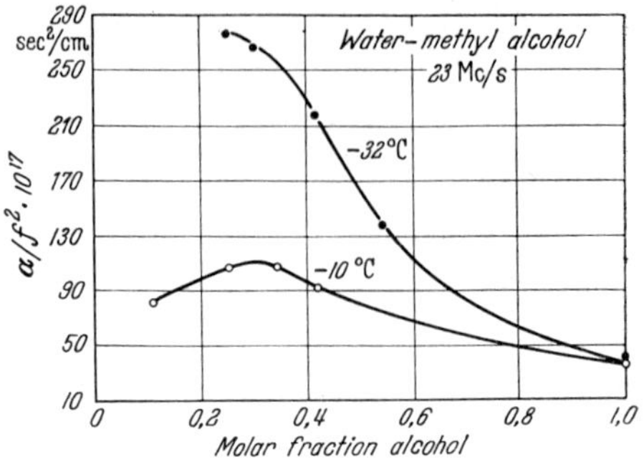

Fig. 38. Sound absorption in the water—methyl alcohol system.

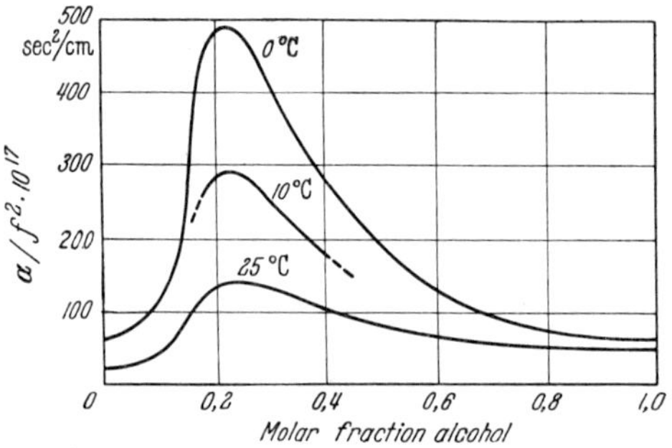

Fig. 39. Sound absorption in water—ethyl alcohol mixtures at various temperatures (22 Mc/sec) (L. R. O. STOREY).

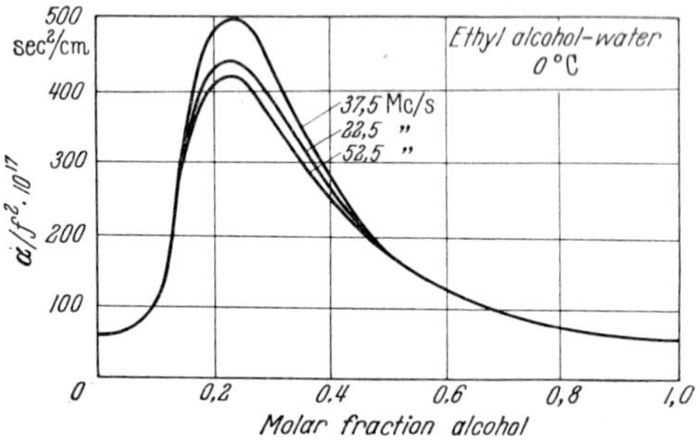

Fig. 40. Sound absorption in water—ethyl alcohol mixtures at various frequencies (0° C) (R. O. STOREY).

The systems formed by water and ethyl alcohol or methyl alcohol have been extensively studied respectively by STOREY and SETTE. In these cases the pure components are associated liquids and the absorption in them is due to the classical sources and to structural relaxation of HALL's type. In their mixtures these causes are operative but some other dissipative process must be present to determine the maximum of absorption coefficient.

[1] M. KRISHNAMURTHI: Proc. Ind. Acad. Sci. A **43**, 106 (1956).
[2] See footnote 2, p. 333.
[3] L. R. O. STOREY: Proc. Phys. Soc. Lond. B **65**, 943 (1952).

In particular in both systems the ratio $\alpha_{\exp}/\alpha_c$ for mixtures having compositions near the absorption maximum changes with temperature in a different way from what is usually true in liquids where the excess absorption is due to alteration of structure by pressure variations. Following a suggestion of BAUER, STOREY assumed that associations of different molecules are in the solution and that the equilibrium among them is altered by temperature changes as in liquids where a chemical equilibrium with a low rate of reaction is present.

Some evidence of the existence of molecular associations in some water—alcohol mixtures is given by other observations: (1) the specific heats of water—alcohol mixtures are non-linear functions of composition; (2) the freezing point curve has a discontinuity for a composition near that for which the sound absorption coefficient has its maximum; (3) the heat of mixing is finite and has a maximum for the same composition; (4) the viscosity coefficient has a similar maximum; (5) the sound velocity in these systems has a maximum whose presence has

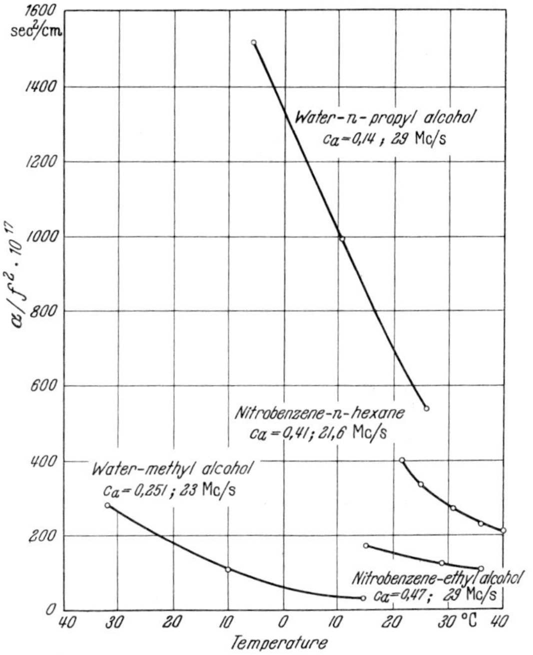

Fig. 41. Temperature dependence of absorption coefficient of mixtures having compositions in proximity to those of absorption maximum of various systems.

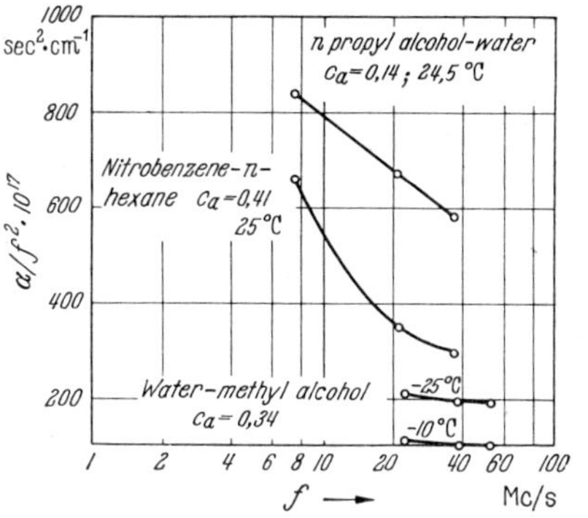

Fig. 42. Frequency dependence of absorption coefficient of mixtures having compositions in proximity to those of absorption maximum of various systems.

been explained on the basis of dynamic equilibria among different kinds of molecular associations. The hypothesis of existence of relaxation phenomena among molecular associations allows one to explain easily the behaviour of water—alcohol mixtures. The term associations is of course used broadly in the sense that it includes any kind of short range order.

The rapid decrease of sound absorption of these mixtures is due to the destruction of associations by thermal agitation. The maximum of absorption of course occurs at a composition for which the proportion of the components are more favourable to the formation of associations, i.e. are about equal to the proportion in the predominant associations. According to the experimental results these prevalent associations are formed by a number of water molecules for one alcohol molecule which is 3, 4, 9 respectively for methyl, ethyl, n-propyl alcohols.

The frequency variation of α/f^2 for these water—alcohol mixtures shows that the relaxation frequencies in the process are either inside or not much beyond the range of experiment. In order to make some evaluation of the mean relaxation frequency the approximate separation of the experimental absorption coefficient into contributions of the various dissipative mechanisms becomes important. These are: (1) viscosity and thermal conductivity (classical absorption); (2) relaxation of structures disturbed by pressure as in the pure components and producing a frequency-dependent isothermal compressibility; (3) relaxation of molecular associations disturbed by temperature variations and producing a frequency-dependent specific heat. The classical contribution can be easily calculated if viscosity coefficient, density and sound velocity are known, because the effect of thermal conductivity can be neglected. The second contribution is difficult to calculate. STOREY, in the case of water—ethyl alcohol mixtures, assumed a linear variation with composition between its known values for water and ethyl alcohol. He thus found at the various frequencies approximate values for the contribution to the absorption coefficient of the thermalrelaxation process. Using the formula

$$\frac{f^2}{\alpha} = A^{-1}\left[1 + \left(\frac{f}{f_{rm}}\right)^2\right] \tag{27.1}$$

and plotting f^2/α vs. f^2 he could calculate a value for f_{rm} assuming that the process had only one relaxation time. The accuracy of measurement and the approximation in the calculation of the contribution of the thermal process does not allow to distinguish if this process happens with one or more relaxation times: probably however a distribution of relaxation times is involved in the equilibria of various associations. STOREY calculated the following relaxation frequencies for the water—ethyl alcohol mixtures of maximum absorptions: (103 ± 5) Mc/sec at 0° and 0.22 alcohol mole fraction; (145 ± 10) Mc/sec at 25° C for 0.25 alcohol mole fraction. SETTE, studying water—methyl alcohol mixtures, observed that STOREY's approximation was crude: the viscosity coefficient and the classical absorption in fact are not linear functions of composition but have maxima; there is no reason therefore why the losses due to structural relaxation of Hall type should follow a linear law. SETTE's investigation seems to show that the same structural changes with composition, which produce the appearance of the new process, alter so greatly the structure of the liquid that no simple hypothesis can be at present done concerning the process bound to a frequency-dependent compressibility. This fact does not allow a reliable calculation of relaxation frequencies of the thermal process: the strong frequency variation of α/f^2 show however that they are not far from the range of experiment: 20 to 60 Mc/sec.

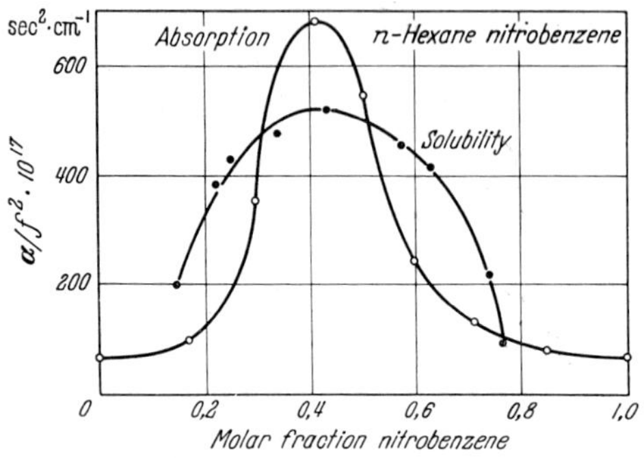

Fig. 43. Sound absorption of n-hexane—nitrobenzene mixtures and solubility curve.

The analysis of results in mixtures of water with methyl and ethyl alcohols seems to indicate that the maxima found in the absorption coefficient in water—alcohol systems is caused by relaxation phenomena due to the slowness with which equilibria of molecular associations follow the changes of temperature produced by sound waves. It seems reasonable to admit that a similar explanation is valid also for those mixtures of polar liquids which show a maximum of the absorption coefficient.

γ) Systems of partially soluble liquids. A thermal relaxation process similar to that now described is responsible for the increase of absorption which may be produced by adding to a liquid another one partially soluble in it. Fig. 43

shows the case of the nitrobenzene—n-hexane[1] system at 25° C and 8 Ms/sec; on the figure is also shown the solubility curve with the consolute temperature of 21.02° C. Figs. 44, 45 (CHYNOWETH-SCHNEIDER[2]) refer to a mixture with 44.6 weight percent of triethyl-amine in water and give the variations of absorption coefficient and velocity as functions of temperature through the critical

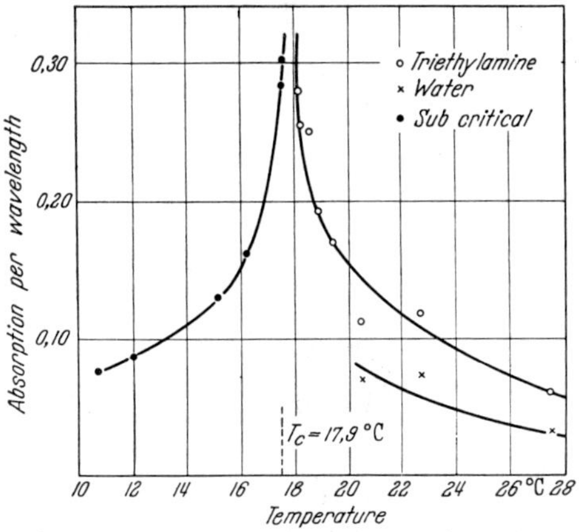

Fig. 44. Sound absorption vs. temperature in a mixture water—triethylamine (44.6 weight percent of triethylamine). Above the critical temperature, two phases are present (A. G. CHYNOWETH and W. G. SCHNEIDER).

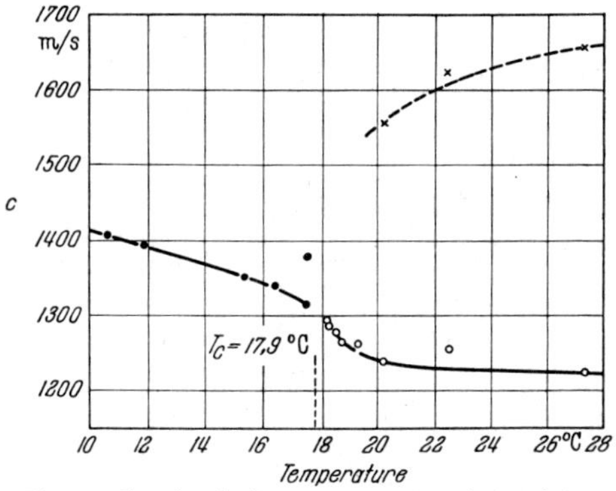

Fig. 45. Sound velocity vs. temperature in a mixture water—triethylamine (44.6 weight percent of triethylamine). Above the critical temperature, two phases are present (A. G. CHYNOWETH and W. G. SCHNEIDER).

region: this system has a minimum critical solution temperature of about 18° C for a mixture with 25 weight percent of amine.

CHYNOWETH and SCHNEIDER have found similar results in a mixture aniline—n-hexane with 74.6 weight percent of hexane. The temperature and frequency variations of α for a mixture nitrobenzene—n-hexane having 0.41 nitrobenzene mole fraction are included in Figs. 41 and 42. Fig. 46 gives the frequency dependence of α/f^2 for the water—triethylamine mixture studied by CHYNOWETH and SCHNEIDER, and by SETTE[1].

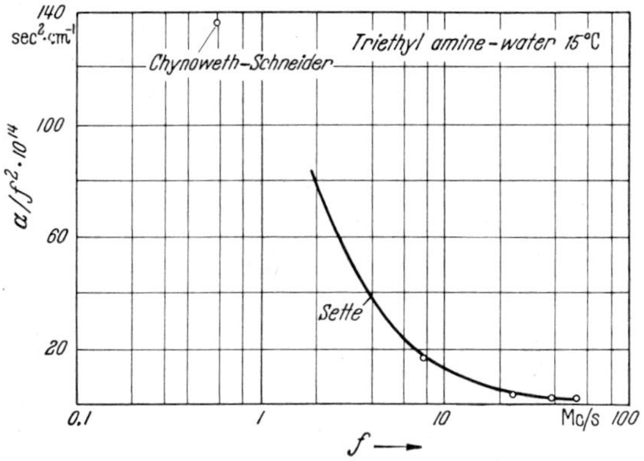

Fig. 46. Sound absorption vs. frequency in a mixture water—triethylamine (44.6 weight percent of triethylamine).

The increase of sound losses in these mixtures in the critical region of solubility is bound to the critical phenomena which take place in the liquid[3]. As is known, the liquid in the critical region is no longer a homogeneous phase but is formed by a mother phase in which clusters of various sizes and compositions are dispersed. The optical phenomenon of the critical opalescence, which is caused by light scattering produced by clusters, shows that their average size is of the order of magnitude of visible light wavelengths.

[1] D. SETTE: Nuovo Cim. Ser. X **1**, 800 (1955).

[2] A. G. CHYNOWETH and W. G. SCHNEIDER: J. Chem. Phys. **19**, 1566 (1951).

[3] Similar dissipative processes are operative in the critical temperature region of pure liquids. See W. G. SCHNEIDER: Canad. J. Chem. **29**, 243 (1951).

Sound propagation in such heterogeneous media undergoes losses of new types in addition to those present in pure components.

The principal cause of additional absorption could be: (1) scattering of sound energy; (2) increase of viscosity losses due to the heterogeneity of the liquid; (3) relaxation phenomena in the equilibrium of clusters.

It is to be observed that since the sizes of clusters are much smaller than the sound wavelengths (between 0.3 and 0.003 cm) the scattering process has no importance. These conclusions based on the results of optical opalescence experiments are confirmed by sound absorption measurements at various frequencies. The absorption coefficient produced by scattering [see Eq. (17.1)] depends upon the fourth power of frequency and therefore α/f^2 should increase with f^2 while the experiments show (Figs. 42 and 46) that it decreases when the frequency rises.

STOKES' calculation of the absorption coefficient due to viscosity is made using the hypothesis of a homogeneous liquid. R. LUCAS[1] extended the calculations to the case of a liquid in which there are density fluctuations. SETTE applied LUCAS' formula to the case of water—triethylamine systems for which data on the chemical potential in the critical zone are available and the composition of clusters can be determined. SETTE found that the losses due to viscosity, according to LUCAS' formula are considerably higher then those given by STOKES' relation, especially at low frequencies; they are however some orders of magnitude smaller than those found experimentally in the megacycle region. It is therefore concluded that the high absorption coefficient found in mixtures of partially soluble liquids near the critical region are essentially due to relaxation processes in the equilibrium of clusters of different size and composition among themselves and with the mother phase. The distribution of molecules in the clusters is strongly dependent on temperature and the temperature variations produced by sound alter the equilibria. The cause of losses in this kind of mixtures, therefore, is practically the same as that found in mixtures of polar liquids which show a maximum of the absorption coefficient; the molecules of the two components aggregate in various forms (associations or clusters) and the relative equilibria are disturbed by temperature variations produced by sound waves so that thermal relaxation is set up.

Of course the clusters can have various sizes and compositions and many equilibria are involved in a solution of partially mixable substances near the critical region. A wide distribution of relaxation times is to be expected. An approximate evaluation of the range of relaxation frequencies in the water-triethylamine with 44.6 weight percent of amine obtained by SETTE from the excess of absorption coefficient vs. frequency, indicates the range 2.5 to 30 Mc per sec.

δ) Systems of polar liquids showing a minimum in the absorption coefficient curve. Some binary mixtures of strongly polar or associated liquids show an absorption coefficient curve with a definite minimum. Such behaviour has been found in the systems aniline—nitrobenzene, aniline—ethyl alcohol[2], benzyl alcohol—ethyl alcohol and benzyl alcohol—isopropyl alcohol[3]. Although the shapes of the curves are the same as those found in systems of two unassociated liquids with similar absorption coefficients, the origin of relaxation processes is different in the pure liquids and in the mixtures. In the present case we deal with components which are strongly polar or associated liquids. Moreover, in some of the mixtures, it has been found that the ratio α_{exp}/α_c does not much vary with

[1] R. LUCAS: J. Phys. Radium **8**, 41 (1937).
[2] D. SETTE: Acustica **5**, 194 (1955).
[3] M. KRISHNAMURTHI: Proc. Ind. Acad. Sci. A **43**, 106 (1956).

temperature while the absorption coefficient decreases fast when the temperature increases. This suggests that the main dissipative process causing excess absorption is probably to be found in structural relaxation phenomena of the kind present in pure liquids, i.e. it is caused by pressure variations produced by the waves and is therefore of a nature different from that of the structural process found in the preceding categories of mixtures.

C. Dependence of sound velocity on the chemical and structural nature of the liquid.

28. Introduction. In the preceding divisions of this paper it has been shown how dispersion of sound velocity can be produced by various processes. The existence of relaxation phenomena in the frequency range of experiments is responsible for the deviation of the experimental absorption coefficient from its classical value found in most liquids. Only in a few cases, however, dispersion of velocity has been found: usually the relaxation frequencies are well above the accessible range or the velocity variations expected are so small as to require higher precision than that of normal methods.

The values of velocity measured at various frequencies therefore are usually equal to the low frequency velocity. This velocity, as has been mentioned, is given by

$$c^2 = \frac{1}{\varrho\,\chi_{\mathrm{ad}}} \tag{28.1}$$

and it has been extensively used to determine χ_{ad} and the ratio of specific heat $\gamma = \chi_{\mathrm{ad}}/\chi_{\mathrm{is}}$ if the isothermal compressibility is known.

Recently numerous researches have been performed to clarify the relations between sound velocity and other molecular properties. The success of such tentative work, which had a semi-empirical origin but soon found theoretical support, shows that the velocity of propagation of a mechanical disturbance, i.e. sound velocity, has to be considered a primary property of liquids in a molecular kinetic theory and not a secondary property derived from compressibility as in normal thermodynamics.

A short account of the relations between sound velocity and molecular properties will be given in the present Part C.

29. Sound velocity and VAN DER WAALS' equation. A first relation between sound velocity and a molecular property has been found by SCHAAFFS[1] assuming for the liquid the validity of a VAN DER WAALS' equation:

$$\left[p + \frac{\varrho^2}{M^2}\,a(T,\varrho)\right]\left[\frac{M}{\varrho} - b(T,\varrho)\right] = RT \tag{29.1}$$

with a and b functions of ϱ and T instead of constants as assumed in gases. It is then possible to find the velocity c using the equation:

$$c^2 = \gamma\,\frac{dp}{d\varrho}\,. \tag{29.2}$$

The molecular radius is related to b and it can be expressed as a function of c using (29.1) and (29.2). SCHAAFFS obtains:

$$r_m = \sqrt[3]{\frac{3}{16\pi N_A}\,\frac{M}{\varrho}\left[1 - \frac{RT\gamma}{Mc^2}\left(\sqrt{1 + \frac{1}{3}\,\frac{Mc^2}{\gamma RT}} - 1\right)\right]} \tag{29.3}$$

with N_A the Avogadro number.

[1] W. SCHAAFFS: Z. Physik **114**, 110 (1939); **115**, 69 (1940).

The values of r_m obtained by means of (29.3) for various molecules are in excellent agreement with those obtained by other methods.

Eq. (29.2) can be solved to give c. SCHAAFFS obtains, at atmospheric pressure,

$$c = \sqrt{\frac{\gamma R T}{M}\left[\frac{\frac{1}{3}}{\left(1-\frac{b}{V}\right)^2} - \frac{2}{\left(1-\frac{b}{V}\right)}\right]} \tag{29.4}$$

where $V = M/\varrho$ is the molecular volume.

Because the covolume b can be found by addition of atomic terms in the molecule, one would think that Eq. (29.4) would permit the calculation of a sound velocity to compare with the experimental one. Unfortunately this is not possible because the ratio of specific heats is usually not determined and because $\left(1-\frac{b}{V}\right)$ is a very small quantity and therefore great variations of c can be produced by small errors in b.

Eq. (29.4) however is useful to clarify some relations existing between sound velocity and other properties. SCHAAFFS[1] has used (29.4) to explain some of the empirical rules that PARTHASARATHY[2] established between velocity, molecular weight, density, and molecular size. Differentiation of (29.4) in fact shows that sound velocity increases when γ, ϱ and b raise or when the molecular weight decreases.

PARTHASARATHY'S first rule, for instance, says that aromatic compounds have usually higher velocities than the aliphatic ones; this is due to the bigger densities of aromatic substances.

Another rule of PARTHASARATHY establishes that the substitution in a molecule of one atom by a heavier one to obtain a new compound produces a decrease of velocity; this is due to the increase of molecular weight and is true if large variations of ϱ and b are not produced at the same time.

30. SCHAAFFS' theory of velocity and chemical composition. α) *Semiempirical relation.* Considerations based on Eq. (29.4) brought SCHAAFFS[3] to empirically examine the dependence of c on the ratio B/V where B is the effective volume occupied by molecules per mole, i.e. $\frac{4\pi}{3} r_m^3 N_a$ where r_m is the molecular radius. As is well known, B is related to the covolume b by the relation

$$b = 4B \tag{30.1}$$

obtained with the van der Waals assumption of elastic collisions between molecules. The ratio

$$r_i = \frac{B}{V} \tag{30.2}$$

is called by SCHAAFFS "space filling".

Fig. 47 shows the experimental values of the product cV for many organic compounds formed of C, N, O, H atoms as a function of molecular refraction, M_R, (sodium D line) which can be assumed to be approximately proportional to B. It is evident that the experimental points lie close to a straight line. If one considers that the proportionality between M_R and B is only approximate and differences of the value of B for a molecule are always found if either mechanical or optical methods are used for its determination, it seems plausible to assume

[1] W. SCHAAFFS: Ann. Phys., Lpz. **40**, 393 (1941).

[2] S. PARTHASARATHY: Current Sci. **6**, 322 (1938).

[3] W. SCHAAFFS: Z. phys. Chem. **194**, 39, 66 (1944); and [*21*].

that a linear relation occurs between c and r_f for compounds formed by C, H, N, O atoms and that the values of B, like those of M_R and b, can be formed by adding the contributions of the atoms entering in the molecule:

$$\left.\begin{aligned} c &= \boldsymbol{W} r_f = \boldsymbol{W}\frac{B}{V} \\ &= \boldsymbol{W}\frac{\sum_i (z_i A_i)}{V} \end{aligned}\right\} \qquad (30.3)$$

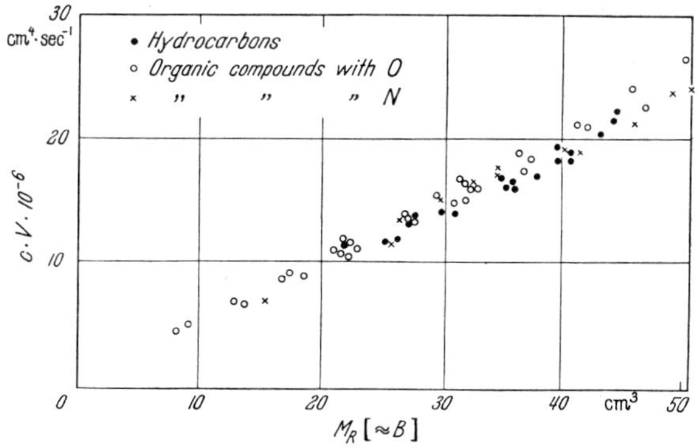

Fig. 47. cV versus molecular refraction (W. SCHAAFFS).

where z_i is the number of a type of atom present in the molecule and the addition is to be extended to all kinds of atoms in the molecule. The constant $\boldsymbol{W}$ has an approximate value of 5000 m/sec. Eq. (30.3) has been used to determine first the atomic contributions and next to calculate a sound velocity to compare with the experimental value for many compounds. The agreement between calculated and experimental velocities is very satisfactory for compounds formed by C, H, O, N atoms. Fig. 48 gives the product cV as a function of $\sum_i (z_i A_i)$ for numerous compounds; it has been obtained by SCHAAFFS using values for the atomic contributions which were found in a

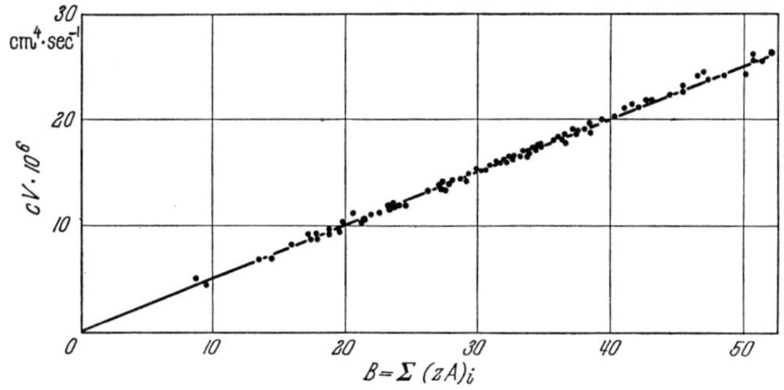

Fig. 48. cV versus $\sum_i (ZA)_i$ for 94 substances formed by H, O, N, Cl atoms (W. SCHAAFFS).

first calculation without taking into account the improvements of the theory which we will discuss below; the agreement however between the straight line given by (30.3) and the experimental values is satisfactory.

The simple relation (30.3) fails in the cases of organic compounds in which either heavy atoms (Cl, Br) or groups like NO_2 are present. The deviation rises regularly when the number of atoms or groups in the molecule increases.

In order to explain these deviations SCHAAFFS observes that the relation (30.1) is valid with the assumption of elastic collisions among molecules; the reality is better described by

$$b = s B \qquad (30.4)$$

with s a factor which characterizes the collision (collision factor). Then Eq. (29.4) is written:

$$c = \sqrt{\frac{\gamma RT}{M}\left[\frac{\frac{1}{3}}{(1-s r_f)^2} - \frac{2}{(1-s r_f)}\right]} \qquad (30.5)$$

and one is brought to consider the experimental dependence of c on $s r_f$ at constant temperature. This can be done by considering homologous series (primary alcohols, etc.) as in Fig. 49 where c is plotted versus $s r_f$. Isomer curves given by Eq. (30.5) produce bands if one allows γ to assume values in a narrow range; on the same diagrams are plotted the experimental values of c for the various members of a series and a band is obtained for each series. What is important to observe is that all the bands for many series, seem to approximate the same value of velocity when $M \to \infty$:

$$c_\infty = 1600 \text{ m/sec}.$$

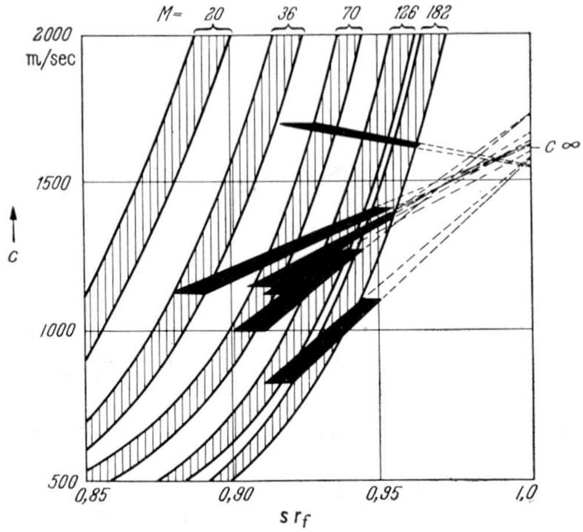

Fig. 49. Sound velocity of homologous series versus $s \times r_f$. The series are (from the top of the figure); ethylene glycols; primary alcohols; fatty acids; 1-olefins; paraffin; alkyloidides. Isomer bands are also shown.

The reason for the different slopes of the curves which approximate straight lines for the various homologous series is believed to lie in the values of the collision factor s.

Through considerations of this kind SCHAAFFS establishes a general formula for the sound velocity at constant temperature:

$$c = c_\infty \, s \, r_f; \tag{30.6}$$

i.e. the sound velocity is proportional to the factor which describes the elasticity of collisions and to the space filling. The collision factor in general can be written

$$s = s_n \left(1 - \frac{r_{f0}}{r_f}\right), \tag{30.7}$$

where s_n is the value of s for simple organic compounds and r_{f0} assumes values appreciably different from zero when heavy atoms or particular groups are present in the molecule.

The value of s_n found by SCHAAFFS [*21*] for pure hydrocarbons with no dipole moment is 2.85. For simple liquids, therefore, for which r_{f0} can to a first approximation be assumed zero, (30.6) and (30.7) yield

$$c = c_\infty \, s_n \, r_f = 1600 \times 2.85 \, r_f$$
$$= 4450 \, r_f \text{ m/sec},$$

in agreement with Eq. (30.3).

β) Theoretical treatment. Eqs. (30.3), (30.6) and (30.7) which have been established by SCHAAFFS by means of a semi-empirical procedure find support in a theoretical treatment by ALTENBURG[1].

This author considers a liquid as formed by a cubic lattice of particles and assumes that the resistence of the liquid to shearing stresses is zero. Then during sound propagation only the intermolecular forces between molecules which are in the direction of propagation are of importance, and it is possible to extend to this case a formula for the velocity of propagation of mechanical disturbances in a plane lattice. Assuming that the potential energy is formed by an attractive part, proportional to $1/d^6$ (LONDON) and a repulsive part proportional to $1/d^{12}$

[1] K. ALTENBURG: Z. phys. Chem. **195**, 145 (1950).

(LENNARD-JONES), d being the distance between two molecules, ALTENBURG finds for the sound velocity:

$$c = \sqrt{6 N_A^3} \frac{1}{V} \sqrt{\frac{C^*}{M}} \tag{30.8}$$

where C^* is the proportionality factor in the expression of the potential due to the attractive force. If the close-packed arrangement of spheres is assumed instead of that of a cubic lattice for the molecules of the liquid, Eq. (30.8) changes only in the numerical factor which becomes $\sqrt{4.25 N_A^3}$.

The term $\sqrt{C^*/M}$ is a molecular quantity proportional to the potential of attractive forces and can be derived by adding the contributions of the atoms which enter into the molecule.

$$\sqrt{\frac{C^*}{M}} = \sum_i \sqrt{\frac{C_i^*}{M_i}},$$

M_i being the atomic weights.

In fact LONDON has shown that the long-range intermolecular forces are additive and therefore the potential of the attractive force exerted by one molecule upon another is the addition of the potentials between each atom of the first molecule and the second molecule.

Eq. (30.8) therefore is analogous to (30.3). Furthermore, ALTENBURG applying LONDON's quantum-mechanical calculations, finds

$$c V \sim \sqrt{\frac{h e}{m \sqrt{m \delta}}} B \tag{30.9}$$

where h is the Planck constant, and according to LONDON, the molecules are treated as quasi-elastic dipoles of charge e, mass m, and polarizability δ. Because δ is approximately proportional to M the denominator of the fraction in (30.9) is proportional to M^2. It can be shown that the number of electrons important in determining the intermolecular forces is proportional to the square of the number of electrons of a molecule. Moreover for molecules formed by atoms of similar atomic weight, the number of electrons is approximately proportional to the mass of the molecules. In these cases the numerator and denominator of the fraction in (30.9) are both proportional to M^2, i.e. the factor in front of B is constant. This is in agreement with Eq. (30.3) of SCHAAFFS. If, however, heavy atoms such as halogenes enter into the molecules, the mass of the molecules increases more than the number of electrons and the factor in front of B becomes smaller. This qualitative indication is in agreement with Eqs. (30.6) and (30.7).

ALTENBURG[1] also has found relations connecting the sound velocity with other molecular properties which in general seem in pretty good agreement with experiments. We remember the relation to surface tension, σ, calculated assuming the liquid molecules arranged in a face-centred cubic lattice:

$$c = 5.663 \sqrt{\sigma} \sqrt[6]{\frac{N_A}{\varrho^2 M}} \text{ cm/sec}, \tag{30.10}$$

and with parachor,

$$c = 5.663 \frac{P_a^2 \varrho^2}{M^2} \sqrt[6]{\frac{N_A}{\varrho^2 M}}. \tag{30.11}$$

[1] K. ALTENBURG: Kolloid-Z. **117**, 153 (1950).

As is well known the parachor of a molecule

$$P_a = \frac{M}{\varrho_{\mathrm{liq}} - \varrho_{\mathrm{gas}}}\,\sigma^{\frac{1}{4}} \tag{30.12}$$

is approximately temperature independent and can be obtained adding the parachors of the atoms.

γ) Atomic addenda. Returning now to Eqs. (30.6) and (30.7) they can be easily be written in a way more suited to practical calculations. The molecular weight and B can be expressed as sums of atomic contributions. The quantity r_{f0} can be written

$$r_{f0} = \frac{\beta}{\beta + B} \tag{30.13}$$

Table 12. *External addenda for some bonds* (W. SCHAAFFS).

Bond	External addendum A
H—	1.06
=C<	3.36
>C<	3.06
—C≡	3.66
O=(C)	3.82
(C)—O—(C)	1.64
(C)—O—(H)	4.53
(C)—N=(C)	4.35
(C)—N<(C)(C)	5.20
(H)—N<(C)(C)	5.80
(C)—N<(H)(H)	6.42
N≡(C)	5.45
NO_2—(C)	12.00
Cl—(C)	6.92
Br—(C)	13.20
I—(C)	16.00

Table 13. *Internal addenda for some bonds* (W. SCHAAFFS).

Bond	Internal addendum
CH_3—(C)—	0.10
OH—(C)	0.16
COOH—(C)	1.30
NO_2—(C)	1.20
Cl—(C)—	0.25 near 1 Cl atom 0.52 near 2 Cl atoms 0.75 near 3 Cl atoms 0.87 near 4 or more Cl atoms
Cl—(C)<	0.87
Br—(C)—	4.20 near 1 Br atom 4.50 near 2 Br atoms 6.00 near 3 or more Br atoms
Br—(C)<	4.75
I—(C)—	4.60 near 1 I atom

where β has the dimension of a volume and characterizes the singularities produced in the potential curve by the introduction of heavy atoms or groups in the molecule. Also β can be expressed as a sum of atomic (internal) addenda,

$$\beta = \sum_i z_i \beta_i . \tag{30.14}$$

Eqs. (30.6) and (30.7) can be written ($\boldsymbol{W} = c_\infty s_n$)

$$c = \boldsymbol{W} \varrho \frac{B}{M} - \boldsymbol{W} \frac{1}{1 + \frac{B}{\beta}} \tag{30.15}$$

and M, B, β can be calculated using atomic addenda.

Tables 12 and 13 give the values calculated by SCHAAFFS for the more usual external (A_i) and internal (β_i) addenda. Table 14 gives for many compounds the experimental velocity and that calculated by SCHAAFFS. Probably an internal addendum exists for each atom but only when the addenda are sufficiently high does their need become evident in the calculation. In the laste column of the table are given the values of the second (corrective, Δc_{corr}) term in (30.15). The agreement between experiment and theory seems very satisfactory and the deviations are probably due to peculiarities of the molecules with are not taken into account in this simple theory.

Table 14. *Measured and calculated values of sound velocity* (W. SCHAAFFS).

Liquid	Formula	Density	Sound velocity (m/sec) measured	Sound velocity (m/sec) calculated	Δc_{corr}
			Hydrocarbons.		
Benzene	C_6H_6	0.878	1326	1326	
Toluene	C_7H_8	0.866	1228	1327	
o-Xylene	C_8H_{10}	0.871	1360	1347	
m-Xylene	C_8H_{10}	0.863	1340	1335	
p-Xylene	C_8H_{10}	0.860	1330	1331	
Indene	C_9H_8	0.998	1475	1471	
Tetralin	$C_{10}H_{12}$	0.967	1492	1468	
Cyclohexane	C_6H_{12}	0.779	1284	1284	
Cyclohexene	C_6H_{10}	0.811	1305	1304	
Methylcyclohexane	C_7H_{14}	0.764	1247	1247	12
Hydrindene	C_9H_{10}	0.910	1403	1369	
Cis-Decalin	$C_{10}H_{18}$	0.896	1451	1435	
Trans-Decalin	$C_{10}H_{18}$	0.870	1403	1392	
			Organic compounds with O=(C) *bonds.*		
Acetophenone	C_8H_8O	1.026	1496	1482	
Benzaldehyde	C_7H_6O	1.046	1479	1480	
Cinnamaldehyde	C_9H_8O	1.112	1570	1593	
Benzylacetone	$C_{10}H_{12}O$	0.989	1514	1463	
Ethylphenylxetone	$C_9H_{10}O$	1.009	1498	1470	10
Cyclohexanone	$C_6H_{10}O$	0.948	1443	1428	
			Organic compounds with OH *groups.*		
Benzylalcohol	C_7H_8O	1.045	1540	1538	20
Carvacrol	$C_{10}H_{14}O$	0.976	1475	1466	31
O-Cresol	C_7H_8O	1.046	1523	1538	20
Cyclohexanol	$C_6H_{12}O$	0.962	1493	1500	20
1-Linaloöl	$C_{10}H_{18}O$	0.863	1341	1359	21
Furfuryl alcohol	$C_5H_6O_2$	1.135	1467	1470	24
			Organic compounds with nitrogen atoms.		
Diethylaniline	$C_{10}H_{15}N$	0.934	1482	1476	
Ethylbenzylaniline	$C_{15}H_{17}N$	1.029	1586	1574	
Aniline	C_6H_7N	1.022	1656	1657	
O-Toluidine	C_7H_9N	0.998	1634	1630	
m-Toluidine	C_7H_9N	0.989	1620	1613	
Cyclohexylamine	$C_6H_{13}N$	0.819	1435	1420	
Ethanolamine	C_2H_7ON	1.018	1741	1781	
			Organic compounds with chlorine atoms.		
Chlorobenzene	C_6H_5Cl	1.107	1291	1295	116
m-Dichlorobenzene	$C_6H_4Cl_2$	1.287	1295	1295	193
o-Chlorotoluene	C_7H_7Cl	1.085	1344	1334	101
m-Chlorotoluene	C_7H_7Cl	1.070	1326	1313	101
p-Chlorotoluene	C_7H_7Cl	1.066	1316	1305	101
α-Chloronaphthalene	$C_{10}H_7Cl$	1.192	1483	1481	81
1-2-4 Trichlorobenzene	$C_6H_3Cl_3$	1.456	1301	1324	250
Trichloroethylene	C_2HCl_3	1.477	1049	1052	370
Acethyl chloride	C_2H_3OCl	1.103	1060	1088	183
Perchloroethylene	C_2Cl_4	1.614	1066	1082	408
			Organic compounds with bromine atoms.		
Ethyl bromide	C_2H_5Br	1.461	900	820	662
n-Butyl bromide	C_4H_9Br	1.275	990	968	490
n-Amyl bromide	$C_5H_{11}Br$	1.223	981	1024	430
n-Octyl bromide	$C_8H_{17}Br$	1.166	1182	1192	320
m-Methylcyclohexylbromide	$C_7H_{13}Br$	1.259	1194	1173	365
p-Methylcyclohexylbromide	$C_7H_{13}Br$	1.267	1189	1183	365
Methylenbromide	CH_2Br_2	2.484	963	1025	985
Ethylene bromide	$C_2H_4Br_2$	2.178	1009	1014	871
Propylene bromide	$C_3H_6Br_2$	1.941	995	995	795
Bromoform	$CHBr_3$	2.890	928	925	1300
Acetylene tetrabromide	$C_2H_2Br_4$	2.963	1041	1060	1270

δ) Sound velocity and dipole moment. SCHAAFFS[1] uses the sound velocity to calculate dipole moments, μ, of molecules. For substances for which $\beta \ll B$

$$\mu = \sqrt{\frac{9\,kT}{4\pi N_A}\left[P_z - \frac{cV}{2\boldsymbol{W}} - \sqrt{\left(\frac{cV}{2\boldsymbol{W}}\right)^2 + \beta V}\right]} \tag{30.16}$$

where P_z is the molecular polarization. Eq. (30.16) gives results which compare well with those found by means of molecular refraction.

31. Sound velocity and molecular volume. RAO's formula. *α) Rao's formula.* An empirical relation has been established by M. R. RAO[2] between sound velocity

Table 15. *Sound velocity, density and $\mathscr{R}$* (M. R. RAO).

Liquid	Temperature °C	Sound velocity m/sec	Density g/cm³	$\mathscr{R}$	Liquid	Temperature °C	Sound velocity m/sec	Dersity g/cm³	$\mathscr{R}$
Benzene	10	1375	0.8896	975.7	Chlorobenzene	0	1362.5	1.1279	1106
	20	1324	0.8790	975		10	1322.5	1.1180	1105
	30	1278	0.8684	975.4		20	1284.5	1.1060	1106
	40	1231	0.8576	975.4		30	1248	1.0980	1104
	50	1184	0.8467	975.2		40	1212	1.0844	1106
						50	1178	1.0730	1108
Toluene	0	1414	0.8848	1168	Heptane	0	1235	0.7005	1533
	10	1370.5	0.8752	1168		10	1196	0.6920	1536
	20	1327.5	0.8657	1169		20	1154	0.6826	1538
	30	1284.5	0.8563	1169		30	1112	0.6751	1536
	40	1242	0.8474	1168		40	1070	0.6665	1536
	50	1199	0.8378	1168		50	1028	0.6579	1536
Carbon tetrachloride	0	1008	1.6327	944.3	Methyl alcohol	0	1187	0.8100	418.6
	10	970	1.6134	944.1		10	1154	0.8007	419.5
	20	935	1.5939	943.4		20	1121	0.7913	420.4
	30	904	1.5748	944.3		30	1088	0.7818	421.3
	40	873.5	1.5557	945.0		40	1156	0.7723	422.3
	50	843	1.5361	945.8		50	1023.5	0.7627	423.3

and molecular volume valid for unassociated liquids. Considering in fact the variations of sound velocity and density of these substances, RAO found for the ratio

$$\frac{\dfrac{1}{c}\dfrac{\partial c}{\partial T}}{\dfrac{1}{V}\dfrac{\partial V}{\partial T}} = -3.03 \approx -3. \tag{31.1}$$

Eq. (31.1) yields by integration RAO's formula:

$$\sqrt[3]{c}\,V = \sqrt[3]{c}\,\frac{M}{\varrho} = \text{const} = \mathscr{R}. \tag{31.2}$$

Table 15 gives $\mathscr{R}$ calculated at different temperatures for various substances. It is evident that $\mathscr{R}$ is constant for unassociated liquids. $\mathscr{R}$ has been at times called molar sound velocity, but as it has not the dimension of a velocity this denomination may originate confusion and its use is not recommended.

If the adiabatic compressibility χ_{ad} is introduced in (31.2) one obtains

$$\sqrt[6]{\varrho^7}\,\sqrt[6]{\chi_{\text{ad}}} = \frac{M}{\mathscr{R}} \tag{31.3}$$

[1] W. SCHAAFS: Z. phys. Chem. **194**, 170 (1944) and [*21*].

[2] M. R. RAO: Current Sci. **8**, 510 (1939). — Indian J. Phys. **14**, 109 (1940). — J. Chem. Phys. **9**, 682 (1941).

and therefore also the left-hand side of this expression must be temperature independent. RAO[1] has successfully shown that the similar expression $\left(\varrho\sqrt[7]{\chi_{\mathrm{ad}}}\right)$ is not only independent of temperature but also independent of pressure. The same happens for $\varrho\sqrt[7]{\chi_{\mathrm{is}}}$ as has been found by WADA[2] (Table 16). This author has also shown that both $\varrho\sqrt[7]{\chi_{\mathrm{ad}}}$ and $\varrho\sqrt[7]{\chi_{\mathrm{is}}}$ are molecular expressions which can be obtained by addition of atomic addenda.

Table 16. *Temperature and pressure dependence of* $\varrho\sqrt[7]{\chi_{\mathrm{is}}}$ (Y. WADA).

Toluene				Acetone			
Temperature °C	ϱ (g/cm³)	$\chi_{\mathrm{is}}\cdot 10^{12}$ cm²/dyne	$\varrho\sqrt[7]{\chi_{\mathrm{is}}}$	Pressure (atm)	ϱ (g/cm³)	$\chi_{\mathrm{is}}\cdot 10^{12}$ cm²/dyne	$\varrho\sqrt[7]{\chi_{\mathrm{is}}}$
0	0.8845	78	1.648	1000	0.8529	55.9	1.515
10	0.8754	84	1.648	2000	0.8952	42.5	1.530
20	0.8664	90	1.648	3000	0.9288	32.1	1.525
30	0.8573	96	1.645	4000	0.9554	25.5	1.517
40	0.8484	103	1.645	5000	0.9778	21.7	1.518
50	0.8369	111	1.645	6000	0.9978	19.2	1.522
60	0.8309	120	1.647	7000	1.0160	17.3	1.527

β) Atomic and bond addenda. According to RAO, the quantity $\mathcal{R}$ for an unassociated pure liquid is formed by addenda of the atoms which enter into the molecule:

$$\sqrt[3]{c}\,V = \mathcal{R} = \sum_i z_i\, a_i\,. \tag{31.4}$$

Table 17. *Atomic addenda* (R. T. LAGEMANN and W. S. DUNBAR).

	Souders viscosity Eq. (31.5)	Parachor	Molecular refraction	$\mathcal{R}$	Covalent radius Å
H	2.7	15.4	1.100	92.5	0.30
C	50.2	9.2	2.418	10	0.77
N	37	17.5	—	—	0.70
O	29.7	20.0	1.525	74	0.66
F	—	25.5	1.00	—	0.64
Cl	60	55	5.967	227	0.99
Br	79	69	8.865	245	1.14
I	110	90	13.900	340	1.33
CH_2	55.6	40	4.618	195	—
Double bond .	−15.5	19	1.733	110	—
Triple bond .	—	38	2.398	—	—

The addition is to be extended to all atoms in the molecule. Table 17 gives the average values of addenda[3] for $\mathcal{R}$ as well as for other molecular properties. In the table also some corrections have been indicated to be introduced when double bondings are present in the molecules.

LAGEMANN, CORRY and DUNBAR[3,4] have shown that the correct value of $\mathcal{R}$ can also be obtained by adding values established for each type of bond in the molecule. Table 18 gives the corresponding addenda for $\mathcal{R}$ and for other molecular properties.

[1] M. R. RAO: J. Chem. Phys. **14**, 699 (1946).
[2] Y. WADA: J. Phys. Soc. Japan **4**, 280 (1949).
[3] R. T. LAGEMANN and W. S. DUNBAR: J. Phys. Chem. **49**, 428 (1945).
[4] R. T. LAGEMANN and J. E. CORRY: J. Chem. Phys. **10**, 759 (1942).

The use of either atomic or bond addenda is a procedure which gives good results in many simple cases. It however does not take into account peculiarities of the molecules which of course have an effect on $\mathcal{R}$. At times in fact the values obtained for an addendum differ according to the compounds used for the calculation[1]. For instance BACCAREDDA[2] has studied the values of $\mathcal{R}$ in some series

Table 18. *Bond addenda* (R. T. LAGEMANN and W. S. DUNBAR).

Bond	Refraction	Parachor	$\mathcal{R}$	Longitudinal polarizability	Bond length Å
C—H	1.705	17.7	95.2	7.2	1.07
C—F	1.60	26.0	—	—	1.41
C—Cl	6.51	54.9	230	35.3	1.76
C—Br	9.47	68.1	247	—	1.91
C—I	14.51	97.2	305	—	2.10
C—S	4.59	—	—	—	1.81
C—N	1.54	—	—	—	1.47
C—O	1.425	7.0	34.5	—	1.43
C—C	1.209	4.6	4.25	18.2	1.54
H—H	2.08	35.2	—	5.55	0.60
H—Cl	—	67.8	—	31.3	1.29
H—O	1.73	26.4	99	—	0.99
Cl—Cl	—	111.5	—	66.0	1.98
C=C	4.15	28.7	129	30.2	1.33
C=S	10.61	72.1	319	—	1.61
C=O	3.42	37.4	186	—	1.22
C≡N	4.77	63.3	285	—	1.15
C≡C	6.025	53.2	—	36.8	1.20

of isomers finding differences depending on the particularities of the molecules. BACCAREDDA and NATTA[3] studied various polymers and established that the ratio of the experimental velocity to the velocity calculated through RAO's formula using atomic addenda depends upon the presence of branches into the molecules. They introduce therefore the above mentioned ratio as a shape factor.

γ) Rao's constant and other molecular properties. In homologous series the constant $\mathcal{R}$ is a linear function of other molecular properties as the molecular weight (M), the molecular refraction (M_R), the parachor (P_a), the covolume b, the magnetic molecular rotation R_m, the critical volume (V_c) the viscosity constant defined (SAUDERS) by:

$$I = (2.9 + \log_{10}\log_{10}\eta)\,\frac{M}{\varrho} \tag{31.5}$$

where η is expressed in millipoise.

The relation between $\mathcal{R}$ and one of these quantities, say X, is given by:

$$\mathcal{R} = a_0 + a_1 X. \tag{31.6}$$

The coefficients a_0 and a_1 are given in Table 19 according to RAO[4] and to LAGEMANN and DUNBAR[5].

[1] R. T. LAGEMANN, J. S. EVANS and D. R. MCMILLAN: J. Amer. Chem. Soc. **70**, 2996 (1948).
[2] M. BACCAREDDA: Ric. Sci. **19**, 358 (1949).
[3] G. NATTA and M. BACCAREDDA: Gazz. chim. ital. **79**, 364 (1949).
[4] M. R. RAO: J. Chem. Phys. **9**, 682 (1941).
[5] R. T. LAGEMANN and W. S. DUNBAR: J. Phys. Chem. **49**, 428 (1945).

Table 19. *Constants in the Eqs. (31.6)* (R. T. LAGEMANN and W. S. DUNBAR).

Series	M		M_R		P_a	
	a_0	a_1	a_0	a_1	a_0	a_1
Paraffins	+155	13.97	101.4	41.89	16.67	4.935
Esters of acetic acid	−206	14.01	172.2	38.61	46.87	4.551
Monohydric alcohols	−32	14	81.63	41.70	27.38	5.072
Benzene hydrocarbons	−120	14.02	−59.10	39.61	41.31	4.939

Series	I		b		R_m	
	a_0	a_1	a_0	a_1	a_0	a_1
Paraffins	150.3	3.550	220.6	144.400	89.7	189.8
Esters of acetic acid	46.17	4.552	150.7	140.100	281.3	169.4
Monohydric alcohols	31.57	3.454	−313.6	247.300	123.4	180.9
Benzene hydrocarbons	−27.75	4.035	195.8	147.300	−111.7	186.9

A special application of the relation between $\mathcal{R}$ and M_R has been found. It permits the calculation of the molecular weight of a polymer[1]:

$$M = \frac{a_0\,\varrho}{c^{\frac{1}{3}} - a_1 \dfrac{n^2-1}{n^2+2}} \tag{31.7}$$

where n is the refractive index.

LAGEMANN and DUNBAR[2] also established a relation between $\mathcal{R}$ and either the boiling point temperature, T_b, or the critical temperature in homologous series:

$$T^* = a_0 + a_1 \log_{10}\mathcal{R} \tag{31.8}$$

where a_0 and a_1 have different values according as T^* is the critical or the boiling point temperature.

RAO's relation can be used to obtain an expression for the temperature-dependence of velocity in unassociated liquids. In these liquids, in fact

$$\varrho = \bar{\varrho} + \varrho_0\left(1 - \frac{T}{T_c}\right)^{0.3}, \tag{31.9}$$

where $\bar{\varrho}$ is the vapor density at temperature T, ϱ_0 is the liquid density at $T=0$ ($1/\varrho_0$ is approximately equal to the critical volume) and T_c is the critical temperature.

At moderate temperatures $\bar{\varrho}$ is negligible and

$$c = c_0\left(1 - \frac{T}{T_c}\right)^{0.9}. \tag{31.10}$$

The curve c versus T given by (31.10) is almost linear and is in agreement with experimental results.

LAGEMANN, MCMILLAN and WOLF[3] have established an empirical relation between the temperature coefficient of velocity and molecular weight

$$\frac{\Delta c}{\Delta T} M^{\frac{1}{2}} = 39.0 \quad \mathrm{m \cdot sec^{-1}\,{}^{\circ}C^{-1}\,g^{\frac{1}{2}}} \tag{31.11}$$

which agrees in many liquids within 6% with experiment. It has however no general validity[4].

[1] W. WEISSLER, J. W. FITZGERALD and J. RESNICK: J. Appl. Phys. **18**, 434 (1937).
[2] R. T. LAGEMANN and W. S. DUNBAR: J. Phys. Chem. **49**, 428 (1945).
[3] R. T. LAGEMANN, D. R. MCMILLAN and W. E. WOOLF: J. Chem. Phys. **17**, 368 (1949).
[4] G. W. MARKS: J. Acoust. Soc. Amer. **27**, 680 (1955).

δ) *Rao's formula and molecular associations.* RAO's formula is valid only for unassociated liquids. When applied to associated substances, $\mathscr{R}$ is temperature-dependent and it increases with temperature. Probably this is due to the fact that in calculations one uses the molecular weight of simple molecules, whereas one should consider the weights of the associated groups which decrease in size and number when the temperature is raised. Some times the ratio $\mathscr{R}_T/\mathscr{R}_0$ has been taken as an indication of the variation of association with temperature. ($\mathscr{R}_0$ is relative to a reference temperature T_0.) Fig. 50[1] gives this ratio in toluene, water and methyl alcohol; T_0 is the melting point temperature. Toluene is practically unassociated and the ratio stays constant ($=1$), while in the other two liquids in which association is present the ratio decreases.

ε) *Theoretical explanation of Rao's formula.* Some attempts have been made to find a theoretical basis for the empirical RAO's formula.

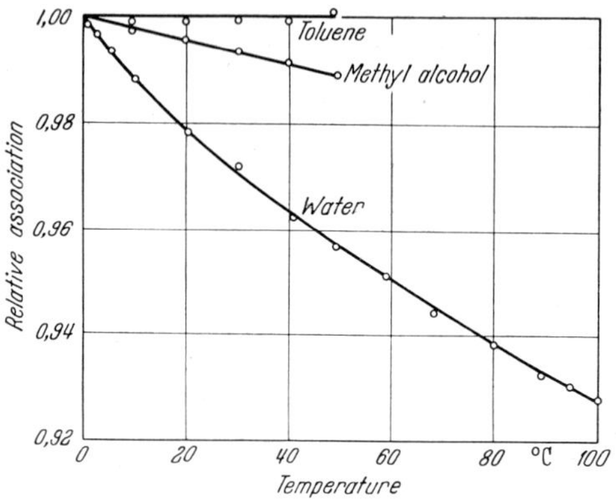

Fig. 50. Relative association vs. temperature (A. WEISSLER).

ALTENBURG[2] applied his theory (Sect. 30β) to the calculation of the lefthand side of Eq. (31.1), obtaining

$$\frac{\frac{1}{c}\frac{\partial c}{\partial T}}{\frac{1}{\varrho}\frac{\partial \varrho}{\partial T}} = \frac{19}{6} = 3.17. \tag{31.12}$$

This result is important because it shows that RAO's formula can be explained on the same general ideas which justify SCHAAFFS' results. The meaning of $\mathscr{R}$ remains still to be clarified, as also the reasons of its relation to atomic addenda. Recently SCHAAFFS[3] has suggested an interpretation of RAO's formula using Eq. (30.6) which explains also the additivity. If r_m and l are the molecular radius and the length of edges of the cubic cell, B and V are given by:

$$B = \frac{4\pi}{3} r_m^3 N_A, \quad V = l^3 N_A. \tag{31.13}$$

Then Eq. (30.6) can be used to obtain

$$\sqrt[3]{c}\, V = \sqrt[3]{c_\infty}\, \sqrt[3]{\frac{4\pi}{3} s}\, (r_m l^2 N_A). \tag{31.14}$$

The equation is similar to RAO's formula. SCHAAFFS suggests writing (31.14) in the form

$$\sqrt[3]{\frac{c}{c_\infty}}\, V = \sqrt[3]{\frac{4\pi s}{3}}\, (r_m l^2 N_A). \tag{31.15}$$

Then the dimension of both sides is that of a volume, and the additivity can be understood because it has been already established for various characteristic volumes of molecules as V, B, b, etc.

SCHAAFFS, moreover, finds an explanation of the temperature independence of $\mathscr{R}/\sqrt[3]{c_\infty}$ (and of $\mathscr{R}$); this volume in fact has a value always intermediate between the volumes $\frac{4\pi}{3} V$ and B. The volume of the elementary cell l^3 and V increase

[1] A. WEISSLER: J. Chem. Phys. **15**, 210 (1947).
[2] K. ALTENBURG: Kolloid-Z. **117**, 153 (1950).
[3] W. SCHAAFFS: Acustica **4**, 635 (1954).

slightly with temperature: in benzene, for instance, l^3 increases 11% between melting and boiling points. On the other hand, r_m^3 and B in organic substances decrease with temperature. This can be seen by means of sound velocity measurements using Eq. (30.6) solved for B. Therefore a volume must exist between B and V which does not vary with temperature and this seems to be $\mathcal{R}/\sqrt[3]{c_\infty}$.

This analysis shows that RAO's formula is valid for those organic substances for which B decreases with temperature, but it is not a rule valid for all kinds of liquids.

32. Intermolecular forces and sound velocity. The velocity of propagation of a mechanical disturbance in a liquid strongly depends on the nature of the forces which the molecules exchange. ALTENBURG's theoretical calculation of an expression similar to the semi-empirical relation found by SCHAAFFS, shows clearly how intermolecular forces are at the foundation of this formula. SCHAAFFS' treatment, however, with the use of atomic addenda, does not make evident the dependence of velocity upon intermolecular forces. PARSHAD[1] has suggested some considerations which although of a qualitative nature are useful in explaining some characteristic aspects of sound velocity in liquids. The interaction energy between two molecules has the form

$$W = \frac{C_r^*}{d^n} - \frac{C_a^*}{d^6}, \tag{32.1}$$

where constants C_r^* and C_a^* correspond to the repulsive and attractive forces and d is the distance. The repulsive forces decrease with a power n of the distance which is between 9 and 12; according to LENNARD-JONES it should be 12.

The attractive forces are essentially of these types:

(a) Dispersion forces (LONDON); the corresponding interaction energy is:

$$W = -\frac{3}{4}\,\frac{\zeta_1\zeta_2}{d^6}\,V^* \tag{32.2}$$

where ζ's are the polarizabilities and V^* the excitation potential (approximately equal to the ionization potential).

(b) Induction forces (DEBYE): the interaction energy is

$$W = -\frac{\mu_2^2\zeta_1 + \mu_1^2\zeta_2}{d^6} \tag{32.3}$$

where the μ's are dipole moments.

(c) KEESOM forces between polar molecules:

$$W = -\frac{2}{3}\,\frac{\mu_1^2\mu^2}{k\,T\,d^6}. \tag{32.4}$$

All attractive forces depend upon $1/d^6$.

The distances between molecules in liquids are often of the same order of magnitude as dipole lengths so that usually it is necessary to consider not only the dipole moment of the whole molecule, but also the real distribution of charges. For instance in *p*-dichlorbenzene the dipole moment of the molecule is zero, but there are two strong $c-d$ dipoles which surely produce interactions.

The position of dynamic equilibrium of molecules depends upon C_a^*, C_r^* and the thermal agitation. Of course the equilibrium distance becomes smaller and smaller when the cohesive energy, i.e. C_a^* gets bigger and bigger.

[1] R. PARSHAD: Indian J. Phys. **19**, 47 (1945).

Because the cohesive energy varies with $1/d^6$ when the equilibrium distance decreases, it increases the variation of energy required to move the molecules from the equilibrium, i.e. the compressibility of the substance gets smaller. In other words, the compressibility decreases when the cohesive energy increases.

According to PARSHAD, the formation of molecular associations in a liquid produces a decrease of cohesive energy involved in sound propagation, because when groups of molecules are formed they move as unities and therefore the cohesive energy among them is of importance in sound propagation. The cohesive energy among groups is rather small because the cohesive energy of single molecules is mainly spent in holding together the molecules of the group.

The general ideas now mentioned are useful to clarify some aspects of the behaviour of sound velocity in pure liquids and in mixtures.

PARTHASARATHY[1] investigated experimentally the dependence of sound velocity on weight, shape length of molecules, viscosity, dipole moment, presence of double bonds, etc. These rules as well as their exceptions can be explained by means of various methods. PARSHAD's treatment is useful in giving a qualitative description of the phenomena.

33. Variations of sound velocity with temperature and pressure. Sound velocity decreases when temperature rises, in all liquids tested up to the present with exception of water. The coefficient $\Delta c/\Delta T$ in organic liquids goes from 2 to 6 m/sec per degree.

In unassociated liquids we have already seen the validity of RAO's relation which allows one to calculate the changes of velocity by means of the variation of volume with temperature. ALTENBURG in his theoretical treatment of sound velocity considers the effects of temperature and of an external pressure as volume effects. Changes of temperature or of pressure produce variations of the distance between molecules (d) and this distance influences the sound velocity directly and indirectly through the value of the intermolecular forces. ALTENBURG[2] established the relation:

$$c \approx c_0 \left(1 - \frac{19}{2} \frac{d - d_0}{d_0}\right) \tag{33.1}$$

where d_0 and c_0 refer to fixed temperature (for instance melting point) and pressure, and $(d - d_0)$ is the variation of distance between molecules produced by changes either of temperature or of pressure.

If associations are present inside the liquid the observed variations of velocity with temperature are partly due to the aforementioned volume effect and partly to the destruction of associations produced by increase of thermal agitation when the temperature rises. According to PARSHAD's considerations a decrease of the number of molecular associations in a liquid produces an increase of cohesive energy involved in sound propagation and therefore a decrease of compressibility: i.e., in general a rise of velocity.

The most characteristic case of an associated liquid is water. Fig. 51 gives the results obtained by PANCHOLY[3] in H_2O and D_2O. The behaviour is similar in the two cases: in normal water the velocity maximum (1.557 m/sec) is reached at 74° C. WILLARD[4] has suggested the following empirical relation for the velocity in water:

$$c_{°t} = 1.557 - 0.0245\,(74 - {}^\circ t) \tag{33.2}$$

with °t meaning the centigrade temperature.

[1] S. PARTHASARATHY: Current Sci. **6**, 322 (1938).
[2] K. ALTENBURG: Kolloid-Z. **122**, 35 (1951).
[3] M. PANCHOLY: J. Acoust. Soc. Amer. **25**, 1003 (1953).
[4] G. W. WILLARD: J. Acoust. Soc. Amer. **19**, 235 (1947).

This behaviour of velocity can be explained on the basis of destruction of association and volume effect. The increase of velocity in the first part of the curve of Fig. 51 is due to the gradual destruction of association with consequent increase of cohesive energy involved in sound propagation produced by thermal agitation; this effect is so big that any volume effect is masked. When almost all associations are destroyed the volume effect produces a decrease of velocity with temperature as in the other liquids.

Some measurements of sound velocity vs. pressure have been performed in a few organic liquids by SWANSON[1], BIQUARD[2], and CARNEVALE and LITOVITZ[3]. Figs. 52 and 53 give the results of BIQUARD, and of CARNEVALE and LITOVITZ.

Values of velocity in water as a function of pressure have been obtained by HOLTON[4], by SMITH and LAWSON[5], and by LITOVITZ and CARNEVALE[6].

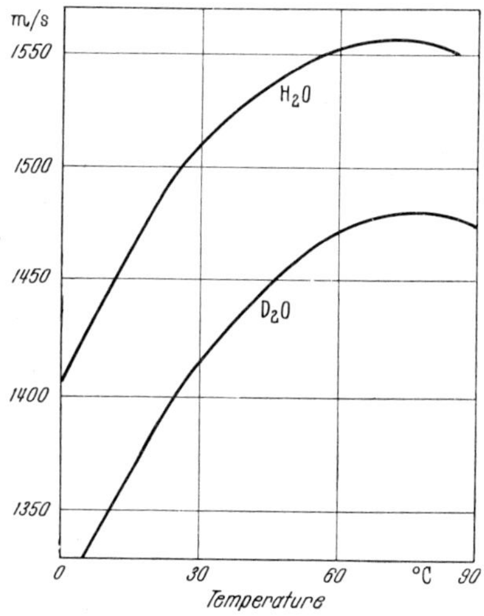

Fig. 51. Temperature dependence of sound velocity in H_2O and D_2O (M. PANCHOLY).

In all liquids the velocity increases with pressure as is required by a volume effect. ALTENBURG[7] has modified Eq. (33.1) for the case that the variation of distance is produced by a pressure variation;

$$c = c_T \left[1 + \tfrac{19}{6}\, \Phi(\Theta^*) \int\limits_0^P \chi_{\text{is}}\, d p\right] \tag{33.3}$$

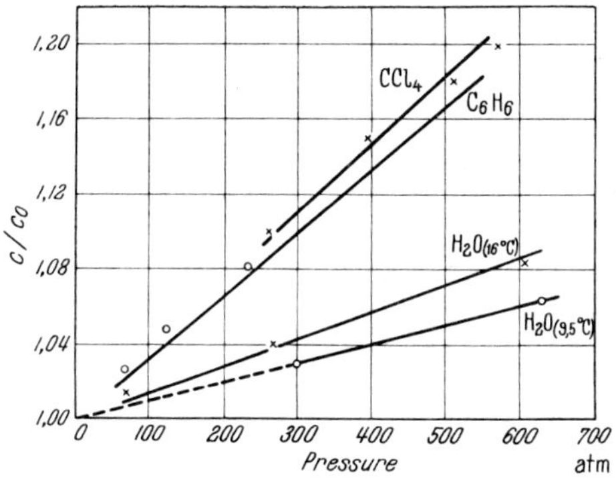

Fig. 52. Sound velocity vs. pressure in some liquids (P. BIQUARD).

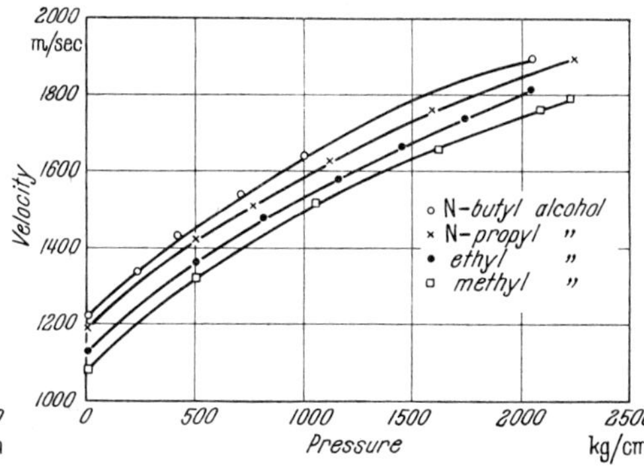

Fig. 53. Sound velocity vs. pressure in some primary alcohols (E. CARNEVALE and T. A. LITOVITZ).

where c_T is the velocity at excess pressure zero at the temperature of experiment and χ_{is} is the isothermal compressibility. Φ is a function of the reduced tempera-

[1] J. CH. SWANSON: J. Chem. Phys. **2**, 689 (1934).
[2] P. BIQUARD: C. R. Acad. Sci. Paris **206**, 897 (1938). — Rev. Acoust. **8**, 130 (1939).
[3] E. H. CARNEVALE and R. A. LITOVITZ: J. Acoust. Soc. Amer. **27**, 547 (1955).
[4] G. HOLTON: J. Appl. Phys. **22**, 1407 (1951).
[5] A. H. SMITH and A. W. LAWSON: J. Chem. Phys. **22**, 351 (1954).
[6] T. A. LITOVITZ and E. H. CARNEVALE: J. Appl. Phys. **26**, 816 (1955).
[7] K. ALTENBURG: Kolloid-Z. **122**, 35 (1951).

Table 20. *Calculated and measured values of* $\frac{1}{c}\frac{\partial c}{\partial p}$ (K. ALTENBURG).

Liquid	$\chi \cdot 10^6$ (atm^{-1})	Θ^*	$\Phi(\Theta^*)$	$\frac{1}{c}\frac{\partial c}{\partial p} \cdot 10^5$ (atm^{-1}) theoretical		experimental
Ethyl bromide	(100)	0.223	1.34	42	51	43
Carbon tetrachloride	96	0.110	1.13	34	41	50
Chloroform	89	0.154	1.20	34	40	38
Ether	162	0.306	1.56	80	96	88
Pentane	(150)	0.308	1.54	73	87	92
Carbon disulphide	82	0.135	1.17	30	36	39
Benzene	84	0.111	1.14	30	36	33
Toluene	80	0.052	1.06	27	32	34
Aniline	42.5	−0.098	0.91	12	14	21

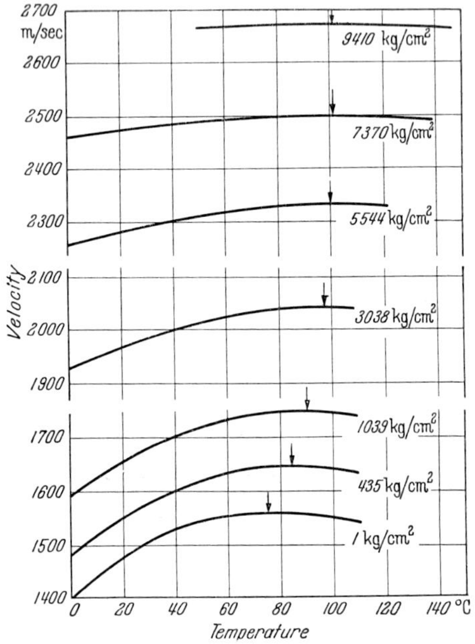

Fig. 54. Sound velocity in water vs. pressure (A. H. SMITH and A. W. LAWSON).

ture (T_0 = melting point; T_c = critical temperature) $\Theta^* = \frac{T-T_0}{T_c-T_0}$.

$$\Phi(\Theta^*) = \frac{1-\frac{1}{3}\frac{7}{24}\log(1-\Theta^*)}{1+\frac{19}{2}\frac{7}{72}\log(1-\Theta^*)}. \qquad (33.4)$$

Table 20 gives the result of ALTENBURG's calculation compared with SWANSON's measurements for the ratio

$$\frac{1}{c_T}\frac{\partial c}{\partial p} = \frac{19}{6}\chi\,\Phi(\Theta^*) \qquad (33.5)$$

in the range 1 to 300 atm.

The theoretical values of $\frac{1}{c}\frac{\partial c}{\partial p}$ in the fifth column of Table 20 are calculated by means of (33.5) using data from the literature for the various quantities; no empirical constants are involved. The calculated values are on the average 20% smaller than the experimental ones. Small variations of the factor $\frac{19}{6}=3.17$ in Eq. (33.5) are, however, sufficient to improve the agreement; column 6 gives the theoretical values calculated by using a numerical factor 3.8 instead of 3.17.

As mentioned in Sect. 31α, RAO and WADA have found that some expressions formed by means of density and compressibility are independent of variation of pressure as well as of temperature. A similar observation has been made by LITOVITZ and CARNEVALE for the expression $\sqrt[3]{c}\,V$.

Fig. 54 gives the results of velocity measurements in water at different pressures obtained by SMITH and LAWSON. It is interesting to observe that the maximum shifts towards higher temperature and the curves become flatter as pressure increases. HOLTON reached an opposite conclusion with regard to the shift of the maximum, but SMITH and LAWSON's results find some support in the few measurements of LITOVITZ and CARNEVALE. SMITH and LAWSON's analysis of their results seem to give support to HALL's model for the structure of water.

34. Sound velocity in liquid mixtures. The sound velocity in a liquid binary mixture is a function of composition whose form strongly depends on the nature and intensity of the interactions that molecules either of the same or of different kinds exert; in particular the formation or destruction of molecular associations in changes of composition bears directly on the sound velocity. For these reasons, no general theoretical treatment which allows the calculation of the velocity vs. composition curves is available and we shall only indicate the more characteristic cases.

SCHAAFFS[1] has found in a few mixtures the validity of a linear dependence of velocity on weight concentration. Examples are benzene—chlorobenzene; benzene—p-dichlorobenzene, carbon tetrachloride—acetone; carbon tetrachloride—n-heptane.

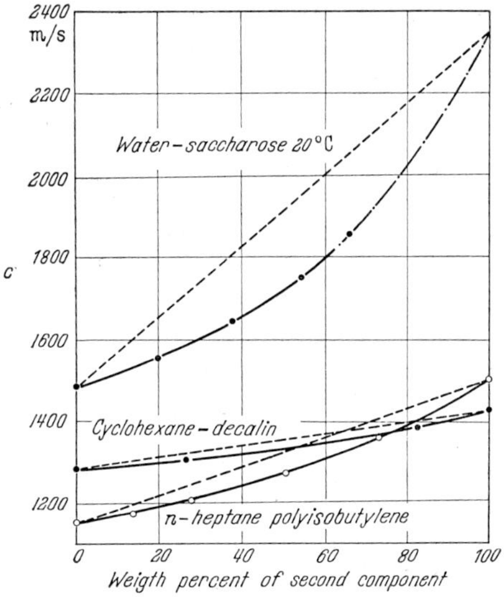

Fig. 55. Sound velocity in some mixtures: experimental values and theoretical curves (full lines) (G. NATTA and M. BACCAREDDA).

Some binary systems show the property that each component keeps its specific volume, and the specific volume of the mixture is obtained by adding the contributions of the two components. According to NATTA and BACCAREDDA[2] in these cases molecules of one type are not appreciably affected by the presence of molecules of the other type. These authors developed a formula which expresses that the time needed for a mechanical pulse to pass through the mixture is the sum of the times which would be required to pass successively through two layers each formed by one of the two components and having thickness proportional to the relative volume concentration. NATTA-BACCAREDDA's formula can be written, using volume concentration (y) or weight concentration (x) of components 1,

$$c_y = \frac{1}{\dfrac{y}{c_1} + \dfrac{(1-y)}{c_2}}, \tag{34.1}$$

$$c_x = \frac{1}{\dfrac{x}{c_1 \varrho_1} + \dfrac{1-x}{c_2 \varrho_2}}. \tag{34.2}$$

In Fig. 55 some examples are given of the application of these formulae. The full lines are those obtained by Eq. (34.2) and agree well with experiment. The dashed lines would instead correspond to a linear dependence of c on the weight concentration.

Although these results are satisfactory, the application of (34.1) and (34.2) is not general and there are exceptions in the class of mixtures for which the specific volume has the aforementioned property.

An important group of binary mixtures is that of systems formed by water and another component which may be acetone, a primary alcohol, acetic acid,

[1] W. SCHAAFFS: Z. Physik **105**, 658 (1937).
[2] G. NATTA and M. BACCAREDDA: Atti Accad. Lincei Roma **4**, 360 (1948).

some glycols, ether, etc. In these systems the velocity reaches a maximum at an intermediate concentration. Fig. 56 gives GIACOMINI'S[1] results in the system water—ethyl alcohol at different temperatures. Both pure components, especially water, are associated liquids and when they are mixed the molecules may form three different kinds of association: water—water, alcohol—alcohol and alcohol—water. According to PARSHAD[2] when alcohol is added to water a dynamical equilibrium among different associations is established and practically destruction of water associations takes place without appreciable formation of water—

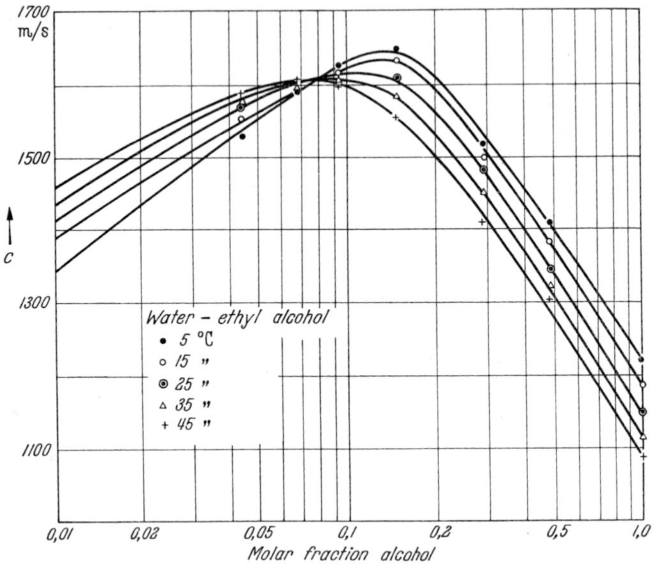

Fig. 56. Sound velocity in water—ethyl alcohol mixtures (A. GIACOMINI).

alcohol groups. Therefore the number of molecules randomly distributed increases as is suggested by measurements of vapour pressure and of dielectric polarizability. The decrease of number of associations produces an increase of cohesive energy involved in sound propagation and determines the increase of velocity which is observed when alcohol is added to water. Moreover BUTLER[3] has calculated the interaction energy between two water molecules (5.25 kcal) and that between the OH group of alcohol and a water molecule (5.6 kcal). From this calculation it is evident that the water—water associations are broken up by alcohol molecules, and it is possible to find the concentration to which the maximum cohesive energy (maximum sound velocity) corresponds in the various water—alcohol systems.

When the temperature is raised the associations in pure water are partly destroyed and smaller quantities of alcohols are needed to complete the dissociation: this explains the decrease of the height of maximum sound velocity and its shift to lower alcohol concentrations shown in Fig. 56.

---

[1] A. GIACOMINI: Acta Pontificia Acad. Sci. **6**, 87 (1942). — J. Acoust. Soc. Amer. **19**, 701 (1947).

[2] R. PARSHAD: Indian J. Phys. **15**, 323 (1941).

[3] See R. PARSHAD: Indian J. Phys. **15**, 323 (1941).

Analogous results[1] can be obtained if the dissociation in the water used for the mixture is produced, instead by means of a temperature rise, by adding small quantities of a salt as is shown in Fig. 57.

The mixtures carbon tetrachloride—ethyl alcohol and carbon tetrachloride—methyl alcohol have been extensively studied [*19*]. The velocity vs. composition curves show a minimum which at 18° C is reached for about 0.04 molar concentration of ethyl alcohol and 0.1 molar concentration of methyl alcohol. It is believed that this minimum is due to the formation of dimers of alcohol. When the temperature rises the minimum shifts towards higher concentration because thermal agitation makes the formation of associations more difficult. Fig. 58 gives DERENZINI and GIACOMINI'S[2] results in carbon tetrachloride—ethyl alcohol mixtures.

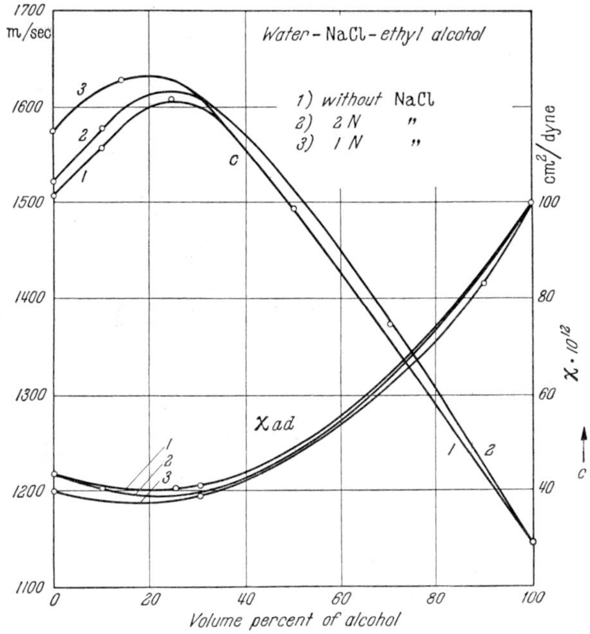

Fig. 57. Sound velocity and adiabatic compressibility in mixtures of water, ethyl alcohol and sodium chloride (R. PARSHAD).

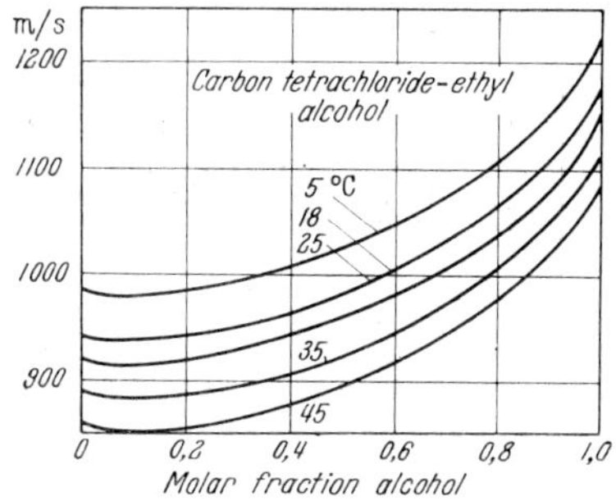

Fig. 58. Sound velocity in carbon tetrachloride—ethyl alcohol mixtures (T. DERENZINI and A. GIACOMINI).

In Fig. 59 are given the curves of velocity and compressibility in the system benzene—ethyl alcohol[3]; both show an inflection. This behaviour can be qualitatively explained[4] by considering the tendency of alcohol molecules to associate and the opposite influence exerted on them by the benzene molecules. The benzene molecules in fact have high polarizability and their planar shape perpendicular to the axis of polarizability can produce strong induction and dispersion forces on alcohol molecules opposing the formation of alcohol—alcohol associations.

The few examples of binary mixtures examined show how the behaviour of compressibility and sound velocity can, at least in a qualitative way, be explained by an analysis of the interactions that tųe molecules of the system exchange.

This, of course, makes possible the use of sound velocity measurements to get information on the nature of the intermolecular forces in binary systems.

---

[1] R. PARSHAD: J. Acoust. Soc. Amer. **21**, 175 (1949).
[2] T. DERENZINI and A. GIACOMINI: Ric. Sci. **13**, 27 (1942).
[3] P. TUOMIKOSKI and U. NURMI: Comment. Phys. Math. Helsinki **10**, 11 (1940).
[4] R. PARSHAD: Indian J. Phys. **16**, 1 (1942).

Some attempts have been made to examine in binary mixtures the change with composition of the expressions:

$$\mathcal{R} = \frac{M}{\varrho\, c^{\frac{1}{3}}}, \qquad \mathcal{B} = \frac{M}{\varrho}\, \chi^{\frac{1}{7}}, \tag{34.3}$$

which correspond respectively to Rao's and Wada's formula (Sect. 31α) and which have values independent of temperature in pure unassociated liquids. Nomoto[1] has calculated the two expres-

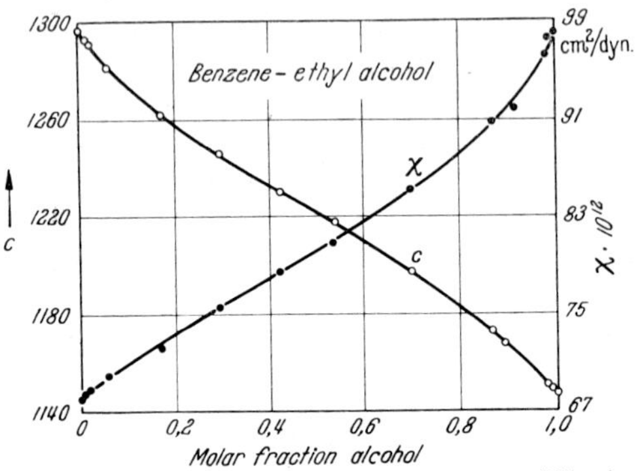

Fig. 59. Sound velocity and adiabatic compressibility in benzene—ethyl alcohol mixtures (P. Tuomikoski and U. Nurmi).

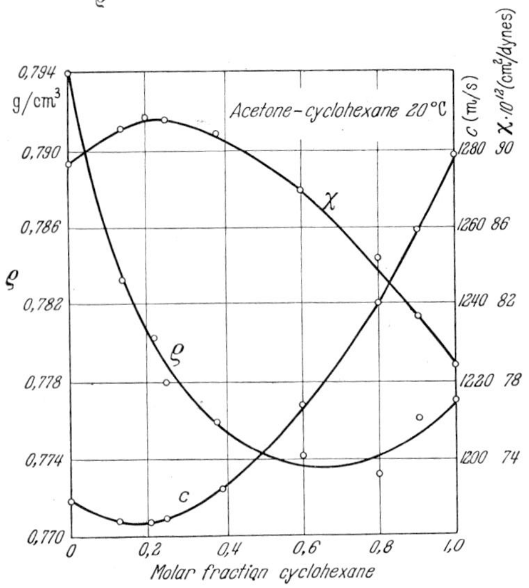

Fig. 60. Sound velocity, density and adiabatic compressibility in acetone—cyclohexane mixtures (I. Gabrielli and G. Poiani).

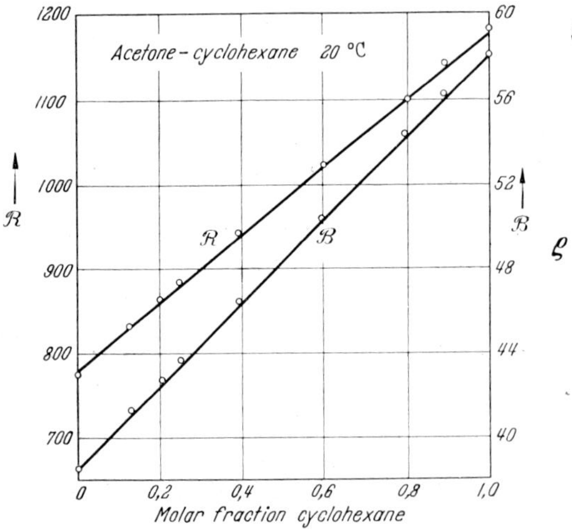

Fig. 61. $\mathcal{R}$ and $\mathcal{B}$ in acetone—cyclohexane mixtures (O. Nomoto).

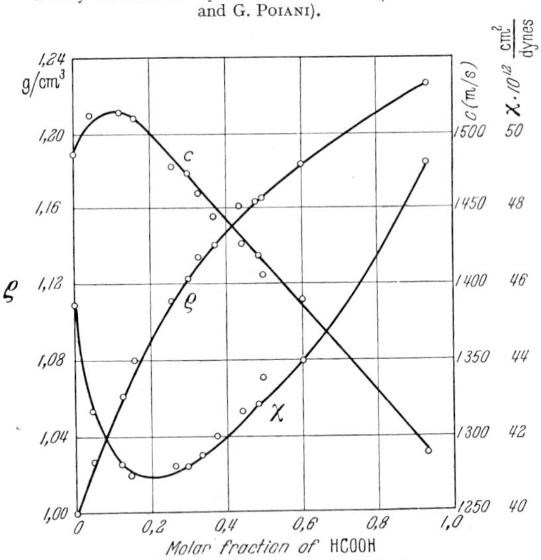

Fig. 62. Sound velocity, density and adiabatic compressibility in water—formic acid mixtures (I. G. Mikhailov).

sions (34.3) in a large number of mixtures of various kinds, including some formed by associated components such as water—acetone and water—alcohol. He finds that $\mathcal{R}$ and $\mathcal{B}$ have a linear form in many systems for which neither sound velocity nor compressibility behave linearly. Figs. 60[2] and 61 respectively

---

[1] O. Nomoto: J. Phys. Soc. Japan **8**, 553 (1953). — J. Chem. Phys. **21**, 950 (1953).

[2] Experimental results by I. Gabrielli and G. Poiani: Ric. Sci. **11**, 619 (1952).

give c, ϱ, χ and $\mathcal{R}$, $\mathcal{B}$ in the system acetons—cyclohexane. Figs. 62 and 63[1] refer to the mixtures water—acetic acid. Similar results where obtained by MARKS[2]. The latter author finds also the validity of the following expression for the velocity of mixtures at various temperatures.

$$\left(\frac{\Delta c}{\Delta T} M^{\frac{1}{2}}\right) = a_1 N_1 + a_2 \tag{34.4}$$

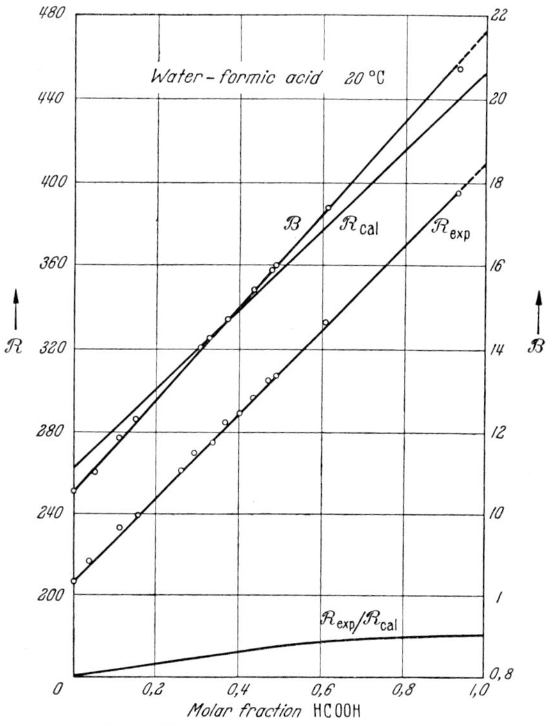

Fig. 63. $\mathcal{R}$ and $\mathcal{B}$ in water—formic acid mixtures (O. NOMOTO).

where a_1 and a_2 are suitable constants and N_1 the mole fraction of one component. Eq. (34.4) holds if association or dissociation does not occur.

Bibliography.

Books and collections of papers on ultrasonics in which the subject of the present article is treated.

[*1*] BERGMANN, L.: Der Ultraschall, 6. Aufl. Zürich 1954.
[*2*] MASON, W. P.: Piezoelectric Crystals and their applications to ultrasonics. New York 1950.
[*3*] VIGOUREUX, P.: Ultrasonics. London 1950.
[*8*] Atti Convegno Internazionale di Ultracustica (Roma 1950). Suppl. Nuovo Cim. Vol. VII, No. 2 (1950).
[*5*] Colloquium over Ultrasonore Trillingen. Koninklijke Vlaasme Ac., Brussel 1951.
[*6*] RICHARDSON, E. G.: Ultrasonic Physics. London 1952.
[*7*] Communications du Congrès International sur le traitement par les ultrasons (Centre de Recherches S.I.M.) Marseille 1955.
[*7a*] HERZFELD, K. F., and T. A. LITOVITZ: Absorption and dispersion of ultrasonic waves. New York: Academic Press 1959. [Note added in proof.]

[1] Experimental results by I. G. MIKHAILOV: Dokl. Akad. Nauk USSR. **31**, 550 (1941).
[2] G. W. MARKS: J. Acoust. Soc. Amer. **27**, 680 (1955).

The following review articles treat extensively the subjects of sound dispersion and absorption. These paper have extensive lists of literature.

[*8*] RICHARDS, W. T.: Supersonic Phenomena. Rev. Mod. Phys. **11**, 36 (1939).
[*9*] KITTEL, C.: Ultrasonics research and the properties of matter. Progr. Phys. **11**, 205 (1948).
[*10*] SKUDRZYCK, E.: Die Theorie der inneren Reibung in Gasen und Flüssigkeiten und die Schallabsorption. Acta phys. Austriaca **2**, 148 (1948).
[*11*] SETTE, D.: L'assorbimento delle onde ultrasonore nei liquidi. Suppl. Nuovo Cim. **6**, 1 (1949).
[*12*] KNESER, H. O.: Molekulare Schallabsorption und Dispersion. Ergebn. exakt. Naturw. **22**, 121 (1949).
[*13*] MARKHAM, J. J., R. T. BEYER and R. B. LINDSAY: Absorption of sound in fluids. Rev. Mod. Phys. **23**, 353 (1951).
[*14*] PINKERTON, J. M. M.: On the interpretation of ultrasonic absorption measurements in liquids. In Ref. [*5*], above.
[*15*] KARIM, S. M., and L. ROSENHEAD: The second coefficient of viscosity of liquids and gases. Rev. Mod. Phys. **24**, 108 (1952).
[*16*] TRUESDELL, C.: Precise theory of the absorption and dispersion of forced plane infinitesimal waves according to the Navier-Stokes equation. J. Rat. Mech. and Analysis **2**, 643 (1953).
[*17*] HERZFELD, K. F.: Relaxation phenomena in gases, in the book: Thermodynamics and Physics of matter. Princeton 1955.

The following paper is a review of recent contribution of Russian physicists.

[*18*] BEYER, R. T.: Recent research in ultrasonics and physical acoustics in the USSR. Suppl. Nuovo Cim., Ser. X **4**, 33 (1956).

The following review articles treat the relation between sound velocity and molecular composition and structure. A wide list of literature can be found in them.

[*19*] SETTE, D.: Velocità di propagazione degli ultrasuoni nelle mescolanze liquide. Ric. Sci. **19**, 1338 (1949).
[*20*] SETTE, D.: Velocità degli ultrasuoni nei liquidi puri e struttura molecolare. Ric. Sci. **20**, 102 (1950).
[*21*] SCHAAFFS, W.: Schallgeschwindigkeit und Molekülstruktur in Flüssigkeiten. Ergebn. exakt. Naturw. **25**, 109 (1951).

Dispersion and Absorption of Sound in High Polymers.

By

WARREN P. MASON.

With 53 Figures.

1. Introduction. High polymer materials exist in the form of liquids, rubbers, and solids depending on the temperature, the length of the polymer chain and the degree of cross bonding to other polymer chains. Even in the solid state, materials such as polyethylene and nylon may be partly crystalline with liquid-like regions joining the crystalline regions. The liquid-like structure of rubbers accounts for their ability to stretch, and it is this feature, coupled with the use of carbon black, that causes them to wear so well in automobile tires. Plastics and rubbers are the materials that can take the greatest strains without fatigueing; and they outwear such materials as metals and glasses. Toughness, mechanical shock resistance, ultimate elongation and strength are determined by the ease with which the polymer molecules can be displaced without breaking the piece. It is no accident that polymer substances are used in body armor to deflect bullets.

The molecular polymer chain is the fundamental building block of the rubber or plastic materials, and it is the motion of parts or segments of the chains that determines the response to a mechanical stress. Even those "long-time" qualities of plastics, such as creep and stress relaxation, apparently result from the integrated displacements or rapidly oscillating segments of the chains. The displacement of chain segments is accompanied by loss of energy to adjacent segments and ultimately into heat. The amount of heat generated in automobile tires due to the stretching they undergo is of considerable importance in determining the lasting quality of the tire. Natural rubber's low internal friction for both compressional[1] and shear waves[2] is famous for its low hysteresis heating. The high hysteresis loss present in butyl rubber and other polymer materials is advantageous for the braking of automobiles on slippery surfaces[2a]. Such tires do not "sing" as do natural rubber tires.

A wide variety of methods have been used to study the chain and segment motions possible in polymer liquids, rubbers and solids. One method of studying these chain segment motions is to observe the stress relaxation, creep, viscosity, etc., and to relate them to a distribution of molecular relaxation times (and energy barriers), as originated by KUHN[3,4]. This method is particularly good for obtaining the long-time distribution end of the relaxation spectrum, but it is not capable of determining the very short time relaxations occurring for single chain segment motions.

---

[1] GEHMAN, WOODFORD and STAMBAUGH: Industr. Engng. Chem. **33**, 1032 (1941).
[2] DILLON, PRETTYMAN and HALL: J. Appl. Phys. **15**, 309 (1944).
[2a] J. A. GREENWOOD and D. TABOR: Proc. Roy. Soc. Lond. **71**, 989—1001 (1958).
[3] KUHN: Z. phys. Chem. B **42**, 1 (1939).
[4] SIMHA: J. Appl. Phys. **13**, 201 (1942).

Another approach is to strain polymers with periodic waves over a very wide spectrum of wavelengths, eventually going to frequencies comparable to those of the thermal vibrations of significant groups or segments of the macromolecules. The resulting velocity dispersion or attenuation relaxation can then be examined and activation energies determined by observing the variation of relaxation frequencies with temperature. Recently, shifts with hydrostatic pressures have been observed[5a, 5b]. This acoustic spectrum determination is similar to the investigation of the dielectric constant dispersion and absorption that has been carried out for many materials by using electromagnetic waves. In fact for some materials such as glycerol[6], the relaxation frequencies are the same for both methods. It is not true that they always occur at the same frequencies for the reason that the chain segments are driven in a different manner by the two processes. To drive the chain by electromagnetic waves requires that the chain have dipole moments. All the dipole moments of a given chain segment are driven alike by the electric field whereas a mechanical stress takes hold of the segment in a different manner and may cause a different relaxation frequency. Furthermore, since the material does not have to be polar for a mechanical wave to act on it, many more relaxations can be investigated mechanically than can be investigated electrically.

Both shear and longitudinal mechanical waves have been used in polymer studies. For polymers in solution, shear waves are required because the effect of a few added polymer molecules on the bulk stiffness is negligible, but the effect of a few added molecules on the shear viscosity and stiffness is significant. Hence, shear waves are a necessity for interpreting the effects of chemical changes and additions. Even for rubbers and solids, shear waves can give information on compressional viscosity and its relaxation spectrum which cannot be obtained by longitudinal waves alone.

During the last few years a large number of investigators have employed ultrasonic techniques in investigating the mechanical properties of polymers. A number of the instruments employed are described in Chap. II. Among the investigators may be mentioned the pioneering wave studies of FERRY and collaborators[7, 8] on concentrated solutions of polymers, which have suggested intrinsic relations of the chain molecules in a highly plasticized semisolid state; the work of NOLLE[9] and IVEY, MROWCA and GUTH[10] on the mechanical properties of rubber; the work of BAKER, HEISS, MASON, and MCSKIMIN[11–13] on the relaxations of polymer molecules in dilute solutions and the relaxations found in long chain liquids and solids; the work of HOPKINS on soft polymer rubbers[14]; the work and theories of ROUSE and coworkers[15, 16], and of F. BUECHE[17a] and B. ZIMM[17b], on polymer molecules in solutions; and the work of LAMB[5b] and

[5a] CARNEVALE, KENDALL and LITOVITZ: Paper B 2, 49th meeting of Acoust. Soc. of America, June 30, 1955. J. Chem. Phys. **26**, 465 (1957).

[5b] A. J. BARLOW and J. LAMB: Proc. Roy. Soc. Lond. A **253**, 52 (1959).

[6] LITOVITZ, LYON and PESELNICK: J. Acoust. Soc. Amer. **26**, 566–577 (1954).

[7] FERRY, SAWYER and ASHWORTH: J. Polymer Sci. **1947**, 593, for a general review.

[8] J. D. FERRY: J. Amer. Chem. Soc. **72**, 3746 (1950).

[9] NOLLE: J. Polymer Sci. **15**, 1 (1950). — J. Appl. Phys. **19**, 753 (1948).

[10] IVEY, MROWCA and GUTH: J. Appl. Phys. **20**, 486 (1949).

[11] BAKER and HEISS: Bell Syst. Techn. J. **31**, 306–356 (1952) (a review paper).

[12] MASON and MCSKIMIN: Bell Syst. Techn. J. **31**, 122–171 (1952) (a review paper).

[13] BAKER, MASON and HEISS: J. Polymer Sci. **8**, 129–155 (1952).

[14] I. L. HOPKINS: Trans. Amer. Soc. Mech. Engrs. **73**, 195 (1951).

[15] P. E. ROUSE jr.: J. Chem. Phys. **21**, No. 7, 1272–1280 (1953).

[16] K. SITTEL, P. E. ROUSE jr. and E. D. BAILEY: J. Appl. Phys. **25**, 1312–1320 (1954).

[17a] F. BUECHE: J. Chem. Phys. **20**, 1959 (1952); **22**, 603 (1954).

[17b] BRUNO H. ZIMM: J. Chem. Phys. **24**, 269 (1956). See also Chap. I, Rheology, Vol. 3. New York, Academic Press 1960.

LITOVITZ[6,18] and collaborators on high frequency measurements of many polymer liquids and the effects of pressure[5a, 5b] on some.

Polymer solids have been studied extensively by KOLSKY[19] and his coworkers at the Imperial Chemical Industries of England, by the wave propagation and impedance techniques, while HOFF[20] and coworkers, also at the Imperial Chemical Industries, Inc., have used both mechanical and electrical measurements at low temperatures to investigate the effects of added groups on the polymer chains.

The next sections describe measurements made on polymers in solution, polymer liquids, polymer rubbers, and solid polymers and some of the conclusions and generalizations that can be drawn from them. An interpretation is described which employs linear and three-dimensional networks. This allows one to interpret the results in terms of four network parameters. The work described is mainly on the physical side. The chemical work necessary to determine molecular weights, molecular size, etc., will be found in other references[11, 21-24].

I. Phenomenological methods for characterizing relaxations.

A good description of many of the properties of polymers can be obtained by setting up phenomenological models of the processes taking place in the molecules. This is probably not as fundamental a method as the network description considered later, but it has been applied extensively in relating the mechanical properties to assumed mechanisms of the polymer molecules. In any case it is usually the first step in discussing a more fundamental mechanism. Hence it is the purpose of this section to describe several standard models of this type.

2. Maxwell models of elastic moduli. The theories of elasticity in solids and viscosities in liquids are initially based on solids for which elasticity is unaccompanied by flow and liquids for which flow is not accompanied by elastic effects. However, there are materials whose mechanical properties cannot be adequately defined unless one simultaneously considers both viscous and elastic effects.

The first case of this type considered was the Maxwellian[25] relaxation for which a material can respond to a stress by two different mechanisms, elasticity, and flow. Maxwell devised this model to consider the relaxation time associated with a change in shape of a volume of gas or liquid. He conceived the idea that if the shape of a volume of liquid or gas were instantaneously changed, this change would be opposed by elastic forces. However, in the course of a very short time (the Maxwellian relaxation time) the molecules will move so that all the elastic stresses are relieved and the conditions are restored to the original state before the change in shape. MAXWELL's model, which is shown in mechanical and equivalent electrical form in Fig. 1, applies quite well for the shear properties

---

[18] T. A. LITOVITZ and T. LYON: J. Acoust. Soc. Amer. **26**, 577—581 (1954).

[19] For example, see H. KOLSKY, Stress Waves in Solids, (London: Oxford Press 1953), for a summary of a number of the papers. Later paper are: J. J. BENBOW: Proc. Phys. Soc. Lond. B **67**, 120 (1954). — H. KOLSKY: Proc. 2nd Int. Congress on Rheology. London: Butterworth Scientific Publ. 1954. — H. KOLSKY: Phil. Mag. **45**, 712 (1954).

[20] E. A. HOFF, D. W. ROBINSON and A. H. WILLBOURN: Part. I. J. Polymer Sci. **13**, 565 (1954); Part II **18**, 161 (1955).

[21] P. J. FLORY: J. Amer. Chem. Soc. **65**, 372 (1943).

[22] FOX and FLORY: J. Phys. Colloid. Chem. **55**, 221 (1951).

[23] BAKER: Ind. Engng. Chem. **41**, 511 (1949).

[24] P. J. FLORY: Principles of Polymer Chemistry. Ithaca, N.Y.: Cornell Univ. Press 1953.

[25] J. C. MAXWELL: On the Dynamic Theory of Gases. Phil. Trans. Roy. Soc. Lond. **157**, 49—88 (1867). — Phil. Mag., Ser. IV **35**, 129—145, 185—217 (1868).

of simple liquids and short chain polymer liquids. Mathematically the model can be expressed in the form

$$\frac{d S_{12}}{dt} = \frac{T_{12}}{\eta} + \frac{1}{\mu} \frac{d T_{12}}{dt} \tag{2.1}$$

where the first term expresses the viscous relation between the rate of change of the shearing strain S_{12} in terms of the applied shearing stress T_{12} and the coefficient of shear viscosity η, while the second term represents the elastic relation between the strain and stress, where μ is the shearing modulus. To determine the Maxwellian relaxation time, we consider the following problem. The sample is quickly forced to assume a deformation S_{12} and then constrained so that it retains this deformed shape. Although the deformation cannot change

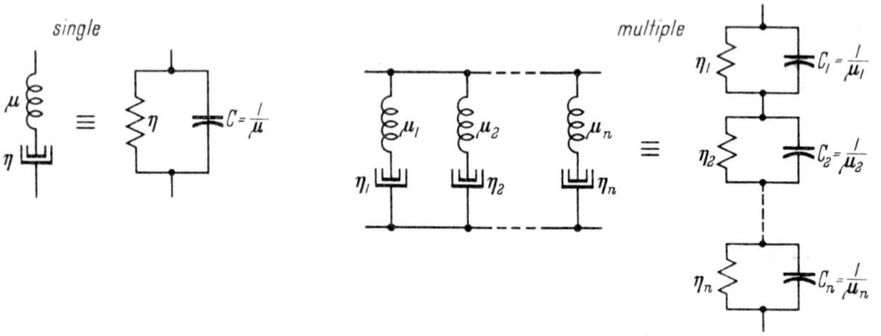

Fig. 1. Maxwell model, multiple Maxwell model and equivalent electrical circuits.

under these conditions, the internal flow gradually relaxes the stress so that smaller stresses are required to maintain the shape. Since the strain does not change, $d S_{12}/dt = 0$, and the equation reduces to

$$\frac{1}{\mu} \frac{dT_{12}}{dt} + \frac{T_{12}}{\eta} = 0. \tag{2.2}$$

A solution of this equation is

$$T_{12} = T_{12_0} e^{-\mu t/\eta}. \tag{2.3}$$

After a time

$$t_0 = \frac{\eta}{\mu} \tag{2.4}$$

the stress will have relaxed to (1/e)-th of its original value. The time t_0 is called the Maxwell relaxation time. For a polymer liquid such as polymerized castor oil[26] the shear stiffness is about 1.2×10^7 dynes/cm², while the viscosity at room temperature is 18 poises. Hence the relaxation time is 1.5×10^{-6} seconds which is well within the range of the shear impedance measuring instruments of Chap. II. If MAXWELL's concept is correct, all liquids should have a shear elasticity and a relaxation time. For liquids having an instantaneous shear elasticity of 10^{10} dynes/cm² and a viscosity of 0.01 Poise (values in the range of ordinary light liquids) the relaxation time is in the order of 10^{-12} seconds and hence is much too small to be measurable by any ultrasonic measuring instruments so far devised. Only viscosities can be measured for such liquids.

The properties of simple and viscoelastic liquids can be measured by using sinusoidal vibrations produced by the transducers and instruments described in

[26] See W. P. MASON: Piezoelectric Crystals and Their Application to Ultrasonics, Chap. XIV, p. 345. D. Van Nostrand Co 1950.

Chap. II. For sinusoidal vibrations, Eq. (2.1) takes the form*

$$T_{12} = \left(\frac{j\,\omega\,\eta}{1+j\,(\omega\,\eta/\mu)}\right) S_{12} = \left(\frac{j\,\omega\,\eta}{1+j\,\omega/\omega_0}\right) S_{12} \tag{2.5}$$

where $f_0 = \omega_0/2\pi$ is the relaxation frequency given by

$$f_0 = \frac{\mu/\eta}{2\pi} = \frac{1}{2\pi\,t_0}. \tag{2.6}$$

Hence the relaxation frequency is the inverse of 2π times the Maxwellian relaxation time. To determine the transmission of shear waves in a Maxwellian liquid, we insert Eq. (2.5) in the Newtonian equation

$$\varrho\,\frac{\partial^2 u}{\partial t^2} = \frac{\partial\,T_{12}}{\partial\,y} \tag{2.7}$$

where u is the displacement in the x direction. For a plane shear wave propagated along the y direction, this equation becomes for simple harmonic motion, since $S_{12} = \partial u/\partial y$

$$\omega^2\,\varrho\,u + \frac{j\,\omega\,\eta}{1+j\,\omega/\omega_0}\,\frac{d^2 u}{d\,y^2} = 0. \tag{2.8}$$

For a frequency much below the angular relaxation frequency ω_0, this equation takes the form

$$u = A\,\mathrm{e}^{-\sqrt{j\,\omega\,\varrho/\eta}\,y} = A\,\mathrm{e}^{-\sqrt{\pi f\varrho/\eta}\,(1+j)\,y}. \tag{2.9}$$

Hence the attenuation and phase shift for this medium are equal. For example, for a light liquid like water having a density of 1.0, a viscosity of about 0.01 poises, measured at a frequency of 1000 cycles, the attenuation and phase shift are 560 nepers or radians per centimeter. These values are so high that measurements of wave motion are impossible in such liquids. The characteristic impedance Z_0 defined as the ratio of the stress to the particle velocity $-\dot{u}$, can be measured by instruments discussed in Chap. II. From Eq. (2.5), the stress is

$$T_{12} = j\,\omega\,\eta\,\frac{\partial u}{\partial y} = -j\,A\,\omega\,\eta\,\sqrt{\pi f\,\varrho/\eta}\,(1+j)\,\mathrm{e}^{-\sqrt{\pi f\varrho/\eta}\,(1+j)\,y}. \tag{2.10}$$

The particle velocity $\dot{u}$ is

$$-\dot{u} = -j\,\omega\,A\,\mathrm{e}^{-\sqrt{\pi f\varrho/\eta}\,(1+j)\,y} \tag{2.11}$$

and hence

$$Z_0 = \sqrt{\pi f\,\eta\,\varrho}\,(1+j). \tag{2.12}$$

Hence the impedance has equal resistance and positive reactance values that increase in proportion to the square root of the frequency.

For a complete Maxwell element, the solution of Eq. (2.8) becomes

$$A + jB = \frac{1}{\sqrt{2}}\left[\frac{-\omega^2\varrho\,\mu}{\omega_0^2\,\eta} + \sqrt{\frac{\omega^4\varrho^2\mu^2}{\omega_0^4\,\eta^4} + \frac{\omega^2\varrho^2\mu^2}{\omega_0^2\,\eta^2}}\right]^{\frac{1}{2}} + j\cdot\frac{1}{\sqrt{2}}\left[\frac{\omega^2\varrho\,\mu}{\omega_0^2\,\eta^2} + \sqrt{\frac{\omega^4\varrho^2\mu^2}{\omega_0^4\,\eta^4} + \frac{\omega^2\varrho^2\mu^2}{\omega_0^2\,\eta^2}}\right]^{\frac{1}{2}} \tag{2.13}$$

while the expression for the characteristic impedance becomes

$$R + jX = \left[\frac{\frac{\omega^2\varrho\,\mu}{\omega_0^2} + \sqrt{\frac{\omega^4}{\omega_0^4}\,\varrho^2\mu^2 + \frac{\omega^2}{\omega_0^2}\,\varrho^2\mu^2}}{2\left(1+\frac{\omega^2}{\omega_0^2}\right)}\right]^{\frac{1}{2}} + j\left[\frac{-\frac{\omega^2\varrho\,\mu}{\omega_0^2} + \sqrt{\frac{\omega^4\varrho^2\mu^2}{\omega_0^4} + \frac{\omega^2\varrho^2\mu^2}{\omega_0^2}}}{2\left(1+\frac{\omega^2}{\omega_0^2}\right)}\right]^{\frac{1}{2}}. \tag{2.14}$$

* The symbol j has been used throughout for the imaginary unit.

Figs. 2 and 3 show the values of resistance and reactance and attenuation and phase shift (in nepers and radians) plotted as a function of the ratio of f, the frequency, to the relaxation frequency f_0. Well below the relaxation frequency, the resistance and reactance terms are equal, while well above the relaxation frequency the resistance approaches the characteristic impedance $\sqrt{\mu\varrho}$ per square centimeter while the reactance approaches zero. For large frequencies, the attenuation approaches the value

$$A \to \sqrt{\varrho\mu}/2\eta \tag{2.15}$$

while the phase shift becomes

$$B \to \frac{\omega}{V} \quad \text{where} \quad V = \sqrt{\frac{\mu}{\varrho}}. \tag{2.16}$$

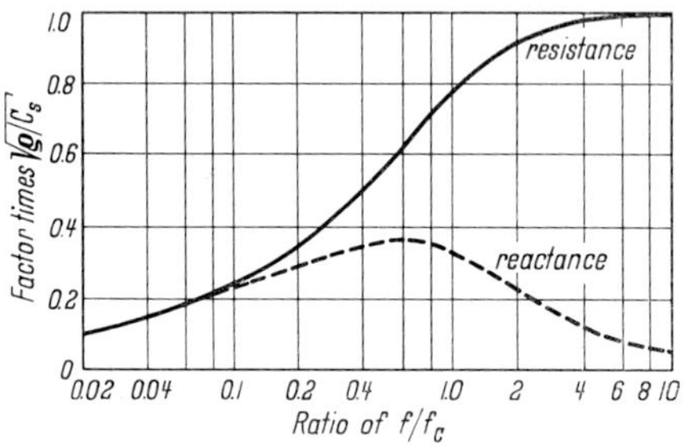

Fig. 2. Resistance and reactance of a medium coupled by a Maxwell element.

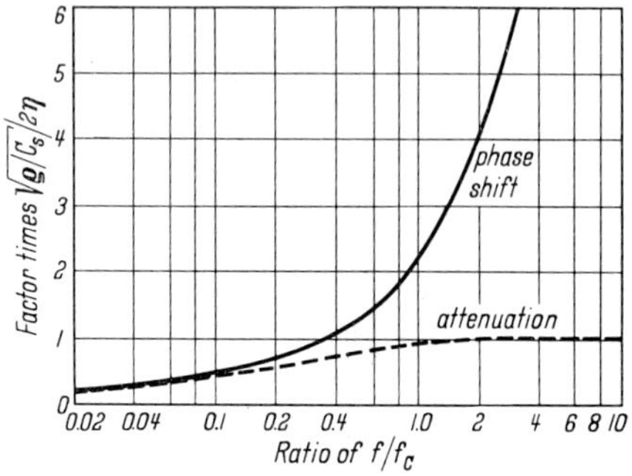

Fig. 3. Phase shift and attenuation per unit length of a medium coupled by a Maxwell element.

For polymer liquids, there are a large number of relaxation frequencies having different values of η_i and ω_i, the viscosity and relaxation frequency. For this case, Eq. (2.8) can be generalized to the form

$$\omega^2\mu\varrho + \sum_{i=1}^{n} \frac{j\omega\,\eta_i}{1+j\omega/\omega_i}\,\frac{d^2u}{dy^2} = \omega^2\varrho\mu + \sum_{i=1}^{n}\left[\frac{\mu_i\left(\frac{\omega^2}{\omega_i^2}+j\,\frac{\omega}{\omega_i}\right)}{1+\frac{\omega^2}{\omega_i^2}}\right]\frac{d^2u}{dy^2} = 0 \tag{2.17}$$

where $\omega_i = \mu_i/\eta_i$. A solution for this equation is of the form

$$u = A\,e^{-\Gamma y} \tag{2.18}$$

where

$$\Gamma = (A + jB) = \left[\frac{-\omega^2\varrho}{\sum_{i=1}^{n}\frac{\mu_i\left(\frac{\omega^2}{\omega_i^2}+j\,\frac{\omega}{\omega_i}\right)}{\left(1+\frac{\omega^2}{\omega_i^2}\right)}}\right]^{\frac{1}{2}}. \tag{2.19}$$

Since $\Gamma Z_0 = (A + jB)(R + jX) = j\omega\varrho$, the measurable characteristic impedance Z_0 takes the form

$$Z_0 = R + jX = \left[\varrho\sum_{i=1}^{n}\mu_i\,\frac{\left(\frac{\omega^2}{\omega_i^2}+j\,\frac{\omega}{\omega_i}\right)}{\left(1+\frac{\omega^2}{\omega_i^2}\right)}\right]^{\frac{1}{2}}. \tag{2.20}$$

For very low frequencies, i.e., below the lowest relaxation frequency, the impedance is

$$R + jX = \sqrt{j\varrho\omega \sum_{i=1}^{n} \eta_i} = (1+j)\sqrt{\pi f \varrho \sum_{i=1}^{n} \eta_i} \tag{2.21}$$

while for frequencies much larger than the highest relaxation frequency

$$R = \sqrt{\varrho \sum_{i=1}^{n} \mu_i}\,. \tag{2.22}$$

For intermediate values, the resistance and reactance terms can be calculated from (2.20) if values of μ_i and ω_i are given or assumed. Examples are discussed later.

A modification of MAXWELL's model is useful in discussing the characteristics of a polymer dissolved in a solvent. For such a solution, the viscosity is greatly enhanced at low frequency by the motion of the polymer coils through the solvent; but at higher frequencies, parts of the chains are immobilized and the viscosity becomes less while the stiffness of the solution increases. At very high frequencies no part of the chain can move and the viscosity reduces nearly to the solvent viscosity. For a number of relaxation frequencies, this action can be represented by the model of Fig. 4 which shows the elements of the network both in mechanical and equivalent electrical form. With this model the stress-strain and strain-rate equations are

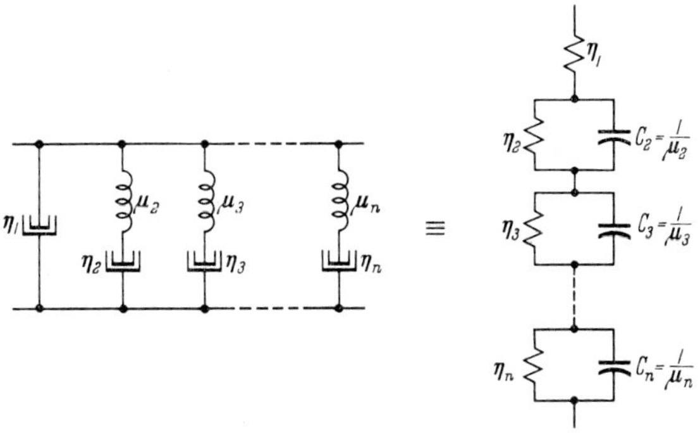

Fig. 4. Modified Maxwell elements for use for long chain polymers in solution.

$$T_{12} = \eta_1 \frac{\partial S_{12}}{\partial t} + \sum_{i=2}^{n} \frac{1}{\dfrac{1}{\eta_i \dfrac{\partial S_{12}}{\partial t}} + \dfrac{1}{\mu_i S_{12}}} \tag{2.23}$$

where η_1 is the solvent viscosity, η_i the viscosity associated with the segment motions which have also the shear stiffness μ_i.

In analyzing the results of single frequency measurements, it is simpler to consider only one molecular viscosity and one shear stiffness. Then Eq. (2.23) is replaced by a single value of $i=2$. Inserting this relation in Eq. (2.7) and solving for the propagation constant $\Gamma = A + jB$ and the characteristic impedance $Z_0 = R + jX$, we find

$$\left.\begin{aligned} \Gamma = A + jB &= \sqrt{\frac{-\varrho\mu\eta_2^2 + j\left[\omega\varrho\eta_2^2\eta_1 + \dfrac{\varrho\mu^2}{\omega}(\eta_1+\eta_2)\right]}{\eta_1^2\eta_2^2 + \dfrac{\mu^2}{\omega^2}(\eta_1+\eta_2)^2}}\,, \\ Z_0 = R + jX &= \sqrt{\frac{\varrho\mu\eta_2^2 + j\left[\omega\varrho\eta_1\eta_2^2 + \dfrac{\varrho\mu^2}{\omega}(\eta_1+\eta_2)\right]}{\eta_2^2 + \dfrac{\mu^2}{\omega^2}}}\,. \end{aligned}\right\} \tag{2.24}$$

The shear impedance devices described in Chap. II can measure R and X for a range of frequencies. A third measurement is the static viscosity $\eta_1 + \eta_2$. Hence, solving these equations simultaneously for the values of η_1, η_2, and μ, we find

$$\left.\begin{aligned} \eta_1 &= \frac{2RX}{\omega\varrho} - \frac{(R^2 - X^2)^2/\omega\varrho}{\omega\varrho(\eta_1+\eta_2) - 2RX}, \qquad \eta_2 = \eta_1 + \eta_2 - \eta_1, \\ \mu &= \frac{(R^2 - X^2)\,\omega\,\eta_2}{\omega\varrho(\eta_1+\eta_2) - 2RX}. \end{aligned}\right\} \tag{2.25}$$

Since R, X, and $\eta_1 + \eta_2$ are measured by the crystal and the zero frequency measurement of the viscosity, all the quantities can be determined. Data of this sort are discussed in Chap. III.

3. Voigt models. MAXWELL's simple model pertains mainly to liquids or materials that have flow under statically applied stresses. Early attempts to generalize the classical elastic theory so as to include dissipation and elastic dispersion effects were made by O. MEYER[27] and W. VOIGT[28]. The generalizations consists in regarding the stress as a function not only of the strain but also the strain rate. Thus in the case of tension applied to a bar, the tensile stress T_{11} and the tensile strain S_{11} are assumed to be related by the equation

$$T_{11} = Y_0 S_{11} + \eta \frac{dS_{11}}{dt}. \tag{3.1}$$

A body which satisfies this type of relation is known as a Voigt solid.

For a shear wave the elastic constant is μ. Inserting this equation in the Newtonian force equation (2.7), the equation of propagation becomes

$$\omega^2 \varrho u + (\mu + j\omega\eta)\frac{d^2u}{dy^2} = 0. \tag{3.2}$$

This equation has solutions for the propagation constant Γ and the characteristic impedance Z_0 given by

$$\left.\begin{aligned} \Gamma &= A + jB = j\omega\sqrt{\frac{\varrho}{\mu + j\omega\eta}} \approx \frac{2\pi^2 f^2 \eta}{\varrho V_s^3} + \frac{j\omega}{V_s} \quad \text{where} \quad V_s = \sqrt{\frac{\mu}{\varrho}}, \\ Z_0 &= R + jX = \sqrt{\varrho(\mu + j\omega\eta)}. \end{aligned}\right\} \tag{3.3}$$

When the characteristic impedance Z_0 is used to evaluate the shear stiffness μ and the shear viscosity η, we find

$$\mu = \frac{R^2 - X^2}{\varrho}; \qquad \eta = \frac{2RX}{\omega\varrho}. \tag{3.4}$$

In some cases the shear stiffness is written in the form $\mu + j\mu'$, i.e., a real and imaginary part. For this case

$$\mu = \frac{R^2 - X^2}{\varrho}; \qquad \mu' = \omega\eta = \frac{2RX}{\varrho}. \tag{3.5}$$

The most common method for expressing the shear stiffness or viscosity of a polymer material is to determine the μ and η values of Eq. (3.4) or the μ and μ' values of Eq. (3.5) over the complete frequency range. These values are not generally constant with frequency, since a large number of relaxation processes

[27] Zur Theorie der inneren Reibung. J. reine angew. Math. **58**, 130 (1874).

[28] Über innere Reibung fester Körper, insbesondere der Metalle. Ann. d. Phys. **47**, 671 (1892).

are involved. A commonly employed procedure is then to analyze the measured values of μ and η in terms of a multiple distribution of Voigt models having the equivalent circuits in mechanical and equivalent electrical form shown by Fig. 5. An alternate procedure is to analyze μ and η' in terms of a series of Maxwell models such as shown on Fig. 1.

For a series of Maxwell models, the complex stiffness becomes

$$\eta - \frac{j\mu}{\omega} = \frac{\mu' - j\mu}{\omega} = \sum_i \frac{\eta_i}{1 + \frac{j\omega}{\omega_i}} = \sum_i \frac{\eta}{1 + \frac{\omega^2}{\omega_i^2}} - j\omega \sum_i \frac{\frac{\eta_i^2}{\mu_i}}{1 + \frac{\omega^2}{\omega_i^2}} \tag{3.6}$$

where

$$\omega_i = \frac{\mu_i}{\eta_i}.$$

Hence at low frequencies the viscosity η is the sum of the individual viscosities of all the relaxation elements, i.e.,

$$\eta = \sum_i \eta_i \tag{3.7}$$

while at high frequencies, i.e., for frequencies above the highest relaxation frequency

$$\mu = \sum_i \mu_i. \tag{3.8}$$

For the modified Maxwell model it is the difference between the measured viscosity and the solvent viscosity that is equal to the real sum on the right side of Eq. (3.6) while the shear stiffness of the medium is equal to the imaginary part of (3.6). These expressions are used in the Rouse-Bueche-Zimm theory of polymer molecules in solution.

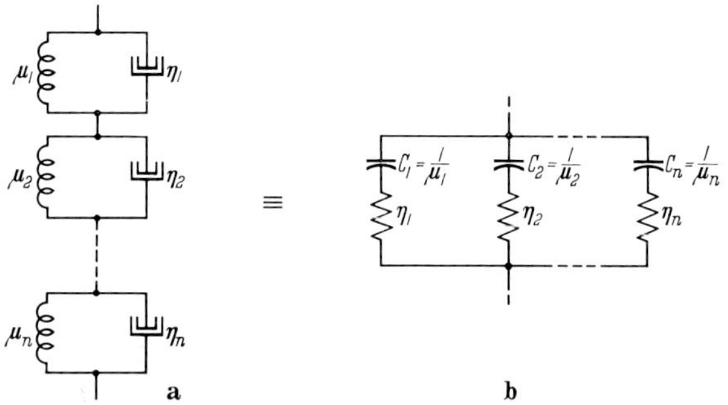

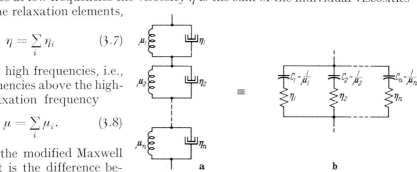

Fig. 5a and b. Multiple Voigt model and equivalent electrical circuit.

Similar expressions can be obtained for the shear viscosity and shear stiffness of a series of Voigt elements of the type shown by Fig. 5. If we write the result in terms of admittances, we have

$$\frac{1}{\eta - \frac{j\mu}{\omega}} = \sum_i \frac{1}{\eta_i - \frac{j\mu_i}{\omega}} = \sum_i \frac{1}{\eta_i\left(1 + \frac{\omega_i^2}{\omega^2}\right)} + \frac{j}{\omega} \sum_i \frac{\frac{\mu_i}{\eta_i^2}}{\left(1 + \frac{\omega_i^2}{\omega^2}\right)}. \tag{3.9}$$

Hence at zero frequency and infinite frequency

$$\frac{1}{\mu} = \sum \frac{1}{\mu_i}; \quad \frac{1}{\eta} = \sum \frac{1}{\eta_i}. \tag{3.10}$$

Several methods have been used to evaluate the relaxation frequency distribution for given measured curves. One simple method is the cut and try one of assuming discrete relaxation frequencies with definite values of η_i and altering the constants until a reasonable fit is obtained for the measured values. This gives usable results only if the distribution is not too broad. Another method is to assume a continuous distribution of relaxation frequencies or times τ_i related to the relaxation frequencies by the equation

$$\tau_i = \frac{1}{2\pi f_i} = \frac{1}{\omega_i}. \tag{3.11}$$

With this substitution the summation of (3.6) becomes

$$\mu(j\omega) = j\,\omega \int_0^\infty \frac{\eta(\tau)}{1+j\,\omega\,\tau}\,d\tau + \mu(0) \qquad (3.12)$$

where $\mu(j\omega)$ is the complex shearing modulus. If $\mu(j\omega)$ is given as an analytic function from a zero to an infinite frequency, the integral can be inverted by employing Fourier integral transforms. This is not usually a profitable method since μ is measured over a finite frequency range. Recently, however, ROESLER and co-workers[29] have shown that an iteration method or a Fourier series expansion method can be used to determine the relaxation spectra with better precision than can be obtained by an inversion of the infinite integral. They have applied their method to the data on polyisobutylene given by the Bureau of Standards cooperative program (see Chap. IV). In the present chapter, the network method of analysis is followed and this automatically determines the relaxation distribution. Hence other methods of determining the relaxation spectra will not be discussed further.

Stress relaxation and creep methods have also been used extensively in measuring the properties of polymers. These are related to the complex elastic modulus by equations of the type[30]

$$\mu(j\,\omega) = j\,\omega \int_0^\infty e^{-j\omega\tau}\,\psi(\tau)\,d\tau + \mu_0 \qquad (3.13)$$

where $\psi(\tau)$ is the stress relaxation function. Conversely by applying a Fourier transform one has

$$\psi(t) = \frac{2}{\pi}\int_0^\infty \frac{\mu_1(\omega)}{\omega}\sin\omega t\,d\omega = \frac{2}{\pi}\int_0^\infty \frac{\mu_2(\omega)}{\omega}\cos\omega t\,d\omega \qquad (3.14)$$

where $\mu(j\omega) = \mu_1(\omega) + j\mu_2(\omega)$. In a similar way the creep $\varphi(t)$ function can be related to the complex compliance function by equations of the type

$$J_1(\omega) = \int_0^\infty \frac{d\varphi(\tau)}{d\tau}\cos\omega\,\tau\,d\tau; \qquad J_2(\omega) = -\int_0^\infty \frac{d\varphi(\tau)}{d\tau}\sin\omega\,\tau\,d\tau. \qquad (3.15)$$

Since only physical acoustic methods employing sinusoidal vibrations are discussed in this chapter, the relations will not be considered further.

II. Special instruments for measuring the properties of polymers.

Sound waves do not usually propagate very far in polymer liquids and to some extent polymer solids on account of the high internal friction associated with the motions of polymer segments. As a result, the usual wave transmission techniques used for solids have not been very successful. This is particulary true for shear waves which are necessary for the interpretation of the properties of polymer molecules in solution and consequently a series of measuring instruments have been devised which measure the loading or characteristic impedance

[29] F. C. ROESLER: Proc. Phys. Soc. Lond. B **68**, 89 (1955). — F. C. ROESLER and W. A. TWYMAN: Proc. Phys. Soc. Lond. B **68**, 97 (1955).

[30] See for example, B. GROSS: Mathematical Structure of the Theories of Viscoelasticity. Paris: Hermann & Cie. 1953.

the medium rather than the wave velocity and attenuation. Since these instruments have been developed almost exclusively for polymer measurements, it is the purpose of this section to describe their theory and operation*.

4. Impedance methods for measuring highly attenuating liquids and solids. For materials having very high attenuations per wave length, the ordinary wave propagation methods are not applicable since the wave propagation does not extend far enough into the medium to provide reliable results. Such waves do, however, apply a loading effect on the transducers, which can be measured by measuring the electrical impedance changes produced in the transducer input by the mechanical loading. Such measurements have been used in measuring

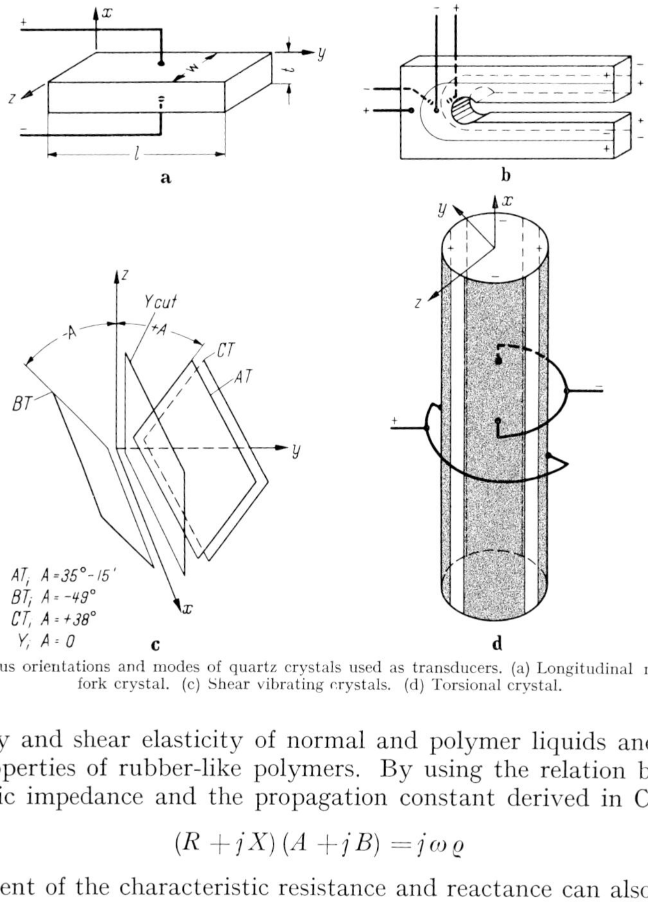

Fig. 6a—d. Various orientations and modes of quartz crystals used as transducers. (a) Longitudinal mode. (b) Tuning fork crystal. (c) Shear vibrating crystals. (d) Torsional crystal.

the viscosity and shear elasticity of normal and polymer liquids and solutions, and the properties of rubber-like polymers. By using the relation between the characteristic impedance and the propagation constant derived in Chap. I,

$$(R + jX)(A + jB) = j\omega\varrho \tag{4.1}$$

a measurement of the characteristic resistance and reactance can also determine the attenuation and phase constants per unit length.

One of the first transducers used for this purpose[31] was the torsional quartz crystal shown by Fig. 6. This crystal was attached to a vacuum tube socket as shown by Fig. 7. This crystal produces a pure torsional mode and generates a shear wave in the cylindrical medium. If the distance that the wave propagates

* See also Chap. 11, Rheology; Theory and Applications, Vol. II, New York: Academic Press 1958, for a description of a number of measuring instruments.

[31] W. P. Mason: Measurement of the Viscosity and Shear Elasticity of Liquids by Means of a Torsionally Vibrating Crystal. Trans. Amer. Soc. Mech. Engrs. **69**, 359—367 (1947).

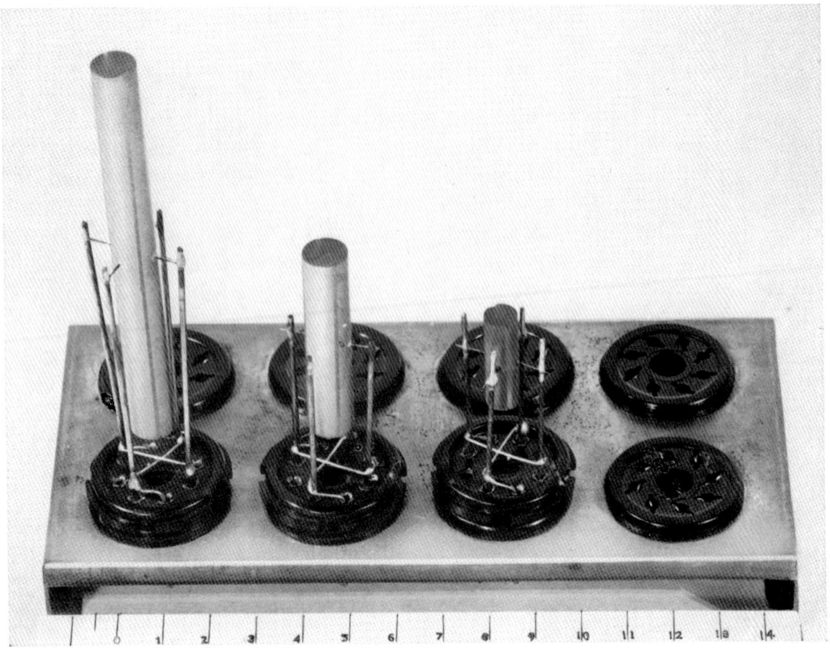

a

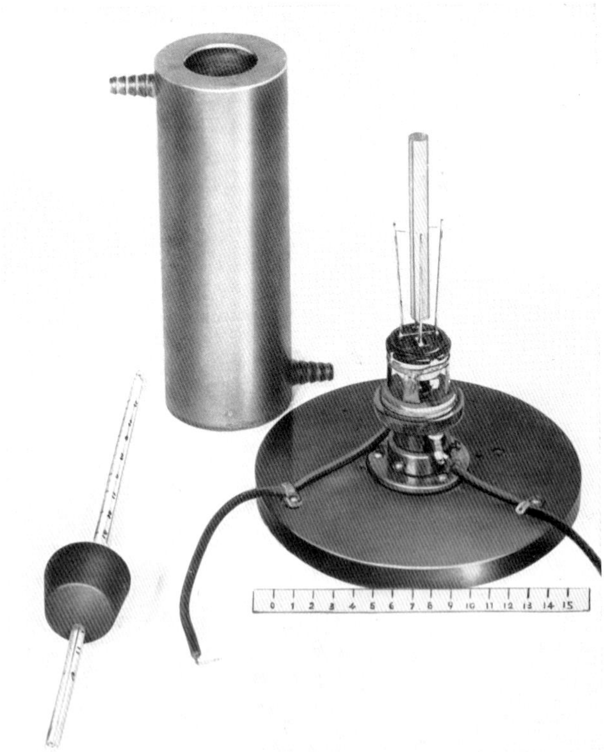

b

Fig. 7. (a) Photograph of 40, 80 and 150 kc torsional crystals. (b) Torsional crystal mounted in temperature controlled chamber.

into the medium is small—as is usually the case—a shear wave in a cylindrical medium will have the same characteristic impedance as for a plane shear wave. For a purely viscous medium this is equal to [cf. Eq. (2.12)]

$$Z_0 = R + jX = \sqrt{\pi f \eta \varrho}\,(1+j)$$

where f is the frequency, η the viscosity and ϱ the density. Some liquids, particularly polymer liquids, have a shear elasticity at high frequencies due to the fact that the separate chains cannot slide past each other in the time of a cycle and they act as though they were connected together in the manner of a solid body. If such a liquid has a single relaxation frequency, the characteristic impedance is given by formula (2.14), viz.

$$R + jX = \left[\frac{\omega^2\eta^2\varrho C + \sqrt{\omega^4\eta^4\varrho^2C^2 + \omega^2\eta^2\varrho}}{2(1+\omega^2\eta^2C^2)}\right]^{\frac{1}{2}} + j\left[\frac{-\omega^2\eta^2 C + \sqrt{\omega^4\eta^4\varrho^2C^2 + \omega^2\eta^2\varrho}}{2(1+\omega^2\eta^2C^2)}\right]^{\frac{1}{2}}.$$

Hence the resistance becomes larger than the reactance.

For waves propagated into the cylindrical medium for some distance, there is a slight difference between the plane wave characteristic impedance and the cylindrical characteristic impedance as discussed by McSkimin[32]. The relation is

$$\left.\begin{aligned} Z_K &= \frac{Z}{j\left[\dfrac{J_1(ka) - jY_0(ka)}{J_1(ka) - jY_1(ka)} - \dfrac{2}{ka}\right]} \\ &\text{where} \\ ka &= \frac{\varrho\omega a}{Z_K} \end{aligned}\right\} \quad (4.2)$$

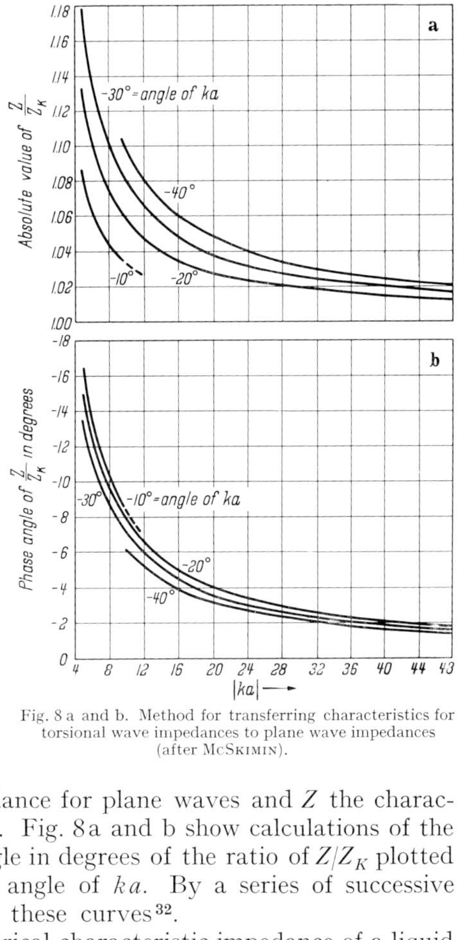

Fig. 8a and b. Method for transferring characteristics for torsional wave impedances to plane wave impedances (after McSkimin).

and $Y_0(ka)$ and $Y_1(ka)$ are Bessel's functions of the second kind. In this equation ϱ is the density, a the radius, $\omega = 2\pi f$, Z_K is the characteristic impedance for plane waves and Z the characteristic impedance for cylindrical waves. Fig. 8a and b show calculations of the absolute value of Z/Z_K and the phase angle in degrees of the ratio of Z/Z_K plotted against the absolute values and phase angle of ka. By a series of successive approximations Z_K can be found from these curves[32].

The method for measuring the cylindrical characteristic impedance of a liquid by means of the torsional crystal is to first measure the resonant resistance and the resonant frequency of the crystal in vacuum. The liquid or solution to be measured is then introduced in the cylinder surrounding the crystal. The temperature of the liquid can be controlled by means of a circulating liquid. The resonant frequency and the resistance of the crystal surrounded by the liquid are then measured and the difference ΔR_E and Δf are determined. From the

[32] H. J. McSkimin: Measurement of Dynamic Shear Viscosity and Stiffness of Viscous Liquids by Means of Traveling Torsional Waves. J. Acoust. Soc. Amer. **24**, 355—365 (1952).

equivalent circuit of the crystal it has been shown[31] that ΔR_E and Δf are given by

$$\left.\begin{aligned}\Delta R_E &= \frac{r}{2\pi f_R^2 C_0 I}\left[a^3 + \frac{a^4}{l}\right] R = K_1 R,\\ \Delta f &= -\left[\frac{a^3 + a^4/l}{2I}\right] X = -K_2 X,\end{aligned}\right\} \tag{4.3}$$

where r is the ratio of capacitances of the torsional crystal, f_R the frequency of resonance, C_0 the static capacitance of the crystal, $I = \pi \varrho_c a^4/2$ is the moment of inertia of the crystal, a the radius of the crystal and l its length. An alternate and more exact way of determining K_1 and K_2 is to use liquids of known density and viscosity and to evaluate K_1 and K_2 from a number of measurements.

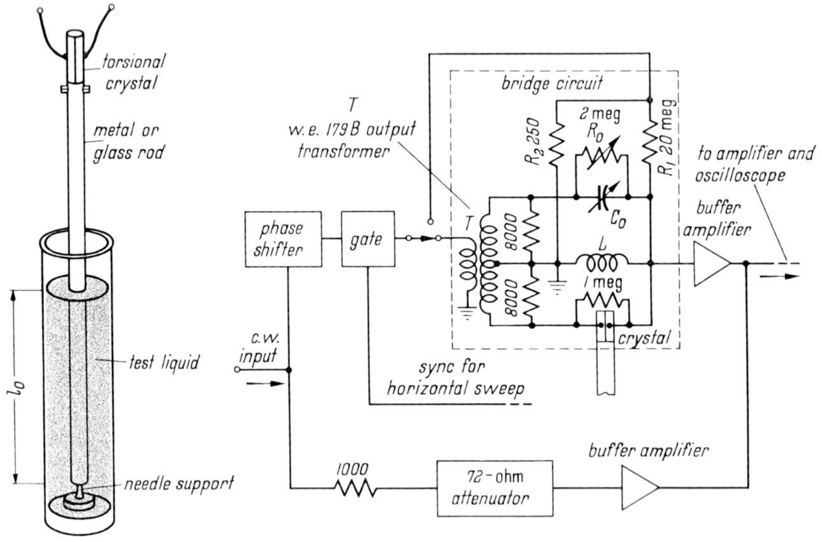

Fig. 9a and b. Torsional wave impedance measuring system for liquids and polymers (after McSKIMIN).

The torsional crystal is very sensitive and can measure the viscosity of a gas. However, for liquids having viscosities greater than 10 poises, the mechanical loading is so large that simple resonance frequency and resistance measurements can no longer be relied on to give accurate results. Such high viscosity liquids can be measured by means of the torsional wave pulse method[32] whose components are shown by Fig. 9. A torsional quartz crystal is soldered or cemented onto a cylindrical metal or glass rod supported at one end by a needle point. Using the circuit of Fig. 9b for which the crystal acts as one component of an electrical bridge, a pulse of a time duration determined by the time necessary to time separate out successive reflections in the rod is impressed on the sending crystal. On account of the bridge balance, the initial pulse applied to the buffer amplifier is small enough not to overload it. Reflections actuate the torsional crystal and produce a voltage that is not balanced out by the bridge, and these produce a series of pulses spaced in time and dying out at a rate determined by the attenuation in the rod. This is usually made out of a nickel iron which has a very low temperature coefficient of velocity[33].

[33] M. E. FINE and W. C. ELLIS: Amer. Inst. Mech. Engrs. J. Metals 3, 761 (1951). Compositions similar to rods d and e can be made to have nearly a zero coefficient of velocity.

The process of measurement consists in establishing a balance in phase and amplitude in the rod in air by adjusting the frequency impressed and the balancing attenuation in the lower arm. The rod is then immersed for a definite length in the liquid to be measured. This results in a change in attenuation and a change in phase which can be measured by rebalancing the attenuation in the attenuator and changing the phase. For a rod of low temperature coefficient, the phase change ΔB can be measured by the amount of frequency change required to rebalance the circuit. A water jacket is usually placed around the system in order to controll and vary the temperature. When the change in attenuation ΔA expressed in nepers (1 neper = 8.68 db) and the change in phase ΔB, expressed in radians, are measured, the torsional impedance of the liquid is given by the equation

$$Z_c = \left(\frac{\varrho V}{4}\right) \frac{a}{l} [\Delta A + j \Delta B] \tag{4.4}$$

where a is the radius and l the length of the rod covered by the liquid. For very viscous liquids a correction to plane wave impedances can be made by Eq. (4.2).

A somewhat similar device[34] has recently been marketed under the name of the ultra-Visconson. This consists of a thin magnetostrictive blade in which a longitudinal wave is excited by an applied electric pulse. This wave is damped by the viscous drag of the end immersed in a liquid and the change in attenuation and phase are used to actuate an analog computer which calculates the equivalent viscosity and stiffness of the liquid. It should be pointed out that since the rod can expand sidewise by virtue of its POISSON's ratio, it can also send out longitudinal waves and theoretically a correction should be made for this as discussed later for the tuning fork crystal. For very viscous liquids this correction may be small and this device has been used successfully in measuring the viscosity of blood as a function of time during the clotting period, in following the viscosity of a thermosetting resin, etc., and appears to be a very useful factory tool in following the changes in a plastic mixture as the process proceeds.

The processes so far described for measuring viscosity are useful in the frequency ranges from 20 kilocycles to several hundred kilocycles. To completely characterize a polymer reaction, it is usually necessary to have much lower and much higher frequency ranges. For the higher frequency range, a single device has so far been proposed[35a]. As shown by Fig. 10, this device operates by reflecting a shear wave at a small angle of incidence from a polished surface in a fused silica rod. Such a wave is reflected as a shear wave and by loading the surface with a liquid or solution whose viscosity and shear stiffnesses are to be measured, a change in amplitude and phase occur in the reflections. The experimental circuit is shown by Fig. 10b. This device can measure the shear impedances of liquids from viscosities as low as water to long chain polymer liquids with viscosities as high as 100000 poises. The frequency range covered is from about 3 megacycles up to 100 megacycles. A number of measurements using this device are discussed in Chap. III and IV.

By using the technique recently employed by BÖMMEL[35b] and DRANSFELD, the frequency range for the reflectance technique can be extended to frequencies

[34] W. ROTH and I. R. RICH: A New Method for Continuous Viscosity Measurement. General Theory of the Ultra-Visconson. J. Appl. Phys. **24**, 940—950 (1953).

[35a] W. P. MASON, W. O. BAKER, H. J. MCSKIMIN and J. H. HEISS: Measurements of Shear Elasticity and Viscosity of Liquids at Ultrasonic Frequencies. Phys. Rev. **75**, 936—946 (1949). This device was the work of H. J. MCSKIMIN. It has recently been improved by incorporating the comparison circuit in the same block as the measuring circuit. This lowers the temperature stability requirement and also allows the measurement of the shear properties of a liquid under pressure.

[35b] H. E. BÖMMEL and K. DRANSFELD: Phys. Rev. **117**, 1245—1252 (1960).

as high as 1000 MC. By inserting a rod of AC cut quartz in a wave guide, shear waves can be generated at the surface of the rod which can be propagated as a plane wave down the axis of the rod. For a short rod, the attenuation is sufficiently low so that a number of reflections can be seen. By immersing one end in a liquid, changes in the reflected attenuation and phase shift occur which can be measured by comparing the reflected pulse with that from an identical rod not immersed in a fluid. While this system is not as sensitive as the one shown by Fig. 10b, it can be used to measure the shear properties of relatively light and heavy liquids. This system has the advantage that by changing the tuning of the wave guide, a wide range of frequencies can be obtained by using the same rods.

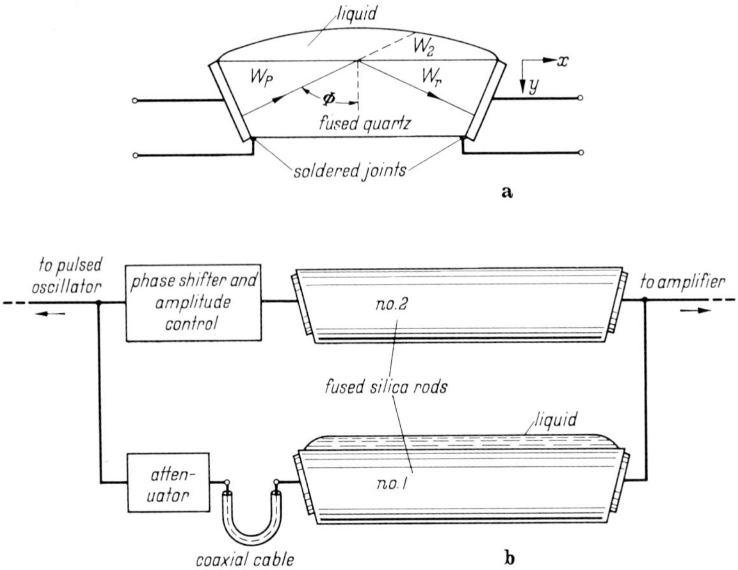

Fig. 10a and b. Shear reflectance method for measuring shear wave impedance of liquids and polymers (after McSKIMIN).

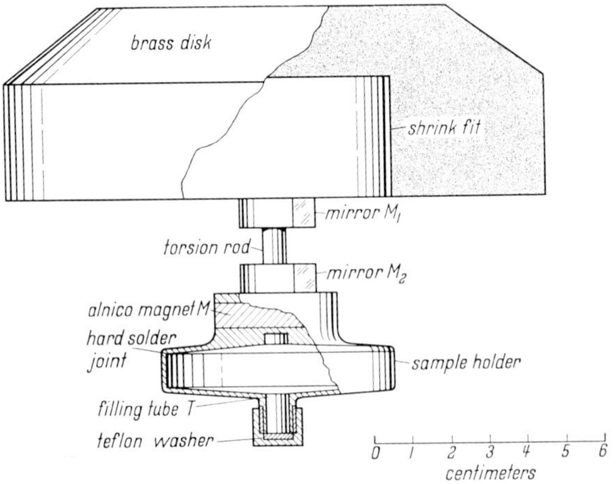

Fig. 11. Torsional pendulum for measuring shear viscosity and shear elasticity of polymer solutions at low frequencies.

In the low frequency range, a number of devices have been employed. For low viscosity, low impedance liquids, a very elegant method is the torsional pendulum method of SITTEL, ROUSE and BAILEY[36]. The pendulum consists of a massive upper bob attached to a smaller lower bob by means of a torsional rod whose length can be varied to control the frequency as shown by Fig. 11. The lower bob is set in motion by a magnetic

[36] K. SITTEL, P. E. ROUSE jr. and E. D. BAILEY: J. Appl. Phys. 25, 1312—1320 (1954).

driving system which is then cut off. The frequency of oscillation is measured by a counter method and the rate of dying down is measured by a mirror system. Starting at a given amplitude, oscillations occur until they are cut off at a predetermined lower amplitude. The number of cycles and their rate are determined by a counter and a chronograph. The lower bob is then filled with a liquid to be measured, and the change in frequency and change in damping are measured. From these the mechanical resistance and reactance can be measured by formulae similar to Eqs. (4.3). The constants K_1 and K_2 can be evaluated by mean is of known liquids.

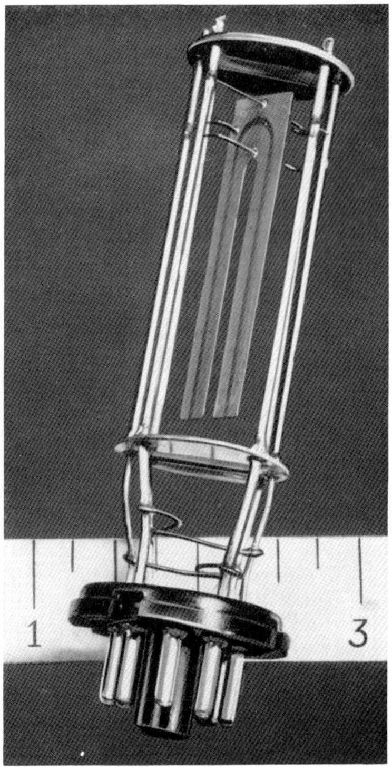

Fig. 12. Photograph of a mounted tuning fork crystal.

Another method used for lower frequencies, i.e., 500 cycles to 10000 cycles is the crystal tuning fork whose photograph is shown by Fig. 12. This is immersed in a liquid in a container such as shown by Fig. 7 and measurements are made of the change in frequency and change in resonant resistance as was done with the torsional crystal. Most of the loading is due to the viscous drag along the large flat surface but also there is a small amount of longitudinal loading due to the thin sides which can introduce a longitudinal wave in the liquid. Since the thickness is very small (usually about 0.5 to 1.0 mm) this loading is mostly a mass loading as can be seen from the radiation impedance curve for a piston[37]. Furthermore, the added mass is proportional to the density of the medium so that we have two correction terms for the added mass, one proportional to the density of the medium and the other having a reactance proportional to $\sqrt{\pi f_c \eta \varrho}$, the positive reactance term of the viscous drag. If we introduce these two reactance terms in the resonant circuit of the crystal it can be shown that

$$\Delta R_E = K_1 \sqrt{\pi f \eta \varrho}\,; \qquad \Delta f = \frac{K_3 R + K_2 \sqrt{\pi f_c \eta \varrho}}{1 + \frac{2 K_3 \varrho}{f_c} + \frac{3}{2} \frac{K_2}{f_c} \sqrt{\pi f_c \eta \varrho}}\,. \tag{4.5}$$

Since the transducer has not been previously described, some experimental data are shown in Table 1 which verify that these equations agree with the measured

Table 1.

Liquid	Temperatur °C	ϱ	η	Measurement frequency	ΔR_E Ohms	Measured Δf	$\sqrt{\pi f \eta \varrho}$	K_1	$\sqrt{\pi f_c \eta \varrho}$	Δf Cal.
Cyclohexane . .	32.5	0.766	0.0075	2347	4020000	74.7	6.51	617000	6.64	74.9
Benzine	32.0	0.865	0.00541	2340	3520000	81.7	5.86	600000	5.99	81.9
CCl_4	30.5	1.573	0.0084	2281	5960000	140.7	9.74	612000	10.05	140.8
Dioctal sebocate	31.5	0.907	0.143	2302	19000000	119.7	30.65	619000	31.5	119.9

[37] For example, see W. P. MASON: Electromechanical Transducers and Wave Filters, p. 149. New York: D. Van Nostrand 1948.

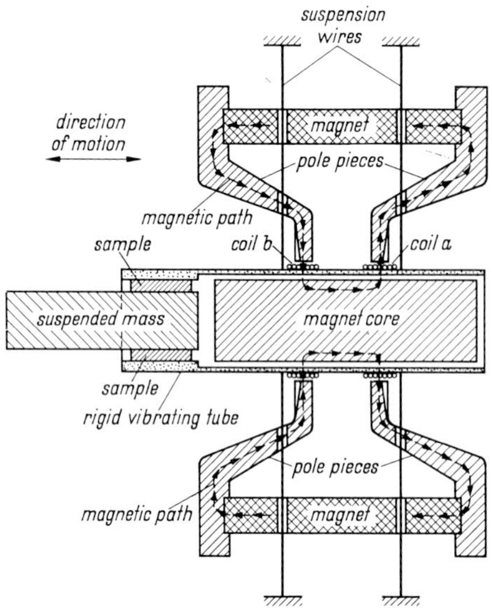

Fig. 13. Electromechanical transducer for measuring the shear impedance of rubbers and solids (after FITZGERALD and FERRY).

results obtained from a number of calibrating liquids of different densities and viscosities. This transducer has been used in evaluating the viscosity and shear stiffness of some polymer solutions discussed in Chap. III. The crystal frequency f_c in vacuum is 2421.7 cycles, $K_2 = 1.56$; $K_3 = 90.8$. Hence the calculated Δf agrees with the measured values within 0.2 cycles which is in the order of the accuracy of the measurement. The constancy of $K_1 \approx 612\,000$ indicates that the resistance added by the longitudinal component is negligible.

For higher impedance solutions and quasi-solid polymers, several other devices have been used. For fairly viscous solutions SMITH, FERRY and SCHREMP[38] have described a transducer for vibrating the solution in shear. The shear impedance of the liquid is deduced from the change in the electrical impedance at the input of the transducer by employing standard transducer equations. For higher impedances a double transducer has been developed[39] as shown by Fig. 13. Here a rigid tube supported by 8 wires is driven by the coil a and the motion resulting is determined by the voltage generated in the pickup coil b. Since this is a moving coil type of transducer, no phase angle corrections for eddy currents occur and the usual transducer equations are valid. The sample to be measured is inserted between a fixed mass and the moving tube and the load is reflected in the motional impedance of the transducer. The fixed electrical impedance is balanced out in one arm of the bridge and the mechanical impedance of the load is determined from the ratio and phase angle of the driving current i_a to the pickup voltage V_B.

For higher impedance plastics a horizontal pendulum and a tun-

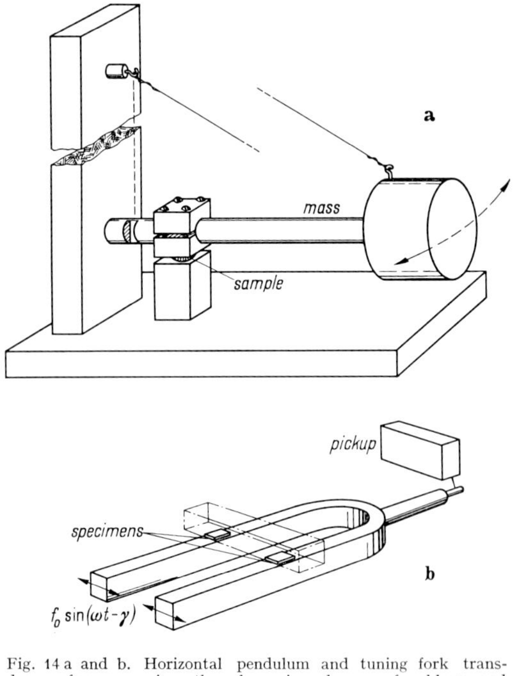

Fig. 14a and b. Horizontal pendulum and tuning fork transducers for measuring the shear impedances of rubbers and solids (after RORDEN and GRIECO).

[38] SMITH, FERRY and SCHREMP: J. Appl. Phys. **20**, 144 (1949).
[39] E. R. FITZGERALD and J. D. FERRY: J. Colloid Sci. **8**, 1 (1953). A commercial shear impedometer of this type is made by the Atlantic Research Corp., Alexandria, Va.

ing fork transducer were developed by RORDEN and GRIECO[40] after a suggestion of R. L. WEGEL. These two devices are shown by Figs. 14a and b. The principle is similar to the other shear transducers in that a change in frequency and a change in damping is brought about by the shear impedance of the polymer which is attached rigidly to a fixed block on one side and to the moving block on the pendulum or tuning fork. Calibrations for any position of attachment of the sample can be had by inserting known weights at these points and observing the change in pitch. The horizontal pendulum can be used in the range from 1 cycle to 10 cycles, the pitch being varied by controlling the position and amount of mass on the ends of the rod. The tuning fork transducer can be driven in several of its modes and can be used in the frequency range form 100 cycles to 10000 cycles.

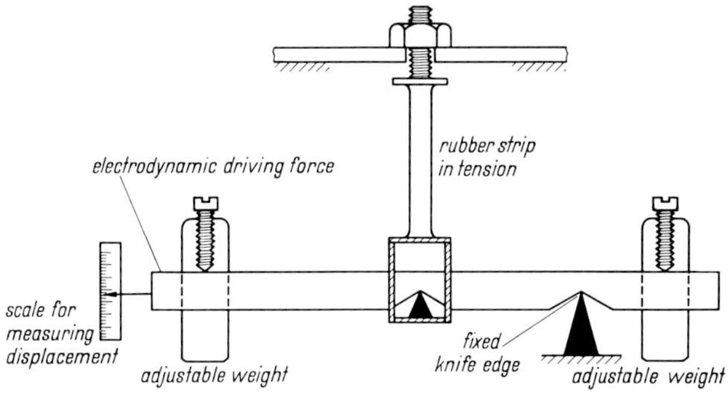

Fig. 15. Rocking beam oscillator for measuring YOUNG's modulus and associated internal friction in rubbers (after NOLLE).

There is a slight error arising from the free edges of the specimen which must be evaluated if accurate results are to be obtained. A correction has been calculated by W. T. READ[41].

A similar device for measuring the complex YOUNG's modulus of a rubber sample is the rocking beam oscillator of A. W. NOLLE[42]. This device, as shown by Fig. 15 consists of a weighted beam which is supported by a rubber strip in tension. The beam is set in oscillation by an electrodynamic driving force and the resonant frequency and Q of the resonance curve are measured by determining the frequency difference between the two 3 db points. The stiffness can be calibrated by replacing the rubber strip by a spring of known stiffness. This device has been used in the frequency range from 0.1 to 30 cycles per second.

5. Methods for measuring bulk moduli and associated compressional viscosities. A number of measurements of longitudinal and shear wave complex moduli (as discussed in Chap. IV) show that there is a compressional viscosity associated with the bulk modulus. Recently[43] several instruments have been devised for measuring directly the compressibilities of solids and their associated imaginary components. Fig. 16 shows the form of a device used by McKINNEY, EDELMAN and MARVIN. Two barium titanate transducers of the barium, calcium, lead titanate compositions are mounted on the inside of a heavy steel frame in which a small cavity is drilled. The liquid or solid to be measured is put in the cavity

[40] H. C. RORDEN and A. GRIECO: Measurement of Dynamic Internal Dissipation and Elasticity of Soft Plastics. J. Appl. Phys. **22**, 842—845 (1951).

[41] W. T. READ: Effect of Stress Free Edges in Plane Shear of a Flat Body. J. Appl. Mech. **17**, 349—353 (1950).

[42] A. W. NOLLE: J. Appl. Phys. **19**, 753 (1948).

[43] J. E. McKINNEY, S. EDELMAN and R. S. MARVIN: J. Appl. Phys. **27**, 425—431 (1956). — W. PHILLIPPOFF and J. BRODNYAN: J. Appl. Phys. **26**, 846 (1955).

which is filled with an oil of a known compressibility. In order to eliminate air bubbles, the system is put under a static pressure of 100 kg/cm². The device operates from frequencies of 50 to 10000 cycles. The measurement consists in balancing the pickup voltage from the titanate, generated by a voltage applied to the other titanate, by a resistance capacitance circuit. It can be calibrated in terms of liquids and solids with known compressibilities. Measurements show compressional viscosities associated with many polymers.

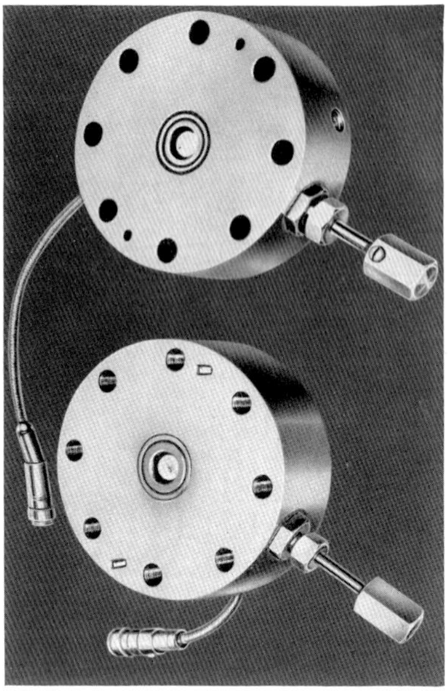

Fig. 16. Device for measuring compressibility and compressional viscosities (after McKINNEY, EDELMAN and MARVIN).

III. Long chain polymer molecules in solutions.

6. Measurements. The mechanical properties of long chain polymers depend on the interactions of segments of the polymer chain with other segments of the same polymer chain (intra-chain reactions) and on the interaction with segments of different chains (interchain reactions). In order to study steric hindrance and restricted rotations about bonds, it is necessary to study the properties of single molecules alone free from interchain reaction. Also where configurational or quasi-configurational displacements are important as they are in elongations greater than 20%, flexibility of single chains needs to be understood.

In order to study the motions possible in single chains, one has to dissolve them in a solvent until they are diluted to such an extent that single molecules can exist without appreciable entanglement with other molecules. A study[12,13] has been made of solutions of two different chain lengths of polyisobutylene dissolved in cyclohexane and since wider frequency measurements have been made on these solutions than for any other solutions reported in the literature, a rather complete discussion will be given for these cases.

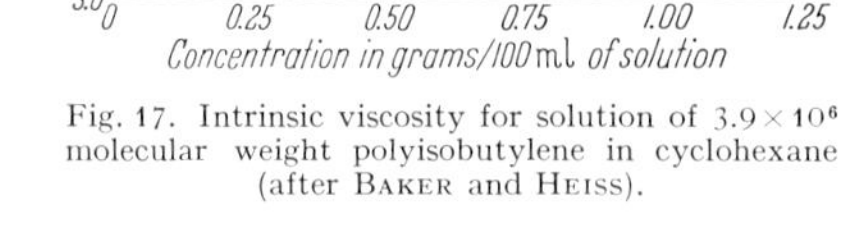

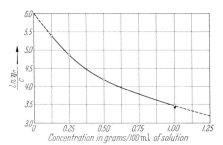

Fig. 17. Intrinsic viscosity for solution of 3.9×10^6 molecular weight polyisobutylene in cyclohexane (after BAKER and HEISS).

The static shear viscosity of the longer chain molecule solutions has been measured as a function of the concentration c, i.e., the number of grams of the polymer per 100 cm³ of solution, and the relative viscosity, i.e., the ratio of the viscosity of the solution to the viscosity of the solvent, was determined. When one takes the natural logarithm of the relative viscosity and divides by the cocentration, the curve of Fig. 17 results. Extrapolating this to zero concentration one obtains the intrinsic viscosity $[\eta]$, which in this case is 6. In the limit this definition gives also $[\eta] = (\eta_r - 1)/c$ as $c \to 0$. Studies by FOX and FLORY[22] have related the intrinsic viscosity of polyisobutylene in cyclohexane to the viscosity average molecular weight and for this case the average molecular weight $\overline{M}_\eta$

is 3.9×10^6. The other chain length has a molecular weight of $\overline{M}_\eta = 1.18 \times 10^6$ giving nearly a four to one factor between the two chain lengths.

A relation between the intrinsic viscosity $[\eta]$ and the average separation between chain ends has recently been established by FLORY and co-workers[44]. This takes the form

$$[\eta] = \Phi(\overline{r^2})^{\frac{3}{2}}/M \tag{6.1}$$

where $\overline{r^2}$ is the mean square separation of chain ends, M the molecular weight, and Φ a constant which appears to have the same value for all linear polymers. Fig. 18 shows a plot of this relation over an intrinsic viscosity range of 100 to 1. For the two polymer solutions the values of $\sqrt{\overline{r^2}}$ are about 1200 and 2080 Å, respectively. Hence, it is seen that the number of molecules that will fill one cubic centimeter of volume with only an occasional contact is for the shorter chain length

$$\left.\begin{aligned} 1 &= \frac{\pi}{6} N\,(1200 \times 10^{-8})^3 \\ \text{or}\quad N &\approx 1.1 \times 10^{15} \text{ molecules per cm}^3. \end{aligned}\right\} \tag{6.2}$$

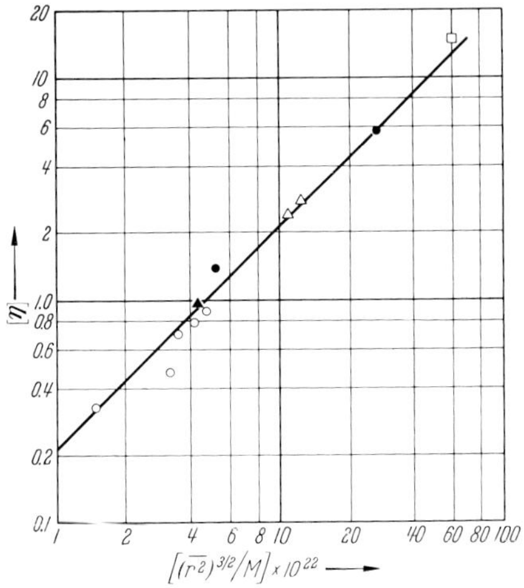

Fig. 18. Plot of intrinsic viscosity $[\eta]$ as a function of the mean square chain separation and the molecular weight for linear polymers (after NEWMAN, KRIGBAUM, LANGIER, and FLORY).

Since the weight of a molecule of 1.18×10^6 molecular weight is

$$\left.\begin{aligned} &1.18 \times 10^6 \times 1.66 \times 10^{-24} \\ &= 1.96 \times 10^{-18} \text{grams} \end{aligned}\right\} \tag{6.3}$$

it takes about

$$\left.\begin{aligned} &1.1 \times 10^{15} \times 1.96 \times 10^{-18} \\ &= 0.0022 \text{ grams per cm}^3, \end{aligned}\right\} \tag{6.4}$$

or about 0.22 gram per 100 cm³ to be essentially separated. For the larger molecular wight molecule, it takes about 0.14 grams per 100 cm³ to have essentially no entanglement.

Using the torsional crystal described in Chapter II some dynamic measurements have been made on the mechanical properties of the two solutions of polyisobutylene chains dissolved in cyclohexane. The polyisobutylene chain has the repeating element shown by Fig. 19, and each link has a molecular weight of 56. The two solutions labelled respectively 120 X and 80X have the viscosity average molecular weights of 3.9×10^6 and 1.18×10^6. Static viscosity measurements were made for the two solutions and on the solvent cyclohexane, and for a one percent solution, i.e., 1 gram per 100 cm³, the viscosities are shown by Fig. 20, plotted against $1/T$. The activation energies for the three liquids are, respectively 3.1, 3.7, and 3.9 kilocalories per mole for the cyclohexane, the 80X solution and the 120X solution.

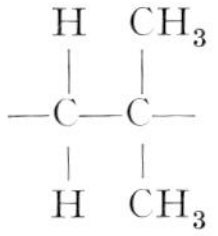

Fig. 19. Repeating element of polyisobutylene.

The first dynamic measurements were made for various concentrations and the results were interpreted in terms of the modified Maxwell relaxation model discussed in Chapter I. From the measured mechanical resistance, reactance and the static viscosity, the element values can be derived from Eq. (2.25). Fig. 21

[44] NEWMAN, KRIGBAUM, LANGIER and FLORY: J. Polymer Sci. **14**, 451–462 (1954).

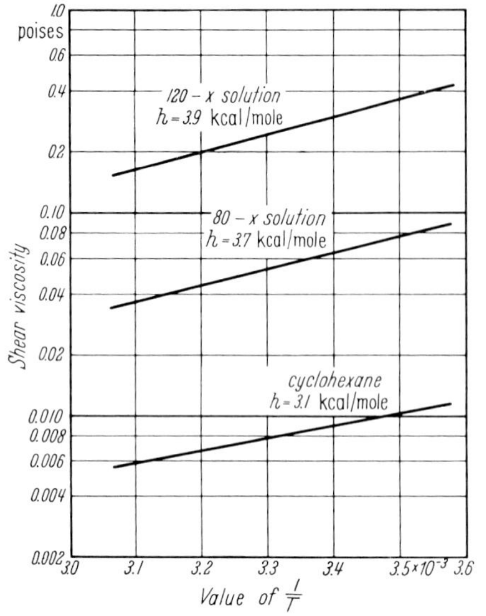

Fig. 20. Viscosity of cyclohexane and 80× and 120× solutions of polyisobutylene in cyclohexane (after J. H. HEISS).

shows the values of η_A, η_B, and μ_B plotted against the concentration in grams per 100 cm³ of solution for a temperature of 25° C and a frequency of 20 kc. The series viscosity η_A is initially the solvent viscosity 0.0086 poise at 25° C and increases only by 50%, up to a concentration of 1 gram per 100 cm³. The additions due to the polymer molecules are mainly represented by the η_B, μ_B values. As can be seen, η_B is nearly proportional to the concentration up to 0.3 gram per 100 cm³, but then increases more rapidly with concentration indicating the presence of some entanglement between the chains. Not much effect is found for the shear stiffness of the molecules which increases nearly in proportion to the concentration. Fig. 22 shows a similar measurement for the $120X$ solution at 7.5° C and 20 kc and here the η_B value is considerably more curved than that for the lower molecular weight solution indicating considerably more entanglement for the higher molecular weight measurements. Up to 0.15 gram per cm³, the viscosity is approximately a straight line relationship.

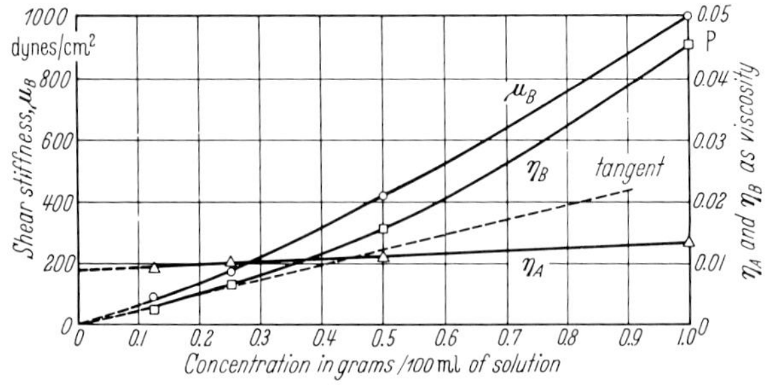

Fig. 21. Parameters of modified Maxwell model as a function of concentration for 80× solution at 25° C.

Both of these measurements show that the shear stiffness of the solution is directly proportional to the concentration and does not show much entanglement effect. This has been checked up to 5% concentration and the stiffness is only 35% larger than 5 times that at 1% concentration.

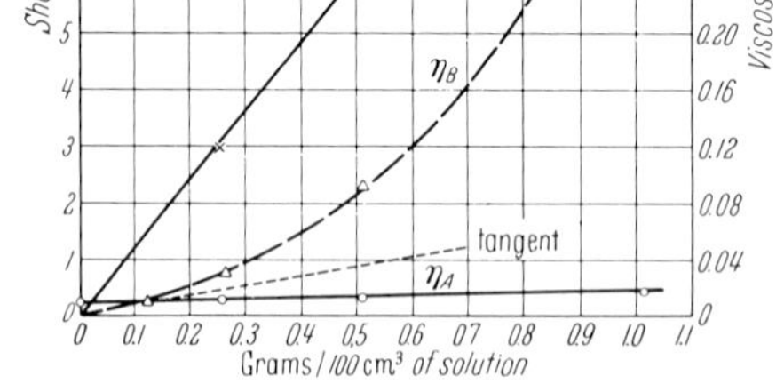

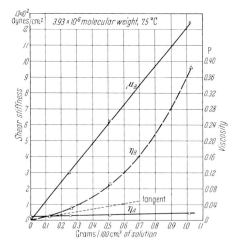

Fig. 22. Parameters of modified Maxwell model as a function of concentration for 120× solution at 7.5° C.

To determine possible relaxations, it is necessary to measure a solution over a wide frequency range. Since the 1% solution does not show much entanglement effect, measurements have been made from 2.4 kilocycles to 14 megacycles by the various techniques described in Sect. 3. The measurements were made for three temperatures and the measured values are shown by Table 2. The static measurements for the $120X$ and $80X$ solutions are given together with measurements at 2422 cycles by the tuning fork method, 20, 40, 80 and 150 kc by the torsional crystal method and one measurement at 14 Mc by the shear wave reflectance method for the 120 X solution.

From the resistance and reactance measurements, the Voigt viscosity and shear stiffness values are calculated. These are given since it is easier to compare the measurements with theory on this basis. Finally, in the last column, the difference between the measured viscosity and the solvent viscosity is given.

Table 2. *Measurements of 80-X and 120-X solutions of polyisobutylene in cyclohexane.*

120-X static measurement.				80-X static measurement.			
Temperature °C	ηs	η_0	ϱ	Temperature °C	ηs	η_0	ϱ
7.5	0.012	0.41	0.785	7.5	0.012	0.085	0.79
25.0	0.0086	0.273	0.771	25	0.0086	0.0586	0.77
50	0.0057	0.168	0.75	50	0.0057	0.0362	0.75

2422 cycle measurements.						2422 cycle measurements.					
Temperature °C	R	X	$\mu = (R^2-X^2)/\varrho$	$\eta_1 = \dfrac{2RX}{\omega\varrho}$	$\eta_1 - \eta s$	Temperature °C	R	X	μ	η_1	$\eta_1 - \eta s$
7.5	20.8	9.85	427	0.0344	0.0224	7.5	15.6	11.0	153	0.0285	0.0185
25	19.9	9.1	409	0.0311	0.0225	25	14.0	10.0	125	0.0236	0.0150
50	17.8	8.0	335	0.025	0.0193	50	11.5	8.3	84	0.0167	0.011

20 kc measurements						20 kc measurements					
7.5	42.7	28.8	1250	0.0249	0.0129	7.5	42.1	28.0	1240	0.0238	0.0118
25	38.7	24.4	1165	0.0194	0.011	25	35.9	24.0	930	0.0178	0.0092
50	34.6	20.5	1030	0.015	0.0093	50	33.4	21.0	897	0.0148	0.0091

40 kc measurements						40 kc measurements					
7.5	53.9	36.8	2000	0.0201	0.0081	7.5	52.2	37.8	1640	0.0199	0.0079
25	45.4	31.6	1370	0.0148	0.0062	25	45.2	31.7	1350	0.0147	0.0061
50	40.3	25.8	1270	0.0111	0.0048	50	38.6	25.8	1100	0.0105	0.0048

80 kc measurements						80 kc measurements					
7.5	70.7	52	2770	0.0188	0.0068	7.5	68.7	53.0	2420	0.01835	0.0065
25	59.4	44.5	2000	0.0136	0.005	25	59.4	44.5	1990	0.01365	0.00505
50	51.4	36.1	1790	0.00985	0.0041	50	48.4	36.1	1382	0.00925	0.00355

150 kc measurements					
25	77.2	59.5	3020	0.0126	0.004

14 Mc measurements					
25	584	524	84000	0.00906	0.00086

Fig. 23 shows a plot of the shear stiffness and difference between the measured viscosity and solution viscosity for the 25° C measurements for both solutions.

7. Theoretical interpretation of solution measurements. It appears that the best interpretation of the effect of long chain molecules on the dynamic properties of solutions—at least for the lower frequency relaxations—is given in Rouse's[15], Bueche's[17a] and Zimm's[17b] theories of the linear properties of dilute solutions of polymers which use the normal coordinate method. Rouse, for example, assumes that the polymer molecule can be divided into N segments of "such a length that the segment is just long enough so that at equilibrium the separation of its ends obeys, to a first approximation, a Gaussian probability function, i.e., if one end of the submolecule is located at the origin of a system of

Cartesian coordinates, the probability $\psi(x, y, z)\, dx\, dy\, dz$ that the other end will be in the volume $dx\, dy\, dz$ lying between x and $x + dy$, y and $y + dy$, z and $z + dz$ is given by

$$\psi(x, y, z)\, dx\, dy\, dz = \left(\frac{\beta}{\pi}\right)^{\frac{3}{2}} e^{-\beta(x^2+y^2+z^2)}\, dx\, dy\, dz \quad \text{where} \quad \beta = 3/2\sigma^2, \tag{7.1}$$

σ^2 is the mean square separation". These are the same equations as have been applied to long chain rubber molecules.

The measurements of Fig. 23 at high frequencies show that the viscosity of the polymer solution is only about 10% higher than the viscosity of the solvent alone. This result strongly supports the hypothesis that the primary effect of the velocity gradient is to carry each segment along with the liquid. The motion, however, will disturb the equilibrium distribution of molecules, and thermal agitation will cause a redistribution of positions with a subsequent motion of the polymer segments through the liquid. At low frequencies for which rearrangements for the whole molecule can take place in a time less than the time of a cycle of the applied stress, this effect manifests itself in an increased viscosity of the solution over that of the solvent. As the frequency becomes higher, there is not time for all redistributions to become complete and the polymer motion lags behind the applied stress giving a complex viscosity or a shear stiffness effect. At the highest frequencies no complete motions can occur, and the reaction of the polymer molecule tothe statistical reorientation effect is a stiffness reactance for which a displacement of the polymer segments can take place, but no motion through the liquid occurs. Under this condition, the viscosity is the viscosity of the solvent and the only effect of the polymer molecule is to introduce a stiffness reaction to the reorienting forces.

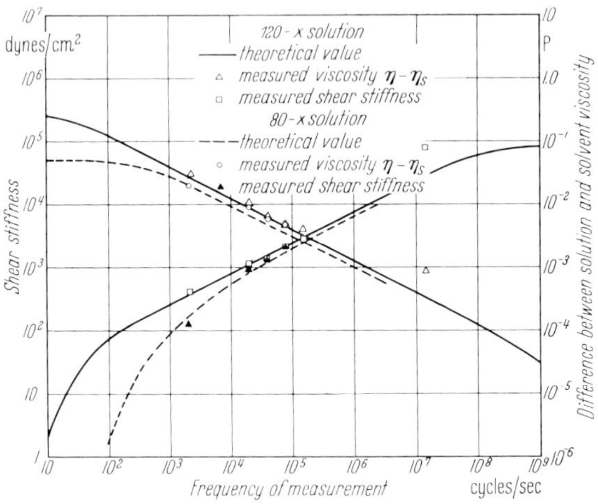

Fig. 23. Measurements of shear stiffness and difference between solution and solvent viscosity for 1% 80× and 120× solutions as a function of the frequency.

The most complete calculation of the dynamic properties of polymer molecules in dilute solutions is the calculation of Zimm[17b]. This takes account not only of the viscosity of separate chain segments but also of the hydrodynamic interaction between chain segments. The results obtained are similar to those of Rouse and Bueche, i.e., the effect of the interaction is to produce a definite viscosity for each chain segment. Zimm considers that the molecule can be represented by a series of $N+1$ identical beads separated by N springs whose values are determined by the Brownian motions of the segment ends. The effect of the external currents caused by the shearing motions of the transducers is to alter the equilibrium Brownian motions and to impart a motion to the separate segments of the chain. By applying the equation of continuity to the probability function ψ, and the force equation

$$F_{x_i} = -kT\,\partial \ln \Psi/\partial x_i; \qquad F_{y_i} = -kT\,\partial \ln \Psi/\partial y_i; \qquad F_{z_i} = -kT \ln \Psi/\partial z_i \tag{7.2}$$

a differential equation in Ψ is derived which involves the constants of the network.

ROUSE and ZIMM have calculated the reorienting displacements and their effects on the energy dissipation due to a polymer network of N segments and have shown that the effect of this rearrangement is to add to the viscosity of the solvent a value η_A and a stiffness μ_A equal to

$$\eta_A = n\,k T \sum_{p=1}^{N} \frac{\tau_p}{1+\omega^2 \tau_p^2}\,; \qquad \mu_A = n\,k T \sum_{p=1}^{N} \frac{\omega^2 \tau_p^2}{1+\omega^2\,\tau_p^2} \tag{7.3}$$

where n is the number of polymer molecules per cm³, k is BOLTZMANN's constant, T the absolute temperature, ω the angular measuring frequency and τ_p a series of relaxation times given by the equation

$$\tau_p = \sigma^2 \Big/ \left[24\,B\,k T \sin^2 \frac{p\pi}{2(N+1)}\right]. \tag{7.4}$$

In this equation N is the number of polymer segments, p a series of integers starting from 1, and B is the mobility of a single subchain end defined as the ratio of the reorienting force to the velocity produced. B is the reciprocal of the force required to pull the chain segment through the liquid at unit velocity. Each relaxation time associated with a particular value of p corresponds to a particular mode of coordination of the motions of the segment of the molecule. The longest relaxation time is that for $p=1$ and this corresponds to a configurational relaxation of the molecule as a whole.

Neither σ^2, B or N are measurable values on this theory but a relation between them can be obtained at zero frequency for which

$$\eta_0 = \eta_S + n\,kT \sum_{p=1}^{N} \tau_p = \eta_S + \frac{n\sigma^2}{24\,B} \sum_{p=1}^{N} \left[\frac{1}{\sin \dfrac{p\pi}{2(N+1)}}\right]^2 = \eta_S + \frac{n\sigma^2 N(N+2)}{36\,B} \tag{7.5}$$

Since $n = N_A\,c/M$, where N_A is AVOGADRO's number, c the concentration and M the molecular weight we find for the intrinsic viscosity

$$[\eta_0] = \lim_{c\to 0} \frac{(\eta_0 - \eta_S)}{(c\,\eta_S)} = \frac{N_A\,N^2\,\sigma^2}{36\,M B\,\eta_S}. \tag{7.6}$$

Practically all the viscosity terms are contained in the first few relaxation terms, and Rouse makes the approximation that

$$\sin \frac{p\pi}{2(N+1)} \approx \frac{p\pi}{2(N+1)} \tag{7.7}$$

which is valid for $p < N/5$. Then

$$\tau_p = \frac{\sigma^2 (N+1)^2}{6\pi^2\,p^2\,B\,kT}. \tag{7.8}$$

Comparing this with (7.5), we have

$$\tau_p = \frac{6(\eta_0 - \eta_S)}{\pi^2\,p^2\,n\,kT}. \tag{7.9}$$

Hence to this order of approximation, the effect of the polymer molecule is independent of the number N of secondary loops.

A calculation of the parameters of this equation have been given by ROUSE with the results shown in Table 3.

In this table η_A is the difference between the measured viscosity and the solvent viscosity at angular frequency ω, η_S the solvent viscosity, η_0 the solution viscosity and μ_A the Voigt stiffness of the medium.

Since all these quantities can be derived for the two solutions of Fig. 23, a test of the theory can be made. For the two solutions, we find for 25° C

$$\left.\begin{array}{llll} 120\text{-}X; & \eta_0-\eta_S=0.265 \text{ poise}; & n=1.54\times 10^{15}; & nkT=63.5 \\ 80\text{-}X; & \eta_0-\eta_S=0.05 \text{ poise}; & n=5.16\times 10^{15}; & nkT=210. \end{array}\right\} \quad (7.10)$$

A plot of the equations for the two solutions are shown by the full and dashed lines of Fig. 23. Up to the 150 kilocycle measurements the agreement is probably within the experimental error. The high frequency measurements are discussed later and it is shown that a short time relaxation has to be introduced to get good agreement.

If one applies the Rouse equations to the 7.5 and 50° C measurements of Table 2, as good an agreement results. The form of the equation agrees with the TOBOLSKY[45]-LEADERMAN[45]-FERRY[46] reduction formula for which all the relaxation elements have stiffnesses which increase in proportion to the temperature, and viscosities all of which obey the same activation energy equations. Reduced variables are based on the equation for the sum of relaxation frequencies

Table 3. *Theoretical values of the viscosities and shear elasticities as a function of ω.*

$\omega\tau_1$	$(\eta_A)/(\eta_0-\eta_S)$	μ_A/nkT
0.1	0.9939	0.01072
0.2	0.9762	0.04162
0.5	0.8758	0.2203
1.0	0.6861	0.5785
2.0	0.4776	1.076
5.0	0.3003	1.982
10.0	0.2135	3.012
20.0	0.1511	4.476
50.0	0.0955	7.351
100.0	0.0676	10.60

$$\left.\begin{aligned} \mu' &= \sum_{i=1}^{N} \frac{\mu_i \tau_i^2 \omega^2}{1+\tau_i^2\omega^2}; \\ \eta' &= \sum_{i=1}^{N} \frac{\eta_i}{1+\tau_i^2\omega^2} \\ &= \sum_{i=1}^{N} \frac{\mu_i \tau_i}{1+\tau_i^2\omega^2} \end{aligned}\right\} \quad (7.11)$$

where μ_i is the shear modulus associated with the i-th relaxation time τ_i, and η_0, the static shear viscosity is $\sum_{i=1}^{N}\eta_i = \sum_{i=1}^{N}\mu_i\tau_i$. It is then assumed that all μ_i depend identically on, and are proportional to, absolute temperatures and concentrations, and one has

$$\mu_i = \mu_{i_0}\frac{TC}{T_0 C_0} \quad (7.12)$$

where μ_{i_0} is the value of μ_i at the reference temperature and concentration, and T and C are the absolute temperature and concentration for μ_i.

It is further assumed that all τ_r depend identically on temperature and concentration and that there are proportionality constants a_T and a_C such that

$$\tau_i = a_T a_C \tau_{i_0},$$

where τ_{i_0} is the i-th relaxation time in the reference state. When these assumptions are incorporated into the expressions for the dynamic rigidity and viscosity, it appears that if a reduced dynamic modulus μ'_R, a reduced dynamic viscosity and a reduced frequency are defined as

$$\mu'_R = \mu'\frac{T_0 C_0}{TC}; \quad \eta_R = \frac{\eta'}{\eta_0}; \quad \omega_R = a_T a_C \omega \quad (7.13)$$

[45] A. V. TOBOLSKY and R. D. ANDREWS: J. Chem. Phys. **11**, 125—134 (1943). See also H. LEADERMAN: Elastic and Creep Properties of Filamentous Materials and Other High Polymers, p. 30. Washington, D.C.: Textile Foundations 1943.

[46] J. D. FERRY: J. Amer. Chem. Soc. **72**, 3746 (1950). — FERRY, FITZGERALD, GRANDINE and WILLIAMS: Ind. Engng. Chem. **44**, 713 (1952). — WILLIAMS, LANDEL and FERRY: J. Amer. Chem. Soc. **77**, 3701 (1955).

data taken under a variety of conditions should form a single curve which gives parameters of interest for the reference state. The unknown constants $a_T\, a_C$ can be evaluated from the observation that

$$\eta_0 = \sum_i \mu_i \tau_i = \frac{TC}{T_0 C_0} a_T a_C \sum_i \mu_{i_0} \tau_{i_0} = \frac{TC}{T_0 C_0} a_T a_C \eta_{i0}.$$

Hence

$$a_T a_C = \frac{\eta_0 T_0 C_0}{\eta_{i_0} TC} \tag{7.14}$$

and hence with the choice of a standard state such that C_0 and η_{i_0} are unity, the reduced frequency variable becomes

$$\omega_R = \omega \eta_0 T_0 / TC. \tag{7.15}$$

Recent work by BARLOW and LAMB[5b] has shown that the effect of pressure can be incorporated in the Tobolsky-Leaderman-Ferry reduction formula. Three types of lubricating oils were investigated. It was found that by plotting all the impedance measurements against the reduced frequency of Eq. (7.15), single curves were obtained for both the resistance and reactance terms. The viscosity η_0 was the viscosity measured at the hydrostatic pressure used. This finding has important consequences for lubrication theory since oils are usually under high hydrostatic pressure and hence viscoelastic effects may be expected at the frequencies for which gear teeth mesh. BARLOW and LAMB found a correlation between relaxation spectra and the hydrocarbon types. In order of ascending frequency spectra the correlation was tri-aromatics, di-aromatics, mono-aromatics and saturates. Further, it was found that higher naphthenic saturates lead to higher values of shear moduli μ_∞.

An interesting relation for a_T has been pointed out by WILLIAMS, LANDEL and FERRY[46]. In the supercooled region, which extends from above the glass temperature T_g to about 100° C above the glass temperature, a universal equation of the form

$$\log_{10} a_T = 17.44\,(T - T_g)/(51.6 + T - T_g) \tag{7.16}$$

has been shown to hold experimentally. Above this temperature the viscosity depends on details of the molecular structure while as the glass temperature is approached, the reduction formula becomes invalid.

An interpretation in terms of the free volume of the polymer has been given. In terms of the ratio of the free volume to the total volume, the viscosity of a liquid can be expressed as

$$\ln \eta = \ln A + \frac{1}{f}.$$

From (7.14) the value of a_T can be written

$$a_T = \frac{\eta T_g \varrho_g}{\eta_g T \varrho}.$$

Neglecting the variations of T and ϱ compared to η,

$$\log_{10} a_T = \frac{1}{2.303}\left(\frac{1}{f} - \frac{1}{f_g}\right). \tag{7.17}$$

The dependence of the free volume on temperature is taken by several authors to be the difference between the thermal expansion coefficients above and below the glass transition temperature. Thus, $f = f_g + (\alpha_2 - \alpha_1)(T - T_g)$. Substituting in (7.17) we find

$$\log_{10} a_T = -\frac{(T - T_g)}{2.303 f_g} \Big/ \left(\frac{f_g}{(\alpha_2 - \alpha_1)} + T - T_g\right). \tag{7.18}$$

This is identical in form with Eq. (7.16) and equating constants $\alpha_2 - \alpha_1 = 4.8 \times 10^{-4}/°C$ and $f_g = 0.025$. The difference in temperature expansion coefficients for most polymers are in this range.

A consequence of this type of relationship is that the activation energy for viscous flow will depend markedly on how close the temperature is to the glass temperature. From the relation

$$\Delta H = R \frac{d \ln a_T}{(1/T)}$$

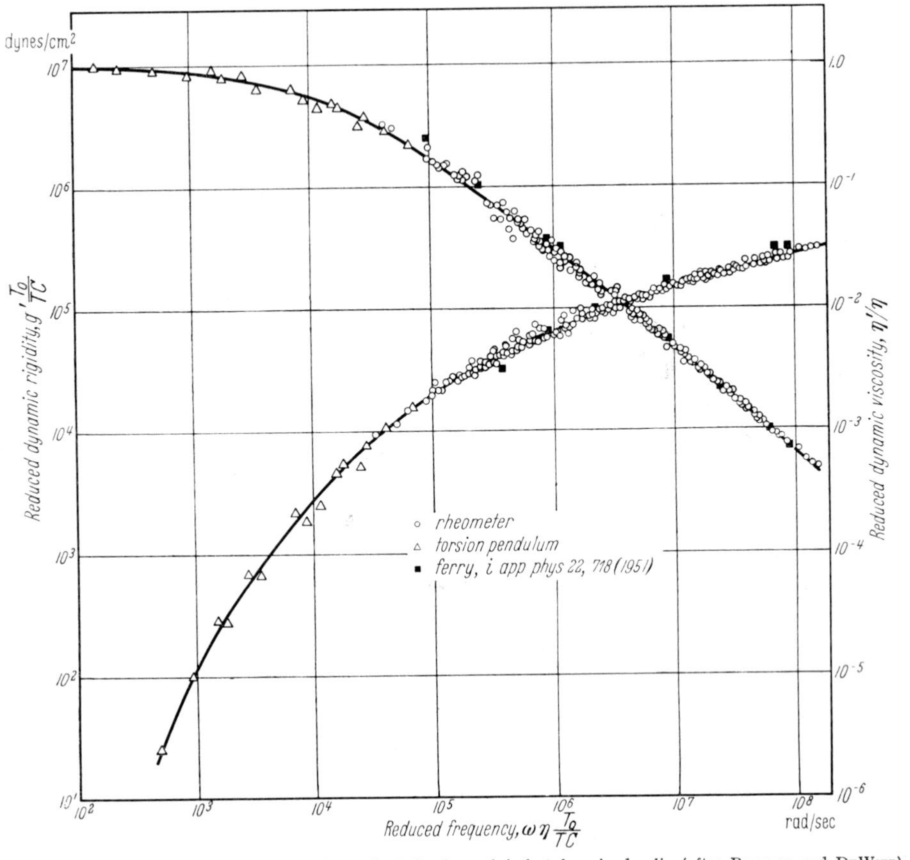

Fig. 24. Reduced dynamic viscosity and shear elasticity for polyisobutylene in decalin (after PADDEN and DEWITT).

one finds

$$\Delta H = R\left[T^2/(\alpha_2 - \alpha_1)\right] \Big/ \left(\frac{f_g}{\alpha_2 - \alpha_1} + T - T_g\right)^2 \approx \frac{2.08 \times 10^3 R T^2}{(51.6 + T - T_g)^2}. \qquad (7.19)$$

Close agreement is found with this equation for a number of polymer liquids.

Fig. 24 shows measurements[47] of the reduced dynamic variables for polyisobutylene (Vistanex B-100) in a decalin solvent for concentrations of 5 to 22%, temperatures from 5 to 35° C and frequencies from 0.005 to 100 cycles per second. As can be seen, all the points lie on one line which agrees well with the theoretical formula of ROUSE-BUECHE-ZIMM. A number of other polymers and solvents have been investigated—principally by FERRY and his co-workers—and sub-

[47] F. J. PADDEN and T. W. DEWITT: J. Appl. Phys. 25, 1086—1091 (1954).

stantial agreement with the reduced variable formula has been obtained for all the solutions considered. It should be pointed out, however, that for frequencies so high that the glassy state is approximated, this reduction formula falls down. For this case the stiffness increases as the temperature is lowered and a change in activation energy occurs as discussed in Chap. IV.

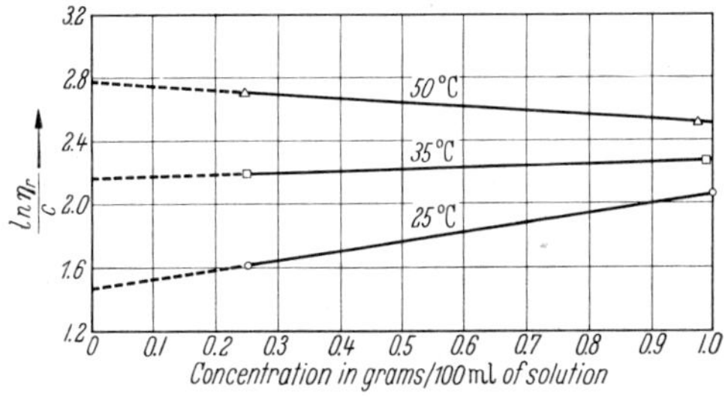

Fig. 25. Intrinsic viscosity of 3.9×10^6 molecular weight polyisobutylene in benzene for 3 temperatures (after BAKER and HEISS).

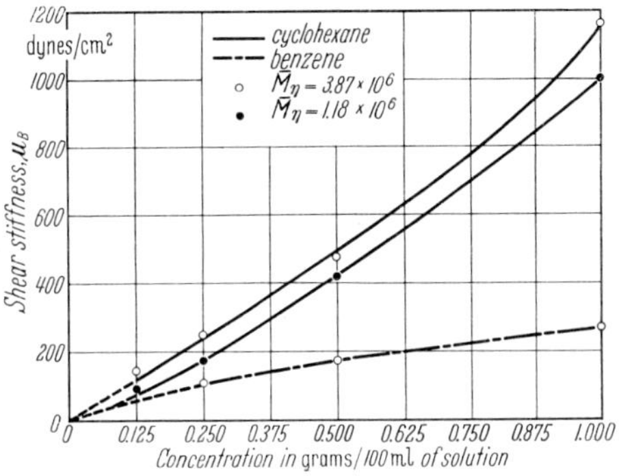

Fig. 26. Comparison of shear stiffness of polyisobutylene in cyclohexane and benzene as a function of the concentration (after BAKER and HEISS).

The ROUSE-BUECHE-ZIMM formula is also useful when the same polymer is dissolved in different solvents. It is well known that the extent of a molecule depends on how good a solvent is used. For a poor solvent the average distance between the ends of the molecule decreases and consequently the constants change. Fig. 25 shows the logarithm of the ratio of the relative viscosity divided by the concentration for the 3.9×10^6 molecular polyisobutylene dissolved in benzene which is a poor solvent. For the three temperatures, 25, 35, and 50° C, the intrinsic viscosity varies from 1.5 to 2.75 and according to Eq. (6.1) and Fig. 18, the $\sqrt{\overline{r^2}}$ average root-mean-square end separation should be, respectively, 1400 to 1700 Å.

The effect on the shear stiffness at 20 kc and 25° C is shown by Fig. 26. The cause of this lower stiffness according to the Rouse-Bueche-Zimm formula is the lower relative viscosity measured for benzene due to the smaller separation $\overline{r^{\circ}}$ of the segment ends. Fig. 27 shows measurements[16] of low molecular weight polyisobutylene in various solvents and the difference in η_A, and the shear stiffnesses μ_A, are very marked. The solid lines represent a calculation from the Rouse Zimm formula. Fig. 28a and b show[16] the viscosity and shear elasticity of another polymer polystyrene in toluene at 30.3° C measured as a function of frequency. As shown by the solid lines, the measured results are

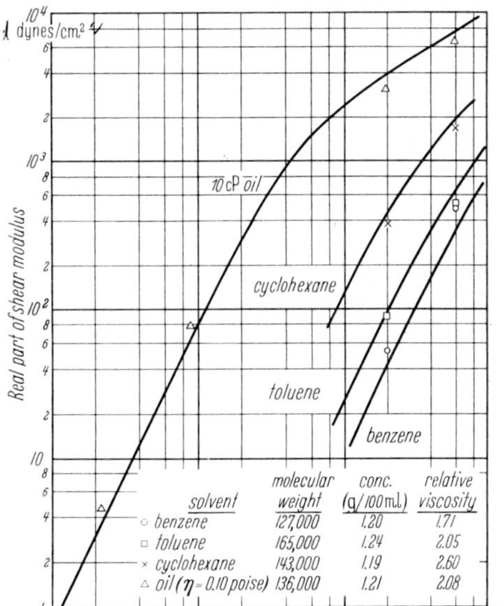

Fig. 27. Shear stiffness of low molecular weight polyisobutylene in several solvents as a function of frequency. Solid lines show theoretical results from ROUSE's formula (after SITTEL, ROUSE and BAILEY).

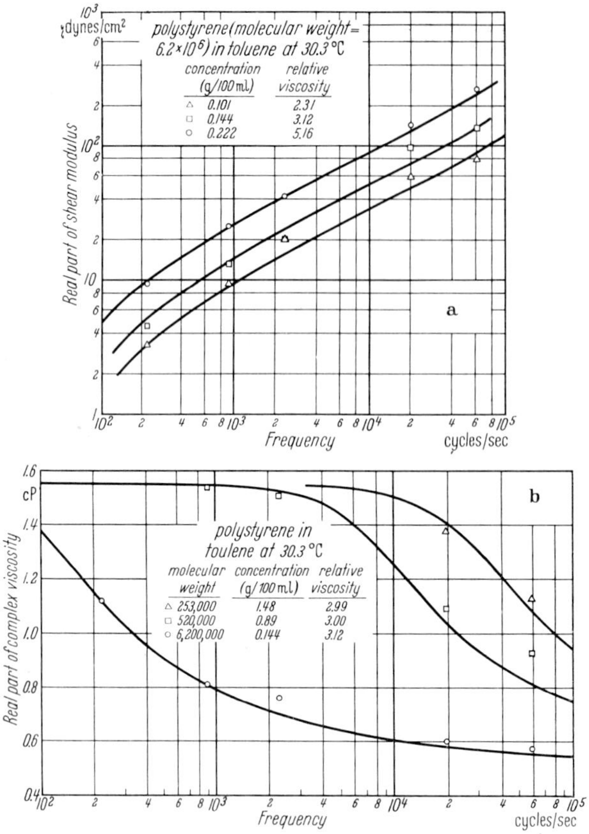

Fig. 28. Shear stiffness and viscosity of polystyrene in toluene for several concentrations. Solid lines show calculation from ROUSE's formula (after SITTEL, ROUSE and BAILEY).

in good agreement with the theory. A number of other polymers have been measured[13,16] in solvents and all the linear molecules agree well with the Rouse Bueche-Zimm formula.

8. Modification of network model for high frequencies. If one extends the calculations of ROUSE-BUECHE-ZIMM to high frequencies, it is evident from Fig. 23 that the 14 Mc measurements are definitely removed from the curve. The part of the curve for high frequencies is somewhat indeterminate since the number N of segments is not determined by the Rouse-Bueche-Zimm theory. However, the effect of a larger number of segments would be to extend the straight line portion to higher frequencies and hence it is evident that the high frequency measurements are definitely removed from the curve. This might be expected since it has been pointed out by ROUSE himself that the short time relaxation mechanisms have been neglected. In order to find out how to introduce the short time relaxation effects, a further consideration is given to the Rouse-Bueche-Zimm model.

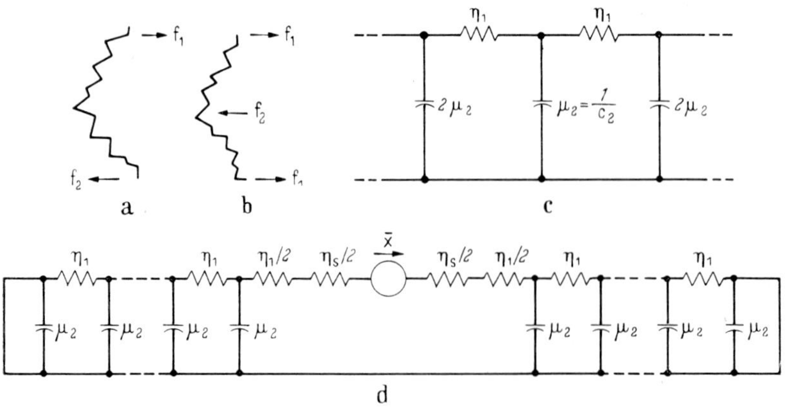

Fig. 29 a—d. Polymer motions and equivalent electrical circuit for polymer chains in a solvent.

This model consists of $N+1$ beads joined together by N springs. The viscous resistance of the bead moving through the solvent is inversely proportional to the mobility B. Since the viscosity of cyclohexane has been found to be unchanged at 14 megacycles with respect to its static value, the viscous resistance of the bead should be unchanged for the high frequency measurement. This value should be determined by the viscous drag of the complete segment as shown in Fig. 29a and can be represented in the model by an equivalent sphere of radius a. According to STOKES' law this drag is given by the equation

$$\frac{1}{B}=6\pi a \eta_s \tag{8.1}$$

where η_s is the viscosity of the solvent.

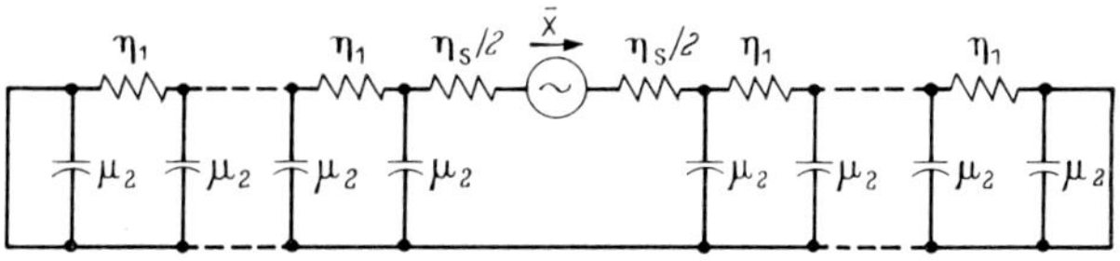

Fig. 30. Equivalent circuit for a single polymer molecule in a solvent.

The spring between the beads represents the stress-strain relationship between the ends of the segments. If the stress is applied slowly enough, so that equilibrium is established in a time less than that of a cycle of the applied stress, the stress strain relation can be represented by a spring which has a stiffness $\mu_2=1/C_2$ in the equivalent electrical circuit of Fig. 29c. Energy is stored in the

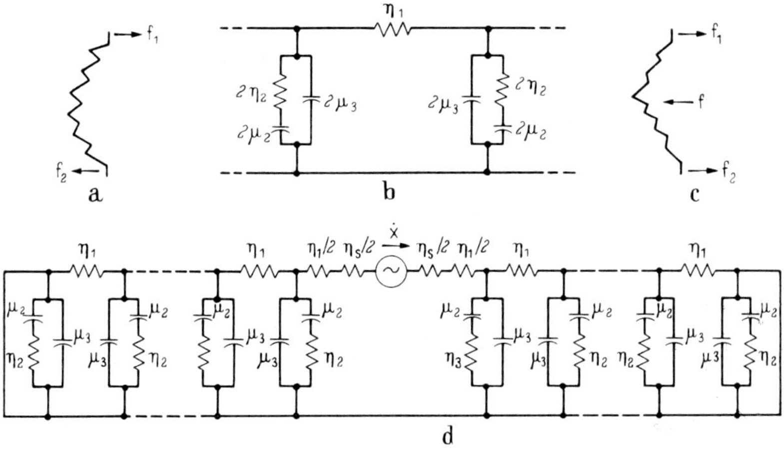

Fig. 31 a—d. Modification in equivalent circuit to take account of thermodynamic relaxation and structural stiffness.

motion since an increase in the length of the chain is involved. Suppose now that the stress is applied in a time much shorter than the time required to establish thermal equilibrium in the chain. The chain will still displace but with a stiffness determined by the intrinsic stiffness of the chain, i.e., that due to the mechanical bending of the joints. If the displacement is held constant for a period of time, thermal agitation will cause the separate polymer units to move in a direction to relieve the stress and after a period of time characterized by a relaxation time τ, thermodynamic equilibrium will be established and the stress will be determined by the thermodynamic stiffness μ_2. This type of stress-strain-time relation is represented by the equivalent electrical network of Fig. 31 for which $2\mu_3$ represents the intrinsic stiffness of the molecule, $2\mu_2$ the thermodynamic stiffness of the molecule and the ratio

$$\frac{\eta_2}{\mu_2}=\tau \tag{8.2}$$

the relaxation time required to establish thermodynamic equilibrium. One section of this type of network is shown by Fig. 31b.

Since energy from the liquid in motion enters the network through the beads, the same type of solution given by ROUSE[16] and ZIMM[17b] could be employed. However, a simpler method for determining the normal modes was pointed out by GROSS[48] and this is used to evaluate the networks of Figs. 29d and 31d. GROSS showed that all the normal modes of the network could be obtained by feeding all the vibrational energy from the liquid in at one point of the ladder network and expanding its impedance about the roots of the network which all lie along the negative real axis of the complex plane. These result in a series of normal modes identical with those of the Rouse-Bueche-Zimm theory. It appears that when all the energy is fed into the network at one point, the same normal modes occur as the ones resulting from the network type of feeding characteristic of the Rouse-Bueche-Zimm theory. Since this method agrees with the more complicated calculations and is much simpler to use, it is employed to investigate the changes in the network required to take account of the high frequency results.

For a midshunt section of Fig. 29c, we can write the equations

$$F_1 = \dot{s}_A \eta_1 + F_2; \qquad (\dot{s}_1 - \dot{s}_A) = \frac{j F_1 \omega}{2\mu_2}; \qquad (\dot{s}_A - \dot{s}_2) = \frac{j F_2 \omega}{2\mu_2} \tag{8.3}$$

where $\dot{s}_1$ is the input velocity of a segment and $\dot{s}_2$ the output velocity of the segment. We can rearrange these equations into the form

$$\left.\begin{aligned} \dot{s}_2 &= \left(1 + \frac{j\omega\eta_1}{2\mu_2}\right)\dot{s}_1 + j\frac{F_1\omega}{\mu_2}\left(1 + \frac{j\omega\eta_1}{4\mu_2}\right), \\ F_2 &= F_1\left(1 + \frac{j\omega\eta_1}{2\mu_2}\right) - \dot{s}_1\eta_1. \end{aligned}\right\} \tag{8.4}$$

Comparing these with the cannonical form of writing the transmission equations

$$\dot{s}_2 = \dot{s}_1 \cosh\Gamma - \frac{F_1}{Z_0}\sinh\Gamma; \qquad F_2 = F_1\cosh\Gamma - \dot{s}_1 Z_0 \sinh\Gamma \tag{8.5}$$

where $\Gamma = A + jB$ is the propagation constant and $Z_0 = R + jX$ is the characteristic impedance of the network, we have

$$\cosh\Gamma = 1 + \frac{j\omega\eta_1}{2\mu_2} = 1 + \frac{j\omega}{2\omega_0}; \qquad Z_0 = \eta_1\sqrt{-j\frac{\omega_0}{\omega\left(1 + \frac{j\omega}{4\omega_0}\right)}} \tag{8.6a}$$

where $\omega_0 = \mu_2/\eta_1$. For the midseries type, with $\eta_1/2$ on each end and μ_2 at the central position, the same expression is obtained for $\cosh\Gamma$ but Z_0 becomes

$$Z_0 = \frac{\eta_1}{2}\sqrt{1 - 4j\,\omega_0/\omega}. \tag{8.6b}$$

The closest physical embodiment for such a network appears to be the representation shown by Fig. 30. Here a source of vibration is coupled to the two halves of the network through the viscosity of the solvent. Since at very high frequencies, the segment moves with the fluid, the viscosity reduces to the solvent viscosity in accord with the Rouse-Bueche-Zimm theory. A rearrangement of

[48] B. GROSS [J. Polymer Sci. **20**, 123 (1956)] has shown that a ladder network similar to Fig. 29d gives identical results to the Rouse-Bueche-Zimm theory. Ladder networks of this type were first introduced into the theory of viscoelastic polymers by BLIZZARD [J. Appl. Phys. **22**, 730 (1951)]. The network energized at its midpoint appears to be closer to a physical representation of a polymer molecule than one energized on one end.

the complete segment can take place and hence a stiffness determined by the complete segment occurs. Hence a full shunt termination is indicated. This network is not in the desired form, but can be made so if we add a viscosity $\eta_1/2$ in series with each of the networks, as shown by Fig. 29d. After calculating the characteristic impedance one has to subtract η_1 to obtain the representation of Fig. 30.

When the transmission equation is written in the form of (8.5), it is well known that for N sections the relations between the output force and velocity and the input force and velocity can be written in the form

$$\left.\begin{aligned} F_N &= F_1 \cosh N\Gamma - \dot{s}_1 Z_0 \sinh N\Gamma; \\ \dot{s}_N &= \dot{s}_1 \cosh N\Gamma - \frac{F_1}{Z_0} \sinh N\Gamma. \end{aligned}\right\} \tag{8.7}$$

When we are dealing with a molecule which is free to move on each end and fed from a source at the center, the two output forces are zero and the ratio of the force F_1 to the velocity $\dot{s}_1$ is

$$Z(j\omega) = F_1/\dot{s}_1 = Z_0 \tanh \frac{N+1}{2} \Gamma \tag{8.8}$$

since half of the $N+1$ sections are in each network. Both sections are in series so that twice the impedance of (8.8) is the load impedance of the long chain molecule.

The energy to feed this chain comes from the shear rate $\dot{s}_{12}$ of the motion of the liquid and hence the energy dissipated in the solution is

$$\dot{s}_{12}^2 \operatorname{Re}\left[\eta_S - \eta_1 + 2 Z_0 \tanh \frac{N+1}{2} \Gamma\right]. \tag{8.9}$$

As a first approximation valid in the region under consideration

$$2 Z_0 \tanh \frac{N+1}{2} \Gamma = 2\eta_1 \sqrt{\frac{-j\omega_0}{\omega}} \tanh \frac{N+1}{2} \sqrt{\frac{j\omega}{\omega_0}}. \tag{8.10}$$

At very low frequencies the tanh is equal to its argument and hence the energy dissipated is

$$\dot{s}_{12}^2 |\eta_S - \eta_1 + (N+1)\eta_1| = \dot{s}_{12}^2 |\eta_S + \eta_0 - \eta_S| \tag{8.11}$$

so that $N\eta_1 = \eta_0 - \eta_S$ where η_0 is the solution viscosity and η_S the solvent viscosity. To determine the shear elastic constant μ_2, we show that the impedance of (8.8) can be made equal to the high frequency value of (7.3) if we pick $\mu_2 = \frac{N n k T}{2}$.

As long as

$$\frac{N+1}{2} \sqrt{\frac{\omega}{2\omega_0}} \tag{8.12}$$

is greater than 2, the value of the argument is greater than $2(1+j)$ and

$$\tanh(2+2j) = \frac{0.965 + j\,2.04}{1 + j\,1.96} = 1.025 - j\,0.03 \tag{8.13}$$

and hence, within less than three percent the value of $\tanh(2+j2)$ is equal to unity and approaches it more closely as the argument gets larger. Therefore the impedance approaches at high frequencies

$$2 Z_0 - \eta_1 = \eta_1 \sqrt{\frac{1 - 4j\mu_2}{\eta_1 \omega}} = -j \frac{2\mu_2}{\omega}. \tag{8.14}$$

This can be made identical with Eq. (7.3) if $\mu_2 = \frac{N n k T}{2}$, for at high frequencies (7.3) becomes

$$Z_R(j\omega) = \frac{-j n k T}{\omega} \sum_{p=1}^{N} \frac{\omega^2 \tau_p^2}{1+\omega^2 \tau_p^2} = \frac{-j N n k T}{\omega} \quad \text{when} \quad \omega \to \infty. \tag{8.15}$$

Hence $\mu_2 = \frac{N n k T}{2}$ and from (7.5)

$$\eta_1 = \frac{\eta_0 - \eta_S}{N} = \frac{\eta \sigma^2 (N+2)}{36 B}. \tag{8.16}$$

By expanding (8.10) in a series of partial fractions, GROSS[48] has shown that the expansion gives identically Eq. (7.3) with the relaxation times of (7.4). Hence since the characteristic impedance Z_0 has meaning for all values of p up to $p = N$, we can use $2Z_0 - \eta_1$, whose real and imaginary values are given in (8.6) to investigate the applicability of the polymer representation of Fig. 30 for very high frequencies. The result of a detailed calculation for the 120-X solution is shown by the solid lines of Fig. 23, assuming $N = 700$ to agree with later measurements. The experimental results do not agree with the theoretical values for frequencies above 10^6 cycles. Hence, as discussed above, it is apparent that some short time relaxations have been neglected.

One can work out the characteristic impedance Z_0 and the propagation constant Γ for the more general network of Fig. 31d in a similar way to that already employed, and it can be shown that the energy dissipated in such a chain with the ends free is

$$\dot{s}_{12}^2 \operatorname{Re}\left[\eta_S - \eta_1 + 2 Z_0 \tanh \frac{N+1}{2} \Gamma\right] \tag{8.17}$$

where

$$\left.\begin{aligned} \cosh \Gamma &= 1 + \frac{j\omega}{2\omega_1}\left(\frac{1 + j\omega/\omega_3}{1 + j\omega/\omega_2}\right) \\ \omega_1 &= \left(\frac{\mu_2 \mu_3}{\mu_2 + \mu_3}\right)\frac{1}{\eta_1}; \quad \omega_2 = \frac{\mu_2}{\eta_2}; \quad \omega_3 = \frac{\mu_2 + \mu_3}{\eta_2}. \end{aligned}\right\} \tag{8.18}$$

with

For a mid series and a mid shunt termination, the characteristic impedance are respectively

$$Z_0 = \frac{\eta_1}{2}\sqrt{1 - \frac{j 4 \mu_2 \mu_3}{\omega \eta_1 (\mu_2 + \mu_3)}\left[\frac{1 + j\omega/\omega_2}{1 + j\omega/\omega_3}\right]} \quad \text{mid series,} \tag{8.19a}$$

$$Z_0 = \frac{\frac{-j}{\omega}\left(\frac{\mu_2 \mu_3}{\mu_2 + \mu_3}\right)\left(\frac{1 + j\omega/\omega_2}{1 + j\omega/\omega_3}\right)}{\sqrt{\frac{1}{4} - \frac{j\omega_1}{\omega}\left(\frac{1 + j\omega/\omega_2}{1 + j\omega/\omega_3}\right)}} \quad \text{mid shunt}. \tag{8.19b}$$

For frequencies for which $\omega \ll \omega_3$; $\omega < \omega_1$; $\omega < \omega_2$ these equations reduce to

$$Z_0 = \eta_1 \sqrt{\frac{-j\omega_1}{\omega}}; \quad \Gamma = \sqrt{\frac{j\omega}{\omega_1}} \tag{8.20}$$

and hence at low frequencies the results reduce to the network of Fig. 30. The theoretical results are still valid for this molecular representation at frequencies below f_1. On the other hand, at high frequencies for which $\tanh N\Gamma/2$ reduces to unity, the characteristic impedance for the mid-series termination reduces to

$$2 Z_0 = \frac{-2 j \mu_3}{\omega}. \tag{8.21}$$

If we take a low value of ω — (10^4) — and a high value — (8.8×10^7), the four parameters of the network can be solved for, with the results:

$$\left.\begin{array}{ll} \mu_2 = 2.2\times 10^4 \text{ dynes/cm}^2; & \mu_3 = 1.9\times 10^5 \text{ dynes/cm}^2; \\ \eta_1 = 3.8\times 10^{-4} \text{ poises}; & \eta_2 = 1.1\times 10^{-2} \text{ poises}. \end{array}\right\} \tag{8.22}$$

With these values the viscosity and stiffness curves resulting are shown by the solid lines of Fig. 32 and a very good agreement with the measured result is found.

These values allow a determination of the number of independent segments in the chain of 3.9×10^6 atomic weight. N is determined by taking the ratio of the measured static viscosity $(\eta_0 - \eta_s) = 0.265$ to η_1 or

$$N = \frac{0.265}{3.8\times 10^{-4}} = 700 \tag{8.23}$$

corresponding to a segment length of

$$\frac{3.9\times 10^6}{56\times 700} = 100 \tag{8.24}$$

monomer units. The third element of the network, the coupling stiffness μ_2, is from Eq. (8.14) and Eq. (7.3)

$$\left.\begin{array}{l} \mu_2 = \dfrac{N n k T}{2} = \dfrac{700\times 63.5}{2} \\ \approx 22000 \text{ dynes/cm}^2. \end{array}\right\} \tag{8.25}$$

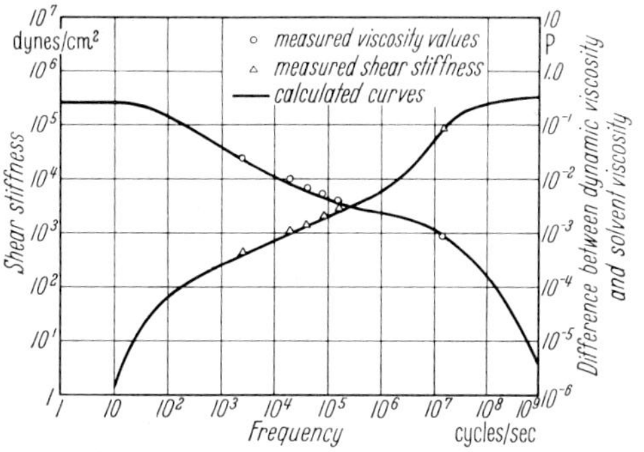

Fig. 32. Calculation of shear stiffness and viscosity for 120× solution taking account of thermodynamic relaxation and structural stiffness.

Hence we conclude that measurements of the shear impedance of polymer solution allows one to estimate the number N of independent segments of the molecule, the thermodynamic coupling stiffness between adjacent segments, and the thermal relaxation time

$$\tau = \frac{\eta_2}{\mu_2} = \frac{1.1\times 10^{-2}}{2.2\times 10^4} = 5\times 10^{-7} \text{ sec} \tag{8.26}$$

occurring when the shape of the chain is altered. For values of ω greater than the reciprocal of this time, mechanical stiffness to bending occurs and this appears to be about 9 times the thermal stiffness for this chain length. Since this stiffness is determined by constraints rather than by thermodynamic agitation, the reduction formula of Eqs. (7.13) is not valid in the high frequency region for which $\omega > 1/\tau$.

Several checks can be made on the value of 100 monomer units for the smallest chain segments. From the Rouse-Bueche-Zimm theory, the difference between the solution viscosity and the solvent viscosity is

$$\eta_0 - \eta_S \approx \frac{n\,\sigma^2 N^2}{36\,B}. \tag{8.27}$$

Since $n = 1.54\times 10^{15}$ molecules per cm³, $N = 700$ we find

$$\frac{\sigma^2}{B} = 1.27\times 10^{-20}. \tag{8.28}$$

The distance σ between chain ends can be calculated from the well-known relation

$$\frac{M}{\sigma^2} = \text{const} \approx 0.9\times 10^{+16} \tag{8.29}$$

where M is the molecular weight of the segment. The value of the constant for polyisobutylene is equal to $0.9\times10^{+16}$ from Fig. 18 and the equivalent $[\eta]$ corresponds to $M=3.9\times10^6$. Hence for a molecular weight of $100\times56=5600$, the value of $\sigma^2=6.25\times10^{-13}$. Introducing this value in (8.28) the value of $1/B$ becomes 2.04×10^{-8}. From (8.1) since the solvent viscosity is 0.0086, the viscous drag on the polymer segment is equivalent to that of a sphere of radius 12.5×10^{-8} cm which appear to be a reasonable value to represent a polymer chain of length equal to 340×10^{-8} cm, with a chain end separation of about 79×10^{-8} cm. If the chain segment was taken as 12 monomer units, as has been suggested for some polymers, the radius of the equivalent sphere would have to be about 1.5×10^{-8} cm which would be too small to represent a chain segment of 37×10^{-8} cm long with a value of σ equal to 27×10^{-8}.

Another check on the length comes from independent evidence given by Fig. 35 of Chap. IV which shows for the pure liquid a polymer segment of very similar length. This length may be determined by the average distance between cross lengths to other polymers. However, if there were a smaller segment length possible for the linear chain, one would expect a leveling off of the shear stiffness and viscosity at a lower molecular weight than is observed.

IV. Properties of polymer liquids.

9. Measured results. A number of measurements have been made of the shear viscosity and stiffness of pure polymer liquids over a wide frequency range, and the results depend as might be expected on the type of chain and the chain

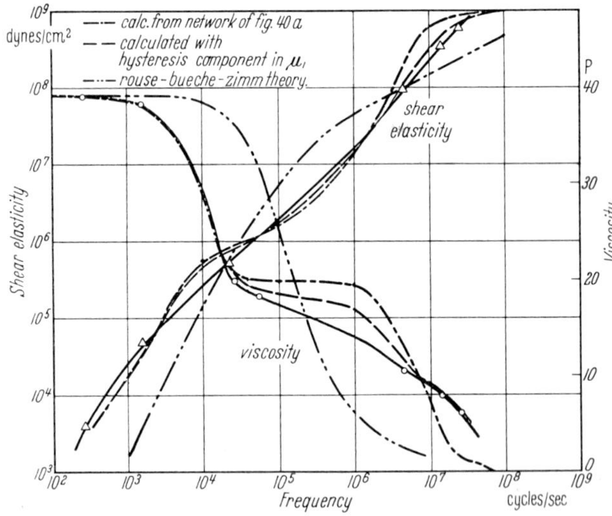

Fig. 33. Measurements for 1660 molecular weight polyisobutylene liquid.

length. One of the most complete measurements[49] made on a light liquid is that shown by Fig. 33. These measurements were made for a polyisobutylene liquid of viscosity average molecular weight of 1660. Since the polyisobutylene chain, as shown by Fig. 19, has a molecular weight of 56 for each repeating element,

[49] In the low frequency range the measurements were made by the tuning fork method of Fig. 14 by I. L. HOPKINS, Trans. Amer. Soc. Mech. Engrs. **73**, 195 (1951) and J. Appl. Phys. **24**, 1300 (1953), while the high frequency measurements were made by H. J. MCSKIMIN using the shear wave device of Fig. 10.

this chain has about 30 repeating elements. The curve shows evidence for a double relaxation as will be discussed later.

Some measurements given previously[12] for polyisobutylene chains of various lengths were recalculated and plotted in terms of reduced frequency, shear stiffness, and viscosity. Only the longest three chains were used. These had, respectively, 56, 74, and 147 repeating elements. The results are shown by Fig. 34. For stiffnesses below about 5×10^7, all the frequency and temperature measurements fall on one curve; but above this stiffness value, the lower temperature values are higher in stiffness than are the high temperature values[49a]. This indicates that the mechanisms which produce the high frequency stiffnesses are not of thermodynamic origin but rather are produced by mechanical constraints on the chain bending motion, and hence the stiffnesses decrease as the temperature increases as does the stiffness of a solid material. All the reduced viscosity measurements fall on a single curve. The final

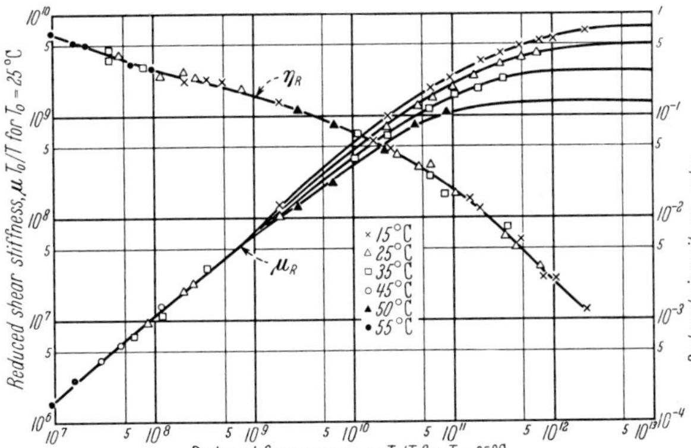

Fig. 34. Reduced shear stiffness and viscosity for polyisobutylene for molecular weights from 3100 to 8300.

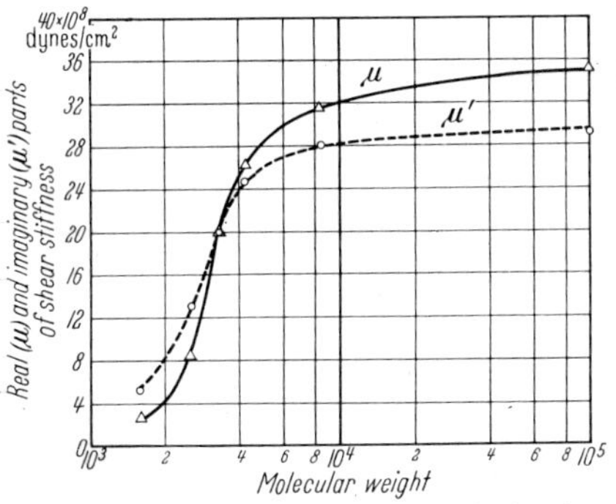

Fig. 35. Real and imaginary parts of the shear stiffness for polyisobutylene liquids of molecular weights from 2×10^3 to 10^5. Measuring frequency is 10^7 cycles. Temperature is 25° C (after MASON, BAKER, MCSKIMIN and HEISS).

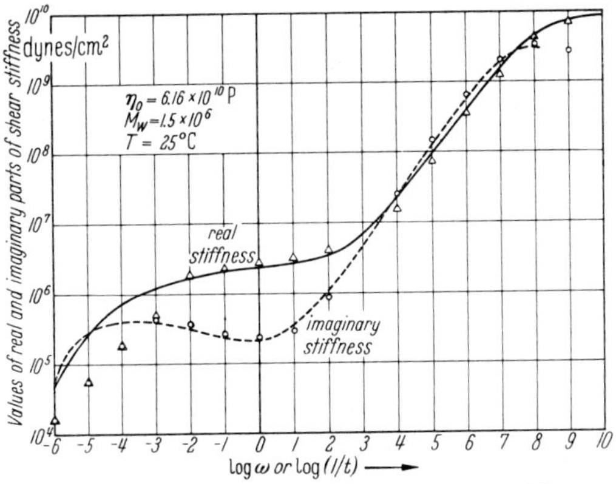

Fig. 36. Real and imaginary stiffness components of Bureau of Standards polyisobutylene of 1.5×10^6 molecular weight (after MARVIN). Triangles and circles represent calculated real and imaginary stiffnesses from network of Fig. 40.

stiffness values shown are taken from the Bureau of Standards measurements discussed below, and it is evident that at very high frequencies the stiffnesses are independent of the molecular weight. Some indications of the chain segment lengths operative are shown by the real and imaginary parts of the stiffness measurements[50] of Fig. 35. The knee of the curve occurs at a molecular weight of about 5600

[49a] Similar results have been found by LITOVITZ and associates for a series of associated liquids. See "Absorption and Dispersion of Ultrasonic Waves" (KARL F. HERZFELD and THEODORE A. LITOVITZ), pp. 479—483. chap. XII: Academic Press 1959.

[50] MASON, BAKER, MCSKIMIN and HEISS: Phys. Rev. **75**, 936—946 (1949), Fig. 11.

which corresponds to 100 repeating elements per segment length. The stiffness increases somewhat above this by a chain articulation effect, but the indicated segment length is about 100 repeating elements.

The most complete measurements of a single long chain substance made are those represented by the cooperative project of the Bureau of Standards[51] on the measurements of a polyisobutylene rubber having chains with an average

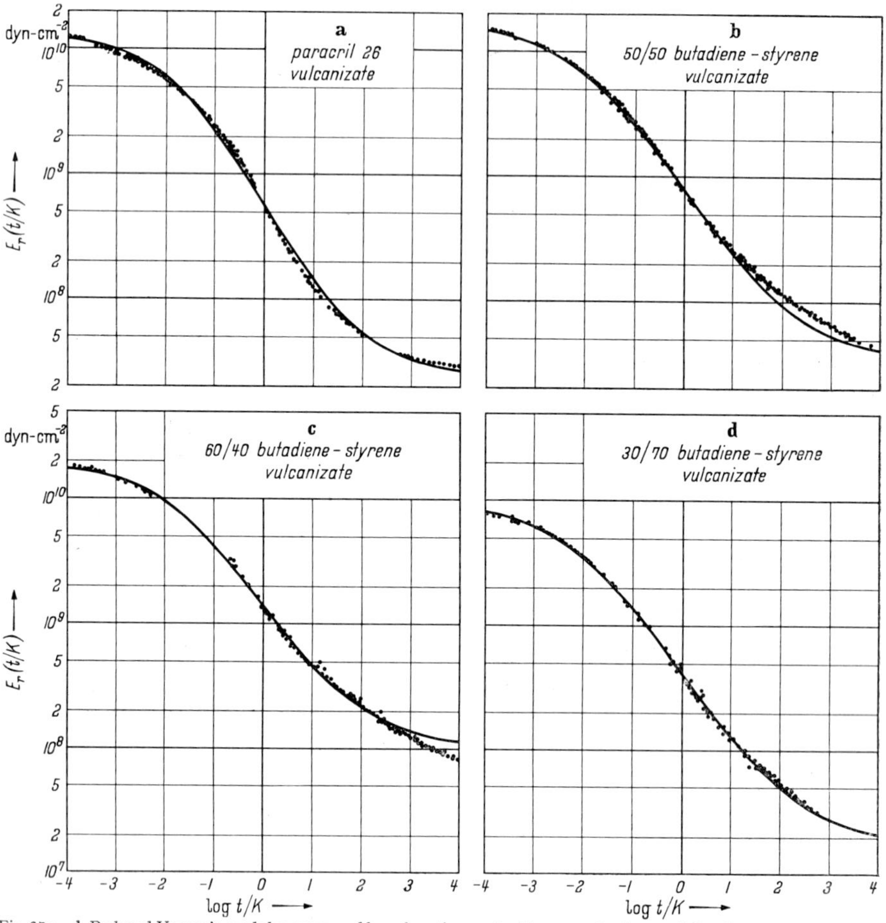

Fig. 37a—d. Reduced YOUNG's modulus measured by relaxation method for several polymers (after CATSIFF and TOBOLSKY)

molecular weight of 1 500 000. This material has the appearance of a rubbery solid, but it will flow for stresses applied over a long period of time. Fig. 36 shows the shear stiffness and viscosity-angular frequency product plotted against the angular frequency ω. As can be seen, there is a plateau covering many factors of 10 in frequency for which the stiffness is nearly a constant.

A large number of other long chain molecules have also been measured, a large share of them by the stress relaxation method[52]. For example, Fig. 37 shows master curves for four compositions of butadiene-styrene copolymers plotted as a

[51] R. S. MARVIN: Proc. 2nd Int. Congress of Rheology, pp. 156—163. London: Butterworth Scientific Publications 1954.

[52] For example, see E. CATSIFF and A. V. TOBOSLKY: J. Appl. Phys. 25, 1092—1097 (1954).

function of log t/K where t is the time since a strain has been applied to the specimen (inverse of ω) in hours and K is a characteristic time for each polymer which is a function of temperature only. The relaxation energy is related to K by the equation

$$H = 2.303\,R\,\frac{d\log K}{d(1/T)} \tag{9.1}$$

where R is the gas constant which is about 2 calories per mole per degree K. All these YOUNG's moduli—which are about 3 times the shear moduli—follow a very similar curve to the polyisobutylene modulus of Fig. 36.

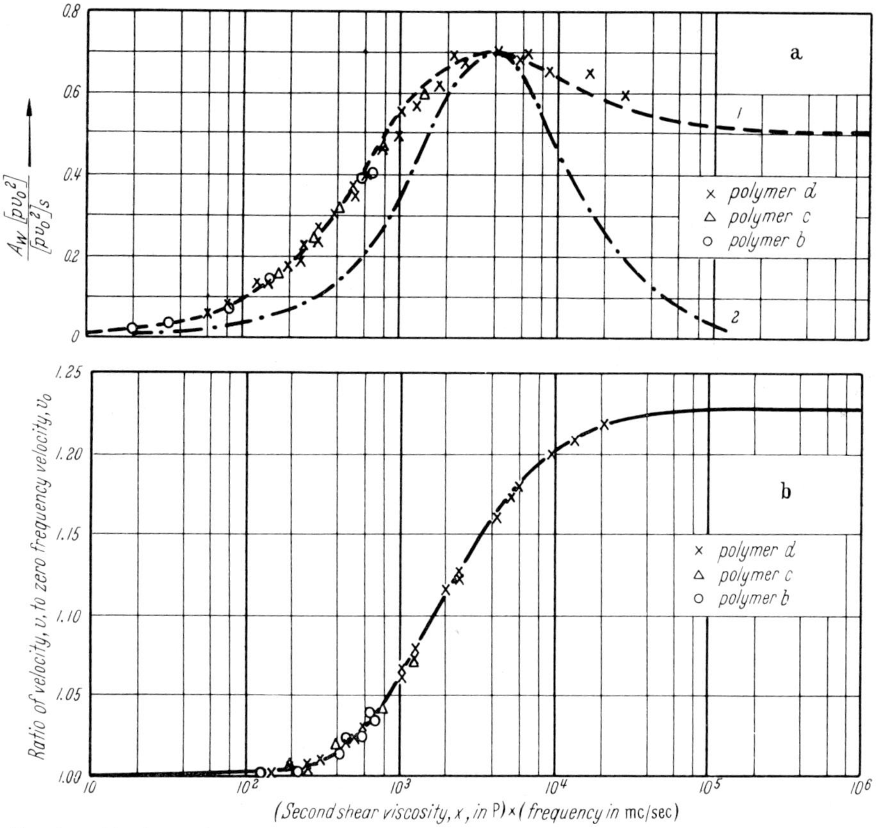

Fig. 38 a and b. Attenuation per wavelength and velocity dispersion of three polyisobutylene polymer liquids (after MASON, BAKER, McSKIMIN, and HEISS).

All the dynamic measurements for pure liquids discussed so far have been made by the shear wave techniques. A number of measurements have also been made by longitudinal wave techniques. Fig. 38a and b show the attenuation per wave length and the velocity of polyisobutylene liquids[53] of molecular weights 2520, 3350, and 4170 plotted against a "second" shear viscosity having an activation energy of 12 kilocalories per mole rather than the 16 kilocalories for viscous flow. It is evident that a broad relaxation is taking place. The curve for a single relaxation is shown by the dot-dash line. The actual measurements are dissymmetrical and approach a constant value independent of frequency for high frequencies. This type of loss indicates a hysteresis type loss for which a constant loss per cycle occurs.

[53] W. P. MASON, W. O. BAKER, H. J. McSKIMIN and J. H. HEISS: Phys. Rev. **77** (1948).

Further evidence for a hysteresis type loss in polymers is given by the work of LITOVITZ[54a] and LYON. Fig. 39a shows the attenuation in nepers/cm for glycerol as a function of frequency for several different temperatures. In this frequency range the attenuation can be represented by an equation

$$A = B + Hf \qquad (9.2)$$

where the part proportional to the frequency is a hysteresis component. If B and H are plotted against $1/T$ as shown by Fig. 39b, an activation energy of 13.8 kcal results for the hysteresis component H. This is about $\frac{1}{3}$ of that for viscous flow. A possible explanation for this effect is considered in Sect. 10.

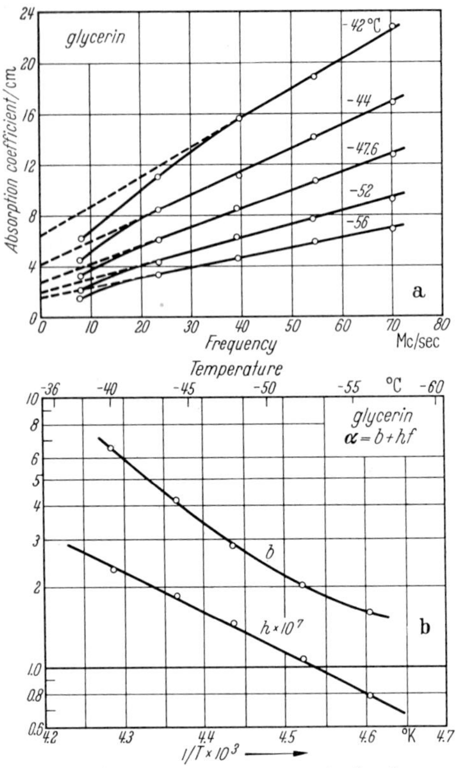

Fig. 39. (a) Attenuation measurements in glycerin as a function of frequency. (b) Evaluation of hysteresis component as a function of temperature (after LITOVITZ and LYON).

When both shear and longitudinal wave measurements have been made on the same liquid, one can determine whether all the loss is due to shear viscosity processes or whether some is due to volume viscosity. At a given frequency and temperature, the attenuation is given by the equation

$$A = \frac{2\pi^2 f^2}{\varrho V_L^3} (\chi + 2\eta) \qquad (9.3)$$

η where χ is the compressional viscosity, is the shear viscosity, and $V_L = \sqrt{(\lambda + 2\mu)/\varrho}$ is the longitudinal velocity. The following table shows measurements of these quantities for three polyisobutylene liquids at 8 Mc and 30° C. It is evident that there is a compressional viscosity χ about one-fourth as large as the shear viscosity.

Polymer mol. weight	$\lambda+2\mu$ in dynes/cm²	$\chi+2\eta$ Poise	μ dynes/cm²	η Poise	λ dynes/cm²	χ Poise
2520	2.01×10^{10}	50	0.2×10^{10}	22	1.61×10^{10}	6
3350	2.26	93	0.27	41	1.72	11
4170	2.56	155	0.3	69	1.88	17

The origin of compressional viscosity has been studied for associated liquids by HERZFELD and LITOVITZ[54b]. They find that the activation energy for compressional viscosity is closely equal to that for shear viscosity. In the case of water the compressional viscosity has been shown to result from two competing crystal structures which have different volumes. The effect of a compressional wave is to change the equilibrium between the two forms causing more of the close

[54a] T. A. LITOVITZ and T. LYON: J. Acoust. Soc. Amer. **26**, 577—581 (1954).

[54b] K. F. HERZFELD and T. A. LITOVITZ: Absorption and Dispersion of Ultrasonic Waves. New York and London: Academic Press 1959. See Chap. XII and Sect. 109—113.

packed structure in the compressional phase and more of the open structure in the rarification phase. The lag of the rate of change between the phases behind the applied pressure is the origin of the volume viscosity. The activation energy is determined by the potential maximum which has to be overcome in going from one phase to the other.

For glycerine and other associated liquids, a simple two state model is not sufficient to represent the results. This is to be expected for more complicated liquids since all of the molecules do not have the same configurations. The activation energy for motion of one part of the molecule from one position to another depends on the number of nearest neighbors and on the orientation of the segment with respect to its neighbors. Hence a distribution of activation energies and related relaxation times is to be expected. HERZFELD and LITOVITZ discuss the probable cause for volume viscosity in associated liquids and conclude that the evidence points to structural relaxations rather than to specific heat relaxations existing in the "Kneser type" unassociated liquids. The values of compressional viscosity are in the order of 1 to 3 times that for shear viscosity in associated liquids, but for polymer liquids the compressional viscosity is usually smaller than the shear viscosity.

10. Possible theoretical interpretation. A pure polymer liquid differs from a polymer molecule in solution in that there are intra-chain connections as well as inter-chain connections. Hence the molecule cannot be considered as a linear network, but must in general be considered as part of a three dimensional network.

Very short networks, however, can be considered as linear networks. FERRY, LANDEL, and WILLIAMS[55] have attempted to fit a Rouse-Bueche-Zimm type curve to the shear stiffness of a low molecular weight polymer on the assumption that the solvent has the same viscosity as the solution. The result of such a calculation is shown by the dash two dot lines of Fig. 33 and as can be seen the fit is not good. Since the Rouse-Bueche-Zimm type of curve requires a polymer with a number of segments, this is not surprising. A much better fit is obtained by considering that a polymer is a two relaxation network having the strcucture of Fig. 40a. For such a short network, the mid shunt termination is considered to be more appropriate than the mid series termination of Chap. VIII. For the three dimensional network of Fig. 40b, it is also simpler to employ the mid shunt termination. This type of termination results is $4\mu_3$ being the high frequency stiffness rather than $2\mu_3$ of Eq. (8.21). The thermodynamic stiffness μ_2 is equal to $(\frac{1}{4})\,(N n\, kT)$. With these changes, the fit to any viscosity, shear stiffness data is substantially the same as the mid series network.

It is readily shown that the impedance of such a network is given by the equation

$$Z = \frac{\eta_1\left(1 + j\,\frac{\omega}{\omega_2}\right)}{1 + \frac{j\,\omega}{\mu_2}\left(\eta_1\left(1 + \frac{\mu_2}{\mu_3}\right) + \eta_2\right) - \frac{\omega^2}{\omega_2\,\omega_3}}\,; \qquad \omega_2 = \frac{\mu_2}{\eta_2}\,; \qquad \omega_3 = \frac{4\,\mu_3}{\eta_1}\,. \tag{10.1}$$

The best values for matching the measured curves are

$$\left.\begin{aligned} \eta_1 &= 39 \text{ poise}; & \mu_2 &= 6\times 10^5 \text{ dynes/cm}^2;\\ \eta_2 &= \frac{\eta_1}{4} = 9.75 \text{ poise}; & \mu_3 &= 2.5\times 10^8 \text{ dynes/cm}^2. \end{aligned}\right\} \tag{10.2}$$

[55] See J. D. FERRY, R. F. LANDEL and M. L. WILLIAMS: J. Appl. Phys. **26**, 359–363 (1955).

With these values the dashed lines of Fig. 33 result. Since the liquid actually represents a range of molecular weights, a smoothing out of the calculation will be obtained and a fair match obtained except at the higher frequencies. At 25° C the density of this liquids is 0.866 so that the value of $n\,kT$ becomes

$$\left(\frac{0.866}{1660\times 1.66\times 10^{-24}}\right)(1.38\times 10^{-16}\times 300) = 13\times 10^{6}. \tag{10.3}$$

Hence the theoretical expression for the shear impedance μ_2 from Eq. (8.25) would yield a value of $N = 0.12$ which indicates that the two halves of the network

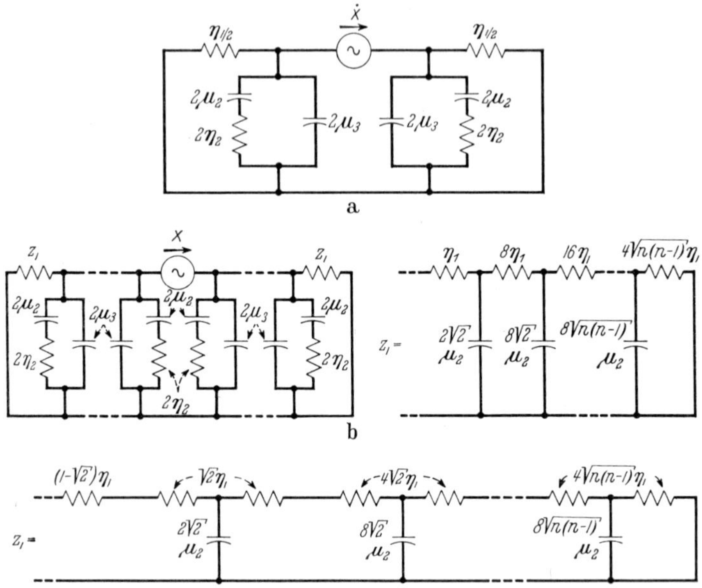

Fig. 40 a—c. Modification of a network of a linear polymer to take account of coupling of single loops to adjacent chains.

are not sufficiently long to develop the full thermodynamic coupling stiffness. In the same way, the viscosity associated with each half segment is 19 poise compared to the value of 58 poise that appears from longer chain measurements. At the highest frequencies the stiffness to bending results in a stiffness of the liquid of about 10^9 dynes/cm².

At the highest frequencies the viscosity decreases much too slowly for any combination of relaxation elements. The same is true for Fig. 34 for longer chain elements where the effective viscosity is decreasing inversely proportional to the frequency even when the stiffness is independent of frequency. One obtains this type of action if the stiffness to bending has a hysteresis component for then the impedance of the medium becomes

$$Z = \frac{4\,[\mu_3' - j\,\mu_3]}{\omega} \tag{10.4}$$

where μ_3' is the hysteresis component of the bending stiffness μ_3. The dot-dash line of Fig. 33 shows the effect of replacing μ_3 by the expression in (10.4) with μ_3' equal to $0.4\,\mu_3$. The agreement at the higher frequencies is much better.

This hysteresis type loss is very widespread in solid materials. For example it has been observed in metals, glasses and solid polymer materials. In the first two types of materials, this type of loss has been shown to be of a relaxational nature and to be due to much smaller elements than those involved in viscous flow. The relaxational nature of the processes for these two types of materials is shown by the curves of Fig. 41. These show internal friction[56a, b, c] and modulus change measurements for single crystals of copper and of bars of soda lime glass. The Q^{-1} curves for copper at 12 kilocycles and the YOUNG's modulus change $\Delta Y/Y_0$, also measured at 12 kilocycles over a temperature range were measured by neutron irradiating one copper crystal while the internal friction at 300° K as a function of the frequency was measured on another crystal. At 12 kilocycles

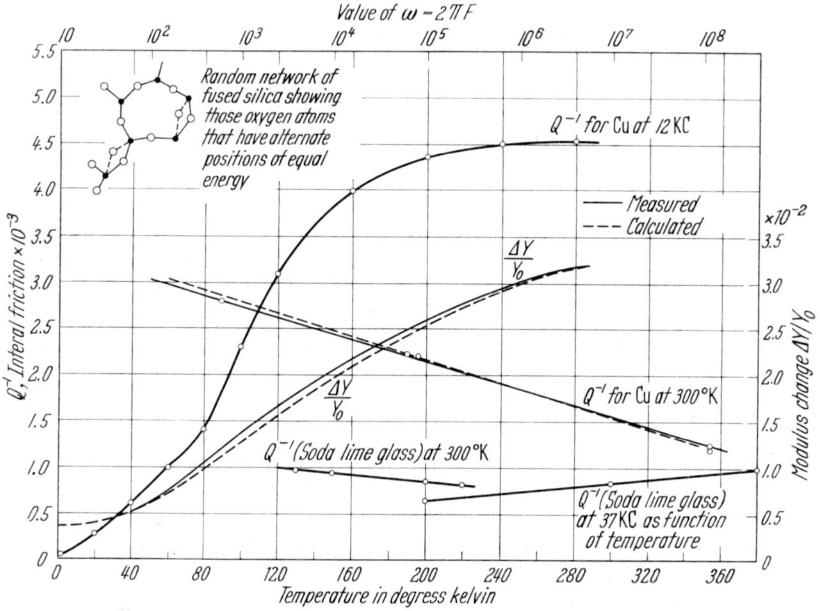

Fig. 41. Curves showing internal friction, Q^{-1}, versus frequency and temperature and the change in elastic modulus of a copper single crystal caused by neutron irradiation (solid lines). Dot dash lines are theoretical curves confirming that the changes are consistent with a series of relaxation processes. Network shows random network for glass and postulated motions showing cause of a distribution of relaxation processes.

this does not have as high an internal friction as the first crystal. Internal friction values plotted against frequency at 300° K and against temperature at a frequency of 37 kilocycles are given for a soda lime glass.

To show that these measurements support a relaxational interpretation, we can make use of the relaxational equations

$$Q^{-1} = \sum_{i=j}^{n} \frac{A_i\,\omega/\omega_i}{1+(\omega/\omega_i)^2}\,, \tag{10.5}$$

$$\frac{\Delta Y_0}{Y_0} = \sum_{i=j}^{n} \frac{A_i}{1+(\omega/\omega_i)^2}\,, \tag{10.6}$$

$$\omega_i = \omega_0\, e^{-H_i/RT} \tag{10.7}$$

[56a] The internal friction and modulus changes for irradiated copper crystals are taken from a paper by D.O. THOMPSON and D.K. HOLMES: J. Appl. Phys. **30**, 525 (1959).

[56b] The internal friction for a copper crystal as a function of frequency is taken from Fig. 99, p. 244, "Physical Acoustics and the Properties of Solids (W.P. MASON). New York: D. Van Nostrand 1958.

[56c] The internal friction against frequency for soda lime glass is given by R.L. WEGEL and H. WALTHER: Physics **6**, 141 (1935). The variation with temperature in Fig. 10, 17, Ref. 56b.

which relate the internal friction and modulus change to a series of relaxation frequencies. These relaxation frequencies are related to a series of activation energies H_i by Eq. (10.7). In this equation, the constant terms ω_0, is for a motion involving single or a few atoms,

$$\omega_0 \approx 10^{13}. \tag{10.8}$$

For a dislocation relaxation such as occurs for the copper crystals,

$$\omega_0 \approx 5 \times 10^{11}, \tag{10.9}$$

since it involves the motion of a complete segment in a potential well of the PEIERLS' energy barrier type.

Although the measurements of Fig. 41 require a continuous distribution of activation energies, an acceptable approximation is obtained by taking activation energies in the ratio

$$\frac{H_{i+1}}{H_i} = 1.11 \tag{10.10}$$

and taking values of the series of constants A_i as

$$A_i = 1.16\, Q_i^{-1} \quad \text{at} \quad T = T_i. \tag{10.11}$$

With these values a smooth curve results for a flat temperature Q^{-1} curve or for a slowly varying Q^{-1} versus frequency curve.

If we evaluate the values of A_i for the internal friction versus temperature curves for soda lime glass, it requires activation energies from

$$H = 6.9 \text{ kilocalories to } 13 \text{ kilocalories} \tag{10.12}$$

to cover the temperature range from 200 to 400° K. The circles on this curve show the results of summing the series of (10.5) with A_i values determined from (10.11) and frequencies determined from (10.7) with $\omega_0 \approx 10^{13}$. This same serie allows one to evaluate the internal friction Q^{-1} as a function of the frequency for a constant temperature. The circles on the Q^{-1} versus frequency curve at 300° K represent the results of this calculation.

The element causing the internal friction Q^{-1} for fused silica and glass has received considerable attention[56d] and rather conclusive evidence has been obtained that it is associated with the bent Si—O—Si bonds. The network of fused silica is illustrated by the figure at the top of Fig. 41. This figure is a pictorial representation of the random network concept for glass. It is evident that although most of the bonds are nearly straight, some of them have a divergence from a straight line. X-ray evidence shows this divergence to be at least ±5°. It is obvious that there are equivalent states for which mechanical and electrostatic energies are nearly equal. Hence thermal energy can make the oxygen take up these positions alternately and successively. An ultrasonic wave can bias one of the wells with respect to the other and hence can alter the probable length of time in each well. As a result, the lag in returning to the equilibrium ratio is the source of the relaxation.

In fused silica, the distribution of bond lengths results in an internal friction peak at low temperatures which satisfies[56d] the frequency-temperature relation

$$\omega_0 = 5 \times 10^{13}\, e^{-1300/RT}. \tag{10.13}$$

By analyzing the frequency and temperature variation of this relaxation, it was shown that it required a distribution of bond angles from zero to 8° with a cor-

[56d] A discussion of the evidence for an internal friction associated with bent bonds is given in Ref. 56b, Chap. X.

responding activation energy range from 0 to 4000 calories per mole. The weighting factors A_i are much higher for the low activation energies than for the high. The weighting factors A_i, which determine the change in modulus for each activation energy range, appear to flatten off above activation energies of 8000 calories per mole, at a value of about $\frac{1}{100}$ of the peak value. The result is a nearly constant internal friction from 200 up to 525° K. Above this temperature, internal friction peaks associated with the displacements of ions in fused silica begin to occur. The range from 200 to 525° K—which requires an activation energy range from 8 to 20 kilocalories—appears to be associated with bent bonds in the range from 12 to 20°. There are many fewer of them than of the lower angle bonds, but each one contributes considerably more to the modulus change $\Delta Y_0/Y_0$ and hence to A_t. Above activation energies of 20 kilocalories per mole, impurity ions can begin to diffuse and these produce more internal friction than do the bent bonds.

For glasses with their interstitial atoms such as sodium, the lattice is considerably more distorted than for fused silica. There is still an internal friction peak at low temperatures, but the ratio of its height to the background loss at higher temperatures is much less than in fused silica. The activation energies for these bent bond displacements are considerably less than those involved in viscous flow.

The data for copper also show that the "hysteresis" type loss, which results in only a 2 to 1 variation of Q^{-1} for a frequency range from 10^2 to 10^7 cycles, is also of a relaxational type. In this case both the modulus change and the internal friction change due to dislocation pinning by neutron irradiation are measured as well as the Q^{-1} values versus frequency. The dot dash lines show the calculated $\Delta Y/Y_0$ and the calculated Q^{-1} plotted against frequency calculated from Eqs. (10.5) and (10.6) when the A_i values are determined from the values of Q^{-1} measured at 12 kilocycles as a function of the temperature. For the Q^{-1} curve versus frequently, the A_i values are lowered in the ratio of the 300° K measurements at 12 kilocycles — $\omega = 7.5 \times 10^4$ — to the 12 kilocycle measurements at 300° K for the top curve. The agreement of these two sets of data with that calculated from (10.5) and (10.6) shows conclusively that this "hysteresis" type loss is of a relaxational nature. The mechanism for this effect in metals is probably connected with dislocations which are not present in a polymer material.

For a polymer material, the nearest parallel is probably the bent bond mechanism present for a glass. The viscous flow mechanism for a polymer is generally thought to be due to the smallest chain segment which can move as a concerted unit. It is probable that monimer, dimer or higher number of units can still move from one position in the fluid to another under the effect of thermal agitation. Ultrasonic waves can bias this motion and the lag behind the impressed stress is the origin of the "hysteresis" type loss. If all of these types of motions are considered, a wide range of activation energies should result, all of them considerably less than that associated with viscous flow. For associated liquids [54a, b] the activation energy for hysteresis components is from $\frac{1}{3}$ to $\frac{1}{5}$ that for viscous flow.

The shear stiffness and viscosity of all the polymer liquids is nearly independent of the molecular weight above the rubbery region, i.e., above stiffnesses of about 10^7 dynes/cm². This is evident from the data of Fig. 34 and 36. If the curves above stiffnesses of 10^7 of Fig. 34 are converted to shear stiffness and imaginary stiffnesses and plotted on Fig. 36 for a 25° C case, the curves nearly overlap even though the molecular weight increases from 8250 to 1.5×10^6. Hence in this high frequency region it is only the reactions pertaining to chain segments that are operative in producing the high frequency values.

Interpretions of the two plateaus of the real and imaginary shear stiffnesses of a polymer liquid as shown, for example, by Fig. 36 have been given in terms of the Rouse-Bueche-Zimm theory[55]. With the extension of this theory to higher frequencies by the data of Sect. 8, it appears that a more logical interpretation can be given in terms of the four element network, which reduces to the Rouse-Bueche-Zimm theory at low frequencies, but introduces an intrinsic stiffness to bending above frequencies for which thermodynamic equilibrium occurs. Since the high frequency plateau has to do only with the motion of chain segments between entanglement points, one can consider only the four elements of the chain segment, the viscosity η_1, the thermodynamic stiffness μ_2, the thermodynamic relaxation viscosity, η_2, and μ_3 the stiffness to bending. These are all shown by Fig. 40a for a single section. For a long chain network there is a high attenuation and it is the characteristic impedance $2Z_0$ that will be measured by shear wave techniques. The characteristic impedance for such a series of sections has already been worked out and is given in Eq. (8.19b). To obtain the modification due to hysteresis we replace ω_3 by $\omega_3(1+j\,0.4)$ since

$$\omega_3 = \frac{\mu_3(1+j\,0.4)}{\eta_2} = \omega_3(1+j\,0.4). \tag{10.14}$$

For the 1.5×10^6 molecular weight polyisobutylene, the thermodynamic stiffness μ_2 for the liquid is

$$\mu_2 = \frac{1}{4}\left(\frac{0.914\times6.025\times10^{23}}{56\times100}\right)1.38\times10^{-16}\times298 \approx 1.0\times10^6\ \text{dynes/cm}^2. \tag{10.15}$$

The stiffness $4\mu_3$ at very high frequencies is 10^{10} dynes/cm² so that

$$\mu_3 = 2.5\times10^9\ \text{dynes/cm}^2. \tag{10.16}$$

The vicosity η_1 can best be determined from the value of the stiffness and viscosity midway between the rubber range and the glassy range, for (8.19b) reduces to

$$2\sqrt{\frac{\mu_3\,\eta_1(0.4-j)}{\omega}} = 1.65\sqrt{\frac{\mu_3\,\eta_1}{\omega}}\,(1-j\,0.675). \tag{10.17}$$

Hence the hysteresis effect causes the imaginary part of the stiffness to be 48% larger than the real part in agreement with the measurements of Fig. 36. Determining η_1 for a value of $\omega=3\times10^6$, we find

$$\eta_1 = 58\ \text{poises}. \tag{10.18}$$

The data of Fig. 34 for molecular weights of about 10000 give

$$\mu_3 = 1.5\times10^9; \quad \eta_1 = 50\ \text{poises}, \tag{10.19}$$

showing that both elements increase slightly as a function of the molecular weight. This is probably due to the slight increase in density which occurs as the molecular weight increases. This has the effect of crowding the chains slightly closer and making it more difficult for them to move.

The final element η_2 is not too well determined by the measurements but later determinations show that it is about

$$\eta_2 = 4500\ \text{poise} \quad \text{giving} \quad \tau_2 = \frac{\eta_2}{\mu_2} = 4.5\times10^{-3}\ \text{sec}. \tag{10.20}$$

With these values the calculated stiffness, real and imaginary, are shown by the open circles and triangles of Fig. 36. The lower values of ω are obtained using the modification of the network for low frequencies discussed below.

The measured values in the rubber-like region depend very markedly on the molecular weight of the liquid as can be seen by comparing Fig. 34 with Fig. 36. For high molecular weights, a region of nearly constant elasticity extends from about $\omega = 10^3$ to $\omega \approx 10^{-4}$, a range of nearly 10^7 cycles. This is due to the coupling of segment motion to adjacent chains. Several suggestions on how to incorporate this reaction into the network have been made[17a, 55] but it appears to the writer that the most logical method is to incorporate the chain as part of a three-dimensional network.

The data of Fig. 35 indicate that when the chain length is 100 repeating monomer units or longer, the mechanical impedance tends to become independent of the molecular weight. Similar results are obtained in the evaluation of the thermodynamic stiffness constant μ_2. It has been suggested[55] that this chain segment length is a measure of the average separation of the entanglement points between the chain under consideration and adjacent chains of the liquid.

A simple network based on these considerations is the one shown by Fig. 40b. Each segment, having a viscosity η_1 is assumed to be coupled to adjacent chains by means of the thermal motions of the segments. The adjacent chains in turn couple to other chains by means of thermal motions, so that the total number of chains driven increase as the square of the distance from the original chain. These adjacent chains dissipate energy in proportion to the number of segments driven. Since there are more segments to set in motion in the adjacent layers, on account of their larger volume, this has to be a tapered network of the kind shown by Fig. 40b. If the inner segment has a volume per unit length of πr_0^2, the next layer will have a volume $\pi[(3r_0)^2 - r_0^2]$ or 8 times that of the first layer. The N-th layer will have a viscosity

$$[(2N+1)^2 - (2N-1)^2]\,\eta_1 = 8N\eta_1 \tag{10.21}$$

where η_1 is the viscosity of a single segment uncoupled to any adjacent segments. The value of this was determined by the high frequency measurements and was found to be

$$\eta_1 = 50\left(\frac{\text{MW}}{10000}\right)^{0.05} \text{ poises.} \tag{10.22}$$

The thermodynamic stiffnesses between adjacent layers also increases with the distance from the center, since there are more molecules to interact with each other, and is taken as the square root of the product of the number of molecules in each layer. Hence

$$\mu = \mu_2\sqrt{64N(N+1)} \approx 8N\mu_2 \tag{10.23}$$

where μ_2 is the thermodynamic stiffness between two elements of a chain. This was evaluated to be 1.0×10^6 dynes/cm² for the B.S. polyisobutylene.

The length of the sidewise chain connected to the main chain is in the order of the main chain but may be somewhat longer on account of VAN DER WAAL'S coupling to adjacent chains. Experimentally, the best agreement with the measured viscosity is determined if the chain is taken as 2.35 times as long as the length determined by the molecular weight. At very low frequencies, the thermodynamic coupling is sufficient to actuate the whole three dimensional network and the viscosity is equal to the number of separate segments times the viscosity η_1 of each. If there are $2.35N$ segments in each side chain, where N is the number of segments for a chain of a given molecular weight, the total number of segments in each side chain is

$$1 + 8(1 + 2 + \cdots + 2.35N) = 8\,\frac{(2.35N-1)(2.35N+1)}{2} \approx 22N^2. \tag{10.24}$$

Since there are $2.35N$ of the side chains along the main chain, the total number of segments will be $52N^3$. Multiplying this value by the viscosity of a single segment, given by (10.22), the viscosity-molecular weight relationship of polyisobutylene on this model should be

$$\left.\begin{aligned}\eta_0 &= 50\left(\frac{\mathrm{MW}}{10000}\right)^{0.05} 52N^3 = 50\times 52\left(\frac{\mathrm{MW}}{56\times 100}\right)^3\left(\frac{\mathrm{MW}}{10000}\right)^{0.5}\\ &= 9.3\times 10^{-9}\,(\mathrm{MW})^{3.05}\end{aligned}\right\} \tag{10.25}$$

valid for molecular weights above 10000.

The following table shows a comparison of this formula with the measurements of FOX and FLORY[57] on the viscosity of polyisobutylene at 25° C.

Molecular weight	Measured η_0 in poise	n=number of repeating elements	N=number of segments	Calculated viscosity from (10.25)
11200	22000	200	2.0	20800
80000	5.9×10^6	1430	14.3	8.2×10^6
660000	2.9×10^9	11500	115	5.2×10^9
1500000*	6.16×10^{10}	26800	268	5.85×10^{10}

As the frequency increases, the sidewise distance that a vibration can penetrate is reduced and at a frequency greater than

$$\omega = \frac{2\sqrt{2}\,\mu_2}{\eta_1} = \frac{2.83\times 10^6}{58} = 4.9\times 10^4 \tag{10.26}$$

the molecule acts again as a single chain molecule with a viscosity $\eta_1 = 58$ poise for the Bureau of Standards polyisobutylene and hence the calculations given previously are valid above $\omega = 10^6\ \mathrm{sec}^{-1}$. For values of $\omega = 10^4$ and 10^5, the impedance of the side chain can be approximated by taking the first few elements and the values shown for $\omega = 10^4$ and 10^5 are calculated in this way.

Unfortunately, this type of tapered network cannot be solved by the image parameter method. However, when $\omega \ll \mu_2/\eta_1$, a differential equation can be derived whose solution can be obtained. To derive the equations we note that the network can be divided as shown in Fig. 40c into a series of sections whose viscosities increase in the sequence $4\sqrt{N_1(N_1+1)}$ and whose coupling stiffnesses increase also in the sequence $8\sqrt{N_1(N_1+1)}$. For the N-th section we can write

$$F_N - F_{N-1} = -8\sqrt{N(N-1)}\,\eta_1 \dot{s}_{N-1}; \qquad \dot{s}_N - \dot{s}_{N-1} = \frac{-j F_{N-1}\omega}{8\sqrt{N(N-1)}\,\mu_2} \tag{10.27}$$

if we neglect ω/ω_0 compared to unity, where $\omega_0 = \mu_2/\eta_1$. Since each section has an elementary length r_0, these section equations reduce to the differential equations

$$\frac{\partial F}{\partial r} = \frac{-8\sqrt{N(N-1)}\,r_0\,\eta_1\,\dot{s}}{r_0^2} = \frac{-8\,\eta_1 r\,\dot{s}}{r_0^2}; \qquad \frac{\partial \dot{s}}{\partial r} = \frac{-jF\omega}{8r\,\mu_2}. \tag{10.28}$$

If we eliminate $\dot{s}$ from the equations, the differential equation for the force becomes

$$r\frac{\partial}{\partial r}\left(\frac{1}{r}\frac{\partial F}{\partial r}\right) = \frac{\partial^2 F}{\partial r^2} - \frac{1}{r}\frac{\partial F}{\partial r} = \frac{j\omega\eta_1}{\mu_2 r_0^2}F. \tag{10.29}$$

[57] T. G. FOX and P. J. FLORY: J. Amer. Chem. Soc. **70**, 2384—2395 (1948).
* Bureau of Standards polyisobutylene.

This equation has the solution

$$F = r[A J_1(\beta r) + B Y_1(\beta r)] \quad \text{where} \quad \beta = \frac{1}{r_0}\sqrt{\frac{-j\omega\eta_1}{\mu_2}}. \tag{10.30}$$

When $r_1 = N r_0$ the force must vanish so that the impedance looking into the sidebranch is

$$Z_S = \frac{F}{\dot{s}} = \frac{8\eta_1}{r_0^2}\,\frac{F}{\left(-\frac{1}{r}\frac{\partial F}{\partial r}\right)} = 8\sqrt{\frac{j\eta_1\mu_2}{\omega}}\left[\frac{-J_1(\beta r_0) + [J_1(\beta r_1)/Y_1(\beta r_1)]\,Y_1(\beta r_0)}{J_0(\beta r_0) - [J_1(\beta r_1)/Y_1(\beta r_1)]\,Y_0(\beta r_0)}\right]. \tag{10.31}$$

For very small values of ω from the series expansions of these functions, we find

$$Z_S = 8\sqrt{\frac{j\eta_1\mu_2}{\omega}}\left[\sqrt{\frac{-j\omega\eta_1}{\mu_2}}\,\frac{r_1^2}{2r_0^2}\right] = 4\eta_1\left(\frac{r_1}{r_0}\right)^2 = 4\eta_1 N_0^2 \tag{10.32}$$

in agreement with the static method. When

$$\sqrt{\frac{\eta_1}{\mu_2}}\,\frac{N_0}{\sqrt{2}} > 4 \tag{10.33}$$

the ratio of $J_1(\beta r_1)$ to $Y_1(\beta r_1)$ reduces to j and for $\frac{\omega\eta_1}{\mu_2} \ll 1$ we can replace the remaining terms by their series expansions and this results in

$$Z_S = \frac{\left(\frac{16}{\pi}\frac{\omega_0}{\omega} - 4\right)\eta_1}{0.5 - j\frac{2}{\pi}\left[\gamma + \log_e \frac{1}{2}\sqrt{\frac{\omega}{\omega_0}}\right]} \tag{10.34}$$

where γ is EULER's constant 0.5772. Intermediate values can be obtained from tables of BESSEL's functions for complex arguments. Using this value of Z_S below $\omega = 10^2$, in the expression for the characteristic impedance,

$$2Z_0 = \frac{-j\frac{2\mu_2}{\omega}\left(\frac{1+\frac{j\omega}{\omega_2}}{1+\frac{j\omega}{\omega_3}\left(\frac{1-j0.4}{1.16}\right)}\right)}{\sqrt{0.25 - \frac{j\mu_2}{\omega Z_S}\left(\frac{1+\frac{j\omega}{\omega_2}}{1+\frac{j\omega}{\omega_3}\left(\frac{1-j0.4}{1.16}\right)}\right)}}, \tag{10.35}$$

the calculated values are shown by the triangles and circles of Fig. 36. A fairly good agreement is obtained except at the low end. For this region the rise in impedance seems to come about a factor of 10 higher in frequency than the measurements.

V. Measurements of rubbers at low strain amplitudes.

11. Rubbers are also made from long chain polymer molecules but differ from polymer liquids in that a cross linking or interlocking of the molecules occurs at a few places along their length to form a three-dimensional network. Between locking points we have long chain polymer molecules with freely rotating segments. Hence the higher frequency or lower temperature properties, which depend on the motions of relatively few segments, may be expected to be very similar to those for polymer liquids.

Shear wave measurements of rubbers indeed show almost identical properties to those of polymer liquids. Fig. 42 shows[14] measurements of several polymer rubbers and as can be seen from the shear stiffness $g=\mu$ and the shear viscosity η,

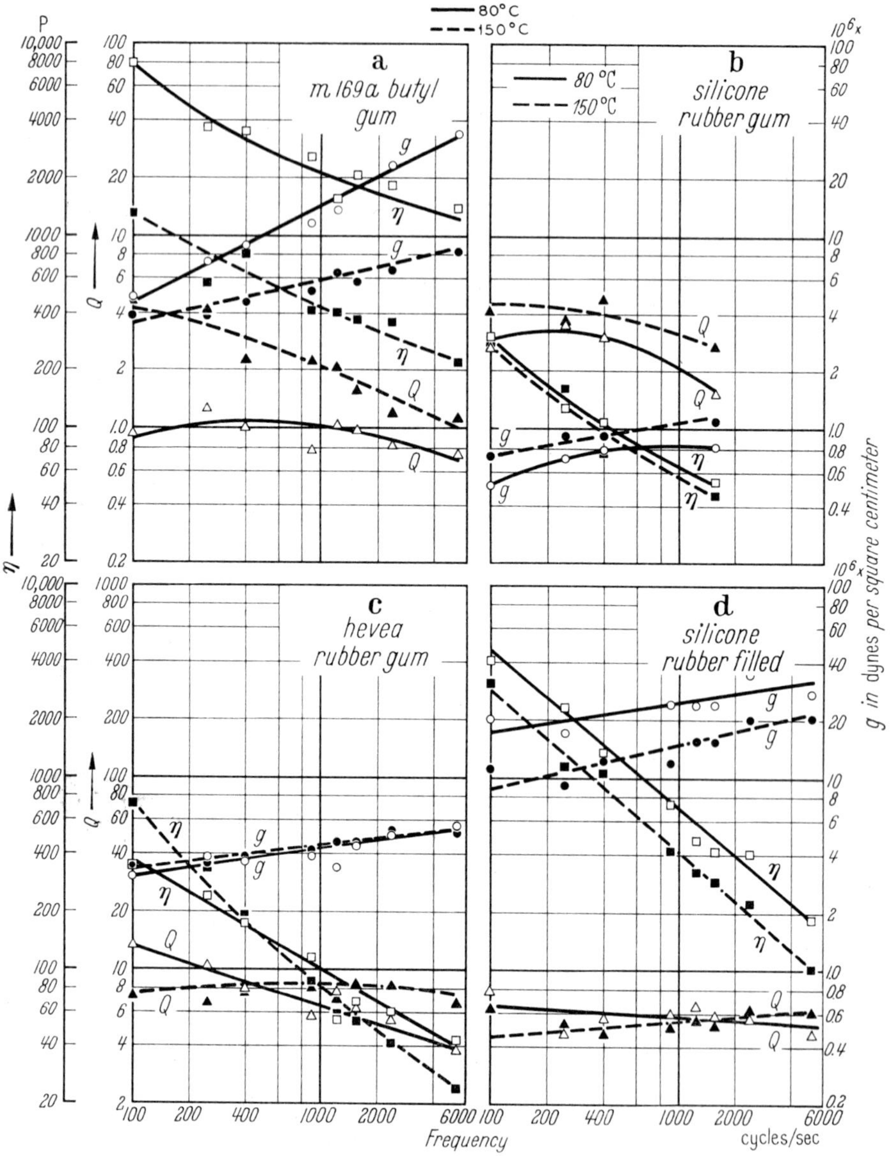

Fig. 42 a—d. Measurement of the shear stiffness and viscosity of several polymer rubbers (after I. L. HOPKINS).

have long plateaus of slowly rising stiffness and slowly decreasing viscosity in the rubber range of 10^6 to 10^7 dynes per square cm, and a more rapidly rising stiffness and falling viscosity in the region of the glassy state. Both Hevea (natural) rubber and silicone rubber gum show a rising stiffness with increase in temperature in agreement with the thermodynamic stiffness concept. The effect of loading silicone rubber with a carbon black is shown by Fig. 42d. Both the shear stiffness and shear viscosity are considerably increased due probably to a reduction in the effective segment volume.

Longitudinal wave measurements of rubbers have been made at considerably higher frequencies[9,10]. Fig. 43 shows[9] a contour of the elastic and dissipative properties of Buna rubber as a function of frequency and temperature and it is evident that the results are very similar to the results of Fig. 39 for polyiso-

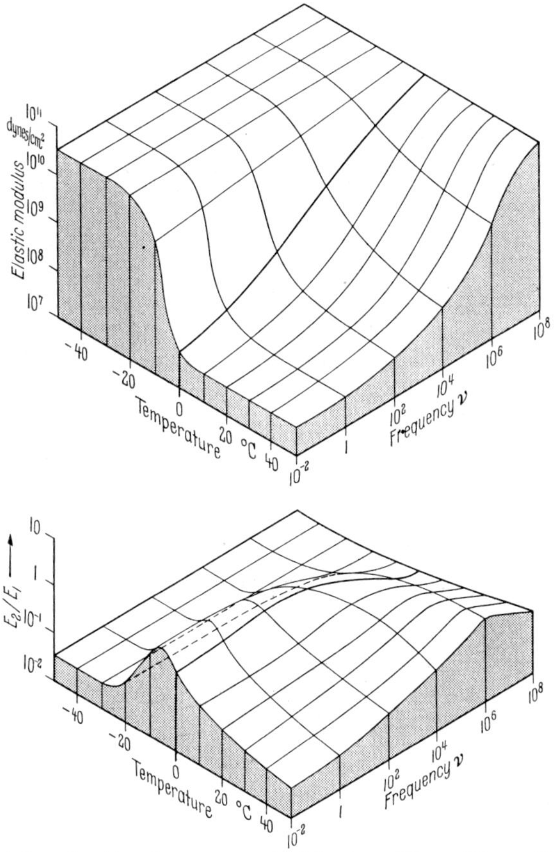

Fig. 43. Contour map of the real and imaginary components of the shear stiffness of Buna rubber (after A. W. NOLLE)

butylene liquids. Measurements[10] for natural rubber show similar peaks indicative of the motions of single chain segments. These measurements all show the dissymmetry of the attenuation peak which is indicative of hysteresis effects.

The principle differences between the mechanical properties of polymer rubber, and liquids occurs in the static or low frequency range. In this range polymer liquids show a viscosity while polymer rubbers show a stiffness. Fig. 44 shows[58] the real and imaginary part of the shear stiffness of natural and GRS rubber. These were obtained by means of a torsional pendulum working in the frequency range from 2×10^{-3} cycles to 1 cycle with measurements made at temperatures from -80 to $+65°$ C. To obtain a complete curve, the segments for one temperature range were made to fit another by multiplying by a factor a_T whose

[58] L. J. ZAPAS, S. L. SHUFTER and T. W. DEWITT: J. Polymer Sci. **18**, 245—257 (1955).

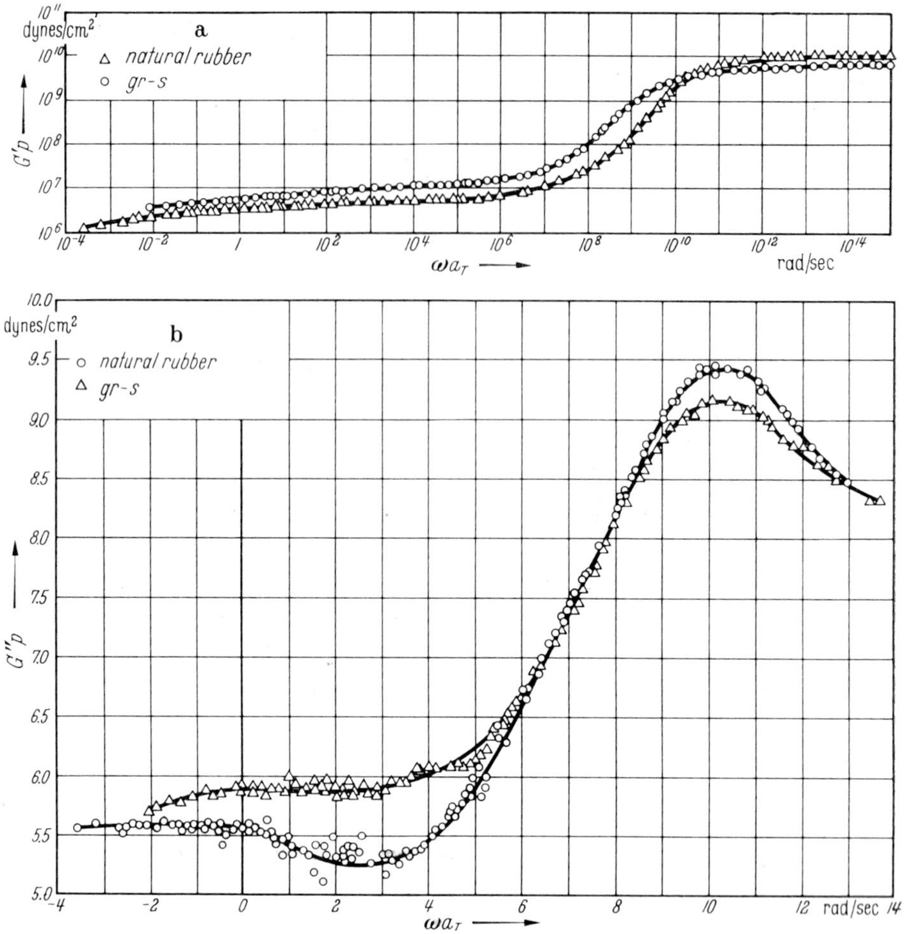

Fig. 44. (a) Shear stiffness and (b) imaginary part of shear stiffness of natural (Hevea) and GRS rubber (after ZAPAS, SHUFTER and DEWITT).

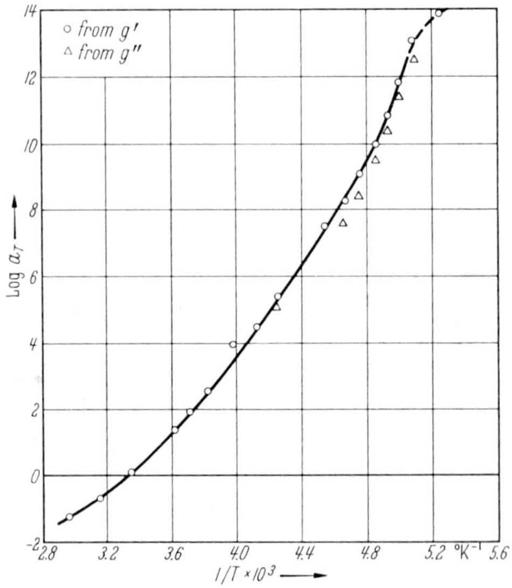

Fig. 45. Logarithm of the shifting factor a_T for natural rubber plotted against $1/T$ (after ZAPAS, SHUFTER and DEWITT).

value as a function of temperatures is shown by Fig. 45. a_T has an activation energy of about 35 kilocalories per mole.

Rubbers differ from polymer liquids in that they are cross linked between chains at a few places so that they are solids rather than liquids. The effect of this cross linking is to make the effective length of each chain much longer than the length corresponding to the molecular weight. On the three dimensional model of Fig. 40, the effective chain length becomes very large and the viscosity approaches infinity. The impedance of a side chain approaches the value given in Eq. (10.34) for all values of ω. If we insert this value into the expression for the characteristic impedance, we find at low frequencies

$$2Z_0 = \frac{-j\,\frac{\mu_2}{\omega}}{\sqrt{0.25 - j\,\frac{\left(\pi 0.5 - j\,\frac{2}{\pi}\left(\lambda + \log_e \frac{1}{2}\sqrt{\frac{\omega}{\omega_0}}\right)\right)}{16}}}\,. \tag{11.1}$$

Fig. 46a and b. Polymer chain arrangements responsible for crystallinity in polymers. (a) Unstretched state. (b) Stretched state (after TRELOAR).

If we take $\omega_0 a_T \approx 10^6$ to agree with the measurements, the shear stiffness should decrease by a factor of 2 for a range of $\omega_0 a_T$ from 10^{-4} to 10^4 in relatively good agreement with the measurements of Fig. 44. The imaginary part of the stiffness should have a ratio of about $\frac{1}{30}$ of the shear stiffness at the low values of ω as compared to about $\frac{1}{10}$ for the measurements.

Rubbers may also exhibit the phenomena of crystallinity which corresponds to the close atomic bonding of adjacent chains as shown schematically by Fig. 46. For unstretched rubber this orienting effect of segments of the molecules into randomly oriented crystallites may take weeks or months and is accompanied by such manifestations as latent heat of crystallization, change of specific volume and increase in elastic constants. If the molecules are oriented by stretching as shown by Fig. 46b, this crystallization can take place in a fraction of a second.

VI. Elastic properties of polymer solids.

12. The elastic properties of polymer solids have been used to some extent to study the nature of chemical bonding in the materials. BENBOW[19] has studied the elastic and damping properties in shear vibrations of two polymer glasses in the frequency range from 10^{-3} cycles to 10^4 cycles, as a function of the temperature. An organic glass is used to denote liquids which do not crystallize when the temperature is reduced, but steadily increase in viscosity whatever the

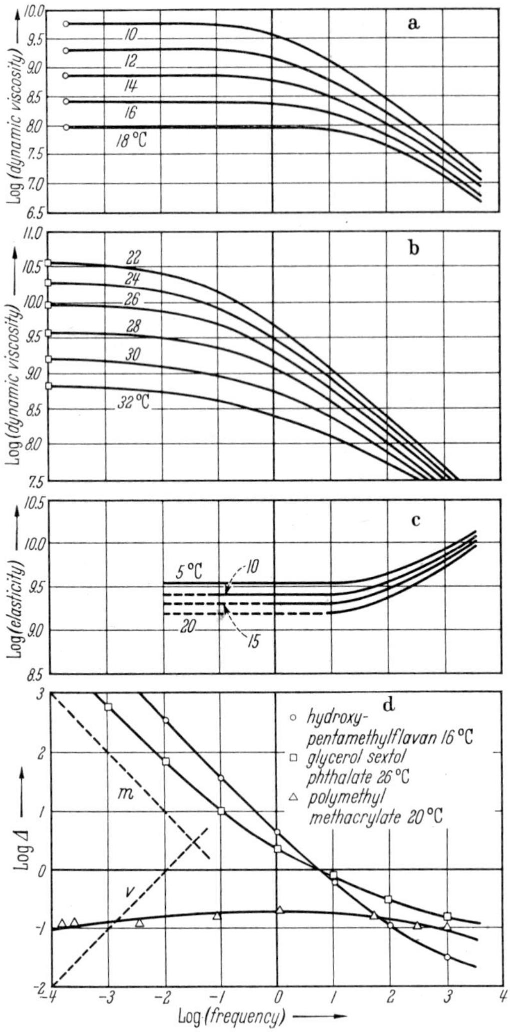

Fig. 47 a—d. Dynamic viscosities and YOUNG's moduli for three polymer glasses (after J. J. BENBOW).

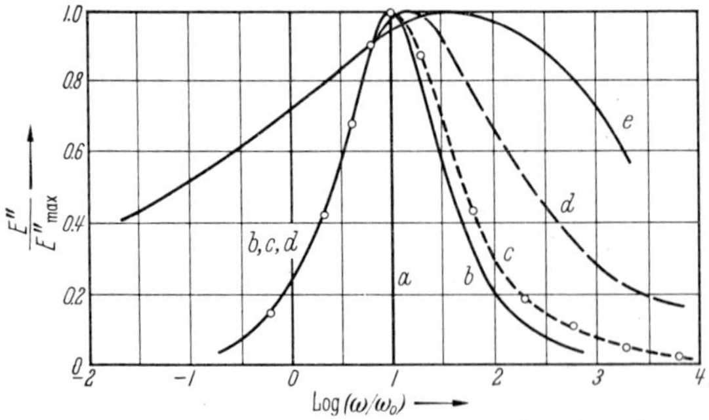

Fig. 48. Plot of the ratio of imaginary to real YOUNG's modulus against the logarithm of ω/ω_0 for three polymer glasses. Curve b is theoretical curve for a single relaxation for a Maxwell body (after J. J. BENBOW).

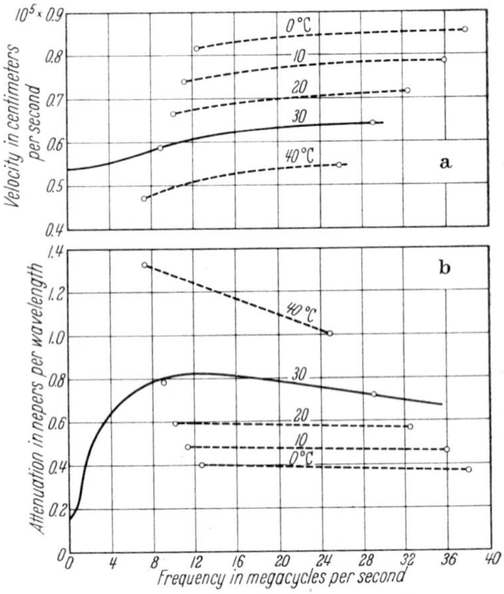

Fig. 49 a and b. Shear velocity (a) and shear attenuation (b) for polyethylene as a function of frequency and temperature (after MCSKIMIN).

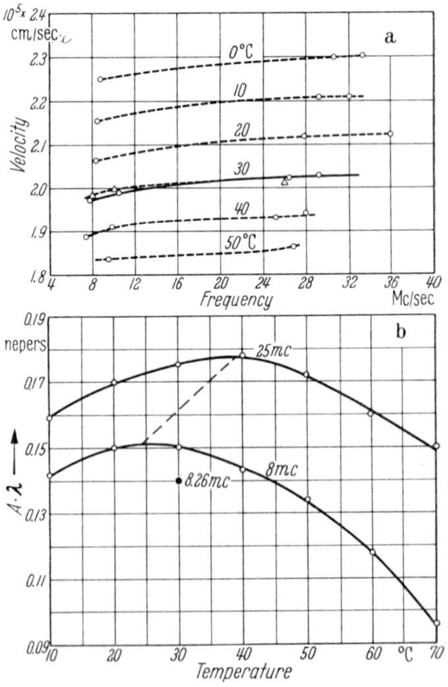

Fig. 50 a and b. Longitudinal velocity (a) and longitudinal attenuation (b) for polyethylene as a function of frequency and temperature (after MCSKIMIN).

rate of cooling. The glasses studied were 2′-hydroxy 2:4:4:6:5′-pentamethylflavan[59] and glycerol sextol phthalate. The results are shown by Fig. 47 for which the dynamic shear modulus and the dynamic viscosity are plotted in terms of a Maxwell body. The hydroxy-pentamenthylflavan behaves like a Maxwell body out to a frequency of 10 cycles after which the viscosity drops and the elastic modulus μ rises. The log of the decrement Δ is plotted on Fig. 47d and is compared with that for polymethyl methacrylate. Fig. 48 shows the ratio of the imaginary component of the elastic constant to the real component, and it is seen that hydroxy-pentamethylflavan has nearly the form of a single relaxation. Glycerol sextol phthalate has a considerable broader curve while polymethyl methacrylate has a very broad curve. The chemical nature of the hydroxy-pentamethylflavan is quite well defined and it is unlikely that there is much association between its molecules. Glycerol sextol phthalate contains hydroxyl groups free to form hydrogen bonds, and

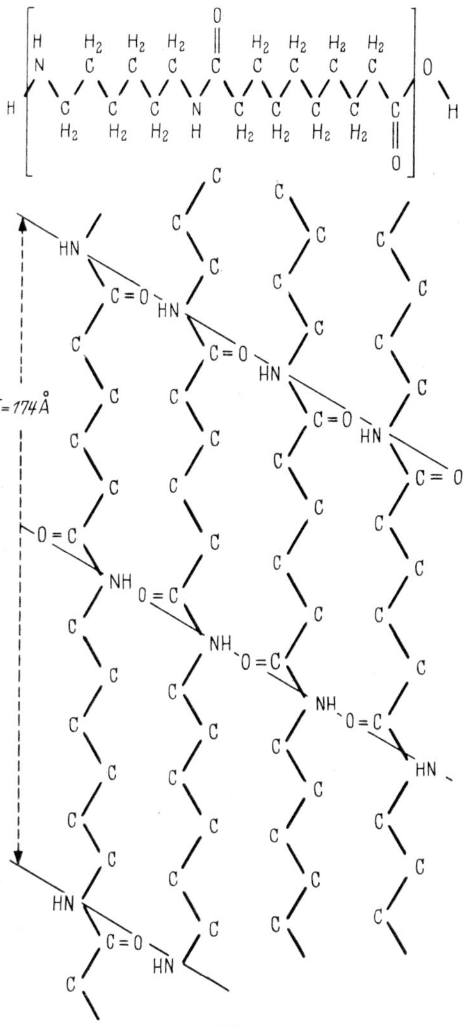

Fig. 51.

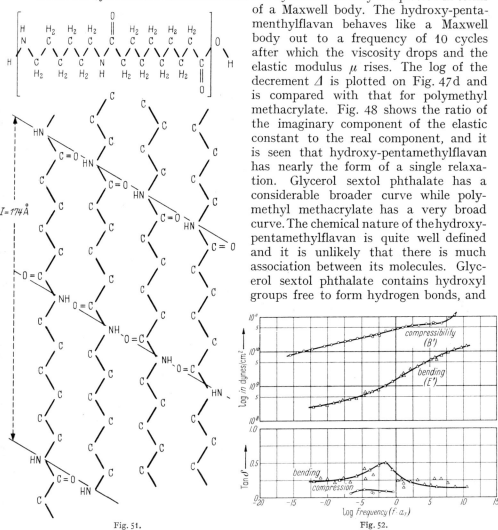

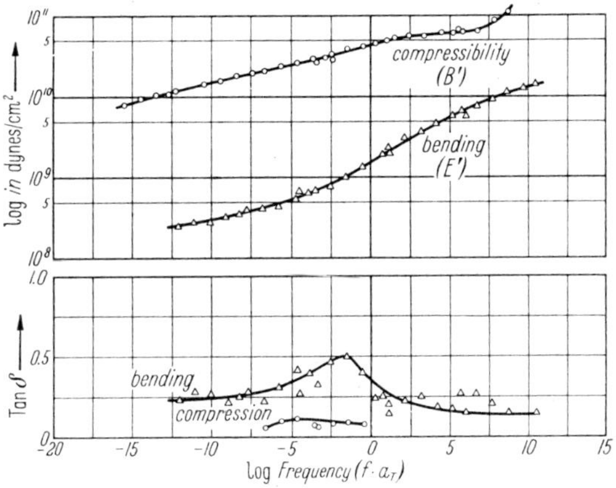

Fig. 52.

Fig. 51. Structure of nylon 6-6 showing hydrogen bonding.

Fig. 52. Elastic compressibility and YOUNG's modulus and associated tan δ's for polyethylene plotted against a reduced frequency (after PHILLIPPOFF and BRODNYAN).

hence it provides an example of an organic glass capable of considerable intermolecular association. Polymethyl metacrylate is a highly cross-linked polymer. The conclusion is drawn that there is a correlation between the width of the relaxation curve and the degree of chemical association.

Some of the less cross linked polymers show relaxations which appear to be associated with the motions of the shortest segment lengths. Fig. 49 shows measurements[12] of the shear modulus of polyethylene of "equilibrium" crystal-

[59] W. BAKER, R. F. CURTIS and J. F. W. MCOMIE: J. Chem. Soc. Lond. **1952**, 1774.

linity and average molecular weight corresponding to an intrinsic viscosity in xylene $[\eta]$ of 0.89 at 85° C. These measurements can be fitted by a single relaxation mechanism having a relaxation frequency of 8 megacycles for a temperature

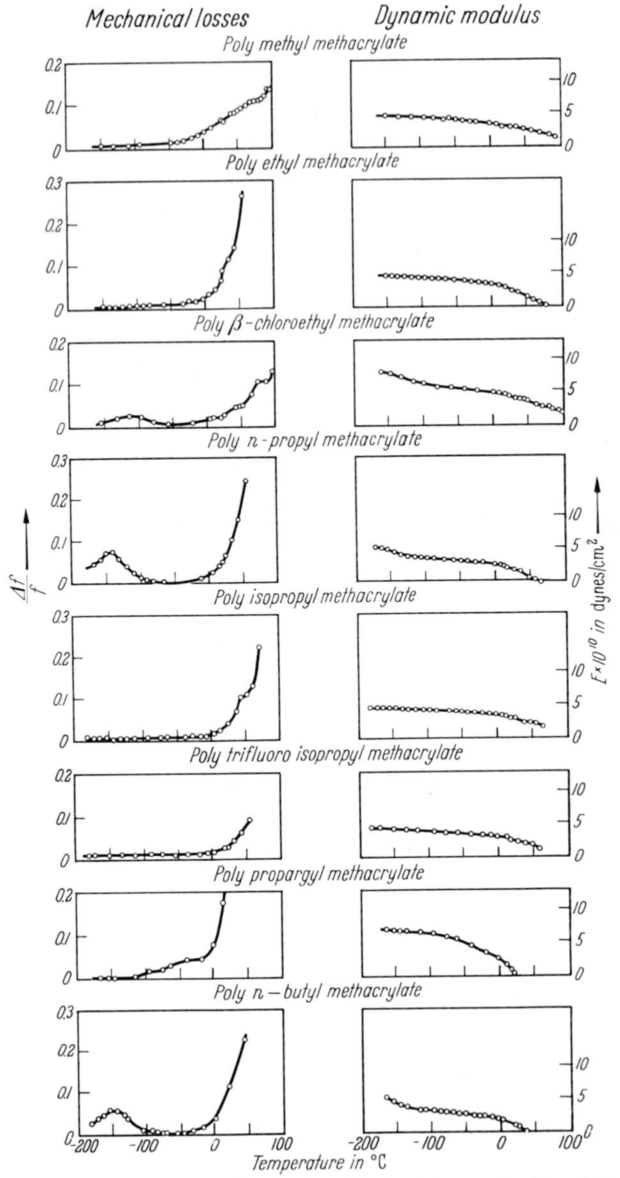

Fig. 53. Internal friction and dynamic moduli for a number of metacrylates as a function of the temperatures (after HOFF, ROBINSON and WILLBOURN).

of 30° C. The corresponding longitudinal measurements are shown by Fig. 50 and a definite relaxation having an activation energy of (12 ± 2) kilocalories per mole is indicated. If we compare the two sets of measurements it appears that most of the loss is accounted for by the shear dissipative mechanisms, but a compressional viscosity about $\frac{1}{4}$ of the shear viscosity is indicated. Similar relaxations were found for nylon 6-6 and nylon 6-10. In these materials the bonding is due to hydrogen bonds between adjacent chains, as shown by Fig. 51 and chain segments are in the order of 6 to 10 repeating units. These materials show compressional viscosities of the same order as the shear viscosities. The λ constants show a normal temperature variation while the shear constants show a relaxation process. Polyethylene has also been investigated in a lower frequency range by PHILLIPOFF and BRODNYAN[60] both for bending vibrations and by a new compressional technique which measures directly the real and imaginary parts of the compressibility. Fig. 52 shows the YOUNG's modulus and compressibility and the values of the phase angle tan δ plotted on a reduced frequency scale. The value of tan δ for compression is smaller than that for bending in agreement with the above measurements at higher frequencies.

For materials more highly cross linked, the smallest chain segment relaxation disappears, but HOFF and coworkers[20] have found relaxations at low temperatures which appear to be related to the presence of side groups on the main chain. Fig. 53 shows measurements of the mechanical loss, defined as $\Delta f/f$, or $1/Q$ and the dynamic modulus for a number of metacrylates. In addition to the glass rubber transitions appearing at the higher temperatures, there are some loss peaks and associated dispersion of the elastic constant appearing at temperatures below $-100°$ C. These have been interpreted as due to motions of the flexible side groups attached to the main chain.

---

[60] W. PHILLIPOFF and J. BRODNYAN: J. Appl. Phys. **26**, 846–849 (1955).

Sachverzeichnis.

(Deutsch-Englisch.)

Bei gleicher Schreibweise in beiden Sprachen sind die Stichwörter nur einmal aufgeführt.

Subject Index.

(English-German.)

Where English and German spelling of a word is identical the German version is omitted.